Hazards XVI

Analysing the past, planning the future

Institution of Chemical Engineers, Rugby UK

Hazards XVI
Analysing the past, planning the future

Orders for this publication should be directed as follows:

Institution of Chemical Engineers,
Davis Building,
165-189 Railway Terrace, RUGBY
Warwickshire, CV21 3HQ, UK

Tel: +44 1788 578214
Tel: +44 1788 560833

Copyright © 2001
Institution of Chemical Engineers
A Registered Charity

Hazards XVI
Analysing the past, planning the future

A three-day symposium organised by the Institution of Chemical Engineers (North West Branch) and held at UMIST, Manchester, UK, 6–8 November, 2001.

This book contains the papers and posters presented at Hazard XVI.
There is also an accompanying CD-ROM.

Organising Committee

M.F.Pantony (Chairman)	Consultant
M.J.Adams	Consultant
G.R.Astbury	Avecia Ltd
S.R.Beattie	Syngenta plc
D.C.Bull	Firebrand International Ltd
A.L.Clarke	NOVA Chemicals
H.R.Cripps	Consultant
K.Dixon-Jackson	Ciba Speciality Chemicals plc
R.F.Evans	Health and Safety Executive
N.Gibson	Burgoyne Consultants Ltd
I. Hymes	Environment Agency
I.Kempsell	British Nuclear Fuels plc
T.A.Kletz	Consultant
G.A.Lunn	Health and Safety Laboratory
R.S.Mason	Consultant
M.McBride	Health and Safety Laboratory
I.F.McConvey	AstraZeneca
G.S.Melville	Burgoyne Consultants Ltd
N.Morton	Health and Safety Executive
M.L.Preston	Consultant
R.C.Santon	Health and Safety Executive
A.I.Thompson	Consultant

Corresponding members of the committee

R.P.Cleaver	Advantica Technologies Ltd
R.L.Rogers	Inburex GmbH

INSTITUTION OF CHEMICAL ENGINEERS

SYMPOSIUM SERIES NO. 148
ISBN 0-85295-441-7

Sponsors

This symposium is supported by the Health and Safety Executive (HSE) and the Environment Agency, sponsored by:

Advantica Technologies Ltd.
Arthur D Little

It is co-sponsored by:

Centre for Chemical Process Safety (AIChE)
Society of Chemical Industry
Chemical Industries Association
The Royal Society of Chemistry
European Process Safety Centre (EPSC)
Safety and Reliability Society
IChemE Subject Groups for 'Safety and Loss Prevention' and 'Environmental Protection'

Printed by Bell and Bain, Glasgow, Scotland, UK

Preface

The primary aim of the Environment Agency is to protect and improve the environment and make a contribution towards the delivery of sustainable development.

In partnership with others the Agency has ensured a significant reduction in routine emissions of pollutants from UK regulated industries over recent years. These reductions contribute to a cleaner, greener environment in our communities. The Agency is well aware that such improvements can be set back, at a stroke, by one major industrial accident. Beyond negative environmental impacts companies are finding that the damage to their reputation caused by such events are at least as important to them as the costs of clean-up or any fines imposed by the courts.

The importance of accident prevention measures in the UK is enshrined within the recent Control of Major Accident Hazard (COMAH) Regulations 1999 and the Pollution Prevention and Control Regulations (PPC) 2000. The Agency plays a central role in both regimes and considers the prevention of polluting accidents to be an important aspect of our work to achieve sustainable development.

The Agency recognises that every incident or near miss provides an opportunity for learning lessons and we are keen to play our part in this process of continual improvement. Our paper to the symposium looks at such lessons learned. We are delighted to be supporting the Institution of Chemical Engineers at this symposium.

Dr Martin G Bigg
Head of Process Industries Regulation
Environment Agency

Contents

Risk assessment and analysis (continued)   (Session 9)
Emergency planning and environmental protection

Safety culture (continued)   (Session 10)

Safe process design (continued)   (Session 11)

Safety culture (continued)   (Session 12)

Lessons from COMAH   (Session 14)

Posters

ACCIDENT INVESTIGATION – MISSED OPPORTUNITIES

Trevor Kletz

Department of Chemical Engineering, Loughborough University LE11 3TU, UK

After paying the high price of an accident, we often miss opportunities to learn from it:

- We find only a single cause, often the final triggering event.

- We find only immediate causes and do not look for ways of avoiding the hazards or for weaknesses in the management system.

- We list human error as a cause without saying what sort of error though different actions are needed to prevent those due to ignorance, those due to slips or lapses of attention and those due to non-compliance.

- We list causes we can do little about.

- We change procedures rather than designs.

- We do not help others to learn as much as they could from our experiences.

- We forget the lessons learned and the accident happens again. We need better training, by describing accidents first rather than principles, as accidents grab our attention; we need discussion rather that lecturing, so that more is remembered; we need databases that can present relevant information without the user having to ask for it.

Finally, we ask if legislation can produce improvements.

Keywords: Accident investigation, discussions, training, human error, databases, memory.

...the ICI knowledge was no more prodigious than elsewhere, just that the company was prepared to be more open about it. – Jim McQuaid[1]

INTRODUCTION

The chemical industry is a much safer place to work than many industries with fewer inherent hazards[2]. Nevertheless, almost all the accidents that have occurred need not have occurred. Most of them have happened before and have been described in published reports. Someone knew how to prevent them even if the people on the job at the time did not. There is something seriously wrong with our safety training and the availability of information if preventable accidents keep on happening.

Having paid the price of an accident, minor or serious (or narrowly missed), we often neglect the opportunity to learn from it. Failures should be seen as educational experiences for both the individual and the organisation. Seven major opportunities, summarised above, are frequently missed, the first five during the preparation of the report and the other two afterwards. Having paid the "tuition fee", we should learn the lessons.

ACCIDENT REPORTS ARE OFTEN ONE-DIMENSIONAL

Often, accident reports identify only a single cause, though many people, from the chemist who chose the process, through the designers, down to the last link in the chain, the operator, had an opportunity to prevent the accident. The single cause identified is usually this last link in the chain of events that led to the accident, such as an operator closing the wrong valve or a mechanic breaking the wrong joint.

Just as we are blind to all but one of the octaves in the electromagnetic spectrum so we are blind to many of the opportunities for preventing an accident. We find one cause and say, "Job done".

ACCIDENT REPORTS ARE OFTEN SUPERFICIAL

Even when we find more than one cause, we often find only immediate causes. We should look beyond them for ways of avoiding the hazards, such as inherently safer design, and for weaknesses in the management system. For example, could less hazardous raw materials have been used? Could more safety features have been included in the design? Were the operators adequately trained and instructed? If a mechanic opened up the wrong piece of equipment, why wasn't there a better system for identifying it? Saying, "The pump you repaired last week is giving trouble again" is a recipe for an accident. Were previous incidents overlooked because the results were, by good fortune, only trivial? The emphasis should shift from blaming the operator to removing opportunities for error or identifying weaknesses in the design and management systems.

When investigators are asked to look for underlying or root causes they sometimes call the causes they have found root causes. For example, a report said that the root cause of a flange leak was fitting the wrong size of gasket. But that was an immediate cause. To find the root cause we would have to ask if the right size of gasket was in stock and it not, why not; if the fitter who installed the gasket knew the possible consequences of fitting the wrong size and if not, why not; if there had been other cases of poor craftsmanship and if they were overlooked; and so on.

Most commentators on the disaster at Bhopal in 1984 missed the most important lesson that can be drawn from it: the material that leaked and killed over 2000 people was not a product or raw material but an intermediate. It was convenient to store it but not essential to do so and afterwards many companies did reduce their stocks of hazardous intermediates, often using them as they were made and replacing 50 or more tonnes in a tank by a few kilograms in a pipeline. For ten years since the explosion at Flixborough in 1974, the importance of keeping stocks of hazardous chemicals as low as possible had been advocated. Though reducing stocks saves money as well as increasing safety little had been done. If we can avoid hazards we can often design plants that are cheaper as well as safer.

The report on a serious explosion[3] that killed four men shows how easily underlying causes can be missed. The explosion occurred in a building where ethylene gas was processed at high pressure. A leak from a badly made joint was ignited by an unknown cause. After the explosion many changes were made to improve the standard of joint-making: better training, tools and inspection.

Poor joint-making and frequent leaks had been tolerated for a long time as all sources of ignition had been eliminated and so leaks could not ignite, or so it was believed. Though the plant was part of a large group the individual parts were independent so far as technology was concerned. The other plants in the group had never believed that leaks of flammable gas could not ignite. Experience had taught them that sources of ignition are liable to turn up, even though we do everything we can to remove known sources, and therefore strenuous efforts must be made to prevent leaks and good ventilation provided to disperse any that do occur. Unfortunately the managers of the plant involved in the explosion had hardly any technical contact with the other plants, though their sites adjoined. Handling flammable gases at high pressure was, they believed, a specialized technology and little could be learnt from those who handled them at lower pressures. The plant was a monastery, a group of people isolating themselves from the outside world. The explosion blew down the monastery walls.

If the management of the plant where the explosion occurred had been less insular and more willing to compare experiences with other people in the group, or if the directors of the group had allowed the component parts less autonomy, the explosion might never have occurred. The senior managers of the plant and the group probably never realised or discussed the need for a change in policy. The leak was due to a badly made joint and so joints must be made correctly in future. No expense was spared to achieve this aim but the underlying weaknesses in the company organization and plant design were not recognized. However, some years later, during a recession, parts of the group were merged.

The causes listed in accident reports sometimes tell us more about the investigators' beliefs and background than about the accidents.

WE LIST HUMAN ERROR AS A CAUSE

Human error is far too vague a term to be useful. We should ask, "What sort of error?"

- Was it due to poor training or instructions? If so we need improve them and perhaps simplify the task.

- Was it due to a deliberate decision not to follow instructions or recognized good practice? If so, we need to explain the reasons for the instructions as we do not live in a society in which people will simply do what they are told. We should, if possible, simplify the task – if an incorrect method is easier than the correct one it is difficult to persuade everyone to use the correct method - and we should check from time to time that instructions are being followed.

- Was the task beyond the ability of the person asked to do it, perhaps beyond anyone's? If so, we need to redesign the task.

- Was it a slip or lapse of attention? If so, it no use telling people to be more a careful, we should remove opportunities for error by changing the design or method of working[4].

WE LIST CAUSES THAT DO NOT POINT TO EFFECTIVE ACTIONS

For example, a source of ignition is often listed as the cause of a fire or explosion. But, as we have just seen, it is impossible on the industrial scale to eliminate all sources of ignition with 100% certainty. While we try to remove as many as possible it is more important to prevent the formation of flammable mixtures.

For example, which is the more dangerous action on a plant that handles flammable liquids: to bring in a box of matches or to bring in a bucket? Many people would say that it is more dangerous to bring in the matches, but nobody would knowingly strike them in the presence of a leak and in a well-run plant leaks are small and infrequent. If a bucket is allowed in, however, it may be used for collecting drips or taking samples. A flammable mixture will be present above the surface of the liquid and may be ignited by a stray source of ignition. Of the two "causes" of the subsequent fire, the bucket is the easier to avoid.

I am not, of course, suggesting that we allowed unrestricted use of matches on our plants but I do suggest that we keep out open containers as thoroughly as we keep out matches.

Instead of listing causes we should list the actions needed to prevent a recurrence. This forces to people to ask themselves if and how the so-called cause can be prevented in future.

WE CHANGE PROCEDURES RATHER THAN DESIGNS

When making recommendation to prevent an accident our first choice should be to see if we can remove the hazard – the inherently safer approach. For example, could we use a non-flammable solvent instead of a flammable one? Even if is impossible on the existing plant we should note it for the future.

The second best choice is to control the hazard with protective equipment, preferably passive equipment as it does not have to be switched on. As a last (but frequent) resort we may have to depend on procedures. Thus, as a protection against fire, insulation (passive) is usually better than water spray turned on automatically (active), but that is usually better than water spray turned on by people (procedural). In some companies, however, the default action is to consider a change in procedures first, sometimes because it is cheaper but more often because it has become a custom and practice carried on unthinkingly. Figure 1 describes an example.

WE DO NOT LET OTHERS LEARN FROM OUR EXPERIENCE

Many companies restrict the circulation of incident reports as they do not want everyone, even everyone in the company, to know that they have blundered but this will not prevent the incident happening again. We should circulate the essential messages widely, in the company and elsewhere, so that others can learn from them, for several reasons:

- *Moral:* if we have information that might prevent another accident we have a duty to pass it on.

- *Pragmatic:* if we tell other organizations about our accidents they may tell us about theirs.

- *Economic:* we would like our competitors to spend as much as we do on safety.

- *The industry is one: every accident effects its reputation.* To misquote the well-known words of John Donne,

> *No plant is an Island, entire of itself; every plant is a piece of the Continent, a part of the main. Any plant's loss diminishes us, because we are involved in the Industry: and therefore never send to know for whom the Inquiry sitteth; it sitteth for thee.*

WE FORGET THE LESSONS LEARNED AND ALLOW THE ACCIDENT TO HAPPEN AGAIN

Even when we prepare a good report and circulate it widely, all too often it is read, filed and forgotten. Organizations have no memory. Only people have memories and after a few years they move on taking their memories with them. Procedures introduced after an accident are allowed to lapse and some years later the accident happens again, even on the plant where it happened before. If by good fortune the results of an accident are not serious, the lessons are forgotten even more quickly. This is the most serious of the missed opportunities and will be considered more fully than the others. Reference 5 describes many examples but here is a more recent one[6]:

During cold weather a water line froze and ruptured inside a building. Damage was fortunately not very serious. Three years later the same line froze and ruptured again. The heating in the building was not operating and the water line was near the door. The basement was flooded and two 15 m^3 tanks floated, reached the ceiling and pushed it up by 0.5 m. The incident occurred at a nuclear site. Can we blame the public for doubting the nuclear industry's ability to operate reactors safely when they let the same water line freeze and rupture twice?

The following actions can prevent the same accidents recurring so often:

- Include in every instruction, code and standard a note on the reasons for it and accounts of accidents that would not have occurred if the instruction etc had been followed. Once we forget the origins of our practices they become "cut flowers"; severed from their roots they wither and die.

- Never remove equipment before we know why it was installed. Never abandon a procedure before we know why it was adopted.

- Describe old accidents as well as recent ones, other companies' accidents as well as our own, in safety bulletins and discuss them at safety meetings.

- Follow up at regular intervals to see that the recommendations made after accidents are being followed, in design as well as operations.

- Remember that the first step down the road to an accident occurs when someone turns a blind eye to a missing blind.

- Include important accidents of the past in the training of undergraduates and company employees.

- Keep a folder of old accident reports in every control room. It should be compulsory reading for new employees and others should look through it from time to time.

- Read more books, which tell us what is old as well as magazines that tell us what is new.

- We cannot stop downsizing but we can make sure that employees at all levels have adequate knowledge and experience. A business historian has described excessive downsizing as producing the corporate equivalent of Alzheimer's disease[7].

- Devise better retrieval systems so that we can find, more easily than at present, details of past accidents, in our own and other companies, and the recommendations made afterwards. We need systems in which the computer will automatically draw our attention to information that is relevant to what we are typing (or reading), as described below.

Of course, everyone forgets the past. An historian of football found that fans would condense the first hundred years of their team's history into two sentences and then describe the last few seasons in painstaking detail. But engineers' poor memories have more serious results.

WEAKNESSES IN SAFETY TRAINING

There is something seriously wrong with our safety education when so many accidents repeat themselves so often. The first weakness is that *it is often too theoretical*. It starts with principles, codes and standards. It tells us what we should do and why we should do it and warns us that we may have accidents if we do not follow the advice. If anyone is still reading or listening it may then go on the describe some of the accidents.

We should start by describing accidents and draw the lessons from them, for two reasons. First, accidents grab our attention and make us read on, or sit up and listen. Suppose an article describes a management system for the control of plant and process modifications. We probably glance at it and put it aside to read later, and you know what that means. If it is a talk we may yawn and think, "Another management system designed by the safety department that the people on the plant won't follow once the novelty wears off". In contrast, if someone describes accidents caused by modifications made without sufficient thought we are more likely to read on or listen and consider how we might prevent them in the plants under our control.

We remember stories about accidents far better than we remember naked advice. We all remember the stories about Adam and Eve and Noah's Ark far better than all the "dos and don'ts" in the Bible.

The second reason why we should start with accident reports is that the accident is the important bit: it tells us what actually happened. We may not agree with the author's recommendations but we would be foolish to ignore the event. If the accident could happen on our plant we know we should take steps to prevent it, though not always those that the report recommends.

A second weakness with our safety training is that it usually consists of *talking to people rather than discussing with them*. Instead of describing an accident and the recommendations made afterwards, outline the story and let the audience question you to find out the rest of the facts, the facts that they think are important and that they want to know. Then let them say what *they think* ought to be done to prevent it happening again. More will be remembered and the audience will be more committed than if they were merely told what to do.

Jared Diamond writes, "Contrary to popular assumptions cherished by modern literate societies, I suspect that we still learn best in the way we did during most of out evolutionary history – not by reading but through direct experience... For us the lessons that really sink in aren't always those learned from books, despite what historians and poets would like us to believe. Instead, we absorb most deeply the lessons based on our personal experience, as everybody did 5400 years ago[8]."

Once someone has blown up a plant they rarely do so again, at least not in the same way. But when he or she leaves the successor lacks the experience. Discussing accidents is not as effective a learning experience as letting them happen but it is the best simulation available and is a lot better than reading a report or listening to a talk.

WHICH REPORTS SHOULD BE DISCUSSED?

We should choose for discussion accidents that bring out important messages such as the need for permits-to-work, the control of modifications, inherently safer designs and so on. In addition, we should:

- If possible, discuss accidents that occurred locally. The audience cannot then say, "We wouldn't do anything as stupid as the people on that plant".

- Draw attention to the missed opportunities described above, in particular to the fact that many people have opportunities to prevent accidents, starting with the chemist who chooses the process, through the engineers who design the plant and ending with the operator who closed the wrong valve. Operators often fall into the traps that others have laid for them and are the people with least responsibility.

- Choose simple accidents. Many engineers are fascinated by complex stories in which someone had to puzzle out some unusual causes. Most accidents are not like that but have quite simple causes. After a fire, one company gave a lot of publicity to an unusual source of ignition and successfully distracted attention from the poor design and management that allowed four tons of hot hydrocarbon to leak out of the plant. No one asked why it leaked or how the company was going to prevent it leaking again.

Undergraduate training should include discussion of some accidents, chosen because they illustrate important safety principles such as the need for inherently safer design, the identification and assessment of hazards, the science of fires and explosions and the need to look below the immediate technical causes for ways of avoiding the hazard and for weaknesses in the management system. Discussion, as already mentioned, is more effective than lecturing but more time-consuming.

If universities do not provide this sort of training industry should provide it. In any case, new recruits will need training on the specific hazards of the industry.

SAFETY DATABASES SHOULD BE ACTIVE AND FUZZY

Accident databases should, in theory, keep the memory of past incidents alive and prevent repetitions, but they have been used less than expected. A major reason is that we look in a database only when we suspect that there might be a hazard. If we don't suspect there may be a hazard we don't look.

In conventional searching the computer is passive and the user is active. The user has to ask the database if there is any information on, say, accidents involving particular substances, operations or equipment. The user has to suspect that there may be a hazard or he or she will not look. We need a system in which the user is passive and the computer is active. With such a system, if someone is using a word processor, a design program or a Hazop recording program and types "X" (or perhaps even makes a diary entry that there is going to be a meeting on X) the computer will signal that the database contains information on this substance, subject or equipment. A click of the mouse will then display the data. As I type these words the spellcheck and grammar check programs are running in the background drawing my attention to my (frequent) spelling and grammar errors. In a similar way, a safety database could draw attention to any subject on which it has data. Filters could prevent it repeatedly referring to the same hazard.

A program of this type has been developed for medical use. Without the doctor taking any action the program reviews the information on symptoms, treatment, diagnosis etc already entered for other purposes and suggests treatments that the doctor may have overlooked or not be aware of[9].

When we are aware that there is or may be a hazard and carry out conventional searching it is hindered by another weakness: it is hit or miss. We either get a "hit" or we don't. Suppose we are looking in a safety database to see if there are any reports on accidents involving the transport of sulphuric acid. Most search engines will display them or tell us there are none. A "fuzzy" search engine will offer us reports on the transport of other minerals acids or perhaps on the storage of sulphuric acid. This is done by arranging keywords in a sort of family tree. If the there are no reports on the keyword, the system will offer reports on its parents or siblings.

There is ample power in modern computers to do all that I suggest. We just need someone willing to develop the software. It will be more difficult to consolidate various databases into one and to make the program compatible with all the various word processor, design, Hazop and control programs in use.

At Loughborough we have demonstrated the feasibility of fuzzy searching and carried out some work on active computing[10,11,12,13].

CULTURAL AND PSYCHOLOGICAL BLOCKS

Perhaps there are cultural and psychological blocks, which encourage us to forget the lessons of the past.

- We live in a society that values the new more the old, probably the first society to do so. *Old* used to imply enduring value, whether applied to an article, a practice or knowledge.

Anything old had to be good to have lasted so long. Now it suggests obsolete or at least obsolescent.

- We find it difficult to change old beliefs and ways of thinking. In the 19th century people found it difficult to accept Darwinism because they has been brought up to believe in the literal truth of the Bible.

- A psychological block is that life is easier to bear if we can forget the errors we have made in the past. Perhaps we are programmed to do so.

The first step toward overcoming these blocks is to realise that they exist and that engineering requires a different approach. "It is the success of engineering which holds back the growth of engineering knowledge, and its failures which provide the seeds for its future development[14]."

CAN THE LAW HELP?

The Health and Safety Commission have issued *Discussion* and *Consultative Documents*[15], which propose that companies and other organisations should be required by law to investigate accidents that occur on their premises. Will this reduce accidents?

It could but whether or not it will depends on a number of factors:

- Companies could be obliged to follow the follow the first five "opportunities" listed in this paper, but the requirement will be effective only if the Health and Safety Executive (HSE) reads a significant proportion of the reports to see if the underlying causes are found, if suitable recommendations are made and if they are carried out. Will they have the resources to do so? It is easy to tell companies what they should do. It is much more difficult to check that they are doing it thoroughly and not just going through the motions to satisfy the letter of the law.

- Will the law state that its purpose it to investigate accidents *so that action can be taken to prevent them happening again, not to attribute blame?* Industry is coming to realise that many people could have prevented almost every accident but the press and politicians seem more interested in finding someone to blame. (On 18 October 2000, the day after the Hatfield train crash, the *Daily Telegraph*'s front page banner headline was "Who is to blame this time?") When discussing crimes they look for the underlying causes such as poverty, upbringing, ill-treatment and peer-group pressure. In contrast, when discussing industrial accidents, instead of looking for the changes in designs and procedures that could prevent them, they assume they are due to managers putting profit before safety. If the law is interpreted in this spirit it will divert attention away from effective action and will do more harm than good.

Remember the words of the report on the tip collapse at Aberfan in 1966 which killed 144 people, most of then children[16]: "Not villains, but decent men, led astray by foolishness or by ignorance or by both in combination, are responsible for what happened at Aberfan". The problem is not how to stop bad people hurting other people but how to stop good people hurting other people.

To quote John Humphreys, "Responsibility has been redefined to include being seen to do something, anything, in response to transient public sentiment often generated by television images, rather than coolly assessing what are realistically the best options"[17].

- Will the HSE be able to insist that the reports are published, anonymously if companies wish, so that others can learn from them?

- Most important of all, there is no mention in the HSE *Documents* of the need to see that the lessons of the past are remembered or the methods by which this can be done. Yet unless the information in accident reports is spread and remembered the work involved in the investigation is largely wasted. At best it produces only a local and temporary improvement.

Afterthought

I remember the first time I rode a public bus... I vividly recall the sensation of seeing familiar sights from a new perspective. My seat on the bus was several feet higher than my usual position in the back seat of the family car. I could see over fences, into yards that been hidden before, over the side of the bridge to the river below. My world had expanded. –

Ann Baldwin[18]

We need to look over fences and see the many opportunities we have to learn from accidents.

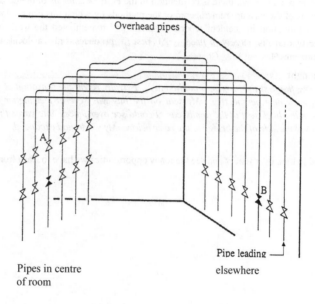

Overhead pipes

A

B

Pipe leading ⎯ elsewhere

Pipes in centre
of room

Figure 1 The fine adjustment valve A had to be changed. The operator closed the valve below it. To complete the isolation, he intended to close the valve on the other side of the room in the pipe leading to valve A. He overlooked the double bends overhead and closed valve B, the one opposite valve A. Both of the valves that were closed were the third from the ends of their rows. Note that the bends in the overhead pipes are in the horizontal plane. When valve A was unbolted the pressure of the gas in the line caused the topwork to fly off and hit the wall.

The report on the incident recommended various changes in procedures. Colour coding of the pipes or valves would have been more effective but was not considered. A common failing is to look for changes to procedures first; to consider changes in design only when changes in procedure are not possible; and to consider ways of removing the hazard rather than controlling it only as a last resort.

1. McQuaid, J., 2001, Review of *By Accident – A Life Preventing them in Industry, Process Safety & Environmental Protection*, 79B: 58.

2. Sanders, R., 1999, *Chemical Process Safety – Learning from Case Histories,* Butterworth-Heinemann, Boston, MA, Chapter 1.

3. Kletz, T. A., 2001, *Learning from Accidents*, 3rd edition, Butterworth-Heinemann, Oxford, UK, Chapter 4.

4. Kletz, T. A., 2001, *An Engineer's View of Human Error*, 3rd edition, Institution of Chemical Engineers, Rugby UK.

5. Kletz, T. A., 1993, *Lessons from Disaster - How Organisations have No Memory and Accidents Recur*, Institution of Chemical Engineers, Rugby UK.

6. Anon., 2000, Freeze protection problems cause damage and loss of fire protection, *Operating Experience Summary,* No 2000-3, Office of Nuclear and Facility Safety, US Dept. of Energy, Washington, DC.

7. Kransdorf, A., 1996, *The Guardian,* 12 October, p. 19.

8. Diamond, J., 2000, Threescore and ten, *Natural History*, Dec 2000/Jan 2001, p. 24.

9. Anstead, M., 1999, More needles, less haystack, *Daily Telegraph Appointments Supplement*, 18 November, p. 1.

10. Chung, P. W. H. and Jefferson, M., 1988, A fuzzy approach to accessing accident databases, *Applied Intelligence*, 9: 129.

11. Iliffe, R. E., Chung, P. W. H., and Kletz, T. A., 1999, More Effective Permit-to-Work Systems, *Proc Safety Env Protection*, 77B: 69.

12. Iliffe, R. E., Chung, P. W. H., and Kletz, T. A., 1998, Hierarchical Indexing, Some lessons from Indexing Incident Databases, *International Seminar on Accident Databases as a Management Tool*, Antwerp, Belgium, November.

13. Iliffe, R. E., Chung, P. W. H., Kletz, T. A., and Preston, M. L., 2000, The Application of Active Databases to the Problems of Human Error in Industry, *J Loss Prev Process Industries*, 13:19.

14. Blockley, D. I. and Henderson, J. R., 1980, *Proc Inst Civ Eng*, Part 1, 68:719.

15. Health and Safety Commission, 1998, *A new duty to investigate accidents, Discussion Document,* HSE Books, Sudbury, UK. A *Consultative Document* with the same title was published in 2001.

16 1966, *Report of the Tribunal appointed to inquire into the disaster at Aberfan on October 21st 1966*, HMSO, London, paragraph 47.

17. Humphrys, J., 1999, *Devil's Advocate,* Hutchison, London, UK, page 63.

18. Baldwin, A. D., 1995, Letter: *Biblical Archaeology Review*, May/June, p. 50.

A JANUS APPROACH TO SAFETY

Dr. John Bond
Centre for Maritime and Industrial Safety Technology, Heriot-Watt University Research Park, Edinburgh, EH14 4AP

Growing public unease over safety and environmental matters is leading to more litigation whether in the civil or the criminal court. It seem probable that the 21st Century defendants will have to show that they have learnt and put into practice the lessons taught by previous accidents not only within their organisation but also outside it. This paper will give some examples from different industries where lessons were not learnt and a notable one where the lessons were shared to the benefit of the public. The process of learning lessons, based on a management system, in design, inspection, maintenance and all operational work is discussed.
The importance of the professionalism of engineers and scientists and the necessity for them to share lessons learnt for the benefit of the employees, the public, the environment and their company is discussed.
Industry must share information on accidents to satisfy the community's concern for greater safety.

Keywords: Accident database, Learning lessons, Duty of care, Hazard identification, Professional engineer

INTRODUCTION

Janus was a god of the ancient Romans who is depicted as having two faces, one looking backwards and the other to the front. He was a guardian of beginnings and the month of January is named after him because he looked back to the past year and forward to the year to come. The Janus approach to safety may suggest itself to us, looking to the past to learn what has happened and to the future to identify what could happen.

If hindsight is defined as wisdom after the event, learning lessons from accidents is a process of converting hindsight into foresight and the Janus approach becomes an active concept. The necessary precautions then become a matter of engineering common sense.

Growing public unease over safety and environmental matters is leading to more litigation both in the civil and the criminal court. It seems probable that defendants in the 21st Century will have to show that they have learnt, and put into practice, the lessons taught by previous accidents not only within their own organisation but also outside it. Given modern communications and the electronic storage and retrieval of accident data, ignorance will no longer be acceptable as a mitigating factor.

WHY LEARN LESSONS?

It may seem obvious that lessons have to be learnt yet it is becoming clear that this is not always the case. It should not be necessary to have a regulation requiring an accident to be investigated and yet a regulation (1) to do just that has now been put forward in a consultative document. It is therefore worth stating the practical reasons why accidents should be investigated.

- To understand what happened.

- To prevent it recurring.
- To protect people.
- To protect equipment and material.
- To meet statutory requirements.
- To protect profits.

It follows that the lessons taught by investigation of the accident have to be learnt; otherwise the accident will recur and the loss both in human and monetary terms will be repeated. But the lessons have to be learnt not only for present purposes but for future occasions where they might be relevant. These lessons should also be shared with others.

The investigation of accidents is often not made in sufficient depth once the basic cause has been established. For example, the cause could simply be attributed to an operator opening the wrong valve. This could indeed be the basic cause but it must be further explored. The operator may have received inadequate training; he may have been incorrectly assessed as competent to carry out the requirements of the job. Delving further back, it may be found there was no management system in place to ensure that all operators were fully trained before being authorised to operate the relevant plant.

The important requirement in an organisation is for a management system covering not only the thorough investigation of accidents but also the use of lessons learnt from within and outside the organisation in all design and risk assessment work (2).

DO WE LEARN LESSONS?

It is often said that the only thing that history teaches us is that we do not learn from it. Here are a few examples from various industries, some going back in time.

1. We have recently heard a lot about Deep Vein Thrombosis (DVT) or Economy Class Syndrome which has lead to the swelling of the leg and blood clots due to cramped conditions in aircraft flying long distances. This is no new problem. It occurred in the equally cramped conditions of stage coaches as Count Leopold Berchtold recounted in 1789 when he published 'An Essay to Direct and Extend the Enquires of Patriotic Travellers' (3):

   "Travellers in carriages are very liable to have their legs swelled; in order to prevent being thus incommoded, it will be advisable to wear shoes rather than boots, to untie the garters, to alight now and then, and to walk as often as opportunity permits, which will favour circulation."

2. This year a report in the Sunday newspaper (4) stated:

   "Seven people including two children were crushed to death in a stampede at Johannesburg's main Park Station when passengers stormed towards a stairway where a gate had been closed ahead of a train's departure."

   This tragedy is an all too frequent echo of earlier instances of crowds rushing down stairways with fatal results.

- Towards the end of the bank holiday in April 1892 the crowds who had been enjoying themselves on Hampstead Heath noticed an approaching rain cloud, decided to call it a day and rushed to the nearest station (3). The stairway down to the platforms at Hampstead Heath Station was soon jammed with a seething mass of passengers; somebody tripped and fell, but still the crowds came. Two adults and six children were killed. A passenger on a train arriving at the height of the crush described the scene in a letter to the *Hampstead and Highgate Express*:-

> *"A most painful sight met my gaze. The station seemed like a howling wilderness, shrieking, bustling, and cries of women and children made it a scene almost indescribable."*

3. The *Marchioness* Disaster.

This disaster occurred on the River Thames in 1989 when a dredger, the *Bowbelle,* rammed and sank the pleasure vessel, the *Marchioness*, and 51 people died. The official inquiry said that the basic cause was the poor lookout on both vessels. It described the accident as "a catastrophe which should never have happened." The *Bowbelle* collided with a passenger launch, the *Pride of Greenwich*, in June 1983. Measures were put in place to improve lookouts and communications but these had fallen into disuse by 1989.

- In 1878 the *Bywell Castle* collided with the *Princess Alice* with 750 passengers on board. 640 passengers were killed. The jurors at the subsequent inquest stated (5):

> *"The investigation ... has brought to light the existence of a state of things on the river which no man in his senses can contemplate without a shudder. It appears that there are no rules whatever to guide captains of vessels. All is left to the chapter of accidents - to the chance that vessels will somehow or other manage to pass one another without coming into collision."*

4. The Loss Prevention Bulletin (6) reported three incidents involving the failure of trap doors used on pigs and high pressure scrubbers on pipelines. The first occurred in 1971 on an offshore installation, the second in 1988 on a shore-based plant with a fatality and the third in 1991 on an offshore installation with a damage cost of £7 million. In each case the failure of the 'yoke type' closure device on the trap door occurred resulting in the pressure release of the pig and pipeline. In the 1971 incident the pressure was released from 87.5 bar with the end closure blowing off with hinge and two clamps. In the 1988 incident the pressure had reached 200 bars in a gas scrubber when the closure door was projected across the site approximately 70 metres with other debris scattered over 170 metres away. In the 1991 incident a pig trap door became detached at a pressure of 79.3 bar. The end closure demolished a crane and caused widespread damage to a module structure.

The cause of these incidents was attributed to the failure of a nut retaining box. In 1986 an appendix to ASME 8 was issued and these closures would not have met the revised code but all three were designed before the code was promulgated. Nevertheless this type of closure is found in many pig traps, scrubbers, condensate coalescers, large filters, etc. It was concluded that if the first "....incident had been made common knowledge, then there is a high probability that the other incidents may not have occurred."

5. The Texaco refinery explosion and fires (7) occurred after a serious electrical storm in 1994. The crude distillation unit was shut down following a fire started by the lightning. An explosion occurred five hours later as a result of a major release of hydrocarbons. The incident was caused by hydrocarbon being pumped into a vessel that was closed at the outlet and the only escape was to a flare system which could not cope with the quantities involved. An outlet pipe failed and released 20 tonnes of hydrocarbon. The HSE report states in paragraph 127:

> "All the key elements of the incident, and the lessons drawn from it, have been seen and publicised before in major accidents around the world. Those who are responsible for operating hazardous plants must have systems in place that bring to their attention these lessons of history."

The report then makes the first recommendation:

> "Safety management systems should include means of storing, retrieving and reviewing incident information from the history of similar plants."

6. Road tanker with the wrong documentation.
On the 3 October 1996 at Avonmouth a road tanker containing sodium chlorite was offloaded into a tank containing epichlorohydrin (8). This occurred because the wrong documentation had been picked up at a ferry crossing. The Chemical Industries Association found that this was not the first incident of this kind and could easily have been avoided if the previous incidents had been reported and shared.

The answer to the question raised at the beginning of this section is very clear. We do not learn lessons from the incidents that occur in many industrial situations. Trevor Kletz has also shown this to be the case (9 and 10) and has stated the reason:

> "It might seem to an outsider that industrial accidents occur because we do not know how to prevent them. In fact they occur because we do not use the knowledge that is available. Organisations do not learn from the past or, rather, individuals learn but they leave the organisation, taking their knowledge with them, and the organisation as a whole forgets."

There have been others in the past who have also stated that lessons must be learnt. After a fire at a theatre in England in 1887, when 188 people were killed, the investigating officer's report (11) concluded:

> "The saddest part of this matter is that no lesson of any kind has been taught by the event, as everyone who has studied the subject either theoretically or practically knew beyond any possibility of a doubt what the whole action of the fire and smoke would be under such circumstances, and moreover, the lessons and warning of recent years had prepared all concerned for the terrible catastrophe precisely as it actually occurred."

More recently a report by the US Environmental Protection Agency and Chemical Emergency Preparedness and Protection Agency (12) describes the recurring causes of recent chemical accidents. The report describes nine accidents in the petrochemical industries which had the following common factors:

- Inadequate hazard review or process hazards analysis.
- Installation of pollution control equipment without adequate hazard analysis and inadequate management of change procedures.
- Use of inappropriate or poorly designed equipment
- Inadequate indications of process condition.
- Warnings went unheeded

There is, however, one notable case where lessons were learnt to the great benefit of air passengers and the companies. Some here will remember the series of accidents that happened with the BOAC Comet passenger aircraft, starting in January 1954 with the disintegration in flight of G-ALYP, followed by G-ALYY in April 1954. The investigation involved the pressure testing of a whole aircraft in a water tank. After subjecting the aircraft to simulated pressure fluctuations the main cause of the failure of the aircraft was found to be fatigue cracks at the corner of the windows. This information was released to the whole industry so that aircraft of the future could take advantage of the lessons learnt. The industry and passengers all benefited from this approach. If the information had not been released, how many more lives would have been lost before other aircraft manufacturers discovered the problem of fatigue cracks at window corners can only be imagined.

WHERE CAN WE FIND LESSONS FROM PAST ACCIDENTS?

Information on past accidents is available from a number of databases including MHIDAS from AEA Technology and FACTS from TNO, but these and many others are often based on information taken from the media. The media, however, are usually only interested in the event and not the causes. The Accident Database of the Institution of Chemical Engineers (8) is based on full reports taken from:

- The Loss Prevention Bulletin
- Reports in journals
- Official reports from Regulatory Authorities
- Confidential reports from companies.

The only other source of information for these lessons, apart from the files of ones own organisation, is the published literature, but searching through it is time-consuming and unreliable. It is well known that the indexing and abstraction systems are inadequate. Only a dedicated accident database can provide a solution to the problem, as shown in the next section.

WHERE CAN WE USE LESSONS FROM PAST ACCIDENTS?

Risk management and risk control are essential features in the avoidance of accidents, and the first stage in any of the methods used is identifying the hazards (see Figure 1) associated with the project or operation. Lessons learnt from accidents (or near-misses) are a vital part of the following operations where hazards have to be identified:

- Design work

- Hazard and Operability Studies
- Risk Assessment
- Writing Permits to Work
- Writing operating instructions
- Safety Audits
- Review Procedures
- Inspections
- Audits

Identifying hazards is the key to almost all operational work and is done automatically in much of our every day work. We look each way before crossing the road but in our technical work it is important that we use not only the hazards that we retain in our memory but also use the hazards identified by others and contained in the memory bank of a database.

A scenario for the use of The Accident Database in the petrochemical industry could be the design of a distillation column for ethylene oxide. The professionalism of the design engineer would require him to consider what accidents had occurred on such equipment. He would want to ensure that his design did not have the problems that others had experienced and which had caused fatalities, injuries to people, damage to equipment (see Figure 2) or discharges to the atmosphere of toxic chemicals. He would therefore seek information on such accidents and the causes. He would discover when consulting The Accident Database (8) that there had been at least eight explosions involving distillation columns and ethylene oxide and that the lessons learnt were of a similar nature. Table 1 gives a very brief description of the incidents and lessons learnt.

It is clear that all these accidents have a similar cause:
- Leak from flange or weld
- Reaction in the insulation with water
- Auto-oxidation catalysed by rust with heating from an insulation fire

If these had been recognised and shared after the accidents in the 1950s or 1960s the design engineers would have been able to prevent most of the subsequent explosions in the ethylene oxide plants with a consequent prevention of fatalities, injuries, pollution and loss of profits.

PROFESSIONALISM

The Engineering Council

A Royal Charter established the Engineering Council in 1981 and one objective was:

"..... to advance education in, and to promote the science and practice of engineering (including relevant technology) for the public benefit and thereby to promote industry and commerce....."

The Engineering Council seeks to achieve this objective by a number of aims including:

- Increasing awareness of the essential and beneficial part engineering plays in all aspects of modern life.
- Spreading best engineering practice to improve the efficiency and competitiveness of business.
- Advancing engineering knowledge through education and training.

These aims are achieved in a number of ways including:

- Stressing the need for a proper balance between efficiency, public safety and the needs of the environment when carrying out engineering activities.

Chartered Engineers, Incorporated Engineers and Engineering Technicians registered with the Engineering Council undertake a duty to the community under the "Code and Rules of Conduct" (12) rule 1:

> "A registrant shall at all times and in all aspects:
> (a) take all reasonable care to avoid creating any danger of death, injury or ill-health to any person or of damage to property by any act or omission whilst carrying out his/her work, save to the extent that the creation of such danger is lawfully authorised;
> (b) take all reasonable care to protect the working and living environments of himself/herself and others and to ensure the efficient use of materials and resources;
> (c) conduct himself/herself so as to safeguard the public interest in matters of safety and health and in a manner consistent with the dignity and reputation of the engineering profession; and
> (d) notwithstanding the provisions of any of the Rules or Codes of professional Practice, comply with all laws and regulations applicable to his/her professional work."

In the Notes for Guidance it is stated:

> "The important feature of this Rule (viz 1(d)) is that more is demanded of the registrant than bare compliance with existing law. Full compliance is required, not only in the letter but also in the spirit. Ambiguities or loopholes in the law, regulations, etc, must not be exploited in an effort to reduce costs if engineering judgement shows that safety or the environment would be jeopardised as a result. In safety and environmental matters the statutory requirements should be regarded as no more than minima. Even when these requirements have been satisified, the Council still looks to the registrant to take such further measures as his or her engineering judgement shows to be necessary for securing public safety and preservation of the environment, in accordance with Rule 1."

Guidelines on Risk Issues (13) published by the Engineering Council in section 6 Communications states:
> " Engineers should pay particular attention to effective feedback on incidents and 'near misses', so that lessons can be learned."

The Institution of Chemical Engineers

The Institution of Chemical Engineers was founded in 1922 and incorporated by Royal Charter in 1957. Section 12 (b) (ii) of the By-laws (14) states:

> "Every Corporate Member shall at all times so order his conduct as to uphold the dignity and reputation of his profession and safeguard the public interest in matters of safety, health and otherwise. He shall exercise his professional skill and judgement to the best of his ability and discharge his professional responsibilities with integrity."

The Rules of Professional Conduct (14) states in section 4:

> "A member shall take all reasonable care in his work to minimise the risk of death, injury, or ill-health to any person, or of damage to property. In his work, a member shall respect all laws and statutory regulations applicable to the design, operation and maintenance of chemical and processing plant. In addition a member shall have due regard for the need to protect working and living environments, and the need to ensure efficient use of natural raw materials and resources."

The Royal Society of Chemistry

In the Code of Conduct and Guidance on Professional Practice (15) and the section on 'The Chemist and Society' it is stated:

> "As members of the Society, chemists have social responsibilities arising from their fundamental duty to serve the public interest, particularly in the fields of health, safety and the environment."

> "Chemists have a duty to identify the hazards and assess the risks of scientific and technological activities and processes. They must strive for the highest standards of care in their own workplace and take an active interest in safety throughout the organisation. They have a right to protest about malpractice, while maintaining a sense of proportion, and they can expect the support of the Society if their efforts are unavailing."

Technical Integrity and Competence

Technical integrity has been defined (16):

> "Technical integrity is concerned with the development of the design such that it is carried out by well trained personnel, who have been assessed competent, in accordance with recognised, sound practices and procedures and such that there is adequate provision by way of reviews and audits, to ensure the design intent is unimpaired in any way that could cause undue risk or harm to people or damage to the environment."

The question of competence is also mentioned in this reference (16) from the Australian Institute of Engineers:

"The ability to perform the activities within the occupation or function to the standard expected in employment."

Engineering and management staff in a company must display both integrity and competence in their respective spheres of responsibility. They must also demand it of any outside contractors they employ. The importance of not causing undue risk requires the engineer to use his training and experience to search in all reasonable places to identify hazards that may not be known to him from his own experience but which may be found in the experience of other persons.

The Professional Person

Under the Health and Safety at Work Act 1974 everybody has a duty of care towards others but the professionally qualified engineer or scientist has an additional duty because of his membership of a professional organisation. This additional duty results from the training he will have received to identify the hazards involved in his work. There is a general requirement to achieve a risk as low as reasonably practical (ALARP).

The ALARP principle is an important concept that requires a professional person:

- To balance the cost involved against the benefit.
- To consider other ways of carrying out the work which lowers the risk but which is also practical.
- To identify not only those hazards that a professional might reasonably be expected to know but also those that can be established by consulting:
  - other persons
  - books
  - databases
  - other sources.

The professional must use all resources he considers appropriate in order to reduce the risks to himself, to others at his place of work and to the public at large, as well as reducing the impact on the environment. If these resources are withheld or not available, then it is incumbent on the professional to draw this to the attention of a superior authority.

CONCLUSIONS

The report by the US Environmental Protection Agency and Chemical Emergency Preparedness and Protection Office (12) concludes with a statement that is only too familiar:

"From the perspective of the individual facility manager, catastrophic events are so rare that they may appear to be essentially impossible, and the circumstances and causes of an accident at a distant facility in a different industry sector may seem irrelevant. However, from our nation-wide perspective at EPA and OSHA, while chemical accidents are not routine, they are a monthly or even weekly occurrence, and there is much to learn from the story behind the accident. Catastrophic chemical accidents still occur too often. Furthermore, when we look beyond the obvious to the underlying systemic causes of an accident, we see that the same root and contributing causes keep popping up again and again. This indicates that government and industry are not doing a good enough job at sharing accident information and implementing lessons learned."

The learning of lessons from accidents is becoming an important part of the professionalism of the engineer and scientist. Public demand for the lessons to be learnt and headed will increase and industry must respond to this reasonable request. If we fail to meet this request the industry must expect demands for the Government to impose statutory regulations.

REFERENCES

1. "A new duty to investigate accidents" HSE Consultative Document CD169
2. Mellin, B.E. and Bond, J. " Learning Lessons from Accidents - The Problems facing an Organisation" Hazards XV IChemE Symposium Series 2000
3. Bond, J. "The Hazards of Life and All That" IOP Publishing 1996 ISBN 0-7503-0360-3
4. IPP Independent on Sunday 4th March 2001
5. Neal, Wendy. "With Disastrous Consequences" Hisarlik Press 1992 ISBN 1 874312 00 1
6. "Failure of Pig Traps - the importance of learning lessons" Loss Prevention Bulletin Issue 124.
7. "The explosion and fires at the Texaco Refinery, Milford Haven, 24 July 1994" HSE Books ISBN 0 7176 1413 1.
8. The Accident Database. The Institution of Chemical Engineers.
9. Kletz, Trevor., "Lessons from Disasters. How organisations have no memory and accidents recur." Institution of Chemical Engineers. 1993 ISBN 0 85295 307 0
10. Kletz, T. "Learning from Accidents in Industry." Butterworth 1988. ISBN 0 408 02696 0
11. Report on the Fire at the Theatre Royal, Exeter, in 1887. Captain E. M. Shaw, Chief Officer of the London Metropolitan Fire Brigade.
12. Beike, James C., "Recurring Causes of Recent Chemical Accidents" US. Environmental Protection Agency, Chemical Emergency Preparedness and Prevention Office. Mary Kay Process Safety Centre.
13. "Codes and Rules of Conduct" Engineering Council
14. "Guidelines on Risk Issues" The Engineering Council 1993. ISBN 0-9516611-7-5
15. Institution of Chemical Engineers . Royal Charter, By-laws, Rules of Professional Conduct and Disciplinary Regulations. 1999.
16. Royal Society of Chemistry. Code of Conduct and Guidance on Professional Practice. 1999.
17. Bale, E.A. and Edwards, D.W., "Technical Integrity - An Engineer's View." Trans IChemE. Vol 78, Part B, September 2000

FIGURE 1 - RISK ASSESSMENT PROCESS - GENERAL

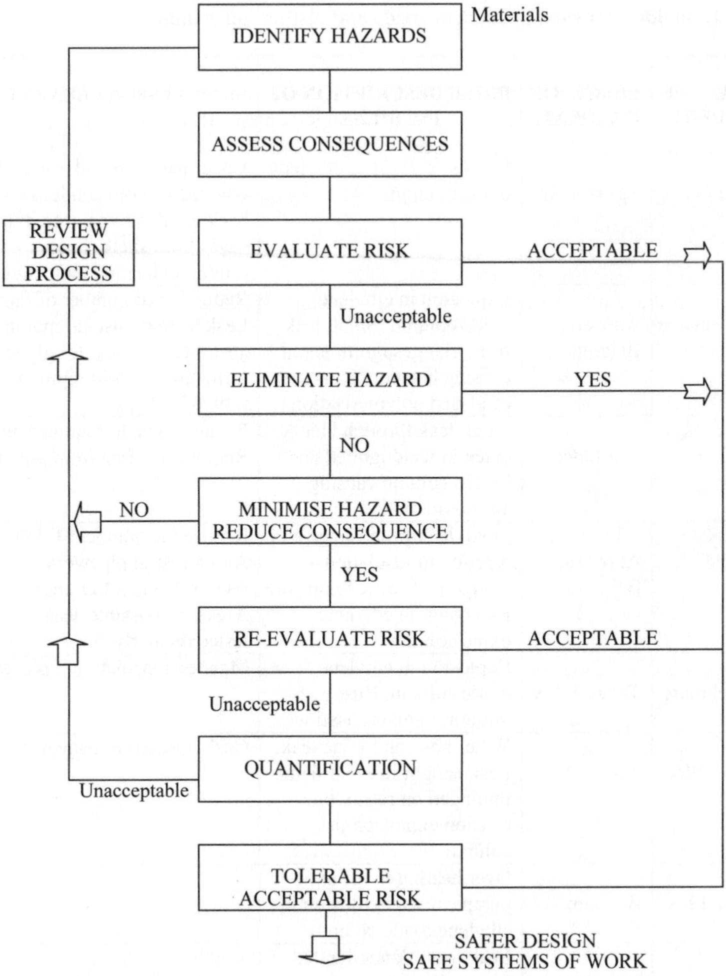

```
                    ┌──────────────────────┐   Materials
                    │   IDENTIFY HAZARDS   │
                    └──────────────────────┘

                    ┌──────────────────────┐
                    │ ASSESS CONSEQUENCES  │
                    └──────────────────────┘

  ┌──────────┐      ┌──────────────────────┐
  │ REVIEW   │      │    EVALUATE RISK     │──────── ACCEPTABLE ⇨
  │ DESIGN   │      └──────────────────────┘
  │ PROCESS  │
  └──────────┘           Unacceptable

      ⇧           ┌──────────────────────┐
                  │   ELIMINATE HAZARD   │──────── YES ⇨
                  └──────────────────────┘

                          NO

    ⇦  NO        ┌──────────────────────┐
                 │   MINIMISE HAZARD    │
                 │  REDUCE CONSEQUENCE  │
                 └──────────────────────┘

                         YES

      ⇧          ┌──────────────────────┐
                 │   RE-EVALUATE RISK   │──────── ACCEPTABLE
                 └──────────────────────┘

               Unacceptable

                 ┌──────────────────────┐
 Unacceptable    │    QUANTIFICATION    │
                 └──────────────────────┘

                 ┌──────────────────────┐
                 │      TOLERABLE       │
                 │   ACCEPTABLE RISK    │
                 └──────────────────────┘

                         ⇩        SAFER DESIGN
                              SAFE SYSTEMS OF WORK
```

Table 1. Incidents involving ethylene oxide and distillation column

DATE OF INCIDENT	PLACE OF INCIDENT	BRIEF DESCRIPTION OF INCIDENT	LESSONS LEARNT
12/3/1991	Texas, USA	Explosion in ethylene oxide column	Upper part of reboiler must be covered. Avoid condensate backup. Positive purge of inert gases from shell. Ensure minimum heating temperature
7/3/1989	Antwerp, Belgium	Explosion in ethylene oxide column. Small leak from flanges igniting and causing hotspot. Rust catalysed polymerisation	Reduction of number of flanges. Leak testing. Insulation non-absorbent and test for glycol formation. Avoid piping with no flow of EO gas
1989	Not stated	Small leak through hair crack in weld ignited and heated column causing auto-oxidation	Flanges to be left uninsulated Remove any rust from pipework
3/7/1987	Antwerp, Belgium	Small leak from flange and reaction in insulation ignited and caused hotspot. Explosion in ethylene oxide column	Reduce the number of flanges Avoid rust in pipework Avoid stagnant EO lines Areas of possible leak should be tested regularly
24 February 1969	Texas, USA	Explosion in ethylene oxide column. Rust initiating polymerisation.	Magnesia insulation replaced
4 July 1969		Water hose on flange leak. Leak caught fire and flame impinged on reflux line causing explosion in column.	Gasket material inadequate
3 June 1964	Belgium	Over heating in reflux pump caused explosion in ethylene oxide column	
1955	Unknown	Leak from flange ignited and impinged on column leading to explosion	

Figure 2. The results of an explosion in an ethylene oxide distillation column.

HOW THE STUDY OF ACCIDENT CASE HISTORIES CAN PREVENT RUNAWAY REACTION ACCIDENTS TO OCCUR AGAIN

Jean-Louis GUSTIN

RHODIA – RHODITECH, 24, avenue Jean-Jaurès 69153 Décines Charpieu France

The study of accident case histories is of utmost importance to prevent the repetition of the same accidents or of accidents with the same causes. This is especially true in the field of runaway reaction accidents.

In the study of accident case histories, the following considerations should be addressed:
- Description of the process and of the chemistry involved.
- Description of the accident circumstances and consequences.
- Identification of the accident causes with special attention to the chemistry.
- Review of the relevant literature to determine if the same accident has occurred earlier.
- Comparison of the accident circumstances with other accidents/incidents where the same cause/chemistry was involved.
- Lessons learned: considerations and factors, which would provide a warning to prevent the same type of accident to occur again.

In this paper, the above approach will be applied to the following accidents:
- the Seveso accident (1976)
- the Bhopal accident (1984)
- the Griesheim accident (1993)
- the frequent Phenol + Formaldehyde runaway reaction
- the accidental bulk polymerisation of reactive monomers with consideration of vinyl acetate and acrylic acid.

It will be shown that the study of accident case histories could greatly reduce the rate of occurrence of runaway reaction accidents.

Keywords: Runaway Reactions, case histories.

INTRODUCTION

The Seveso II regulation requires that for any chemical process concerned by the regulation, a hazard study be completed where the accident case histories known in the same process elsewhere or in related processes should be collected and analysed. This new requirement will ensure that the lessons learned from accidents occurred in the chemical industry as a whole, will help to improve process safety at least in the European Community.

The study of accident case histories will develop. Some processes with bad safety records will be identified and labelled as unsafe. Ignoring this information or neglecting to collect it and to analyse it, will increase liability in case of occurrence of a well known accident scenario.

The study of accident case histories is of great interest in the field of runaway reaction accidents. It helps to identify the contributing factors and scenarios of the accidents, allowing reaching general conclusions, which may apply to related processes or chemistry.

In the manufacture of fine chemicals or pharmaceuticals, some frequent reactions or the use of particular reactants, may present a hazard. It is therefore useful to record incidents and accidents to learn the lessons from it, to prevent these problems to occur again.

A simple method to collect the information on accidents and incidents would be the following:

- Provide a description of the process and of the chemistry involved.
- Describe the accident circumstances and consequences.
- Identify the accident causes with special attention to the chemistry.

- Review the relevant literature to determine if the same accident has occurred earlier.
- Compare the accident circumstances with other accidents or incidents where the same cause/chemistry was involved.
- Identify the considerations and factors, which would provide a warning to prevent the same accident to occur again.

This method of analysis will be exemplified considering well known accidents thoroughly described in the literature or frequent accidents occurring always the same, thus proving the interest of this exercise to prevent accidents from occurring again.

THE SEVESO ACCIDENT ON 10 JULY 1976

This accident had a very important influence on the regulation applied to the chemical industry in the European Community.

The Seveso accident occurred in a process to produce 2,4,5 trichlorophenol by alkaline hydrolysis of 1,2,4,5 tetrachlorobenzene.

As pointed out by Grewer[1] there are two different processes to carry out this reaction. The "old" process is the so-called "Methanol process", a German process where methanolic caustic soda is used for the hydrolysis reaction. This process, very similar to the process involved in the Griesheim accident, is a pressure process operating under the solvent autogeneous pressure i.e. 20 barG in a temperature range of 165°C-180°C[1].

A slightly different process, the Boehringer process[2] operates at a temperature of 140°C thus with a lower pressure but with longer cycle time.

According to Grewer[1] the drawbacks of this process are that no reflux cooling is possible under the process pressure and that caustic soda is not completely soluble in methanol at the process temperature, causing the caustic soda heat of dissolution to add to the heat of reaction of the hydrolysis reaction of $\Delta H = -180$ kJ/mole. This process had four known incidents before the Seveso accident.

The Seveso process is the "Glycol – Xylene" process carried out under ambient pressure. The synthesis reaction is:

This process is a total batch process. At the beginning of the operation, 3235 kg of Ethylene Glycol, 603 kg of Xylene, 2000 kg of solid 1,2,4,5 tetrachlorobenzene and 1000 kg of solid sodium hydroxide, were charged into a 10 m³ stirred reactor equipped with a condenser and a water separator to remove water from the condensate and return xylene into the reactor. The equivalent ratio NaOH / 1,2,4,5 TCB is 2,7. There is an excess of 0.7 equivalent caustic soda with respect to 1,2,4,5 TCB.

The choice of solvents appears to be correct. Caustic soda is soluble in glycol and the organic reactant and product are soluble in xylene. Xylene allows the removal of water by azeotropic distillation. This helps the hydrolysis reaction to go to completion. The reaction mixture should be homogeneous, except for the sodium chloride by product, which should be solid after water removal.

The reaction mixture was heated to 170°C using 12 barG steam with a saturation temperature of 190°C. The reaction mixture was kept at 170°C for four hours and the water – xylene azeotrope was distilled. Then all the xylene and 500 kg of glycol were distilled off by vacuum distillation. Then, on the Saturday of the accident, as the hydrolysis of the phenate with aqueous HCl could not be carried out immediately, and had to be delayed until the following Monday, the steam valve to the heating coil was closed and stirring was stopped 15 minute later at 05:00. This was done to keep the reactor warm over the week-end to prevent the phenate crystallisation. A runaway reaction caused the bursting disc to open at 12:37 i.e. 7.5 hours later, while the reactor was unattended. The whole reactor inventory was released and sprayed over the neighbourhood with a tetrachlorodibenzodioxin content of 3500 ppm. Approximately 2 kg TCDD were released during the reaction vessel blow-down.

There are many variations in the process description published by various authors and details are missing like the reactor volume and material of construction, the reaction temperature, the temperature at which the reactor was left on Saturday morning, whether the steam valve was leaking or not, whether the atmospheric pressure had been re-established with nitrogen or the reactor connected to the atmosphere through some vent line or the reactor completely isolated[1, 3, 4, 5].

A precise drawing of the process is not even available, nor the size of the famous bursting disc. Considering the cost of this accident for the chemical industry as a whole, these details should be made available.

WHAT ARE THE CAUSES OF THE SEVESO ACCIDENT ?

The Seveso accident was caused by the thermal instability of the final reaction mixture after distillation of the xylene and a part of the glycol charge, under vacuum. Most probably the cause of the instability is the presence of anhydrous caustic soda in excess and glycol in the final reaction mixture. In such conditions glycol is not only a solvent but reacts with caustic soda to produce sodium glycoxide and water [5].

$$CH_2OH - CH_2OH + NaOH \rightarrow CH_2OH - CH_2ONa + H_2O$$

$$CH_2OH - CH_2ONa + NaOH \rightarrow CH_2ONa - CH_2ONa + H_2O$$

Dehydration of the reaction mixture by vacuum distillation of the xylene/water azeotrope helps this reaction to proceed.

Diethylene glycol is also formed under alkaline conditions.

$$2\ CH_2OH - CH_2OH \rightarrow CH_2OH - CH_2 - O - CH_2 - CH_2OH + H_2O$$

Other reactions are known at higher temperature:

In 1859, by heating a mixture of KOH and glycol at 250°C, Wurtz[6] obtained potassium oxalate and hydrogen.

$$CH_2OH - CH_2OH + 2\ KOH \rightarrow K_2C_2O_4 + 4H_2.$$

In 1904, by heating an equimolar mixture of ethylene glycol and caustic soda at 230°C-284°C, Nef[7] obtained hydrogen, di and tri ethylene glycol, methanol, ethanol, sodium formate, sodium acetate, sodium oxalate and sodium carbonate. The following reaction mechanism was proved by new experiments carried out at 250°C-350°C by Fry and Schulze[8]:

$$CH_2OH - CH_2OH + 2\ NaOH \rightarrow CH_2ONa - CH_2ONa + 2H_2O.$$

$$CH_2ONa - CH_2ONa + 4\ NaOH \rightarrow C(ONa)_3 - C(ONa)_3 + 4H_2.$$

$$C(ONa)_3\ C(ONa)_3 + 2\ H_2O \rightarrow C_2O_4Na_2 + 4NaOH.$$

Then, the sum of the above reactions is as follows:

$$CH_2OH - CH_2OH + 2\ NaOH \rightarrow C_2O_4Na_2 + 4H_2$$

Then:

$$C_2O_4Na_2 + NaOH \rightarrow HCO_2Na + Na_2CO_3$$

$$HCO_2Na + NaOH \rightarrow Na_2CO_3 + H_2$$

Thus one can write the following reaction:

$$CH_2OH - CH_2OH + 4NaOH \rightarrow 2Na_2CO_3 + 5H_2$$

The gas produced by these reactions is mainly hydrogen. The gas production onset temperature is about 150°C. Gas production increases with temperature and some other gases are obtained in smaller quantity: ethylene, ethane, CO, CH_4, at higher temperature. The decomposition exotherm onset temperature under temperature scan conditions in open and closed test cell is about 230°C-250°C. However the exothermic decomposition of sodium glycoxide and polyglycoxide in glycol and polyglycol solutions is autocatalytic. In isothermal exposures in open VSP test cell, the exotherm initiation may be obtained at 190°C after a long induction period. The autocatalytic nature of sodium glycoxide decomposition may also be deduced from the reaction mechanism as written above.

Cardillo and Girelli [9] studied the reaction of glycol and diethylene glycol with different proportions of caustic soda. Mixtures with 10 % to 30 % caustic soda exhibited exotherms onset temperature of 225°C-230°C. The sample heat of decomposition was 90 to 160 J/g for glycol and 150 to 200 J/g for diethylene glycol.

In the production of polyglycols, accidents occurred during the vacuum distillation of polyglycols over their sodium glycoxides. The sodium polyglycoxide happened to decompose in the column bottom. In the USA, the DIERS in a round robin exercise, studied the decomposition of tetraethylene glycol sodium salt in a tetraethylene glycol solution. The decomposition was best obtained in open cell tests as recommended by the DIERS.

In the Seveso accident, depending on the sodium glycoxide concentration in the reaction mixture, the glycoxide decomposition may have been active at temperatures as low as 160°C or 170°C and may have accelerated later after an induction period. There is no need to assume overheating of the reaction mass or a leak of steam in the limpet coil.

LESSONS LEARNED

In this accident, the cause of the runaway reaction is to have allowed the final reaction mixture after dehydration and evaporation of the solvents, to stay in the reactor at the process temperature for a long period of time, without checking the reaction mixture thermal stability over this period of time.

The rupture disc was not sized on a runaway reaction scenario. Therefore there was no release containment system. The R.D. design basis was to protect the reactor from overpressure during nitrogen push transfer of the reaction mass. It is frequent in multipurpose plants that the emergency relief vents are designed on scenarios independent of the chemistry being made. i.e. the fire case, full heating etc., not necessitating a release containment system. Should a runaway reaction occur, a two-phase flow of the reaction mixture could be sprayed over the neighbourhood. Therefore it would be necessary to review any emergency relief vent to check if a release containment system is necessary in case of runaway reaction. This is a very demanding program.

THE BHOPAL ACCIDENT IN THE NIGHT OF SUNDAY 2 DECEMBER 1984

The facility of Union Carbide India Ltd (UCIL) in Bhopal was built to manufacture Carbaryl by reaction of methyl isocyanate on alpha naphtol.

There were five main plants on the site:

- a carbon monoxide plant
- a phosgene plant where phosgene was produced by reaction of CO with chlorine
- the MIC plant where phosgene was reacted with monomethylamine (MMA) to produce methyl isocyanate
- the Sevin plant where alpha naphtol was produced and reacted with MIC to produce carbaryl
- a pesticide formulation plant.

This facility was situated in a town of 800.000 inhabitants.

Only the MIC plant was involved in the disaster. This plant was described in various papers and books concerning this accident and in ref. [4] and [5].

In the MIC plant, phosgene and MMA are reacted in a gas phase reactor at high temperature to produce methyl carbamoyl chloride (MCC):

$$COCl_2 + CH_3NH_2 \rightarrow CH_3NHCOCl + HCl$$

The outflow of the reactor is quenched with chloroform, the process solvent. After separation of unreacted phosgene, MCC is thermally decomposed into MIC and HCl in a pyrolyzer:

$$CH_3 NH COCl \rightarrow CH_3NCO + HCl$$

Finally MIC is separated from chloroform by distillation in the MIC refining still. Only high purity MIC is sent to the MIC storage vessels.

There were three MIC underground storage tanks. One, n° 619 was empty, the two other tanks were in use. The MIC storage vessels are horizontal cylinders of 57 m^3 nominal capacity each, designed for vacuum and 2.8 barG at 121°C. The storage vessels are pressure vessels allowing a nitrogen pressure of 0.7 to 1,7 barG, to prevent any liquid ingress and help pumping. The MIC was pumped and circulated through a refrigeration unit using chloroform as heat-transfer fluid. The material of construction was 304L stainless steel. The MIC storage vessels were equipped with a combination of a rupture disc and a pressure safety valve in series, with a set pressure of 2,8 barG. The PSV outlet was collected to a vent gas header directed to a scrubber with a circulation of caustic soda solution. The vent gas scrubber capacity was of 4 tonnes of MIC in 30 minutes, then less than 2 tonnes per hour due to the absence of cooling. To obtain this capacity, it was necessary to add 50 % caustic soda to the scrubber when necessary. Both the process vent header and the relief vent header were collected to the scrubber and could also be diverted to the plant flare, as a back-up of the scrubber. The gas scrubber exit was through a 30 m high stack directed to the atmosphere.

The MIC plant was shut-down on 22 October 1984 and was never restarted. The 610 storage tank inventory was 41 tonnes of impure MIC contaminated by 750 kg to 1300 kg chloroform, probably coming from wrong operating conditions in the MIC refining still during plant shut-down. The MIC storage tank cooling system was taken out of service in June 1984. The accident occurred on 2 December 1984 i.e. six weeks after the plant shut-down. Experimental study of the runaway reaction led to the conclusion that 500 kg to 1000 kg water must have entered the tank.

The reaction of MIC with water gives CO_2 and MMA, which further react with MIC to produce DMU:

$$CH_3NCO + H_2O \rightarrow CH_3NH_2 + CO_2$$

$$CH_3NH_2 + CH_3NCO \longrightarrow CH_3NH-\underset{\underset{O}{\|}}{C}-NH.CH_3$$

The heat produced by the above reactions caused MIC polymerisation and the formation of many by-products. The vessel pressure increased due to CO_2 production and MIC vapour pressure. When the PSV discharged, there was probably significant liquid carry over. An estimate of 36 tonnes of material was released, of which 25 tonnes of MIC vapour. The storage vessel did not rupture. The PSV release mass flow-rate was well above the vent gas scrubber capacity. Obviously, the vent gas scrubber design basis was far from taking into account a release mass flow-rate of 10 tonnes/hour of a two-phase flow of the storage vessel inventory. The presence of 7-10 % MMA hydrochloride in the tank residue proved the presence of HCl in the tank, probably coming from upstream in the process.

WHEN DID THE WATER ARRIVE IN 610 STORAGE TANK ?

It is obvious that the water came after the plant shutdown. As there was no circulation in the storage tank after the refrigeration unit shut-down, the water could remain separated in a layer and unreacted for a long time at ambient temperature.

WHERE DID THE WATER COME FROM ?

Considering accidents with isocyanates in general, they occur during plant shut-down due to the use of washing water for cleaning equipments during shut-down. Examples are valve explosions where water or isocyanates came into contact, explosion in pumps, eruption in containers where water and isocyanates are inadvertently mixed. The water may have been cleaning water or water coming from leaks in the plant on heat exchangers and admitted in the 610 storage tank after plant shut-down.

HOW COULD THIS OCCUR ?

This process was a high-tech continuous process with inventories of toxic and flammable products. It was consistent with a large continuous consumption of MIC. If the MIC demand was only occasional, due to problems down-stream, the plant could only start and stop just for the timely MIC consumption, and to fill the underground storage tanks. During the transient shut-down conditions, the MIC purity may have been out of specifications.

This plant design came from the USA in the seventies, from a region where the chemical industry was developed, and large inventories of toxic and flammable materials not considered as a hazard. This type of awareness came later, after the Bhopal accident. Such a disaster had never occurred before.

LESSONS LEARNED

The scenario which led to the Bhopal disaster was very simple and common. If the production of large inventories of such reactive and toxic products had been avoided, if such a process had been installed far from populated areas, the consequences would have been minor.

This accident proves that continuous processes are not less dangerous than batch processes and that they don't exclude large inventories of toxic chemicals.

The occurrence of a runaway reaction due to water ingress in the MIC storage vessel was not taken into account in the vent scrubber design, nor was the possibility of liquid carry-over in the relief system vent line. A proper release containment system was not provided.

THE GRIESHEIM ACCIDENT ON FEBRUARY 22, 1993

On February 22, 1993, a runaway reaction occurred at the Griesheim plant of Hoechst A.G. during which about 10 tons of a reaction mixture were released through a pressure safety valve. The two-phase release was carried over by the north wind and spread over the south part of the factory, the river Main banks and two suburbs of Frankfurt: Schwanheim and

Goldstein. The area concerned by the yellow deposit was of 300.000 m². It was the most serious accident occurred in this company over 130 years[10].

The process concerned was the reaction of ortho chloro nitrobenzene with methanolic caustic soda to produce ortho nitroanisole.

This reaction was carried out in a 36 m³ reaction vessel at a reaction temperature of 80°C and an absolute pressure of 10 bar[11, 12]. The process was a semi-batch process in which 2800 litres of methanol and 5800 litres of o-nitrochlorobenzene were charged to the reaction vessel under stirring. The agitator was then turned off and the liquid level in the reaction vessel was checked manually by opening the manhole cover. The agitator was then restarted and the reactor inventory was heated to about 80°C. Then 15800 litres of cold 15 % wt methanolic caustic soda were introduced over five hours while keeping the reaction mixture temperature at 80°C by cooling through a jacket.

Nitrogen blanketing of the reactor gas phase was achieved after the cold initial charge by applying an additional 3 bar nitrogen pressure to the reactor gas phase, to reduce the oxygen concentration to less than 8 % vol. This oxygen partial pressure was allowed to prevent secondary reactions. Thus no solvent reflux was provided and the process was a pressure process.

The accident enquiry proved that on the operation of the night of 21 to 22 February which was the night of "Rosenmontag" the following failures occurred:

- the agitator was not restarted after checking the reactor liquid level.
- During the introduction of the cold methanolic caustic soda, heating was applied to the reactor to obtain the usual temperature of 80°C whereas cooling was normally necessary.
- After sampling of the reaction mixture to check conversion, the agitator was unfortunately restarted. This was done when the conversion ratio of o-nitrochlorobenzene was only 45 % in the reaction mixture. On mixing the reactor inventory a runaway reaction occurred where the temperature could reach at least 160°C and the pressure 16 barG. The reactor was equipped with a pressure safety valve with a set pressure of 16 barG. The PSV was actuated and its size was large enough to allow liquid carry over. The heat of reaction of the desired reaction was of 140 kJ/mole o-nitrochlorobenzene between 80°C and 120°C, corresponding to an adiabatic temperature rise of ca.100°C. However secondary decomposition reactions involving the nitro group were initiated when the agitation was restarted, with a heat of reaction of 390 kJ/mole[13]. This was also proven by the chemical analysis of the yellow deposit showing significant concentration in azo and azoxy derivatives[10]. It was argued that the side reactions were possible due to a lack of oxygen in the reaction mixture because the reactants were in separate layers in the reactor. The other cause is the high temperature obtained during the runaway reaction.

WHAT ARE THE GENERIC CAUSES OF THE ACCIDENT ?

The most frequent cause of accident in semi-batch processes is the absence of agitation during introduction of the controlling reactant. This was achieved in the Griesheim accident.

This process could have been identified as safety critical since an aromatic nitrocompound was reacted under strong alkaline conditions. It is known that the thermal stability of organic nitrocompounds is lowered by a large extend under alkaline conditions.

The process was operated manually whereas one would expect a computer control for such a process in a 36 m^3 reactor.

There was an alarm if the agitator failed but probably no alarm if the agitator was not started when necessary. This is a frequent short-coming in semi-batch processes.

There was a pressure safety valve on the reactor for another reason and therefore no release collection system was provided. However, should a runaway reaction occur, a two phase release of the vessel inventory was possible.

DID THIS ACCIDENT OCCUR BEFORE ?

The answer is yes. In a document provided by Sumitomo Chemical Ltd[14], a list of chemical accidents occurred in Japan between 1971 and 1981 is given, among which the following:

In a process to manufacture o-nitroanisole from o-chloronitrobenzene, by adding o-nitrochlorobenzene in caustic methanol solution, abnormal reaction occurred when the stirrer was restarted after the stoppage. Nine were injured.

LESSONS LEARNED

- A process where an organic nitrocompound is reacted under strong alkaline conditions should be considered as safety critical.
- In a semi-batch process with high exotherm potential, agitation should be controlled by a computer and safety interlocks. No action should be undertaken if the agitator is not running.
- Pressure safety valves on reactors with a runaway reaction potential, should be reviewed to check for the necessity of a release containment system.
- The products of the runaway reaction, involving side reactions or subsequent decomposition reactions are very different from the desired reaction products. So are their toxic properties. Therefore, the need for a release containment system should not be discussed on the basis of the normal reaction products but on those of the runaway reaction.
- The accidents occurred on the same process should be known by the plant manager and considered in safety reviews.
- This accident had an unexpected mediatic impact – see ref.[15] – and probably caused the withdrawal of the company from the chemical industry.
- A commission was created by the federal government of the FRG to determine the minimum knowledge required to be allowed to run a process[16]. This was added to the German regulation. This accident had an influence on the regulation applied to the Chemical Industry in Germany.

THE PHENOL + FORMALDEHYDE RUNAWAY REACTION

The phenol + formaldehyde reaction is commonly used in the chemical industry to manufacture formo-phenolic resins. This reaction caused many runaway reaction accidents[17]. The hazards of this reaction was exemplified in previous papers[18, 19] by considering a Resole base catalysed reaction where the formaldehyde to phenol molar ratio was R = 1,897. This process includes two separate reaction steps: the methylolation reaction and the salification of the methylolated phenol.

In the methylolation step, formaldehyde is reacted with phenol to obtain a methylolated phenol, in the presence of a catalytic quantity of caustic soda.

The reaction is carried out in a stirred reactor equipped with a condenser. The reactor can be heated or cooled through a jacket.

Phenol is charged to the reactor with the catalytic amount of caustic soda. The reaction mixture temperature is set to 60°C and 37 % wt formaldehyde aqueous solution is introduced over two hours under temperature control by cooling. The reaction mixture is then kept at 60°C to allow the reaction to come to completion. Then the reactor is cooled to 50°C.

In the salification step, a stoichiometric amount of 30 % wt caustic soda is introduced over 30 minutes under temperature control at 50°C, to obtain a phenate.

There is a well known dangerous process deviation which consists of forgetting to introduce the catalytic quantity of caustic soda in the methylolation step, not detecting the mistake and starting the introduction of the stoichiometric amount of caustic soda in the salification step. Obviously, the reactant of the salification step is the catalyst of the previous methylolation step. Should this process deviation occur, the exothermic methylolation reaction is initiated when the whole inventory of formaldehyde is present and unreacted. The fast temperature rise will trigger the polymerisation reaction causing the reactor to pressurise and often to explode, together with the gelification of the reactor inventory.

The gelification reaction is:

The absence of catalyst in the methylolation step may remain undetected because it has no effect on the reactor temperature which is controlled at 60°C. An experimental study of this worst case scenario based on Vent Sizing Package experiments was carried out, where a pressure surge to 37 bar abs. and a maximum heat-rate of 680°C/min. were obtained. See figure 1. The reaction mixture is a high vapour system. The venting requirement for the worst case scenario is a rupture disc of 1 metre in diameter for 30 tonne inventory reactors, like those exploding in the recent period. Atmospheric venting is necessary to prevent the vent blockage by the reaction mixture gelification.

Other process deviations may also cause problems in relation to reactant accumulation or reaction mixture instability. The methylolation final reaction mixture may polymerise a few degree Celsius above 60°C. The corresponding adiabatic temperature rise is 100°C.

During formaldehyde injection in the methylolation step, accumulation of the controlling reactant and its subsequent reaction may initiate the reaction mixture polymerisation above 60°C. The causes of formaldehyde accumulation are: too low a temperature, too high a reactant feed rate, no agitation.

The loss of cooling or a wrong temperature control may also cause the reaction mixture polymerisation. The methylolation final reaction mixture is not stable even at ambient temperature and cannot be safely stored or transported. Gelification proceeds slowly at ambient temperature.

The process considered is therefore safety critical and a number of safety interlocks are recommended to prevent runaway reaction accidents:

1. Interlocks to prevent wrong reactant introduction in the methylolation step.
   - The formaldehyde introduction must not be allowed if the catalytic quantity of caustic soda has not been previously introduced.
   - The formaldehyde introduction must be interrupted if the cooling demand is not obtained in the reactor jacket cooling loop.
   - The catalyst must not be introduced after the beginning of formaldehyde injection.
   - The introduction of the controlling reactant, formaldehyde, must be prevented or interrupted if there is no agitation.
2. Interlocks to prevent the controlling reactant accumulation:
   - Low temperature interlock interrupting the formaldehyde introduction.
   - Limitation of the formaldehyde feed-rate by a diaphragm.
3. Interlocks to prevent the reaction mixture polymerisation by too high a temperature:
   - High temperature interlock interrupting formaldehyde introduction and providing full cooling capacity on the reactor jacket.

In addition, the methylolation final reaction mixture must not be kept for a long period of time without temperature control in a large reactor at the process temperature or under ambient temperature, because the polymerisation proceeds slowly and may speed up.

The merit of high integrity interlocks may be taken into account to reduce runaway reaction accident scenarios, thus reducing the reactor venting requirement.

THE ACCIDENTAL BULK POLYMERISATION OF REACTIVE MONOMERS

The bulk polymerisation of reactive monomers like vinyl acetate, acrylic acid and others, is not currently used in industrial processes, due to the violence of the reaction. However this type of reaction is frequently involved in polymerisation accidents concerning the storage of recycled monomers and premix vessels.

Recycled monomers are obtained in processes where the polymerisation conversion ratio is not 100 %. The unreacted monomers are recovered and stored to be recycled in the polymerisation process. Theses monomers may contain a very low polymerisation inhibitor concentration and some traces of polymerisation initiator. They are much less stable than commercial inhibited monomers.

The use of premix of polymerisation initiator dissolved in the monomers appears to be frequent in polymerisation processes. This allows the introduction of the polymerisation initiator in the polymerisation process, not necessitating the use of a solvent to dissolve the initiator.

These premix with a high concentration of initiator are very unstable and give very violent polymerisation. The accidents are also frequent. This can be easily understood.

The kinetic behaviour of radical chain polymerisations has been presented by Flory[20]. In this theory, the rate of monomer consumption is referred as the rate of polymerisation.

$$R_p = -\frac{d[M]}{dt} = k_p[M][P]$$

where [M] is the monomer concentration, [P] is the polymer radical concentration and k_p is the propagation rate constant.

According to the theory of Flory, the rate of polymerisation is controlled by the initiator concentration[20, 21].

$$R_p = -\frac{d[M]}{dt} = k_p[M](k_d \, f[I]/k_t)^{1/2}$$

where k_d is the initiator decomposition rate constant, k_t the termination rate constant, [I] the initiator concentration, f the fraction of initiator radicals successfully reacting with the monomer.

Consequently, the rate of polymerisation is an Arrhenius function with first order with respect to the monomer concentration and half order with respect to the initiator concentration which controls the population of polymer radicals.

Considering the maximum rate of polymerisation, the higher the initiator concentration, the faster the maximum rate of polymerisation. This explains the very violent polymerisation observed in premix vessel polymerisation accidents, where very high initiator concentration is present. See figure 2.

In the case of commercial monomer storage, the induction period is the time necessary for the monomer thermally generated radicals to consume the inhibitor concentration[20]

$$t = \frac{[Z]}{k_o e^{-E/RT} \cdot [M]} \qquad t = \frac{m[Z]}{k_o e^{-E/RT} \cdot [M]}$$

depending on whether one or more monomer radicals react with each molecule of inhibitor Z. This way not be the case if a polymerisation catalyst is present and if the inhibitor is eliminated first. Then the isothermal induction period is:

$$t = \frac{m[Z]}{k_o e^{-E/RT} \cdot [M] + k_{do} e^{-Ed/RT}[I]}$$

In this case, the polymerisation inhibitor is consumed by the monomer thermal generation of radicals and by the decomposition of the polymerisation initiator. Under moderate temperature where the polymerisation initiator is active and the thermal generation of monomer radicals negligible compared to that of the initiator, the above equation reduces to:

$$t = \frac{m[Z]}{k_{do} \cdot e^{-Ed/RT}[I]}$$

In this case, the polymerisation isothermal induction period is an Arrhenius function of the inhibitor and polymerisation initiator concentrations with an activation energy Ed characteristic of the polymerisation initiator.

This allows a much shorter polymerisation isothermal induction period than in commercial monomer storage. Consequently the probability of having a polymerisation incident in premix vessels or in recovered monomer storage vessels is much higher than in commercial monomer storage vessels and the polymerisation is faster or more violent. Therefore these process situations should be excluded where possible or carefully controlled.

CONCLUSION

The accident case histories discussed in this paper as well as the consideration of two processes where well identified runaway reaction scenarios are known, emphasise the interest of a good understanding of process relevant chemistry.

An effort devoted to the study of the process relevant literature could certainly help to prevent such accidents. A special attention should be paid to possible or frequent process deviations such as the absence of agitation, abnormal residence time, cooling or cleaning fluid ingress to the process side.

The side reactions occurring in case of process deviation should be taken into account. Abnormal toxic products may be obtained together with increased reaction exotherm.

When an emergency relief vent is provided, based on a runaway reaction scenario, the design of a release containment system with sufficient capacity should be included in the project. Also, the revision of existing vents with consideration of possible runaway reaction scenarios should lead to the installation of release containment systems. The assessment of the release toxic properties should take into account possible side reactions and not only the normal synthesis reaction. This could influence the design and size of the release containment system.

The general conclusion that continuous processes are safer than semi-batch processes should be revised taking into account the Bhopal accident circumstances. An oversized continuous process producing toxic products may lead to very unsafe conditions due to the product or intermediate inventories. The reduction or elimination of toxic products inventories should be considered as a priority and should be taken into account in process design.

The care taken to the core process design should also be applied to more neglected operations such as reactant recycling, premix preparation, product storage facilities. Again, a good knowledge of the product properties and of the chemistry involved is necessary.

The use of high integrity safety interlocks should be preferred to manual operation, to prevent simple process deviations such as the absence of agitation, or control catalyst introduction in a reaction mixture.

The above conclusions are only a small part of the lessons learned from the study of these well-known accidents. They emphasise the interest of this activity to complement hazards studies based on risk assessment methods.

LITERATURE

1.   Grewer Th., "Thermal Hazards of Chemical Reactions", Industrial Safety Series, vol. 4, 324-328, Elsevier.
2.   Braun R., Schönbucher A., "Simulation von Semibatchprozessen am Beispiel einer komplexen chemischen Reaktion", Chemische Reaktionen, Erkennung und Beherrschung sicherheitstechnisch relevanter Zustände und Ablaufe. Praxis des Sicherheitstechnik, vol. 4, 35 Tutzing-Symposion (1997), 157-169, Dechema e.V.
3.   Bretherick, Handbook of Chemical Reactive Hazards, p. 680.

4.   Ralph King, "Safety in the Process Industries", Butterworth Heinemann, 1990, 83-89.
5.   V.C. Marshall, "Major Chemical Hazards", John Wiley and Sons, 1987, 356-369.
6.   Wurtz A., "Mémoire sur les glycols ou alcools diatoniques". Ann. Chim. Phys., 3, 400 (1859).
7.   Nef J. U., "Ueber das Verhalten der Glycole und des Glycerins gegen Aetzalkalien und gegen Oxydationsmittel", Annalen, 335, 310 (1904)
8.   Fry H.S., Schulze E.L., "The liberation of hydrogen from carbon compounds. IV The interaction of glycol and glycerol with fused caustic alkalies", J. Am. Chem. Soc., 50, 1131 (1928).
9.   P. Cardillo, A. Girelli, "Comportamento termico di miscele NaOH/glicol etilenico e NaOH/glicol dietilenico. La chimica e l'industria, 64, n° 12, 781 (1982).
10.   Vennen H., "Störfälle in Serie ?", Hoechst im Dialog, 1993.
11.   Klais O., Wörsdörfer U., Westphal F., "Griesheim runaway reaction – Thermochemical investigation" in "Safety and Runaway Reactions, Major accident Hazards Bureau, Joint Research Centre, European Commission, 1997, 23-30.
12.   Klais O., Wörsdörfer U., "Ergebnisse der thermochemischen Untersuchungen zum Störfall im Werk Griesheim". Praxis der Sicherheitstechnik vol. 4, Dechema e.V., Frankfurt am Main, 1997, 41-81.
13.   Klais O., Wörsdörfer U., Westphal F., "Thermochemische Untersuchung zum Störfall Griesheim", Chem. Ing. Tech. 66 (1994) n° 9, 1169-1170.
14.   Sumitomo chemical Ltd, "Accident case histories of reactive materials" – case n° 36, 1973.
15.   Kepplinger H.M., Hartung U., "Störfall – Fieber. Wie ein Unfall zum Schlüsselereignis einer Unfallserie wird", Alber-Broschur-Kommunikation. Verlag Karl Alber GmbH, Freiburg/München (1995).
16.   TAABMU, "Technischer Ausschuss für Anlagensicherheit" "Leitfaden Erkennen und Beherrschen exothermer chemischer Reaktionen" TAA-GS-05, 12.04.1994.
17.   The British Plastic Federation Thermosetting Material Group, "Guidelines for the Safe production of Phenolic Resins". British Plastic Federation, London, 1979.
18.   Gustin J.L., Fillion J., Treand G., El Biyaali K., "The phenol + Formaldehyde runaway reaction, vent sizing for reactor protection". J. Loss Prev. Process Ind. 6 (2) 1993, 103-113.
19.   Gustin J.L., "Choice of Runaway Reaction Scenarios for vent sizing based on pseudo-adiabatic calorimetric techniques". 1st Symposium on Runaway Reactions, Pressure Relief Design and Effluent Handling, March 11-13, 1998, New Orleans, Louisiana. A.I.Ch.E., New York. G.A. Melhem and H.G. Fischer editors.
20.   Ham G.E., "Kinetics and Mechanisms of Polymerisations", Marcel Dekker Inc., New York, 1967.
21.   Gustin J.L., "Understanding vinyl acetate polymerization accidents", I.Chem.E. Symposium Series n° 144, 387-403.

FIGURE 1

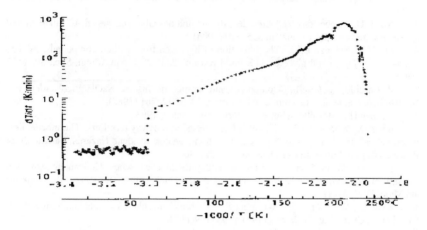

Figure 1: VSP test. Heat rate curve of the worst credible scenario
Phenol + Formaldehyde runaway reaction as described.

FIGURE 2

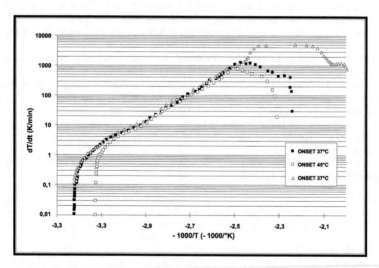

Figure 2: VSP closed cell experiment. Polymerisation of vinyl acetate monomers with 1.8 %
w/w dilauroyl peroxide initiated by a constant temperature exposures at 37°C and 45°C. Heat
rate curves.

A SYSTEMATIC APPROACH TO REACTIVE CHEMICALS ANALYSIS

M. Sam Mannan, William J. Rogers, and Abdulrehman Aldeeb
Mary Kay O'Connor Process Safety Center, Chemical Engineering Department, Texas A&M University System, College Station, Texas 77843-3122, USA (mannan@tamu.edu)

Reactive chemicals are chemicals that can, under certain conditions, release very large and potentially dangerous amounts of energy. Reactive chemicals can lead to reactions that differ from the routine mainly in the rate at which they progress. A chemical reaction can be considered routine if the reaction rate is relatively slow or can be easily controlled. It is this question of rate of reaction and ability to control that marks certain chemicals as warranting special precautions and the label "reactive chemical." The primary difficulty in identifying reactive chemicals stems from the variety of conditions under which certain chemicals can undergo an uncontrollable hazardous reaction. Some chemicals are simply unstable and can vigorously polymerize, decompose or condense, or become self-reactive. Other chemicals can react violently when exposed to common environmental chemicals or conditions. A major difficulty, which arises when one considers the problem as a whole, is that it is often not appreciated that the reactive chemical hazards is seldom a unique characteristic of the chemical or the process itself but highly dependent on the process conditions and mode of operation. For example, a simple property such as flash point can be used to determine the fire or explosion hazard of a substance. In contrast, the identification of a reactive hazard requires the detailed evaluation of both the properties of the substances used and the operating conditions. The dilemma is that many so-called "benign" reactions can become highly reactive or undergo a runaway reaction under slightly different conditions or the introduction of minute impurities. This paper provides a background of the reactive chemicals problem including a summary of chemical incidents that can be attributed to reactive chemical events. Based on the extent of the problem, a systematic approach to reactive chemicals analysis is suggested. The approach is a tiered framework where one can start with simple screening tools based on thermophysical property and thermodynamic analysis, use of quantum mechanics and transitional state theory, and finally the use of experimental measurements.

Keywords: Process Safety, Reactive Chemicals Analysis, Loss Prevention, Quantum Mechanics, Calorimetric Measurements

INTRODUCTION

Some chemicals react spontaneously with very common chemicals in the environment such as water or the components of the atmosphere. Many pure metals for example will oxidize on exposure to the atmosphere. Many chemicals are stable except when combined with certain other chemicals.

Some chemicals require very little energy of activation to initiate a spontaneous reaction. If the reaction is exothermic the energy initially produced may accelerate a continued reaction and a release of energy too violent to be controlled. Temperature, shock, static, or light may trigger an uncontrollable reaction. In some combinations one chemical will act as a catalyst reducing the amount of energy normally needed to initiate or sustain a reaction.

Spontaneous decomposition or changes in physical state, even at a slow rate, may create a reactive hazard by creating a less stable chemical. For some chemicals this decomposition is rapid and violent. For others it is so slow as to be imperceptible but results in a byproduct with a much higher reactivity hazard. Peroxides, which can form when certain organic chemicals are exposed to air, will radically increase the hazards of working with those chemicals. The formation of shock sensitive picric acid crystals from an aqueous solution is a serious hazard created by a simple physical state change in the same chemical.

There are some additional hazardous conditions that are not usually attributed to "reactive chemicals" but should be mentioned. Extreme differences in physical state can cause an uncontrollable release of energy. For example, bringing a hot liquid such as an oil into contact with a liquid with a lower boiling point such as water will cause instantaneous vaporization of the lower boiling point liquid and a violent release of energy.

CHARACTERIZATION OF CHEMICAL REACTIVITY

Many procedures have been suggested in the recent literature for categorizing reactive chemicals. Since the needs for an assessment procedure varies from one industry to another, much effort has been addressed to this subject. A generalized approach to an assessment process stills remains an ultimate goal. A successful approach should be based on an understanding of the stoichiometry, thermodynamics, and kinetics of the reactive system and ideally should require minimum time and inexpensive procedures. In this section we will refer to some of the relevant work during the last few years.

Application of thermal analysis techniques to evaluate reactive chemical hazards has been a major concern for researchers. Zatka (1979) discussed the ability to solve, to some extent, the reactivity questions of substances and reaction mixtures by using commercial differential scanning calorimeter (DSC) and differential thermal analysis (DTA) equipment. In 1985, Kohlbrand presented an experimental procedure to test the runaway potential of reactive chemicals. He suggested using the DSC as a first step and then the accelerated rate calorimeter (ARC) in a more advanced reactivity investigation, especially for pilot plant operations. Gygax (1990) suggested a two-level thermal analysis procedure. The first level was to determine the energy potential and the temperature region of significant thermal activity using microthermal analysis and isoperibolic experiments. The second level was to determine the thermokinetic parameters of the overall reaction using isothermal and adiabatic experiments.

Estimating process safety parameters is another goal of applying thermal analysis testing. Kellet et al. (1997) suggested the use of dynamic DSC and isothermal DSC measurements to evaluate the time to maximum rate under adiabatic conditions (ΔTMR_{ad}) and comparing to values based on simulation. They concluded that this estimation method is useful for preliminary screening procedures for reactive chemical hazard evaluation.

Many other studies were conducted to present the uses of calorimetry in reactivity evaluations or to present modified calorimeters. LeBlond et al. (1996) presented the importance of using reaction calorimetry to obtain high quality kinetics parameters even for complex multi-step reactions. Since adiabatic conditions are maintained during runaway reactions, adiabatic calorimeters are considered the most representative of the behavior of real processes. Sempere et al. (1997) studied the suitability of using various adiabatic equipment in evaluating exothermic reaction hazards such as for decompositions. Heldt and Anderson (1996) discussed the application of modified adiabatic calorimeters to perform chemical reactivity analysis. Townsend and Tou (1980) presented development of accelerated rate calorimeter (ARC) to study reactions taking place under adiabatic conditions to provide time-temperature-pressure data. Fauske (1998) described the use of the reactive system screening tool (RSST) as an early testing step for evaluating reactive chemical hazards.

For each of the suggested techniques there are advantages and disadvantages. Kars and Visser (1996) suggested as a screening tool the shell-modified Sikares calorimeter, which combines some advantages of adiabatic and DSC techniques. Other researchers conducted studies to compare the various techniques. Duh et al. (1996) performed a study to compare the Arrhenius parameters obtained from isothermal, adiabatic, and temperature programmed methods. Leonhardt and Hugo (1997) presented comparisons of thermokinetic data obtained by isothermal, isoperiolic, adiabatic, and temperature programmed measurements. Pastré et al. (2000) conducted a comparison between adiabatic calorimetric and dynamic DSC measurements to estimate time to maximum rate (TMR$_{ad}$).

Estimating reliable kinetic parameters of the main reaction pathway is essential for reactive chemical hazard evaluation. Calorimetric analysis will provide acceptable parameters for homogeneous and one-dimensional chemical systems. However, laboratory investigations are expensive and time-consuming when systems are more complicated. Also, the measured parameters are often not of high accuracy, making reliable thermal hazard evaluation more difficult or impossible [Maria & Heinzle 1998].

Researchers have suggested novel simplification techniques for complex reactions, to reduce the experimental effort. Grewer et al. (1999) discussed the application of calculations based on theoretical models to predict thermodynamic parameters of primary and secondary reactions using the Chemical Thermodynamic and Energy Release Program (CHETAH). Laboratory investigation could then be implemented in case the theoretical approach failed. Maria & Heinzle (1998) suggested those kinetic parameters to be measured from isothermal concentration data and simulated to other kinetic parameters of similar known reactive systems available in databank to help define the reaction pathway. These kinetic parameters could be verified using temperature programmed-DSC. Liaw et al. (2000) developed a mathematical model to predict thermal hazard parameters by simulating adiabatic calorimeter data. Marco et al. (2000) performed isothermal reaction concentration-time experiments and obtained the kinetic equation describing the chemical reaction. The simulation results were compared to temperature-time data for the same reaction obtained from near-adiabatic advanced reactive system screening tool (ARSST) experiment. The combination of isothermal concentration-time results with temperature-time results can help to determine more accurate kinetic parameters and reaction pathways.

Introducing theoretical models of computational chemistry and statistical thermodynamics for predicting thermodynamic parameters was discussed by Bruneton et al. (1997 & 1998). Knowing the system thermodynamics helps focus on the most energetic and therefore the most potentially hazardous reaction pathways.

SYSTEMATIC APPROACH

An evaluation of chemical reactivity must be based on essential information, which includes:

- process operating conditions
- process chemistry mechanisms
- conditions under which chemical reactive hazards can appear
- parameters for quantifying reactive chemicals hazards

Defining these conditions and parameters helps simulate the chemical process for optimum safe and economical operating conditions. Evaluating this information is not an easy task. Laboratory testing has been the traditional approach to evaluate chemical reactivity. This approach is practical for simple systems, but may not be applicable for more complex systems. Because of the large number of chemical compounds and different reaction scenarios, evaluation can be very expensive and time consuming. Moreover, in case of a complex reactive system, experimental procedures will provide an overall evaluation of system thermodynamics and kinetics data but will not explain reaction pathways. In fact, system analysis is required beyond laboratory measurements.

Discussed in this paper is a systematic approach to chemical reactivity characterization that consists of three levels, as shown in Figure 1. In each level, the reactive system is evaluated to understand the reaction chemistry, identify the possibility of thermal exothermal activity, and quantify the reactive chemical hazards. The three evaluation levels are:

1. screening evaluation
2. computation evaluation
3. experimental analysis

In the screening evaluation level, reactants, products, and operating conditions are identified. Literature and databases are searched for relevant data for the various substances in the chemical system.   Relevant data include physical and chemical properties, thermodynamics, kinetics, incidents, and case studies. In addition, in this level, some computations and measurements are made for a preliminary reactivity evaluation. In this evaluation level, some chemicals or reactions that clearly present no hazardous potential can be excluded from further evaluation.

In the second level, all possible reaction pathways are proposed and their feasibility is evaluated based on available information or on predicted properties using numerical techniques such as computational quantum chemistry, statistical thermodynamics, and transition state theory. The non-feasible and non-hazardous reaction pathways are excluded and the remaining ones are tested in the third level of evaluation.

The third level includes experimental analysis. At this level, the numbers of reactions and chemicals to be tested are reduced. More screening tests are performed to exclude more reaction possibilities and to direct the most hazardous reactions to the more advanced experimental techniques. In each of the three evaluation levels, predicting or calculating stoichiometric, thermodynamic, and kinetic parameters are the main objectives and many reaction pathways are thereby excluded from the need for expensive experimental analysis.

Each of these three levels is discussed in the following sections.

LEVEL 1: SCREENING

The screening level is of great importance for the evaluation of chemical reactivity. Screening may include many simple tools to identify thermal hazards of any chemical. Some of these tools are:

1. literature review
2. oxygen balance criterion
3. molecular structure considerations
4. chemical incompatibility

Determining possible reactants, products, operating temperature and pressure ranges, and any other parameters that may affect the process will identify a reactive system. Once the reactive system is identified, the literature is searched for determining some of the stoichiometric, thermodynamic and kinetic parameters based on previously studied systems with similar components. This information may be used in more advanced evaluation levels. Searching the literature also may yield information about incidents due to the same or similar chemicals.

Oxygen balance calculations are used within the screening level as the amount of oxygen, expressed as weight percent, liberated as a result of complete conversion of the material to relatively simple oxidized molecules. This oxygen balance relates to the number of oxygen and reducing atoms in the substance itself. If all reducing atoms can be oxidized completely without excess oxygen, the oxygen balance is zero, and the energy generation of the substance is maximum and is independent of the external oxygen concentration. For molecules containing the elements carbon, hydrogen, and oxygen, oxygen balance is expressed by:

$$\text{Oxygen Balance} = \frac{-1600\left[2x+\left(\dfrac{y}{2}\right)-z\right]}{MW}$$

where x is the number of carbon atoms, y is the number of hydrogen atoms, z is the number of oxygen atoms, and MW is the molecular weight.

A criterion for the value of this balance was proposed, because, in some cases the results of this simple tool may be misleading by bearing no necessary relationship to hazard potential. Shanley & Melhem (1995) studied some familiar compounds of known hazard potential, and found that oxygen balance values do not correlate well with the known hazard potential of these compounds. More detailed discussion is provided in [Shanley & Melhem 1995] [CCPS 1995].

The molecular structure of the various components is another screening tool. Some typical structural similarities in high-energy substances are the relative degree of unsaturation, high proportion or high local concentration of nitrogen in the molecular structure, and nitrogen-to-hydrogen bonds [Bretherick 1987]. Some of the well-known molecular structures are used for identifying the presence of reactive chemical hazards, as shown in Tables 1 and 2.

The existence of any of these functional groups and their unstable structure may be an indication for thermal instability, but this is not guaranteed. For example, the presence of a nitro group attached to a long aliphatic chain does not show a thermal hazard possibility, even though the nitro group is one of the unstable structures. On the other hand, the initial absence of unstable groups is no guarantee for long-term stability of the compound. For example, some aldehydes and ethers are easily converted to peroxides by reaction with oxygen from air [CCPS 1995]. The list of unstable structures in Table 1 is not comprehensive, but it is a tool for reactivity indications.

Knowing the molecular structure of each compound in the system may be used for calculating exothermic potential. Various methods have been used such as heat of formation method [CCPS 1995], and average bond energy summation [Craven 1987]. These methods depend on values of heat of formation of various molecules or bond energy, which are often available in the literature. High accuracy is not an objective for these methods, but preliminary evaluations and indications are useful for screening purposes.

The hazards resulting from inadvertent mixing of chemicals such as explosion, fire, excessive increase in pressure or heat or the release of toxic vapors is addressed as chemical incompatibility, which is a well-recognized problem. Much effort was required for developing chemicals incompatibility charts and tables, which are available in the literature [Winder & Zarie 2000] [Hofelich et al. 1994]. Incompatibility is a matter of degree, however, many parameters such as temperature, amount of material, maximum process pressure, and time of mixing may affect the degree of hazard. Hence, when using the available incompatibility charts and tables, system conditions must be specified. In cases where chemicals of interest are not tabulated, a simple mixing test may help provide an indication of incompatibility, which may require advanced testing. More advanced compatibility analysis evaluation methods are available [Hofelich et al. 1994] [Duh et al. 1997].

As shown above, there are many preliminary screening tools. The indications are that these tools should be used with caution. In some cases, the screening level evaluation may result in excluding some obviously safe compounds or reactions from further investigation procedures.

LEVEL 2: COMPUTATIONAL MODELS

Maintaining the safe operation limits for any chemical process is a primary goal of reactive chemical hazard evaluation. Simulating the dynamic behavior of the process ideally will determine process safe operating conditions. Process simulation is often not possible because of insufficient information. This information includes possible reaction pathways and stoichiometries, thermodynamic parameters, and kinetics of the primary and secondary reactions. However, as shown in the previous section, such information is not usually available in the literature or in databanks, especially, for less common and new systems.

To evaluate the potential of reactive chemical hazards, process parameters must be estimated. An experimental approach, in which the possible exothermic reactions are reproduced in the laboratory, could be taken. However, starting with this approach directly, without additional screening steps was found to be time consuming and expensive, due to the large number of possible reaction pathways, even for relatively simple systems. Also, highly unexpected exothermic secondary reactions may dictate the magnitude and time scales of heat releases during the runaway, and increase the difficulty of interpreting the data of currently used experimental techniques [Bruneton et al. 1998].

In this approach, a computational screening tier is proposed, as illustrated in Figure 2. Identification of the stoichiometries of the reactions that drive thermal instability is a major factor to understanding safety issues of a reactive system. Also, identification of the various possible pathways is the first step to start this computational screening tier.

In most reactive systems, primary reactants and products are known, but products of the secondary reactions are not known. Initially, as shown in Figure 2, a set of possible reaction pathways must be proposed. The basis of this step may vary depending on the system. Available information of similar systems may be used to build this set of possible pathways. Experimental information about the products formed and the subsequent chemistry is another basis for building this set of possible pathways.

The main objective of this computational screening tier is to exclude (eliminate) any infeasible or non-hazardous pathways and to evaluate the reactive chemical hazards for the remaining reactions through the estimated stoichiometries, thermodynamic, and kinetic parameters of the reaction system.

Once the reactants and products are identified or proposed, missing thermodynamic parameters can be estimated using the following numerical methods:

1. molecular group contribution methods
2. statistical thermodynamics combined with computational quantum chemistry methods

Molecular contribution methods are theoretical techniques, which use bond and group contributions in known chemical structures to estimate thermodynamic parameters (e.g. Gibbs free energy, heat of formation and heat of reaction) of the system.

Many different group contribution methods are available; however, the method of Benson (1970) which is used in the CHETAH program is the most widely acceptable one. Molecular group contribution methods are preliminary screening tools to detect sufficiently

46

unstable molecules. Sometimes they are not able to predict the thermodynamics of certain molecules, because some groups are not implemented in these methods [Bruneton et al. 1997]. In fact, these methods are based on correlations obtained from a large number of experimental values of thermodynamic properties for common molecules. Occasionally, these methods are unable to differentiate between the various molecular configurations such as isomers, leading to large deviations in the calculated enthalpies. In such cases, implementation of computational quantum chemistry is the next step for the evaluation of system thermodynamics.

Computational quantum chemistry is based on molecular quantum theory when the motion and distribution of electrons is described in terms of electron probability distributions or molecular orbital [Bruneton et al. 1997]. Numerical techniques have been developed to perform the quantum chemistry calculations. Among the most known techniques are Density Functional Theory (DFT), Hartree-Fock (HF), and semi-empirical parameter techniques. The fundamental quantum chemistry methods, which are also called ab-initio methods, are coupling with statistical thermodynamics to estimate thermodynamic properties, such as enthalpy and entropy of formation of the reactants and products, enthalpy and entropy of the reaction, Gibbs free energy of the ideal gas reaction, and Gibbs free energy of mixing of the reaction.

Predicting thermodynamic information will help, as shown in Figure 2, in excluding infeasible reactions (pathways) and non-hazardous molecules of the proposed pathways. The amount of energy released in any exothermic reaction is not the only key issue in evaluating the hazard of reactive chemicals, although it is essential. The energetic reactions (pathways) will be carried to a more advanced evaluation. The rate (kinetics) at which this energy can be released is the most critical issue. Evaluating the kinetics (activation energy, rate constant) of the reaction system can be challenging or infeasible in case of a complex system of reaction pathways.

A second step of numerical calculations is proposed. Combining computational quantum chemistry (ab-initio methods) with Transition State Theory (TST) calculations is an approach to evaluate reactive system kinetics. Utilizing ab-initio and TST calculations depends on identifying the stoichiometry of the reactions, and then identifying the elementary steps involved in these reactions. The GAUSSIAN package is a commercial software application of ab-initio calculations. More theory and practice of this package is found in [Hinchlifle, 1994]. Unfortunately, applying TST calculations for predicting kinetics may not be useful for some complex systems, but coupling the predicted thermodynamic parameters with concentration-time experimental data is another way to estimate the kinetics of a reactive system.

At the end of this theoretical reactive system evaluation, we conclude that the ability to predict accurate kinetics depends partly on the predicted stoichiometry of the system, which was performed at the beginning and throughout this computational tier. The most exothermic reactions could be further investigated by means of the experimental analysis tier.

LEVEL 3: EXPERIMENTAL METHODS

Most of the safety and thermal reaction risk estimations are based on the exact characterization of a reaction system, including knowledge of the reaction stoichiometry, thermodynamic, and kinetic parameters.

An exact determination of the reaction parameters by traditional means requires extensive and time-consuming laboratory investigations, which may not be cost-effective for many specialty chemicals or immediately applicable to large-scale production purposes due to the variability in raw materials and operating conditions [Maria & Heinzle 1998]. However, as shown in the previous section, the results using the theoretical computational thermodynamics and kinetics approaches are very dependent on the initial assumptions and process conditions used in the evaluation process. Incorrect assumptions may result in the hazards of the system being greatly over or underestimated. As a result, the parameter prediction process is not safe enough for the most energetic reactions within the system.

In such cases, where the theoretical approach is indicating a potential for exothermal activity (chemical reactivity), a more thorough investigation is required for more exact parameter determinations. Up to this point, theoretical computational methods helped to exclude non-hazardous reaction pathways, indicating the most exothermal reactions, and predicting reliable stoichiometric, thermodynamic, and kinetic parameters. Such knowledge will help to guide the experimental investigations.

For a single reaction, sufficiently accurate estimates of the thermodynamic and kinetic parameters can be achieved by using calorimetric methods [Maria & Heinzle 1998]. However, for more complex reacting systems (more than one reaction), calorimetric methods will provide overall measurements of thermodynamic and kinetic parameters without an explanation of reaction pathways and stoichiometries. Hence, meaningful interpretation of the experimental results based on reaction pathways might be impossible. The previous theoretical approach of reaction pathways and parameter prediction should be performed to develop an approximate model for the reaction mechanism. A reaction mechanism may also be obtained by isothermal time-concentration experiments through a direct measurement of species concentrations and kinetic parameters. Understanding the reacting systems' chemistry is essential for reactivity evaluation, and because of that, a major effort to identify reaction pathways is required by the different means of theoretical approaches, as shown in the previous section, or by experimental approach, as discussed below.

Experimental techniques for chemical reactivity evaluations produce data of varying quality. Mainly, there are four common techniques including temperature-programmed differential scanning calorimeter (DSC), isoperibolic, isothermal, and adiabatic analysis. In this approach these techniques are divided into two levels:

a. screening analysis techniques
b. advanced analysis techniques

Figure 3 illustrates the experimental analysis level of this systematic approach. The screening level contains temperature-programmed DSC and isoperibolic analysis, while the advanced level contains the isothermal and adiabatic analysis techniques. This classification will help to provide the necessary information with the fewest number of expensive and time-consuming experimental analyses.

The screening analysis level will help to meet two objectives:

a. estimation by measurements of the over all heat (energy) released by the system
b. estimation by measurement of the temperature range of exothermal activities

Temperature-programmed DSC is an appropriate beginning for an experimental analysis of a reactive system. In the theoretical part, we may predict a reaction model, but not predict the thermodynamics of this reaction(s), or perhaps be uncertain that the predicted values are accurate enough for reactive chemical assessment. Temperature-programmed DSC, especially the closed cell design, is a screening technique for estimating the energy potential (heat of reaction) of the system by measuring heat flux. This analysis will allow calculation of the adiabatic temperature increase (ΔT_{ad}) according to the following equation:

$$\Delta T_{ad} = \frac{\Delta H}{m \, C_p}$$

where ΔH is heat of reaction, m is reactant substance mass, and C_p is specific heat of reaction mixture. If this adiabatic temperature increase is not major, and if the system temperature is not above its boiling point, the potential hazard of this system may be excluded.

There are some values of (ΔT_{ad}) used as a rule of thumb; the most common is 50°C [Gygax 1990] [Keller et al. 1997]. In general, as a disadvantage of this technique, the heat flux signals will be slightly distorted which affects the kinetic evaluations but does not affect the overall energy determination [Gygax 1990]. Another disadvantage is that the estimate of (ΔT_{ad}) is considered rough in some cases. Hence the interpretation of (ΔT_{ad}) of a system may not be clear, since at the end 50°C is still a rule of thumb. In such cases another screening test is to be performed to find the range of temperatures within which the system is considered active for unexpected or unwanted reactions. Isoperibolic experiments will give more accurate estimate of the temperature range of reactivity.

Measuring the sample temperature while maintaining the cooling temperature constant is the basis for isoperibolic experiments. The maximum adiabatic rise (ΔT_{ad}) is calculated by:

$$\Delta T_{ad} = \frac{U \, A}{m \, C_p} \int_0^\infty (T_s - T_c) \, dt$$

where, U is overall heat transfer coefficient, A is surface area of heat transfer, T_s is reaction mixture temperature, T_c is cooling jacket temperature, and t is time. This estimate will indicate the range of temperatures that should be avoided during chemical processes to eliminate unwanted exothermic reactions. In case the unwanted exothermic reaction initiation temperature is close to or overlapping with the process operating temperature, a more detailed investigation is required.

A more advanced investigation requires the introduction of the thermokinetics approach. On the screening level, knowledge of kinetic parameters was not necessary for reactive chemical evaluation, but in complex systems with many reactions in overlapping temperature ranges, this more elaborate approach is required. This advanced thermokinetics analysis level will help meet three objectives:

a. estimation by measurement of the thermodynamic parameters of the overall reactive system in a more accurate way
b. estimation by measurement of the kinetic parameters of the overall reactive system
c. minimizing the scale-up error factors by using testing conditions that are closer to the actual operating conditions

Although kinetic parameter estimation in these methods is for the overall reactive system, the theoretical approach in predicting the stoichiometery of various pathways can help to reduce the system to simpler and more important reactions for further studies.

Isothermal and adiabatic analyses are two techniques used in very advanced thermal analysis. Isothermal analysis can provide the most accurate heat production rates by maintaining reaction mixture at constant temperature while measuring the heat flux as a function of time. On the other hand, adiabatic analysis is more favored, particularly for large reacting masses. In the real plant situations of thermal runaway, neither the process cooling system, nor the reaction container will be able to dissipate the huge amount of energy released. The increasing reactant mass temperature will increase the rate of reaction exponentially, leading to more heat production while adiabatic conditions are maintained. The data obtained in either the isothermal or adiabatic analysis are then used to calculate the thermodynamic and kinetic parameters of the system. In both analyses, it is difficult to maintain perfect isothermal or adiabatic conditions. This will be reflected on the results, and therefore it should be considered during parameter calculations and reactivity hazard evaluation. Several sophisticated instrumental designs of isothermal and adiabatic reaction calorimeters with advanced features are available. Calculating times to runaway and to maximum rate reactions are possible with this level of thermal analysis data. A detailed discussion of these methods is available in Gygax (1990).

Up to this point, only temperature-time experimental data were used to evaluate reactive chemical hazards. At the beginning of our presentation to this systematic approach, we mentioned the knowledge of reaction pathways for a sufficient understanding of our experimental data. However, accurate determination of kinetic parameters for complex reactive systems may not be possible without isothermal concentration-time experimental data. As shown in Figure 3, experimental concentration-time data will help to characterize reaction pathways and hence verify the proposed pathways. Isothermal concentration-time experimental data can be coupled to experimental thermal analysis data or simulated from other similar systems whose kinetic parameters are known or available in databanks. These simulated systems may help initially to predict the reaction pathways, and hence to increase the confidence in the analysis.

SUMMARY OF THE PROPOSED SYSTEMATIC METHOD
The proposed systematic approach, as shown in Figure 1, focuses on determining stoichiometric, thermodynamic, and kinetic parameters of any chemical process by utilizing theoretical and experimental methods.

The first level of this approach was to screen the reactive system based on the available information in databanks or literature. Also, simple structure instability and chemical incompatibility considerations were evaluated. Because these considerations are used as a screening tool, the results should be used with caution.

In the second reactivity evaluation level, theoretical methods are used to help find the reaction pathways, and to predict thermodynamic and kinetic parameters. For predicting thermodynamics, two levels of theoretical techniques are discussed: molecular group contribution methods and statistical thermodynamics combined with computational quantum chemistry methods (ab-initio methods). Molecular group contribution methods depend on thermodynamic data available in databanks for similar molecular groups, which makes its usage limited to the available data. Ab-initio methods are more advanced techniques based on quantum molecular theory. These methods may be used to predict thermodynamics if the molecular group contribution methods fail, but more knowledge and experience is needed to utilize ab-initio methods. Predicting system kinetics is possible using computational quantum chemistry with transition state theory. Depending on the complexity of the system, the predicted values may not be accurate enough to be used for reactivity analysis. Experimental analysis should be used for missing parameters or for more accurate measurements.

After excluding non-feasible and non-hazardous pathways based on the theoretical methods, experimental methods are used to complete the reactivity analysis. Temperature-programmed DSC and isoperibolic techniques are used for screening experimental analyses. More advanced analysis of isothermal and adiabatic methods are used for more accurate measurements. System complexity and degree of accuracy are factors affecting the experimental technique selection.

CONCLUSIONS
Both the ability to evaluate reactive chemical hazards in process chemistry and the ability to determine process safe operating boundaries will enhance not only the safety and operability of processes but will help in determining their optimum operating conditions.

ACKNOWLEDGEMENTS
This research was funded by the Mary Kay O'Connor Process Safety Center of the Department of Chemical Engineering at Texas A&M University.

REFERENCES
Benson, S. (1970). 'Thermochemical kinetics', 2nd ed., John Wiley, Inc., New York.

Bretherick, L. (1987). Reactive chemical hazards: an overview, Proceedings of the International Symposium on Prevention of Major Chemical Accidents, American Institute of Chemical Engineers/Center for Chemical Process Safety, New York, 4.1-4.15.

Bruneton, C., Hoff, C., and Barton, P. (1997). Computer aided identification of chemical reaction hazards, *Computers Chem. Engng.*, 21, Suppl., S311-S317.

Bruneton, C., Hoff, C., and Barton, P. (1998). Thermal stability analysis via elucidation of hazardous reaction stoichiometries, *Computers Chem. Engng.*, 22, 6, 735-745.

Carven, A. (1987). A simple method of estimating exothermicity by average bond energy summation, 'Hazardous from pressure: exothermic reactions, unstable substances, pressure relief, and accidental discharge', Institution of Chemical Engineers, Symposium Series 102, 97-111.

Center for Chemical Process safety (CCPS) (1995). 'Guidelines for chemical reactivity evaluation and application to process design', American Institute of Chemical Engineers/Center for Chemical Process Safety, New York.

Duh, Y., Lee, C., Hsu, C., Hwang, D., and Kao, C. (1997). Chemical incompatibility of nitrocompounds, *J. of Hazardous Materials*, 53, 183-194.

Duh, Y., Hsu, C., Kao, C., and Yu, S. (1996). Applications of reaction calorimetry in reaction kinetics and thermal hazard evaluation, *Thermochimica Acta*, 285, 67-79.

Fauske, H. (1998). The reactive system screening tool (RSST): an easy, inexpensive approach to the DIERS procedure, *Process Safety Progress*, 17, 3, 190-195.

Grewer, T., Frurip, D., and Harrison, B. (1999). Prediction of thermal hazards of chemical reactions, *J. of Loss Prevention in the Process Industries*, 12, 391-398.

Gygax, R. (1990). Scaleup principles for assessing thermal runaway risks, *Chemical Engineering Progress*, 2, 53-60.

Heldt, K. & Anderson, H. (1996). Application of an adiabatic calorimeter with safety concept, *Thermochimica Acta*, 271, 189-194.

Hinchliffe, A. (1994). Modeling molecular structure, Wiley Tutorial Series in Theoretical Chemistry.

Hofelich, T., Frurip, D., and Powers, J. (1994). The determination of compatibility via thermal analysis and mathematical modeling, *Process Safety Progress*, 13, 4, 227-233.

Kars, J. and Visser, C. (1996). Shell-modified Sikarex calorimeter as a screening tool for runaway0 reactions, *Thermochimica Acta*, 289, 155-165.

Keller, A., Stark, D., Fierz, Heinzle, E., and Hungerbühler, K. (1997). Estimation of the time to maximum rate using dynamic DSC experiments, *J. of Loss Prevention in the Process Industries*, 10, 1, 31-41.

Kohlbrand, H. (1985). Reactive chemical screening for pilot-plant safety, *Chemical Engineering Progress*, 4, 52-56.

LeBlond, C., Wang, J., Larsen, R., Orella, C, Forman, A., Landau, R., Laquidara, J., Sowa, J., Blackmond, D., and Sun, Y. (1996). Reaction calorimetry as an in-situ kinetic tool for characterizing complex reactions, *Thermochimica Acta*, 289, 189-207.

Leonhardt, J. & Hugo, P. (1997). Comparison of thermokinetic data obtained by isothermal, isoperibolic, adiabatic and temperature programmed measurements, *J. of Thermal Analysis*, 49, 1535-1551.

Liaw, H., Yur, C., and Lin, Y. (2000). A mathematical model for predicting thermal hazard data, *J. of Loss Prevention in the Process Ind*ustries, 13, 499-507.

Marco, E., Cuartielles, S., Peña, J., and Santamaria, J. (2000). Simulation of the decomposition of di-cumyl peroxide in an ARSST unit, *Thermochimica Acta*, 362, 49-58.

Maria, G. & Heinzle, E. (1998). Kinetic system identification by using short-cut techniques in early safety assessment of chemical processes, *J. of Loss Prevention in the Process Industries*, 11, 187-206.

Pastré, J., Wörsdörfer, U., Keller, A., and Hungerbühler, K. (2000). Comparison of different methods for estimating TMRad from dynamic DSC measurements with ADT 24 values obtained from adiabatic Dewer experiments, *J. of Loss Prevention in the Process Industries*, 13, 7-17.

Sempere, J., Nomen, R., Serra, R., and Cardillo, P. (1997). Thermal hazard assessment using closed-cell adiabatic calorimetry, *J. of Loss Prevention in the Process Industries*, 10, 55-62.

Shanley, E. & Melhem, G. (1995). The Oxygen balance criterion for thermal hazards assessment, *Process Safety Progress*, 14, 1, 29-31.

Townsend, D. & Tou, J. (1980). Thermal hazard evaluation by an accelerating rate calorimeter, *Thermochimica Acta*, 37, 1-30.

Winder, C. & Zarie, A. (2000). Incompatibilities of chemicals, *J. of Hazardous Materials*, A79, 1-30.

Zatka, A. (1979). Application of thermal analysis in screening for chemical process hazards, Thermochimica Acta, 28, 7-13.

Table 1. Examples of well-known high energetic compound groups and their unstable structure [CCPS 1995].

Compound Group	Unstable Structure	Compound Group	Unstable Structure
acetylenic compounds	$-C \equiv C-$	hydroxylammonium salts	$-N^+- OH\ Z^-$
azo compounds	$-C-N=N-C-$	metal acetylides	$-C \equiv C - M$
alkyl nitrites	$-C-O-N=O$	metal peroxides	$-O-O-M$
alkyl nitrates	$-C-O-NO_2$	metal fulminates	$-C=N-O-M$
alkyl hydroperoxides	$-C-O-O-C-$	N-nitroso compounds	$-N-N=O$
aci-nitro salts	$HO-(O=)N=$	N-nitro compounds	$-N-NO_2$
diazo compounds	$-C-N^+=N^-$	N-halogen compounds	$-N-X$

Table 2. Examples of well-known high energetic compounds and their heat of formation [CCPS 1995].

Compound	Unstable Structure	Heat of Formation (kJ/g)
cyanogen	$N \equiv C - C \equiv N$	+ 5.9
nitrogen trichloride	NCl_3	+ 1.9
acetylene	$H - C \equiv C - H$	+ 8.7
hydrogen cyanide	$H - C \equiv N$	+ 4.8
1, 3 – butadiene	$H_2C = CHCH = CH_2$	+ 2.1

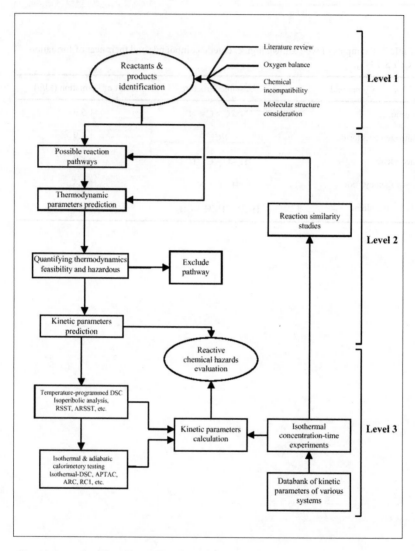

Figure 1: Systematic approach for evaluating chemical reactivity

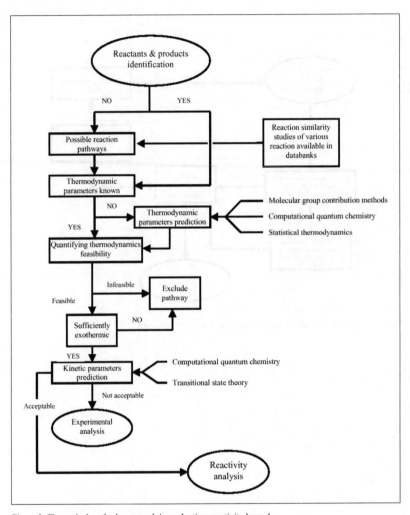

Figure 2: Theoretical methods approach in evaluating reactivity hazard

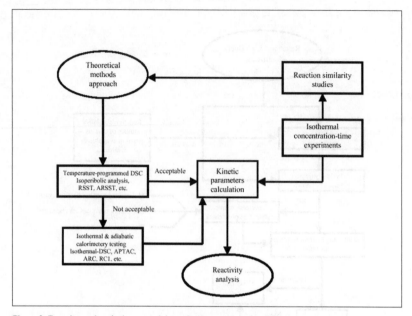

Figure 3: Experimental analysis approach in evaluating reactivity hazard

THE ROLE OF THE CHEMICAL SAFETY BOARD IN PREVENTING CHEMICAL ACCIDENTS

Gerald V. Poje, Ph.D., and Isadore Rosenthal, Ph.D, Board Members U.S. Chemical Safety and Hazard Investigation Board 2175 K Street, NW, Suite 400, Washington, DC 20037 USA

Abstract

The U. S. Chemical Safety and Hazard Investigation Board (CSB) is an independent Federal agency with responsibility for investigating chemical releases, researching safety issues, and recommending improvements in the safety management of chemicals. This paper discusses the history of the Board and its institutional development. Recent investigations are highlighted in addition to safety issues such as process safety management, reactive chemicals, management of change, and the need for better data on chemical release incidents.

Keywords: Process accidents, hazard investigations, United States Chemical Safety Board

Introduction

The U.S. Chemical Safety and Hazard Investigation Board (CSB) is an independent Federal agency whose mission is to investigate–and promote the prevention of–major chemical incidents at industrial facilities. CSB is a scientific investigatory organization; it is not an enforcement body. The U.S. Congress has directed the Board to:

- Conduct root cause investigations and report on findings.
- Conduct special studies on policy, guidelines, regulations, and laws governing chemical safety.
- Establish reporting requirements for chemical incidents within its jurisdiction.

The number and severity of chemical incidents in the United States supported the establishment of CSB. For example, among 14,500 chemical-handling facilities required to file risk management plans with the U.S. Environmental Protection Agency (EPA) in 1999, more than 1,100 reported approximately 1,900 accidents from 1994 through 1999. These incidents resulted in a total of 1,897 injuries, 33 deaths to workers/employees, and evacuation or sheltering in place of over 200,000 people in surrounding communities[1].

The insurance industry recently estimated its direct losses from chemical releases at $1 billion per year. Taking into account indirect losses and losses not covered by insurance companies, overall effects could be conservatively estimated at $3 to 5 billion annually[2].

History and Structure

Following the catastrophic incident at the Union Carbide facility in Bhopal, India, in 1984 and a series of domestic incidents[3] in 1987-1989, the U.S. Congress authorized new chemical accident provisions through the Clean Air Act Amendments of 1990[4]. In addition to new regulatory approaches required of the U.S. Department of Labor's Occupational Safety and Health Administration (OSHA) and EPA, Congress mandated an independent Chemical Safety Board.

CSB began operations in January 1998. Modeled after the National Transportation Safety Board, CSB's authorizing statute provides for five Board Members, including a Chairperson, who are nominated by the President by and with the advice and consent of the

U.S. Senate. Members of the Board are appointed on the basis of technical qualification, professional standing, and demonstrated knowledge in the fields of accident reconstruction, safety engineering, human factors, toxicology, or air pollution regulation. Board members serve a 5-year term. The Board is governed by majority vote. Over the past year, CSB has grown to a staff of 35 with an operating budget of $7.5 million.

Board Functions

Stimulus to Regulatory Assessments and Recommendations

The U.S. Congress explicitly recognized the Board's unique statutory mission, particularly as a stimulus to future regulatory assessments and recommendations, noting:

> The independence of the Board . . . is essential for several reasons. First, it is unlikely that an agency charged both with rule-making and investigating functions would be quick to acknowledge that existing requirements were insufficient to prevent an accident . . . .. Second, the Board is intended as an organizational stimulus to an appropriate amount of regulatory activity by the Environmental Protection Agency [(EPA)] in this area . . . .. A Board which did not operate independent from the [EPA] Administrator's direction would defeat the objective of stimulating regulatory action -- a stimulus created through the organizational tension built into the statutory relationship between the Board and the [Environmental Protection] Agency[5]

In particular, the Board is responsible for issuing periodic reports to Congress; Federal, state, and local agencies; and other interested persons concerned with the safe production, handling, and storage of chemicals. These reports may recommend:

- Measures to reduce the likelihood or consequences of accidental releases and corrective steps to make chemical production, processing, handling, and storage as safe and free from risk of injury as possible.
- Proposals for rules or orders that should be issued by the EPA Administrator or the Secretary of Labor under the Occupational Safety and Health Act to prevent or minimize the consequences of any accidental release causing death, injury, other serious adverse human health effects, or substantial property damage[6].

Independent Investigations

The Board's principal role is to investigate accidents at fixed facilities, determine the conditions and circumstances that led to the event, identify the causes, study chemical safety issues, evaluate the effectiveness of governmental policies and actions related to process chemical safety, and issue safety recommendations.

Congress also recognized that Board investigations have the unique ability to identify serious chemical hazards that are not addressed by OSHA or EPA:

> [T]he investigations conducted by agencies with dual responsibilities tend to focus on violations of existing rules as the cause of the accident almost to the exclusion of other contributing factors for which no enforcement or compliance actions can be taken. The purpose of an accident investigation (as authorized here) is to determine the cause or causes of an accident whether or not those causes were in violation of any current and enforceable requirement. [Senate Report]

The Clean Air Act prohibits the use of any conclusions, findings, or recommendations of the Board relating to any chemical incident from being admitted as evidence or used in any lawsuit arising out of any matter mentioned in an investigation report.

To date, the Board has completed six accident investigations, as summarized below:

- Sierra Chemical Company operated a facility in Mustang, Nevada, which produced explosive boosters used in the mining industry. As the plant began daily operations on January 7, 1998, two massive explosions occurred in sequence, killing four workers and injuring six. The jolts were felt 12miles away in Reno (the larger was the equivalent of a magnitude 2.0 earthquake). The initial explosion occurred in a building that housed explosives-mixing equipment; it is likely that the restart of an interrupted mixing operation triggered the blast. Explosives used in making the boosters included trinitrotoluene (TNT) and Pentolite., Despite the severity of the explosions, there appears to have been little impact offsite because the plant was located in a remote, uninhabited area. The facility was never rebuilt. CSB issued an investigation report on September 28, 1998[7]

- At a Sonat Exploration Company production facility near Pitkin, Louisiana, four oil workers were killed in a vessel failure and fire on March 4, 1998. The incident occurred during startup of a normally unmanned facility. The blast occurred as a result of inadequate design and start-up systems, which led to connection of a high-pressure natural gas stream to an oil and gas separation vessel rated for service at atmospheric pressure. It is not known how much natural gas was contained in the 45-foot vessel at the time of the blast. Although the facility sustained significant damage, no offsite consequences were noted because it was located in a remote area. CSB issued a final investigation report on September 21, 2000.[8]

- On March 27, 1998, at a Union Carbide chemical plant in Taft, Louisiana, two workers were asphyxiated by nitrogen, an odorless and colorless gas. Nitrogen is commonly used in industry to protect materials that are sensitive to oxygen or moisture. The two workers erected a temporary enclosure over an open pipe containing nitrogen to facilitate a black light inspection, unaware that the enclosure also had the effect of trapping the nitrogen. One worker died, and the other sustained severe injuries. There was no significant environmental release. CSB issued a final investigation report on February 23, 1999.[9] Among the recommendations was assessment of the feasibility of adding a warning odorant to nitrogen supplies used in this type of application.

- At the Morton International chemical plant in Paterson, New Jersey, an explosion on April 8, 1998, injured nine workers. The explosion and subsequent fire were caused by a runaway chemical reaction in a 2,000-gallon reactor used to produce a yellow fuel dye (Automate Yellow 96). A vigorous exothermic reaction occurred shortly after the two chemicals used to make the dye were mixed. The temperature in the reactor began to rapidly increase, causing the further exothermic decomposition of the dye and eventually over-pressurizing and rupturing the kettle. The reactor contents were released to the air and distributed into the surrounding urban area. The chemicals released included toxic *ortho*-nitrochlorobenzene. Fallout occurred as far as 0.5 mile from the plant, and residents of a 10 square block area were required to shelter in place. Local authorities issued a health advisory to residents shortly after the incident, though the magnitude of human exposure is unknown. The plant was repaired, but the company discontinued the production of Automate Yellow 96. CSB issued a final investigation report on August 16, 2000.[10]

- On April 9, 1998, at the Herrig Brothers turkey farm in Albert City, Iowa, two volunteer firefighters were killed and seven persons were injured in a propane tank explosion. Two teenagers driving an all-terrain vehicle struck and ruptured the propane lines immediately below the 18,000-gallon storage tank that fed the farm's heating system. The ensuing fire below the tank, which contained about 10,000 gallons of propane, led to a boiling liquid vapor explosion (BLEVE), which resulted in the deaths and injuries. The farm sustained significant damage, but there were no significant offsite consequences. CSB issued a final investigation report on June 23, 1999.[11]

- A catastrophic fire occurred at the <u>Tosco Avon Refinery</u> in Martinez, California, on February 23, 1999. Workers were attempting to replace piping attached to a 150-foot-tall fractionator tower while the process unit was in operation. The line to be removed contained naphtha. Although the job permit called for the line to be drained, steamed, and isolated, these requirements were not met and the work continued. The job was not re-evaluated, nor was the fractionator shut down. During removal of the piping, flammable naphtha was released onto the hot fractionator tower and ignited. The flames engulfed five workers located at different heights on the tower. Four workers were killed, and one sustained serious injuries. CSB issued a final investigation report on March 28, 2001.[12] Recommendations were developed to address deficiencies in maintenance, auditing, and management of change systems.

Hazard Investigations

Causation and recommendations from field investigations often reflect very specific aspects of manufacturing operations, which typically use specialized procedures, equipment, and technologies. However, occasionally in the course of conducting incident investigations, the Board is alerted to significant safety problems that could affect a large number of facilities and are beyond the scope of any one particular investigation. In these cases, CSB conducts a hazard investigation or safety study for industry-wide dissemination. Findings from such an investigation could lead to a variety of recommendations, including proposals for regulatory action.

In 1998, as requested by the U.S. Senate, CSB investigated hazards in the chemical sector from Year 2000 (Y2K) technology problems and issued an investigative report with recommendations.[13] In advocating its recommendations, the Board testified before the Senate, and worked with seven trade associations of the chemical handling industries and with EPA to produce and distribute both a guidance document[14] and a safety alert.[15] The report and the guidance were transmitted to the governors of states and territories, as well as to the major associations of emergency responders and firefighting organizations.

CSB helped to plan and convene a focused roundtable on chemical safety for the President's Council on Y2K. The Board also coordinated its efforts internationally, involving the Intergovernmental Forum on Chemical Safety, the World Health Organization's International Programme on Chemical Safety, and the Organization for Economic Cooperation and Development.

During the Morton International investigation, many stakeholders discussed systemic concerns regarding reactive chemical safety. In the course of this investigation, several other reactive hazards incidents were identified, including Napp Technologies (Lodi, New Jersey, April 21, 1995)[16] and Georgia Pacific Resins (Columbus, Ohio, September, 10, 1997).[17] Thus, in accordance with its congressional mandate, CSB initiated a hazard investigation of reactive chemical process safety.

The objectives of the study are to:

- Determine the scope and significance of reactive chemical incidents.
- Examine how industry, OSHA, and EPA address reactive chemical hazards.

- Determine the differences among companies with regard to reactive chemical policies, practices, testing, and process engineering.
- Analyze the effectiveness of industry and OSHA use of the National Fire Protection Association reactivity rating system[18] for process safety management.
- Develop recommendations for reducing the number and severity of reactive chemical incidents.

Other Safety Research

The Clean Air Act authorizes CSB to conduct research and studies with respect to the potential for accidental releases, where evidence indicates the presence of a potential hazard or hazards. In implementing this objective, the Board has conducted studies in cooperation with Federal, state, and local governmental agencies and organizations in the commercial and nonprofit sectors.

CSB was vested with the responsibility for developing expertise on the content, use, and effectiveness of hazard assessments as a tool for preventing and minimizing the consequences of accidental releases of "extremely"[19] hazardous substances. The Board is also charged with recommending additions to the list of "extremely" hazardous substances (including threshold quantities for such substances) and categories of stationary sources for which hazard assessments apply. In this context, the Board also has explicit responsibility to assess the effectiveness of EPA-mandated risk management plans for accidental chemical releases.

Recommendations

CSB's mission in investigating chemical incidents is to determine the root and contributing causes, promote lessons learned, and advocate recommendations (which are keyed to root causes). The Board's primary focus is to provide guidance in more effectively preventing or mitigating chemical accidents. Analyzing operational failures particular to an incident is a corollary objective.

For example, the Herrig Brothers investigation showed that better firefighter training might have prevented the two fatalities and seven injuries to emergency response personnel. In this incident, an 18,000-gallon cylindrical propane tank exploded following an earlier leak and propane fire. Volunteer firefighters arrived at the scene to find the tank intact, but engulfed in flames. They approached within 100 feet of the tank to set up firefighting equipment, thinking that they were safe as long as they avoided the two ends of the tank.

When the propane tank exploded minutes later, it sent large fragments and shrapnel in all directions. The explosion was categorized as a boiling liquid expanding vapor explosion (BLEVE), which typically occurs when fire weakens the metal of a pressure vessel containing liquefied gas. In such cases, tank failure can be initiated at any point–particularly in the upper section of the tank where there is no stored liquid to provide cooling. Under these circumstances, the sides of the tank do not provide a safety shield, and all personnel should be withdrawn to a safe distance.

CSB determined that the training furnished to Albert City firefighters by the National Propane Gas Association (NPGA) and the Iowa State University Fire Service Institute did not adequately prepare them to respond to a potential BLEVE. The firefighters erroneously thought that the ends of the tank were the most significant hazard and that the sides could be approached in relative safety. The Board recommended to both NPGA and the Fire Service Institute that they modify their training materials and programs to adequately cover response to BLEVEs. Both organizations responded positively and made the requested changes.

The CSB report also noted a significant error in the U.S. Department of Transportation's (DOT) *North American Emergency Response Guidebook*. The *Guidebook* is widely used by personnel responding to hazardous material releases, though it was not directly consulted by firefighters during the Herrig incident. The 1996 edition stated that responders should *"always* stay away from the ends of tanks"* when fighting flammable liquid tank fires. This advice might be thought to imply that that the sides of tanks are safe. As a result of CSB inquiries and consultation, DOT revised the year 2000 guidebook to state that responders should *"always* stay away from tanks engulfed in fire."[20]

Incident Reporting

The Board recognizes the importance of systematically accumulating data on chemical accidents and their consequences. Such data are critical to measure the effectiveness of accident prevention programs and to target future investigation and research resources. In the United States, several Federal agencies have jurisdiction over various kinds of data records for accidental events; however, there is no single Federal source of comprehensive chemical accident data.

Congress authorized CSB to establish regulatory requirements for reporting incidents within the Board's investigatory jurisdiction. The Board has adopted the strategic goal of implementing a system for chemical accident data collection and analysis that can be used to measure prevention effectiveness. This multiyear effort to develop new high quality data is expected to help in predicting the frequency of accidental chemical releases and in identifying which substances and industry segments are most at risk. The Board believes that there is widespread support for data development among other agencies and interested stakeholders in the private sector.

Summary

CSB is a new independent public agency whose mission is to investigate and promote the prevention of major chemical incidents at industrial facilities. As a scientific investigatory organization free of enforcement responsibilities, CSB conducts root cause investigations and safety studies. Through global information technology, the Board's investigation reports are an international resource for preventing chemical accidents.

REFERENCES

[1] See Kleindorfer, P., et al., Center for Risk Management and Decision Processes, The Wharton School, University of Pennsylvania, http://opim.wharton.upenn.edu/risk/downloads/00-1-15.pdf

[2] Estimating Chemical Accident Costs in the United States: A new Analytical Approach, Collins, L., D'Angelo, C, Mattheissen, C., and Perron, M., in Process Industry Accidents, Center for Chemical Process Safety, New York City, pp, 467 – 471, 2000

[3] Among these incidents were: the Phillips Petroleum in Pasadena, TX, the Arco Refinery in Channelview, TX, Marathon Oil in Texas City, TX, Shell Petroleum in Norco, LA.

[4] Clean Air Act, 42 USC 7412

[5] 29 U.S.C. 651 et seq.
[7] http://www.csb.gov/reports/1998/sierra_chem/sierra_fr01.htm
[8] http://www.csb.gov/reports/2000/sonat1_01.htm
[8][9] http://www.csb.gov/reports/1998/union_carbide/98005lafr.htm
[9] http://www.csb.gov/reports/2000/morton/morton_01.htm
[10] http://www.csb.gov/reports/1999/herrig/list_reports.htm
[11] http://www.csb.gov/news/2001/docs/tosco_investigation.doc
[12] http://www.csb.gov/y2k/docs/y2k01.pdf
[13] http://www.csb.gov/news/1999/docs/smefinal.pdf
[14] http://www.csb.gov/news/1999/docs/CEF.pdf
[15] http://www.epa.gov/ceppo/pubs/lodiintr.htm
[16] http://www.epa.gov/ceppo/pubs/gpcasstd.pdf
[17] NFPA 704, Standard System for the Identification of Hazards of Materials for Emergency Response, 1996. In the 1996 standard, the terminology was changed from "reactivity" to "instability."
[18]"Extremely" hazardous substances are a class of materials regulated under Federal law– more specifically, Section 112(r), which deals with the prevention of accidental releases under the Clean Air Act Amendments of 1990.
[19]U.S. Department of Transportation, *2000 Emergency Response Guidebook*, p. 195.

THE THERMAL SCREENING UNIT (TS^U) A TOOL FOR REACTIVE CHEMICAL SCREENING

Jasbir Singh and Cormac Simms
Hazard Evaluation Laboratory Ltd, 50 Moxon St, Barnet, Hertfordshire, EN5 5TS (UK)

The thermal screening unit is an instrument specifically designed for the fast and efficient hazard screening of liquids, solids and heterogeneous systems. The unit provides an alternative device to DSC and DTA for use in hazard assessment and provides information regarding reaction "onset temperatures", rates of temperature rise as well as crucial information regarding the rates and magnitudes of pressure rise in chemical systems. Typical data from the unit is presented together with case studies and a comparison to differential scanning calorimetry (DSC) data.

Keywords: Reaction hazards, Decomposition, Unstable compounds, Hazard screening, Runaway reaction, Exotherm.

INTRODUCTION

Virtually all large multi-national chemical companies are involved with some form of hazard assessment program. An important element of this is reactive chemical testing, which incorporates the assessment of feeds, intermediates and products for thermal stability so that hazards during storage, manufacture and transportation can be accurately assessed. In recent years, even medium and small companies have had to include such testing in the route from the R&D laboratory to full-scale production. Regardless of the size of corporation, the evaluation procedure will frequently include a "screening step" aimed at separating the innocuous chemical materials from those that are potentially hazardous. Typically thermal hazard screening is performed by either a theoretical and/or an experimental investigation.

Theoretical methods of hazard screening are based on mathematical models that are designed to evaluate the potential energy release on the decomposition of the study material into smaller more stable species. In principal such calculations require only a knowledge of heats of formation for the chemical species involved, however, in practice the calculations become more complex because this essential information is not often available in the literature.[1] By employing these techniques it is sometimes possible to make a first guess or estimate of a compounds hazard potential. However, the limitations of theoretical calculations are widely recognised. These include the limited number of predictable reactions that can be assessed and the difficulty of potential side reactions that may have major influence on the magnitude of a runaway reaction and process safety.

A significant draw back of many theoretical calculations is the limited information that is generated regarding the rates and magnitudes of the pressure rises. This information is pre-requisite if a process is to be safely scaled-up, since it is the build up of pressure that will cause the product to be vented from a reactor or worse still cause damage to an industrial plant. These draw backs in conjunction with the considerable user experience required to perform a theoretical calculation makes this approach rarely sufficient to enable direct process scale-up without further downstream experimentation.

Experimental thermal screening methods on the other hand primarily involve the heating of a few milligrams of sample over a user defined temperature range to examine the presence or absence of thermal activity. Classically, these analyses have been performed by popular techniques such as DSC (differential scanning calorimetry) and DTA (differential thermal analysis). However, although these test methods have found widespread application in many areas of chemical research and development, in the area of hazard screening there are numerous shortcomings that are not always recognised. Consequently, many chemical systems are scaled-up on the basis of this hazard assessment data even though it is not always appropriate to do so.

To improve the situation slightly some organisations will supplement the data obtained from DSC and DTA[2] with kinetic studies performed in a reaction calorimeter[3]. Reaction calorimetry is a powerful tool for the elucidation of thermodynamic information from the normal (or desired) reaction. It also enables the operator to examine the profile by which heat is liberated from a reaction. However, in situations where the chemistry is unknown such an instrument should be applied with extreme caution, particularly when there is the possibility of unknown side reaction products since these materials could be potentially more hazardous than the proposed reaction under study. Reaction calorimeters also have the disadvantage that they employ sample volumes in the range 50 ml to 1 litre, which is too large, from both a safety and economical viewpoint for sample screening.

DIFFERENTIAL SCANNING METHODS

GENERAL FEATURES OF DSC/DTA TESTING
In a typical DSC or DTA experiment a few milligrams of sample (often in a sealed metal pan) and an inert reference material are heated together at a defined rate of typically 10 degree Celsius per minute[2]. The temperature of the sample and the reference are monitored and if the temperature of the sample begins to diverge from that of the reference, evidence of thermal activity is inferred. Using this data it is possible to determine an "onset temperature" for the thermal event and measure the amount of heat released.

Using this information the "onset temperature" can be compared with the materials' proposed operating or storage temperature. If these are similar, it might represent a potential hazard. In a similar manner the information relating to energy release can be used to estimate the likely temperature and pressure rise if the exothermic reaction did occur. It is through this type of comparative analysis that DSC/DTA data can be used to estimate the severity of a possible hazard.

The principle benefit of this type of testing is that it can be conducted in just a few hours, requiring limited operator skill. When low running cost is also taken into account, the widespread use of DSC/DTA methods can be easily understood. However, in practice these aspects should be weighed against the many disadvantages that relate to the possible reliability of the data and the potential problems that can ensue from not screening reactions properly.

LIMITATIONS OF DIFFERENTIAL SCANNING DATA
The differential thermal instruments described above are employed for a wide range of analytical determinations in addition to hazard screening. In fact most DSC and DTA applications do not relate to hazard assessment at all and the comments made in this paper will not be concerned with these alternative functions.

A design feature that contributes significantly to the ease of use and low running cost of DSC and DTA is the small mass of sample required which is typically in the milligram scale. From a hazard evaluation perspective, this extremely low sample mass can be a serious disadvantage due to the increased uncertainty in experimental reproducibility. Whilst the testing of pure materials presents no problems, taking a representative sample of a mixture on such a small scale can be difficult. For example, in order to evaluate process intermediates (and sometimes, even products), it is frequently necessary to draw a "live" sample from a reactor. The extraction of such low sample masses that are wholly representative of the system under these conditions can be difficult.

One of the most important pieces of information obtained from thermal scanning devices is the so-called "onset temperature" for exothermic activity. However, it is important to realise that this "onset" threshold is not a fundamental property of a reaction and the measured value depends very much on the instrument sensitivity and the procedure by which the experiment is performed. In Figure 1[4], the onset temperature determined by DSC is compared with that from an adiabatic instrument (in this case the "accelerating rate calorimeter", ARC) using approximately 5g of sample[5]. This information was reported by the Dow Chemical Company from their historical data bank. It shows that in many cases, the "onset temperature" detected by DSC can be as much as 50 °C higher than that reported from adiabatic instruments. In fact in a substantial number of instances the difference between to two methods is as much as 100 °C. (There are several cases where the DSC determined "onset temperature" is lower than that reported by the adiabatic testing, but this can be attributed to the study of non-representative DSC samples).

DSC Vs. ARC Detection Temperatures

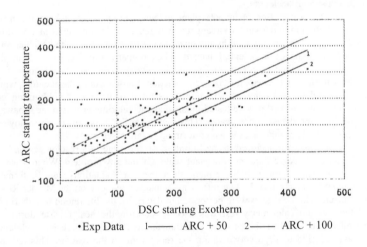

Figure 1: A comparison of "onset temperatures" between DSC and ARC data.

The most significant shortcoming of a DSC or DTA type instrument is that they do not provide any information regarding the pressures generated or the rates of pressure rises measured during a screening a test. The authors are aware that some effort has been made recently to address this problem and produce pressure measuring DSC devices, but so far the data reported has been found to be unclear and noisy and such instruments are limited to only a few psi. However, if the DSC is to be considered as an instrument for accurate hazard assessment and safe process scale-up this information is crucial, since the extent of thermal hazard will be directly represented by the pressure generated during the reaction. It is after all it is the large pressures generated in runaway reactions that generally cause product venting and in extreme cases catastrophic damage to plant and equipment.

Another important factor that needs to be considered when examining the hazard potential of a material is the aspect of time. It is vital to remember that it is not only the amount of energy released that is important but also the rate at which this energy is released (i.e. the reaction kinetics). Although the aspect of DSC scans do partially reflect the kinetics of the chemical system under study the information that is obtained is very often indirect and can be applied in a qualitative manner. The time scales determined bear almost no relation to the real life incident and unless considerable effort and rigour is put into the kinetic analysis, it is not possible to estimate the rates at which events might occur on the plant.

Taking into account all the above points, it is clear that choice of DSC or DTA, as the primary, or worse still only, method of thermal screening can be misleading and if used without information from additional adiabatic calorimeters could be potentially dangerous.

PRACTICAL CASES OF HAZARDS UNDETECTED BY DSC/DTA

There are at least three incidents known to the authors, over the last few years, where major hazardous accidents have resulted, in spite of DSC or DTA data being available. For reasons of confidentiality, it is not possible to give very much detail of these cases but they all resulted in serious accidents.

The first was a fine chemicals plant in New Jersey, USA, where the mixture in a distillation column underwent a violent runaway reaction. This material had been thoroughly tested using a DSC; in this case by the operating chemical company themselves and this had revealed no signs of a potential hazard. The company was experienced in the use of calorimetry and relied on differential scanning techniques for hazard screening followed by reaction calorimetry to check the "desired" reaction. Subsequent to the accident, which caused catastrophic damage to the column plus substantial damage to neighbouring equipment, samples (around 5 to 10g) were tested in an adiabatic calorimeter where the runaway incident was readily reproduced and repeated. This highlights the importance of employing suitable and representable sample sizes when performing hazard assessment.

The second case occurred in the Middle East, this time in a reactor vessel. The process had been run for some time on pilot plant scale without any problem. When it was due to be transferred to the commercial scale plant, three thermal evaluations were performed, two on separate DSC devices (run by two different companies) and one on the Mettler RC-1 reaction calorimeter.[6] The DSC tests were performed to determine the likelihood of a thermal runaway and the reaction calorimetry test was used to confirm the heat release during a normal, controlled batch. When the process was transferred to the large scale, a violent runaway reaction occurred totally overwhelming the relief vent on the reactor. This led to an over-pressurisation of the vessel resulting in large quantities of reactants being discharged as the vessel cover was lifted under pressure. Subsequently the hot vapours released ignited and caused further damage.

The incident in the final example was less dramatic but illustrates an important point. It involved a small company that had recently acquired a DSC as its first hazard evaluation tool. The process required the mixing of two liquids at room temperature, followed by heating to 85 °C before the slow addition of the final reactant to make an organic intermediate for the pharmaceutical industry (Figure 2). Tests had been performed with a mixture of the two reagents added at the start and with samples of the three reactants together. No problem was detected in the first test but the second test indicated some exothermic heat release.

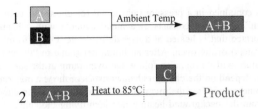

Figure 2: Two preparation of a an organic intermediate

Based on results of the first test, it was decided that the two starting ingredients could be safely pre-mixed in drums ready for charging. However, when this was performed the drums were found to rupture after about 2 hours. Subsequent testing with an adiabatic device (in which pressure data was measured) revealed that while the DSC had correctly reported a lack of exothermic activity, however, it had failed to register the fact that, even at room temperature a considerable amount of gas was being generated albeit at a slow rate. This highlights the necessity for pressure data when scaling up a process.

THE TS^U AS A SCREENING TOOL

ESSENTIAL FEATURES
The TS^U (Thermal Screening Unit) has been developed as an alternative to DSC as a primary thermal screening method. A schematic diagram and a photograph of the TS^U are shown below in Figure 3.

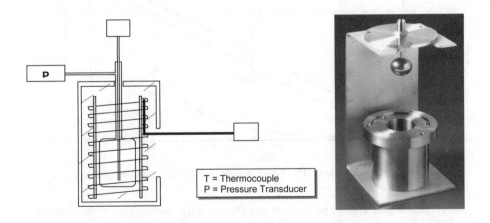

T = Thermocouple
P = Pressure Transducer

Figure 3: Schematic diagram and photograph of the Thermal Screening Unit (TS^U).

The sample is contained in a pressure tight metal (or glass) test cell, suspended in the middle of an "oven". The oven consists of a metal cylinder with a heating coil wrapped around the outer surface that is heated at a user-defined rate. On performing a test the user controls the ramp rate(s) of the oven. After an initial delay due to "thermal lagging" effects the sample temperature will be found to follow the oven ramp at the same rate with a slight "offset" (which will depend on the physical characteristics of the test material such as specific heat). When an exothermic or endothermic process is detected the sample temperature will be found to deviate from the background-heating rate identifying the "onset temperature". The rate of rise in sample temperature (dT/dt) and the maximum value reached, T_{Max} before returning to the background-heating rate reflects important characteristics of the thermal event.

In addition to temperature data, the thermal screening unit is also equipped with a pressure transducer that records changes in sample pressure as the reaction proceeds. This provides the operator with a second method by which sample activity can be identified. This alternative method of sample analysis is particularly useful since it provides a measure of the total pressure generated in the reaction, P_{Max} and the rate of pressure rise (dP/dt). The pressure data also enables very mild exothermic decomposition reactions which result in the production of non-condensable gas to be detected even if the associated temperature rise is too low to be reliably detected.

THERMAL SCREENING OF TOLUENE
The application of the thermal screening unit is illustrated below for the screening of toluene, Figure 4.

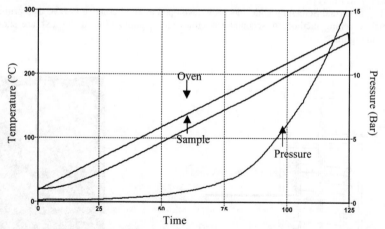

Figure 4: Thermal Screening of HPLC grade toluene (4.8 g) at 2°C/min from ambient temperature to 300 °C.

From Figure 4 it can be observed that after an initial "settling period" the oven and sample temperature ramps are found to run almost parallel to each other, indicating no thermal activity within the solvent. This is exactly what we would expect for an inert material and the trace can essentially be considered as a reference to which other chemical systems can be compared. On examination of the pressure data it is found that the pressure increases with temperature. This increase in pressure is due to the increasing vapour pressure of toluene with temperature. Upon completion of the test the sample is allowed to return back to ambient temperature and pressure. On cooling the pressure temperature curve is identical to that observed for heating confirming that absence of sample activity.

THERMAL SCREENING OF 20% DI-*T*-BUTYL PEROXIDE (DTBP) IN TOLUENE

The thermal screening of 20% DTBP in HPLC grade toluene (4.8g) at 2°C/min is shown below in Figure 4. The reaction consists of the decomposition of an organic peroxide with the formation of ethane gas. This is shown mechanistically in equation (1.1).

$$CH_3)_3C-O-O-C(CH_3)_3 \longrightarrow 2(CH_3)_2CO + C_2H_6$$
(1.1)

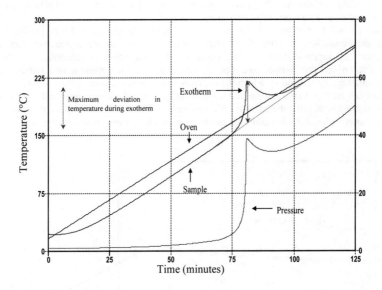

Figure 5: Thermal screening of 20% DTBP in toluene.

From Figure 5, it can be seen that the oven and sample heating traces at the start of the screening are similar to those of just toluene with the establishment of two linear ramps separated by an offset ΔT after an initial settling period. However, once the sample temperature has reached approximately 130 °C a clear deviation from linearity in the sample temperature profile can be detected. This marks the "onset" or "start" of thermal activity in the sample. This deviation from linearity continues to increase as the sample undergoes a thermal runaway until eventually the sample temperature reaches a maximum temperature of almost 50 °C higher than the oven. The peaking in the sample temperature profile indicates the end of the thermal decomposition reaction upon which the temperature is found to fall. The fall in sample temperature continues until it re-establishes a new baseline value which is almost identical to that achieved before the exotherm. The re-establishment of a second baseline after the exotherm is valuable since many decomposition reactions generate by-products that themselves can decompose further at higher temperatures.

In addition to the sample temperature data a wealth of information can be obtained from examination of the associated pressure curve. Similar to the sample temperature response, a clear deviation from the expected vapour pressure curve can be observed in the reaction at approximately 130 °C. In fact it could be argued that the reaction "onset" is clearer in the pressure data than the temperature. Again the shape of the pressure profile provides information on the period over which the reaction occurs. The pressure data also provides additional information about the reaction. On termination of the experiment at 300 °C the sample temperature is found to gradually return to ambient values, but the pressure remains at 14.87 bar. This shows that the decomposition reaction has occurred with the production of non-condensable gas. The knowledge of whether a runaway reaction does or does not proceed with the production of non-condensable gas is significant since it will determine the requirements of the safety system that will be required on scaling up the process. The magnitude of the pressure rise (P_{Max}) in the system is also important since it will also have an influence on the pressure rating of reactor to be employed.

It has already been discussed that from analysis of the temperature and time profile the thermal decomposition of 20% DTBP has been found to provide a reaction "onset temperature" of approximately 130 °C. However, it is important to remember that the determination of an onset temperature is purely subjective and will depend upon a number of factors including; the method by which the experiment has been performed, the thermal mass of the test cell relative to the sample and the method by which the data is analysed. This can be demonstrated by plotting the data in a different manner to determine the onset temperature. Figure 6 shows a plot of dT/dt against temperature for the above decomposition reaction.

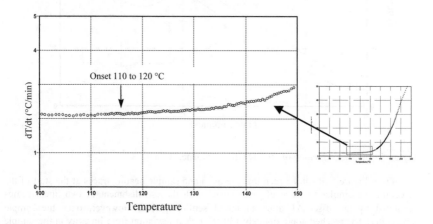

Figure 6: dT/dt versus temperature data for the thermal screening of 20% DTBP in toluene.

In plotting dT/dt against temperature it can be seen that the observable onset temperature for this reaction can now be determined to be in the region of 110 to 120 °C, almost 20°C lower than previously identified from the temperature-time profile and similar to data, reported for larger adiabatic calorimeters. This highlights the importance of careful data analysis during the interpretation of screening data to determine onset temperatures. Also from the plot of dT/dt against temperature it is also easy to determine the rates of temperature rise at different temperatures and to provide an unambiguous measure of the rate of the reaction runaway.

To examine the reproducibility of the thermal screening unit data for this reaction the experiment was repeated eight times and various parameters recorded. These included the maximum rates of temperature and pressure rise and the maximum deviation from the sample baseline during the exotherm to determine the exotherm temperature rise (the baseline was assumed to follow a linear ramp at the specified heating rate of the sample, as shown in Figure 5). A summary of these experiments is given below in Table 1.

Table 1: Experiments on the thermal screening of 20% DTBP in toluene to establish reproducibility.

Experiment Number	1	2	3	4	5	6	7	8
Onset temp (°C)	120	115	115	122	132	120	117	110
Maximum temperature of exotherm (°C)	227	229	229	220	225	231	229	231
Maximum deviation from sample temperature ramp (°C)	68	68	69	53	62	71	68	68
Maximum dT/dt (°C/min)	61	58	52	41	45	59	56	56
Maximum dP/dt (bar/min)	94	119	110	101	-	99.01	-	148

Examination of the maximum deviation of the sample temperature from its baseline value during the exotherm provides an average temperature rise of 65.9 °C ± 3.76 (at 95% confidence) indicating that the magnitude of the temperature rise is reproducible. Measurement of the sample temperature rise therefore provides a suitable method by which the extent of a reaction runaway can be compared. To investigate this hypothesis further the reaction was performed with a 10 % solution of DTBP from which an average temperature rise of 21.86 °C ± 3.17 (at 95% confidence) was observed. This is exactly what would be expected for a lower peroxide charge and re-enforces the qualitative value of using peak heights as a measure of exothermic activity. These trends in reproducibility are also mirrored in the data recorded for dT/dt max, dP/dt max and the maximum observed temperature of the exotherm, suggesting that for similar reacting systems the magnitudes of these quantities provide suitable markers by which reaction runaway potential can be compared.

The width of the exotherm peak is also found to be important diagnostically since the width of the peak will provide some idea of the time period over which the reaction occurs. For the nitrocellulose dye systems that are discussed below we find that the exotherm peaks are extremely narrow revealing that the rate of heat release are much higher and occur over a very short time period.

THERMAL SCREENING RESULTS FROM RECENT STUDIES.

THERMAL SCREENING OF A SERIES OF NITROCELLULOSE DYES

It is well known that nitrocellulose compounds will catalytically decompose in their dry state to give CO, CO_2, H_2O, N_2 and NO. Nitrocellulose pigment dispersions contain up to 50% nitrocellulose, which makes them particularly difficult to handle during manufacturing and processing. These materials have therefore been the focus of both DSC and adiabatic calorimeter studies making them an ideal test series by which the performance of the thermal screening unit can be compared.

A series of nitrocellulose dyes (0.5 g) were heated from ambient temperature to 280 °C at a rate of 2 °C/min to assess their thermal stability. A typical trace for the thermal screening of a yellow nitrocellulose dye is shown below in Figure 7.

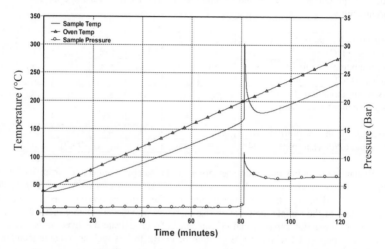

Figure 7: Thermal screening of a nitrocellulose dye at 2 °C/min from ambient to 280 °C.

From Figure 7 it can be clearly seen that the rate of decomposition of nitrocellulose is much greater than that observed previously for the screening of DTBP (dT/dt_{Max} = 269.5 °C/min and dP/dt_{Max} = 550 bar/min compared to 53.5°C/min and 111.8 bar/min for DTBP). This difference in thermal activity is also evident from the width of the sample temperature profile which is significantly narrower than that observed for DTBP, showing that the width of the sample temperature deviation provides evidence of the rate of energy release.

The results obtained during the screening of a series of nitrocellulose dyes are shown below in table 2. From these results the violet pigment can be identified as having the lowest thermal stability with an onset temperature (as determined from a dT/dt against temperature graph) of 127.4 °C and a deflagration temperature of 161 °C. ("Deflagration" is used here to describe the point at which the temperature and pressure begin to rise sharply).

Table 2: Thermal screening of a series of nitrocellulose dyes.

Pigment	Onset Temp (°C)	T_{Max} (°C)	dT/dt_{Max} (°C/min)	dP/dt_{Max} (Bar/min)	$T_{deflagration}$ (°C)	ARC data $T_{deflagration}$ (°C)
Violet	127.4	338.8	318.4	497	157	149
Yellow	139.5	302.5	269.5	550	165	160
Red	149.3	392.8	422.8	630	170	-

Table 2 also shows data for analysis of the same dyes using an accelerating rate calorimeter (ARC) in which the experiment is performed in an adiabatic environment (heat step temperature of 10 °C and a slope sensitivity of 0.02 °C/min). Again the same trend in thermal stability is detected and similar onset and deflagration temperatures recorded. Unfortunately, due to the high pressures that were generated in these experiments it was not possible to analyse these samples by DSC to make a direct comparison. However, other workers have reported an alternative temperature scan DSC procedure in which the onset temperature measured for these dyes where found to give the same trend in thermal stability (no deflagration temperatures recorded).

DETECTION OF ENDOTHERMIC ACTIVITY
In addition to the detection of exothermic processes the thermal screening unit can also be used to detect endothermic reactions. A demonstration of this capability is shown in the thermal screening of 4 g of hydroquinone at 2 °C/min from ambient to 300 °C, shown below in Figure 8.

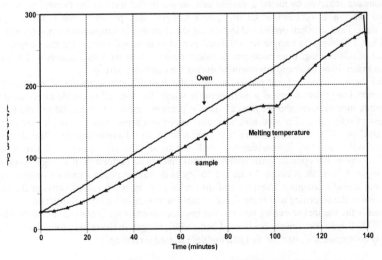

Figure 8: Thermal screening of hydroquinone from ambient to 300 °C at 2 °C/min.

In a similar manner to the screening of liquids, on performing a thermal analysis of a solid sample two linear ramps are generated separated by an offset ΔT. Generally, for solid materials it is found that the offset between the two temperature profiles is slightly greater than that obtained for liquid samples and this can be attributed solely to the differences in heat transfer properties between the two types of materials.

On the detection of endothermic activity the sample temperature trace is observed to peak downwards, similar to what would be expected in a DSC type instrument. Again, the depth of this peak and the aspect of the peak provide a wealth of information regarding the magnitude of the endothermic process and the rate at which it occurs. In the example presented here for the screening of hydroquinone a levelling-off in the sample temperature occurs in the range 171 to 173 °C. This corresponds to the solid-liquid phase transition of the sample and continues for several minutes until the entire sample has melted. This is in excellent agreement to other techniques that report a melting point for hydroquinone in the region 171 to 173 °C.

Again on completion of the sample melting the sample profile re-establishes the initial baseline that was achieved before the thermal activity, enabling secondary thermal events to be identified within the sample. An interesting example of an endothermic process followed by an exotherm is in the thermal screening of L-Ascorbic acid (vitamin C) in which the sample melting at 192-193 °C is immediately proceeded by a violent exothermic runaway due to the decarboxylation and decomposition of the sample producing pressures in excess of 200 bar.

COMPARISON OF THE TS^U WITH ADIABATIC CALORIMETERS

Adiabatic calorimeters such as the ARC[5] or PHI-TEC II[7] are traditionally considered as the most reliable tool for exotherm detection and for generating quantitative kinetic and thermodynamic data with regards reaction severity. In a typical experiment adiabatic conditions are achieved by taking a sample cell similar to that used in the thermal screening unit and placing it between a set of "guard heaters" that precisely match the sample temperature. Tests are then performed by heating the chemical in temperature steps, (typically 10 to 15 °C) holding the sample for a defined period of time and monitoring the sample for evidence of self-heating. If an exotherm is indeed detected then the guard heaters will follow and thus maintain an adiabatic environment during the reaction runaway.

The thermal screening unit possess many of the desirable characteristics of an adiabatic calorimeter. The system contains a thermocouple within the test cell to enable direct sample temperature measurement and the test cell itself is pressure resistant to over 200 bar and has a thickness of 0.65 mm. The screening unit also uses more representative sample sizes than either DSC or DTA again similar to that employed in an adiabatic system. The thermal screening unit, however, is considerably smaller than an adiabatic system and also much simpler to set-up and operate, often enabling many runs to be performed in a single working day or night. When this is coupled with the ability to operate multiple screening units (up to four) from a single computer interface and the scales of economy involved between the two units it makes the screening unit more suited to rapid screening of multiple compounds.

Clearly the thermal screening unit has not been designed to act in competition with ARC or PHI-TEC II type instruments but instead helps to fill the gap in the market for a device that is wholly concerned with routine, fast and multiple hazard screening.

CONCLUSIONS

Although DSC and DTA techniques have been applied with great success to many areas of chemical testing and process development their application to thermal hazard screening has in recent years caused much cause for concern. This is particularly true in the modern chemical manufacturing industry where the pressures on process scale-up and development organisations are continually increasing but the development-cycle time scales are under a constant squeeze. This has resulted in the increasing tendency for quick, single test procedures possibly in combination with reaction calorimetry for thermal stability assessment, which without careful interpretation and experience cannot provide a sufficient guarantee that hazardous processes will not slip through the net.

The thermal screening unit has been developed as tool to address some of these problems associated with modern hazard screening and provide an alternative instrument to DSC and DTA. Importantly the unit employs representative sample sizes in the range 0.5 to 5g. These sample sizes not only provide more realistic information for scale up but also enable a whole range of processes to be examined including heterogeneous systems, air sensitive materials, starting materials and intermediates. The unit also importantly provides pressure information, which enables the study of product storage and provides information on expected reactor pressures if a process were to undergo a runaway reaction. By examining information such as dT/dt_{Max} and dP/dt_{Max} it is also possible to start to gain information on the rates of energy release from a systems. This latter information is beneficial for the design of vent lines and reactor relief systems and will reduce the number of samples that will have to be examined by an adiabatic calorimeter.

REFERENCES

1. Benson, S.W. et al., 1969, *Chem Rev*, **69**, 279.
2. Fenlon, October 1984,W.J., *Plant/Operations Progress*, **3**, No 4, AICHE.
3. Singh, J., Spring 1997, *Plant/Operations Progress*, Vol 16, No 1, 43-49, AICHE.
4. Hoefelich, T.C and Thomas, R,C., 7-9 March, 74-84, 1989, *International Symposium on RunawayReactions*, Boston. Marriot Cambridge, AICHE.
5. Townsend, D,I. And Tau, J.C., 1980, *Thermochim. Acta*, **37**, 1-30.
6. Riesen, 5-6 December 1989, R. *Chemical reaction hazards Conference and Exhibition, London*, IBC Technical services.
7. Singh, J., 1999, *Journal of Thermal Analysis and Calorimetry*, **58**, 193-200.

RUNAWAY REACTION DURING PRODUCTION OF AN AZO DYE INTERMEDIATE.

Stafford Partington* and Simon Waldram[+]
*Holliday Dyes and Chemicals, P.O. Box B22, Leeds Road, Huddersfield, HD2 1UH
[+]Hazard Evaluation Laboratory, 50 Moxon Street, Barnet, HERTS, EN5 5TS

On Sunday 9th June 1996 a violent runaway reaction occurred in a 2.3 m^3 Pfaudler reactor creating a high pressure that led to rupture of the vessel: consequential damage to equipment and buildings was very significant. This paper provides explanations of how and why this accident occurred. At the time of the incident a diazonium ion was being produced for subsequent decomposition to form a phenol. The process had been carried out many hundreds of times before without incident. A combination of isothermal and adiabatic calorimetry was subsequently used to study the thermochemistry of both the desired synthesis reaction, and the undesired decomposition reaction. Plant simulation studies based on this experimental data were then used as an aid to analysing and understanding the events leading up to the accident. In due course the plant was rebuilt and production resumed: some of the strategies used to reduce both the hazards and risks associated with renewed production are discussed. A summary of the overall business impact of the accident is presented.

Keywords: reactor, exotherm, runaway, decomposition, diazonium, adiabatic, calorimetry, business impact

INTRODUCTION

HOLLIDAY DYES AND CHEMICALS
The Holliday company began in 1830 when Read Holliday established a factory in Huddersfield producing ammonia from coal tar waste residues. This was followed in 1856 with the production of magenta and other dyestuffs. L. B. Hollidays were soon in the forefront of the British dye industry and were involved in the formation of the Society of Dyers and Colourists (SDC), and later the British Dyestuff Corporation (which subsequently became ICI in 1926.) New factories were built in 1916 on the current site on Leeds road to manufacture explosives and colourants as part of the war effort. Post war expansion in the 20s and 30s into new higher technology markets, such as fluorescents and transfer-printing dyes, followed. In 1987 L. B. Holliday became the cornerstone of Holliday Chemical Holdings (HCH) who were themselves eventually acquired by Yule Catto in 1998. Since then however, declining markets, severe Eastern competition and escalating site running costs have lead to difficult times and in November 2000 Yule Catto announced the phased closure of the HDC site in Huddersfield.

Over the years Hollidays established a reputation as a quality supplier of dyestuff and chemical intermediates traditionally based on anthraquinone and naphthalene. The diverse molecular structures of the Holliday products necessitated many types of batch and semi-batch reactions including chlorination, hydrochlorination, sulphonation, nitration, cyanation, amination and diazotisation. It was the last of these reactions classes that led to the runaway exotherm that is the subject of this paper.

PRODUCTION OF THE SUBSTITUTED PHENOL
For reasons of commercial sensitivity, full details of the particular chemistry of the reaction that was taking place when this incident occurred cannot be provided. However Figure 1 indicates that an aromatic amine was reacted with a mixture of sulphuric acid and nitrosonium hydrogen sulphate (Nitrosyl Sulphuric Acid, or NSA) to produce the diazonium ion that was then decomposed to form the phenol. It is worth mentioning that this process had been operated over several years, with more than 100 batches per year being made, without incident. All the diazotisations were carried out in a dedicated 2270 litre Pfaudler model AH glass lined reactor. The process equipment was simple in concept and is illustrated in Figure 2.

DETAILS OF THE INCIDENT
The accident was associated with the decomposition stage of the diazo compound that is shown in Figure 1. The graph shown in figure 3 is the actual temperature trace for batch 123 with which the accident was associated. The chart runs from right to left: for clarity a variety of important data have been superimposed on the chart.

We are initially concerned with the first stage of the process that starts with the addition of the amine to be diazotised into 100% sulphuric acid (monhydrate) to give a solution. Typically this takes about 4 hours. Once in solution, and cooled to the correct temperature, NSA is added over 5 hours whilst maintaining the temperature between 30°C and 40°C. At the end of the addition diazotisation is complete.

For batch 123 there were some differences from the norm. During the addition of the amine the temperature rose to about 48°C. When the addition was complete the batch was cooled back to ~ 35°C and the NSA addition started, see point A in figure 3. (Note that the NSA was delivered in drums, there being 4 drums per batch. These were charged individually to a head tank and then run into the reactor contents: an orifice plate in the reactor feed line restricted the maximum flow rate of NSA. The capacity of the head tank was only slightly in excess of one drum.) After a short period the batch had cooled to 30°C, point B. Further addition of NSA took the temperature up to 50°C, point C. The NSA feed was then suspended and the batch temperature was brought down with unintentional over cooling. NSA addition was resumed at 25°C, point D. The batch temperature fell slowly (as a consequence of the cold NSA) to ~ 21°C, point E, and then rose continuously with the last recorded temperature showing 60°C at point F. Shortly after this temperature a massive over pressurisation of the vessel occurred resulting in the pan lid and head gear being blown off the vessel with devastating consequences. The agitator was left on the mezzanine roof but the pan lid itself travelled approximately 150 metres before landing and smashing into an office wall. The main body of the reactor was driven off its mounts and down through the concrete floor below. It would have travelled further but for a steel structure beneath the floor impeding its progress. Thankfully nobody was injured in the incident which happened at 9.30 am on a Sunday morning when site activities were at a minimum. A short video taken a few hours later captures the devastation of the unit, surrounding vessels and equipment.

UNDERSTANDING WHAT WENT WRONG

The simulation in the laboratory of an accident in which a major process vessel has ruptured because of overpressure should not be undertaken lightly. Even on the laboratory scale the hazards from an explosion may be very significant, and a rigorous risk assessment is required before experiments can be started.

The plant in question relied heavily on manual control systems, and data recording was rudimentary. Despite this, the limited process information considered during the early stages of accident investigation indicated clearly that reactor temperature control had been erratic and that eventually the temperature in the reactor had risen out of control. A high pressure had been generated: a relatively small portion of this could be attributed directly to the vapour pressure of the reaction mixture present. The major component of the pressure was therefore due to non-condensable gas production. Such instability of diazonium salts is well documented[1, 2].

THE THERMOCHEMICAL DATA

The thermochemistry of the reactions taking place was examined using the facilities at Hazard Evaluation Laboratory with a combination of isothermal and adiabatic calorimetry. The former was primarily used to study the desired process under operating conditions at, or close to, those that were normally intended. The latter was used to simulate loss of cooling and to understand the severity of the decomposition exotherm(s) that could occur: by working with test cells with a low thermal mass (low ϕ factor) the behaviour of large scale plant can be accurately reproduced.[3]

Isothermal calorimetry
Isothermal calorimetry studies on the production of the diazonium ion were made in the one litre SIMULAR reaction calorimeter[4]. The final stage of this procedure involved the pumped addition of Nitrosyl Sulphuric Acid (NSA) into the remainder of the reaction mixture. In the laboratory this was carried out at temperatures of 50°C, 40°C and 30°C: these temperatures were selected to cover the range of extremes of temperature permitted during plant operations. At some stages of these additions the feed was suspended so as to enable the enthalpy accumulation to be inferred corresponding to intermediate times during the feed addition. Enthalpy accumulation was also calculated when each feed stage was terminated. At 30°C ~ 80% of the reaction enthalpy was released after cessation of the feed: analogous figures at 40°C and 50°C were ~ 28% and ~ 17%. The history of a typical two-stage experiment at 40°C and 30°C is shown in Figure 4.

Adiabatic calorimetry
Adiabatic experiments were made in the PHI TEC II calorimeter[5] in magnetically agitated, low phi factor glass test cells. In the first test the desired diazonium salt was prepared under normal conditions in the laboratory and then charged to the test cell. The test cell was open to the pressure containment vessel in which the calorimeter was housed: this vessel was purged with nitrogen and then initially pressurised to 7 bara so as to minimise evaporative losses from the sample. A heat-wait-search procedure was then started with ~ 5°C steps starting from 30°C. A weak exotherm in excess of the chosen onset threshold of 0.04°Cmin^{-1} was first detected at 43.35°C. However this was not

sustained and after ~ 45 minutes when the sample temperature was 44.25 the self-heat rate fell below the termination threshold and the heat-wait search was resumed. This exotherm could have been the result of a small amount of residual activity from the diazonium salt preparation stage, or the earliest phases of decomposition. At 56.33°C a second exotherm was detected. This was sustained over a period of ~ 150 minutes with the final stages of the exotherm becoming very violent. A maximum temperature of 301.2°C was reached with a corresponding pressure of 16.6 bara. This is illustrated in figure 5. If the test had been conducted in the sealed cell mode, then, at a test cell fill level of ~ 70%, the final pressure in the cell head space would have been several hundred bara. The kinetics of the decomposition reaction are not simple. In figure 6 the self-heat rate is plotted as a function of temperature: the exotherm accelerates to a peak self-heat rate of ~ 100°Cmin^{-1} at 141°C, then subsides briefly before reaching a maximum self-heat rate in excess of 2100°Cmin^{-1}. This self-heat rate is, of course well in excess of that at which true adiabatic conditions can be maintained.

In another adiabatic experiment starting at 30°C nitrosyl sulphuric acid was injected into the reaction mixture prepared after dissolving the amine in the monohydrate. Note that 30°C was the lowest reaction temperature permitted in the HDC process instructions. The resultant exotherm is illustrated in figure 7. The initial exotherm is the direct consequence of the desired reaction, i.e. the formation of the diazonium salt. However the temperature that is reached is sufficient to trigger the violent decomposition exotherm that follows within less than 10 minutes of the start of the experiment. What is even more clear than before is the fact that the decomposition reaction itself involves two stages, see figure 8. The first peak in self-heat rate of 882°Cmin^{-1} occurs at ~150°C and the second of 2700°Cmin^{-1} at 255°C. These figures are in excellent qualitative, and quantitative, agreement with the analogous data shown in figure 6 which it should be recalled is for the decomposition of the diazonium compound when prepared under normal conditions.

SIMULATION

Process simulation was carried out by Dr Alan Wright of BatchCAD Consulting. The main objectives and purposes were to:

- Provide a better understanding of the chemistry and its interaction with process operation, with a view to simulating the possible causes of the incident.
- Provide a simulation and development tool to aid in the design of the process as it was to be re-built.

Using the BatchCAD RATE program the rate constants, and reaction orders, in power law kinetic models for both the diazotisation reaction and the subsequent decomposition reaction were evaluated by curve fitting the model predictions to both the isothermal and adiabatic calorimetry data. For the diazotisation step a model with first order rate dependence on the amine concentration and second order rate dependence on NSA concentration fitted the data best. The Arrhenius constants were evaluated using the isothermal calorimetry data (reaction power output, reaction enthalpy and reactant accumulation) at 30°C, 40°C and 50°C. The model thus developed generated good data fits to all of the experimental results. Enthalpy and rate parameters for the reaction of the water formed during the diazotisation with the monohydrate were determined using a combination of literature and experimental data. The decomposition reaction was modelled using both the adiabatic calorimetry data in figure 5 as well as isothermal data gathered at 110°C. The complete reaction model predictions were then tested for the combined synthesis and decomposition reaction data shown in Figure 7: the overall agreement was reasonable and generated a good measure of confidence in the efficacy of the model and the validity of simulation studies.

A reactor model for a Pfaudler AH series 500 gallon (2270 litre) reactor with water cooling, as being used by HCH at the time of the incident, was developed using the BatchCAD REACTION program. This included information on the physical dimensions of the vessel, the jacket service fluids, the reactor control system and the reactor heat transfer capability. Best estimates of cooling water temperature (which was not logged) and overall heat transfer coefficient were based on experience and those portions of Figure 3 (together with some sections of the temperature trace from earlier in the batch) when reactor cooling was applied fully. On this basis the overall heat transfer coefficient was ~ between 210 and 280 $Wm^{-2}K^{-1}$.

The process charge and feed conditions on the day of the incident were included in the model with estimated NSA feed rates and operation of a safety trip on feed rates if the reactant temperature was outside the 25°C to 36°C range. There was good plant evidence that the reactor agitation system had functioned normally throughout the batch reaction and this assumption was made in the plant model.

A number of causes of the incident were possible including accumulation of unreacted NSA and inadvertent heat input to the reactor, e.g. from a passing steam valve. Reduction of heat transfer capacity due to fouling was possible but this, of course, was already allowed for in that the overall heat transfer coefficient was estimated from the plant data. Many simulations were carried out with the recorded temperature profile of Figure 3 being used as the set point in the simulator feedback controller that was used to regulate the coolant flow. Using these techniques the simulation showed that an addition of 60% of the NSA could have been made in 2 hour 15 minutes for an overall heat transfer coefficient of 210 $Wm^{-2}K^{-1}$. For a value of 280 $Wm^{-2}K^{-1}$, 70% of the NSA could have been added in this same time, or 100% could have been added in 3 hours 30 minutes.

CONCLUSIONS
The combination of laboratory based experimental studies in isothermal and adiabatic calorimeters, and computer simulation of plant behaviour, gave vital insights into the possible causes of the incident. These can be summarised as follows:
1. The reported addition of 75% of the NSA over 2 hours and 15 minutes would have resulted in an accumulation of ~ 30% of unreacted NSA within the reactor.
2. This accumulation alone could not account for the severity of the thermal runaway that took place.
3. The temperature on plant rose from ~ 21°C to ~ 60°C over a period of ~1 hour. This rate of temperature rise could not be reproduced without an additional heat input to the reactor.

4. A constant heat input to the reactor of ~ 34kW throughout this period would have been required, in addition to the reaction enthalpy release, in order for the simulation studies to reproduce the plant runaway.
5. Application of steam to the reactor jacket could have produced a heat input of this magnitude. Thus a steam valve that was inadvertently left open, or a badly leaking steam valve, could have been a contributory cause of the incident.
6. Some other source of additional heat, e.g. resulting from the ingress of water cannot be ruled out.

Some general observations can also be made:

- Operating a semi-batch reactor below the specified temperature range can greatly increase the accumulation of unreacted feed, and hence the potential for a runaway reaction.
- Increased reactant accumulation will raise the Maximum Temperature of the Synthesis Reaction (MTSR) and as a consequence reduce the Time to Maximum Rate (TMR) for any subsequent exotherm, e.g. the decomposition reaction in this case.
- A small additional heat input to a reactor can dramatically reduce the TMR at the end of a semi-batch feed. For example, in the system studied, with the reactor at 35°C and the NSA feed over 5 hours, the TMR at the end of the batch was just over 10 hours. With an additional heat input of only 5 kW to the reactor this falls to ~ 3.5 hours.

THE NEW PLANT

There was an urgent need to resume plant production as soon as possible but neither Hollidays nor the HSE would have allowed re-installation of the original facility. At the time Hollidays were looking at the feasibility of continuous, rather than batch, processing technology in relation to other products. After some small scale trial studies in which a small amount of product was produced it was decided to continue to use a semi-batch process similar to the original one. However the original design would be modified extensively so as to eliminate or reduce hazards where possible and reduce the risks associated with those that remained. Important inputs into the new plant design were the thermochemistry studies and simulations referred to earlier sections.

Safety features for the new plant included:

- Computer control, and data logging, with soft and hard-wired trips and interlocks.
- Prevention of the possibility of a rapid NSA dump charge by pump metering and drum charging.
- Reactor weight monitoring and control via the use of load cells.
- Header tank weight monitoring and control via the use of load cells for accurate NSA weight charge.

A pressure relief vent on the reactor would not be an appropriate basis of safety for coping with any potential runaway reaction and consequent over-pressurisation. The relief line would have to be sized in accordance with the DIERS principles, as outlined the HSE "Workbook for chemical reactor relief system sizing"[6], and, because of the very high rates of pressurisation, would be impossibly large. A far better policy was to devise a process design that would not allow an exothermic decomposition runaway to occur. This was achieved by ensuring that if temperature control was not within defined limits then the contents of the vessel would be dumped before any exotherm could develop into a hazardous event. This was achieved by having a special Pfaudler reactor manufactured with 2 bottom outlets of sufficient capacity to permit rapid dumping of the contents into an appropriately sized quench tank. This revised plant layout is shown in Figure 9. General aspects of the design of such a system, and specification of the necessary amount of quench fluid to be present, are discussed in an HSE Contract Research Report CRR 100/1996,[7]. Pressure relief vent sizing could then be specified to cope with other specific, and less arduous, maloperations: this resulted in an acceptable pressure relief line size of 150 mm.

BUSINESS IMPACT

When a catastrophic event such as this accident occurs there is inevitably a major impact on the company's business. This usually extends far beyond the product stream involved and is only revealed long after the damage to the plant and the fabric of the building have been assessed and catalogued. Some of the major costs associated with this accident are summarised below:

- Cost of new installation: £1.0 M
- Business interruption: £1.1 M
- Re-instatement of surrounding plant/buildings: £0.5 M
- Fines and costs: £0.1 M

However there were many other factors too that are more difficult to quantify in purely financial terms. These include:

- Opportunities for competitors to increase their market share of the business.
- Existing customers now insisting on dual sourcing of their chemical feedstocks.
- Additional employee costs.
- Psychological impact on the workforce.
- Deleterious effect of morale.
- Implications, and extra costs, associated with other existing processes that could be candidates for a similar event.
- Preparation of the accident investigation and legal defence using the services of Hammond Suddards.
- Training and re-training of various types, including simulated on- and off-site crisis management (with Link Associates), improvement and strengthening or works emergency teams, accident investigation.

REFERENCES

1.   Bretherick's Handbook of reactive chemical hazards, 6th Edition, 1999, Ed. Urben P. G., Butterworth Heinemann, ISBN 0 7506 3605 X

2.   The accident data base, Institution of Chemical Engineers, ☐ HYPERLINK "mailto:jcheshire@icheme.org.uk" ☐jcheshire@icheme.org.uk☐,   ☐ HYPERLINK "http://www.icheme.org" ☐www.icheme.org☐

3.   Emergency relief system design using DIERS technology. The Design Institute for Emergency Relief Systems (DIERS) Project Manual, 1992, Ed. Fisher H. G., AIChE, ISBN 0 8169 0568 1

4.   Singh J., Reaction calorimetry for process development: recent advances, Process safety progress, 1997, 16, No 1, pages 43 – 50

5.   Singh J., Reliable scale-up of thermal hazards data using the PHI-TEC II calorimeter, Thermochimica Acta, 226, 1993, pages 211 – 220

6.   Etchells J., Wilday J., Workbook for chemical reactor relief system sizing, HSE Books, 1998, CRR 136/1998, ISBN 0 7176 1389 5.

7.   Singh J., Safe disposal of vented reacting fluids, HSE Books, 1996, CRR 100/1996, ISBN 0 7176 1107 8

Figure 1
<u>Routine reaction</u>

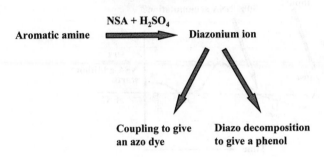

Aromatic amine $\xrightarrow{NSA + H_2SO_4}$ Diazonium ion

Coupling to give an azo dye

Diazo decomposition to give a phenol

Figure 2
<u>Original plant line diagram</u>

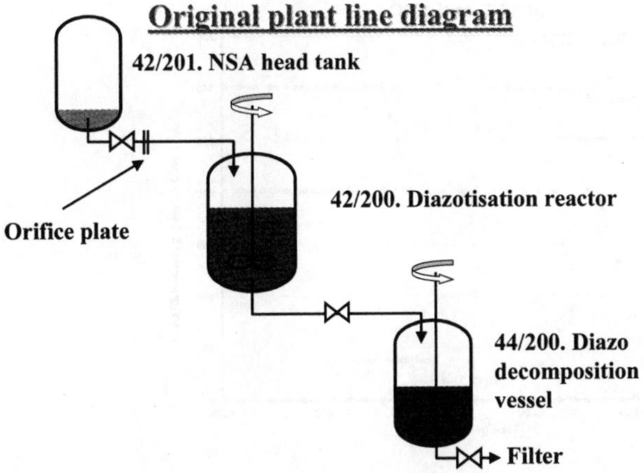

42/201. NSA head tank

Orifice plate

42/200. Diazotisation reactor

44/200. Diazo decomposition vessel

→ Filter

Figure 3
Temperature trace during the NSA addition

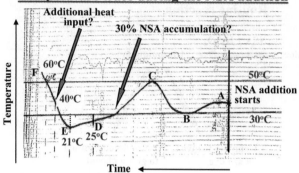

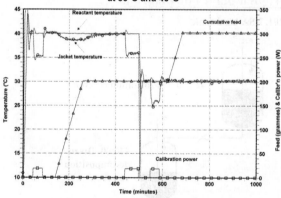

Figure 4. Isothermal calorimetry on the semi-batch addition of NSA at 30°C and 40°C

Figure 5. Decomposition exotherm for the diazonium ion: sample prepared externally in a automated reactor. Open cell test with 7 bara N₂ pressure

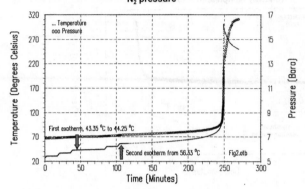

Figure 6. Decomposition exotherm for the diazonium ion: self heat rate versus temperature shows a two stage decomposition

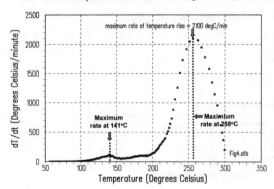

Figure 7. Exotherm for the synthesis reaction and the subsequent diazonium ion decomposition. Open cell test with 7 bara N$_2$ pressure. Runaway complete in ~ 10 minutes

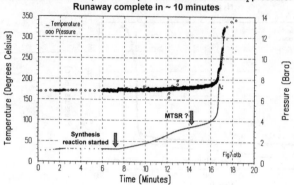

Figure 8. Exotherm for the synthesis reaction and the subsequent diazonium ion decomposition. Open cell test with 7 bara N$_2$ pressure

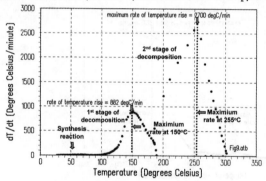

Figure 9
New plant line diagram

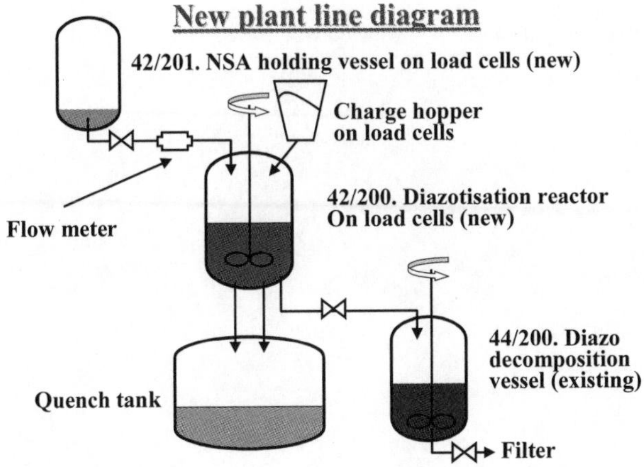

42/201. NSA holding vessel on load cells (new)

Charge hopper
on load cells

42/200. Diazotisation reactor
On load cells (new)

Flow meter

44/200. Diazo
decomposition
vessel (existing)

Quench tank

Filter

LARGE SCALE CALORIMETRY

Dr Peter J. Duggan, S Hollingworth, and M Martin
Avecia

This paper discusses the potential benefits to be gained from accurate measurement of the heat energy output from plant scale reactors. The incorporation of thermocouples and a flow meter into the vessel cooling system permits accurate measurement of the plant scale heat energy output rate and thereby provides an accurate measure of the accumulation of reagents at any given time. This procedure permits safer working and improved understanding of the chemical manufacturing process. The potential benefits from modification of plant scale reactors include a reduced number of incidents in the chemical industry together with improved optimisation of the process on the plant.

As above

Calorimetry, isothermal, heat-balance, heat-loss,

INTRODUCTION

Statistics show that the highest numbers of hazard and safety related incidents per specific chemical process occur with high energy systems, see "Chemical Reaction Hazards" by Barton and Rogers, reference 1. Specific reference is given to polymerisations, nitrations, and sulphonations, i.e. all highly energetic systems. It should be noted that less energetic systems could also give rise to significant chemical reaction hazards. The key feature is the amount of stored energy during plant processing, i.e. the product of potential heat energy release and accumulation. Further analysis shows that a lack of understanding of the balance between process heat energy output and available vessel cooling capacity is a major factor in many of these incidents. Process maloperations are responsible for the next highest number of chemical reaction hazards. Overall, it can be deduced that many parts of the chemical industry suffer from a lack of knowledge or appreciation of the potential heat energy output of a given manufacturing process and in particular of the kinetic parameters associated with the process, i.e. the rate of heat generation.

Highly energetic processes and other moderately energetic processes often have the potential for uncontrolled reaction to give rise to excessive heat energy output leading to vessel over-pressurisation and possible ejection of the batch from the reactor, etc. The consequence of runaway chemical processes can be very costly and can involve loss of life as well as loss of plant, loss of manufacturing capability, loss of morale, bad publicity, etc. As well as cost implications, legislative pressure from various government bodies requires that the chemical industry examine properly a proposed process to establish if it gives rise to a potential chemical reaction hazard and if so to determine safe operating conditions.

The most usual processing methodology is based upon semi-batch operation and the most usually Basis of Safety for a semi-batch chemical manufacturing process is based upon process control. Process control usually involves the controlled addition of a key reagent to the remaining materials whilst maintaining the batch at a given set temperature. To facilitate operation, many chemical manufacturers will pre-determine the rate of addition by examination of the proposed process in the laboratory using a calorimeter.

There are a number of commercial isothermal calorimeters available, for example the HEL Simular, Mettler Toledo RC1, etc. Furthermore, some companies have developed their own system, for example the power compensation heat flow calorimeter developed by Avecia, figure 1. Use of these calorimeters allows examination of a given proposed manufacturing process under the proposed normal operating conditions. Note: It is also possible to use the calorimeter to examine certain maloperations, for example rapid addition, omission of catalyst, etc.

The isothermal calorimeter produces a kinetic profile, i.e. process power output versus time, of the given proposed process. This data can be processed to allow determination of the required vessel cooling system for a given addition rate or vice versa. From a hazards viewpoint, the data can be used to determine if there is a build up or potentially dangerous accumulation of reagents and therefore if the process gives rise to excessive amounts of stored potential energy. As a result of the calorimetric analysis in the laboratory, the proposed process may be revised to avoid a potentially dangerous accumulation of reagents. Once a process has been examined and safe-operating conditions defined, it is possible to consider the scale up of the process to a manufacturing scale. This procedure of examination of a proposed process in a calorimeter prior to operation on a manufacturing scale is in common use throughout the chemical industry. It should be noted that the isothermal calorimeter represents only one component of a more comprehensive package of experimentation, which may be used to examine a given proposed process. Never the less the isothermal calorimeter is most frequently used to determine the required vessel cooling system for a chemical manufacturing process.

The use of calorimeters has improved the safety performance of the chemical industry. However and despite increased availability and use of calorimeters, the chemical industry still suffers from an unacceptably high number of incidents, which are due to excessive and often unexpected heat energy outputs from a given chemical processing system. The archives abound with such examples. As an example and typical of the unexpected behaviour that can occur in a chemical manufacturing process, a minor incident occurred during a pilot scale reductive acylation which was being operated by a UK chemical manufacturing company.

CASE HISTORY

A typical chemical manufacturing process incident was the subject of an earlier paper, reference 2. A brief synopsis of the incident is provided below to illustrate the need for accurate measurement of the heat energy output from larger scale reactors.

The process had been examined, using heat flow calorimetry, prior to the start of manufacture and safe-operating conditions had been established. The process had been operated for several years without incident and was considered safe and robust.

The process itself required the addition of an aromatic nitro body to an agitated batch comprising an anhydride and acid together with finely divided iron. Calorimetric examination had established the reaction kinetic profile and a suitable addition regime had been established, see figure 2.

The chosen basis of safety was process control requiring addition of the nitro body to the batch over a minimum number of hours whilst maintaining the batch at a given set temperature. The processing methodology was considered safe and had been operated many times always giving the product in good yield and quality and without giving rise to a chemical reaction hazard. The process was considered robust.

The incident batch occurred at the start of a new campaign in which a different grade of iron was being used. In fact the new grade was more finely divided and was considered to be of a higher specification than the earlier grade, which had been used successfully for many years. Charging of the batch was carried out as usual and there were no indications that anything unusual was occurring. The operator had recorded that the start of the addition of the nitro species had been accompanied by a temperature spike, which was the normal observation. The addition of the nitro body was completed over the normal period to the batch at the given set temperature. The were no further temperature deviations. In accord with normal practice at the end of the addition the batch was sampled for analysis. Analytical results were available within about 30 minutes and indicated that the reaction was only 10 to 20% complete. Coincident with the obtaining of the analytical results it was found that the pilot scale batch was self-heating at a rapid rate. The batch self-heated to boil and thereafter to eject a considerable portion of the batch from the reactor. The details of the incident batch, i.e. the time temperature profile, are shown in figure 3.

The incident was minor in nature, mainly due to small scale of operation, but it does serve to illustrate that despite the best of intentions and the use of modern sophisticated calorimeters incidents still occur.

A detailed and extensive investigation into the incident batch was carried out and the cause of the incident was found to involve the use of the new "improved" grade of iron. The finely divided iron was shown to have an extensive surface coating of iron oxide, which in practice prevented the desired reductive alkylation from occurring. It is worth noting that the surface coating was not comprehensive and some of the iron was active. The active portion produced a temperature kick, which the operator took to indicate that the process was progressing in the normal manner. Once the non oxide-coated material had been consumed the bulk inactive material failed to react with the nitro body, which was being charged in a controlled manner. Thus despite charging the reagent in a controlled manner, a potentially dangerous "All-in" batch was generated. With time the oxide layer was removed by the acid, i.e. pickling, and the "All-in" batch reacted with the consequence detailed above.

The process was re-examined in a heat flow calorimeter using the new grade of iron, see figure 4. Addition of the nitro body was carried out over five hours to the batch at 25°C. The process power output profile shows the accumulation of reagents and subsequent resultant very rapid reaction, which overwhelms the reactor cooling system. Analysis shows that about 80% of the total process power output occurs after the addition of reagents is complete. The initial part of the reaction is comparable to the earlier calorimetric data confirming the presence of some normal active iron.

The above small scale minor incident is typical of the scenario which can affect many chemical manufacturing processes. The lack of accurate measurement of heat energy output from larger scale reactors, and in particular plant scale reactors, has led to many serious incidents in the chemical industry. It is the purpose of this paper to highlight the potential dangers and to propose safer working practices.

Controlled Additions

It is worth considering what is meant by controlled addition. Frequently a Basis of Safety will call for the addition of a key reagent to be made to the batch in a controlled manner whilst maintaining the batch at a given set temperature. In general it is assumed that the batch will behave in a similar manner to the laboratory calorimeter experiment and that the addition procedure will avoid any potentially dangerous accumulation of reagents. As shown above this hypothesis can be wrong.

Furthermore, consider a simple yet frequent maloperation of failure to charge a catalyst at the start of processing. The above precaution, i.e. add at a rate balanced to cooling, has little, if any benefit and affords no protection to the plant and operators. In the event of omission of a key catalyst the subsequent addition of reagents would be carried out with little, or no, process heat energy output and would generate a batch, which apart from catalyst could be considered to be "all-in". There are many examples of such batches suddenly and without warning undergoing rapid reaction leading to serious chemical reaction hazards. However, the identified safety precautions had been followed and the reagent was charged in a controlled manner to the batch at the given set temperature.

In the above nitro reaction process, to provide a means for future safe operation it was decided to revise the addition procedure such that the nitro body would be charged to batch portionwise with analysis of the batch prior to each subsequent addition. The next aliquot addition would only be carried out provided that the previous analysis had proved that there was an acceptable level of reagents present. In this way it was possible to identify if a potentially dangerous accumulation of reagents was present in the batch prior to the continued addition of the key reagent.

The revised processing methodology did provide a means of ensuring safe operation but was time consuming and the required analysis was costly. Such procedures were thought necessary to prevent a reoccurrence of the incident. However, alternative safe practices were not readily available.

Large Scale Calorimeter

It is recognised that it is often impractical to provide controlled additions of energetic reagents together with frequent analysis of the progress of the reaction. One alternative has been introduced within Avecia with some expected success as well as unexpected benefit to the business.

A plant scale reactor within Avecia has been modified to incorporate a pair of matched thermocouples into the vessel cooling system, i.e. to measure the difference in coolant temperature of the fluid entering and exiting the vessel jacket coolant system. A flow meter provides an accurate measure of the rate of flow of coolant through the vessel jacket. A third thermocouple monitors the batch contents temperature. The data is then processed according to heat flow and heat balance principles.

In one example, the reactor was used to carry out a manufacture involving a highly energetic metallation of a reactive organic compound via an organometallic species. The process was examined in a laboratory-based calorimeter and the heat of reaction determined and the kinetic profile of the reaction established under normal operating conditions, see figure 5. A Basis of Safety was written and the associated precautions were incorporated into the works process operating instructions.

The process was operated on a plant manufacturing scale using the modified reactor as described above.

The progress of the process reaction on the plant was followed using the various thermocouples and coolant flow meter. Figure 6 shows the process operated with batch temperature control at -40°C. The addition was completed in two hours and the batch temperature was maintained at about -36°C to -39°C. Note: The coolant temperature dropped from -40°C at the start of the addition to a minimum value of -68°C during the addition. Once the addition was completed, the vessel coolant temperature returned to the jacket temperature, i.e. within about 45 minutes after the addition was completed. It can be seen that the addition is immediately exothermic and that a small accumulation of reagents is generated. Analysis provided an accurate thermodynamic profile of the progress of the process. Two techniques were employed, i.e. heat balance calorimetry and heat flow calorimetry.

Heat Flow Principles

Heat flow calorimeter depends upon knowledge of the heat transfer coefficient of the batch/vessel together with the temperature differential between the batch and the jacket cooling system.

$$\text{Rate of Process Energy Output} = UA(T_b - T_j)$$

where:

U is the heat transfer coefficient of the batch / reactor
A is the available vessel / jacket cooling area
T_b is the temperature of the batch in the reactor
T_j is the temperature of the coolant in the vessel jacket

Heat Balance Principles

In heat balance calorimetry a differential thermocouple, or a matched pair of thermocouples, is used to provide a measure of the heat energy gained by the fluid passing through the vessel cooling system, i.e. the process heat energy lost from the batch to the vessel cooling system. The product of the coolant temperature differential, i.e. the difference between the cooling fluid temperature entering and leaving the vessel jacket cooling system, and the coolant flow rate will provide an accurate measure of the rate of heat dissipation from the batch to the coolant system.

Rate of Process Energy Output = $(T_{J2}-T_{J1})$ x Flow rate x Specific Heat of the Coolant

Results

The results of the analysis were very encouraging and both heat flow and heat balance analyses were consistent with the data obtained from the experimental scale isothermal calorimeter, which operated, by power compensation heat flow calorimetry..

Analysis of the proposed process using the laboratory based isothermal power compensation calorimeter had indicated that the heat of reaction associated with the addition of the key reagent was -15 k calories per mole of reagent.

Heat flow analysis of the plant scale process indicated that the manufacturing scale heat of reaction value was -14.1 to -15.2 k calories per mole. Furthermore the peak power output in terms of Watts of heat energy evolved per unit mass were very comparable between the laboratory based isothermal calorimeter and the modified plant scale reactor.

Overall, a number of batches have been monitored and the results are very consistent. It is reassuring to know that the laboratory calorimeters can, if used properly, provide an accurate measure / model of the energy profile obtained in a plant scale manufacturing reactor.

Benefits

Increased Efficiency: Processes can be monitored to ensure that the addition profile is matched to the available vessel cooling system. In practice, with notable and well-publicised exceptions, most processes operate well within the available vessel cooling capacity. This can mean that addition periods are unnecessarily extended. In the example above, the addition rate has been modified, i.e. increased, such that there is a time saving of about 20% by comparison to the original plant operation.

Improved Safety: Continued analysis of the progress of a reaction allows the ready identification of any potentially dangerous build up of unreacted reagents. Note: It is possible for the analysis to be carried out on line and therefore the chemist or plant operator can readily determine the progress of a reaction at any time.

Increased Confidence: Confidence in operating the process is increased. Continual evaluation of the process heat energy output together with knowledge of the progress of the addition permits analysis to ensure that a potential hazardous build-up of reagents does not occur. Under such circumstances the addition of further reagent is suspended and technical advice is obtained.

Optimised Cooling Efficiency: A further unexpected benefit has been forthcoming in that analysis of the batch / vessel heat transfer proprieties has shown that the cooling system is more efficient at certain temperatures. It had been thought previously that improved cooling would be achieved by reducing the coolant temperature to a minimal value. In practice the calorimetric analysis has shown that improved cooling is achieved by the use of coolant at a specific temperature value at which the characteristics of the coolant system are utilised to their full potential. This has enabled the batch time to be reduced with the consequential gain in production and therefore manufacturing costs have been reduced.

Conclusions

Overall, the incorporation of heat flow and heat balance analysis into the plant scale manufacturing capability has provided a step improvement in the safety of our plant. The accurate matching of reagent addition rate to the available vessel cooling system is apparent. Furthermore the matching of the addition rate to the amount of accumulation of reagent in the batch allows safer working and reduced risk of a serious chemical reaction hazard associated with operation of our processes.

References:

1.   Barton and Rogers
2.   PJ Duggan Hazards XIII

Figure 1: Power Compensation Isothermal Calorimeter as used in Avecia.

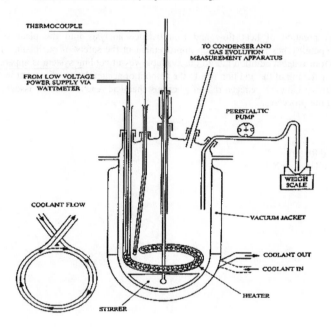

Incident process normal profile:

ORIGINAL PROCESS GRANULAR IRON

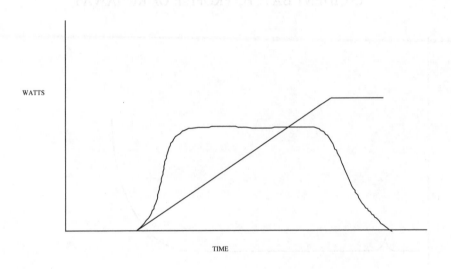

Incident batch: profile of runaway:

INCIDENT BATCH; PROFILE OF RUNAWAY

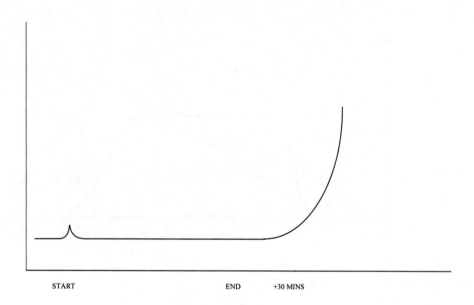

START   END   +30 MINS

Isothermal Calorimetry: of Incident Batch

MODIFIED PROCESS USING FINELY DIVIDED IRON

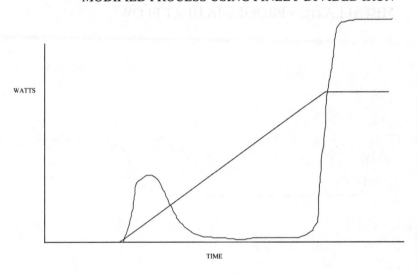

metallation Profile:

METALLATION PROFILE IN HEAT FLOW

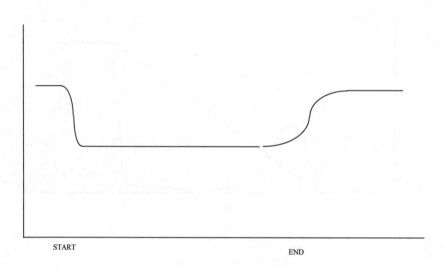

START

END

Metallation with Batch Temperature Control at –40 °C

METALLATION

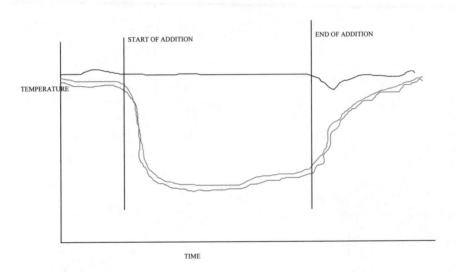

NON-ISOTHERMAL HEAT-FLOW CALORIMETRY FOR BATCH AND SEMI-BATCH PROCESS DEVELOPMENT

Dr. Jim Bickerton & Dr. Allan W. Timms

JB Safety Consultancy & Great Lakes (UK) Ltd.

Non-isothermal heat flow calorimetry, Enthalpy of Reaction, Baseline construction, Experimental errors.

INTRODUCTION

Heat flow calorimetry has been used extensively to measure isothermal heats and energies of commercially important synthesis reactions. In common with other calorimetry techniques, some measurement principle is calibrated against a known heat flow. The unknown heat flow due to the reaction of interest is compared with the calibration heat flow, and so can be evaluated. If the calibration and measurement experiments are as identical as possible, then the (unknown) errors will cancel, being common to both experiments.

The technique has not been widely applied to non-isothermal reactions, presumably due to the difficulties arising as a result of the changing reactor temperature. Recent advances in computing technology have now made accurate temperature control possible, and so non-isothermal operation has become a practical proposition. In this paper we describe how a modern isothermal calorimeter (SIMULAR) [1] has been used to measure the heat of reaction of both a well-documented test reaction (methanolysis of acetic anhydride) and of a commercially useful synthesis reaction.

PRINCIPLE OF OPERATION

ISOTHERMAL OPERATION.

A sophisticated control system is used to keep the calorimeter at a set temperature. In isothermal calorimetry this is a constant value, and in non-isothermal calorimetry the reactor temperature is a function of time. The controlling effect in isothermal calorimetry as implemented in the commercially available calorimeter, SIMULAR [1] is the temperature of the oil circulated through the reactor jacket:

Heat flow to and from the calorimeter is described by the relationship

$$(1) \quad q_f = U.A.(T_R - T_J)$$

where q_f is the heat flow from reactor to jacket, T_R and T_J are the temperatures of the reactor and jacket respectively, A is the effective heat transfer area and U is the heat transfer coefficient. The equation describes differential heat flow – i.e. the heat flow over unit time. Integration of q_f over the period of the reaction is necessary to determine the total heat (or energy) of the reaction.

Typical experiments using this technique involve one or more electrical calibration steps. The reactor contents are heated electrically and the power to the heater is measured directly. The heat flow from the reactor at equilibrium is equal to the heat input to the heater, and so the U.A term in equation (1) above can be found. The heat flow from the calorimeter at any time can be calculated from the observed temperatures of the reactor contents and jacket. The U.A term depends on a number of variables, such as the fill level in the reactor, the thermal conductivity of the reactor contents and so on. Carrying out a number of electrical calibrations during a measurement may be necessary to determine the changing values of U.A as the reaction or process simulation proceeds.

NON-ISOTHERMAL OPERATION

In the real world, at least some useful synthetic reactions are carried out over a range of temperatures. To study these reactions isothermally is to deviate from normal plant operating conditions and may lead to erroneous conclusions. The question then arises as to whether the calorimeter can be operated non-isothermally.

In isothermal operation, the baseline or zero heat flow condition is easily established. However, in non-isothermal operation, the control system is actively changing the temperature in the calorimeter. In this case a baseline can only be established if the control action is reasonably reproducible. Figure 1 below shows how the time temperature data for two separate temperature ramps can be superimposed.

Figure 1 here.

It can be seen that the control action for each ramp is virtually identical. This means that if a thermal event occurs during the ramp then there will be a detectable effect in the control system response (See Figure 2).

Figure 2 here.

In non-isothermal experiments, it is also necessary to estimate the amount of heat (or energy) which is used to change the temperature of the reactor contents:

$$(2) \qquad q_{Acc} = C.\frac{dT}{dt}$$

where C is the overall heat capacity of the calorimeter and contents, dT/dt is the change in temperature per unit time and q_{Acc} is the amount of power needed to bring about the temperature change.

Determination of the heat capacity of the reactor (i.e. calorimeter) is not easily possible for a number of reasons. For instance, it is not possible to define how much of the glass in the reactor walls is to be included in a conventional heat capacity determination. Similarly, the contribution of any reactor fittings, such as the thermometer probe, cannot be easily defined.

Two approaches have been used for the present paper. The first approach has been to define a calorimeter "constant" (E_{cal}) which includes the effective part of the calorimeter and its contents (Accumulation Heat Methodology). The software supplied with the calorimeter (WinCalc ™) was used. The calorimeter constant is measured in separate calibration steps, done before and after the reaction. The drawback with this approach is definition of the baseline for the heat flow integration. Under isothermal conditions the baseline heat flow is easily defined. The question of baselines for the non-isothermal experiment is not so clear.

As far as we are aware, equation 2 has never been used to determine the heat flow, and subsequently, after integration, the energy released for a system which has been deliberately perturbed from isothermal conditions – i.e. the temperature of the system is deliberately ramped up between two set temperatures.

The second approach takes as its baseline the temperature data from the calibration steps. No attempt is made to calculate a separate calibration constant. The assumption is that systematic errors are common to both measurement and calibration experiments and therefore cancel out.

EXPERIMENTAL.

REACTION OF ACETIC ANHYDRIDE AND METHANOL – UNCATALYSED REACTION.
The reaction was carried out by addition of acetic anhydride to methanol at 20°C followed by ramping the reactor temperature up to 50°C over 1 hour followed by a stir out at 50°C. Calibrations for both UA and the heat capacity of the reactor and contents were carried out before and after the reaction. The experiment is depicted graphically in Figure 3.

Figure 3 here.

Accumulation Heat Methodology.
The measured value of E_{cal} pre-reaction is an underestimate since at this point no acetic anhydride has been added to the vessel. It has been corrected by addition of the heat capacity of the acetic anhydride. E_{cal} used in the calculation is the mean of the two values.

Inspection of the graph (Figure 3) indicates that the feed of acetic anhydride to methanol at 20°C is slightly endothermic (+0.9kJ/mol) as calculated by normal methods. Clearly, during the final stir out stage at 50°C reaction is still taking place since the oil inlet temperature is still rising. Reaction is therefore occurring over the heat up and stir out periods.

Interpolation of both the baseline and the change in UA were not straight forward. These parameters were interpolated following the reactor temperature. In any event, the total change in UA was less than 3% over the reaction and is probably not significant. The final result for the molar heat of reaction was –59.3 kJ/mol of acetic anhydride for the heat up ramp and final stir out. This figure breaks down as +23.4 kJ as total heat flow and -82.8kJ/mol accumulated in the reactor contents. The overall heat of reaction is therefore –58.4kJ/mol of acetic anhydride. This compares reasonably well with the generally accepted value of about -66kJ/mol [2] for an uncatalysed reaction.

Residual Differences Methodology.
This method relies on the fact that two separate temperature ramps can be almost perfectly superimposed (Figure 1). Subtraction of the mean reactor - jacket temperature differences of the two calibration ramps from those for the reaction ramp yields the temperature differences due to the chemical reaction alone. Integration of these residual differences affords the enthalpy of reaction. A consistent method has been employed to calculate the enthalpy of reaction in the stir out step. The total enthalpy measured was –59kJ/mol of acetic anhydride charged. This is in fair agreement with both the heat accumulation methodology and the literature value.

Figure 4 here

REACTION OF ACETIC ANHYDRIDE AND METHANOL – CATALYSED REACTION.
The experiment was repeated but a trace of sulphuric acid catalyst was added part way into the heat up stage. The same quantities of raw materials were used in this experiment and the calibration data from the first experiment were applied. The time temperature details are depicted in Figure 5.

Figure 5 here.

Accumulation Heat Methodology.

The results were calculated in an identical manner to the previous case using identical values for UA and the specific heat capacities. The result of −76.1kJ/mol compares very well with the generally accepted value of −74.8kJ/mol [3] for the catalysed reaction. In principle, using calibration data from previous experiments is probably unsound. In this case however, careful attention to detail was taken in assembling the experiment and the data plotted with the calibration data from the previous experiment justifies this strategy.

Residual Differences Methodology.

The residual differences gives an enthalpy of reaction of −65kJ/mol of acetic anhydride. This is a little low compared with the literature value and the value calculated by the accumulation heat methodology.

Figure 6 here.

A REACTION OF INDUSTRIAL IMPORTANCE.

For reasons of commercial sensitivity, the chemistry of this real example can only be represented in general terms. A solid raw material (A) is suspended in a solvent with stirring. The second reagent is added over a period of time. This addition is exothermic and converts the starting material into a new insoluble intermediate (B). The reaction mixture is then slowly heated at a constant rate to an elevated temperature to convert the intermediate (B) into the product (C). During this stage a gas is evolved. The heat of reaction of this stage had never been measured previously although adiabatic reaction calorimetry had indicated that the reaction may be endothermic. Again appropriate calibration and specific heat determination stages were included in the experimental plan. The experimental time temperature data are depicted in Figure 7.

Figure 7 here.

Accumulation Heat Methodology.

The feed of the raw material was exothermic while the heat up stage was strongly endothermic (Figure 6). The enthalpy of reaction for the heat up stage only (not on a molar basis) was calculated as +97kJ. It is interesting to note that the energy released curve is almost an exact mirror image of the gas evolved curve. This is expected as the amount of gas released is proportional to the extent of the reaction, in turn proportional to the heat of reaction. Furthermore, during the initial part of the reaction some energy is absorbed and no gas is evolved, indicating a minimum two stage mechanism.

Figure 8 here.

Residual Differences Methodology.

The residual differences are plotted in Figure 7 and Figure 8 shows the integrated enthalpy curve. The enthalpy of reaction quoted on the same basis as above is +90kJ. The agreement between the two results is fair although, again, the residual differences method has given a lower result than the accumulation heat methodology.

Figure 9 here.

Figure 10 here.

DISCUSSION.

The three experiments reported above show that reasonable results can be achieved using a modern heat flow calorimeter in non-isothermal mode. Unfortunately, because of the calibration problems the experiments are necessarily time consuming. The industrially important reaction took 42 hours to complete.

The results calculated for the two reference reactions agree well with the accepted best values. This shows that the general calculation methods used for isothermal calorimetry are also valid for non-isothermal work. Of the two calculation methods used, the residual differences method appears to give slightly lower results than the heat accumulation methodology. It is not immediately clear why this is so.

Experimental errors in isothermal heat flow calorimetry are normally minimised by allowing the calorimeter to reach equilibrium. Under non-isothermal conditions the equilibria are much more dynamic and it is likely that systematic errors are larger as a result. Traditionally, calorimetrists design experiments so that the measurement and the calibration are as near identical as practically possible. This allows the systematic errors to cancel completely in the calculation. The reproducibility of the temperature ramps which is possible using a modern computer controlled calorimeter will contribute to reduced errors.

It is interesting to note that in the industrially important example, the order in the experiment of UA determination followed by the ramp stage is probably not the best. This is almost certainly linked to the fact that the raw material (A) dissolved on heating. On cooling back, the material crystallised in a different form and crystallised on the walls of the calorimeter. This undoubtedly introduced a significant error in UA. A better arrangement would have been to carry out the ramp stage first, followed by the UA determination.

In the industrially important example, the measured enthalpy relates to an overall effect which includes a variety of physical state changes as well as the reaction. Of course, this information is exactly that which a Process Design Engineer requires.

CONCLUSION.

* Heat flow calorimetry is a viable practical means of determining the enthalpy of reactions carried out under non-isothermal conditions.

* There are a number of sources of error in addition to those normally present in isothermal heat flow calorimetry.

* Errors associated with the temperature ramps can be significantly reduced by keeping the calibration and measurement experiments practically identical.

* Modern computer controlled instrument helps significantly in the reduction of the errors between experiments.

References:

1.   J. Singh, 1997, *"Reaction Calorimetry for Process Development: Recent Advances"*, *Process Safety Progress, Volume 16, No1, Spring, AIchE (New York),* 43-49.
2.   T. K. Wright & C. W. Butterworth, 1987, *IChemE Symp. Series No: 102, UMIST*: 85.
3.   Barton & Rogers, 1997, *Chemical Reaction Hazards*: 22.

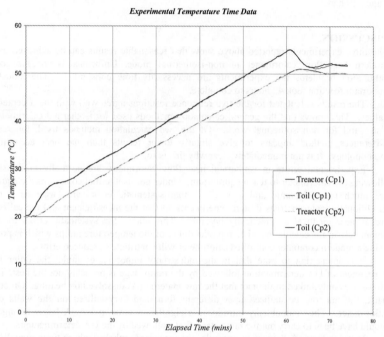

Figure 1: Time Temperature Data from two Separate Temperature Ramps Superimposed.

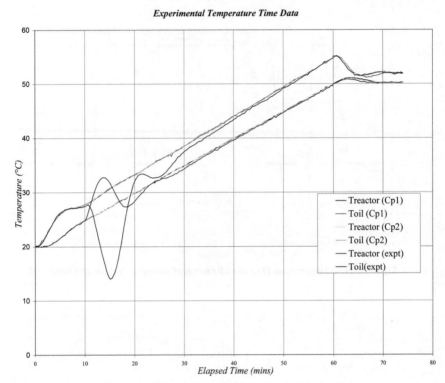

Figure 2: Experimental Data for Catalysed Reaction Superimposed on data from two calibrations.

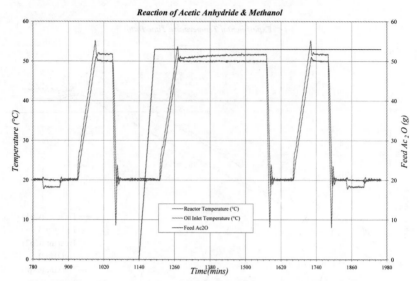

Figure 3: Time Temperature Data from Reaction of Acetic Anhydride and Methanol.

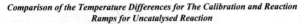

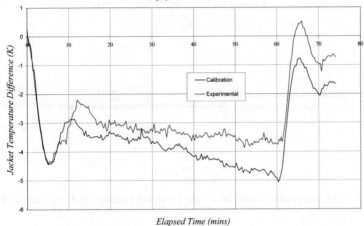

Figure 4: Jacket Temperature Differences for Calibration Ramp and Experiment for Uncatalysed Reaction.

Acid Catalysed Reaction of Acetic Anhydride and Methanol

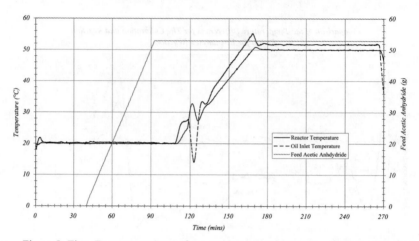

Figure 5: Time Temperature Data from Acid Catalysed Reaction of Acetic Anhydride and Methanol.

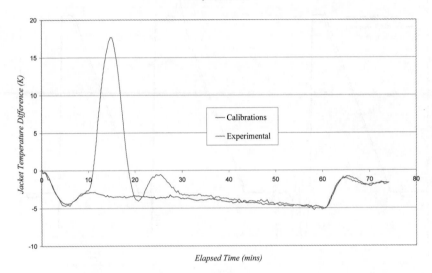

Comparison of the Temperature Differences for The Calibration and Reaction Ramps for Catalysed Reaction

Figure 6: Jacket Temperature Differences for Calibration Ramp and Experiment for Catalysed Reaction.

Non-Isothermal Industrially Important Reaction

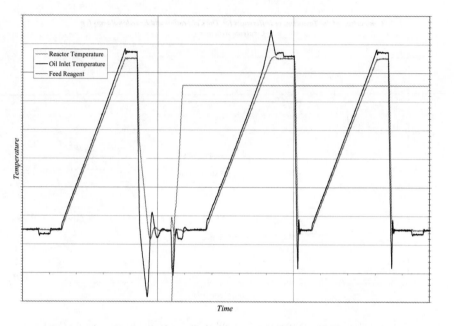

Figure 7: Time Temperature Data from an Industrially Important Example.

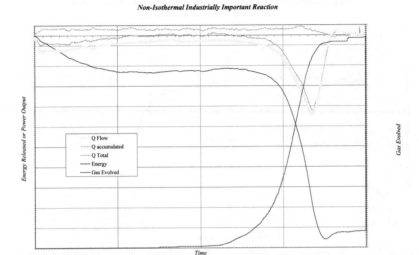

Figure 8: Energy Released for Industrially Important Example.

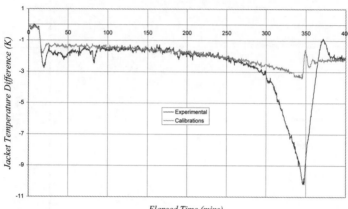

Temperature Differences for the Calibration and Measurement Ramps from the Industrially Important Reaction.

Elapsed Time (mins)

Figure 9: Jacket Temperature Differences for Calibration Ramp and Experiment for Industrially Important Reaction.

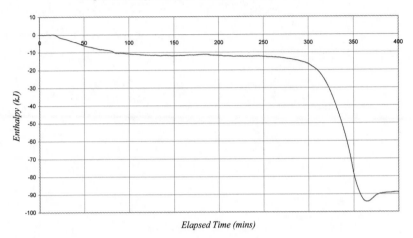

Integrated Enthalpy Change for the Industrially Important Reaction

Figure 10:Integrated Enthalpy Change for the Industrially Important Reaction.

MIS-IDENTIFICATION OF CHEMICALS

M. Powell-Price[a] and G.W. Suter[b]

[a]European Process Safety Centre, 165-189 Railway Terrace, Rugby, Warwickshire, CV21 3HQ, UK

[b]Swiss Institute for Safety and Security, WKL 127.P.60, CH-4002 Basle, Switzerland

This paper reports on work carried out by the European Process Safety Centre (EPSC) Contact Group on *Safety Issues in Batch Production*

The mis-identification of chemicals is a perennial safety issue. A number of serious incidents and near-misses have arisen through chemicals being incorrectly identified in both continuous and batch processes. However, the nature of batch production makes it particularly vulnerable to such incidents of Mis-Identification, due to the following characteristics:

- The use of multi-purpose plants, with different chemicals used in different production campaigns;
- The large variety of chemicals kept ready for use in a plant;
- The use of containers (i.e. bags, pallets, FIBC, etc), as opposed to supply via fixed pipes;
- The greater use of organisational versus technical safety measures.

For these reasons the European Process Safety Centre (EPSC) Safety Issues in Batch Production Contact Group choose this topic for investigation.

Keywords: Mis-identification, Chemical Handling, Hazard Identification, Protective and Preventative measures

BACKGROUND

The EPSC Contact Group on *Safety Issues in Batch Production* was formed in 1998 to investigate issues specific to Batch Production. The Group's first project investigated the issues involved with the transfer of processes from site to site, company to company or from development to production[1].

On completion the Contact Group chose to focus on the mis-identification of chemicals. The impetus for this topic was a number of recent incidents that had been attributed to incorrect identification or substitution of chemicals and the lack of clear guidance or advice in the literature. For the purpose of the project, and this paper, the mis-identification of chemicals was taken to refer to any chemical, other than that intended, reaching the process through the incorrect action, or inaction, of personnel.

INTRODUCTION

Mis-identification is by no means specific to Batch Chemistry or Production and can occur in any operation. However, there are facets of batch production that make it vulnerable to such incidents. These facets can be characterised by:

- The use of multi-purpose plants, with different chemicals used in different production campaigns;
- The large variety of chemicals kept ready for use in a plant;
- The use of containers (i.e. bags, pallets, FIBC, etc) as opposed to supply via fixed pipes;
- The greater use of organisational versus technical safety measures.

The aim of the investigation and subsequent report[2] was to provide a summary of the information exchanged between EPSC members on their company's approach to avoiding the mis-identification of chemicals.

A literature study undertaken at the start of the project revealed very little guidance on the methods available specifically for the prevention of mis-identification. There were, of course, general procedures outlined in Safety Management Systems[3] and more specific procedures for handling chemicals in later publications[4].

This paper includes the key findings from the benchmarking of the approaches taken by EPSC member companies to prevent mis-identification incidents. This benchmarking revealed a range of techniques from simple approaches, requiring the double checking of key stages, to complex systems involving bar codes and computer systems.

RISK ANALYSIS

Risk Analysis, with a special focus on mis-identification of chemicals and hazardous interactions, is a prerequisite for safe material flow through any process and the effective use of any additional measures.

A procedure for Hazard Identification is a vital for safe operation. Hazard Identification can be used to highlight possible hazards and then enable the company to target resources, procedures, measures, etc at the most significant hazards. There are many publications covering the topic of Hazard Identification [5,6,7].

One key finding was that Hazard Studies would often "start-at-the-gate" assuming that material entering the site was of the correct type and to specification. From experience, and the material presented, it is clear that this assumption is not valid. Therefore care should be taken when selecting the boundaries for a hazard study and any assumption(s) made.

Interaction matrices represent in a concise manner the possible hazardous interactions between chemicals present in a given plant and between chemicals and construction materials. The large number of possible interactions in a multi-purpose plant may render a "one-by-one" consideration impractical if not impossible. Class formation similar to that in Bretherick's[8] may be a good solution of this problem, some examples of classes being e.g. "strong acids", "peroxides", "amines".

Hazard Identification and Risk Assessment must be conducted to ensure that safe operation is maintained and the most effective procedures are utilised.

PREVENTATIVE AND PROTECTIVE MEASURES

A comprehensive and robust system of document verification is one essential element of a safe procedure for avoiding the possibility of mis-identification of chemicals. However established procedures for handling documentation are not in themselves foolproof, and other methods of identification may be required. The Contact Group provided information on a number of other additional measures used by various companies and these included:

LABELLING

All packages should be clearly labelled to allow easy and positive identification of the contents. Essential features of such a labelling system are:
- Highly visible labelling;
- Labelling on all packages of a delivery unit e.g. a pallet;
- Robust labels e.g. high adhesion, weather proof etc;
- Material name written in large easily readable characters;
- Avoiding the use of similar names, especially similar abbreviations.

The similarity of chemical names can be a significant problem when trying to avoid the mis-identification of chemicals. Shortened names or abbreviations have been introduced to allow easier communication and better distinction between chemicals with similar scientific names, but the increase in the number of these abbreviations has meant that it is evitable that some will become similar to each other. Moreover, cases have been reported where the abbreviation has inadvertently been identical to a molecular formula of a completely different chemical. One example is when "AAA" (Aceto-Acet-Anilide) and "AAOT" (Aceto-Acet-Ortho-Toluidide) were exchanged in the supply chain, with the mis-identification only caught by an attentive operator. A second near-miss occurred in a development laboratory where "KBR" (Potassium Bromide) was ordered for a synthesis though Copper Bronze (Kupferbronze) was the intended material. The error was readily identified when the chemical was delivered. In addition, the changes within the process industries, such as the increasing number of company mergers, has had the effect of merging different systems of abbreviations, a significant risk, if not carefully controlled.

SAMPLING AND ANALYSIS

Sampling and analysis may be used to support other methods of identification. Whilst analysis can provide the definitive identification of a chemical care must be exercised to ensure that mis-identification does not arise during or after the analysis step. On-line sampling systems are becoming more readily available through the development of miniaturised electronic systems. Although analysis can identify the chemical present there are some situations when analysis is not suitable or feasible. These include when the product is hazardous to health, thus introducing a significant risk to the individual involved or when it becomes unworkable to sample every container of product (i.e. a pallet containing about twenty 25 kg bags).

Some companies utilise a "just-in-time" system of delivery for materials to site. This allows the inherent safety improvement of reducing inventory, but can lead to pressures to allow material through from delivery to the production unit as quickly as possible. The procedures in place to analyse the chemicals should be suitable for both the hazard of the chemical, its possible incompatibility with other chemicals on site, the quantity of containers and the length of time before the product will be required for use.

BAR-CODES

Bar-codes are an additional measure that can be used in the supply chain to avoid the mis-identification of chemicals. In addition to their use in the supply chain, one member company has used a system of bar-coding for nearly two years at an individual plant.

On the company's site, all vessel charge points and transfer booths were equipped with a bar-code reader. Operators, supervisors and managers were all provided with bar-coded name badges so they could be identified. This allowed for each charge to be coded, and therefore, linked to a specific operator and, where supervisory checks were required, these could be programmed in. The computer control system verifies that the materials are correct and also automatically time stamps each input, charge and action.

Where practical, the bar-code read charges were combined with load cell measurements to ensure exact charges. It also allowed bar-coded batch labels to be printed that could further improve the accuracy and efficiency of the process.

The equipment involved had been found suitable for industrial use. The system provided excellent automated checks on both material type and quantity (either by number of bags etc. or via comparison with load cell results) for all manual-charging operations. Although not infallible, it would clearly reduce the potential for "operator error" to very low levels. This was true if the current system used for manual charging operations and manual controls were maintained.

An industry wide system of coding would further increase the effectiveness of the system. However, ultimately, it was felt that bar coding was only an aid to chemical identification and not a replacement for current procedures.

KEY-LOCKS

Key lock systems take many forms, one of which involves the use of locks and keys to stop any unauthorised use of materials from rail or road tanks entering the site. On arrival at the site all containers go through site security. Information regarding the tank contents is transferred and the analytical department notified. A sample is taken and analysed and a universal lock fitted by the analytical department that prohibits any unauthorised removal of the chemical. Once the analysis is complete the universal lock is removed and a substance specific lock attached to the tank. The plant or unit requiring the substance is then informed and the tank moved to storage ready for use. When required, the plant or unit is able to open the substance specific lock and unload the container. Once the chemical has been used, the plant places an order with the purchasing department and the specification is sent to both the purchasing department and analytical department. The chemical is then reordered, site security is notified of its arrival and the process begins again.

The system is applicable when there are regular consignments of chemicals in bulk quantity. It is particularly useful when deliveries of chemicals are scheduled on a "just-in-time" basis. The technique is suitable for any bulk quantity where there is only one unique method of removing the material from the transport container i.e. valve, coupling etc.

SECOND SIGNATORY OR "4-EYES"

The second signatory or "4-eyes" principle is the method by which operations are first conducted by one operator and signed signifying that the correct procedure, operation etc had been followed. A second operator then countersigns the form signifying that the procedure has indeed been conducted correctly.

This technique of double signatories or "4-eyes" is most applicable when the operations being undertaken have the potential for producing hazardous situations if the procedure is incorrectly followed or the wrong chemical is added. The procedure is particularly useful when used in operations that require a high operator input, but in which it may be difficult to provide physical means of ensuring correct operation. For example, these can include batch operations, particularly multi-batch operations where there is a heavy load on operators. The procedure is also applicable for procedures that are only required intermittently (e.g. cleaning, maintenance, occasional batches).

To work most effectively the "4-eyes" principle should be used sparingly and only when secondary checks are needed due to there being a significant hazard. If the method is used too frequently on low hazard situations, there is the possibility that the method will be devalued and operators may begin to perform unauthorised tasks. When using "4-eyes" principles operators should be fully trained in the method and the reasons behind its use fully explained. The workload on any operator must be monitored with the reasons for any increase in workload fully explained to the operator, particularly when additional "4-eyes" procedures are introduced.

One limitation is that the first operator could assume that the second operator will check the consignment, operation etc. and the second operator could assume the first has conducted the tests etc. This can lead to a situation where operations take place under the "safety" of double checks, but in effect these double checks mean that neither operator conducts the inspections, operations etc. This can be avoided through appropriate training and the explanation of the importance of the procedure and only using the procedure when the hazard warrants it.

Incidents have been reported where one or more secondary-checks have failed to reveal an error[9,10].

SEGREGATED STORAGE IN STAGING AREA

Segregated Storage can be utilised throughout the entire the supply chain, but in practice it is particularly used in staging areas (these are the areas where materials are stored immediately prior to it being used in production, as compared to warehouse areas). This method can be utilised at the start of the supply chain and at later stages. Segregated storage can take many forms ranging from "soft" procedure based segregation to "hard" physical measures. Specific storage areas can be dedicated to specific products or barriers can be used to separate two or more incompatible materials. This can involve mechanical measures (e.g. walls, cages, separate buildings) or the use of a barrier of an "inert" chemical that does not have a hazardous reaction with either of the first two.

A segregated storage approach is applicable to most facilities and is a significant first step in ensuring the correct delivery of chemicals. This approach must include a rigorous documentation procedure, be regularly audited and employees trained in its use and the reasons for it.

TRAINING

Training cannot be seen as an independent method of preventing the mis-identification of chemicals but should be seen as a requirement for the effective implementation of those measures that are in place. Training can cover formal induction training, refresher training and regular group discussions. In order to minimise the risk of mis-identification it is important that training:

- Describes the measures that need to be followed for safe operation;
- Emphasises the importance of the checks and cross-checks that are in place;
- Provides the operators with an appreciation of the consequences that may arise if the systems fail.

BULK PRODUCTS

Bulk handling presents specific problems and provides certain benefits in the avoidance of mis-identification. The use of bulk chemicals can make identification simpler as there will be less sampling and analysis required to establish the identity of the material. This is particularly true when compared to sampling methods required for pallets, bags, and FIBC's. Problems occur if there is a mis-identification, for whatever reason as the quantity involved is likely to be significantly greater (tonnes versus kilos) and hence the consequence of any incident will be greater. Therefore bulk chemicals require similar techniques to those described earlier, but there will be variations in their application if the benefits of delivery in bulk are to be maximised while the associated hazards are minimised.

The UK Chemical Industries Association (CIA) produced a guidance document[11] in 1999 which focused on offloading products into bulk storage. This guidance deliberately concentrated on the supplier and customer interaction with the bulk load. It advised the implementation of a system independent of the supply chain. This was seen as having the advantage that the supplier and/or customer can introduce systems that reduce the potential for product crossover and are independent of those parts of the supply chain over which they have little control.

EMERGENCY PLANNING

Whatever system is in place to prevent mis-identification it is still vitally important to have prepared, documented and implemented an appropriate emergency plan. This emergency plan will need to be explained to all personnel, who need to be trained and competent in both the plan as a whole and their specific roles.

FINDINGS

STEPS TO MINIMISE THE HAZARD

Whilst there is no simple and unique solution to the problem the following steps can be used to ensure that the hazard is fully identified and appropriate controls in place:

Interaction matrix
Construct an interaction matrix to help identify hazardous interactions.

Hazard identification
Conduct a study to identify where the possibility exists for mis-identification to occur. (This may be in addition to conducting a HAZOP study).

Supply chain
Consider the importance of ensuring correct delivery of materials. For bulk chemicals reference should be made to the CIA Guide[11].

Labelling
Robust and accurate labelling is a must and a basis of safe operation. Considerations for labelling are discussed earlier in this paper.

Additional measures
Where the mis-identification of chemicals could lead to serious consequences, to either humans or the environment, additional measures will be required. One or more of the following approaches may be required to reduce the hazard or risk to tolerable levels:

- Segregated storage;
- Second signatory;
- Sampling and analysis;
- Key-locks;
- Bar-codes.

MOST INCIDENTS CAUSED BY HUMAN ERROR

From recent incidents and the experience of the Contact Group members, it was felt that most of the incidents where chemicals have been mis-identified could be attributed, at least in some way, to human error. This may over simplify the cause as it can be argued that human error stems from procedural, training, and management system failures. Although it would be simple to say that to reduce the likelihood of mis-identification humans need to be taken out of the loop, in batch production (particularly multi-purpose) this is not feasible.

The *human factor* plays a crucial role in Batch Processing in this area. Thus procedures, organisational measures and checks that are in place to confirm the identity of chemicals should be reviewed to confirm that they are "fit for human nature" e.g.:

- Ergonomically suitable;
- Short and simple;
- Not jeopardizing efficiency targets;

- Not too repetitive

The attentiveness of the operator is key to solving, or avoiding, the problem of mis-identification. This attentiveness can be enhanced through:

- The correct use of training;
- Raising awareness of the problem:
- Considering ergonomics in plant design and material supply chain;
- Consideration and limitation of work load stress; and
- Promoting a working environment where operators feel a degree of self-responsibility.

AN ONGOING PROBLEM

The Contact Group felt that there was a perpetual safety problem in the mis-identification of chemicals within a supply chain. Within processes there are opportunities to use inherent safety principles to substitute or eliminate steps that have such hazards. However, short of producing all raw materials on each site, there will always be the need for transportation of raw materials to site and the removal of product from site thus, reinforcing the scope for mis-identification of chemicals within the supply chain.

ACKNOWLEDGEMENTS

The authors wish to acknowledge the contributions made by following companies and institutions to this paper:

Akcros Chemicals   *Eutech*
BASF AG   *Novartis*
Bayer AG   *Rhodia*
Ciba Specialty Chemicals *Swiss Institute of Safety and Security*
Clariant GmbH   *Unilever*
EC JRC   *VTT Automation*

REFERENCES

1. EPSC, 2000, *Member-only* Report No. 17 - Safety Management for Process Transfer of Batch and Semi-Batch Process.
2. EPSC, 2000, *Member-only* Report No. 21 - The Mis-identification of Chemicals.
3. EPSC, 1994, Safety Management Systems.
4. EPSC, 2000, Safety, Health and Environmental Management Systems for Small to Medium Sized Enterprises: 66-67.
5. EPSC, CIA & IChemE, 2000, HAZOP: Guide to Best Practice in the Process and Chemical Industries.
6. Wells, G., 1997, Hazard Identification and Risk Assessment, IChemE.
7. CCPS, 1992, Guidelines for Hazard Evaluation Procedures, 2nd Edition.
8. 1999, Bretherick's Handbook of Reactive Chemical hazards, 6th Edition, Butterworth-Heinemann.
9. 2001, Action following the explosion at Albright & Wilson UK Ltd, Avonmouth on 3 October 1996, *Loss Prevention Bulletin,* Issue 153: 9-10.
10. June 2001, Supply of the wrong chemical leads to a release of hydrogen sulphide gas, *Loss Prevention Bulletin,* Issue 159: 4-5.
11. CIA, 1999, Bulk storage - procedures for off loading products into bulk storage at plants and terminals.

EVALUATION OF THE UN VENT SIZING METHOD FOR ORGANIC PEROXIDE PORTABLE TANKS

J A Hare* and W D Adams**
*   Health and Safety Laboratory, Buxton, Derbyshire, SK17 9JN
**   Hazardous Installations Division, Health and Safety Executive, Merseyside L20 3RA
© Crown Copyright 2001. Reproduced with the permission of the Controller of Her Majesty's Stationary Office

Type F organic peroxides are permitted for transport in portable tanks. Emergency Relief Systems have to be fitted to tanks intended for the transport of such peroxides. The United Nations Manual of Tests and Criteria includes a method to determine the minimum required emergency vent area using a 10 dm^3 test apparatus. The 10 dm^3 test apparatus is electrically heated (to simulate a fire) and the vent area is then scaled-up on vessel volume.

The Design Institute for Emergency Relief Systems (DIERS) has also produced methods to size the vents for gas generating runaway reaction systems including the decomposition of organic peroxides. These methods make use adiabatic calorimeters and vent sizing equations that consider if the vent will have to pass a two-phase gas-liquid flow or a single-phase gas-only flow.

The UN vent sizing method is evaluated and large-scale trials on organic peroxide decomposition described. DIERS vent-sizing calculations for two-phase homogeneous flow and gas-only flow are compared with the large scale test results.

Keywords: organic peroxides portable tanks, emergency relief systems, vent sizing.

INTRODUCTION

Runaway chemical reactions, if not adequately prevented or mitigated, can give rise to major accidents (e.g. Seveso, Bhopal). Pressure relief (venting) is a commonly used method of mitigation which, if properly designed, will prevent failure of the vessel, thereby averting a major accident.

Type F organic peroxides, which may undergo self accelerating decomposition, can be transported in tanks or intermediate bulk containers (IBCs) provided that these are fitted with adequately sized emergency pressure relief devices. The current state of the art for the design of pressure relief systems for runaway chemical reactions has been developed following research by the Design Institute for Emergency Relief Systems (DIERS) research consortium in the USA (Fisher et al[1]). However, the United Nations Manual of Tests and Criteria (UN[2]) includes a test method "Example of a Test Method for Vent Sizing", to determine the "required emergency vent capacity to be fitted to a specific portable tank for a particular organic peroxide". This method involves determining the critical orifice diameter by electrical heating (at a rate to simulate fire engulfment) of the peroxide in a 10 dm^3 vessel and then using area to volume scaling to calculate the minimum vent area for the tank. Experts in vent sizing have expressed serious doubts as to the applicability of this method.

However, as the method is relatively easy to apply, it is being increasingly used. The Hazardous Installations Division of HSE therefore commissioned HSL to perform an evaluation of the UN method in order to establish whether and under what circumstances it may be unsafe.

DANGEROUS GOODS TRANSPORT

UK legislation on the transport of dangerous goods implements two European Council directives (94/55/EC and 96/49/EC) which require EU member states to align their domestic transport legislation within the provisions of ADR (ECE[3]) and RID (ECE[4]). ADR is the European agreement concerning the international carriage of dangerous goods by road and RID is the European agreement concerning the international transport of dangerous goods by rail. As there is so much international trade in goods, there are agreements which control the way in which such goods are transported internationally. The UN Recommendations on the Transport of Dangerous Goods (UN[5]) forms the basis for the main European agreements for the transport of dangerous goods by road (ADR) and rail (RID) and international agreements for the transport of dangerous goods by sea (IMO) and air (ICAO).

UN VENT SIZING METHOD

The UN vent sizing method is based on some experimental work which indicates that, for organic peroxide formulations, the ratio of the minimum emergency vent area to the tank capacity is constant and can be determined using a reduced scale tank of 10 dm^3 capacity. DIERS methodology suggests that area to volume scaling applies only if the phase and density of the material vented is the same at both scales. A small-scale test may vent a gas-only flow, whereas a large-scale test may vent a two-phase flow. The higher density of the two-phase release requires the vent to carry a larger mass flow and so the vent must be considerably larger than application of the simple area to volume scaling would suggest.

The UN Model Regulation 4.2.1.13 permits the transport of type F organic peroxides in portable tanks. Model Regulation 4.2.4 has a table listing all organic peroxide mixtures which are permitted for transport in portable tanks. The possibility of self-accelerating decomposition and fire engulfment should be taken into account for tank transport of organic peroxides (Model Regulation 4.2.1.13.2). Tanks intended for the transport of organic peroxides should be fitted with emergency relief devices (Model Regulation 4.2.1.13.6). The emergency relief device (Model Regulation 4.2.1.13.8) should be designed to vent all decomposition products and vapours evolved during a period of not less than one hour of complete fire engulfment as calculated by the formula:

$$q = 70961 \ F \ A^{0.82} \tag{1}$$

and where F = 1 for non insulated vessels and, for insulated vessels, is given by:

$$F = U \ (923 - T_{PO}) \ / \ 47032 \tag{2}$$

The set pressure of the emergency relief device is set above that of the pressure relief device used for non-emergency situations. The emergency device is dimensioned so that the maximum pressure in the tank never exceeds the test pressure of the tank (Model Regulation 4.2.1.13.8). The minimum test pressure for a portable tank should be 4.0 barg (Model Regulation 4.2.1.13.4). The pressure relief device (normally a bursting disc) is designed to prevent any pressure build up in the portable tank due to decomposition products and vapours at a temperature of 50°C (Model Regulation 4.2.1.13.7). Bursting disc pressures are normally set in the range 3.0 to 3.5 barg so that they do not activate unnecessarily during transport. The UN method (Manual of Tests and Criteria - Appendix 5) is given as an example method of how to determine the size of the emergency relief device. Other methods may be used provided that they adequately size the emergency relief device. The 10 dm^3 UN tests would be undertaken to provide data for the design of emergency relief devices for the particular tank concerned. For insulated portable tanks the capacity of the emergency relief device shall be determined assuming a loss of insulation from 1% of the surface area (Model Regulation 4.2.1.13.9).

Complete fire engulfment was defined in the 1994 test method as a heat load of 110 kW m^{-2}; so that the heat absorption was proportional to the wetted area. The current definition for compete fire engulfment is based on API 520 (API[6]) without prompt fire fighting or good drainage; here the heat load is proportional to the wetted area to the power of 0.82. The heating rate to be used in the UN test is calculated from the sum of the heat load directly and indirectly to the exposed surface.

The UN test apparatus consists of a stainless steel tank with a gross volume of 10 dm^3 which is fitted with an extra bursting disc (set at 80% of the design pressure of the 10 dm^3 vessel) for safety reasons. The 10 dm^3 tank is fitted with a 1 mm opening which simulates the tank PRV (this is scaled using vent area to tank volume ratio) and a bursting disc assembly with a variable aperture orifice plate which simulates tank emergency venting (also scaled using vent area to tank volume ratio). The outer surface of the tank below liquid level is heated at a constant rate independent of the heat generated by the peroxide. A method is given to calculate the heating rate to be used in the test. The temperatures in the liquid and gas phase are measured as well as the tank pressure. The UN test vessel is unlikely to fail catastrophically during the testing process because of the protection of the extra bursting disc and also the largest diameter orifice available is used in the initial testing.

The minimum or suitable portable tank vent area (A_p) is calculated from the minimum orifice vent area (A_t) determined in a test in which the maximum pressure is not more than the test pressure of the portable tank, where the test vessel has volume (V_t) and the portable tank (V_p):

$$A_p = V_p (A_t / V_t) \tag{3}$$

DIERS VENT SIZING METHODOLOGY

For gassy systems the vent is designed for the maximum rate of gas evolution which generally occurs at the maximum temperature (Leung[7]). This is because there is no latent heat for cooling and thus the reaction temperature is not controlled by venting. A volumetric balance is achieved with the maximum volumetric gas generation rate being equal to the volumetric discharge rate. The relationship can be represented as:

$$(dQ/dt)_{g,max} = W / \rho_e \tag{4}$$

The volumetric gas generation rate is evaluated based on the experimental measurement of the rate of pressure rise data in a small scale adiabatic calorimeter. The maximum rate of gas evolution is obtained from the experiment using:

$$(dQ/dt)_{g,max} = (m_o / m_t) (V_f / P_m) (dP/dt)_{max} \tag{5}$$

There are now two approaches to calculate the mass flow rate (W) that the vent should be able to deal with: firstly and more rigorously to assume a two-phase relief and secondly to assume a gas only relief.

HOMOGENEOUS TWO-PHASE RELIEF

The exiting fluid density can be calculated from the vessel average density, which assumes homogeneous vessel venting, thus:

$$\rho_e = m_o / V \tag{6}$$

The required mass flowrate, W, is then calculated as:

$$W = \rho_e \, (dQ/dt)_{g,max} = (dQ/dt)_{g,max} \, (m_o / V) \tag{7}$$

Thus the ideal vent area (A), which is calculated from the required mass flowrate and the vent capacity (G), is:

$$A = (W / G) = (dQ/dt)_{g,max} \, (m_o / V \, G) \tag{8}$$

The mass flux G can be calculated using the Omega solution for the Homogeneous Equilibrium Model (HEM) (Leung[8]). A gassy system will generate a non flashing flow (since no vapour is being generated) with the value of omega lying between 0 and 1. The basic Omega equation is:

$$G = G^* \, (P_o \, \rho_e)^{1/2} \tag{9}$$

GAS-ONLY RELIEF

Here the exiting fluid density is calculated as for an ideal gas:

$$\rho_e = \rho_g = P \, M_W / R \, T \tag{10}$$

The gas mass flux can be calculated using equation 9:

$$G = G^* \, P \, (M_W / RT)^{1/2} \tag{11}$$

G^* equals 0.61 for an isentropic coefficient (k) value of 1.0 for choked isothermal flow, which is the worst case. Choked flow is the maximum flow rate of a compressible fluid (gas or two-phase) for a given upstream pressure.

We can now calculate the vent area using equations (4) and (11):

$$A = W/G = (dQ/dt)_{g,max} \, \rho_e / \, G^* \, P \, (M_W / RT)^{1/2} \tag{12}$$

Then using equation (10) to replace the exiting fluid density:

$$A = (dQ/dt)_{g,max} \, (M_W / RT)^{1/2} / \, G^* \tag{13}$$

Thus for choked flow:

$$A = ((dQ/dt)_{g,max} / 0.61) \, (M_W / RT)^{1/2} \tag{14}$$

FAUSKE'S RECENT GASSY EQUATION

Fauske[9,10] argues that the vent area may be calculated as for an ideal gas (13). Fauske then assumes that the critical value of G^* equals 2/3 instead of the true value of 0.61 and also introduces a discharge coefficient (C_D) to obtain:

$$A = (3/2) \, ((dQ/dt)_{g,max}/C_D) \, (M_W/RT)^{1/2} \tag{15}$$

Then substituting equation (5) into equation (15):

$$A = (3 / 2\ C_D)\ (m_o\ V_f\ (dP/dt)_{max} / m_t\ P_m)\ (M_W/RT)^{1/2} \tag{16}$$

The initial mass in the reactor can be calculated in terms of the reactor volume and the reactant density (Note equation (17) assumes that the vessel is always liquid full):

$$m_o = V\ \rho_r \tag{17}$$

Thus an expression for the vent area per unit volume can be obtained:

$$A/V = (3 / 2\ C_D)\ (\rho_r\ V_f\ (dP/dt)_{max} / m_t\ P_m)\ (M_W/RT)^{1/2} \tag{18}$$

HARE'S SIMPLIFIED GASSY EQUATION

This simplified vent sizing equation uses the DIERS[1] gassy equation and takes account of two phase flow. The equation solves the DIERS gassy vent sizing equation (equation 8) with the mass flux G calculated using a reliable two-phase flow method. The maximum rate of gas evolution can be calculated from the small scale maximum pressure rate using the temperature corrected version[1] of equation (5), which is reproduced here:

$$(dQ/dt)_{g,max} = (m_o/m_t)\ (V_f/P_m)\ (dP/dt)_{max}\ (T_t/T_c) \tag{19}$$

A suitable equation is required to calculate the two-phase (gas / non-flashing liquid) flow characteristic of gassy systems (Etchells and Wilday[11]). One approach is to use the Omega method (Leung[8]):

$$G = G^*\ (P_o / v_e)^{1/2} \tag{20}$$

Using the Omega method for a gassy system requires knowledge of the vessel void fraction (α_o) and the isentropic coefficient of the gas (k) as omega would be calculated as:

$$\omega = \alpha_o / k \tag{21}$$

Graphs of G^* and critical pressure ratio (η_c) versus Omega are available and the Omega method also allows corrections to be made for friction and backpressure. An alternative approach is to use Tangren's method (Tangren et al.[12]), which although it assumes isothermal flow instead of the adiabatic flow assumed by the Omega method, gives very similar results for choked flow. For this simplified analysis, choked flow will be assumed. Tangren's method requires the critical pressure ratio (Leung & Fauske[13]) to be calculated first:

$$\eta_c = \left[2.016 + \left(\tfrac{1-a_0}{2a_0} \right)^{0.7} \right]^{-0.714} \tag{22}$$

where α_o is the void fraction entering the relief system from the upstream vessel. The value of G, using Tangren's method, can now be calculated:

$$G = \sqrt{\frac{P_0}{v_e}}\ \frac{\left(\tfrac{2}{a_0} \left[\left(\tfrac{1-a_0}{a_0} \right)(1-\eta) - \ln\eta \right] \right)^{0.5}}{\tfrac{1}{\eta} + \left(\tfrac{1-a_0}{a_0} \right)} \tag{23}$$

It will be seen that equation (23) can be rewritten as equation (20) except that G^* is calculated using Tangren's method. The exiting fluid specific volume (v_e) is the reciprocal of the exiting fluid density (ρ_e) and so equation (20) can be written as equation (9). Equation (9) can now be substituted into equation (8) to give an equation for the vent area, also replacing the upstream vessel pressure (P_o) with the maximum allowable pressure (P_m):

$$A = (dQ/dt)_{g,max} \, (\rho_e / P_m)^{1/2} \, (1 / G^*) \tag{24}$$

Making the homogeneous vessel assumption means that the exiting fluid density (ρ_e) is assumed to equal the vessel average density (ρ_o) which is calculated using equation (6). The vessel two phase density can also be calculated from the void fraction (α_o) and the density of the liquid phase in the reactor (ρ_f) as:

$$\rho_o = (1-\alpha_o) \, \rho_f \tag{25}$$

Now replacing ρ_e in equation (24) with $(1-\alpha_o) \, \rho_f$ from equation (25):

$$A = ((dQ/dt)_{g,max} \, (\rho_f / P_m)^{1/2} \, ((1-\alpha_o)^{1/2} / G^*) \tag{26}$$

HSL GAS-ONLY AND TWO-PHASE VENT SIZING CALCULATIONS
The results of large scale tests will be compared with DIERS gas-only and homogeneous vessel two-phase vent sizing calculations. There are a limited number of large scale tests available. It is important to consider peroxide / solvent mixtures of varying reactivities. The large scale data should include maximum pressures and vent areas for vessels of various sizes or batch masses. Adiabatic data is also needed for the same peroxide / solvent mixture using a similar external heating rate to perform the DIERS vent sizing calculation. The UN vent sizing method is based on the assumption that the ratio of the vent area to tank capacity is constant and can be determined using a reduced scale tank of 10 dm^3 capacity. Graphs will be generated for three systems showing maximum pressure versus vent area per unit volume or mass. The graphs will show experimental test data and DIERS calculated vent sizes. The three systems selected for the vent sizing comparisons are:

- 37.5% by weight of bis (3,5,5-trimethyl hexanoyl) peroxide in isododecane,
- tert-butyl peroxy-2-ethylhexanoate in isoparaffinic solvent, and
- technical pure dicumyl peroxide.

The DIERS vent sizing equations used in this analysis will be summarised here for ease of reference. The maximum rate of gas generation is calculated using equation (5). Hare's simplified gassy equation (equation 26) will be used as the homogenous vessel two-phase flow vent sizing equation. Equation (16) (Fauske's gassy equation without the assumption of that the vessel is always liquid full) will be used as the gas-only flow vent sizing equation. Note that equation (16) implies the use of equation (5) to calculate the maximum rate of gas evolution. For both homogeneous vessel two-phase and gas-only vent sizing methods backpressure corrections will be ignored but friction will be allowed for.

SYSTEM 1 - BIS (3,5,5-TRIMETHYL HEXANOYL) PEROXIDE
The first system for study is 37.5% by weight of bis (3,5,5-trimethyl hexanoyl) peroxide in isododecane. Akzo Nobel market this peroxide mixture as Trigonox 36-CD37.5 - UN No 3119. It is available either as a 900 kg IBC or portable tank. Data on this system was included in papers by de Groot et al[14,15] and Wakker and de Groot[16]. Schuurman[17] gave HSL a

tabulated summary of this data for 8.3, 9, 33 and 234 dm³ vessels. The fill levels were 60, 80 and 90%. Schuurman[18] also provided decomposition data for the system. The major gaseous product is carbon dioxide (molecular weight 44 kg kmol⁻¹). The adiabatic data necessary to perform the vent sizing calculations was based on papers by Fauske[9,10,19,20,21]. Fauske performed his RSST test with an external heating rate (fire simulation) of about 0.8°C min⁻¹.

Figure 1 is a plot of maximum pressure versus vent area per unit volume (A/V). It shows experimental and calculated maximum pressures for homogeneous vessel two-phase flow and gas-only flow vent sizing. Calculated maximum pressure versus (A/V) lines are shown only for an 80% fill level.

The adiabatic data came from an RSST experiment. The RSST can only be operated as an "open system" where the test cell is connected to a much larger capacity containment vessel in which the pressure is measured. Open system tests are recommended by DIERS for gassy systems and have the advantage that effects of gas solubility in the solvent are limited. The two-phase vent sizing method, which made the homogeneous vessel assumption, would appear to be overly conservative. Gas-only flow vent sizing fits the experimental data better. The UN vent sizing method seems to be applicable to this system because experimental data from different vessel volumes lie on the same curve.

SYSTEM 2 - TERT-BUTYL PEROXY-2-ETHYLHEXANOATE

The second system for study is tert-butyl peroxy-2-ethylhexanoate in organic mineral solvent. HSL undertook some pilot plant tests using 20% by weight of this peroxy ester in an isoparafinic solvent catalysed by cobalt accelerator (Etchells et al.[22]). The HSL tests simulated a runaway reaction in a chemical reactor and investigated the vent size required. The reactor volume is 340 dm³. The vent area was not varied, but tests were performed using 100, 150, 200 and 250 dm³ batch volumes. Akzo data on 25 and 30% by weight of tert-butyl peroxy-2-ethylhexanoate in isododecane was available from Schuurman and Wakker[23] and Schuurman[24]. The 30% by weight formulation is marketed by Akzo as Trigonox 21-C30 UN No 3119 and is supplied as a portable tank. The Akzo tests were performed using 8.3 and 10.2 dm³ vessels which are normally run 90% full. The external heating rate was the main variable.

Schuurman[18] also provided decomposition data for the system. The major gaseous product is carbon dioxide (molecular weight 44 kg kmol⁻¹). The adiabatic data necessary to perform the vent sizing calculations was based on HSL Phi Tec tests for the 20% by weight mixture performed with accelerator concentrations of 1% and 0%. Note that the HSL adiabatic tests were initiated at 95°C with no imposed external heating rates. Three sets of adiabatic data were available for each accelerator concentration: Closed cell- raw pressure rate; closed cell - dissolved gas corrected rate and open cell pressure rate. The pressure rates and free volumes vary between the data sets. For closed system tests, the measured pressure is reduced due to dissolved gas, therefore dissolved gas corrected pressure rates were generated.

Figures 2 and 3 are plots of maximum pressure versus vent area per unit mass (A/m$_o$), showing gas-only flow and homogeneous vessel two-phase flow vent sizing respectively. Vent area per unit mass is used as the X-axis because the HSL tests were performed using the same vessel but with different batch volumes. The HSL pilot tests are of interest, even though they are not fire simulations, because they show the effect of scale-up and explore the validity of the DIERS gas-only and homogeneous two-phase vent sizing methods. In Figure 3, the 1% accelerator calculations are for a fill level of 74% (the largest fill used) and the 0% accelerator calculations are for a fill level of 90%. Note: only Akzo data with low maximum pressures due to lower heating rates have been included in the figures.

Considering firstly the HSL data. Assuming gas-only flow for vent sizing was never conservative. Using homogeneous two-phase flow for vent sizing was conservative for closed system tests provided allowance was made for dissolved gas; otherwise it was non conservative. Using homogeneous two-phase flow for vent sizing was overly conservative for open system tests. The experimental density was less than the homogeneous density; i.e. more gas and less liquid in the two-phase flow. Using the experimental density rather than the homogeneous density, a better prediction of the experimental mass flux was achieved. The flow regime seemed to be bubbly rather than homogeneous. The UN vent method does not appear to be applicable to this system.

Considering secondly the Akzo data. Adiabatic data was not available for the external heating rates used in the Akzo experiments, whereas the HSL adiabatic tests were performed without external heating. Thus for the 30% peroxyester tests, most of the predicted maximum pressures for homogeneous two-phase flow fell below the experimental values, apart from those based on open cell data. This shows the importance of performing an adiabatic test with the same external heating rate as used in the experiment. The other factor was the differences in peroxide concentration and the choice of solvent. This shows the importance of performing an adiabatic test using the same reaction mixture as used in the experiment.

SYSTEM 3 - NEAT DICUMYL PEROXIDE.
The third system for study is dicumyl peroxide. This system is of interest because of the incident at Calhoun in 1990 involving 1.7 m^3 (450 US gallon) tanks (NTSB[25]). Hercules, whose chemical (Di-Cup 99 wt% solid UN 3109 type F solid) and tanks (DOT spec 57) were involved in the incident, later carried out some tests using 0.22 m^3 (58 US gallon) tanks (Gove[26]) with an external heating rate of 0.8 °C min^{-1}. Later the Organic Peroxide Producers Safety Division (OPPSD) had some 10 dm^3 tests carried out at a variety of external heating rates between 2 and 9°C min^{-1} (Plowright[27]). Finally OPPSD carried out a fire engulfment tests on a 1.74 m^3 (460 US gall) tank (McCloskey[28] and Coffey[29]). For this test the equivalent heating rate was calculated to be 6°C min^{-1}. Schuurman[18] also provided decomposition data for the system. The major gaseous product is methane (molecular weight 16 kg kmol^{-1}). The adiabatic data necessary to perform the vent sizing calculations was based on papers by Fauske[9,10,19,20,21]. Fauske performed his RSST test with an external heating rate (fire simulation) of about 1°C min^{-1}.

Figure 4 is a plot of maximum pressure versus vent area per unit volume (A/V). It shows experimental and calculated maximum pressures for homogeneous vessel two-phase flow and gas-only flow vent sizing. Calculated maximum pressure versus (A/V) lines are shown only for an 80% fill level.

Gas-only flow vent sizing calculations fit reasonably with the 58 US gall tests (0.8°C min^{-1}), and the OPPSD 10 dm^3 (2°C min^{-1}) and 1.74 m^3 (460 US gall) (6°C min^{-1}) tests. However tests on vessels with higher external heating rates show much higher pressures. This shows the necessity of performing an adiabatic test with the same external heating rate. Homogeneous two-phase vent sizing was overly conservative. The OPPSD 10 dm^3 tests used a high heating rate of 9°C min^{-1} and so cannot really be compared with the calculated vent sizes. Fauske[19] thought that the reaction mechanism changed from homogeneous to propagating. The UN vent sizing method would appear to be applicable to this system.

DISCUSSION

UN VENT SIZING METHOD

The initial test proposal assumed a heat load of 110 kW m^{-2}. This is typical of the heat flux usually given for open pool fires. However much higher heat fluxes are possible with jet fires (250 to 300 kW m^{-2}). The current UN method uses a heat load calculation method consistent with API 520. This results in a significantly lower heat load than would be produced using 110 kW m^{-2}. Thus the external heating applied to the test vessel, used to simulate fire engulfment, may not be adequate. Assuming that only pool fires are conceivable as the external heat flux is not conservative. The Calhoun incident showed that large fireballs can be generated on a trailer carrying a number of IBCs. Also jet fires could occur when the portable tank is being loaded or unloaded at the chemical plant rather than on the road. Only the tank surface below the liquid level is heated. This is not the worst case.

FUNDAMENTALS OF DIERS VENT SIZING

DIERS vent sizing methods are for the maximum gas generation rate, which is the worst case for gassy systems. Homogeneous two-phase flow is the worst case and this was the basis of the early DIERS work. It was recognised that this can be overly conservative and therefore DIERS gas only flow methods have been developed. Care needs to be taken however in assuming that no liquid carry over occurs. A small amount of liquid carry over (much less than the homogeneous vessel assumption) can cause a larger vent to be required. Assuming gas only flow would then produce an undersized vent.

DISCUSSION OF HSL VENT SIZING CALCULATIONS

The intention here was to compare the available experimental data with vent sizing calculations performed using the DIERS gas-only and homogeneous two-phase flow vent sizing methods. Note that there is only a limited amount of experimental data available. One particular problem was obtaining reliable adiabatic data for the same peroxide concentration with a comparable external heating rate.

- For system 1 (3,5,5-trimethyl hexanoyl peroxide) DIERS gas-only flow vent sizing and the UN method both seemed applicable.
- For system 2 (tert-butyl peroxy ethyl hexanoate) the experimental HSL data indicated a bubbly two-phase venting mixture. The DIERS gas-only flow vent sizing and UN methods were shown not to be safe. DIERS homogeneous two-phase vent sizing was shown to be conservative provided either open system test data or closed system dissolved gas corrected data was used. A fair vent sizing comparison could not be made with the Akzo data because adiabatic data was not available with the higher peroxide concentration, the different solvent and the variety of external heating rates.
- For system 3 (dicumyl peroxide), some tests with low external heating rates and larger vessels seemed to fit the DIERS gas-only flow vent sizing and UN methods. A fair vent sizing comparison could not be done with tests using high external heating rates because of the lack of adiabatic data.

Two-phase flow is caused by liquid level swell. If the level swell is low, then gas-only flow occurs. In practice, the vent flow is often two-phase but with a lower density than predicted by the homogeneous vessel assumption. For accurate vent sizing, if two phase flow occurs, a method is required to calculate the actual density (not the homogeneous density) and therefore the mass flux of the venting mixture. However if gas only flow is predicted, it is important to know the molecular weight of the gas products and this is not always easy to determine. For the gas evolution rate calculation, closed cell tests are affected by gas

141

solubility if there is a solvent present and this causes problems if the intended maximum pressure is lower than the test cell pressure at the maximum pressure rate. For open cell tests a temperature correction should be made.

The HSL validation work was only able to consider a limited number of large scale tests because of the lack of published data. System 1 is the most commonly quoted example of the validity of the UN vent sizing approach. A range of systems needs to be considered to show the general validity of the UN method.

CONCLUSIONS

There may be potential problems with how the UN method assesses the effect of heat flux on the venting and decomposition of the organic peroxide as it only considers pool fires and only the wetted surface of the tank is used to calculate the heat transfer.

Only a limited amount of reliable validation has been possible in terms of comparisons with the DIERS vent sizing methods. For those experimental data available, the UN test was conservative for two cases but non-conservative for one case. However to make definitive conclusions would require considerably more experimental data.

The UN vents sizing method may not be valid in all peroxide venting cases and other methodology may need to be developed. The UN method would seem to be applicable to largely gas-only flow venting. If there were a significant amount of two-phase flow then the DIERS homogeneous method would seem to be applicable. The problem arises for intermediate cases where there is a low liquid fraction two-phase flow. Here the UN method would not be safe and the DIERS homogeneous method would be overly conservative. Again to make definitive conclusions would require considerably more experimental data.

NOMENCLATURE

A	Vent area, m^2
A_w	Wetted area, m^2
A_p	Portable tank vent area, m^2
A_t	Test vessel vent area, m^2
C_D	Discharge coefficient (assumed to be 1.0 for this analysis)
F	Insulation factor
G	(Two-phase) mass flux, $kg\ m^{-2}\ s^{-1}$
G	Mass flux, $kg\ m^{-2}\ s^{-1}$
G^*	Dimensionless mass flux
K	Heat conductivity of insulation layer, $W\ m^{-1}\ K^{-1}$
k	Isentropic coefficient
L	Thickness of insulation layer, m
M_W	Molecular weight of gas, $kg\ kmol^{-1}$
m_o	Reaction mass, kg
m_t	Test sample mass, kg
P_m	Maximum allowable pressure, Pa
P_o	Upstream vessel pressure, Pa
P	Pressure, Pa
$(dP/dt)_{max}$	Maximum pressure rate, $Pa\ s^{-1}$
q	Heat absorption, W
$(dQ/dt)_{g,max}$	Maximum rate of gas evolution, $m^3\ s^{-1}$
R	Gas constant = $8314\ J\ kmol^{-1}\ K^{-1}$
T_{PO}	Temperature of the peroxide at the relieving conditions, K
T	Temperature, K

T_t	Temperature in test cell, K
T_c	Temperature in containment volume, K
U	Heat transfer coefficient of the insulation (K/L), W m^{-2} K^{-1}
V	Reactor vessel volume, m^3
V_f	Free volume (either test cell free space (closed cell) or containment volume (open cell)), m^3
V_p	Portable tank volume, m^3
V_t	Test vessel volume, m^3
v_e	Exiting fluid specific volume, m^3 kg^{-1}
W	Vent mass flow rate, kg s^{-1}
α_o	Void fraction
ρ_e	Exiting fluid density, kg m^{-3}
ρ_g	Gas density, kg m^{-3}
α_o	Void fraction
ρ_o	Vessel two phase density, kg m^{-3}
ρ_f	Liquid (reactant) density, kg m^{-3}
η_c	Critical pressure ratio
η	Pressure ratio
ω	Omega, dimensionless number

ACKNOWLEDGEMENTS

P Schuurman of Akzo Nobel, Deventer, The Netherlands, who provided a significant amount of experimental data on the organic peroxides. J C Etchells of Technology Division, Health and Safety Executive, Merseyside who was the sponsor for all the experimental work at the Health and Safety Laboratory on System 2 (tert-butyl peroxy-2-ethylhexanoate).

The views expressed in this paper are the views of the authors and should not necessarily be taken as those of the Health and Safety Executive.

REFERENCES

1.   Fisher HG et al, "Emergency relief system design using DIERS technology - The DIERS project manual", AIChE, New York, 1992
2.   United Nations, "Recommendations on the transport of dangerous goods - Manual of Tests and Criteria", 3rd revised edition, United Nations, Geneva, 1999
3.   ECE, "European agreement concerning the international carriage of dangerous goods by road (ADR) and protocol of signature", United Nations, Geneva, 1998 and 2001
4.   ECE, "European agreement concerning the international carriage of dangerous goods by rail (RID) and protocol of signature", United Nations, Geneva, 1998 and 2001
5.   United Nations, "Recommendations on the transport of dangerous goods - Model regulations", 11th revised edition, United Nations, Geneva, 1999
6.   American Petroleum Institute (API), Recommended Practice RP520, Part 1 1993
7.   Leung JC, "Chemical process relief system design seminar" held at Decines, France, September 1998.
8.   Leung JC, "The Omega method for discharge rate calculations", International Symposium on Runaway Reactions and Pressure Relief Design, Boston, August 1995.
9.   Fauske HK, "The reactive system screening tool (RSST): An easy inexpensive approach to the DIERS procedure", Process Safety Progress, Vol 17, No 3, p190-195, Fall 1998.

10.   Fauske HK, "The reactive system screening tool (RSST): An easy inexpensive approach to the DIERS procedure", International Symposium on Runaway Reactions, Pressure Relief Design and Effluent Handling, New Orleans, March 1998.

11.   Etchells J and Wilday J, "Workbook for chemical reactor relief system sizing", HSE Contract Research Report, 136/1998, 1998

12.   Tangren RF, Dodge CH and Seifert J, Journal of Applied Physics, Vol 20, No 7, p637-645, 1949.

13.   Leung JC and Fauske HK, "Runaway system characterisation and vent sizing based on DIERS methodology", Plant Operations Progress, Vol 6, No 2, p77-83, April 1987

14.   de Groot JJ, Groothuizen ThM and Verhoeff J, "Relief venting of thermal explosions", Loss Prevention and Safety Promotion in the Process Industries, 3rd International Symposium, Basle, Vol 3, p13/944-13/955, September 1980.

15.   de Groot JJ, Groothuizen ThM and Verhoeff J, "Safety aspects of organic peroxides in bulk tanks", Industrial and Engineering Chemistry, Process Design and Development, Vol 20, p131-138, 1981.

16.   Wakker JP and de Groot JJ, "Venting of decompositions of energetic liquids using a bottom vent", Process Plant Safety, Symposium Proceedings, AIChE, Vol 2, p55-71, 1996.

17.   Schuurman P, "Bulk experiments Bis (3,5,5-trimethyl hexanoyl) peroxide 37.5% w/w in isododecane", private communication to HSL, September 1996.

18.   Schuurman P, "Akzo Nobel: Technical bulletins on thermal decomposition mechanisms on Trigonox 21, Trigonox 36 and Perkadox BC", private communication to HSL, April 2000

19.   Fauske HK, "The RSST provides pressure relief requirements for organic peroxides", FAI Process Safety News, Spring 1998.

20.   Fauske HK, "Advances in relief system design", 22nd US DIERS Users Group Meeting, Charleston, October 1998.

21.   Fauske HK, "Advances in chemical reaction hazard evaluation: Prevention and accommodation", 23rd US DIERS Users Group Meeting, Las Vegas, April 1999.

22.   Etchells JC, Snee TJ and Wilday AJ, "Relief system sizing for exothermic runaway: The UK Strategy", International Symposium on Runaway Reactions, Pressure Relief Design, and Effluent Handling (New Orleans), AIChE, p135-162, March 1998.

23.   Schuurman P and Wakker JP, "Emergency relief sizing of organic peroxide tank - container by venting tests", OECD-IGUS EOS meeting, Boston, March 1994

24.   Schuuram P, "Trigonox 21 = tert.butylperoxy-2-ethylhexanoate = Tx21", private communication to HSL, March 2000

25.   National Transportation Safety Board (NTSB), Highway Accident Report "Multiple-vehicle collisions due during limited visibility (fog) on Interstate 57 near Calhoun, Tennessee, December 11, 1990", PB92-916202, NTSB/HAR-92/02, 1992

26.   Gove SH, "Emergency pressure relief for intermediate bulk containers containing dicumyl peroxide - Incident report and test data", 18th US DIERS Users Group Meeting, Houston, February 1996.

27.   Plowright JD, "Thermal decomposition testing of organic peroxides: New 10 litre test data", OECD-IGUS EOS Meeting, Stockholm, May 1999.

28.   McCloskey C, "Fire engulfment test of an IBC filled with dicumyl peroxide",OECD-IGUS EOS Meeting, Buxton, December 1999.

29.   Coffey MV, "Emergency venting testing", OECD-IGUS EOS Meeting, Buxton, April 2000

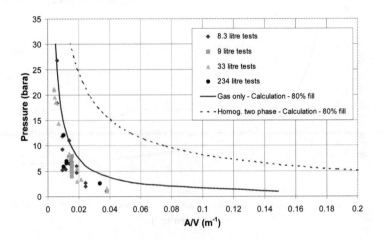

Figure 1. Bis (3,5,5-trimethyl hexanoyl) peroxide (37.5% w/w) in isododecane

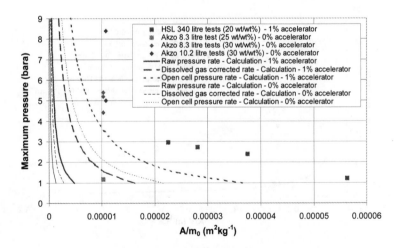

Figure 2. Peroxyester in solvent (Gas only flow)

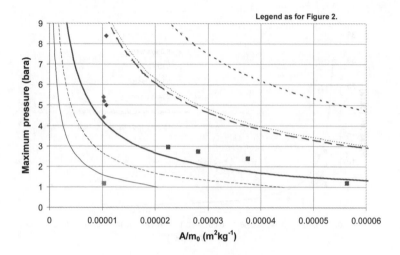

Figure 3. Peroxyester in solvent (Homogeneous two-phase flow)

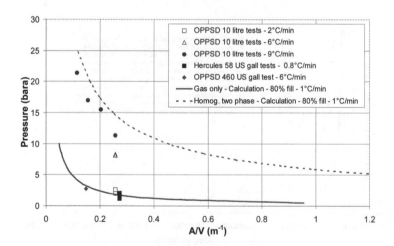

Figure 4. Dicumyl peroxide

CONSEQUENCES OF JET-FIRE INTERACTION WITH VESSELS CONTAINING PRESSURISED, REACTIVE CHEMICALS

T Roberts*, I Buckland**, H Beckett*, J Hare* and M Royle*

*   Health and Safety Laboratory, Buxton, Derbyshire SK17 9JN
** Technology Division, Health and Safety Executive, Merseyside L20 3QZ

Current practice for the protection of pressure vessels containing reactive, flammable chemicals is typically based upon liquefied petroleum gas (LPG) standards for protection against hydrocarbon pool fires. However, this may not be appropriate. It is well recognised, that the more challenging incident scenario is a jet-fire, wherever pressurised, or pressure liquefied flammable materials are handled. In particular, a reactive chemical fuelled jet-fire may well be more severe than a hydrocarbon pool fire. Additionally, LPG is not a self-reactive chemical. As such, the level of heat transfer that a vessel containing a reactive chemical may be exposed to without incident, could well be significantly lower than an LPG vessel could withstand.

Chemicals undergoing decomposition or self-reaction (e.g. polymerisation) at elevated temperatures may require additional levels of protection to prevent or control a runaway reaction triggered by the input of energy from an external fire. There is insufficient knowledge of the safe allowable heat input to self-reactive chemicals that are held in pressure vessels. Additionally, the adequacy of pressure relief devices sized using current standards in such circumstances is uncertain.

In this paper, work is described to:
- determine, by calorimetry, the effect of heat on chemicals (1,3-butadiene and propylene oxide) capable of exothermic self reaction;
- assess the feasibility of carrying out calorimetry on pressure liquefied gases, including calorimetric tests which simulate fire situations; and
- compare the jet flame characteristics of 1,3-butadiene with a propane jet in an intermediate scale test.

The results are discussed in terms of the likelihood of thermal runaway, the vent sizing requirements of the pressure relief device and the protective effect of thermal insulation.

Keywords: self-reactive, 1,3-butadiene, propylene oxide, vent sizing, fire protection, jet fires.

INTRODUCTION

Current practice for the protection of pressure vessels containing reactive, flammable chemicals is typically based upon liquefied petroleum gas (LPG) standards for protection against hydrocarbon pool fires. The appropriateness of this may be questioned on two fronts. LPG is not a self-reactive chemical, where the levels of fire protection are intended to prevent the pressure vessel itself from reaching its critical failure temperature (> 400 °C). In the case of a self-reactive chemical, the critical temperature is likely to be the substantially lower one of that leading to the onset (< 350 °C) of exothermic runaway. Further, the more likely incident scenario involving plant containing pressurised flammable materials may well be a jet-fire rather than a pool fire. Jet fires are typically more severe than pool fires because of their high heat fluxes and high mechanical erosive effects. This has been confirmed by numerous workers, including HSL[1].

For chemicals undergoing decomposition or self-reaction (e.g. polymerisation) at elevated temperatures, there is insufficient knowledge of the amount of heating that they may be safety exposed to when held in pressure vessels. Such information is needed to correctly design an adequate fire protection system to be certain that a runaway reaction, which otherwise might be triggered by the heat from an external fire, may be prevented or controlled. Additionally the adequacy of pressure relief sized using current standards in such circumstances is uncertain.

HSE's Technology Division commissioned a feasibility study of methods to assess the effectiveness of pressure relief and fire protection in a jet fire. The work described in this paper concerns the determination of the:

- Effect of heat, using adiabatic calorimetry, on two substances capable of self-reaction viz. 1,3-butadiene and propylene oxide;
- Performance of fire simulation calorimetry on 1,3-butadiene;
- Jet flame characteristics of 1,3-butadiene in comparison with a propane jet fire in an intermediate scale test; and
- Size of pressure relief device required.

ADIABATIC CALORIMETRY

A literature review (Keaney[2]) confirmed that adiabatic calorimetry on selected reactive chemicals was necessary to determine kinetic parameters and give an indication of the temperatures and pressures likely to be reached. There is particular concern for vessels provided with thermal insulation, including vessels where the fire protection is by a passive fire protection material.

The reactive chemicals selected as being most suitable for the purposes of jet fire testing and calorimetry were propylene oxide and 1,3-butadiene. Adiabatic studies were undertaken using a Phi-Tec 2 (Singh[3]) and a Columbia Scientific Industries ARC™ accelerating rate calorimeter (Townsend & Tou[4]). Most of the calorimetry was performed with the Phi-Tec but one Accelerating Rate Calorimeter run was performed on propylene oxide where this fell outside of the operating range of the Phi-Tec calorimeter.

In the Phi-tec calorimeter, the sample is held in a thin-walled stainless steel container which is surrounded by electrical heaters, the whole assembly is installed inside a stainless steel pressure vessel. Heat transfer to or from the sample can be controlled by varying the temperature of the electrical heaters. Adiabatic conditions can be achieved by matching the temperature of the heaters to that of the sample. Alternatively, a steady heat input can be obtained by programming the electrical heaters to maintain a temperature a fixed amount above the sample temperature. If the pressure in the test cell increases, rupture of the thin walled container is prevented by automatically increasing the pressure of nitrogen in the external pressure vessel.

When measurements are required on a substance having a low boiling point and therefore a high vapour pressure at the temperature of interest, the effect of the elevated pressure required in the external pressure vessel is to significantly increase heat losses from the sample container. In addition to this effect, additional heat losses may be observed due to refluxing of the sample in the fill line of the sample container.

TEST PROCEDURES FOR THE ADIABATIC CALORIMETRY

PROPYLENE OXIDE

Propylene oxide is a colourless flammable liquid with a boiling point of 34 °C. In large tanks, it is usually stored under ca. 8 bar nitrogen pressure. For the calorimetry, propylene oxide was cooled in a refrigerator to approximately 5 °C and then filled into a pre-weighed test cell using a syringe.

1,3-BUTADIENE

1,3-butadiene is a colourless reactive gas with a boiling point of –4.4 °C. It is stored liquefied under its own vapour pressure. 1,3-butadiene is normally supplied with an added polymerisation inhibitor, in this case t-butyl catechol. Liquid 1,3-butadiene was condensed in a type 1a Phi-Tec test cell (magnetically stirred, low phi factor) using a cooling bath consisting of solid carbon dioxide and 2-propanol.

In order to configure the Phi-Tec calorimeter such that measurements could be made on 1,3-butadiene it was necessary to develop a method to allow for both the heat losses due to operating in a high-pressure regime and also those heat losses due to reflux. This was done by running several calibration tests with a sample vessel filled with butane, a substance with a similar pressure temperature profile to 1,3-butadiene but with no tendency to self-heat. The data obtained for heat losses with butane were then programmed into the calorimeter control and used to obtain self-heating measurements on 1,3-butadiene. With this type of heat loss compensation, care is required as it is possible for self-heating to be detected, when not actually present, due to excessive heat input from the calorimeter heaters.

RESULTS FROM ADIABATIC CALORIMETRY

PROPYLENE OXIDE

Pure propylene oxide was tested in the Phi-Tec and showed no tendency to self-heat up to a temperature of 216 °C. Due to the limiting operating range of the Phi-Tec calorimeter, a single test performed using the ARC. Self heating became detectable at a temperature of 300 °C, at which temperature the pressure of propylene oxide was of the order of 140 bara. It was concluded from these tests that pure propylene oxide was insufficiently reactive to pursue this type of investigation.

Although pure propylene oxide was relatively stable up to temperatures of approximately 300 °C, it should be noted that propylene oxide has a tendency to undergo base catalysed exothermic polymerisation at ambient temperature (Freeder and Snee[5]). Provided that there were no local hot spots on the tank shell and no catalysis, propylene oxide vapour would be vented at temperatures up to 300 °C before thermal runaway would occur.

1,3-BUTADIENE

Initial tests with 1,3-butadiene gave heat losses such that it was impossible to detect an exotherm below 160 °C. The large heat losses and hence the extremely low level of exotherm sensitivity enabled a plot of 1,3-butadiene vapour pressure to be obtained from these tests. In addition to the heat loss problems, it was found that taking a 1,3-butadiene exotherm to conclusion resulted in an explosive decomposition causing significant damage to the calorimeter. In subsequent tests, attempts were made to automatically switch off the calorimeter before violent decomposition occurred. These attempts were unsuccessful due to the calorimeter having no cooling nor quench facility.

The result from a Phi-Tec test on 1,3-butadiene is given in Table 1. The specific heat for 1,3-butadiene (liquid) is taken as 2.055 J g^{-1} K^{-1}. In this test the calorimeter heaters were switched off at 190°C, but at this temperature the heat generation from the polymerisation of 1,3-butadiene was sufficient for the reaction to continue to completion. The plots of temperature and pressure versus time are shown in Figure 1. The plots of LOG [dT/dt] versus reciprocal temperature and pressure versus temperature are compared later in Figures 2 and 3 with the corresponding fire simulation data. The measured vapour pressure data for 1,3-butadiene in the Phi-Tec compares well (see Figure 2) with the data derived from the Antoine constants ($\log_{10}$[pressure(mm)] = 6.859 − (935.5/{temperature(°C)-239})) provided by Braker and Mossman[6].

Table 1. PHI-TEC EXPT. WITH 1,3-BUTADIENE WITHOUT FIRE SIMULATION

Run No	Sample mass (g)	T_{onset} (°C)	T_{max} (°C)	ΔT_u (K)	P_{max} (bara)	dT/dt_{max} (K min^{-1})	ϕ factor	ΔT_{ad} (K)	ΔH_r (J g^{-1})
pa98	44	114	321	207	87.4	83.7	1.14	236	485

1,3-butadiene shows self-heating from around 114°C. At this temperature, the pressure in the container due to 1,3-butadiene vapour is around 25 bara. Significant rates of self-heating are not obtained until the 1,3-butadiene is heated above its critical temperature at which point the pressure is of the order of 40 bara. It would be expected that higher rates of self-heating would be obtained at lower temperatures in the case of external heating or if the inhibitor had been consumed. In the case of jet fire impingement onto a tank of 1,3-butadiene, the local heat input could be so severe as to cause local decomposition, the products from which may catalyse the reaction of the remaining 1,3-butadiene, thereby causing a runaway at lower temperature.

FIRE SIMULATION CALORIMETRY

Singh[3] indicates that fire simulation calorimetry may be performed using the Phi-Tec adiabatic calorimeter. It is claimed that the Phi-Tec can achieve rates of external heating which are representative of fire heat inputs from design codes such as API RP 520[7] to industrial-scale vessels. Typical rates of temperature rise from external heating of 0.5 K min^{-1} are quoted. Fire simulation calorimetry was carried out in the Phi-Tec to:

(a)   Obtain data for validation of calculation methods using adiabatic calorimetric data.
(b)   Gain experience with, and evaluate the use of, the Phi-Tec calorimeter for this purpose.

The method of simulating external heat input using the Phi-Tec, involves increasing the temperature of the calorimeter heaters above that of the sample by an amount appropriate to the heat input required. This method is limited by the operating software since the maximum allowable temperature difference is 30 °C. The heat loss compensation system also uses this method and, for a substance like 1,3-butadiene, this effectively limits the additional temperature available for fire simulation to approximately 15°C. This equates to a heat input of 1 W. The calorimeter was first calibrated so that the heat input to the sample as a result of a given heater lead (in degrees above sample temperature) was known. This calibration was performed using a low ϕ factor magnetically stirred test cell filled with 70g dimethyl phthalate. The calibration indicated a linear relationship having the equation:

$$Q = 0.0713.T_{ad} \tag{1}$$

It can be seen from this calibration that a relatively large temperature difference gives only a small additional heat input.

A single fire simulation run was performed on 1,3-butadiene using the Phi-Tec calorimeter. The conditions and results for the run are given in Table 2. An additional heat input of approximately 1 W was used. Assuming a specific heat for 1,3-butadiene liquid of 2.055 J g^1 K^{-1}, this gives an additional heating rate for the 40g of 1,3-butadiene in the test cell of 0.78 K min^{-1} (25 W kg^{-1}). The actual heating rate measured in the initial period, before self heating, was approximately 0.8 K min^{-1}. This equates to a total additional heat input of 8370 J over the measured temperature range. Jet fire impingement (Roberts et al.[8 & 9]) onto a two tonne tank of propane results in a heat input of approximately 1000 W kg^{-1} or 24 K min^{-1}. To simulate a heat input of this order in the Phi-Tec is impractical. It is usual, however, to encounter larger tanks, for example a road or rail tanker would be about 20 tonnes and a static storage tank could be around 80 tonnes, in which case the rates of temperature rise would be accordingly lower. A jet fire is a more severe fire than a pool fire that is assumed by current codes in setting fire relief requirements. The heat input from API RP 520 would lead to a heating rate of approximately 2 K min^{-1}.

Table 2. FIRE SIMULATION RESULTS ON 1,3-BUTADIENE

Run No	Sample mass (g)	T_{onset} (°C)	T_{max} (°C)	ΔT_u (K)	P_{max} (bara)	dT/dt_{max} (K min^{-1})	ϕ factor	ΔT_{ad} (K)	ΔH_r (J g^{-1})
PA99	40	115	488	448	93	518	1.15	515.2	1059

Note: Less 209 J g^{-1} additional heat input

In this fire simulation test, the additional heating has the additional effect of precluding any heat losses, and therefore the effect of self-heating becomes evident where the gradient of the temperature trace deviates from the straight line of the additional heating. The onset of self-heating becomes apparent at 115°C. Figures 2 and 3 compare tests PA98 (performed without external heating) and PA99 (performed with external heating). Figure 2 shows that the pressure for PA99 is generally higher at a given temperature than for PA98. This is because of the lower conversion at a given temperature for the externally heated experiment compared to the experiment without external heating. The initial reaction is expected to be dimerisation mainly to 4-vinylcyclohexene, which is less volatile than 1,3-butadiene and therefore a lower conversion results in a higher pressure. Figure 3 shows log [temperature rate] versus temperature data for both experiments. There is also good agreement in onset temperatures between the two experiments (114°C for PA98 and 115°C for PA99) confirming that the external heating does not affect this important parameter.

The results indicated that, with the heat-input method used, small heat flux fires on unprotected vessels or larger fires on protected (deluge or insulation) vessels can be imitated experimentally.

FIRE TRIALS WITH 1,3-BUTADIENE

SAFETY CONSIDERATIONS

1,3-butadiene was selected for the fire trials since it was one of the least toxic of the pressure liquefied reactive chemicals (e.g. carbonyl sulphide, diborane, ethylene, germane, vinyl chloride). However, 1,3-butadiene is a carcinogen and mutagen. Risk assessments, including gas dispersion modelling, indicated that a continuous release of 0.1 kg s^{-1} was the maximum allowable for the 400 m radius safety distance available on HSL's Buxton site. Hence it was necessary to design the fuel supply system such that it could be shut-off remotely at very short notice and would fail safe (i.e. closed) in the event of failure. With these restrictions, it was considered that six 60 kg cylinders of 1,3-butadiene could be safely handled at one time.

The flammability properties (Braker & Mossman[6]) of 1,3-butadiene are compared with those of propane in Table 3.

Table 3. 1,3-BUTADIENE AND PROPANE FLAMMABILITY PROPERTIES

Property	1,3-Butadiene	Propane
Boiling point	-.4.4 °C	-42.1 °C
Vapour pressure (21.1 °C)	2.49 bar	8.53 bar
Relative vapour density	1.88	1.55
Flash point	-76 °C	-104 °C
Auto-ignition temperature	420 °C	468 °C
Lower flammability limit (by volume)	2%	2.2 %
Upper flammability (by volume)	11.5%	9.5%
Heat of combustion (liquid)	44.2 MJ kg^{-1}	46.0 MJ kg^{-1}

1,3-Butadiene may undergo exothermic decomposition. If a runaway reaction is initiated, the cylinder could explode causing burns from the resulting fireball or missile damage. The calorimetry suggested that a runaway reaction is not likely to occur in a cylinder at temperatures below 100 °C. However, verbal advice from the supplier suggested that the cylinders may be safely heated to no more than 30 °C although the safety data sheet indicated 50 °C. Approximately 30 °C was used for the experiments.

JET FIRE SCENARIOS
There are two basic jet fire scenarios:

(a)   A vapour jet fire resulting from puncture, weld, flange or valve failure of a tank above the liquid level or failure of vapour take-off pipework.
(b)   A flashing liquid jet fire resulting from puncture, weld, flange or valve failure of a tank below the liquid level or failure of liquid take-off pipework.

FIRE TEST PROCEDURE
The properties of vapour only and flashing liquid propane jets have previously been investigated[10] and determination made of acceptable scaling between the two. It was therefore decided to use a version of the jet-fire resistance test (JFRT)[11] of passive fire protection materials with the flame recirculation chamber modified to incorporate a copper pipe calorimeter (28 mm o.d., 7.3 m exposed length and 0.642 m^2 exposed area). This was located at the known position of maximum heat flux within the open-fronted box used to give a re-circulating fireball in front of the test specimen. Heat flux to the calorimeter could then be measured for jet flames produced by different fuels and for a range of flow rates. The assembled test piece was supported on two steel stands bolted to a pair of concrete blocks, which were positioned on the 15 m x 15 m test pad (see Figure 4). For the fire tests, two fuels were used:

- 1,3-Butadiene vapour supplied from cylinders, immersed in a hot water bath to aid vaporisation, providing a vapour rate of 0.05 kg s^{-1};
- Liquid 1,3-butadiene, supplied from cylinders pressurised to 3.45 barg with nitrogen, providing a liquid flow rate of 0.844 kg s^{-1}; and
- Propane vapour supplied from a 10 tonne storage facility via a hot water vaporiser.

As vapour flow is at a much lower flow rate than liquid flow, 1,3-butadiene vapour fire trials were performed first. Liquid 1,3-butadiene fire trials were then performed until the cylinders were nearly empty. Finally, the propane vapour fire trials were performed to provide a comparison.

In each test, a steady flow of water was established through the pipe calorimeter. The fuel was then released and ignited and the water from the calorimeter collected over a timed period. The 1,3-butadiene flow rate was estimated by weighing the cylinders before and after the tests and the propane vapour flow by a calibrated flow meter. The in and out water temperatures and the flame temperatures along the vertical centre line were measured with type K, stainless steel sheathed thermocouples.

RESULTS FROM FIRE TRIALS

1,3-BUTADIENE VAPOUR
Two successful 1,3-butadiene vapour trials (BD03 and BD04) were performed. In each trial, the 1,3-butadiene burnt with bright orange flames in the flame re-circulation chamber (see Figure 5), with duller orange flames above the flame re-circulation chamber and black smoke was produced at the tips of the flames. The measurements from 1,3-butadiene vapour fire trials BD03 and BD04 are summarised in Table 4.

LIQUID 1,3-BUTADIENE
One liquid 1,3-butadiene fire trial (BD05) was performed. In this trial the liquid 1,3-butadiene burnt producing copious quantities of black smoke (see Figure 6). After the jet was extinguished, a considerable amount of liquid 1,3-butadiene remained burning within the flame re-circulation chamber. A summary of the measurements taken is given in Table 5.

Table 4. 1,3-BUTADIENE VAPOUR TRIAL DATA

Parameter	Trial	
	BD03	BD04
Jet duration (s)	324	237
Mass of fuel used (kg)	15.6	11.4
Vapour mass flow rate (kg s^{-1})	0.048	0.048
Water flow rate (kg s^{-1})	1.42	0.80
Mean temperature difference (K)	18.6	22.9
Beginning and end time for mean (s)	100 -250	60 - 180

Table 5. 1,3-BUTADIENE LIQUID FIRE TRIAL DATA

Parameter	Trial BD05
Jet duration (s)	288
Mass of fuel used (kg)	243
Liquid mass flow rate (kg s^{-1})	0.844
Water flow rate (kg s^{-1})	0.82
Mean temperature difference (K)	2.54
Beginning and end time for mean (s)	90 - 240

PROPANE VAPOUR

Two propane vapour trials (BD07 and BD08) were performed in order to determine the heat flux at the jet fire resistance test rate of 0.3 kg s^{-1} and the equivalent 1,3-butadiene vapour rate of 0.05 kg s^{-1}. The flames observed (BD07) at 0.3 kg s^{-1} were typical of those observed in a jet fire resistance test (see Figure 7) whereas the flames from a 0.05 kg s^{-1} propane vapour jet fire (BD08) were smaller in size (see Figure 8), particularly in regard to the depth of the fireball formed in front of the flame re-circulation chamber. However, the flames appeared brighter in colour and slightly larger than those from the corresponding 1,3-butadiene vapour jet fire (see Figure 5). Measurements from propane vapour fire trials BD07 and BD08 are summarised in Table 6.

Table 6. PROPANE VAPOUR TRIAL DATA

Parameter	Trial	
	BD07	BD08
Jet duration (s)	175	780
Mass of fuel used (kg)	52.5	39
Vapour mass flow rate (kg s^{-1})	0.300	0.050
Water flow rate (kg s^{-1})	2.01	1.39
Mean temperature difference (K)	9.1	14.1
Beginning and end time for mean (s)	50 - 170	140 - 800

DISCUSSION OF FIRE TRIAL RESULTS

The main aim of this phase of the project was to determine if the fires obtained from 1,3-butadiene were more severe than the fires used to assess the fire resistance of passive fire protection materials. A discussion of the various parameters is given as follows.

FLAME TEMPERATURES

The flame temperatures, measured at 0.3 m intervals (from the bottom) up the centre line of the re-circulation chamber by shielded thermocouples ca. 12 cm proud of the surface, are summarised in Table 7.

Table 7. FLAME TEMPERATURE RANGES

Trial	Description	Flame temperatures (Celsius)			
		TC07 (0.3 m)	TC08 (0.6 m)	TC09 (0.9 m)	TC10 (1.2 m)
BD03	1,3-butadiene vapour (0.05 kg s^{-1})	900 - 1100	1100 to 1150	1200 to 1250	1200 to 1250
BD04	1,3-butadiene vapour (0.05 kg s^{-1})	1050 to 1100	1100 to 1150	1150 to 1200	1200 to 1250
BD05	1,3-butadiene liquid (0.84 kg s^{-1})	-13 to 0	-13 to 0	300 to 400	500 to 600
BD05	Burning 1,3-butadiene liquid	600 to 900	800 to 900	850 to 1020	900 to 1050
BD07	Propane vapour (0.30 kg s^{-1})	500 to 600	700 to 800	800 to 900	900 to 1000
BD08	Propane vapour (0.05 kg s^{-1})	600 to 750	830 to 970	1000 to 1100	1100 to 1200

In each trial, the maximum temperature always occurred at the top position (0.3 m from the top of the flame re-circulation chamber). The results are discussed as follows:

1,3-butadiene vapour flames: The flame temperatures were similar at equivalent positions for the 1,3-butadiene vapour trials and were consistent with the very similar flames observed in each trial.

Flashing liquid 1,3-butadiene flames: At the lowest two positions, the temperatures measured during the jet phase of the liquid 1,3-butadiene trial indicated that these thermocouples were being engulfed in a two phase mixture of flashing liquid and vapour at or below the boiling point of -4 °C. The burning liquid left after the jet was extinguished gave temperatures about 200 °C lower than the 1,3-butadiene vapour jets. The results indicate that a release of liquid 1,3-butadiene close to a vessel is likely to result in the surface being cooled at the impact point and burning liquid forming a pool fire underneath, if there is no drainage.

Propane vapour flames: The results from the propane vapour trials were somewhat surprising in that the temperatures measured at a flow rate of 0.3 kg s^{-1} were nearly 200 °C below those measured at a flow rate of 0.05 kg s^{-1}. This suggests that, at the higher flow rate, incomplete combustion is occurring at the thermocouples positioned 12 cm from the rear surface of the flame re-circulation chamber.

1,3-butadiene versus propane: The flame temperatures from the 0.05 kg s^{-1} propane jet were slightly below those from the corresponding 1,3-butadiene jets. This may be due to the particular combination of gas velocity (the 1,3-butadiene pressure was 1.2 barg and the propane pressure 1.6 barg) and release distance used.

HEAT FLUXES
The mean heat fluxes were calculated using the expression:

$$I = (dm/dt \cdot C_w \cdot \Delta T_w) / (S \cdot \sigma) \tag{2}$$

The calculated heat fluxes are summarised in Table 8.

Table 8. HEAT FLUXES

Trial	Description	Mean water flow rate (kg s^{-1})	Mean temperature rise (K)	Mean heat flux (kW m^{-2})
BD03	1,3-butadiene vapour (0.05 kg s^{-1})	1.42	18.6	181
BD04	1,3-butadiene vapour (0.05 kg s^{-1})	0.8	22.9	126
BD05	1,3-butadiene liquid^a (0.84 kg s^{-1})	0.82	2.54	14
BD05	Mean burning liquid 1,3-butadiene^c	0.82 ^{b}	6.63	37
BD05	Maximum burning liquid 1,3-butadiene^c	0.82 ^{b}	17.42	98
BD07	Propane vapour (0.30 kg s^{-1})	2.01	9.1	125
BD08	Propane vapour (0.05 kg s^{-1})	1.39	14.1	134

Notes: a   Measured during jet impingement.
         b   Assuming no changes to water flow after the measurement period.
         c   Measured after impingement had ceased.

The mean heat fluxes (125 and 134 kW m^{-2}) measured from burning propane vapour were similar to the 126 kW m^{-2} measured during the second 1,3-butadiene vapour trial (BD04) but were below the 181 kW m^{-2} measured during the first 1,3-butadiene vapour trial (BD03), performed when the cylinders were full. The liquid impingement result was very low indicating that the calorimeter was being cooled by unburnt liquid. After impingement had ceased, the mean burning liquid heat flux was only 37 kW m^{-2} and the maximum 98 kW m^{-2}. The heat fluxes measured should be treated with caution as the results are clearly influenced by the cooling effect of unburnt gas on the calorimeter. If the jet had been at a greater stand-off distance (e.g. 1.5 m instead of the JFRT 1.0 m) then the cooling effects may have been much lower and the mean measured heat fluxes higher.

The heat fluxes measured with a pipe calorimeter impinged by a 1.7 kg s^{-1} flashing liquid propane fire (Roberts et al. [8 & 9]) and by a kerosene pool fire (Moodie et al.[12]), were in the ranges 180 - 200 kW m^{-2} and 75 - 85 kW m^{-2} respectively. In an early version of the Jet Fire Resistance Test, Shirvill and Wighus[13] measured (using heat flux meters) heat fluxes in the range 190 (near the jet impingement point) to 280 kW m^{-2}. In general (apart from the mean burning liquid 1,3-butadiene heat flux) the measured heat fluxes were higher than the values measured by Moodie et.al. in a kerosene pool fire and the value assumed by API for pool-fire pressure relief calculations.

FIRE PROTECTION

Even though the unburnt gas effects probably indicate an underestimate of the heat fluxes, visual observation and measured flame temperatures suggest that the flames and heat fluxes are less severe than those achieved in the jet fire resistance test[11] for passive fire protection (PFP) materials. Hence, unless the reactive chemical actually reacts with the PFP, the JFRT should be adequate for assessing the fire performance of material used to protect vessels containing pressurised reactive chemicals. For reactive chemicals, the PFP needs to:

• Protect the wall of the vessel from reaching a temperature where weakening can occur;
• If possible, prevent a runaway reaction from being initiated; and

- Reduce the heat transfer to the vessel so that a relief device with a practical vent size can be used.

The vent sizing requirements are discussed in the next section.

VENT SIZING

The rate of a chemical reaction increases with temperature and many reactions of commercial interest are exothermic. A runaway reaction occurs when the rate of heat generation due to the reaction exceeds the rate of heat loss from the vessel. The rate of heat generation is an exponential function of temperature whereas the rate of heat loss is a linear function of temperature. The major heat loss from a tank will be by convection and radiation to the atmosphere. The runaway reaction will also rapidly increase the pressure of a closed system: the vapour pressure will increase with temperature; this is a vapour pressure system. To avoid the design pressure of the vessel being exceeded, vessels are normally fitted with a pressure relief valve, which will be activated at a set pressure. The diameter of the relief system must be carefully selected. Two-phase flow often occurs from runaway reaction systems. This is because the liquid level in the vessel rises, particularly after vent opening due to the amount of vapour being produced in the reaction liquid. Hence liquid as well as vapour leave the reactor via the vent. A vent sized for vapour flow alone will be inadequate. The calculation of the vent area is a two-stage process: the vent mass flux is first calculated and secondly the vent area calculated from the mass flux, rate of heat generation and any permitted overpressure. The vessel pressure is allowed to exceed the set pressure and rise to a maximum pressure, which is not higher than the design pressure plus permitted accumulation. In this way the required vent area may be reduced from that if no overpressure above the set pressure was allowed.

For a system where the pressure is due to vapour, the simplest mass flux equation (which neglects friction) is the Equilibrium Rate Model (ERM) (Fauske[14]):

$$G = (dP/dT)_m (T_m / C_{pm})^{1/2} \qquad (3)$$

The subscript, m, refers to mean conditions between the set pressure and the maximum pressure. The commonly used vent sizing equation for a vapour pressure exothermic reaction system is the Leung Equation (Leung[15]):

$$A = m_o\, q_m\, /\, G\, [\{(V/m_o)(h_{fgm}/v_{fgm})\}^{1/2} + \{C_{pm}\, \Delta T\}^{1/2}]^2 \qquad (4)$$

The heat release rate per unit mass is calculated using the following equation:

$$q = C_p\, (dT/dt) \qquad (5)$$

The Leung equation was developed for chemical reactors where the heat input is primarily from the exothermic reaction and there is no external heating. For a vessel containing reactive chemical exposed to fire, the would be the dominant heat source and therefore the Leung equation has been modified (Wilday & Daskalakis[16]) to include the effect of external heating on the heat release rate per unit mass. This modified Leung equation again is only for vapour pressure systems and can be used where the external heating is due to fire. The modified value of the heat release rate per unit mass is given by:

$$q_{modifed} = q + 2Q / m_o \qquad (6)$$

The rate of temperature rise due to external heating which needs to be applied in the small-scale test is given by:

$$(dT/dt)_{external} = Q / m_o \, C_p \qquad (7)$$

After a small-scale test has been performed with the additional heat input, it is necessary to calculate the rate of temperature rise due to the reaction, in order to calculate the reaction heat release rate per unit mass:

$$(dT/dt)_{reaction} = (dT/dt)_{measured} - (dT/dt)_{external} \qquad (8)$$

$$q = C_p \, (dT/dt)_{reaction} \qquad (9)$$

The above equations have been used to calculate vent sizes for an example vessel. These calculations have been performed, with the data from a Phi Tec experiments on 1,3-butadiene. Vent sizing calculations were performed for a small vessel of 2 m^3 capacity containing 800 kg of 1,3-butadiene (80% filling). The heat input from the fire was assumed to be 33.2 kW. This requires an external temperature rise rate of 0.8°C min^{-1} calculated using equation (7). The vent sizing calculations use a vent opening pressure of 25 bara with a maximum allowable pressure of 27.5 bara.

API 520[7] / Parry[17] can be used to calculated the heat flux for the small vessel. Taking the vessel to be a vertical cylinder of equal height and diameter of 1.37 m. The wetted surface area can be calculated as 6.19 m^2. API 520[6] / Parry[17] give the following equation to calculate the heat input assuming prompt fire fighting and good drainage:

$$Q \, (kW) = 43.2 \, F \, S_W^{0.82} \qquad (10)$$

The heat input for the small vessel can thus be calculated as (193 kW x F). The API codes allow the environmental factor (F) to take account of insulation. To achieve a heat input of 33.2 kW as used in the vent sizing calculation would require an insulation thickness of about 2 inches (F = 0.15).

The required vent size for the small vessel can then be calculated using API 520[7] and BSI[18] if it is assumed that:

• Vapour-only flow occurs instead of the two-phase flow assumed by the ERM; and
• The vapour is produced purely by the effect of the external heating at 33.2 kW and not by the runaway reaction.

The required relief rate is calculated as:

$$W = Q / h_{fg} \qquad (11)$$

The vent mass flux for vapour only flow can be calculated as:

$$G = C_d \, C_{sv} \, P \, (M_w/Z_o \, T)^{1/2} \, F_B \qquad (12)$$

The required vent area A is finally obtained as:

$$A = W/G \tag{13}$$

The calculated vent diameters for runaway reaction alone, runaway and external heating and external heating alone are shown in Table 9. For this size of vessel the vapour-only vent size for fire relief alone (external heating) is more than the required relief area for runaway reaction alone (two-phase relief) but less than the required relief area for fire (external heating) and runaway reaction (two-phase relief). However, for larger vessel sizes, the required vent size for runaway reaction could exceed that for external fire alone.

Table 9. SUMMARY OF VENT SIZING CALCULATIONS

External heating (kW)	Runaway reaction (kW)	Vent diameter (mm)	External Heating
None	7	2.62	None
33	5	8.16	Experimental
33	None	5.47	Calculated

DISCUSSION ON VENT SIZING

VENT SIZING

The vent sizing calculations shown in Table 9 confirm that larger vent sizes are needed if an external fire initiates a runaway reaction than for external fire alone. It is therefore important to take account of the possibility of thermal runaway when sizing vents on vessel containing reactive chemicals. As well as increasing the necessary size of the vent, it will be necessary to design the vent system for the two-phase flow that is to be expected. This will include venting to a safe place, which does not feed the fire, and the possibility of a catch tank or quench tank for the vented liquid.

Vent sizing calculations for runaway reaction with external heating require data from fire simulation calorimetry. Simulation of large storage vessels, with lower surface areas per unit mass, will require lower heat input rates to the calorimeter than simulation of smaller vessels.

The vent sizing calculations in Table 9 assume the API 520 fire heat input into a small, 2 m³, vessel with a 2 inch thickness of insulation. For this case, the fire heat input rate is significant compared with the rate of heat evolved by the runaway reaction and the external heat input can be simulated using fire simulation calorimetry. This size of vessel was chosen as being typical of processing equipment whilst large enough that fire simulation calorimetry is possible; for smaller vessels the higher heat input rates required in such calorimetry may not be feasible.

For typical storage vessels of up to about 80 tonnes capacity, the rate of heat input from an external fire will be very low compared with the heat evolved by a runaway reaction and is probably negligible in terms of carrying out vent sizing for a runaway. However, if the external fire had a long enough duration to initiate a runaway reaction, a larger vent would be required for the runaway reaction than for external fire.

If external heating was from a jet fire, rather than a pool fire, higher heating rates (e.g. by approximately an order of magnitude for a 2 m³ vessel) would result. Fire simulation calorimetry would not be always be feasible, either because simulation of a small process vessel would necessitate a very high rate of external heating or because a large storage vessel would necessitate an infeasibly low rate. In such cases, it may be possible to correct calorimetric data to add the effects of external heating using a method analogous to that to correct for thermal inertia (sample heat loss) (Townsend & Tou[4]). However, any such data correction procedures would require development, validation and definition of their conditions of applicability.

CONCLUSIONS

The following conclusions are made:

(a)   The flames and heat fluxes from 1,3-butadiene jet fires are less severe than those use in the jet fire resistance test for passive fire protection materials. Hence, unless the reactive chemical actual reacts with the fire protection, the jet fire test should be adequate for assessing the fire performance of material used to protect vessels containing pressurised reactive chemicals providing they have similar burning rates and heats of combustion to 1,3-butadiene.

(b)   For reactive chemicals, the passive fire protection needs to:

- protect the wall of the vessel from reaching a temperature where weakening can occur;
- if possible, prevent a runaway reaction from being initiated; and
- reduce the heat transfer to the vessel so that a relief device with a practical vent size can be used.

(c)   For reactive chemicals, vent sizing for external fire needs to consider whether the fire will give rise to a runaway reaction. If so, two-phase venting will be expected and larger required vent sizes will result.

(d)   Fire simulation calorimetry may be required to obtain data for vent sizing but will not be feasible for all sizes of process equipment and storage vessels. A methodology needs to be developed and validated for correcting calorimeter data for the heat input from an external fire.

(e)   Whilst API 520 provides a link between insulation and the vent size required, it does not take account of specific fire protection methods such as water deluge or intumescent passive fire protection.

NOMENCLATURE

A	Vent area, m^2
C_d	Discharge coefficient
C_{sv}	Flow correction factor, function of isentropic coefficient
C_w	Specific heat of water, $4.180 \ kJ \ kg^{-1} \ K^{-1}$
C_p	Reaction mixture specific heat capacity, $J \ kg^{-1} \ K^{-1}$
dm/dt	Water mass flow rate, $kg \ s^{-1}$
dP/dT	Rate of change of pressure with temperature, $Pa \ K^{-1}$
$(dT/dt)_{external}$	Rate of temperature rise due to external heating, $K \ s^{-1}$
dT/dt_{max}	Maximum rate of temperature rise, $K \ min^{-1}$

ΔH_r	Heat of reaction, J g^{-1}
ΔT	Temperature difference between temperatures at the relief set pressure and the maximum accumulated pressure, K
ΔT_u	Uncorrected adiabatic temperature rise, K
ΔT_{ad}	Corrected adiabatic temperature rise, K
ρT_w	Water temperature rise, K
F	Environmental factor
F_B	Back pressure correction factor
G	Mass flux, kg m^{-2} s^{-1}
h_{fg}	Latent heat of reaction mixture, J kg^{-1}
I	Heat flux, kW m^{-2}
m_o	Reactant mass, kg
M_W	Molecular weight, 54.092 gmol g^{-1} kmol kg^{-1}
P	Vessel pressure, Pa
P_{max}	Maximum pressure, bara
ϕ factor	1 + (heat capacity of test cell/heat capacity of sample)
q	Heat release rate per unit mass of reactant, W kg^{-1}
$q_{modifed}$	Heat released from reactant plus external heat, W kg^{-1}
Q	Heat input, W
S	Surface area exposed to flame, 0.642 m^2 experiment;
S_W	Effective wetted surface area of vessel, 6.19 m^2 vent sizing
σ	Absorptivity of copper surface (surface blackened), 0.95
T	Reactant temperature, K
T_{ad}	Difference between the sample temperature and the calorimeter heater temperature, K
T_{max}	Maximum temperature, °C
T_{onset}	Onset temperature, °C
V	Vessel volume, m^3
v_{fg}	Difference between vapour specific volume and liquid specific volume, m^3 kg^{-1}
W	required relief rate, kg s^{-1}
Z_o	Compressibility factor

REFERENCES

1.   Roberts, T. A., Gosse, A. and Hawksworth, S., 2000, Thermal radiation from fireballs on failure of liquefied petroleum gas storage vessels, *Trans. IChemE Hazards*, Vol. 78, Part B: 184 – 192.

2.   Keaney A. and Roberts T. A., 1996, Hazard consequences of jet-fire interactions with vessels containing pressurised reactive chemicals, HSL Internal Report, PS/96/12.

3.   Singh J., 1992, Phi-Tec: Enhanced vent sizing calorimeter - application and comparison with existing devices, International Symposium on Runaway Reactions, p313-330, AIChE, New York.

4.   Townsend D. I. and Tou J. C., 1980, Thermal hazard evaluation by an accelerating rate calorimeter, *Thermochimica Acta*, Vol 37: 1.

5.   Freeder B. G. and Snee T. J., 1988, Alkali-catalysed polymerisation of ethylene oxide and propylene oxide - hazard evaluation using accelerating rate calorimetry, *J.Loss Prev. Process Ind.*, 1988, Vol 1: 164-168.

6.   Braker W. and Mossman A. L., 1980, Matheson Gas Data Book, 6th edition, Matheson Gas Products, Secaucus, New Jersey, 1980.

7.   American Petroleum Institute, 2000, Sizing, selection, and installation of pressure - relieving devices in refineries. Part 1 - Sizing and Selection, Recommended Practice 520, Washington DC, January 2000.

8.   Roberts T. A. and Beckett H., 1996, Hazard consequences of jet-fire interactions with vessels containing pressurised liquids: Project R04.029 final report, HSL Internal Report PS/96/03.

9.   Roberts T. A., Medonos S. and Shirvill L. C., 2000, Review of the response of pressurised process vessels and equipment to fire attack, HSE Offshore Safety Report OTO 2000 051.

10.   Roberts T. A., Brown D., Beckett H. and Buckland I., 1995, Comparison of the effects of different fire test regimes on passive fire protection material, I.Chem.E. Symp. Series No. 139, pp. 253 - 266.

11.   Jet Fire Test Working Group, 1995, Jet Fire Resistance Test of Passive Fire Protection Materials, HSE Offshore Technology Report OTI 95 634.

12.   Moodie K., Cowley L. T., et al., 1988, Fire engulfment tests on a 5 tonne LPG tank, J. Haz. Mats., Vol. 20: 55 - 71.

13.   Shirvill L. and Wighus L., 1992, A method of testing resistance to jet fires, Advances in EP Research, Vol. 2: 12 - 13.

14.   Fauske H. K., 1985, Flashing flows – Some practical guidelines for emergency releases, Plant Operations Progress, Vol 4, No 3: 132-134.

15.   Leung J. C., 1986, Simplified vent sizing equations for emergency relief requirements in reactors and storage vessels, AIChE Journal, Vol 32, No 10: 1622-1634.

16.   Wilday A.J. and Daskalakis G., 1994, Pressure relief design for chemical reactors exposed to external fire, Paper 53c, AIChE Summer National Meeting, August 1994.

17.   Parry C. F., 1994, Relief systems handbook, IChemE, Rugby, 1994 reprint.

18.   BSI 1984, BS 6759: part 3: 1984, Specification for safety valves for process fluids.

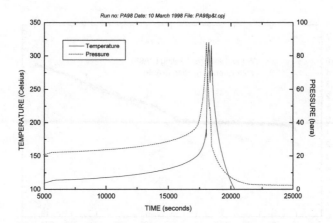

Figure 1. TEMPERATURE AND PRESSURE VERSUS TIME FOR 1,3-BUTADIENE

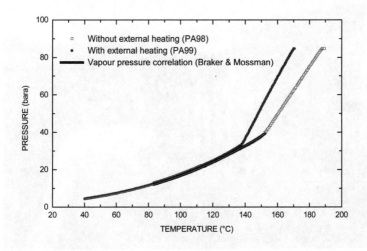

Figure 2. PRESSURE VERSUS TEMPERATURE FOR 1,3-BUATADIENE

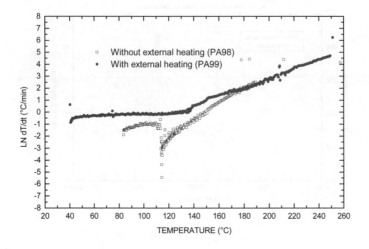

Figure 3. LOG [HEATING RATE] VERSUS TEMPERATURE FOR 1,3-BUTADIENE

Figure 4. PIPE CALORIMETER IN POSITION

Figure 5. FLAMES FROM 1,3-BUTADIENE VAPOUR

Figure 6. FLAMES FROM LIQUID 1,3-BUTADIENE

Figure 7. FLAMES FROM 0.3 KG S^{-1} PROPANE VAPOUR

Figure 8. FLAMES FROM 0.05 KG S^{-1} PROPANE VAPOUR

AN EXPERIMENTAL STUDY OF SPREADING LIQUID POOLS

R.P. Cleaver, P.S. Cronin and J.A. Evans

Advantica Technologies Ltd, Ashby Road, Loughborough, Leicestershire, LE11 3GR and

I.L. Hirst HSE, St Anne's House, Stanley Precinct, Bootle, Merseyside, L20 3RA

Assessment of the hazards posed by the storage of flammable or toxic liquids in large tanks can be assisted by the used of mathematical models to calculate the consequences of leakages. These consequences may include fires or explosions from dispersion of flammable vapours, harm to persons from inhalation of toxic vapours or harm to the environment. One component of such models is a mathematical representation of the spreading of a liquid pool, and in recent years a number of pool spread models have been proposed and implemented.

However, there are a number of issues in the formulation of the spreading models that have yet to be resolved. In particular, one area of uncertainty is the boundary condition applied at the front of the spreading pool. Boundary conditions which are generally accepted as applicable to the spread of oil on water and to the dispersion of a cloud of dense gas in air may not be applicable to the spread of a liquid on land, as the balance of competing physical phenomena at the spread front is different. Resolution of the uncertainties this creates has been hampered by a lack of reliable experimental data at a large scale. As a result, the Health and Safety Executive have contracted Advantica to carry out a series of "liquid spread on land" experiments at their Spadeadam Test Site to provide a sufficiently detailed database to resolve this issue. This paper gives details of the experimental programme and presents selected results from it.

KEYWORDS: Liquid pool spread, Consequence assessment, release behaviour, experimental data

INTRODUCTION

Assessment of the hazards posed by the storage of flammable or toxic liquids in large tanks can be assisted by the use of mathematical models to calculate the consequences of leakages. These consequences may include fires or explosions from dispersion of flammable vapours, harm to persons from inhalation of toxic vapours or harm to the environment. One component of such models is a mathematical representation of the spreading of a liquid pool, and in recent years a number of pool spread models have been proposed and implemented [1,2].

However, there are a number of issues in the formulation of the spreading models that have yet to be resolved. In particular, one area of uncertainty is the boundary condition applied at the front of the spreading pool; in this respect the modelling described in Webber[1] is fundamentally different to that described in Linden et al[2], for example, and in a number of other software models known to be in use. Boundary conditions which are generally accepted as applicable to the spread of oil on water and to the dispersion of a cloud of dense gas in air may not be applicable to the spread of a liquid on land, as the balance of competing physical phenomena at the spread front is quite different. Although information is available from a variety of sources [3,4,5,] resolution of the uncertainties this creates has been hampered by a lack of reliable experimental data at a large scale. As a result, the Health and Safety Executive have contracted Advantica to carry out a series of "liquid spread on land" experiments at their Spadeadam Test Site to provide a sufficiently detailed database to resolve this issue, as well as to allow more general validation.

The large scale of the test rig means that the experiments also have a direct bearing on issues of a practical nature. Most tanks used for storage of flammable or toxic liquids in the United Kingdom have capacities less than 50,000 cubic metres, although several tanks exist with capacities in excess of 100,000 cubic metres. The test tank constructed at Spadeadam replicates a tank of about 150,000 cubic metres capacity at a linear scale of one-twentieth, or, alternatively a tank of about 20,000 cubic metres capacity at a linear scale of one-tenth.

From an initial fill height of up to 1.8 m, water was released through a slot at the base of the tank and was free to spread over distances of up to 10 m on a specially constructed horizontal concrete surface. The size of the slot was such that the tank emptied completely in about thirty seconds. More rapid releases can be imagined, and indeed have occurred in practice when storage tanks have failed catastrophically. But the rate of release in these tests was judged adequate for the intended purpose of the tests. Experiments were carried out investigating not only the rate at which the pool spread, but also its interaction with a retaining bund wall of the type that is often encountered. The amount of the liquid that is able to flow over the retaining walls in this interaction is a quantity of particular interest in hazard assessment. Consequently, estimates of the proportion of the liquid that escaped from the bunded area in this way, the "overtopping fraction", were also made in the experiments.

In the following Sections, details of the experimental programme are presented and a number of the results are discussed. This includes a description of the experimental rig and associated instrumentation; an overview of the test programme; examples of the results and, finally, a discussion of the results and the implications these may have.

EXPERIMENTAL DETAILS

THE TEST RIG
The release vessel was designed to represent at 1/20th scale a quadrant of a 70m diameter storage tank. The lower section of the vessel was constructed from a section of curved mild steel with a 3.5m diameter. Elsewhere, the shape of the vessel was modified slightly in order to strengthen the vessel whilst maintaining the required cross-sectional area to represent a quadrant of a cylindrical tank, as shown on Figure 1.

For all of the tests, the vessel was filled with water at ambient temperature. A slot was cut around the circumference of the lower section of the vessel wall, and into it was fastened a quarter-circular strip of mild steel containing a slit of 25 mm height, through which the water could be released. The water was held in the vessel initially by an array of five flaps. On the outside of the tank was a pneumatically controlled mechanism that opened or closed the flaps; thereby allowing water to flow freely out of the tank for a controlled period of time.

The release mechanism was controlled by a PC based SCADA system, connected to a sequence timer system that co-ordinated the operation of the liquid release mechanism and the instrumentation.

Bund walls were fabricated from mild steel and set up on a flat 15m square concrete pad with the release vessel at one corner. Thirteen different bund configurations were used, 9 circular and 4 square. All configurations were sized to give nominally the same liquid containment volume. The two sides of the 90° quadrant were enclosed with 250mm deep flat plate, and were assumed to act as walls of symmetry. Perspex sections were fitted into one of the side walls to allow video records to be made of the water flow.

For some tests, 1 circular and 2 semi circular sections were installed within the bund to represent the appropriate parts of a regular array of additional tanks. The sections were fabricated from 200mm wide flat steel strip rolled to a 3.5m diameter.

INSTRUMENTATION
A scale was marked on the inside of the vessel to show the level of water within it above the bottom of the slit. In addition, a pressure transducer was fitted in the vessel at a height that was level with the top of the slit. During the experiments, the signal from the pressure transducer was recorded on a transient recorder sampling at 200Hz, from which the rate of flow of water out of the vessel was inferred.

The movement of water across the bund floor was monitored using up to 60 resistance probes, fixed in position on the concrete bund floor using terminal block. The resistance probes consist of two electrodes separated by gap (typically 5-10 mm), which provides a high electrical resistance. The arrival of the water lowers the resistance across the gap and triggers a TTL voltage step output from a purpose-built electronic circuit. This voltage acts to terminate a computer based counting register on a counter board. Counting was started when the release was initiated, and thus, using the known count frequency, a measure of the time of arrival of the water front at a specific probe location was obtained. The accuracy of the system has been checked by comparison with cine records and has been shown to indicate arrival times with an accuracy of better than 1 millisecond.

Water that overtopped the bund was caught in a polythene sheet attached to the (outside) edge of the bund and was then pumped into calibrated containers to measure its volume.

Up to four video cameras were used in the experiments; the images being recorded on MiniDV video tape. Video timers provided a timescale for the images on the video tape. One camera was used to provide general images of the release, another provided an overhead view of the floor of the bund whilst the other two cameras were used to monitor items of specific interest, for example, the time of arrival of the water front at the bund wall, or the release of water in the vicinity of the tank.

EXPERIMENTAL PROGRAMME
In the first of two Test Phases, 37 experiments were carried out to examine liquid spread over flat uninterrupted terrain and interaction with a single, circular bund wall. Three nominal fill heights were used for these tests: 1.45m, 1.6m and 1.8m, chosen to give water volumes approximately equal to 90%, 100% and 110% of the bund capacity. Different combinations of bund location and height were investigated and bunds with face angles, relative to the oncoming water front, of either 30 degrees, 45 degrees or 90 degrees were used.

In the Phase 1 experiments, the resistance probes were positioned as shown in Figure 2. Probes deployed along two radial lines monitored the general progress of the front, and probes located along circular arcs gave information about the radial symmetry of the flow.

In Phase 2, 22 experiments investigated releases into square bunded areas, in some cases with obstructions present. Figure 3 illustrates the different configurations. In all of these cases, the bunds walls presented a vertical face to the oncoming water.

EXPERIMENTAL RESULTS
Figure 4 shows the variation of the height of water remaining in the vessel with time for three representative experiments carried out with the three initial fill levels. The experimental values were inferred from the measurements of pressure made at the base of the vessel. The data recorded by the pressure transducer inevitably contain some random, high frequency noise and, possibly, other, more physically-based oscillations, superposed on the signal recording the changing head of water as the tank empties. Such oscillations are particularly apparent in the first few seconds immediately following the opening of the flaps to release the water. As a result, some form of time averaging is required to remove this high frequency component from the data if they are to be differentiated numerically in order to infer a

representative flow rate from the vessel. The curves shown in Figure 4 were produced using 0.5 second time averaging to remove the high frequency oscillations. Also shown on this Figure are predicted values obtained using the Bernoulli equation for the outflow velocity and the measured value for the area available for outflow, assuming a discharge coefficient with a value of 0.64. The agreement between the values inferred from the measurements and the predictions is very close. This gives some confidence that the measurements were made correctly and that the release mechanism worked as intended.

Figure 5 shows the time of arrival of the water front plotted against distance from the release vessel for representative tests carried out with the three initial fill levels. These measurements were made in experiments in which the bund wall located 10m from what would have been the centre of a cylindrical vessel (referred to hereafter as the 'centre of the vessel').

The time of detection of water at the resistance probes was used to infer the velocity of the front. Using the time difference between arrival of water at adjacent resistance probes along a radial line was found to give a local velocity with a significant amount of variability. Consistent with this, local variations in progress can be observed on the video records. However, a smooth polynomial curve was fitted to all of the time of arrival data collected in experiments with the same initial fill height in the vessel and this curve was differentiated to obtain an 'averaged' front velocity. A comparison of this inferred 'average' velocity with one particular set of 'local' velocity data is shown in Figure 6.

It should be noted that an examination of the video records and time of arrival records of the experiments suggests that the disruption to the flow caused by the presence of the resistance probes may have slowed the progress of the front slightly along the line of the probes. The size of the terminal block used to hold the resistance probe wires close to ground level was approximately 14mm and it was observed that there was a small wake-like region created in the lee of each probe. The video records suggest that these wake-like regions did not spread to affect the radial outflow at other locations. The maximum effect this produced appears to have occurred in the tests with the greatest initial fill level in the tank. In this case, the maximum difference in the time of arrival of the flow along the line of the probes and elsewhere at a distance of 10m (i.e arrival at the bund wall in the relevant tests) is about 0.5 secs. This suggests that the average speed of progress inferred from the resistance probe measurements systematically underestimates the true value by 0.05 m/s at most (compared with an observed value of about 0.37 m/s – corresponding to a discrepancy of about 13% in the values obtained from the resistance probe data along the 45 degree radial line). Whilst such differences should be born in mind if the data are used to compare with the predictions of mathematical models, they are of a smaller magnitude than differences in the predictions models currently in use.

The volume of water that overtopped the bund in each experiment was found to vary with the initial fill height, the profile of the bund wall and its distance from the vessel. As an example, Figure 7 shows how, in a number of the Phase 1 experiments, the amount varies with the wall angle and distance of the bund from the vessel.

DISCUSSION

As yet, only the data collected in the Phase 1 experiments have been examined in detail. This phase has provided data on the spreading of water released from the base of a tank, that at a scale of 1:20, represents a 70m diameter storage tank. The release and the surrounding geometrical arrangement are of a simple nature and this means that the flow that is produced can be simulated in a straightforward manner by mathematical models for liquid spread over land. Hence, the results from the experiments provide a dataset that can be used for the development or validation of mathematical models.

The interaction of the spreading front with a number of different bunds has been examined and the amount of water, if any, overtopping the bunds has been determined. A number of observations can be made on the data, as follows.

Firstly, as can be seen from Figure 4, the outflow from the vessel is in close agreement with expectations from theory. Also, the initial velocity of the water flowing out of the vessel is consistent as a starting value for the inferred spreading velocity data, such as that shown in Figure 5.

Within the programme, a number of experiments were carried out with the same initial head in the tank. A comparison of the spreading behaviour in these experiments gives some idea of the repeatability of the observed behaviour. It is found that there is some variation in the time of arrival at a given distance from the tank (of the order of 10 to 20%) in any one experiment. However, the results from all of the experiments, taken before interaction with the bund wall, show similar behaviour. If the time of arrival is plotted against distance from the 'centre' of the vessel, the measurements lie in a band of relatively narrow width, indicating a good degree of reproducibility in flow behaviour. Figures 5 and 6 illustrate this for the results obtained with one particular initial fill level in the vessel. Results such as those shown in Figure 5 and 6 provide the data that can be used to help investigate a number of issues. For example, the observed spreading velocity may be used to test the significance of using different boundary conditions at the front of the spreading pool within the mathematical models for pool spread on land. This should enable many of the existing uncertainties to be resolved.

The measurements of the amount of water overtopping the bund have also been examined. As Figure 7 demonstrates, if a large enough release occurs from the full perimeter of the tank, the water is capable of overtopping the bund walls, even if the bunded area has the capacity to hold all of the water that is released. Based on these results, it appears that the amount that overtops the bund decreases as the distance of the bund wall from the vessel increases (note: the bund heights were chosen to ensure that the bunded volume had nominally the same capacity in each case.). The amount also appears to be sensitive to the bund wall angle. Of the designs that were tested, the vertical bund wall was the most effective at retaining the water within the bund in this case.

It is expected that the results from the second Phase of experiments will shed further light on the release behaviour in situations that are more likely to be encountered in practice. Finally, it is noted that many of the mathematical models include the effects of parameters such as the surface tension and viscosity of the liquid within their formulation. Hence, once the existing uncertainties in the spreading behaviour have been resolved, it should be possible to use the models to define a specific, limited, programme of further experiments to provide data to confirm the influence of these parameters.

REFERENCES

1. Webber, D.M., A Model for Pool Spreading and Vaporisation and its Implementation in the Computer Code G*A*S*P", Report SRD/HSE/R507, September 1990.
2. Linden, P., Daish, N., Dalziel, S., Halford, A., Jackson, M., Hirst, I., Perroux, J., Wiersma, S. 'LSMS : A New Model For Spills Of LNG And Other Hazardous Liquids', Proceedings of 1998 International Gas Research Conference, San Diego, November 8th - 11th.
3. Greenspan, H.P. and Johansson, A.V. An experimental study of flow over an impounding dyke. Studies in Applied Mathematics, 64, 211-233, 1981.

4. Moorhouse, J and Carpenter, R.J. Factors affecting vapour evolution rates from liquefied gas spills. I Chem E North Western Branch, Hazards Symposium, 1986.
5. 5.Sharifi, T. An experimental study of the catastrophic failure of storage tanks. Ph D Thesis. University of London, Imperial College of Science and Technolocgy, Dept. of Chem Eng. And Chem. Technology, 1987.

DISCLAIMER
This paper describes work funded by the Health and Safety Executive. Its contents, including any opinions and/or conclusions expressed, are those of the authors alone and do not necessarily reflect HSE policy.

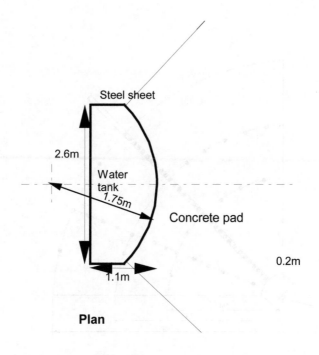

Plan

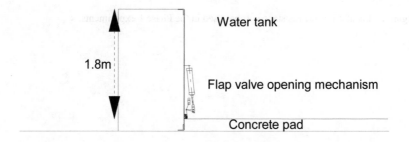

Elevation

Figure 1. Diagram showing the design of the experimental rig.

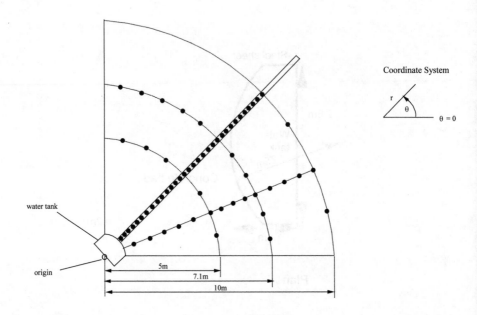

Figure 2. Location of the resistance probes used in the Phase 1 experiments.

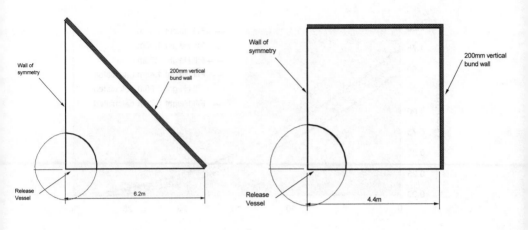

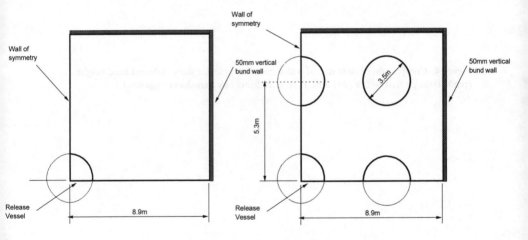

Figure 3. Four arrangements of bunding investigated in Phase 2 of the experimental programme.

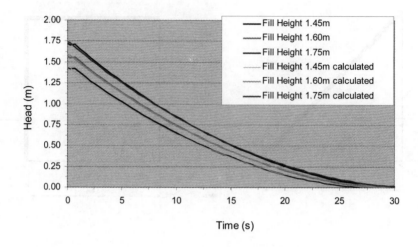

Figure 4. Comparison of flow rate of water from the tanks for three different head heights. (predictions plotted with a zero time shift, as indicated by transducer response).

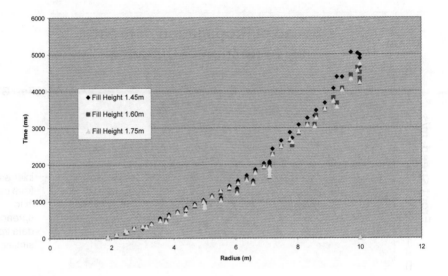

Figure 5. Comparison of spreading data for three tests using different heads of water initially in the tank.

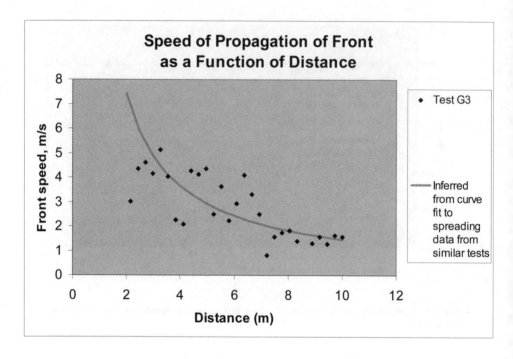

Figure 6. Comparison of frontal speed inferred from resistance data along a radial line in Test G3 with the values inferred from a curve fit to all the data collected in similar experiments.

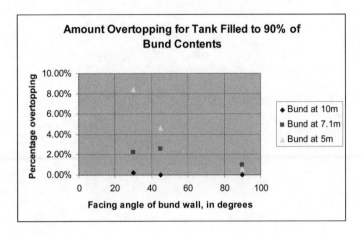

Figure 7. Amount of water overtopping the bund for bunds with different wall angles facing the oncoming flow. Results are shown for experiments in which the vessel was filled to 90% of the capacity of the surrounding bund.

PROJECT ON LOSS OF CONTAINMENT POTENTIAL FROM TANKS CONTAINING HAZARDOUS SUBSTANCES

A Khandelwal
Unit 3 Land Division, Hazardous Installations Directorate, Health & Safety Executive, Newcastle Under Lyme
© Crown Copyright 2001. Reproduced with the permission of the Controller of Her Majesty's Stationery Office.

Losses of containment from tanks have led to a number of serious incidents and accidents. A project was, therefore, initiated within Unit 3 of Land Division of HSE's Hazardous Installation Directorate (HID) to gather information on the potential for loss of containment, and the measures currently in use to mitigate the possible consequences. The work was carried out with a view to identifying benchmarks for simple alarm/automatic protection systems designed to reduce the incidence of tank overfilling, and other protection measures to prevent loss of containment. Thirteen sites - within Wales and the West of England were visited over a 6-month period as part of this project. Sites chosen contained more than 5 fixed tanks storing a variety of substances. Sites with large, complex storage facilities, such as refineries or large chemical plants were excluded.

The key findings of this work were:

1.   Wide variations existed in standards in design, selection, fabrication, installation, inspection and maintenance of tanks, bunds, alarms, trips, valves, and fittings. Appropriate enforcement action was taken where companies failed to comply with the law.

2.   Most of the sites visited had made little effort in carrying out risk assessments on loss of containment. Few had identified safety critical items.

3.   In many instances tanks were not fitted with adequate level alarms and trips. The tanks were old and no records existed of these being 'fit for the purpose'. Bunds were also inadequate in size and were constructed of inappropriate materials.

4.   Most of the sites visited paid little attention to the inspection, testing and maintenance of isolation valves, pipe work and fittings. Failure of these has in the past lead to loss of containment.

5.   On a number of sites, pumps and other items were found to have been located inside the bund where a catastrophic failure of a tank could lead to a serious incident.

6.   On many sites no consideration had been given to the use of Remotely Operated Shut Off Valves (ROSOV's), in the event of an emergency.

7.   In many instances, separation distances were inadequate, bunds were excessively crowded with tanks, piping had been poorly installed through the bund wall and bunds were cluttered.

8.   In most cases housekeeping was poor and there were build ups of rainwater, potentially flammable materials, inside tank and pump bunds.

Appropriate design features to prevent loss of containment are discussed. Internal HSE guidance is being prepared for inspectors, giving details of the survey and offering advice on the circumstances where enforcement action would be appropriate. HID's inspection strategy relating to this matter is being developed and the potential for loss of containment from tanks containing hazardous substances may now become one of the issues raised routinely during planned inspections to chemical manufacturing and storage sites.

Keywords: Loss of tank containment, Overfilling protection, Bunding and Tank farm protective measures.

INTRODUCTION

There have been a number of EC reportable incidents involving loss of containment of hazardous substances from storage tanks. Incidents, which have been reported to the HSE, include instances of tank and tank fittings failure, as well as tank overflow from overfilling. A project was initiated within Land Division of the Hazardous Installation Directorate (HID) of HSE to gather information on the potential for loss of containment, and measures to mitigate the possible consequences.

The work was undertaken at establishments to which the Control of Major Accident Hazards (COMAH) Regulations 1999 applied.

The aim of the project was to establish baseline information about the potential for loss of containment, and the measures to mitigate possible consequences through visits by specialist inspectors to selected sites.

The scope of the project was to identify measures to prevent loss of containment, including:

- implementation of simple alarm systems;
- scope of inspection and maintenance systems;
- adequacy of bunding arrangements;
- maintenance of containment measures;
- and whether formal risk assessments, have been carried out.

The work was carried out with a view to identifying benchmarks for simple alarm/automatic protection systems, to reduce the incidence of tank overfilling, and of other protection measures to prevent loss of containment.

WORK CARRIED OUT AND PROCEDURES

SELECTION OF SITES

Thirteen sites within Wales and the West of England were selected and visited over a six-month period as part of this project. The sites chosen contained more than 5 fixed tanks and a variety of chemicals. It was not intended that the project should cover sites with large and complex storage facilities such as refineries or large chemical manufacturing sites. Sites that contained tanks storing a variety of substances were preferred.

A range of different types of chemicals - flammables, toxics, and corrosives - were covered in the study and in the majority of cases, the sites had more than one type of chemical in storage.

In all cases, the sites chosen were subject to the Control of Major Accident Hazard Regulations 1999 and included both top tier and lower tier sites.

COMPANY TYPES

The companies chosen were from a range of operational activities and size to provide a good cross section of small, medium and large sites. Tanks of all sizes, from a few m^3 to up to 5,000 m^3 in volume were covered in the study.

PRO FORMA

A pro forma, as attached in Appendix 1, was used to collect information.

On larger sites where there were a large number of tanks and tank farms, a preliminary selection was made before carrying out a detailed inspection and collecting detailed information. The selected tanks and tank farms were chosen on the basis of hazard potential, local factors and the potential for learning from this exercise. In some cases the sites requested a copy of the pro forma so that they could carry out a similar exercise, on their own, on other tanks and tank farm(s) either on the same site or other sites belonging to the company. This was agreed to encourage inquiry, discussions and improvements within the site and the company.

TOPICS
The main topics covered in the project were:

- Risk assessment on loss of containment and identification of safety critical items
- Tanks, including their design, inspection and maintenance
- Bunds, including their size, construction, and lining materials
- Isolation valves, pipe work, flange, fittings, inspection and maintenance
- Alarms and trips
- Housekeeping

KEY FINDINGS AND RESULTS
Wide variations existed in the standards between the various companies visited and even within a site. Some companies were aware of the dangers of minor or catastrophic failure and had a system in place to prevent and deal with these situations. In other cases the companies were totally unaware of the dangers and had taken virtually no steps to prevent loss of containment due to the tank overflow or failure.

Most companies had not carried out a risk assessment, which identified the hazards, and taken measures to avoid loss of containment.

The sections below discuss the findings in more detail.

TANKS
Wide variations existed in tank design, inspection and maintenance regimes within individual company sites and between different companies visited as part of this project.

Types
There were no repeated defects found in a particular type of tank. Tanks inspected included all different types, such as, horizontal, vertical and vertical tiered tanks, and varied widely in their design, state of repair, inspection & maintenance regime.

Some tanks were located at an elevated level and in one case an acid tank located at some 20 - 30 feet up in the air could have sprayed strong acid at tanks located at ground level and a leak could have breached the bund depending on the direction and extent of the failure.

Age
Tank age had little to do with tank integrity and tanks of different age were covered as part of this study. Some new tanks were poorly designed and some very old ones were well designed and maintained. As an example the oldest tank encountered in the survey was built in 1893 and after a thorough refit and examination had received another 10 years lease of life.

Size
There was no correlation between tank size and integrity. Tanks as little as a few thousand liters were found to be badly designed and maintained and tanks very large in size were found

to be perfectly adequately designed and maintained. The smallest tank covered in the study was a few m^3 and the largest was of 5000 m^3 in size.

Contents
Tanks containing all different types of materials were covered in the study. These included COMAH named substances, toxics, flammables, corrosive and other hazardous substances. Although there were no hard and fast rules governing standards versus substances stored within tanks, it was found that in general additional care was exercised in the design and maintenance of tanks containing hazardous inventories and COMAH named substances.

Design Codes
Wide variations existed regarding the design of the tanks. Some tanks included in the project were built to design codes or industry standards. However, a large proportion were built to an unknown standard or were purchased second hand with no records of standards to which they were built.

Material of Construction
Tanks covered in the study were mostly either made of steels or plastics. Plastic tanks were generally built to a standard and appeared in better shape but wide variation existed in steel tank design and their state of repair.

Special Features
Some tanks covered in the study had special coatings and linings. These tended to be well maintained, as the occupiers were aware of their possibility of failure and therefore had better systems in place for regular inspection and maintenance.

Location
In a number of cases the tanks and tank farms were located too close to other tank farms, process plant, offices, other occupied buildings, rivers and other over ground water courses. A loss of containment or a fire in these cases could have led to serious escalation and possible harm to people and environment.

In a number of cases the tank farms also contained materials, which on mixing could generate dangerous by-products or where a catastrophic failure of one tank could bring a flammable liquid in the vicinity, in contact with heated tanks or pipe work.

BUNDS
Wide variations existed both within sites and among companies visited as part of this project. Some bunds were well designed, constructed and managed whilst the others were not adequate for the purpose and were badly maintained.

Size
Most bunds were capable of holding 110% of the contents of the largest vessel.

Design
Different designs were found in use within a site and among companies on tank farms. Some had all the various tanks contained within a single bund whereas in other cases there were bunds within bunds to isolate spillages from specific tanks that were considered incompatible. In some cases the dividing walls were only constructed a few inches high to prevent mixing of

minor spillage whereas in other cases the walls were constructed to full height to prevent the stored material over topping in the event of a catastrophic failure.

Pumps and Pipe work   In a lot of the cases the pumps were inside the bunds and no consideration had been given to the submerging of pumps in the event of a catastrophic failure of one of the tanks, containing either flammable or corrosive chemicals.

Also, in many cases pipes had breached the bund walls without any consideration given to making sure that it had not weakened the wall.

Bund Walls   The walls were also of all different heights, which in some cases made climbing necessary to carry out an inspection. Whilst there is no hard and fast rule regarding the wall height, a height above the eye level makes climbing necessary thus requiring extra effort to carry out an inspection. These bunds normally get left unattended and have therefore suffered from greater chances of having a pipe flange leakage or gasket / bolt failures. The high walls also in some cases did not look strong enough to be able to withstand the catastrophic failure of the tank. In some cases no adequate means had been provided for easy entry into bunds and egress from bunds. Any height that has to be accessed above two meters has to be provided with an appropriate means of access.

Sumps and Drains   Some bunds were laid to slope towards a sump to collect spillages and rainwater or a drain with an outlet valve.

Some drains with an outlet valve were found left open thus negating the whole object of having a bund in the first place.

Sumps with a pump which runs automatically or manually as and when required to pump out accumulated waste or rain water to a suitable location (or some equally effective means), is a better solution for keeping the bunds clean and free of spillages and rainwater, than having a drain with an outlet valve.

Materials of construction   All different materials of constructions were found to be in use on bunds. These included reinforced concrete, bricks, breezeblocks, plastic as well as earth and stone chippings.

Bund walls   Generally these were made of bricks, reinforced concrete, breezeblocks and plastics. In some cases breeze blocks and bricks were plastered over to ensure greater strength and non-permeability. In other cases they were left bare or painted over. In many cases the bund walls were found to be in bad condition due to age, lack of maintenance, supporting of pipe work, cable trays, instrumentation and electrical junction boxes, other miscellaneous items and objects.

Floor   Generally these were reinforced concrete, bricks, and plastic or special acid resistance bricks. In many cases concrete lining had been damaged due to the corrosive action of the chemical.

Lining   In some cases the bund floor and walls had been lined to protect against the attack by the chemical stored. This was particularly important for the storage of corrosive chemicals such as hydrochloric acid where a catastrophic failure of the tank could have put a severe strain on the wall and continued integrity of the wall is of importance to prevent loss of containment.

VALVES AND FITTINGS

Most companies paid little attention to valves and fittings. There was also little consideration given to use of Remotely Operated Shut Off Valves (ROSOV's), or the inspection and testing of valves to ensure isolation, particularly in an emergency situation. In a number of cases these valves were generally left open indefinitely for operational reasons. No consideration was given to making sure that valves had not stuck in an open position and had not deteriorated or developed a leak.

ALARMS AND TRIPS

Wide variations existed regarding alarms and trips among the companies surveyed. Some companies had tanks fitted with alarms as well as trips whereas others were only fitted with alarms, and some relied on manual dipping, gauges and inventory accounting systems.

INSPECTION AND MAINTENANCE

Wide variations existed regarding inspection and planned maintenance among the companies inspected. Some companies did have a regular inspection and maintenance regime whereas the majority of the companies had no such scheme in place for tanks and tank farms. The former generally related to large oil and chemical manufacturing companies or their subsidiaries.

The systems in themselves also varied, with widely differing inspection and maintenance regimes for similar duties.

In some cases inspections were undertaken every few years, but in other cases the gap between frequency of inspection and maintenance was as high as 25 years. The companies that carried out regular inspection again varied in terms of the systems used. In some cases they were still using a manual system but the majority of the companies who carry out regular inspection and maintenance now appear to be using a computer based system. Where these systems were in existence records were generally kept and were available for inspection.

The systems also varied in terms of depth of examination, testing and maintenance. Depending on the type of tank, size, duty and other design features, some companies carried more or less daily visual external examination. In other cases there was limited frequent visual examination, but an infrequent examination to a defined written scheme of examination.

HOUSE KEEPING

Wide variations existed regarding house keeping among the companies inspected. Some companies did have a regular cleaning regime whereas the majority of the companies had no such scheme in place for tanks and tank farms.

DISCUSSION

Discussion below is aimed at guiding industry as well as Regulatory Inspectors to assess whether the company has taken minimum steps to fulfill their statutory obligations.

LOSS OF CONTAINMENT

Loss of containment due to tank overfilling or failure is a real possibility. There are many examples where these have led to harm to people and the environment and cost companies dearly, in terms of, loss of materials, clean up costs and bad publicity.

Whilst it is not possible to totally avoid these failures occurring, the chances of one happening can be reduced and the likely harm it causes to people and the environment can be minimised.

TANKS AND TANK FARMS

Tanks and tank farms occupy a large proportion of any chemical site. They also hold the largest inventory of hazardous materials and a loss of containment could lead to some of the worst problems arising from the site.

In a lot of cases simple, relatively inexpensive, measures can save significant potential for harm to people and environment.

General - Companies should carry out a risk assessment and this overall assessment should be used to derive a policy on protective measures, frequency of inspection and maintenance.

Old tanks/tank farms -If there are no records available regarding the design standard used in the construction and installation of the tank, and the company uses hazardous materials for storage in these tanks, the company should employ a competent person to draw a scheme of examination and prove that the tank is 'fit for the purpose'.

Where codes or industry standards exist they can be used to identify the inspection and maintenance requirements.

New Tanks and Tank Farms - These should be built to current industry standards or codes of practice for their intended service. Where the application is novel and no data exists the company should carry out corrosion studies and other work to identify an appropriate inspection and maintenance regime. This should also be reviewed once a reasonable inspection history has accumulated. .

Incompatible materials should not be grouped together inside a bund; this potential hazard should be designed out whenever new tank farms are being planned or new substances introduced.

BUNDS

Bunds provide a second line of defence in the containment of hazardous chemicals in the event of tank, valve or fitting failure. The size, design, construction, lining, entry and egress from the bunds are important.

The bunds should be constructed to hold at least 110% volume of the largest vessel within the bund. The bund walls and floor should be impermeable to prevent loss of containment and fouling of ground water courses.

All pumps must be located outside the bund, preferable on a small sill with its own bund to catch leaks and minor spills.

Bund walls should not be used to support pipe work, cable trays, instrumentation, electrical equipment and any other miscellaneous items which can cause the weakening of the wall. For the same reason pipe work should not be allowed to breach the bund wall unless special fittings are installed to maintain the bund integrity. A suitable lining should also be applied to the bund floor and wall to prevent attack by spilt chemicals due to a minor leak or a catastrophic failure.

The floors should be laid to a small collection sump fitted with a pump or some other equally effective device to pump out spillages or rainwater as required to a suitable location.

The bund should be kept clean at all times. In many instances this has been found to have been achieved by having housekeeping rules and making it part of the responsibility of the user department.

VALVES AND FITTINGS

Valves and fittings should be inspected regularly to ensure integrity as well as to make sure that valves can be shut to isolate tanks in an emergency.

Consideration should also be given to use of ROSOV's particularly when storing flammable, corrosive and toxic liquids.

ALARMS AND TRIPS

Risk assessment should be used to assess the need for alarm and trips on tanks. Tanks containing toxics and materials whose loss of containment could lead to major harm to people and environment should be fitted with alarms as well as trips.

INSPECTION AND MAINTENANCE

Regular inspection and maintenance plays a vital role in preventing loss of containment. The company should carry out risk assessments to identify the frequency of inspection and quality of maintenance regime required on their plant. As part of this assessment all safety critical items must be identified and the inspection and maintenance regime defined.

HOUSE KEEPING

Good house keeping has a vital role in safety. It reduces the risk of slips, trips and falls and also minimises the risk of fire and incompatible materials mixing together to produce a hazardous substance. Companies should have house keeping rules and should assign individuals for this duty. It should carry out regular inspection and audits to make sure that the rules are being followed and individuals assigned this duty are carrying out their assigned tasks.

SUMMARY OF FINDINGS AND CONCLUSIONS

1. Wide variations existed in standards, in design, selection, fabrication, installation, inspection and maintenance of tanks, bunds, alarms, trips, valves, and fittings. Appropriate enforcement action was taken where the companies had failed to comply with the law.

2. Most sites visited had made little effort to carry out risk assessments on tank containment, which would have enabled them to identify safety critical items.

3. In many instances tanks were not fitted with adequate level alarms and trips, they were old and no records existed of these being 'fit for the purpose'.

4. Bunds of inadequate size, and some constructed of inappropriate materials, were also seen.

5. Most sites visited paid little attention to inspection, testing and maintenance of isolation valves, pipe work and nuts and bolts. These have in the past lead to loss of containment or serious escalation.

6. On a number of sites pumps and other items were found to have been located inside the bund where a catastrophic failure of a tank could lead to a serious incident. On many sites no consideration had been given to the use of ROSOV's in the event of an emergency.

7. In many instances separation distances were inadequate, bunds were excessively crowded with tanks, piping had been poorly installed through the bund wall and bunds were cluttered.

8. In most cases housekeeping was poor and there were build-ups of rainwater, organic-growth, rubbish and spillages inside tank and pump bunds.

CURRENT STATUS AND HID INSPECTION STRATEGY

Internal guidance is now been prepared for inspectors, giving details of the survey, its conclusions and offering advice on the circumstances in which enforcement action would be appropriate. This matter may become one of the issues raised routinely during planned inspections to chemical manufacturing and storage sites.

Hazardous Installation Directorate (HID) inspection strategy is currently being developed and the potential for loss of containment from tanks containing hazardous substances may now become one of the issues raised routinely during planned inspections to chemical manufacturing and storage sites.

Internal guidance will provide benchmarks for the technical standards inspectors would be seeking and those circumstances where formal enforcement action would be considered.

APPENDIX 1

Tank Storage Questionnaire

(Advice on how to complete the questions are shown in italics in Parts A, B and C, which follow)

A. COMMON INFORMATION FOR ALL SITES

1. Site

2. No.'s Employed

3. Business / Process

4. Activity associated with tanks in survey

(e.g. Raw materials storage, blending, intermediate product storage, finished product storage).

B. INFORMATION IN RELATION TO TANKS / TANK FARMS CONCERNING MAINTENANCE, INSPECTION AND BUNDING

1. Type of Tanks

E.g. vertical, horizontal etc. - indicate Nos.

2. Tank Capacities

Approximate contents if full

3. Contents of Tanks

Mark which category(s) are appropriate

Very Toxic

Toxic

Extremely Flammable

Highly Flammable

Flammable

Dangerous to the environment
COMAH named substance
Other

4. When were the vessels installed and to what design standard were they originally built?

5. Does the site have a planned inspection and maintenance system for the vessels?

6. If so, is it a computer-based or a paper-based system?

7. Does the inspection system cover tank fittings and pipe work as well as the vessels?

8. Please comment if there are any special features, which require special inspection procedures (e.g. lined vessels or pipe work).

9. What is the inspection frequency?

(Indicate if there is a standard frequency, or different frequencies for different vessels. Are the venting arrangements, PRVs etc., inspected to the same frequency?).

10. Can the company demonstrate that the inspections have been carried out when due, and remedial maintenance action taken when necessary?

11. Please comment on the general standard of the vessel and pipe work maintenance. Pay special attention to supports for pipe work, and earth bonding arrangements where flammable liquids are stored.

12. Are the vessels bunded? If so, what is the form of construction of the bunds?

13. Has the company carried out an assessment to ensure:

   a)   That the bund is capable of holding the contents of 110% of the largest vessel in the bund?

   b)   That the bund can withstand the full hydrostatic pressure from a complete loss of contents of the largest vessel?

   c)   That the construction of the bund is appropriate for the types of substances stored (e.g., if acid, is the bund lined with acid-resisting coatings / bricks?

14. Please comment on the general standard of maintenance and housekeeping of the bunds. Pay special attention to expansion joints; drain valves through bund walls etc.

C. INFORMATION IN RELATION TO ALARM SYSTEMS ON VESSELS, WHERE APPLICABLE

Questions 1 to 7 are specific to an individual tank and should be completed for all tanks on site. Question 8 is specific to the tank but there may be similarities between tanks. These details should be completed for all tanks, but may be cross-referenced where appropriate. Questions 9 and 10 relate to all alarms and overrides and only need to be completed once per site.

1. Type of Tanks
E.g. Vertical, horizontal, etc. - indicate Nos.

2. Tank Capacities
Approximate contents if full

3. Contents of Tanks
Mark which category(s) are appropriate
Very Toxic
Toxic
Extremely Flammable
Highly Flammable
Flammable
Dangerous to the environment

COMAH named substance

Other

4. Type of Measurement System

Please indicate the most appropriate description.

None

Combined process measurement and alarm

Process measurement and independent alarm

Combined process measurement and automatic interlock

Process measurement and independent automatic interlock

Other *(please give details)*

5. Type of overfill device

If more than one device present please indicate the final or safety critical device

Level

Weight

Mass

Pressure

Other

6. Alarm and Automatic Interlocks

6.1 Risk Assessment

6.1.1 Has the company carried out a risk assessment to identify the safety criticality of the alarm or automatic interlock?

6.2 Has the safety criticality been used to influence the implementation and if so how?

6.3 Alarms and Interlock Trip-point

6.3.1 Is the alarm and/or automatic trip-point documented?

6.3.2 Is the trip-point justified and what factors have been taken into consideration?

7. Alarms

Indicate where and how alarm is displayed. If both local and remote indication, identify the place where the operator is expected to see the alarm

7.1 Display

Local

Remote

Control room

Alarm panel

VDU

7.2 Operator response (alarms only)

7.2.1 Is there a documented procedure for responding to safety critical alarms?

7.2.2 What length of time has been allowed for the operator to respond to the alarm and take corrective action?

8. Maintenance Procedure

8.1 Measuring device

8.1.1 Is the measuring device tested/calibrated to a written procedure?

8.1.2 What is the test frequency and how has it been determined?

8.2 Function test (end to end)

8.2.1 Is a full function test including operation of the measuring device, of any alarm or valve, undertaken?

8.2.2 What is the frequency and how has it been determined?

8.2.3 If full function testing has not been undertaken please indicate what is.

8.3 Isolating valve

8.3.1 Is the valve is tested to a written procedure?

8.3.2 What is the frequency and how has it been determined?

9. Modification of Alarms/Interlocks

9.1 Modification system

What is the system for controlling the modification of alarms and interlocks? Identify key features.

Is the system for controlling the modification of alarm trip points different from above? If yes, please identify key features.

10. Control of Overrides

10.1 Can alarms / interlocks be overridden?

10.2 If yes, identify the override mechanism and key features of the system for controlling overrides.

DIRECTED WATER DELUGE PROTECTION OF LIQUEFIED PETROLEUM GAS VESSELS

T Roberts*, I Buckland** and H Beckett*

* Health and Safety Laboratory, Buxton, Derbyshire SK17 9JN
** Technology Division, Health and Safety Executive, Merseyside L20 3QZ
© Crown Copyright 2001. Reproduced with the permission of the Controller of Her Majesty's Stationery Office.

The adequate fire protection of Liquefied Petroleum Gas (LPG) storage vessels to guard against their catastrophic failure and possibly Boiling Liquid, Expanding Vapour Explosion (BLEVE) is recognised to be of key importance. One means of achieving this is by directed water deluge that, for LPG vessels of 50 tonnes or larger, should be a fixed system on the vessel. The deluge rate currently recommended for such systems is designed to provide adequate protection against hydrocarbon pool fires. However, it is now recognised that the incident scenario most likely to threaten the integrity of such vessels is impingement by a hydrocarbon fuel jet fire. HSE therefore decided to sponsor studies of the effectiveness of directed water systems in protecting against jet fires.

This paper describes the work carried out by the Health and Safety Laboratory (HSL) in which a nominal 2 kg s^{-1} flashing liquid propane jet fire was impinged upon two tonne propane vessels protected by a range of water deluge systems. The results from the work show that a directed water deluge system designed to provide protection against a pool fire (using the minimum recommended rate of 9.8 dm^3 m^{-2} min^{-1}) provides inadequate protection against jet-fires. However, improved designs of water deluge systems proved more successful.

A number of aspects concerning the design of directed water deluge systems were studied, including: type of nozzle and their arrangement, water flow rate and pressure, effect of blocked nozzles and delayed deluge initiation. Critical design parameters are proposed for directed water deluge systems.

Keywords: directed water deluge, propane, LPG, fire protection, jet fires.

INTRODUCTION

An external fire can pose a significant threat to the integrity of a plant containing pressurised flammable materials. The particular purpose of providing fire protection to such vessels is to limit the heat transfer from the heat source to the pressure vessel. This delays the rise in temperature to critical levels, reduces the risk of escalation and gives additional time for emergency actions to be implemented. In respect of one of the means of providing fire protection of LPG storage vessels, namely directed water deluge, the deluge rate recommended[1] is that determined to provide protection against a hydrocarbon pool fire.

The particular water deluge rate recommended of 9.8 dm^3 m^{-2} min^{-1} over the whole of the exposed vessel surface derives from work by Bray[2] and Billinge[3] et al. as adequate for the protection of vessels containing pressure liquefied gases against hydrocarbon pool fires. It is not perhaps surprising that others have proposed comparable application rates with a view to providing similar levels of protection. For example, the National Fire Protection Association[4] in the USA, recommends 10.2 dm^3 m^{-2} min^{-1} as the minimum deluge rate. Whilst the American Petroleum Institute[5] specify a lower minimum requirement of 4.1 dm^3 m^{-2} min^{-1}, in taking account factors such as high-intensity flame impingement, water losses due to wind and partial clogging of water delivery nozzles, the same deluge rate as the NFPA is recommended. The Institute of Petroleum[6], in their model code of safe practice for bulk pressure storage of LPG, recommends that water deluge systems should be designed to permit application of at least 7 dm^3 m^{-2} min^{-1}.

However, it is now recognised that the incident scenario that is potentially most likely to threaten the integrity of such vessels is jet-fire impingement. Jet fires are typically more severe than pool fires because of their high heat fluxes (up to 350 kW m^{-2}) and high mechanical erosive effects. Jet fires have higher velocities and can result in higher rates and higher amounts of heat transfer to a vessel than for a pool fire. HSE's Technology Division therefore sponsored a project to study the critical elements of deluge system design for protection against jet fires.

The experimental programme comprised several phases. The first phase was to determine the effectiveness of water deluge systems designed according to current practice; one designed to deliver the minimum recommended rate of 9.8 dm^3 m^{-2} min^{-1} and one designed to a tentative fire protection industry standard[7] that is used in the UK. The second phase was to investigate whether a directed water deluge system could be made effective against a jet fire. In phase 3 the sensitivity of the system to blocked nozzles and delayed water deluge initiation was investigated. The final phase was to confirm the effectiveness of the system in protecting a vessel containing various degrees of fill of LPG.

DESIGN OF DIRECTED WATER DELUGE SYSTEMS

The design codes currently used in the UK allow a significant degree of flexibility in the specification of directed water deluge systems. The most detailed code, BS 5306 Part 2[8], unfortunately does not explicitly cover water deluge protection of vessels containing pressurised flammable materials, such as LPG. The two other design codes in use are, the Fire Offices' Committee (FOC)[7] *Tentative rules for medium and high velocity water spray systems* (hereafter referred to as the Tentative Rules), and NFPA 15[4] *Water spray fixed systems for fire protection*. Whilst issued as an interim measure in 1979, the Tentative Rules provide the greater detailed guidance on the design of systems for the protection of "storage vessels containing inflammable gases, and liquids at atmospheric and higher pressures" i.e. including LPG vessels. The experimental work has therefore been carried out with regard to the FOC Tentative Rules and NFPA 15 designs are considered in relation to these.

TENTATIVE RULE DESIGN REQUIREMENTS

Different types of spray nozzles may be used in water deluge. Low velocity (LV) nozzles produce a fog-type spray with a fine drop size and a high capacity for heat absorption. High velocity (HV) nozzles produce a spray with a much coarser drop size, with good capabilities for penetrating through turbulent fire gases and convection currents. Medium velocity (MV) nozzles are general purpose, providing a mixture of the properties of low and high velocity sprays, with the result that they can be used in all categories of protection. According to the Tentative Rules, for liquids with flash points less than 66 °C and combustible gases, medium velocity sprays need to be installed with a view to bringing a fire under control and to provide cooling. For horizontal, cylindrical storage vessels, it is specified that protection should be by means of open medium velocity spray nozzles, not less than 6 mm bore, operating at pressures between 1.4 bar and 3.5 bar and should have cone angles between 60° and 125°. The recommendations for the spacing and operation of sprinkler nozzles are based upon "*an application rate of 10 mm min*[-1] *over the vessel surface to limit the heat input to the vessel to 19.0 kJ min*[-1] *per square metre of vessel surface.* [This may be an error – Bray's work[2] suggests that 19 kW m^{-2} is the appropriate value] *It is assumed that the design of the vessel vents will be capable of maintaining the internal pressure within design limits for this heat input.*"

Spray nozzles should be installed in accordance with relevant spray nozzle application charts. There are three different charts corresponding to spray nozzle stand-off distances of 0.45 m, 0.55 m and 0.65 m from the vessel surface. Each chart gives the K-factor for the nozzles for the allowed number of spray rows and spray angle for a given vessel diameter. The K-factor is calculated from:

$$K \quad = \quad \text{Flow rate (dm}^3 \text{ min}^{-1}) / \text{Pressure}^{0.5} \text{ (barg)} \tag{1}$$

and relates the flow rate to the water pressure. The rules specify that, if a spray nozzle with an orifice corresponding to the K-factor value determined from the graph is not commercially available, the next larger orifice should be used. The longitudinal spacing of the spray nozzles is given as a table of discharge angle versus stand-off distance from the vessel. Protection of the ends is provided for, by increasing by one the number of spray nozzles per row indicated by the table for the desired vessel length. The two outer spray nozzles are arranged so that half their output sprays back to cover the vessel end (flat or curved) and half sprays on the vessel shell. For curved vessels above ≥ 3.5 m in diameter, an additional spray nozzle onto the centre of the vessel end is required. Where the plinths supporting the vessel interfere with the water distribution, additional spray nozzles should be provided on the bottom rows of spray nozzles. Further spray nozzles of, for example, 6 mm bore size will be required for the vent, manholes, inlet and outlet points, pumps etc., "*unless the items are well protected by sprayers protecting the vessel surface*".

With respect to the actual water coverage, the Tentative Rules stress in a note that "*it is not acceptable to establish total flow requirements for protection of a vessel by simply adding a given percentage to the theoretical figure obtained by consideration of required density and surface area of vessel and then determining the number of sprayers by dividing the total flow by the output for one spray nozzle*". However, study of the original derivation of the recommended rates suggests that the rate that is quoted is the **delivery rate** to the nozzles divided by the vessel surface area and *not* the amount of water actually delivered to the surface of the vessel.

HSL EXPERIMENTAL DELUGE SYSTEMS

A commercial organisation designed two directed water deluge systems for use in the experimental programme. The first was designed to deliver the minimum recommended application rate of 9.8 dm^3 m^{-2} min^{-1}, and the second to provide a range of configurations within the parameters permitted in accordance with the Tentative Rules. The systems were designed for installation on nominal 2 te LPG vessels, details of which are given below.

SYSTEM DESIGNED TO GIVE THE MINIMUM RECOMMENDED RATE

The system comprised 9 stainless steel, medium velocity, hollow cone (impact type) nozzles (see Figure 1) that were specially made with a nominal 4.7 mm bore and 95° spray angle nozzles, and quoted K factor of 10, arranged in three rows around the vessel (see Figure 2). Four additional nozzles were fitted to prevent formation of dry spots on the vessel behind the supporting legs. The stand-off distance of the nozzles from the vessel surface varied between 0.5 m and 1.0 m as shown in Figure 2. To produce the required coverage, the manufacturer specified a water pressure of 2 barg at each nozzle, Figure 4 shows the spray pattern.

SYSTEM NOMINALLY DESIGNED TO THE TENTATIVE RULES

The system comprised three rows of four stainless steel, medium velocity, hollow cone nozzles (nominal bore 6.8 mm, spray angle of 95°, K-factor 28) with a 1.50 m longitudinal spacing (c.f. 1.57 m specified in the Tentative Rules) and a 0.65 m stand-off distance. For the experimental set-up, the end nozzles were *not* directed half onto the parallel section and half onto the end cap as recommended in the Tentative Rules, nor were the pressure relief valve or top and bottom outlet valves specially protected by dedicated nozzles. Additional nozzles were not required to prevent the formation of dry spots on the vessel behind the legs. Figure 3 shows the positions of the spray nozzles and Figure 5 the spray pattern.

CHARACTERISATION OF DELUGE SYSTEMS

For each type of nozzle, at least 3 were randomly selected and checked by collecting and measuring the amount of water delivered to the nozzle in a specified time at the minimum and maximum water pressures used. The overall flow through the system was measured using a calibrated flow meter. For the non-standard 4.7 mm bore nozzles, the measured K factor was 13.2 compared to 10.0 quoted by the manufacturer. This may have been a calculated, rather than a measured value. The K factor for the 6.8 mm nozzles was found to be the 28.0 stated by the manufacturer.

A key element of the work was to characterise not only the water leaving the nozzles but also the amount of water covering the surface of the target vessels. Davies and Nolan[9, 10] (South Bank University) were tasked with:

- performing a more detailed characterisation of the spray (e.g. trajectories, droplet size and velocity); and
- characterising the water coverage of the vessel (e.g. water film thickness, surface water flow rate).

The measured (contact probe) film thicknesses for the minimum recommended rate system were slightly higher, 1.20 mm compared to 0.95 mm, than the Tentative Rule system but this is probably a function of the measuring technique used. In the early use of the film thickness instrumentation, measurements were made when the probe left the water film rather than when approaching it (as used in other deluge system measurements) and there may have been surface tension effects. The results suggest that, within the limits of experimental error, there was very little difference in water film thickness between the systems. Hence putting more water on the surface of the vessel will lead to an increased flow rate across the surface rather than an increased depth of water film.

The results from the water coverage experiments, measured by sealing a collection device to different points of the vessels surface, are summarised in Table 1. The surface water flow rate values varied considerably across the surface of each of the vessels. In most cases, the surface water flow rate was lowest over the bottom surface of the vessels, suggesting that water running down the tank was falling from the surface of the vessels just after passing the tank equator. The results from the systems where the top and bottom rows were not staggered (as recommended in NFPA 15 but not the Tentative Rules) indicated that the surface water flow rates were generally higher at positions between nozzles, where the spray patterns overlapped. This was confirmed by a series of later, detailed experiments by Davies and Nolan[9, 10]. The effect of increased water concentration between nozzles appears to increase with increasing pressure. The deluge system designed to provide the minimum recommended rate (9.8 dm³ m⁻² min⁻¹) actually gave a mean surface water flow rate well below this. The deluge system designed in accordance with the Tentative Rules gave a mean surface water flow rate nominally in excess of the recommended rate. However, the rate varied significantly across the surface of the vessel.

Table 1. WATER COVERAGE

System	Between (B) or Opposite (O) nozzles	Water pressure (barg)	Surface water flow rate (dm^3 m^{-2} min^{-1})			
			Top front	Front centre	Lower front	Mean
Minimum recommended rate	O/B *	2.0		4.2	4.8	5.1
	O/B *	2.0		7.1	5.5	
	O/B *	7.0		5.0	9.8	8.1
	O/B *	7.0		11.6	6.4	
Tentative Rules	B	1.4		13.7	14.9	10.0 ±4.4
	O	1.4	10.8	8.4	4.3	
	B	2.0		16.4	16.3	10.6 ±4.7
	O	2.0	11.5	8.0	2.8	

*   Top and bottom nozzles staggered

EXPERIMENTAL SET-UP

TARGET VESSELS
Two target vessels were used. The first vessel (see Figure 4) was similar to those used in failure mode trials[11] and was used unpressurised in case it was weakened in the fire trials. The second vessel (see Figure 5) was used from new for validation trials in which it was filled with propane and where the deluge system was expected to prevent the shell temperature from significantly exceeding 100 °C. The dimensions of the vessels are summarised in Table 2.

Each target vessel was mounted on a steel I-beam frame located in a pit in a concrete pad. This pit was filled with water during the trials to protect the support frame.

Table 2. TARGET VESSEL DIMENSIONS

Parameter	Vessel used for phase 1 to 4 trials	Vessel used for phase 5 trials
General shape	Horizontal bullet	Horizontal bullet
End caps	1.9 : 1 Semi-ellipsoidal	2 : 1 Semi-ellipsoidal
Overall length	4064 mm	4064 mm
Length of parallel sections	3276 mm	3370 mm
Outside diameter of parallel sections	1200 mm	1240 mm
Surface area	15.6 m^2	16.3 m^2
Thickness of parallel sections (minimum)	7.1 mm	10 mm
Thickness of end sections (minimum)	7.2 mm	8.5 mm

JET FIRE
The jet fire consisted of a 2 kg s^{-1} flashing-liquid propane discharge from a 80° basic fan nozzle with the long axis of the elliptical opening in a vertical orientation. The supply system consisted of six 1.7 tonne propane storage vessels, which were over- pressurised with nitrogen (nitrogen is slightly soluble in propane but this had only a marginal effect on the flame characteristics) to maintain the propane at just above its vapour pressure at the point of

discharge. Since the nitrogen control system was relatively crude and the trials duration short, the same nitrogen start pressure (11 barg) was used for each experiment. The point of discharge was 1.30 m above the ground and aimed at the centre of the vessel, 0.05 m below its base. The distance between the point of discharge and the target vessel was varied between 1.0, 2.5, 3.0, 3.5 and 4.5 m. The set-up was chosen to expose the vessel to the most onerous conditions of the jet-fire. Discharge 4.5m from the vessel resulting in almost complete fire engulfment (at least 85% of the vessel surface was engulfed, the fall off occurring at the two end caps). Previous work has shown that this is sufficient to bring an unprotected vessel to failure within 5 minutes[11]. At shorter discharge distances to the target vessel, the fire is not so developed, but the force of the discharge is greater.

INSTRUMENTATION
As the primary measure of the success or failure of the deluge systems was the shell temperatures, only details of the type K thermocouple positions on the shell are given here. The metal temperature was measured at a number of points using 3 mm, stainless steel-sheathed, type K thermocouples attached to the surface of the vessel. In each case, a 60 x 12 x 3 mm steel plate was grooved 2.5 mm deep using a 3 mm diameter spherical milling tool. The plate, with the thermocouple in place, was clamped to the vessel and then metal-sprayed in position. The spray coating and plate were ground to a smooth finish. This held each thermocouple tightly to the vessel surface and protected it from direct flame impingement. The thermocouples were positioned as shown in Figures 6 and 7 in terms of their horizontal position left or right of the central weld and the angle from the top around the circumference of the vessel. It was not possible to place the thermocouples symmetrically at the top and bottom of the vessel because of the positions of the valves and support legs.

EXPERIMENTAL PROCEDURE
Before each series of trials, the system was flushed and clean nozzles were fitted in the appropriate pattern. The water pressure was set and checked for correct operation. After starting the deluge and allowing the spray pattern to be established, the propane supply valves were opened and propane ignited. Thereafter, the flame pattern and its effect on the tank were observed and recorded. For the delayed deluge initiation trials, the flame was first established and after the required delay time the water was started and observations made on whether the vessel was adequately cooled. The delay times quoted are the times from ignition of the propane to full water pressure being achieved. The water deluge target tank was heated until one of the following conditions prevailed:

(i)   The tank shell temperatures stabilised at close to 100 °C or less, and no dry spots were observed on areas of the vessel surface remote from the thermocouple locations, showing that the water deluge was effective in protecting the tank;

(ii)   One or more of the tank shell or support feet temperatures exceeded 200 °C and continued to climb, showing that the water deluge was not effective in protecting the tank; or

(iii)   Dry spots were seen to develop on areas of the tank surface remote from the thermocouple locations, showing that the water deluge was not effective in protecting the tank.

In order to minimise any damage to the vessel, the tests were stopped as soon as the temperatures had stabilised or it was clear that they were not going to stabilise. The deluge was continued after the flame was extinguished until the vessel returned to ambient temperature.

For the validation trial on the 20% full propane vessel, before the vessel was filled, the plastic and aluminium level gauge (in the top of the vessel) was replaced by a steel blanking plate in order to prevent premature failure. The water spray was started and set to 2 barg water pressure. The water deluge system was established and stabilised at the required settings before application of the jet fire. The criteria used for the deluge system being effective in protecting the vessel were that the shell temperatures should not exceed 100 °C and no dry spots should develop. The test would be terminated if:

(i)   Dry spots were formed.

(ii)   Any of the measured temperatures exceeded 120 °C.

(iii)   Any of the fittings, e.g. pressure relief valve, showed signs of failure.

Towards the end of the trial, the water deluge was turned off for one minute and then restarted to ascertain if the vessel temperatures would recover. Approximately 5 s was required for the water pressure to build from 0 barg to 2 barg or decay from 2 barg to 0 barg. One minute was chosen as the interval for interruption of the water supply. This was the time required for the vessel surface to reach 300 °C and was considered sufficient to observe any dry spots, which might have been obscured from the monitoring cameras by the steam and flames. The nominal temperature of ca. 300 °C was chosen because, above this, damage to the target vessel was expected to occur. The water deluge was allowed to continue after the flame was extinguished until the vessel surface returned to ambient temperature.

For the nominally empty vessel trial, the vessel was emptied of propane and the pressure transducers and emergency dump line were removed. A plug was removed from the top of the vessel to prevent pressure build up. The plastic and aluminium level gauge was re-inserted in the top of the vessel to determine if the deluge provides sufficient protection of the gauge. The same operating procedure was used as for the filled vessel except that the test was terminated if the shell temperature exceeded 300 °C rather than 120 °C.

EFFECTIVENESS OF THE MINIMUM RECOMMENDED RATE

The effectiveness of the deluge system designed to give the minimum recommended rate was assessed using five different propane release stand-off distances (1.0, 2.5, 3.0, 3.5 and 4.5 m). In order to help avoid damaging the vessel, these trials were performed with the vessel 20% full of water. The initial trials, at a water deluge pressure of 2.0 barg, indicated that the system was not capable of protecting the vessel. The most severe effects to the vessel occurred at a propane stand-off distance of 1.0 m, giving most heat input to the back of the target vessel, and at 3.0 m giving most heat input to the front. The water pressure was then increased in steps to determine if, at higher flow rates, the vessel could be protected using the original nozzle arrangement. Water pressures of 2, 3, 4, 6 and 7.3 barg (the maximum available at the time) were used. The maximum temperatures (over 100 °C) at each circumferential angle are summarised in Table 3, and the maximum temperatures for each pressure are plotted in Figure 8.

At higher water discharge pressures of 6 barg and above), the recorded maximum temperatures fell broadly within the conditions (i) specified for the tests. However, the variation in temperature profiles indicated that the deluge system was not fully controlling the jet fire. The tank temperatures below the water fill level only exceeded 100 °C at the right hand end of the vessel and on the legs. This confirmed that the vapour space wall of the vessel is that which is most vulnerable to excessive heating.

Table 3. MAXIMUM TEMPERATURES FOR TRIALS WITH 3.0 M STAND-OFF

Test No.	Water pressure (barg)	Temperatures over 100 °C (angle at each circumferential position*)								
		A	B	C	D	E	F	G	H	Leg
W26	2				210 (045)	250 (045)	325 (022)	440 (045)	160 (180)	500(R)
W25	3						132 (022)	380 (045)		390 (R)
W24	4				230 (045)	375 (045)	360 (022)	275 (045)		235 (R)
W23	6							125 (045)		170 (R)
W22	7.3					220 (045)	130 (022)	170 (045)		170 (R)

* 0° = top, 090° = front, 180° = bottom and 270° = back

EFFECTIVENESS OF SYSTEM NOMINALLY DESIGNED TO THE TENTATIVE RULES

The effectiveness of the deluge system designed to give the minimum recommended rate was assessed using five different propane release stand-off distances (1.0, 2.5, 3.0, 3.5 and 4.5 m). As the trials on the deluge system designed to give the minimum recommended rate indicated that the maximum heat transfer to the target vessel occurred at 1.0 and 3.0 m propane release stand-off distances, these were used for the trials on the deluge system designed to the Tentative Rules. The system was run at water pressures of 1.4, 2.0, 2.7 and 3.5 barg; i.e within the range permitted by the Tentative Rules. As noted above, due to the effect that the water fill has, it was decided to use the target vessel empty for subsequent trials in order to be able to detect any hot spots at the base of the vessel.

No temperatures over 100 °C were recorded and no dry spots were observed in any of the trials performed with a water pressure of 2.0 barg or more. Even at 1.4 barg water pressure, there were no temperatures of more than 112 °C recorded, although visual observation indicated a dry spot in the trial with a 3.0 m stand-off distance. The results of the trials at 1.4 and 2.0 barg water pressure and with a 3.0 m stand-off distance are compared in Table 4.

Table 4. MAXIMUM TEMPERATURES FOR TRIALS WITH 3.0 M STAND-OFF

Test no.	Water pressure (barg)	Time (min)	Maximum temperature (Celsius) at measurement time (angle at circumferential position - see Figure 6)								
			A	B	C	D	E	F	G	H	Leg
W84	1.4	6	93 (000)	98 (045)	112 (045)	101 (045)	95 (000)	98 (022)	91 (045)	76 (000)	80 (L)
W85	2.0	6	71 (180)	100 (045)	96 (045)	99 (045)	93 (090)	95 (045)	94 (045)	52 (180)	66 (L)

The results suggest that, for the 3.0 m jet-fire stand-off distance, a water deluge pressure of 1.4 barg does not prevent formation of dry spots but pressures of 2.0 barg or more are effective.

EFFECT OF BLOCKED NOZZLES

A survey by Blything[12] of LPG installations fitted with water deluge systems suggested that at least one blocked nozzle was likely to be found on every installation and a reasonable probability of two. Given the relatively high risk of such an occurrence, it was considered advisable to investigate the effects of blocked nozzles. The triangle of nozzles 1.5 m from the right end of the frame were chosen for the trials as any wind tended to skew the flames in this direction. Hence, to determine the effect of blocked nozzles, nozzles 11 (top), 3 (front) +11 (top) and 3 (front) + 7 (back) +11 (top) (see Figure 3) were blocked off in turn. A 2.0 barg water pressure was used with propane jet release point stand-off distances of 1.0 and 3.0 m.

With the top nozzle (11 - see Figure 3) blanked-off, a large dry spot, which extended down the front of the vessel at the F band and towards the E and G bands, started to form after 2 minutes. The maximum temperatures in the E, F and G bands are illustrated in Table 5 with temperatures over 100 °C highlighted.

Table 5. MAXIMUM TEMPERATURES (°C) WITH ONE TOP NOZZLE BLOCKED

Position	Front	E	F	G	Back	E	F	G
Top	0°	231	379		0°	231	379	
	22°	136	438		337°	-	165	
	45°	93	423	94	315°	92	95	92
	67°				292°	93		
Middle	90°	92	91		270°	85	88	
	112°				247°		88	
	135°	80	82	85	225°		83	
Bottom	180°	80	85		180°	80	85	

In the trial (W72) with the top (11) and front (3) nozzles blocked (see Figure 3), dry spots developed within 20 s and the temperatures exceeded 300 °C in the E, F and G bands. The maximum temperatures recorded are indicated in Table 6 with temperatures over 100 °C again highlighted.

Table 6. MAX. TEMP. (°C) WITH ONE TOP & FRONT NOZZLE BLOCKED

Position	Front	E	F	G	Back	E	F	G
Top	0°		386		0°		386	
	22°	221	488		337°		192	
	45°	199	499	95	315°	94	98	95
	67°				292°	94		
Middle	90°	392	447		270°	86	91	
	112°				247°		90	
	135°	277	323	372	225°		87	
Bottom	180°	133	118		180°	133	118	

With three blanked-off nozzles(3, 7 and 11 - see Figure 4), dry spots were first noted after 25 s on the F band. The dry spot increased in area around the front of the vessel and then extended round to the back of the vessel. The temperature reached 400 °C at the F 22°, E 90° and G 135° positions in less than 3 minutes. The maximum temperatures are illustrated in Table 7 with temperatures over 100°C again highlighted.

The results from the single blocked nozzle trials suggest that the water film breaks-down in the region of the blocked nozzle, resulting in a dry patch. The shell temperature in the dry patch can reach a temperature at which there is a significant reduction in steel strength. Hence, even with a single blocked nozzle, there is a real risk of vessel failure in a jet fire, although whether that would inevitably lead to catastrophic failure is unknown at this time.

Table 7. MAX. TEMP. (^{O}C) WITH 1 TOP, FRONT & BACK NOZZLE BLOCKED

Position	Front	E	F	G	Back	E	F	G
Top	0°	255	438		0°			
	22°	290	488		337°		292	
	45°	224	483	193	315°	96	173	96
	67°				292°	97		
Middle	90°	468	470		270°			
	112°				247°		232	
	135°		371	413	225°	342	226	
Bottom	180°	226	314		180°	226	314	

With two or three adjacent blocked nozzles, large dry patches are formed. This would almost certainly allow the shell to reach the temperature (ca. 650 °C) where the vessel would fail. However, though large dry patches are formed, there is still a reduction (by at least a factor of two) compared to the corresponding unprotected tank trial[10] in heat transferred to the vessel. This suggests that additional time would be available, for example, to direct water from a portable fire pump onto the dry patch. It is not clear from the available data as to how effective this would be.

EFFECT OF DELAYED DELUGE INITIATION

Deluge systems may be triggered automatically by gas or flame detection or manually. In most cases, it is likely that a vessel may be enveloped in fire before the deluge system comes fully into action. Accordingly, a series of trials were performed in which the target vessel was enveloped in flame prior to the application of water. The delay time was progressively increased from 17 s to 160 s. The nominal 2 kg s^{-1} propane jet fire used will cause some regions of an unprotected vessel wall[10] to reach temperatures of ca. 650 °C in 160 s. At this temperature, there is a significant risk of catastrophic vessel failure.

Lev and Strachan[13] suggest that 120 °C is the critical steel substrate temperature at which there is breakdown of a water film. The results suggest that the unprotected vessel shell needs to be heated for about 25 s to reach this temperature. Hence, as might be expected, there was full recovery (all shell temperatures at or below 100 °C) with a 17 s and, initially, a 24 s delay. However, in the 24 s delay trial, the temperature started rising after 3 minutes at the F 45° position and reached 208 °C after initially cycling between 100 and 120 °C. In general, dry patches were difficult to see through the flames. However, in this case, visual observation suggested that there was a small dry spot immediately downstream of the thermocouple housing. This may imply that small protrusions on the vessel surface, e.g. from a type approval plate, can have a significant effect on the water film and hence the degree of protection. This effect was not observed in the 32 s delay trial. However, in this case, the temperature at the E 180° position (bottom of vessel) reached 120 °C after two minutes and stayed at this temperature until the flames were extinguished. It is possible that any "shadow" effects are magnified if the vessel is heated above 120 °C before applying the water. In the trial with 44 s delay, all the temperatures recovered to 100 °C except at the 45° position at the centre/front of the vessel where they reduced to 120 °C. However, in the 63 s and 100 s delay trials, all the temperatures recovered within 75 s of applying the water. In the final delay trial (160 s), the vessel was taken to over 600 °C before applying the water. Even under these extreme conditions, where an unprotected vessel would fail[9] within another 90 s, the temperature fell to 100 °C at most, although not all, measuring points. At one position, the temperature reached 299 °C and the temperature was still increasing at about 0.7 K s^{-1}. Hence the vessel was kept at temperatures below which there was no loss in steel strength for delayed deluge application times up to 100 s. It was found, therefore, that recovery (i.e. all temperatures $\leq 100\ °C$) was possible for delay times up to 100 s but this could not always be relied upon.

EFFECT OF THE VESSEL CONTENTS

The previous phases of the experimental work utilised an unpressurised vessel as the jet-fire target. In addition, most of the trials described in the open literature involved using, either water filled or empty, unpressurised target vessels and, therefore, it was considered that validation trial(s) on a vessel filled with propane should be performed. The trials were designed to demonstrate that a water deluge system, shown to protect an unpressurised vessel against a ca. 2 kg s^{-1} flashing liquid propane jet fire, will be effective when applied to a 20% full propane vessel. Two trials were performed:

(a)   A remote controlled long duration trial on a 20% full propane vessel to determine the effectiveness of the system developed;

(b)   A long duration trial on the empty vessel to determine if the vessel contents influenced the results and to allow close observation of the system behaviour.

Each trial incorporated a one-minute period, with the water diverted away from the vessel, to determine if recovery (i.e. all shell temperatures decreasing to 100 °C or below) occurred.

20% FULL VESSEL

The temperatures at bands B, C, D, E and F were reasonably stable, remaining under 100 °C whilst the water deluge was on (for example, see the band D temperatures in Figure 9). The highest shell temperatures experienced by the vessel during the deluge were at the 45° and 90° circumferential positions (on all bands) and the lowest were at the bottom-back of the vessel. All the temperatures of the shell and fittings remained below 100 °C until the water was diverted away from the vessel for one minute after 40 minutes. A photograph showing a typical fire engulfment is shown in Figure 10.

At 40 minutes, whilst the water deluge was diverted for one minute, temperatures around the bottom of the vessel rose typically by about 25 °C. This was true for bands B, C, D, E and G particularly at a circumferential position of 315°. Temperatures around the top of the vessel stayed around 100 °C except at the B and F 90° positions. Here, a hot spot developed and a temperature of 163 °C was recorded at 41 minutes, just before the water deluge was restored. For the next minute, the temperature continued to increase to 235 °C (though the water deluge had been reapplied) but, within a further minute, this had returned to under 100 °C. Thermocouples on or between the valves also recorded temperatures over 100 °C whilst the water deluge was off. These results were consistent with the results from the 63 s delay time trial but not with the 24 s trial where a significant temperature excursion occurred.

At 41 minutes, the combination valve registered a temperature of 157 °C and the vessel shell adjacent to the combination valve registered a temperature of 105 °C. Over the next minute, both increased in temperature to 231 °C and 153 °C, respectively, recovering to below 100 °C when water was reapplied.

The pressure relief valve (PRV) opened after nearly 20.7 minutes at a pressure of 18.2 bara (see Figure 11). It remained open for about 40 s before closing at 15.1 bara. The pressure then rose to 17.9 bara when the PRV opened again. The PRV cycled open and shut 5 times during the trial with the opening pressure slightly lower each time but the closing pressure staying fairly constant. The cycling rate reduced in frequency as the trial progressed but increased again whilst the water was off.

The results suggested that the water deluge system had given 40 minutes fire protection and that this would be maintained as long as water could be supplied at the required rate.

EMPTY PROPANE TANK

The temperatures at bands B, C, D, F and G were reasonably stable, remaining under 100 °C until the water deluge was first turned off at 24 minutes. The only exception was at the band E 45° position (see Figure 12). At this position, the temperature rose above 100 °C after 9.9 minutes and reached 163 °C after a further 30 seconds and then decreased to 100 °C before beginning a major temperature excursion. The temperature reached a maximum of 359 °C at 14 minutes and then reduced to below 100 °C after a further 3 minutes and remained below 100 °C until the water was diverted at 24 minutes.

When the water was diverted at 24 minutes, the shell temperatures rose rapidly reaching a maximum of 410 °C at the C 45° position. The maximum temperatures at each band were all close to the 45° position. When the water was restored to the spray nozzles, the temperatures at all positions, except the 180° positions, were reduced to below 100 °C. At the C, D and E bottom (180°) vessel positions, the temperature reached 185, 237 and 240 °C respectively, by the times the flames were extinguished. This corresponded to observed dry spots. Similar behaviour, with the 180° position temperatures exceeding 100 °C was observed in the 32 s and 160 s delay time trials. Hence it appears that, with the deluge system used, hot spots that do not recover on application of water can develop along the bottom of an empty vessel.

The top fittings reached a maximum temperature of 91 °C before the water was diverted at 24 minutes. The bottom fittings and legs reached a maximum of 88 °C. The front of the PRV reached 328 °C when the water was diverted and the front left leg reached 195 °C. All the top and bottom fittings, and the legs, recovered to below 100 °C when the water was restored. The level gauge, made from aluminium with a plastic lens and Viton seal, was subjected to the empty vessel test (W90) and a subsequent 10 minute demonstration trial (W91) included a total of two minute fire engulfment without water deluge protection. The plastic lens melted but both the aluminium body and the Viton seal remained undamaged. It is likely that it would have continued to hold the pressure if the vessel had contained propane. During the empty vessel trial (W90), the brass pressure relief valve on top of the vessel was subjected to the full protected period of the test and one minute of fire engulfment. Shortly after the jet flames were extinguished and whilst the water deluge was still operating, the PRV spring popped and fell on the floor allowing the valve to remain open. The brass retaining / adjusting ring had distorted causing the threads to disengage.

COMPARISON OF FULL AND EMPTY VESSEL

It would be expected that the biggest differences in temperature would be at the bottom of the vessel since, at this position, the shell of the vessel containing propane will be cooled by the liquid propane inside the vessel as well as the water on the surface. The mean temperatures at the 180° position were nearly 20 °C lower for the 20% full vessel than for the empty vessel.

COMPARISON WITH DELUGE SYSTEM DESIGNED IN ACCORDANCE WITH NFPA 15

HSE had sponsored work (Bennett[14] et al.) to investigate the fire protection afforded by a water deluge system designed to NFPA 15 on a LPG vessel. The vessel had the following dimensions: length of parallel section 7.50 m; depth of end caps 0.64 m; diameter of tank 2.17 m; and area of tank 61.3 m^2. The deluge system was nominally designed for an offshore facility (Shirvill and White[15]) to achieve a minimum application rate of 10.2 dm^3 m^{-2} min^{-1} over the whole exposed surface of the vessel. The deluge system comprised four rows of six stainless steel nozzles (7.4 mm bore, $110°$ spray angle, K factor 34) with ca. 0.65 m stand-off distances. The total water delivery rate was 1064 dm^3 min^{-1}. A 2.4 barg inlet line pressure was used to give a pressure of 1.4 barg at the furthest nozzle. The calculated mean pressure for the system was 1.57 barg. The application rate was therefore nominally 1064 / 61.3 = 17.4 dm^3 m^{-2} min^{-1}. Subsequent characterisation of the system by Davies and Nolan[9, 10] indicated that the actual coverage varied widely over the surface of the vessel, with spot readings as low as 2.6 dm^3 m^{-2} min^{-1} recorded at the top of the vessel. A photograph showing the deluge system in operation is presented in Figure 13.

The tests involved a wider range of propane jet sizes, extending up to 9 kg s^{-1}. The results with a ca. 2 kg s^{-1} propane jet, at 1.0, 3.0 and 5.0 m propane release stand-off distances (the jet was aimed at the centre of the vessel), were similar to those obtained in the HSL trials using the water deluge system designed to deliver the minimum recommended rate when run at 4 barg. This, with a calculated application rate of 16.6 dm^3 m^{-2} min^{-1}, most closely compares with that for the NFPA system of 17.4 dm^3 m^{-2} min^{-1}. In both, hot spots (temperatures above 120 °C) were observed near to the top of the vessel. Similar results were obtained using a 6 kg s^{-1} propane jet. With the 9 kg s^{-1} propane jet hot spots were recorded in the region of the centre/front of the vessel.

The 17.4 dm^3 m^{-2} min^{-1} calculated application rate was considerable lower than the 31 dm^3 m^{-2} min^{-1} shown by HSL to be required to protect an empty shell against a 2 kg s^{-1} jet fire.

CONCLUSIONS

The overall conclusions were as follows:

- Existing industrial directed water deluge systems cannot be relied upon to maintain a water film over the whole of the surface of a vessel in an impinging jet scenario. However, by using additional water (up to double) to the amount normally applied, protection can be provided against at least a ca. 2 kg s^{-1} flashing liquid propane jet fire. Protection might be achieved with lower amounts of water if the deluge system was optimised to give the greatest and most uniform surface water flow rate. At present, no guidance or design tools appear to exist, which allow such optimisation.

- The evidence suggests that industrial deluge systems may be designed to the Tentative Rules or NFPA 15 or to an ad hoc design. Systems designed according to NFPA 15 have fewer restrictions on the nozzle specification and spacial arrangement and, in practice, are likely to deliver less water than a system designed according to the Tentative Rules.

- The apparent current practice of designing directed water deluge systems on the basis of the water exiting the spray nozzles masks the variation in water coverage of the vessel that occurs and is therefore considered to be a poor measure. It is recommended that, instead, the amount of water actually flowing over the surface of the vessel should be used in the design specification.

- The successful performance of directed water deluge systems has been found to be critical upon all the spray nozzles functioning correctly and the deluge system coming fully into action within 100s.

- Indications are that careful attention needs to be given to the provision of additional spray nozzles to protect vessel fittings and where obstructions, such as gantries are present, to ensure they do not disrupt the required flow of water over the vessel surface.

- The above conclusions suggest there is clear need for improved validated guidance on the design of directed water deluge systems.
- The conclusions given above relate to deluge systems for horizontal, cylindrical vessels. Whilst guidance is given in the Tentative Rules for spherical vessels, there is no validation of the requirements. There appears to be no United Kingdom guidance at all on vertical, cylindrical vessels.

REFERENCES

1. LP Gas Association, 1998, Code of Practice 1, Bulk LPG Storage at Fixed Installations Part 1: Design, Installation and Operation of Vessels Located above Ground.
2. Bray, G. A., 1964, Fire protection of liquid petroleum gas storage tanks, *Institute of Gas Engineers Journal,* **Nov**: 776-789.
3. Billinge, K., Moodie, K. and Beckett, H., 1986, The use of water sprays to protect engulfed LPG storage tanks, *5th Int. Symp., Loss Prevention and Safety Promotion in the Process Industries,* Cannes.
4. National Fire Protection Association, 1996, Water spray fixed systems for fire protection, Boston (USA), NFPA.
5. American Petroleum Institute, 1989, Design and construction of liquefied petroleum gas (LPG) installations, Washington D.C. (USA), API.
6. Institute of Petroleum, 1987, Liquefied Petroleum Gas, Vol. 1, Large bulk pressure storage and refrigerated LPG, London (UK), John Wiley and Sons.
7. Fire Offices' Committee, 1979, Tentative rules for medium and high velocity water spray systems.
8. Loss Prevention Council, 1996, Rules for automatic sprinkler installations (including BS 5306: Part 2 : 1996 and the relevant LPC Technical Bulletins to June 1997).
9. Davies, G. and Nolan, P. (to be published), The water film depth and water flow rate on the surface of a Liquefied Petroleum Gas (LPG) tank protected by a water deluge system, *J. Loss Prev. in the Process Industries.*
10. Davies G and Nolan P (to be published), Surface water distributions arising from deluge systems designed to protect industrial liquefied petroleum gas (LPG) tanks from fire, *J. Loss Prev. in the Process* Industries.
11. Roberts, T. A., Gosse, A. and Hawksworth, S., 2000, Thermal radiation from fireballs on failure of liquefied petroleum gas storage vessels, *Trans. IChemE Hazards*, Vol. 78, Part B: 184 – 192.
12. Blything, K. W., 1983, The fire hazards and counter measures for the protection of pressurized liquid petroleum gas storage on industrial sites, UKAEA Report SRD R 263.
13. Lev, Y. and Strachan, D. C., 1989, A study of cooling water requirements for the protection of metal surfaces against thermal radiation, *Fire Technology*, **25**(3): 213-229.
14. Bennett, J. F., Shirvill, L. C. and Pritchard, M. J., 1997, Efficacy of water spray protection against jet fires impinging on LPG storage vessels, HSE Contract Research Report 137/1997, ISBN 0 7176 1395 X.
15. Shirvill, L. C. and White, G. C., 1994, Effectiveness of deluge systems in protecting plant and equipment impacted by high-velocity natural gas jet fires, ICHMT International Symposium on heat and mass transfer in chemical process industry accidents, Rome, 1994.

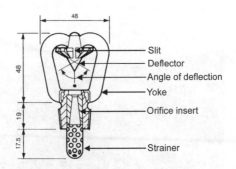

Figure 1. MEDIUM VELOCITY NOZZLE

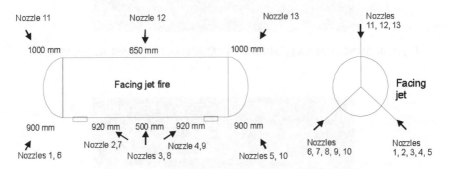

Figure 2. NOZZLE ARRANGEMENT TO GIVE HSE MINIMUM RATE

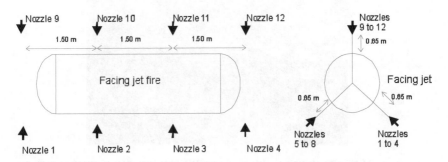

Figure 3. NOZZLE ARRANGEMENT TO GIVE TENTATIVE RULE RATE

Figure 4. MINIMUM RATE SPRAY PATTERN ON UNPRESSURISED VESSEL

Figure 5. TENTATIVE RULE SPRAY PATTERN ON 20% FULL PROPANE TANK

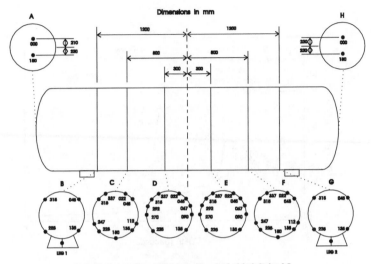

Angles in degrees (0 = top of tank. 90 = front of tank facing jet)

Figure 6. THERMOCOUPLE POSITIONS ON UNPRESSURISED VESSEL

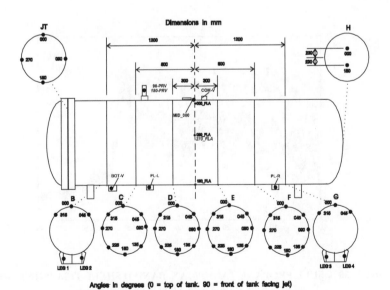

Angles in degrees (0 = top of tank. 90 = front of tank facing jet)

Figure 7. THERMOCOUPLE POSITIONS ON PROPANE TANK

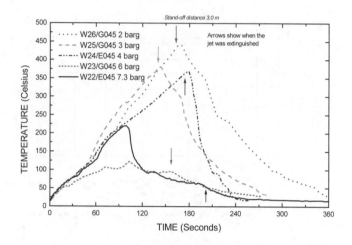

Figure 8. MAXIMUM SHELL TEMPERATURES VS. WATER DELUGE PRESSURE
(Recommended minimum rate system with 3.0 m propane stand-off)

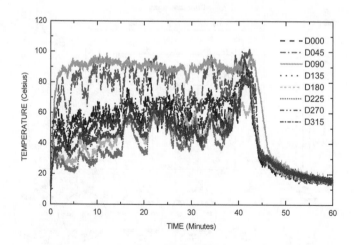

Figure 9. 20% FULL PROPANE TANK: MAX. BAND D SHELL TEMPERATURES
(Tentative Rule system with 3.0 m propane stand-off)

Figure 10. FIRE ENGULFMENT OF 20% FULL PROPANE TANK

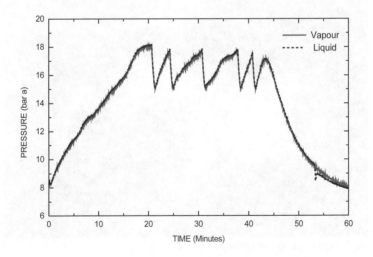

Figure 11. PROPANE VAPOUR AND LIQUID PRESSURES

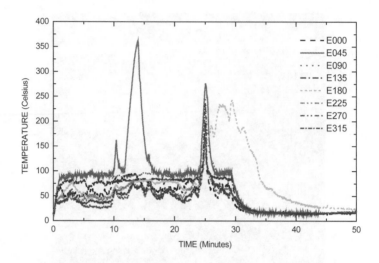

Figure 12. EMPTY TANK BAND E SHELL TEMPERATURES
(Tentative Rule system with 3.0 m propane stand-off)

[Courtesy of J Bennett, Shell Global Solutions]

Figure 13. SHELL DELUGE SYSTEM: FLAMES FROM 2 KG S^{-1} PROPANE JET

EXPLOSION VENTING OF BUCKET ELEVATORS

P Holbrow*, G. A. Lunn*, A. Tyldesley**
*Health and Safety Laboratory, Harpur Hill, Buxton, Derbyshire, SK17 9JN
**Health and Safety Executive,TD5, Magdalen House, Bootle, Merseyside.

This paper is a report of an experimental programme on the explosion protection of bucket elevators by venting. The project was a collaborative effort with funding by the Health and Safety Executive and manufacturers and users of bucket elevators through the British Materials Handling Board. Two bucket elevators were used in the project — a single leg elevator and a twin-leg elevator. Four dusts were used with K_{St} values up to 211 bar m s^{-1} and dust clouds were produced by dust injection and by normal operation. Reduced explosion pressures were measured and guidance has been derived from the results. This guidance is in terms of vent spacing as a function of the K_{St} value of the dust.

INTRODUCTION

Bucket elevators are widely used in the handling of large quantities of bulk powders, and are normally the preferred means of conveying where long vertical lifts are required for free flowing powders/granular products. As such they are to be found in nearly all animal feed mills, bulk grain stores, and many of the larger installations handling powders in the food industry. Powder or granular products inevitably spill from the buckets during operation, and fall down the up-leg of the elevator. The finer materials is likely to remain in suspension, while the coarser material falls back to the boot. At the top of the elevator, while most of the powder will discharge down the off-take chute, some will inevitably be carried over, into the down leg of the elevator. Thus both legs are likely to contain a dust cloud of unknown concentration, constantly agitated by the moving buckets, all the time the elevator is in operation. Various sources of ignition are foreseeable in such units and explosion incidents have been reported.

Explosion venting is one method for explosion protection of bucket elevators. The current Institution of Chemical Engineers guidance requires that the vents – equal in cross sectional area to the limb – are positioned according to the guidance for ducting. Alternatively, a spacing of 6 m between vents is used. The guidance also requires that the top casing and the boot must be explosion relieved[1].

There is, however, no evidence that this guidance spells out the optimum venting requirements of elevators, and there is little published work on elevator explosion tests. Gillis and Fishlock[2] carried out venting and suppression experiments on a twin leg elevator and some guidance was given.

The current project was a collaborative effort by the Health and Safety Executive and manufacturers and users of bucket elevators through the British Materials Handling Board.

EXPERIMENTAL

Two bucket elevators have been used in this programme: a single leg elevator and a double leg elevator. Both elevators were mounted in a tower with access levels at 2.7 m intervals.

SINGLE LEG ELEVATOR
A schematic diagram of the elevator is shown in Figure 1. The single leg steel casing is

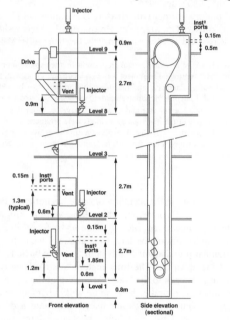

Figure 1 Single leg bucket elevator

rectangular in shape, with a cross section of 1.22 m x 0.945 m in which the chain linked buckets of nominal dimensions 540 mm wide x 280 mm x 390 mm with a spacing of approximately 450 mm, run up and down. It has a fixed speed drive mounted at the head of the elevator powered by an 11 kW motor and gearbox that drives the buckets at a speed of approximately 35 m/min. The drive pulley and a deflector pulley are mounted within the head of the elevator and a return pulley is mounted at the boot of the elevator.

Explosion relief vents were installed at each level, including the top face of the elevator, with dimensions equal to the nominal cross section of the elevator casing (1.22 mm x 0.945 m), apart from level 8 where, because of the restriction of supporting steel members, a slightly smaller vent was installed – 0.945 m x 0.7 m. Plastic vent panel closures were used for the majority of the tests. Stainless steel vent panels were also used in some of the tests.

Dust injection cylinders were located at each of the nine levels at intervals of 2.7 m. Their position at each level alternated from side to side. An ignition source could be fitted at level 1, level 5 or level 9 (see Figure 1).

TWIN LEG ELEVATOR
The twin-leg elevator (Figure 2) was supplied by Carier Bulk Materials Handling Ltd and represents a typical elevator used in the bulk handling industry. The casing was designed to a stronger specification than normal to enable it to withstand the high explosion pressures. The

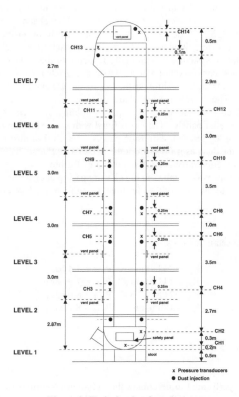

Figure2 Twin leg bucket elevator

elevator head, boot and a 1.5 m long leg section were each hydrostatically tested to 1.5 bar g. The overall height from the base of the boot to the top of the head section was 17.75 m

The maximum dimensions of the steel buckets were 308 mm wide x 175 mm deep x 130 mm high and were bolted to the 320 mm wide rubber belt. The belt was driven by the 0.6 m diameter crowned head pulley at a speed of 3 m/s. Typically, when full to capacity, each bucket would carry approximately 1.7 kg of cornflour or 1.3 kg of milk powder. Discharge takes place by centrifugal action as the buckets pass around the head pulley.

The design clearances are approximately: between the tip of the buckets and the front of the casing: 70 mm, between the sides of the buckets and casing: 41 mm and between the rear of the belt and the casing: 55 mm.

Explosion relief vent openings were installed at approximately 3 m intervals on both legs and measured 305 mm wide x 457 mm high (0.139 m^2). The bottom edge of the first relief panel was 2.875 m from the base. A single explosion vent was located at the side of the head. The cleaning door at the boot was modified to incorporate a safety panel designed protect the boot in the event of excessive pressure. This was covered with a strong burst panel having a bursting pressure in excess of 400 mbar.

Dust could be dispersed into the elevator using a pressure injection system or by a recirculation system. Dust was injected into each leg at each level simultaneously via nozzles located flush with the inside of the casing. Pairs of nozzles were positioned at each level. Seven injector assemblies were fitted to the elevator, one at each floor level.

In the recirculation system dust is initially loaded into the elevator via a chute at the bottom of the up-leg and conveyed to the head where it is discharged into a recycle leg. The discharged dust falls under gravity through the leg to the elevator inlet and is reconveyed back up the elevator. The recycle leg has a square cross section measuring 250 mm x 250 mm and incorporates an intermediate 2 m^3 capacity holding bin. The bin and the leg are protected by explosion relief panels. The bin is fitted with two explosion relief panels on the top face and the recycle leg has four explosion panels. Removal of dust from the elevator is achieved by directing the dust, as it flows from the bin, to a discharge duct by the operation of a diverter valve. The diverter valve is located 3 m below the bin.

The ignition source was installed in the elevator casing at either level 1 upleg (close to the boot), level 7 (close to the head of the elevator) or at an intermediate point in the leg. (See Figure 2).

THE DUSTS
Four dusts have been used in the tests:

Milk Powder:	K_{St} = 86 bar m s^{-1}, P_{max} = 7.4 bar g
Cornflour A:	K_{St} = 144 bar m s^{-1}, P_{max} = 7.9 bar g
Cornflour B:	K_{St} = 211 bar m s^{-1}, P_{max} = 8.0 bar g
Cornflour C:	K_{St} = 180 bar m s^{-1}, P_{max} = 8.7 bar g

EXPERIMENTAL RESULTS

SINGLE LEG ELEVATOR
A series of tests was performed to determine the optimum conditions of injection pressure, dust concentration and ignition delay that produced the highest explosion pressures. The optimum conditions were used throughout the main test programme.

Effect of Ignition Position
Three ignition positions have been used in the complete series of explosion tests – top (level 9), middle (level 5) and bottom (level 1) of the elevator. The results show that any one position is not significantly more hazardous than the others. There was a tendency, where the ignition source was located at level 1 or level 9, for the peak pressure to be measured at level 9. The likely causes of this are the congested elevator head with buckets, drive and deflection pulley wheels all mounted in close proximity – these would tend to cause restriction to the venting of the explosion and possibly enhanced turbulence.

When the igniter was located at level 5 the explosion propagated towards the head and the boot and resulted in peak pressures at a range of locations. Although there was no definite pattern to the location of the peak pressure, its most frequent location was at level 9.

Effect of Moving Buckets
The results showed that operation of the buckets had no significant effect on the reduced explosion pressure compared to when the buckets are stationary.

216

Measurements of Reduced Explosion Pressure
a) Cornflour B
Figure 3 shows all relevant test results using Cornflour B, with the reduced explosion

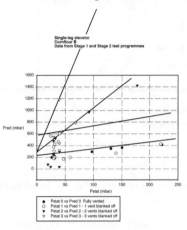

Figure 3 Reduced explosion pressure vs vent bursting pressure

pressure plotted against the vent opening pressure, P_{stat}. The points for different total vent areas have been enveloped by straight lines. From each of these lines, an upper value of the reduced explosion pressure at a P_{stat} of 0.1 bar has been estimated, and these pressures are plotted in Figure 4 against the total vent area. Similarly in Figure 5, reduced explosion pressures when P_{stat} equals 0.05 bar are plotted against total vent area. The total vent areas necessary to limit the reduced explosion pressure to either 0.5 bar g or 1 bar g have been marked on Figures 4 and 5.

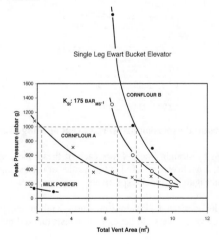

Figure 4 Explosion pressure vs total vent area at a vent opening pressure of 0.1 bar

Single Leg Ewart Bucket Elevator

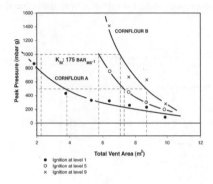

Figure 5 Explosion pressure vs total vent area at a vent bursting pressure of 0.05 bar.

b) Cornflour A

Figure 6 shows all relevant test results using Cornflour A. The points for different total vent

Single-leg elevator
Cornflour A
Data from Stage 1 & Stage 2 test programmes

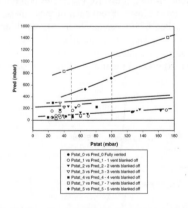

Figure 6 Reduced explosion pressure vs vent opening pressure

areas have been enveloped by straight lines. From each of these lines, upper values of the reduced explosion pressure have been estimated at P_{stat} values of 0.1 bar and 0.05 bar, and are plotted against vent area on Figures 4 and 5 respectively.

c) Milk Powder

Explosions of milk powder generated very low pressures, and, often, pressures were not sufficient to burst any of the vent covers. In the explosion tests that did burst the vent covers, pressures did not rise beyond the bursting pressure of the cover. These results are plotted in Figure 4.

TWIN LEG ELEVATOR

Because there is a relatively large space around the buckets in a single leg elevator, it is generally easy to propagate a flame through the entire casing. Figure 7 shows a cornflour

Figure 7   Cornflour explosion in single leg elevator

explosion that has moved from top to bottom of this elevator and has vented at every level. In a twin-leg elevator, however, the space around and between the buckets is much more limited and it is unclear, at first sight, whether the buckets act as turbulence induces in the flow ahead of the flame and thus cause the explosion to accelerate or act as obstacles to the flame propagation and so decrease the explosion velocity or prevent its propagation altogether.

In order to answer this question, explosion tests were done in which all buckets were removed from the elevator and then replaced in stages until a full complement was re-fitted. The guidance derived from these results is based only on the tests with a full complement of buckets.

Effect of ignition location

Without buckets installed, with the vents at 3 m intervals (fully vented) and using cornflour "A" the most effective location of the ignition source was at the head; with cornflour "B" it was found that the most effective location was at the boot. However, with buckets installed the explosion pressure tended to increase when the igniter was located at level 7. Therefore in the majority of tests, the ignition source was located in the elevator head at level 7. This was at a point in the head where the free volume was greater than elsewhere in the elevator and would allow maximum development of the primary explosion prior to the expanding flames making contact with the elevator walls and buckets.

Effect of bucket spacing – fully vented elevator

Tests were carried out initially without the buckets installed followed by tests with a range of bucket spacings with the buckets running. In principle the presence of the buckets could produce two effects: a) inhibit flame propagation, b) increase turbulence of the flame. The elevator was fully vented, with vents at 3 m intervals with a vent at the head. A range of ignition locations was used.

Table 1 demonstrates the progressive increase in explosion pressure with increased numbers of buckets in the elevator with cornflour "B". However, with cornflour "A" the buckets tended to inhibit flame propagation with accompanying low pressures.

Table 1. Peak explosion pressures – fully vented elevator

	Peak explosion pressure – Cornflour "A"	Peak explosion pressure – Cornflour "B"
No buckets	191	211
Buckets at 3 m spacing	110	314
Buckets at 1 m spacing	273	265
Buckets at 0.28 m spacing	117	519
Buckets at 0.14 m spacing	110	659

Without the buckets installed, both cornflour "A" and "B" propagated flame through the elevator. The more reactive dust, Cornflour "B", produced a slightly higher peak pressure (211 mbar) compared with cornflour "A" (191 mbar).

To test the flame blocking ability of the buckets, they were installed at 3 m spacing and were positioned between the vents in a stationary position. In the stationary mode the buckets prevented propagation of the cornflour "A" flame and the pressure did not exceed the burst pressure of the explosion panels; cornflour "B" flame propagated through the elevator and the explosion pressure increased to 275 mbar. In the running mode, the buckets still inhibited flame propagation with cornflour "A". However, cornflour "B" still propagated through the elevator with the explosion pressure increased further to 314 mbar. This provides evidence that the presence of the buckets increased the turbulence in the case of cornflour "B" but the buckets inhibit flame propagation with cornflour "A" although this was not always the case.

In one test with 1 m spacing of the buckets and the elevator running, with ignition at the head and using cornflour "A", flame propagated past the buckets from the head to the boot after which is propagated up the downleg and produced 273 mbar at the boot – a pressure comparable with cornflour "B" which produced 265 mbar in a nominally identical test.

Explosion tests with varied vent configurations

The peak explosion pressures were measured for a range of vent configurations using four dusts. The buckets were running in all the tests.

Pressure data from the tests with the buckets spaced at 280 mm and 140 mm have been plotted and are presented in Figures 8 and 9 respectively.

Vent spacing was set at 3 m, 6 m and 12m. Generally, flame propagation was rare with cornflour "A" and peak pressures were measured usually close to the ignition – in the head. Cornflour "B" explosions propagated into the elevator legs and to the boot, with peak

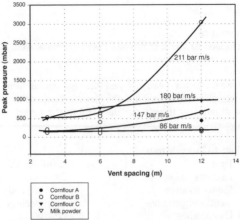

pressures measured either in the boot or the upleg. Explosions of cornflour "C" also

Figure 8 Explosion pressure vs vent spacing. Buckets at 280 mm spacing; Vent opening pressure = 0.1 bar.

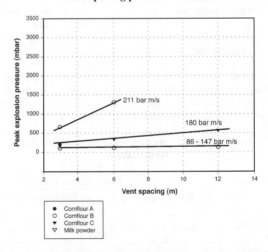

Figure 9 Explosion pressure vs vent spacing. Buckets at 140 mm spacing; Vent opening pressure = 0.1 bar.

propagated into the upleg to the boot and into the downleg. In one test, with a vent spacing of 6m, the primary explosion in the head propagated to the boot via the downleg in the direction of the bucket travel and propagated to level 3 in the upleg. Secondary flame then re-emerged at level 5 in the downleg and persisted for approximately 4 seconds at the vent after which flame re-emerged at level 5 in the upleg and at the head, thus demonstrating how unpredictable flame propagation can sometimes be. No flame propagation took place in any of the milk powder tests.

Tests with the Recycle system

These tests were performed to check that worst case conditions were being tested by dust injection tests and that explosions experienced during actual running were adequately covered by the test programme.

The elevator was cleaned internally and the appropriate vent configuration was installed. Cornflour was manually loaded into the elevator boot and the elevator was run for approximately 3 – 4 minutes to recycle the dust before the igniter was fired. The test conditions were:

Cornflour "A" recycle tests
Dust	:	cornflour "A"
Bucket spacing	:	280 mm
Igniter positions	:	level 7 (hood)
Vent configurations	:	vent spacings 12 m
Dust loading	:	175-200 kg

Cornflour "B" recycle tests
Dust	:	cornflour "B"
Bucket spacing	:	280 mm
Igniter positions	:	level 7 (hood) and part way down the elevator
Vent configurations	:	vent spacings of 3m, 6m and 12m
Dust loading	:	100 kg

In the tests with the recirculation system in use, the peak explosion pressures were significantly less than those developed by similar tests but using the dust injection system. The lower pressures are likely to be the result of a reduction in turbulence and differences in the dust concentration. The comparative data is shown in Table 2.

Table 2. Peak Pressures in the twin leg elevator with different dust cloud formations

Vent spacing	Ignition location	Peak pressure (mbar)	
		Injection system	Recirculation system
3 m	head	519	216
3 m	downleg		194
6 m	head	650	152
6 m	downleg		246
12 m	head	3031	356
12 m	downleg		no ignition of cornflour

Generally, the direction of explosion propagation was into the downleg following the direction of the bucket movement and occasionally into the upleg via the boot.

These tests show that continueing the operation of the elevator after the explosion can extend the duration of the explosion compared to when the dust is injected. In one test, secondary explosions and external explosions continued until the operation of the elevator was switched off after approximately 1.5 minutes. Until the buckets were shut down, their movement continued to feed cornflour to the external flames, perpetuating combustion outside the elevator. Large, sustained fireballs, typically 5m in diameter, were produced in the tests and dust settled out on the platforms under the vent openings were ignited.

DISCUSSION

SINGLE LEG ELEVATOR

Figures 4 and 5 provide the information from which the vent spacing for dusts with different K_{St} values can be estimated. A linear interpolation has been used to estimate reduced explosion pressures for a K_{St} – value of 175 bar m s^{-1}.

Figure 10 shows how the total vent area required to limit reduced explosion pressures to 1.0 bar and 0.5 bar varies with the K_{St} – value when the value of P_{stat} is 0.1 bar and 0.05 bar.

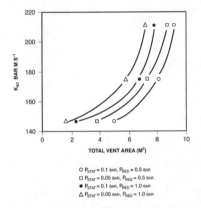

O P_{STAT} = 0.1 BAR, P_{RED} = 0.5 BAR
□ P_{STAT} = 0.05 BAR, P_{RED} = 0.5 BAR
● P_{STAT} = 0.1 BAR, P_{RED} = 1.0 BAR
△ P_{STAT} = 0.05 BAR, P_{RED} = 1.0 BAR

**Figure 10 Total vent area vs K_{St} value.
Single leg elevator**

The relationship between total vent area and vent spacing is shown in Figure 11. The

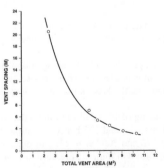

**Figure 11 Vent spacing as a function of total vent area.
Single leg elevator.**

vent spacing is calculated by positioning one vent in the boot and one in the head of the elevator, and distributing the remaining total vent area along the elevator assuming each vent has an area equal to the cross-sectional area of the elevator. The vent spacing for several values of K_{St} and P_{stat} are listed in Table 3. The spacing read from Figure 11 is rounded down to the nearest metre.

Table 3. Vent Spacing

K_{St} bar m s^{-1}	P_{stat} bar g	P_{red} bar g	Vent Spacing (m)
150	0.05	1.0	19
		0.5	10
	0.10	1.0	14
		0.5	7
175	0.05	1.0	7
		0.5	4
	0.10	1.0	5
		0.5	4
200	0.05	1.0	5
		0.5	3
	0.10	1.0	4
		0.5	3

The data from the milk powder tests is shown on Figure 4. In neither of the tests which vented did the reduced explosion pressure exceed the vent opening pressure which was 125 – 135 mbar. In the two tests where venting occurred, the vent nearest the ignition position opened, along with vents approximately 10 – 12 m from the ignition position. It is recommended that a spacing of 10 m will, for dusts of K_{St} equal to 100 bar m s^{-1} limit reduced explosion pressures to the vent bursting pressure if this is no greater than 0.10 bar.

By comparison with the data from other dusts, vents fitted in the boot and head of an elevator will limit the pressures to less than 0.5 bar g for dusts with K_{St} – values of 100 bar m s^{-1} or less.

TWIN LEG ELEVATOR

The reduced explosion pressure data for bucket spacing of 140 mm or 280 mm are combined in Figure 12. This diagram may be used to estimate vent spacing providing:

i)   the vents open at a pressure not exceeding 100 mbar.
ii)   the area of the vent is not less than the cross-sectional area of the elevator leg.
iii) a vent is positioned at the head and a vent is located as close as possible to the boot.

The data suggest that a vent spacing of 10m will limit the reduced explosion pressure to 1 bar for dusts with K_{St} values between 150 and 175 bar m s^{-1} and a spacing of 5m is required for dusts with K_{St} values between 175 and 200 bar m s^{-1}. For dusts with K_{St} values between 100 and 150 bar m s-1 a spacing of 14m will limit the pressure to 1 bar.

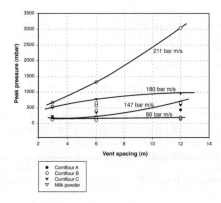

**Figure 12 Explosion pressure vs vent spacing for twin leg elevator.
Vent opening pressure = 0.1 bar.**

GUIDANCE

SINGLE LEG ELEVATORS

Vent openings should have an area equal to the cross-sectional area of the elevator leg and the least requirement is that vents should be fitted in the head and as close as is practicable to the boot. This generally means a vent within 6m of the boot or within the recommended spacing, whichever is the lesser. The spacing between vents along the elevator is listed as a function of the dust K_{St} value, the vent burst pressure and the reduced explosion pressure in Table 3.

For dusts with K_{St} values of 150 bar m s^{-1}, a vent spacing of 6m will limit the reduced explosion pressure to 300 mbar, when the vent static burst pressure is 0.1 bar.

For dusts with a K_{St} value of 80 bar m s^{-1}, a vent spacing of 20m will limit the reduced explosion pressure to 250 mbar.

TWIN LEG ELEVATORS

Vent openings should have area equal to the cross-section of the elevator leg and the least requirement is that vents should be fitted in the head and as close as is practicable to the boot. This generally means within 6m of the boot or within the recommended vent spacing, whichever is the lesser. The static burst pressure of the vent closure should not exceed 0.1 bar.

The spacing of additional vents depends on the K_{St} value of the dust.

a) Although explosions are possible with dusts of low K_{St}, generally the pressures developed by dusts with K_{St} values below 100 bar m s^{-1} are not significant, and no additional vents are required.

b) Dusts with a K_{St} value of 150 bar m s^{-1} are able to develop significant pressures, although the likelihood of explosion propagation through the elevator is low. Vents additional to those at the head and boot may be required on long elevators if the casing is comparatively weak. The graphs in Figures 8, 9 and 12 should be used to estimate the reduced explosion pressure for a given K_{St} value and vent spacing.

c) Dusts with K_{St} values above 150 bar m s^{-1} will propagate explosions, and vents additional to those in the head and boot are required on elevators taller than 6m. The graphs in Figures 8, 9 and 12 should be used to estimate the reduced explosion pressure for a given K_{St} value and vent spacing. The strength of the elevator should then be designed appropriately.

d) No data is available for dusts with K_{St} values greater than 210 bar m s^{-1}.

It is essential that the elevator stop quickly in the event of an explosion. This may be achieved by trip switches on vent panels, but because of uncertainty as to which panels may open, a trip on a single panel is not likely to be reliable. Either a sensitive pressure switch, or switches, or trips fitted to more than one panel are recommended.

Vents should not open into regularly occupied areas, and wherever possible should be either ducted to the outside or fitted with a device that prevents flames emerging (e.g. a Q pipe).

REFERENCES
1. Lunn, Geoff. Guide to Dust Explosion Prevention and Protection. Part 1 – Venting (2nd Edition) Institute of Chemical Engineers, Rugby (1992).

2. Gillis, J.P. and Fishlock, F.H. Explosion Venting and Suppression of Bucket Elevators.

Acknowledgements
The assistance of Steve Andrews, Des Brookes and Andrew Nicol during this project is gratefully acknowledged.

MECHANICAL IGNITION OF DUST ACCUMULATIONS AND THE IGNITION CAPABILITIES OF SMOULDERING NESTS

G.A. Lunn and J. Gummer

Health and Safety Laboratory, Harpur Hill, Buxton, Derbyshire, UK, SK17 9JN

This paper is a report of a research project into ignition of dust accumulations by rotating, contacting surfaces submerged in the dust and the ability of burning accumulations to ignite dust clouds. A relationship has been developed between the temperature of the hot surface and the power expended by friction at the wheel contact point. Considering the complicated nature of both the tests and the various combustion behaviours and physical properties of the dusts studied the overall trend shown by the results is a relatively clear one and a reasonable indication of the maximum temperatures likely to be developed by a given friction power loss for this apparatus can be obtained. The present results show that the onset temperatures for smouldering combustion are similar to the temperatures that lead to combustion when dust deposits are in contact with relatively large surfaces heated electrically. Smouldering nests of dusts prove to be poor ignition sources for explosive dust clouds, but flaming nests were able to ignite clouds of all the dusts used up to the maximum MIT used - 600°C to 675°C. Smouldering nests with temperatures above approximately 700-800°C were, however, able to ignite sulphur clouds.

INTRODUCTION

Hazardous mechanical friction in dust handling plant is usually accidental but surveys of industrial dust explosion incidents show that, in a substantial percentage, friction and mechanical failure and flames and flaming material are known ignition sources[1,2,3]. Research has been done on the potential for ignition by mechanical sparks and frictional heating but there is no generally accepted method of estimating the likelihood of ignition by mechanical sources of dusty environments. The information available in the literature is not sufficiently wide to give a guidance framework with the potential for general use.

This paper is a report of a research project on the ignition of dust deposits due to mechanical friction by rotating, contacting surfaces submerged in the dust and the ability of burning accumulations to ignite dust clouds. Burning nests with different characteristics have been introduced into clouds of dusts covering a range of Minimum Ignition Temperatures (MITs). Various dusts have been subjected to a submerged source of frictional heating and burning dusts with different Train Firing properties have been used as the nest material and the dust clouds have MIT values of approximately 400°C, 500°C and 600°C.

EXPERIMENTAL DETAILS

FRICTION APPARATUS
An apparatus was designed that would produce frictional effects between two rotating metal disks of 150 mm diameter (see Figure 1). The disks are driven independently by two 5.5 kW motors, both capable of a maximum speed of 1450 rpm (giving a speed of 11.38 m/s at the periphery of the disks). The speed can be increased, however, by changing the pulley ratios from 1:1 to 1:2, so enabling a maximum speed of 2900 rpm (peripheral speed 22.76 m/s). Analogue outputs from the controllers allow constant monitoring of the power and torque levels throughout testing.

One of the two disks is fixed in position and the other disk is mounted on a lay (secondary) shaft, driven by a chain drive. This is connected to a sleeve that pivots about the drive shaft, thus allowing radial movement. A loading arm is connected to the sleeve at the pivot point, allowing various loads to be applied.

Figure 1 Friction apparatus.

The power and torque levels of each disk were monitored continuously during each test. The surface temperature of the disks was checked using a UKAS calibrated thermocouple and indicator. Mild steel disks were used on all the tests. All had a diameter of 150mm and thickness of 25mm. To ensure repeatability during the tests, the disks were either skimmed (using a lathe) or changed at regular intervals for new disks. This ensured the disks had a smooth surface before each test.

Initial testing showed that an enclosure was required to keep the dust around the contact area of the two disks. A steel enclosure (approx 3.6 litres) was produced that straddled the disks. This enabled the dust to be contained around the contact point of the two disks. Due to the fine nature of certain dusts, however, material was found to be escaping from the enclosure around the disks. To solve this problem, a second enclosure - volume 7.2 litres - was constructed that completely enclosed the two disks.

Various combinations of load, speed and duration of test were tried for each dust in order to find conditions that would produce burning in the dust deposit.

FINDING SUITABLE SMOULDERING DUSTS
The burning behaviour of a range of dusts was tested by subjecting a line of each dust to a flame ignition source. From the results a number of dusts was selected with characteristics covering a range of cloud Minimum Ignition Temperatures and Layer Ignition values. The values for the dusts selected for the friction apparatus tests are shown in Table 1.

Table 1:Ignitability Characteristics

Dust type	Dust Layer Glow temp (deg C)	Minimum Ignition Temperature (MIT) (deg C)
Sulphur	250-270	280-370
Lycopodium	280	410*
Woodflour	310-320	480-500**
Tea (Earl Grey)	300	510*
Cornflour (st2)	440-450	450-500**
Calcium Stearate	>450	450-500**
Anthraquinone	>450	600-675**

* Measured in BAM oven at HSL.

** Measured in Godbert Greenwald furnace at Syngenta.

Other results were taken from reference 4.

LARGE SCALE VERTICAL TUBE TESTING
A large scale vertical tube apparatus was designed and produced to test the ability of burning nests to ignite dust clouds. The final design consisted of a 2m long perspex tube with an internal diameter of 0.3m. A vibrating hopper and screw feed arrangement was chosen. In this apparatus dust was fed into an air flow in a pipe connected to the top of the 2m long perspex tube. The rate of feed and air flow were both variable to so that a wide range of dust concentrations could be produced (see Figure 2).

Figure 2 Vertical tube apparatus

PRODUCING THE BURNING NEST

For the main series of tests, coherent smouldering or burning nests were to be used as the ignition source in the vertical tube arrangement. In order to obtain sustained combustion some form of airflow either through or over the smouldering dust sample is usually necessary. Several different methods for producing sustained combustion were tried and the best was a bank of dust over which was passed warm air at 50°C. This method allowed sustainable smouldering nests to be created with most dusts. Land Cyclops Ti35+ infrared Thermal Imaging (TI) camera was used to measure the burning temperature of various dusts.

EXPERIMENTAL RESULTS

FRICTION APPARATUS

Discussion of Frictional Heating Results

The results from the friction apparatus tests are discussed in this section in terms of the surface temperature developed by the power expended in the frictional process during the turning of the two wheels against each other. The power expended is calculated from the power-time traces measured during the tests. These traces reveal the total power measured throughout the test and the power expended in the friction process is obtained by subtracting the background power:

Power = Power levels during the test (disk1 + disk2) - Background power (disk 1 + disk2)

Ignition and combustion of the dust has been equated with the onset of smouldering at red heat. Figure 3 shows an example when burning inside the friction apparatus did not occur.

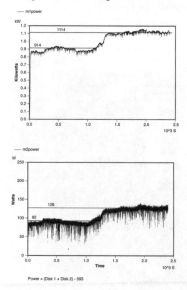

Figure 3 Power traces from a test with wood dust: non-ignition

At approximately 20 minutes into the experiment, there is an increase in the power necessary to rotate the discs. An example for wood dust of a power-time trace in which ignition did occur is shown in Figure 4. At approximately 8 minutes from the end of the test i.e 32 minutes from the start, there is a second increase in the power level. In this example, a smouldering   combustion   began.

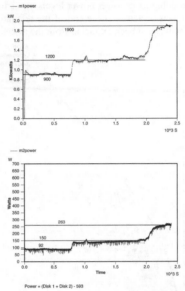

Figure 4 Power traces from a test with wood dust: ignition

The factor determining whether the dust accumulation will ignite is the generation of a critical temperature somewhere in the dust. In this apparatus the highest temperatures measured at the end of the test were always on the disks. Although the bulk dust did experience a rise in temperature over the course of a test, this did not approach the temperature of the disk surface.

The apparatus generates a localised heat source, essentially, although it is an extended one. Rather than a hot spot at the contact point, the heated surface extends round the circumferences of the disks, with generally little variation in temperature. In most tests, however, the disks had different temperatures. Ignition of the dust deposits occurred at a disk surface, but not necessarily at the contact point.

The temperature at the disks arises because of power expended in the friction process. Three variables can affect the power expended - the relative velocity of the disks, the load applied and, to some extent, the dust surrounding the disks. An analysis of the data and considering the power expended at the start of each run indicates that, generally, at a constant relative velocity the power expended increases with load and at a constant load power expended increases with an increase in relative velocity. This is a very general conclusion, however, and there are exceptions in the experimental data. Likewise, the power expended at given conditions of load and relative velocity varies with the dust, but no consistent pattern emerges from the results. The most accessible measurements from the tests are the power expended during the friction process and the temperature generated at the disks.

The temperature at the disks is measured at the close of the tests, and on deriving a relationship between the power expended and the temperature at the rubbing point, it needs to be recognised that the temperatures are a result, not of the average power over the test duration, but of the power expended during the final stages of the test. So in obtaining the data points for Figure 5, which shows the relationship between power expended and the surface temperatures measured, higher or lower power levels occurring earlier in the test have been ignored - only power levels in action at the end of the test have been used. Figures 3 and 4 show how the power levels have been extracted from the traces.

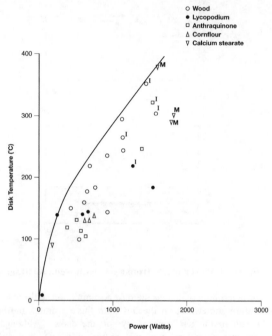

Figure 5 Surface temperature against power expended by friction

Considering the complicated nature of both the tests and the various combustion behaviours and physical properties of the dusts studied the overall trend shown by the results is a relatively clear one and Figure 5 gives a reasonable indication of the temperature developed by a given friction energy loss for this apparatus. If a line is drawn to envelope the experimental points a value can be given to the maximum temperature likely to be produced by a given energy loss.

The conditions that lead to ignition are not, however, typified by the final minutes of the test. Only an analysis of the trace as it develops throughout the test can show what distinguishes an ignition condition from a non-ignition. The example in Figure 3, which is the trace for a wood-dust test that did not lead to ignition, shows that for the first half of the test, 20 minutes approximately, the energy expended amounted to 470 watts. This value is fairly typical of the wood dust tests in the early stages. On the basis of the graph in Figure 5, this energy expenditure would lead to temperatures of approximately 170°C maximum.

Temperatures at this level produce some change in the dust - perhaps charring - which after a time produces an increase in the energy expended in turning the disks. The temperature produced by this higher energy - 649 watts - is measured at 210°C maximum (on the basis of Figure 5) but does not produce an ignition. In Figure 4, burning occurs after a period of approximately five minutes during which the energy expended is 757 watts, producing a maximum temperature of approximately 230°C , on the basis of the graph in Figure 5. From this analysis, then, in this apparatus, if the energy expended is in the region of 700 watts, maximum temperatures of approximately 210°C - 230°C are generated and these are capable of producing smouldering combustion in wood dust. These temperatures compare to 310 - 320 for the 5 mm thick layer test, and 210- 230°C for cones of wood-dust over a small box heated with a constant electrical power[5].

For lycopodium ignition probably occurs in the region of 190°C. A cone of lycopodium over an electrically heated box ignited at temperatures between 175°C and 200°C.

For an St2 Cornflour, the highest rate of energy dissipation was 746 W, which would give a maximum temperature of 230°C, insufficient to cause ignition. The ignition temperature of a 5 mm layer is > 450°C and a cone over an electrically heated box did not ignite at a temperature of 280°C.

Comparisons of some of the wood dust tests where the duration of the tests was curtailed suggest that 20 minutes is required for the disks to reach their maximum temperature. Some tests with wood dust were carried out over a range of test durations with power expended of about 1000 W. The tests suggest that approximately 20 minutes is necessary for extensive smouldering of the dusts to occur.

The results from the mechanical apparatus reveal that a power expended of approaching 1 KW is necessary to generate disk temperatures in the region of 200-240°C in a time of under 40 minutes and probably in the region of 20 minutes. An electrical heating device, at a power of 106 watts requires three to four hours to reach this temperature when covered with a cone of dust. As the power input increases the time to reach a given temperature decreases, but in the end it is the surface temperature generated that is the critical factor in determining the likelihood of ignition.

As the temperature necessary to produce combustion varies with the dust, then it follows from Figure 5, that, generally, the necessary power expended in friction varies also. It is thus difficult to suggest, on the basis of the present results, that there is a limiting relative velocity below which combustion will not occur. For wood dust, no ignitions occurred at a relative velocity below 9.8 m s[-1], at the highest loads used. At lower loads, higher relative velocities were required to produce ignition. Dusts which are more difficult to ignite than wood dust generally require a higher relative velocity if ignition is to occur at a given load.

The question arises as to the practical relevance of these measurements and whether more simple tests could provide data for estimating the risk of frictional ignition of a powder deposit. The present results show that the onset temperatures for smouldering combustion are similar to the temperatures that lead to combustion when dust deposits are in contact with relatively large surfaces heated electrically. A hot surface test, using electrical heating, may be a more realistic way of testing for the likelihood that frictional heating will lead to burning of a dust deposit.

SMOULDERING NESTS AND THE IGNITION OF DUST CLOUDS

Once the risk of combustion in a dust accumulation has been assessed, the danger that a burning dust pocket might ignite an explosive dust atmosphere needs to be estimated.

DETERMINING THE BURNING TEMPERATURE

A review of the literature on the behaviour of smouldering nests indicates that the size and temperature of the nest are important in producing an ignition of dust clouds. The first step in this set of tests was to produce a series of burning nests with dust banked-up as shown in Figures 6 and 7 and ignited using a blow torch. The burning temperature was measured using

Figure 6 Smouldering nest - lycopodium

Figure 7   Burning nest - lycopodium

a thermal imaging camera for a range of conditions - burning with smoulder, burning with flame and burning with warm air applied. The results are given in Table 2

TABLE 2:Burning Temperature of Dust Deposits

Dust tested	Type of burning	Air applied at 50C?	Temperature range (C)
Wood	smouldering	No	690
Wood	with flame	No	730
Wood	smouldering	Yes	850-900
Earl Grey fines	smouldering	Yes	800-940
Lycopodium	with flame	No	650
Lycopodium	with flame	Yes	1056-1173
Lycopodium	with flame	After air removed	820-850
Lycopodium	smouldering	Yes	1,050
Baby milk powder	smouldering	Yes	950-1000
Baby milk powder	smouldering	No	700
Baby milk powder	with flame	Yes	960
Cornflour (st2)	smouldering	No	800
Cornflour (st2)	small pockets of flame	Yes	830
Cornflour (st2)	with flame	Yes	900
Coal dust	smouldering	Yes	>1170
Calcium stearate	with flame	Yes	700
Calcium stearate	with flame	No	900
Anthraquinone	with flame	No	860
Hot coil (used on setup tests)			670-680

A burning nest of dust was positioned inside the vertical tube close to the bottom and its burning mode noted. A dust cloud was then created within the tube using the screw feed arrangement.

In some of the tests the burning nest was dispersed by an air blast from a conical nozzle buried in the dust, to see if the action of breaking-up the smouldering deposit would result in ignition of the dust cloud.

An analysis of the results is shown in Table 3, where the temperature of the nest is divided into three bands - approximately 700°C; 800°C to 900°C;and approximately 1000°C and above. The type of burning is listed, along with the Minimum Ignition Temperature of the dust cloud and whether or not ignition occurred. In the majority of tests where smouldering was the mode of combustion, ignitions did not take place even when high smouldering temperatures were evident and the temperature difference between this temperature and the cloud MIT was high. Only when the nest was dispersed and the temperature difference was high did ignition occur. Sulphur dust clouds were the only ones which would ignite on smouldering nests, but even then the temperature difference between the nest and the cloud MIT was greater than 500°C. By contrast, if flaming combustion took place ignition of a dust cloud was practically guaranteed, even when the flames were small.

A short series of experiments was conducted in which air was supplied to a smouldering nest of dust. The pressure and temperature of the air were varied to see if the burning mode of the sample could be altered.

Tests, involving wood dusts, confirmed that nests burning with a flame could be created from smouldering deposits of dusts by the addition of a suitable air supply.

Table 3:Ignition Conditions.

Temperature of Nest (°C)	Mode of Combustion	MIT of Dust Cloud (°C)	Ignition Y/N
Wood 690	Smoulder	280-370	N
Wood 690	Smoulder	480 - 500	N
Wood 690	Smoulder	410	N
Wood 690	Smoulder	600-675	N
Wood 730	Flames	410	Y
Wood 730	Flames	450 - 500	Y
Wood 730	Flames	600 - 675	Y
St2 Cornflour 830	Flame	450 - 500	Y
Anthraquinone 860	Flame	600 - 675	Y
Tea 800 - 940	Smoulder	510	N
Wood 850-900	Smoulder	280-370	Y
Wood 850 - 900	Smoulder	410	N
Wood 850 - 900	Smoulder	450 - 500	N
Wood 850 - 900	Smoulder	480 - 500	N
Calcium Stearate 900	Flame	450 - 500	Y
Tea 800-940	Smoulder	600 - 675	N
Milk 950 - 1000	Smoulder	410	N
Milk 950 - 1000	Smouldering then	410	Y
Milk 960	dispersed	410	Y
Lycopodium 1050	Flame	410	N
Coal > 1170	Smoulder	410	N
Coal > 1170	Smoulder	410	Y
Coal > 1170	Flame	600 - 675	N
Coal > 1170	Smoulder Flame	600 - 675	Y

DISCUSSION OF THE BURNING NEST RESULTS

The tests on ignition of clouds by burning nests show that smouldering nests are very poor ignition sources, but once flaming combustion occurs ignition of the dusts used is practically a certainty even when the flames are very small. Work at Syngenta[6] on the ignition of dust clouds has shown that clouds can be ignited by various burning or smouldering ignition sources. Three ignition sources - paraformaldehyde, which burns with a flame, $Fe^{3+}(H_2)$, which smoulders, and incandescent particles of saw dust - were used. Sulphur and lycopodium dust clouds of various concentrations were blown over the first two of the ignition sources, and both dusts ignited. The incandescent particles were introduced into the dust clouds soon after the clouds had been produced. The sulphur clouds ignited, but the lycopodium did not.

These tests were repeated with dusts of various MIT values, from 270°C to above 1000°C, as measured in the Godbert Greenwald furnace. With the burning layer, dusts with MITs above 600° to 800°C did not ignite; with the smouldering layer, dusts with MITs above 340°C, approximately, did not ignite; with the incandescent particles, dusts with MITs above about 330°C did not ignite. Some tests using layer ignition sources of various areas and temperatures showed that as the area decreased, for a given temperature, the dust MIT above which a dust cloud did not ignite increased.

The results from the current project are in agreement with those of Syngenta. Smouldering nests did not ignite dust clouds with MIT values above 400°C, but flaming nests were able to ignite clouds of all the dusts used up to the maximum MIT used - 600°C to 675°C. Sulphur clouds were ignited by smouldering nests with temperatures above approximately 700-800°C.

A review of the wider literature also shows that burning nests are poor sources of ignition[7,8,9,10]. The likelihood of ignition of a dust cloud by a hot nest is low if the nest burns only by smouldering   Ignition depends crucially on the production of either flame or incandescent particles and if flaming does take place then the risk of an ignition is very high.

The question then arises as to how likely the production of burning nests is in practice. Despite all the reports of ignition incidents in industrial plant, experimental studies have in the main indicated that transport of nests through industrial plant is not easy. Clearly, the Train Firing Test is the primary method for determining whether a dust deposit will either propagate smouldering or inflame. In practical situations, however, both the temperature and air flow inside dust-handling plant can have an effect on the burning behaviour. If the air above the dust deposit is at a temperature higher than normal room temperature, the requirements for ignition may fall. Layer ignition temperature typically decrease by 40°C-60°C at an air temperature of 100°C.

Various tests have been developed to measure the ignition behaviour of dust deposits in streams of hot air. Similar tests could tell whether smouldering dusts were in danger of flaming. The IChemE Guide, *Prevention of fires and explosions in dryers* described tests developed to simulate various conditions and obtain measurements of the temperature at which exothermic reaction begins[11]. If the dust deposits and surrounding conditions properly simulate practical situations, the temperature at which deposit burning progressed to flaming combustion could be used as a basis for safe procedures with an adequate safety margin incorporated.

CONCLUSIONS

The results of these experiments show that hot surfaces produced by friction are able to initiate smouldering combustion in dust deposits at temperatures similar to those obtained using electrical heating. The power required to produce these temperatures is much higher than when an electrical ignition source is used but ignition occurs at a shorter time. Whereas ignition requires several hours when heated electrically, ignition by mechanical means occurs in less than an hour at a similar surface temperature. A relation between the energy lost by friction and the temperatures developed has been demonstrated.

Clearly, potential ignitions in practice have to be anticipated by determining the type of frictional event likely to occur and applying data and information from a test that is close as practicable to the expected event. In practice, only a limited set of tests to determine the risk of ignition will be available; they will be chosen not only on technical grounds but on cost and time considerations also and they will not cover all likely situations in detail. The effects of scale need to be considered - small areas require less power to produce smouldering than large ones - but the present results are perhaps typical of the frictional heating likely to occur in practical mechanicl equipment.

A practical way forward may be to take a two-track approach. Firstly to develop an electrical heating test to characterise the combustion behaviour of the dust deposit and secondly to generate a set of data on the temperatures likely to be generated in different frictional environments either without the presence of dusts or with an inert dust typical physically of industrial powders. By merging the results of both these series of tests, a practical scheme of assessing ignition risks of dust deposits could be developed.

Burning nests of dust have been shown to be poor sources for ignition of dust clouds if smouldering combustion alone takes place. When flaming combustion occurs, however, ignitions of dust clouds are, to all intents and purposes, guaranteed. Clearly, the Train Firing

Test is the primary method for determining whether a dust deposit will either propagate smouldering or inflame. In practical situations, however, both the temperature and air flow inside dust-handling plant can have an effect on the burning behaviour. If the air above the dust deposit is at a temperature higher than normal room temperature, the requirements for ignition may fall. Layer ignition temperatures typically decrease by 40°C-60°C at an air temperature of 100°C.

Various tests have been developed to measure the ignition behaviour of dust deposits in streams of hot air. Similar tests could tell whether smouldering dusts were in danger of flaming. If the dust deposits and surrounding conditions properly simulate practical situations, the temperature at which deposit burning progressed to flaming combustion could be used as a basis for safe procedures with an adequate safety margin incorporated.

REFERENCES

1. Abbott, J.A. BMHB Survey of dust fire and explosions in the UK 1979-84 (British Materials Handling Board, ISBN 0 85624 4554).

2. Porter, B. Industrial Incidents. Paper presented at Dust Explosions: Assessment, Prevention and Protection, 24th November, London (1989).

3. Jeske, A and Beck, H. Evaluation of dust explosions in the Federal Republic of Germany, EUROPEX Newsletter No 9 p2 (July, 1989).

4. Eckhoff, R. K. Dust explosions in the process industries. 2nd edition. Butterworth Heinemann (1997).

5. Torrent, J. Private Communication. LOM, Madrid, Spain.

6. Bailey, M. and Walker,N. Private Communication. Syngenta, Manchester, UK.

7. Pinkwasser, Th. On the ignition capacity of free-falling smouldering fires. Euromech Colloquium 208, Explosions in Industry. (1986).

8. Zockoll, C. Ignition effect of smouldering pockets in dust-air mixtures. VDI-Berichte. 701, p295. VDI-Verlag GmbH, Dusseldorf (1989).

9. Alfert, F. et al. The ignition capability of nests of smouldering material and hot objects in industrial plants. VDI-Berichte No 701. pp 303-319 (1988).

10. Jaeger, N. Zundwirksamkeit von glimmnestern in staub/luft-gemischem. VDI-Berichte 701, p263. VDI-Verlag, GmbH, Dusseldorf, (1989).

11. Abbot, J. Prevention of fires and explosions in dryers – A User Guide. The Institution of Chemical Engineers. 2nd Edition. Rugby, UK. (1990).

THE FIRE AND EXPLOSION HAZARDS OF DRIED SEWAGE SLUDGE

S.J. Manchester BSc CChem MRSC

Fire and Risk Sciences Division, BRE Ltd, Bucknalls Lane, Garston, Watford, WD25 9XX.

This paper describes the fire and explosion tests that have been undertaken on dried sewage sludge samples from plants throughout the UK, elsewhere in Europe and from around the world. As a result of legislation banning the dumping of sewage sludge at sea, it has become necessary for waste water treatment companies to find alternative means of disposing of sewage sludge. One process used extensively is to dry the sewage sludge to produce a solid granular or pellet product that can be used as fertiliser. During the operation of producing the final dried material fine dust is produced. This dust is combustible and a number of explosion and fire incidents have occurred in drying plants. These incidents have occurred mainly through a general lack of understanding of the hazards posed by the generation of fine dust and the long term storage of large quantities of combustible final product. Dust explosibility tests and self-heating tests on the sewage sludge provide quantitative data, which is used to enable preventative and protective systems to be designed and implemented.

Keywords: dust explosion, self-heating, spontaneous combustion, explosion prevention, explosion protection.

BACKGROUND

The total amount of sewage sludge produced in the UK is currently about 1.1 million tonnes and is expected to grow to 1.5 million tonnes of dry solids by 2005. As a result of legislation banning the dumping of sewage sludge at sea, it has become necessary for the waste water treatment companies to find other means of disposing of sewage sludge. One technique currently used is to dry the sludge to form granules or pellets and then sell this material to use as fertiliser or fuel. There are currently approximately 110 drying plants in Europe, using a number of different processes to dry the sewage sludge. All have the following in common: the production of a combustible solid as granules/pellets and dust. In the presence of sufficient oxygen and with numerous potential sources of ignition present in the process, there is a considerable risk of an explosion or fire occurring.

Since 1997 at least six significant fire and explosion incidents have occurred at sites in the UK and throughout Europe resulting in damage to process equipment. These incidents could have been prevented if the risks had been understood and adequate preventative and protective measures been taken.

The Fire and Risk Sciences Division of BRE has undertaken a number of on-site assessments of sewage sludge drying operations. This has resulted in a large amount of dust explosion, and self-heating tests being conducted on many samples of dried sewage sludge from various stages of the drying process and from many different drying plants. As a result of test work on samples of material from processing plants and site visits, recommendations on the most appropriate safety measures can be given.

INTRODUCTION

In de-watering and drying sewage sludge a large quantity of dust and final dried product is produced, both of which are readily combustible. They will form the fuel in what is known as the "fire triangle". This refers to the necessary requirements for a fire or explosion to occur in any system. The first requirement is the presence of a **fuel,** and in order for the fuel to burn a sufficient quantity of **oxygen** is required. Finally, there must be an **ignition source** present of sufficient energy to ignite the fuel air mixture.

Although dust explosions have been known for over two centuries in industries such as flour milling and coal mining, they were a new phenomenon to the water industry when they started producing large amounts of dust as a consequence of their drying operations on sewage sludge. The fire hazards arising from layers of dust and bulk storage of the final product were also relatively unknown to the water industry. Many drying plants were supplied, installed and commissioned without sufficient thought to the possible fire and explosion risks posed by the production of fine dry dust and final granular/pellet product. As a result a number of fires and explosion incidents occurred, as the conditions required for an ignition of dried sewage sludge material are present during the drying operations of a de-watering plant.

DUST EXPLOSIONS

In order for a dust explosion to occur there must be a dust cloud suspended in the atmosphere. Dusts are generally regarded as having particle sizes less than 500 microns. Sizes larger than this will not be able to be suspended in the atmosphere and hence ignited. Once the dust cloud is created it needs to be of a sufficiently high concentration to be able to be ignited.

Physical and chemical variations can have significant effects on the initiation and progress of a dust explosion. As will be seen later, a general understanding of these effects can be incorporated in explosion prevention and protection techniques. For a dust explosion to propagate, a number of conditions must be satisfied:

- The dust must be combustible.
- The dust must be capable of becoming airborne.
- The dust must have a particle size distribution capable of propagating flame.
- The concentration of the dust suspension must fall within the explosible range.
- An ignition source of sufficient energy capable of initiating flame propagation must be in contact with the dust suspension.
- The atmosphere into which the dust is suspended must contain sufficient oxygen to support and sustain combustion.

Other factors will also have an effect on the sensitivity to ignition and the severity of the explosion, these are:

- The turbulence of the dust cloud.
- The chemical composition of the dust.
- The moisture content of the dust.
- The initial temperature and pressure.

Generally, the severity of an explosion will increase with dry and fine dusts that form a highly turbulent dust cloud. The types of materials that are explosible cover a very diverse range of different materials such as food stuffs (e.g. flour, sugar, coffee, maize), chemicals, pharmaceuticals, dyes/pigments, metals, carbon/coal, rubber, bone meal, paper/wood products and of course, sewage sludge.

The typical characteristics of a dust explosion are: flames, a rapid expansion of combustion gases producing pressures up to about 10 bar, and the possible production of toxic gases such as carbon monoxide and oxides of nitrogen. Many explosion incidents start with a relatively small primary explosion from a localised dust cloud ignition, which then disturbs other dust deposits creating a much larger cloud and a more severe secondary explosion. It is this secondary explosion that usually causes the most damage and risk of injury to personnel.

The types of equipment involved in dust explosions include: mills/grinders, filters, dryers, silos/hoppers, ducts, conveyors, cyclones, and bucket elevators. Many, if not all, of these plant items can be found in a sewage sludge drying process plant.

LEGISLATION
In the UK the Health & Safety at Work Act (1974) is the main legislative framework. It places duties on each of the main parties to industrial activity - employers, self-employed, employees and owners of premises - to ensure the safety of those at work and people who may be affected by a work activity. The Act should ensure that equipment at work is safe to use, but this requirement is extended by the Provision & Use of Work Equipment Regulations 1992. However, the European Union is now the main engine for legislative change.

There are two EU Directives relating to explosion prevention and protection:

- The ATEX-100A-Directive (94/9/EC) requires that measures to prevent ignition of potentially explosive atmospheres by equipment and applies to electrical and mechanical equipment and protective systems.

- The ATEX-137-Directive (1999/92/EC) sets out minimum requirements for improving the safety and health of workers potentially at risk from explosive atmospheres, e.g. undertaking a risk assessment.

The ATEX Directives become mandatory throughout the European Union on 1st July 2003. The approach taken by the Directive is to lay down some essential health and safety requirements which must be met, but gives the task of developing practical means for compliance to the European Standards bodies. Standards bodies such as CEN are mandated to produce standards in support of the Directive. CEN is writing new standards covering risks from non-electrical equipment, explosion protection systems and dust explosibility test methods, including minimum explosible concentration, minimum ignition energy, limiting oxygen concentration, maximum explosion pressure and rate of pressure rise.

DUST EXPLOSION TESTS
In order to comply with ATEX it will be necessary to demonstrate that the requirements of the Directive have been met. This will place an onus on equipment manufacturers to ensure that their products can operate safely in the environment for which they are intended, and on plant operators to provide a safe operating environment. In both these instances, the nature of the dust that is present in the plant will need to be assessed for its explosibility.

The risk of a dust explosion is removed if a dust cloud is never allowed to form, all the potential ignition sources are removed and the concentration of oxidant is reduced to a level that cannot support combustion.

In a sewage sludge drying process the formation of a dust cloud results from the drying and conveying processes that are necessary in order for the final product to be formed and collected. Hence, guaranteeing the non-formation of a dust cloud is not a practical method of dust explosion prevention, except possibly in some plant items in the early stages of the process, before the material enters the dryer where it still contains enough moisture to prohibit dust cloud formation.

This leaves preventative methods relying on the elimination of ignition sources and the reduction of oxygen levels. However, before these two techniques can be applied it is necessary to obtain some data on the ignition properties/behaviour of the dust present in the plant. A number of standard tests are available to provide information of the ignition sensitivity and behaviour of dusts.

DUST LAYER IGNITION

This test, which follows IEC 1241-2-1 : 1994[1], determines the minimum temperature of a hot surface, which will result in the decomposition and/or ignition of a dust layer placed on it. The results are used to define the safe surface temperatures of equipment, exposed to the atmosphere, that may be susceptible to layers of combustible dusts forming on them.

Surfaces in a sewage sludge drying plant that may become hot enough to ignite layers of dusts include the surface of the dryer, motor surfaces, electrical and light fittings. Dust layers that ignite may act as ignition sources for dust explosions and fires in bulk material. Accumulations of dust layers within the plant building, such as on girders and ledges, should be avoided as in the case of an explosion they may be disturbed and act as the fuel for a secondary explosion. This occurs when a small localised explosion disturbs accumulations of dust, thus generating a much larger dust cloud which is then ignited by the first explosion, resulting in a much bigger overall explosion. Noxious fumes will also be produced which could affect the health of personnel in the plant.

Tests undertaken on numerous sewage sludge samples have shown quite a large variation in the results, which fall within the range 150 - 280°C for a 5mm layer. For layers of increased thickness, lower ignition temperatures may be expected. The results of this test are used to specify safe operating surface temperatures for equipment being used in areas where dust is present. Dust hazardous area zoning guidance[2] should be used to ensure all equipment within areas where dust may occur is rated correctly. As the results show large variations from sample to sample it is important that the dust present in a particular process is tested. The results of the test are very dependent of the physical and chemical nature of the material, e.g. particle size, moisture content, composition of the sewage sludge.

MINIMUM IGNITION TEMPERATURE (MIT) OF A DUST CLOUD.

The minimum ignition temperature of a dust suspension is the lowest temperature at which it will ignite spontaneously and propagate flame, the value being particularly relevant to problems involving relatively large heated areas of plant, e.g. the surface of a drier.

The test equipment and method used follows IEC 1241-2-1 : 1994[1]. It involves placing a small amount of dust, typically 0.2g, in a dust holder at the top of a thermostatically controlled "Godbert-Greenwald" furnace (Figure 1). The dust is then dispersed by an air blast forcing the dust vertically downwards through the furnace tube. The criterion for an ignition is that flames should be observed at the bottom end of the tube. If no ignition occurs the temperature of the furnace is increased until an ignition is observed. The temperature of the furnace is then reduced incrementally until flame propagation is no longer observed from the bottom of the furnace for ten consecutive tests.

For the sewage sludge samples tested dust cloud ignition temperatures were found to fall within the range 350 - 550°C, again the values are very dependent on the nature of the sample tested. In the sewage drying plant, dust clouds generated internally within a plant item or externally within the process building, may be ignited if the dust cloud comes into contact with any areas of the plant that may have heated surfaces within this range of temperatures. For example, the inlet to the dryer, the dryer surface or other items of machinery where the surface temperature may exceed the minimum ignition temperature of the dust cloud. A risk assessment will be required in all areas of the plant where dust clouds are present and the classification zoning system for dusts[2] used to ensure all equipment within the zones are rated accordingly.

MINIMUM EXPLOSIBLE CONCENTRATION (MEC)

The minimum explosible concentration is the lowest concentration of powder dispersed as a cloud in air that will, on contact with an ignition source, allow the propagation of flame through the cloud. In situations where the concentration of dust in the atmosphere can be reliably controlled, as might be possible in electrostatic spraying booths, some dust extraction units and lean phase pneumatic conveying equipment, it may be used as a parameter on which explosion protection could be based.

The equipment used for the test is either the vertical tube (Figure 2) or the 20-litre sphere (Figure 3). The vertical tube consists of a perspex tube, volume 1.2 dm^3, mounted on a dispersion cup and fitted with a filter paper bursting disc and two ports for electrodes. The gap between the electrode points is set to 6 mm and the continuous spark of energy 8 - 10 J, generated from a 240V supply through a nominal 14.4 kV transformer. The 20-litre sphere apparatus consists of a spherical chamber with a volume of 20 litres and surrounded by a water jacket. Dust enters the sphere from a 0.6 litre pressurised storage chamber via a pneumatically operated outlet valve. The sample is injected by compressed air and a perforated deflector plate inside the chamber ensures uniform dispersion. The ignition source comprised of two pyrotechnic igniters with a total energy of 10 kJ located in the centre of the explosion chamber.

A weighed sample of the powder is dispersed into the apparatus using a single blast of compressed air form a pre-filled reservoir. A dust cloud forms around the ignition source and ignition is recorded. If the dust ignites the test is repeated at successively lower concentrations until no ignition occurs in ten consecutive tests (three if the sphere is used), using a fresh sample for each test. More details on this test are given in reference 3.

The Minimum Explosible Concentration (MEC) of sewage sludge has been found to fall with the range 50 - 200g/m^3. Most, if not all sewage sludge drying plants will be likely to exceed these values in some parts of the plant and hence reliance on the MEC as a basis of safety is not recommended. However, the information may be required by designers of explosion protection systems.

MINIMUM IGNITION ENERGY (MIE)

Any powder handling operation involving the transportation (e.g. pneumatic conveying or pouring) or agitation (e.g. grinding, micronising, mixing or sieving) of a powder can lead to the build up of electrostatic charge. If rapidly discharged a spark of sufficient energy to ignite a dust cloud may result.

The minimum ignition energy of a dust cloud gives an indication of the sensitivity of the sample to ignition by electric and electrostatic sparks. If a material is found to be sensitive to ignition by this means, then suitable precautions must be taken. Guidance is given in BS5958 Parts 1 & 2[4,5].

The vertical tube apparatus (Figure 2) used for this test consists of a perspex tube placed over a dispersion cup and fitted with a filter paper bursting disc and two electrodes. The electrodes are connected to a circuit which produces a spark of known energy. The spark is generated using a small inductive trickle-charge circuit following IEC 1241-2-3 : 1994[6].

The ignition energy of the sample can be calculated using:

$$E = \frac{1}{2} CV^2 \qquad\qquad (1)$$

where,   E = Spark Energy in Joules
          C = Capacitance of the system is set in Farads
          V = Voltage is measured in Volts

The weighed sample is placed in the dispersion cup and the vertical tube fitted to it. The sample is then dispersed using a single blast of compressed air from a pre-filled reservoir. The dust cloud forms around the spark gap as the spark discharges and an observation is made of any flame propagation away from the ignition source. If flame propagation is observed the energy of the spark is reduced incrementally until a spark energy is reached in which no flame propagation is seen. The quantity of powder used in the tests is varied to cover the most readily ignitable mixture in air.

The majority of the sewage sludge samples tested showed a low sensitivity to ignition from low energy static discharges. Many samples could not be ignited at 500mJ. However, there were some that could be ignited at spark energies of 250mJ, indicating some sewage sludge dust clouds are capable of being ignited at relatively low energy ignition sources. As a minimum requirement all plant items should be earth bonded.

LIMITING OXYGEN CONCENTRATION (LOC) OF A DUST CLOUD

The minimum concentration of oxygen that is necessary for a dust suspension to ignite and propagate flame needs to be known in cases where explosion prevention measures include the use of inert gas. The test apparatus used may be the vertical tube (Figure 2) or 20-litre sphere (Figure 3), and operate at ambient temperatures.

The weighed dust sample is dispersed within the apparatus around the ignition source in known concentrations of oxygen in nitrogen (or carbon dioxide). Once ignition is achieved at a known oxygen concentration, the level of oxygen is reduced until a point is reached where no ignition occurs. The source of ignition is a continuous electric spark of nominal energy 8 – 10 Joules (vertical tube) or two chemical igniters of 1000 J. A full description of the test is given in reference 3.

Values of the LOC obtained for sewage sludge samples tested varied from 9.0 - 12.0 %, using nitrogen and carbon dioxide as the inert gas. Most drying plants use inerting as a basis of safety, the inert gas used is the steam from the water entrained within the sewage sludge. However, it has not yet been determined what effect the use of steam as the inerting agent has on the results of the LOC. No tests are currently available to determine the LOC using steam. This will be the subject of a forthcoming research project funded by the HSE. Until the research project has been completed, the LOC results using nitrogen or carbon dioxide should be viewed with some caution. Large safety margins of at least 4% below the LOC for a particular sample should be used as the safe operating oxygen limit in the plant.

EXPLOSION INDICES (MAXIMUM PRESSURE, RATE OF PRESSURE RISE AND KST)
The determination of the explosion indices is essential quantitative information for explosion protection, based on relief venting[7][8], suppression[8] and containment[8] The severity is characterised by two parameters, the maximum pressure P_{max} and the maximum rate of pressure rise $(dP/dt)_{max}$.

P_{max} is essentially independent of volume, but $(dP/dt)_{max}$ is volume dependent and is therefore related to a volume independent parameter the K_{st} which is defined by an equation known as the Cube Root Law:

$$K_{st} = V^{1/3}.(dP/dt)_{max} \qquad (2)$$

where V is vessel volume in m^3, $(dP/dt)_{max}$ is the maximum rate of pressure rise in bar s^{-1} and K_{st} is a constant in bar m s^{-1}.

The values of K_{st} and P_{max} for a powder are determined under defined conditions in a laboratory test apparatus either $1m^3$ or 20-litre volume. Values of K_{st} are also related to a broader explosion hazard classification, which is used to rank groups of powder according to their K_{st} value. This is the St. classification and Table 1 shows the relationship between K_{st} and St. classification.

Extensive work has been undertaken to relate the K_{st} value to the sizing of the explosion reliefs and suppression systems.

All the test work on sewage sludge samples was undertaken in the 20-litre sphere. The apparatus consists of a spherical chamber with a volume of 20 litres and surrounded by a water jacket (Figure 3). Dust enters the sphere from a 0.6 litre pressurised storage chamber via a pneumatically operated outlet valve. The sample is injected by compressed air and a perforated deflector plate inside the chamber ensures uniform dispersion. The ignition source comprises of two pyrotechnic igniters with a total energy of 10 kJ located in the centre of the explosion chamber.

Explosion pressures are measured for a range of dust concentrations using piezo-electric pressure transducers. The maximum explosion pressure (P_{max}) and the K_{st} of the dust sample tested is defined as the mean values of the maximum values of each test series (total 3 series) over the concentration range close to the observed maxima.

Table 1. St. Classification

K_{st} Bar m s^{-1}	Explosion Classification
0	St. 0
0 – 200	St. 1
200 – 300	St. 2
300	St. 3

Sewage sludge samples tested have shown quite large variations in the values of the maximum pressures and Kst determined in the 20-litre sphere, see Table 2. However, they all fall within the St.1 classification (Table 1) category. St.1 dusts typically include natural products such as flour, grain, wood products and coal. Specific values of pressure and Kst are required for the dust within the process to enable explosion protection systems to be accurately designed.

Table 2 Explosion test data for sewage sludge samples tested at BRE

Explosion test	Results
Layer ignition	150 - 280°C
Minimum ignition temperature	350 - 550°C
Minimum explosible concentration	50 - 200g/m³
Minimum ignition energy	> 250mJ
Limiting oxygen concentration	9 - 12 %
Maximum pressure	7 - 9 bar g
Kst	80 - 200 bar m/s

DUST EXPLOSION PROTECTION

Once all the required data has been accumulated on the driest and finest sample of sewage sludge dust present in the plant, then a risk assessment can be made as to likelihood of an ignition. In the first instance this will be avoiding the formation of dust clouds wherever possible and eliminating all the identified potential ignition sources. If the plant is being run under an inert atmosphere of steam or other inert gas then protocols and procedures should be in-place to ensure that the oxygen levels do not exceed the maximum permissible oxygen concentration. This is typically set at 2 - 4% below the LOC value.

If the above measures cannot be guaranteed or the risk is not sufficiently reduced, then explosion protection measures will be required. The most suitable systems will depend on the nature and position of the plant item, and may include use of one or a combination of the following: relief venting, suppression, containment and isolation

FIRE HAZARDS

Dried sewage sludge is combustible. There are two potential sources of ignition that may lead to a fire hazard, from an external source and from self-heating.

EXTERNAL IGNITION

The high temperatures involved in drying and processing the sewage sludge to form the final product can cause the sewage sludge to smoulder and burn. If deposits of dust are allowed to build-up in areas of the plant where hot dry conditions exist then the temperature may be high enough to ignite the deposit. The level of oxygen required to initiate a smouldering combustion is not known at present, but values considerably less than atmospheric concentration could be sufficient. Hence, either deposits are not allowed to form and remain in the system for long time periods, or the oxygen concentration is kept to a such a low level that combustion cannot be initiated. The HSE research programme of work mentioned earlier is to include work on initiation of smouldering deposits under low oxygen concentrations.

SELF-HEATING

Self-heating can occur in either small volumes of material in warm environments or in bulk deposits held at relatively low ambient temperatures. Self-heating occurs when heat is generated within a material either due to chemical oxidation or biological reactions[9]. If the rate of heat generated within the sample is greater than that lost from the sample to the surroundings, then the heat will gradually increase within the sample. If this continues, then eventually the temperature of the material may reach its auto-ignition temperature leading to ignition.

Smouldering deposits of sewage sludge dust have been found to occur in warm areas of drying plants, where deposits have built-up over a period of time. It is essential that there are no areas within the processing plant where deposits can accumulate. If such areas exist then measures need to be undertaken to ensure these areas are removed or cleaned regularly to remove the deposits.

Bulk storage of the final product, either in silos or storage areas after being bagged, can lead to self-heating and eventual spontaneous combustion. Advice on safe storage volumes, temperatures and times to ignition of sewage sludge products has been given following investigations into the self-heating behaviour. Isothermal self-heating tests[10] have been undertaken on a number of different samples of sewage sludge and the results used to give specific fire safety advice.

Isothermal self-heating tests

Isothermal self-heating tests[9,10] determine the critical ignition temperature of the dried sewage sludge. Thermal ignition theory[9] can then be used to enable the behaviour of the dried sewage sludge to be predicted under specific practical conditions of storage, plant operation and transport.

The tests involve placing the dried sewage sludge material in a cubic wire mesh basket inside an oven set at a particular temperature. The sizes of basket usually chosen are of size 75mm, 100mm, 125mm, 150mm and 200mm. The temperature inside the oven and the temperature of the sample are monitored using thermocouples and continuously logged until ignition has occurred or exothermic reaction takes place. If ignition occurs the test is repeated at a lower oven temperature until no ignition is observed. The procedure is then repeated using three different sizes of basket. In this way the critical ignition temperature for each basket size is determined.

This information can then be used to calculate the critical ignition temperature of any system if the volume and ambient temperature is known. Further calculations can also be performed to assess the time to reach ignition and the hazards arising from placing warm material into a cool store.

From the variety of sewage sludge samples tested the critical ignition temperature values obtained with the basket sizes tested, indicate that the results are very dependent on the form in which the product is tested, i.e. pellets will give different results to granules, which will be different to powders.

Packing Group

It has been determined in the isothermal basket tests that sewage sludge is liable to self-heat. If the sewage sludge is to be transported it needs to meet the requirements of the UN Orange Book Test N.4[11]. This test is similar to the isothermal basket test.

The ability of a substance to undergo oxidative self-heating is determined by exposure of it to air at temperatures of 100°C, 120°C or 140°C in a 25mm or 100mm wire mesh cube. Each sample container is housed in a cubic container cover of stainless steel, slightly larger than the sample container. In order to restrict the effect of air-circulation, this cover is installed in a second stainless steel cage 150 x 150 x 250mm in size.

The sample/container is housed in the cover and hung at the centre of the oven. The oven temperature is raised to 140°C and kept there for 24 hours. The temperature of the sample and oven is recorded continuously.

A positive result is obtained if spontaneous ignition occurs, or if the temperature of the sample exceeds the oven temperature by 60°C. The results of these tests will initially determine whether the substance being tested is classified in Division 4.2, i.e. the substance is regarded as being a hazardous substance for transportation. If the material does come into this category then it will be assigned a packing group, depending on the results of the tests and the quantities of material being transported.

TOXICITY ASSESSMENTS OF COMBUSTION PRODUCTS

A number of assessments have been made by BRE on the toxic products produced when different samples of dried sewage sludge are decomposed under various fire conditions. The test apparatus used in these investigations was the BRE "Purser" Tube Furnace. Details of the test method and the procedure used to estimate the lethal toxic potency of the fire effluent is described in reference 12. The conditions chosen for these studies included non-flaming decomposition (350°C), vitiated flaming conditions (650°C) and vitiated high temperature flaming conditions (900°C). The yields of carbon monoxide, carbon dioxide, smoke density and particulates were measured and estimates were made as to the quantity of acid gases and total organic products.

It was found that the main hazardous products evolved under the fire conditions studied were carbon monoxide and smoke. Some organic products would also be emitted, but these were judged to be unlikely to present a serious health hazard unless they were to occur frequently. The extent of the hazard would then depend on the mass of material decomposed, the individual composition of the sewage sludge, the volume into which the products were dispersed and the ventilation system.

The data obtained from the tube furnace tests enable fire hazard assessments to be made in specific facilities from sewage sludge fires during processing and storage.

CONCLUSIONS

Dried sewage sludge dust is an explosible powder. Measures need to be taken to ensure that the risk of this hazard is reduced as much as possible. The first stage is to undertake a risk assessment of the plant and instigate dust explosion preventative measures. These measures include: trying to minimise dust cloud formation, elimination of potential ignition sources, hazardous zoning of the area within the process building and maintenance of an inert atmosphere with the plant. In addition, explosion protection systems, such as relief venting, suppression, and isolation will also be required as a back-up to these measures.

Fire hazards also exist with dried sewage sludge when present as a dust and also with the final granular/pellet product. Layers or accumulations of dust in warm/hot areas of the plant can lead to smouldering combustion, which can then act as an ignition source for a dust explosion or lead on to larger fires. Procedures need to be in place to ensure dust does not accumulate in areas of the plant where temperature/oxygen conditions could lead to an ignition. The final product is liable to self-heat when stored for long periods of time in bulk containers such as silos or after being bagged and placed in storage areas. Information on safe storage volumes. temperatures and times will be required for the product. If the material is to be transported, then tests need to be undertaken to ensure compliance with regulations concerning the transport of substances liable to self-heat and to enable correct packaging/marking.

Combustion of dried sewage sludge also produces the toxic gas carbon monoxide, as well as smoke. Depending on the quantity of material burning and the building volume/ventilation, this could pose a hazard to workers within the process building. This potential hazard should be included in any risk assessment on the process.

RECOMMENDATIONS FOR FUTURE WORK

- The limiting oxygen concentration data for sewage sludge dust clouds needs to be assessed at high temperature and using steam as the inerting agent. HSE sponsored research work on developing a test method to undertake these assessments should be commissioned this year. The results of this project should then be used to implement additional safety procedures.

- Layer and deposits of dust inside the drying plants may also self-heat to ignition over a period of time, even under low oxygen conditions. The concentration of oxygen and the temperature necessary for this to occur is not known at present. This information is important as it is known that smouldering deposits have been the cause of past incidents. This work also forms part of the HSE sponsored research project.

- Sewage sludge plants need to have a rigorous safety review of their operations to ensure that dust explosion and fire prevention and protection measures are adequate.

REFERENCES

1. IEC 1241-2-1 Part 2, Section 1, Method B "Methods for Determining the Minimum Ignition Temperature of a Dust" 1994.
2. IEC 61241-3. Electrical apparatus for use in the presence of combustible dust - Part 3: Classification of areas where combustible dust are or may be present. 1997.

3. Field, P. Dust explosions. Handbook of Powder Technology Vol. 4, Elsevier, Amsterdam 1982.

4. BS5958 Part 1. Code of Practice for the control of undesirable static electricity. General considerations. British Standards Institution, 1991.

5. BS5958 Part 2. Code of Practice for the control of undesirable static electricity. Recommendations for particular industrial situations. British Standards Institution, 1991.

6. IEC 1241-2-3 Electrical apparatus for the use in the presence of combustible dust - Part 2: Test methods - Section 3: Method for determining the minimum ignition energy of dust/air mixtures. 1994.

7. Lunn, G.A. Guide to Dust Explosion Prevention and Protection. Part 1 - Venting. 2nd Edition. The Institution of Chemical Engineers, Rugby, 1992.

8.   Schofield, C., Abbot, J.A. Guide to Dust Explosion Prevention and Protection. Part 2 - Ignition Prevention, Containment, Inerting, Suppression and Isolation. The Institution of Chemical Engineers, Rugby, 1988.

9.   Bowes, P.C. Self-heating: Evaluating and Controlling the Hazards. HMSO. 1984

10.   Beever, P. F., Spontaneous Combustion - Isothermal Test Methods, Building Research Establishment Information Paper IP23/82 (1982).

11.   United Nations. Recommendations on the Transportation of Dangerous Goods. Manual of tests and criteria. Third revised edition 1999.

12.   Purser, D.A. Fardell, P.J. Rowley, J. Vollam, S.J. An improved tube furnace method for the generation and measurement of toxic combustion products under a wide range of fire conditions. Flame Retardant '94 Conference, London 26-27 January 1994. Proceedings pp 179-200.

Figure 1   Godbert-Greenwald furnace

Figure 2   Hartmann (Vertical) Tube

Figure 3   20-litre sphere

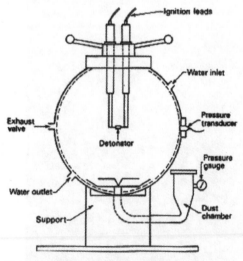

Figure 4   20-litre sphere (schematic)

THERMAL DRYING OF SEWAGE SLUDGE - HSE'S ROLE IN PROMOTING SAFER PLANT.

R.J.Easterby* & A.Tyldesley[+], Health & Safety Executive.
* Midlands Specialist Group, Mclaren Building, Dale End, Birmingham. B4 7NP.
[+] Technology Directorate, Magdalen House, Stanley Precinct, Bootle. L20 3QZ.
© Crown Copyright 2001. Reproduced with the permission of the Controller of Her Majesty's Stationery Office.

UK waste water treatment companies, driven by the need to stop dumping of sewage sludge at sea and the uncertainty of the future of sludge disposal to land, have invested heavily in thermal drying equipment for sewage treatment. The dried sludge products are typically granular, are easy to handle and have a range of potential uses. The product can however give rise to a dust explosion hazard and under certain conditions may smoulder and self-ignite. There has been a rapid growth in the number of thermal drying plants in the UK over the last 3 years, bringing to the waste water treatment companies large-scale chemical engineering challenges outside their previous experience. Several of these, using different technologies, have suffered dust explosions, which, fortunately, despite causing significant damage to equipment, have not resulted in any injuries. This paper describes some of the incidents, which have occurred, highlights common features and outlines HSE's approach to risk reduction in terms of encouraging cooperation with manufacturers and users and producing appropriate guidance. It also describes areas where new work has been needed to establish safe operating conditions.

Keywords: thermal drying, sewage sludge, dust explosion

BACKGROUND

European Directives have caused the UK wastewater industry to change the way in which municipal sewage is handled. Dumping at sea was prohibited from the end of 1998 and the application of raw and treated sewage to agricultural land has been severely restricted. Only material which has undergone what is referred to as "advanced treatment" may now be used on the land. The wastewater treatment companies began to assess the options available to them. Those companies located close to the coast or those with a well-developed agricultural market needed to seek alternative methods of sewage sludge disposal. Many of the companies affected in this way have invested in plant for thermal drying of sewage sludge. The dried product is a granular material which is relatively easy to store and to transport. The thermal drying processes meet the criteria for advanced treatment and make the dried material suitable for agricultural application. The versatility of the product means that it can also be used for landfill, for building materials, for horticulture or as a medium calorific value fuel for heat and power generation.

The first modern UK sludge drying plant was commissioned at the Wessex Water site at Avonmouth in 1992. Of the 20 UK drying plants currently operating or being constructed, five were commissioned in 1998, three each in 1999 and 2000 and a further seven are due to be commissioned in 2001. Driven by impending legislation, the speed of installation of thermal drying technology in the UK wastewater treatment industry has been very rapid indeed. What is unclear is whether the current investment satisfies the immediate needs of the wastewater industry or whether further plants are required to do so. Equally, proven success of the first generation of plants or more demanding legislation may precipitate further development.

TYPES OF DRYING PLANT INSTALLED

The drying plants installed in the UK have encompassed a range of sizes, a number of different drying technologies and several drier manufacturers. The smallest plant is at a seaside location and only operates according to seasonal demand and then only on a day-shift basis. The largest plant which is located on the North East coast accepts municipal sludge both from local pipelines and also from satellite locations which deliver the sludge by ship. When the second phase of this development is complete it will be the largest sludge drying facility in the world, capable of treating 250,000 cubic metres of raw sewage per day and producing 90,000 tonnes per year of dried sludge pellets.

Although there are individual examples in the UK of a belt drier and a fluidised bed drier, the most common driers are drum driers including both rotary and paddle types; in a rotary drier the drum itself rotates whereas in a paddle drier the drum is stationary but an internal paddle rotates. Heat may be supplied directly or indirectly. In a directly heated drier the sewage sludge within the drier is in direct contact either with heated air or with combustion products from a burner system. In an indirect system the heating medium is usually a thermal oil or low-pressure steam, which is held in a jacket around the drier and inside the internal rotating vanes of a paddle drier. A directly heated drier is usually a high velocity system, with a low solids hold-up and the residence time of the sewage sludge in the drier may only be a few seconds. An indirect system is usually a slow moving system with residence times of around an hour and a solids hold-up of several tonnes.

None of the manufacturers of the principal drying equipment are British though they have all had experience in Europe of using their equipment with sewage sludge and other organic and inorganic species. For the water companies and their preferred contractors thermal drying represented a completely new technological challenge.

INCIDENTS OCCURRING

In 1998 and 1999 dust explosions occurred at four of the recently installed plants, which at the time represented up to 50% of the operating plants in the UK. Fortunately no one was injured although there was in each case significant damage caused to equipment and buildings. The explosions were not confined to a particular type of plant and occurred on rotary and paddle drying plants using both direct and indirect drying. All of the incidents occurred during start-up, shutdown or commissioning.

Although differing in detail, the incidents at each of the plants had a number of common features:
- The reactivity of the dried or partially dried sludge had not been fully appreciated.
- There was no effective method to control inertisation during shutdown as well as normal operation; indeed in some cases there were facilities to override oxygen level alarms.
- There was no tolerance to loss of sludge flow. Bearing in mind the variability of the material being handled, flow upsets are foreseeable.
- There was ineffective temperature monitoring and control particularly during shut down periods and in local dead spots.
- Temperature activated quenching systems did not operate or were ineffective.
- There was a lack of explosion protection measures on plant equipment both on the drier and also on the conventional solids handling equipment.

The incidents were not all investigated in detail by HSE. Instead, each of the waste water treatment companies instigated their own internal investigation supported by external consultants experienced in the field of dust explosions. In conjunction with this some of the consultants used their own or other recognised test houses for testing of the dried sludge properties. There was therefore an absence of a co-ordinated approach in investigating the incidents and the recommendations arising, whilst valid for individual cases, were inconsistent. Not all of the waste water treatment companies agreed to adopt their consultants' full recommendations.

About this time HSE, through its Utilities National Group, became aware of the incidents which had occurred, the similarities between them and the rapid growth of this new technology. The Group, with support from local and national specialists, began to look into the topic of thermal drying of sewage sludge.

SAFETY DESIGN

At the design stage of a plant handling a combustible dust, a decision should be made on the type of safety precautions to be adopted. This is often referred to as the "Basis of Safety" and may be embodied in a statement detailing the preventive and protective measures to be followed. Preventive measures include the avoidance of flammable atmospheres by inerting or by control over dust clouds, and the elimination of ignition sources. Protective measures include explosion containment, explosion relief venting and explosion suppression. The Basis of Safety need not be the same for all parts of the plant - in some areas prevention may not be possible - but all areas should be covered. It does not appear that such a formalised approach was taken to any of the first series of drying plants which were installed in the UK in 1998 and 1999. Despite that, for most of the plants it is clear that the basis of safety adopted for the drier itself was prevention based on self-inerting. Under normal operating conditions the water vapour driven off in the drier is sufficient to depress the oxygen concentration to a value below that which supports combustion of the dust, referred to as the limiting oxygen concentration (LOC). However, during times of reduced throughput of sewage sludge or during start-up and shutdown, the LOC may be exceeded. None of the early plants appear to have included systems to maintain inerting by injection of inert species such as nitrogen or steam during these periods; some plants even allowed overriding of oxygen alarms. In the light of earlier experiences some of the more recent plants have included positive inerting systems in their design.

Each of the plants also included conventional solids handling equipment to a greater or lesser degree downstream of the drier. Bucket elevators, screw conveyors, sieve classifiers, mills and pelletisers were all in evidence. With the exception of the product silos, which did generally incorporate some form of protection, the remainder of the solids handling equipment was unprotected. Some of the companies have argued that an inert atmosphere would be present throughout the product handling equipment as a result of being carried through from the drier, although there were no oxygen detectors to support this argument and no equipment for injection of inert species into those areas of plant. Solids handling equipment is notoriously prone to leakage and some plants operate under slight negative pressure, giving a driving force for air to enter the system. An inerting system is unlikely to be effective for this type of equipment unless detailed estimates of leakage rates are made in order to determine the required supply rate of inert gas. Because of the inherent tendency of dried sewage sludge to self-heat and auto-ignite, avoidance of ignition sources is unlikely to be a valid preventative method. Protection of equipment from the effects of a dust explosion, either by explosion venting or by suppression, is likely to be the most appropriate safety precaution for the dried solids handling equipment.

STANDARDS/REGULATIONS/GUIDANCE

Currently no industry standards exist for sewage sludge drying plants in the UK or the US. The most relevant guidance is contained in the 1990 I.Chem.E. publication, *Prevention of fires and explosions in dryers*[1] but few of the suppliers appear to have incorporated its recommendations and it does not cover all the issues. There is in existence a draft European standard[2] and also German publications by DIN[3] and VDMA[4]. Suppliers and users of thermal drying equipment must also comply with the relevant parts of the ATEX Equipment and User Directives in due course[5, 6]. The DIN standard states that the oxygen concentration in the drier must be limited to a value which is within a safe margin of the LOC. It also states that the oxygen concentration within the drier is to be measured continuously. The VDMA standard states that thermal drying plants should take account of fire and explosion risks and be designed in accordance with VDI Guidelines[7]. It does not make reference to the importance of maintaining a low oxygen concentration. Contrary to HSE's current position it accepts that solids processing areas operating below 110°C may use "avoidance of ignition sources" as a preventative measure.

Thermal drying plant is covered by the *Equipment and Protective Systems Intended for Use in Potentially Explosive atmospheres Regulations 1996* [8] (which enacted the ATEX Equipment Directive in the UK). Depending on the age of the equipment there is or there will be a requirement for the supplier to show that equipment and any protective systems conform to relevant safety standards and provide documentation to demonstrate that conformity. Schedule 3 of the Regulations includes more detailed requirements including that the equipment must be designed after due consideration of operating faults and maintenance conditions (this could refer to start-up and shut-down conditions). It also goes into detail on the range of preventive and protective measures available.

The ATEX User Directive[6], which is due to enacted in the UK in conjunction with the Chemical Agents Directive[9], requires users of drying equipment to make an assessment of the specific risks arising from explosive atmospheres, including those arising from dusts, and to classify places where explosive atmospheres may occur into zones (specific zone definitions for combustible dusts are contained in Annex 1 of the Directive). The results of the risk assessment and the area classification will need to be documented and updated in accordance with plant modifications.

HSE UTILITIES NATIONAL GROUP ACTIVITIES

Although there is legislation in place on the supply and use of thermal drying equipment, none of it is industry-specific. There is general HSE guidance in place on the safe handling of combustible dusts[10] and I.Chem.E. publications on dust explosion prevention and protection[11,12]. There is also specific I.Chem.E. guidance on the prevention of fires and explosions in dryers[1]. However, none of these addresses all of the problems associated with sewage sludge drying plants and the HSE Utilities National Group felt that more focussed guidance would be beneficial to equipment suppliers, to waste water companies and also to HSE inspectors. The immediacy of the problem and the very rapid growth in installation of these plants in the UK meant that issue of formal HSE guidance, which may take one or more years would not be appropriate. Instead it was decided to issue interim guidance which would provide information based on the current awareness of the risks from such plant. As and when new information became available as a result of plant operation or from further independent testing it could be incorporated. Finally, it would be issued as formal HSE guidance. It was decided that the most appropriate format would be an internal Operational Circular for use by HSE inspectors, supported by a detailed Information Document (ID) which would also be available to interested parties outside HSE.

An information gathering exercise, including visits to plants already operating in the UK, began in October 1999. A discussion document was prepared in October 2000 and was used as the basis for consultation. In a series of open meetings the major issues were discussed with drying equipment suppliers, with waste water treatment companies and with consultants with experience of the hazards of dried sewage sludge or similar materials. Finally the Information Document, prefaced by the HSE Operational Circular, was issued in July 2001[13].

HSE INFORMATION DOCUMENT
The ID contains information on the principal hazards presented by the drying and ancillary processes. It outlines the need to specify the anticipated range of physical and chemical properties of the sewage sludge raw material and calls for systems to accommodate both longer-term changes and short-term contamination e.g. from petrol spills or from industrial effluent. The document outlines applicable legislation and guidance and gives specific advice on the need for risk assessment and the use appropriate assessment methodologies such as HAZOP and Hazardous Area Classification.

A range of properties may be used to characterise dried sludge. The ID refers to each of these and advises which of the parameters are critical to drier safety design and should be measured at the outset. It gives examples of the wide range of measured values that may be expected. Such variations are more likely to be attributable to real variations in sludge properties rather than unsatisfactory testing procedures and they clearly demonstrate the need for each plant to test its own product and, importantly, to retest it at regular intervals once the plant is running.

The ID contains descriptions of the types of drier which may be used with details of the different drying technologies. It then goes into considerable detail on the principles of drier safety. The need for a Basis of Safety to be established is highlighted and the preference for preventive over protective measures is stressed. The principles of inerting, the importance of maintaining an inert atmosphere at all times and the design and use of equipment to monitor oxygen concentration are considered in some depth. The document stresses the need for accurate and reliable temperature measurement and gives examples of how it may be used to activate water sprays for controlling oxygen concentration or for tackling fires inside drying equipment. The importance of the availability of emergency systems and ensuring that systems do not fail to danger is outlined.

A range of preventive and protective measures is applicable to the product handling plant, storage silos and offloading equipment. The ID refers to each of these and highlights the importance of preventing propagation of a dust explosion through connected plant. It discusses appropriate protective systems for bucket elevators and the selection of equipment for detection and control of fires in storage silos. Although information is not yet available it draws attention to the fact that there may be need to be restrictions on the dimensions of product material stacked on the ground or in bulk containers.

Finally the ID highlights important management issues such as the need for change control procedures for plant modifications and the need for permit to work systems when carrying out hot work or when access to the inside of equipment is sought. Adequate training of operators must include a full understanding of the properties and hazards of dried sludge and knowledge of the appropriate emergency response.

ISSUES ARISING

LIMITING OXYGEN CONCENTRATION

During the course of preparing the ID and especially after consultation with the suppliers and dust consultants, it became apparent that the information available on dried sludge properties, particularly on LOC, was varied and inconsistent. The result of this was that outwardly similar plants were being operated over a wide range of oxygen concentrations (e.g. between 5%v/v and 12%v/v) without adequate justification. In addition to this, doubt was expressed whether the laboratory test results used could be reliably extrapolated to operating plant conditions.

LOC is usually measured in a 20 litre sphere apparatus and the oxygen concentration is adjusted by mixing air with nitrogen or carbon dioxide. The test method, described in a European draft standard[14], calls for the oxygen concentration to be varied in increments of 1%v/v and the test to be carried out over a range of dust concentrations. There is advice in the standard on how to interpret any observed pressure rise.

The test is usually conducted at ambient temperature whereas all the driers operate at temperatures in excess of 100°C. Bartnecht[15] reviewed the information available on LOC measured at elevated temperatures and other non-standard conditions but none of the data relates to dried sludge. His work shows that the measured LOC is expected to fall as the temperature rises. It is also known that the scale of the experimental apparatus and the size of the ignition source do influence the results and that correction factors should be applied to convert the results measured in the 20-litre sphere to operating plant scale. The condition of the product may also influence the LOC result. Apart from expected differences in individual sludges from diverse sources, the experimentally measured LOC may also be affected by the water content of the dried sludge and the particle size of the sample.

Although the test apparatus measures the minimum oxygen concentration which may result in an explosion, it is also desirable to maintain an atmosphere within the drier which will prevent smouldering ignition. Guidance suggests that the LOC for smouldering ignition may be lower than that for a dust explosion and may be affected by the bulk of smouldering material and the time of exposure. Smouldering product is believed to have been the ignition source for several dust explosions centred in sludge driers. It should be remembered that even though the oxygen concentration within the drier may be below that which supports smouldering, depending on the temperature at which the product leaves the inert atmosphere and encounters increased oxygen levels, there may be the potential for smouldering to occur in downstream equipment.

HSE has commissioned a research programme to examine the issues outlined above in order that users will be able to determine safe operating conditions for driers where inerting is the basis of safety. The work will look at the effect of elevated temperature and the effectiveness of steam as an inerting agent for sewage sludge drying and examine whether laboratory testing should always be carried out under operating plant conditions or whether extrapolation may be used. It will also examine whether it is possible to determine the LOC to prevent smouldering ignition and whether it is affected by the bulk of material or exposure time.

To use LOC as a critical operating parameter for drying plant will require continuous and accurate monitoring of the conditions within the plant. Any detection systems used to monitor atmospheres within an operating plant must be reliable and be tolerant to the hot, dusty and water-laden atmosphere prevailing in the drier.

SELF-HEATING PROPERTIES

It is widely understood that dried sludge can react with air and self-heat to spontaneous combustion, particularly if stored for too long and in too great a bulk. This places restrictions on the maximum temperature of product material supplied to storage silos and current practice is for the product to be cooled to 40°C to 50°C prior to bulk storage. Laboratory tests have been used to set the temperature limits but in some cases the safety margin is small. Problems may arise if the product is stored for much longer than normal, particularly during a hot summer period. Also, although most operators will ensure that there is a regular turnover of product in the silos, it is possible that stored material may bridge or "rat-hole" and significant quantities of product may not be emptied from the silo. An additional complexity is that the temperature cycling which occurs in a freely venting silo can cause condensation and the entry of microorganisms. In at least one case this is thought to have contributed to self-heating of product by biological action at a temperature well below the usual limit. Temperature monitoring inside large silos is unlikely to be sufficiently reliable for early warning of smouldering and suppliers are moving towards the use of carbon monoxide detectors. It is possible that the gas detection system could be extended to monitor for the products of biological activity.

CARRIAGE OF DANGEROUS GOODS

Operating experience to date and the results of testing of many samples have suggested that the dried sludge product should be classified as "Dangerous Goods for Transport" under the *Carriage of Dangerous Goods (Classification, Packaging and Labelling) etc. Regulations 1996*[16]. These regulations require persons carrying dangerous goods by road and rail to protect those persons involved in handling and carrying the dangerous goods, members of the emergency services and the public from the potential dangers of such activities. The regulations require the consignor to classify the goods according to their hazards, to package the goods suitably, to provide information about the hazards and to provide information to the vehicle operator/carrier.

The most relevant description for the dried sludge product based on the UN Recommendations is "Self heating solid, organic, N.O.S., UN 3088" (also classified as UN Division 4.2 - "spontaneously combustible substance") [17]. The classification is determined by carrying out tests detailed in the *Approved Requirements and test methods for the classification and packaging of dangerous goods for carriage*[18]. The results of the tests not only determine the classification and appropriate hazard labelling but also the type of packaging which is required - either Packing Group III (minor danger) or Packing Group II (medium danger). Additionally the classification may place restrictions on the quantity of bulk material carried in a single load so that in some cases transport by bulk tanker may not be permissible.

At present the UN test method for a combustible substance, which involves heating various sample sizes at temperatures between 100°C and 140°C, has not been carried out on dried sludge samples. The results from similar isothermal basket tests suggest that it is likely that most samples should be classified as "spontaneously combustible" and that in some cases the more stringent Packing Group II should apply. Further work is needed in this area by the drying plant operators to ensure that the material is correctly classified.

PLANT ISOLATION

Many plants handling explosible dusts consist of a series of containers of various sizes linked together by conveying equipment. If an explosion starts in one location it can spread through the plant, causing damage remote from the initial site of the ignition. Dust clouds can be raised from deposited material by a pressure wave spreading through the system and an explosion can occur even where no dust cloud was initially present. A requirement to restrict the spread of a dust explosion by the use of chokes and baffles has been UK law for 40 years[19]. Two commonly used plant items which are effective in preventing explosion propagation are rotary valves and screw conveyors. However the use of these items can produce dust by attrition of the product, which is undesirable to the operator from a quality control viewpoint. If rotary valves and screw conveyors cannot be used, designers should look at alternatives such as suppressant barriers, rapid acting slam-shut valves and explosion diverting devices. To date, too little attention has been given to these aspects of plant design.

HAZARDOUS AREA CLASSIFICATION

It is a requirement of the ATEX User Directive[6] for the operator to carry out a classification of areas into zones where explosive atmospheres may occur. For plant handling a combustible dust, the zoning exercise must consider not only those areas where a cloud of combustible dust may occur but also layers, heaps and deposits of dust which could subsequently give rise to an explosive atmosphere. Selection of electric equipment designed to prevent dust cloud ignition and with a temperature rating low enough to prevent ignition of dust layers can then follow. In order to carry out this exercise, designers will need to make estimates on the likely cleanliness of drying plant. Newly built plant should be effectively dust-tight and the building should remain relatively clean. However, as plants get older they are likely to develop dust leaks, particularly from any areas which operate above atmospheric pressure. It is difficult to give advice until there is a feel for the housekeeping standards to be expected in a plant which has operated for some time.

CONCLUSION

The use of thermal drying processes for sewage sludge treatment has presented the waste water treatment companies with a new technological challenge which they have had to tackle for the first time on very large-scale plants. The equipment suppliers, despite having had previous experience of operating such plants outside the UK, have not systematically addressed all the fire and explosion risks. A lack of appreciation of the principal hazards together with an absence of adequate controls has resulted in serious incidents at a high proportion of the UK plants. HSE has consulted widely to produce timely guidance which may be used to assist in future plant design and ensure consistency in the enforcement of related health and safety issues. Further research work has been commissioned by HSE to establish critical material properties which may be used to define safe operating parameters.

REFERENCES

1. Abbott, J.A., *Prevention of fires and explosions in dryers.* I.Chem.E. 1990.

2. *Waste water treatment plants. Part 8 - Sludge treatment and storage.* prEN 12255-8, October 2000.

3. *Sewage Treatment Plants. Principles for the Design of Structures and Technical Equipment. Part 10: Specific Principles for Thermal Sludge Drying Equipment.* DIN 19569-10 (Draft), January 2000.

4. *Equipment for Sewage Sludge Drying.* Verband Deutscher Maschinen und Anlagenbau. VDMA 24 437, August 1994.

5. *Approximation of the laws of the Member States concerning equipment and protective systems intended for use in potentially explosive atmospheres.* Directive 94/9/EC of the European Parliament and the Council, 23rd March 1994.

6. *Minimum requirements for improving the safety and health protection of workers potentially at risk from explosive atmospheres.* Directive 99/92/EC of the European Parliament and of the Council, 16th December 1999.

7. *Dust fires and dust explosions - hazards, assessment and protective measures.* Verein Deutscher Ingenieure. VDI 2263, May 1990.

8. *Equipment and Protective Systems Intended for Use in Potentially Explosive Atmospheres Regulations 1996.* (SI 1996/192).

9. *Protection of the health and safety of workers from risks related to chemical agents at work.* Directive 98/24/EC of the European Parliament and of the Council, April 1998.

10. *Safe Handling of Combustible Dusts Precautions against Explosions.* HSE Guidance booklet, HS(G)103, 1994.

11. Lunn G. *Dust Explosion Prevention and Protection. Part 1 - Venting.* I.Chem.E., 1992.

12. Schofield C. & Abbott J.A. *Guide to Dust explosion Prevention and Protection. Part 2 - Ignition Prevention, Containment, Inerting, Suppression and Isolation.* I.Chem. E. 1988.

13. *Control of Health and Safety Risks at Sewage Sludge Drying Plants.* Health and Safety Executive, Information Document HSE 847/9, July 2001.

14. *Determination of explosion characteristics of dust clouds. Part4: Determination of Limiting Oxygen Concentration of dust clouds.* prEN 14034-4, March 2000.

15. Bartnecht, W., *Dust Explosions: course, prevention, protection.* Springer-Verlag, 1989.

16. *Carriage of Dangerous Goods (Classification, Packaging and Labelling) and the Use of Transportable Pressure Receptacles Regulations 1996.* (SI1996/2092).

17. *Approved Carriage List: Information for carriage of dangerous goods by road and rail other than explosives and radioactive substances.* HSE Books L90. 1996.

18. *Approved Requirements and test methods for the classification and packaging of dangerous goods for carriage.* HSE Books L88, 1996.

19. Section 31, Factories Act, 1961.

THE EXPERIMENTAL STUDY AND SIMULATION OF TUBE RUPTURE IN SHELL-AND-TUBE HEAT EXCHANGERS

A.M. Thyer, A.J. Wilday and G. Bankes *
Health and Safety Laboratory, Harpur Hill, Buxton. SK17 9JN
* Health and Safety Executive, Offshore Safety Division, Merton House, Stanley Rd., Bootle. L20 3DL

This paper summarises the findings of a Joint Industry Project to determine the effectiveness of computer simulation models used to predict the consequences of tube rupture in high pressure gas coolers. This was achieved by undertaking an experimental test programme in which tubes carrying a high pressure gas were ruptured inside a full-scale shell-and-tube heat exchanger. The facility was extensively instrumented with strain guages and pressure transducers to allow records of short and long-term pressures/strains in the heat exchanger and relief pipework to be measured. This information was then compared against a number of blind simulations performed by other participating companies to determine the level of accuracy. The experimental data obtained support the use of one-dimensional fluid dynamic models to predict the flowrates, shell pressures and forces on the heat exchanger and connected lines. The relief system opening time and the shell-side friction are important input data to such models. The measurement of opening times of typical bursting discs and safety valves is recommended. The experimental data also support the possibility of using finite element modelling to take account of the effect on the shell of the high pressure pulse being of short duration rather than a static load.

Keywords: heat exchanger, shell-and-tube, tube rupture

INTRODUCTION

There are many shell and tube heat exchangers operating on oil production platforms in the North Sea where high pressure gas is either cooled or heated by the use of a low pressure utility fluid, such as sea water. Such heat exchangers typically have gas on the tube side at 100-250 bar gauge pressure and sea water on the shell side at 5-20 bar. The shell side of exchangers is usually designed to withstand a pressure just above the operating pressure of the liquid. It therefore needs to be protected against tube failure by fitting either bursting discs or pressure relief valves. However, a critical problem for the engineer has been to select a suitable design pressure for the utility (low pressure) side of the exchanger, which will be able to withstand the pressures generated before the chosen pressure relief system is fully effective.

Incidents which have occurred over the past decade clearly illustrate the highly detrimental engineering and financial consequences that can result from a tube rupture. These have ranged from catastrophic failure of the heat exchanger shell with associated mechanical damage to nearby process plant (Brent Delta, Jan 1989) to the ingress of flammable gasses into accommodation modules and process areas (Fulmar Alpha August 1991), fires, personnel injury and mechanical damage as a result of pressurisation of the cooling water system. In many instances the consequential financial losses have been considerable.

The industry has sought to tackle the problem by carrying out quantitative risk assessments as well as employing specialist consultants to undertake computerised dynamic simulations of the pressures generated within the units in the event of a tube failure. These simulations make a number of simplifying assumptions, but the accuracy of their modelling predictions is unknown, because the models have never been validated against experimental data obtained from realistic experiments.

The Institute of Petroleum Heat Exchanger Task Group was therefore set up to progress work to develop confidence in the design methods used by the offshore industry and thereby ensuring that high-pressure heat exchangers are able to withstand possible tube rupture. The terms of reference of the Task Group called for experimental work to provide data sets for validation of the computer codes, the specification of their accuracy, and to establish the range of applicability. A simple "rule of thumb" design criteria for heat exchangers[1,2] was also investigated. Guidelines for use by industry have been produced by the Institute of Petroleum[3].

Work proceeded in phases. The Institute of Petroleum (IP) funded a literature review and survey by Trident Consultants and Foster Wheeler Energy[4], and HSE carried out its own literature review[5]. In the second phase the IP funded work by AEA Technology aimed at producing a simple "rule of thumb" assessment method[1,2], and HSE funded a series of shock tube experiments to allow partial validation of codes in a one-dimensional geometry. Very good agreement was obtained between code predictions and shock tube test[6]. This work showed the one-dimensional computer model was accurate in predicting pressure peaks and profiles in a one-dimensional (shock-tube) geometry. However, experimental results from a representative heat exchanger, which is strongly three-dimensional, were thought necessary to fully validate the codes, establish greater confidence in their predictive capability, and further aid the development of design guidelines. This is the subject of this present paper.

In August 2000 the preceeding five-six years work on heat exchangers came to fruition when The Institute of Petroleum published its guidance document: "guidelines for the design and safe operation of shell-and-tube heat exchangers to withstand tube failure". This document is available through the IP.

DESCRIPTION OF THE TEST FACILITY

The experimental programme was carried out on a typical offshore shell-and-tube heat exchanger, a photograph of which appears as Figure 1. The shell for the heat exchanger was designed and fabricated by Motherwell Bridge Thermal Ltd. following a typical offshore design, and was made from 10 mm carbon steel with an internal diameter of 740 mm and an overall length of 3750 mm. Two main nozzles were fitted along with a number of smaller nozzles to allow internal inspection. The main nozzles were: one of 150 mm diameter for a graphite bursting disc with a specified failure pressure of 10 bar (g), and a 203 mm diameter nozzle to represent part of the cooling water circuit. Other dimensions and nozzle positions are given in Figure 2.

The tube bundle for the heat exchanger was a surplus four-pass bundle containing 566, 19 mm Monel tubes, which was purchased for a nominal fee from Texaco North Sea. Prior to the programme the header was sawn off leaving a flat tubesheet. At the same time the U's were removed leaving straight open ended tubes. This served a dual purpose:

a)   it allowed the easy removal of straight tubes from the bundle; and;
b)   it allowed the tubes to flood with water.

The latter point was necessary to avoid complications for the modellers as a partially air-filled system would give 'spongy' pressure pulses.

Twelve tubes were removed from the tube bundle; 6 were replaced with specially weakened carbon steel tubes to be failed in the test programme, and six with tubes carrying miniature pressure transducers. These were positioned in close proximity to the failure point. Tubes not in use for instruments or compressed air injection were plugged with tapered steel plugs.

The appearance of outlet pipework for the 'cooling water' and relief pipework is illustrated in Figure 3. In order to withstand forces exerted by liquid slugs during tests, this pipework was secured to 10 one tonne concrete blocks and further weighed down with 12 one tonne bags of gravel.

The compressed air system comprised a 0.91 m^3 / minute compressor, feeding a bank of five 0.258 m^3 cylinders. The total reservoir volume at 1 bar was 1.29 m^3 giving 345 m^3 at the maximum working pressure of 275 bar. Air was delivered to the heat exchanger through a 50 mm nominal bore (NB) pipe.

During the tests the heat exchanger was isolated from the air receivers by an air-operated quarter-turn ball valve. The cylinders were then taken to between 20 and 50 % of the nominal failure pressure for the tube under test. At this point air was slowly introduced into the unpressurised tube via a by-pass line fitted with a flow restriction. This avoided a sudden shock-loading of the weakened tube which could have caused it to fail prematurely. Once the pressure was balanced on both sides of the main supply valve, it was opened and the compressor run until the weakened tube in the heat exchanger eventually failed. For the highest pressure test at 150 bar the compressor was run for 3.5 hours.

The mechanical strains in the shell were measured using fourteen two-axis 'tee' type gauges, having a frequency response of around 80 kHz (giving ±1% strain reading accuracy). Pressures were monitored using up to 12 externally mounted transducers on the shell (Kister 701 H, and Druck, PDCR 930), 4 internal transducers (Kistler 601H), with a further 6 transducers being fitted to the discharge pipework.

Two separately-controlled and triggered Nicolet digital logging systems were used. These were configured to log at rates of 100 or 12.5 kHz depending on the frequency response of the instrument. This gave a total logging time ranging from 3.5 to 7 seconds, which was ample to observe short-term transients, a steady state flow period, and pressure decay in the system once the majority of water in the shell had been ejected.

In addition to instrumentation on the shell and discharge pipework, one further pressure transducer was fitted to the compressed air feed pipe. The output from this instrument was logged and used to determine the exact failure pressure of the tube, and to follow the discharge characteristics of the air receivers.

The final feature of the test facility was the use of a large water tank at the end of the 8" water discharge pipe to determine the relative proportion of water venting through this pipe and the bursting disc.

THE TEST PROGRAMME

Four tests were undertaken at failure pressures of 71, 102, 130 and 146 bar.

EXPERIMENTAL RESULTS

The results for Test Three, with a failure pressure of 145.9 bar are described as they are typical of those obtained.

The results obtained were tabulated to include, peak instantaneous pressures/strains, peak long-term values over a 10 ms period, values at 0.5 s, and values at 2.5 s. These are still subject to a nondisclosure period and can be obtained through the Institute of Petroleum. Peak instantaneous pressures are given in Table 1.

Table 1
Test 3 instantaneous peak pressures: burst pressure 145.9 bar

Tranducer	1	2	3	4	5	7	8	9	10	11	12	13	int. top	int. bottom
Peak pressure / bar	20.02	21.09	23.9*	25.7*	17.2*	20.18	34.35 11.8*	18.9*	14.53	145**	16.25	18.98	93.5	37.55
Time to peak / ms	0.88	1.22	-	-	-	2.98	15.53	-	4.88	3.42	2.55		0.33	0.76
Distance from failure point / m	0.84		0.60	0.81	0.65	2.17	2.08	2.85	2.78	2.09	0.29	0.03	0.55	0.27

* Pressure transducer faulty, reading derived from strain gauge results
** Pressure transducer showed two small peaks of around 30-40 bar followed by one at 145 bar, after which it failed.

Examination of the video record for this test indicated a flow velocity in the bursting disc line of 19 m.s⁻¹, with a period of slug-flow lasting approximately 3.9 s. This corresponds reasonably well with the output obtained from the pressure transducer at the mid point of the horizontal run of 150 mm NB pipe, where the pressure peak was around 3.25 s long.

REVIEW OF RESULTS FROM EXPERIMENTAL PROGRAMME

The results obtained show that the initial effects of tube failure are to create a high pressure gas bubble in the vicinity of the failure point, in which the pressure may approach a significant proportion of the source pressure, as proposed by Goyder[2]. During the first few milliseconds after failure a ringing pressure profile is obtained with peaks of around 50 μs duration. These decay rapidly leaving a long-term pressure 0.5 s after failure of between 3 - 4 % of the original source pressure. This may persist for approximately 2 s, after which the pressure falls to approach zero 3.5 s after failure. During this period the compressed air reservoir pressure falls to 80 - 83 % of the source pressure.

Strain profiles show similar trends with an initial peak followed by long-term decay. Here it is likely, however, that the decay in strain readings is both a function of falling pressure and venting of the water in the shell. It was noticed during preparation for the tests that the strain gauges required rebalancing after the shell was filled as it sagged slightly under the load. This was more pronounced in the commissioning test than in the actual experimental tests, as the shell was supported under the tubesheet and the saddle near the domed end,

(Figure 1), rather than on both saddles and the tubesheet. This induced an artificially high bending moment along the exchanger longitudinal axis. However, it is likely that loss of water would result in a slight decrease in the baseline strain reading for the gauges.

Good correlation has been obtained between data sets obtained for the four tests. It was found that pressure pulses in excess of 10 ms duration rose as the tubeside pressure increased, with that at 71 bar being about 6.1 % of the tubeside pressure, and that for 146 bar being 7.7 %. Similar trends were seen in the long-term at 0.5 s after failure (Table 2).

In contrast to the results in Table 2, correlation between peak shell-side and tubeside pressures is poor and no real trend was evident, as can be seen from the data in Table 3 below. This lack of a clear trend will be due, at least in part, to the response and accuracy of the pressure transducers. The Druck strain gauge type transducers tended to overestimate the magnitude of the original pressure pulse due to their inability to withstand the severe mechanical acceleration to which they were exposed during the tests.

Table 2
Mean shell-side pressures as a function of tube failure pressure

Test No.	Failure pressure / bar	Highest pressure over a 10 ms period / bar	% tubeside pressure	Pressure at 0.5 s / bar	% tubeside pressure	Pressure at 1.0 s / bar	% tubeside pressure
1	70.9	4.3 ± 3.8	6.1	2.5 ± 2.0	3.4	2.4 ± 2.0	3.4
2	102.3	8.2 ± 2.9	8.0	4.6 ± 1.4	4.5	4.3 ± 1.2	4.2
4	130 ± 1.4	10.0 ± 4.9	7.7	5.6 ± 3.6	4.3	4.7 ± 3.7	3.6
3	145.9	10.4 ± 3.8	7.1	6.0 ± 1.4	4.1	4.8 ± 1.6	3.2

Table 3
Correlation between tubeside pressure and peak shell-side pressures

Test number	Tubeside pressure / bar	Mean peak shell-side pressure /bar	Mean peak shell pressure as % tubeside pressure
1	70.9	6.8	10
2	102.3	27.1 ± 19.3	26
4	130 ± 1.4	10.7 ± 4.6	8
3	145.9	20.8 ± 6.0	14

Similar trends to those above were seen for the strain gauge results.

Measurement of the volume of water retained in the shell after the test and venting through the relief line also provided useful data in the form of the volume of water venting per unit area of pipe. For the 203 mm NB pipe which was permanently open (apart from a polythene disc to retain a static head of water), the amount vented was 1.4-1.6 $dm^3.cm^{-2}$. For the 150 mm NB pipe attached to the bursting disc a larger volume of 2.3-2.6 $dm^3.cm^{-2}$ was vented. This difference was due to the inertia of the water in the completely filled larger pipe, thus decreasing the rate of discharge. Whereas the 150 mm NB pipe was dry downstream of the bursting disc, thus the only impedance to flow was due to the convoluted path and internal surface roughness of the pipework. Despite this apparently higher contribution for the 150 mm pipework, the quantity venting from each pipe was approximately the same, at about 33 % of the water in the shell.

With the exception of peak pressure, which varied between tests, a reliable trend was observed between the percentage tubeside pressure and the long term pressures in the shell. For instance, pressure peaks exceeding 10 ms duration, range from 6-8 % of the original pressure, and long term pressures 0.5 and 1.0 s after tube rupture vary from 3.5 - 4.5 % and from 3.2 - 4.2 % of the original gas pressure respectively. These pressures are significantly below those originally anticipated , and are well below the design pressure for the shell. Should only one exit have been available, however, considerably greater pressures would have developed with an increased chance of damage occurring to the shell or tube bundle.

Results from the strain gauges displayed similar trends to the pressures and can in many cases be used to back-calculate a reliable causative pressure, especially for pressure peaks over 10 ms duration, or in the longer term at 0.5 s or so. For instantaneous pressures, however, the highly transient nature of the pressure peaks means that the shell has insufficient time to react and generate the full potential strain reading. For different shell materials and thicknesses, however, this will be different and this effect may be a characteristic of the chosen test shell. However, as this was constructed to be representative of units in service, it appears likely that many shells will only develop a fraction of the strain they could potentially develop.

Post-test examination of the shell and tube bundle have shown that although the support baffles for the tube bundle flex, no permanent damage occurred. Thus under the test conditions utilised it is extremely unlikely that baffles would be displaced to slide along the tubes and completely block the shell. A similar conclusion can be drawn for the shell. However, a note of caution should still be aired as the shell was specifically designed and tested to ensure that, whilst it was representative of those in industry, it would not fail prematurely. The highest strain recorded arose in the fourth test, where the failure point was directly facing the shell and approximately 2.5 cm from the inner wall. This strain of 1336 μe, corresponds to a causative pressure of 74.7 bar (57 % of the tubeside pressure). Whilst this was within the shell hydrotest pressure of 84.7 bar, it was approaching it and the point where plastic deformation would occur. However, plastic deformation is not failure, and whilst some enlargement may have resulted, the shell did not fail. Should the shell have been an old one with evidence of internal corrosion (rather than a new unit manufactured specially for the test programme) or should the shell already have been under pressures in excess of 10 bar from cooling water pumps, damage to the shell could have occurred.

Forces in the water discharge pipework on the shell were in line with that predicted prior to the programme. Velocities in the 6" pipe on the bursting disc ranged from 19 -22 ms^{-1}, corresponding to a load of 10-12 tonnes.

Whilst the heat exchanger did not fail catastrophically during this work, the possibility of failure still exists, should the pressures developed be greater, or the shell more responsive towards high speed strain. It is therefore recommended that an understanding of which materials would be more susceptible to damage from strain transients is developed. The studies carried out by Sheffield University in parallel to this project may be used as a basis for this[7].

Apart from the possibility of damage to the heat exchanger, damage to associated pipework could occur. It is therefore recommended that the maximum shell pressure should be used in the calculation of pipe loads, i.e. forces developed with the minimum number of exits from the shell. This would avoid the situation where comparatively small loads were predicted with multiple event paths, all of which were not present when a tube did fail. If this is a potential problem for systems known to have weak pipe supports it may be necessary to upgrade these, or to specify in a permit to work system that the heat exchanger is completely shutdown if valves are closed on pipework leading from it.

These tests have investigated the effectiveness of a bursting disc on the relief system only. There may be many units protected by combinations of bursting discs and pressure relief valves (PRVs), or solely by PRVs. It is widely known that PRVs have a much slower response than bursting discs. This slow response time may allow the development of higher shell pressures, especially if the PRV is the only exit. A continuation study substituting the bursting disc with a PRV is therefore recommended to determine if units fitted with PRVs have a greater chance of catastrophic failure of the shell or downstream pipework.

USE OF EXPERIMENTAL RESULTS

COMPARISON WITH FLUID DYNAMIC MODEL PREDICTIONS

The IP Heat Exchanger Task Group invited those consultants who had the capacity to model the fluid dynamics of tube failure in heat exchangers to join the Task Group and to model the tube rupture experiments. Modelling was to be done with the code they would use commercially and using the same assumptions as appropriate. These consultants all used models which predict the pressures in the heat exchanger shell as a function of time following tube rupture. The modelling was conducted in two phases:

a) "Blind", i.e. without access to the experimental results, modelling of the first three experiments. HSL provided the modellers with details of the experimental rig and operating procedure together with the actual burst pressure of the tube. The purpose of this phase was to test the level of agreement of the codes when used (as they are used commercially) to predict the pressures in the shell following a tube rupture.

b) Further modelling with access to the experimental results. The purpose of this phase was to draw out any conclusions concerning how the models could be improved.

One-dimensional models tend to be used commercially as their accuracy is believed fit for purpose. The alternative of CFD programmes require significantly greater computing time and have higher associated cost. The one-dimensional codes all differ in their detailed implementation, but have certain assumptions in common. All model the compressibility of the water and usually take account of shock waves and their interactions. Some explicitly model the growth of the gas bubble. All make one-dimensional approximations to the flow within the LP side of the heat exchanger. The overall friction is modelled in terms of a loss coefficient which can be obtained from the pressure drop during normal operation.

Three computer models (those of Fluor Daniel, Hydraulic Analysis and W S Atkins) took part in the validation exercise. In phase (a), all were conservative when compared with the experimental results for peak pressure in the shell when run "blind" using commercial modelling assumptions (see Figure 4). These results therefore support the use of a one-dimensional modelling approach.

In phase (b), it was possible to investigate some of the factors giving rise to the spread of predictions shown in Figure 4. It was found that good input data for the models on disc burst time and shell-side friction are important. The results were less sensitive to tube burst time and this work identified that a tube burst time in the range instantaneous to 0.7 ms is appropriate (for carbon steel tubes). Shell-side friction information will usually be available from the heat exchanger designer. Disc burst time, or safety valve opening time, is important and it was recommended that further work be done to measure such parameters. When input assumptions were changed to the agreed best estimate values, the predictions of the models converged and gave good agreement with the experimental data. Some of the differences between model predictions and experimental results could be explained by the fact that the models assume that all the water is driven out of the shell by the gas, but in the experiments significant water remained within the shell.

Guidance has been developed by the Institute of Petroleum[3], giving recommendations for the assumptions to be made when modelling the fluid dynamic aspects of tube rupture in heat exchangers. This should help to ensure that sufficiently accuarate predictions can be obtained using any of the available one-dimensional models.

COMPARISON WITH FINITE ELEMENT MODEL PREDICTIONS

Associated work was carried out at Sheffield University to study the failure criteria for heat exchanger shells subjected to short duration pressure pulses[7,8]. A finite element model of a heat exchanger shell was developed and was validated using both small-scale shock tube data and the large-scale experimental results reported here. Good agreement was obtained.

A finite element model allows failure criteria to be developed, whereby the failure pressure is higher than for static loading if the duration of the pressure pulse is very short. However, if this were to be used for design, such a finite element model would need to be developed for the specific application (shell dimensions, material etc.). The model could then be used to predict the maximum stress developed in response to the short duration high pressure pulse predicted by the fluid dynamic model. This stress could then be compared with the allowable stress within the pressure vessel design code. This possible approach is further discussed in the Institute of Petroleum guidance[3].

CONCLUSIONS

1. Large-scale tube rupture experiments have been carried out on a shell-and-tube heat exchanger, typical of those in use in the North Sea. Experimental data suitable for the validation of both fluid dynamic modelling of the flows/pressures and finite element modelling of the stress in the shell have been generated.

2. The experimental data support the use of one-dimensional fluid dynamic models to predict the flowrates, shell pressures and forces on the heat exchanger and connected lines. The relief system opening time and the shell-side friction are important input data to such models. The measurement of opening times of typical bursting discs and safety valves is recommended.

3. The experimental data also support the possibility of using finite element modelling to take account of the effect on the shell of the high pressure pulse being of short duration rather than a static load.

4. The results of this work have been used in the development of guidance on safe design to take account of tube rupture in shell and tube heat exchangers (Institute of Petroleum, 2000).

ACKNOWLEDGEMENTS

This work was carried out as a Joint Industry Project sponsored by the Institute of Petroleum; the Health and Safety Executive; Amerada Hess; BHP Petroleum; CMPT; Esso Engineering; Fluor Daniel Applied Computer Solutions; Marathon Oil; Mobil North Sea; Phillips Petroleum; Shell International Oil Products; Texaco North Sea; and Total Oil Marine. In-kind support was given by: Fluor Daniel Applied Computer Solutions; Foster Wheeler Energy Ltd.; Hydraulic Analysis Ltd.; IMI Marsden Ltd.; Marathon Oil; Motherwell Bridge Thermal Ltd.; Shell International Oil Products; Texaco North Sea; Trident Consultants Ltd.; and W S Atkins. Related work carried out by the University of Sheffield was funded by the Engineering and Physical Sciences Research Council. We should like to express particular thanks to Mr C Weil (consultant); Dr B Ewan and Mr M Moatamedi (Sheffield University); IMI Marsden Ltd.; Foster Wheeler Energy Ltd.; and Messrs P Kerry, D Bagshaw and E Belfield (HSL).

REFERENCES

1. Goyder HGD (1996). Structural integrity assessment of heat exchangers following a tube rupture. AEA Technology Report AEAT-0347, April 1996

2. Goyder, H.G.D., (1997). Tube rupture in high pressure heat exchangers", ASME Conference, Dallas, 1997.

3. Institute of Petroleum (2000) Guidelines for the design and safe operation of shell and tube heat exchangers to withstand the impact of tube failure, ISBN 0 85293 286 3

4.   Trident (1993) " Report to the Institute of Petroleum on the Development of Design
        Guidelines for Protection Against Over-Pressures in High Pressure Heat Exchangers:
        Phase One", Trident Consultants Ltd and Foster Wheeler Energy, Report J2572,
        known as "The Trident Report".

5.   Wilday A.J. and Thyer A. M. (1995). The protection of heat exchangers against tube
        rupture - literature review. HSE Internal Report, IR/L/RAM/ES/95/11.

6.   Wilday A.J., Thyer A. M. and Ewan, B.C.R., (1996). Shock tube experiments to
        partially model tube rupture in high pressure shell-and-tube heat exchangers. HSE
        Internal Report, RAS/96/12, FS/96/12

7.   Ewan, B C R, (1999), "A study of the failure criteria for vessels under transient
        pressure loadings", Report to EPSRC

8.   Ewan, B C R & Moatamedi, M, (2000), "Design aspects of chemical plant exposed to
        transient pressure loads", submitted to Chem. Eng. Research & Design, Trans IChemE
        Part A

Figure 1
The instrumented heat exchanger before installation in bunker

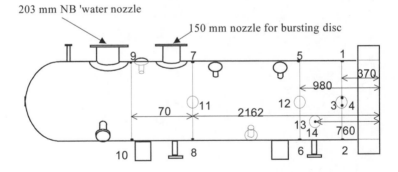

Figure 2
Instrument positions on shell and their separation

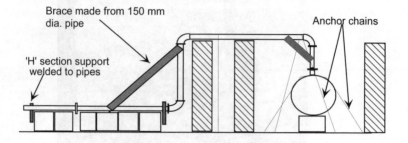

Figure 3
Sketch showing 150 and 203 mm water discharge pipework
and method of securing pipes/heat exchanger in bunker

One tonne bags of gravel on horizontal pipe run outside bunker not shown

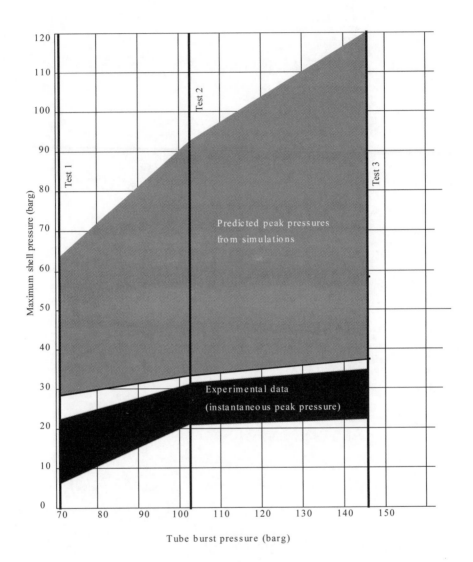

Figure 4
Comparison of experimental data with one dimensional fluid dynamic model predictions

TURBULENCE GENERATED DURING VENTED GASEOUS DEFLA-GRATIONS AND SCALING ISSUE IN EXPLOSION PROTECTION

V.V. Molkov

The University of Ulster, 75 Belfast Road, Carrickfergus, BT38 8PH

The paper presents recent findings in quantitative evaluation of turbulence generated during venting of gaseous deflagrations in empty enclosures without initial turbulence. A correlation dependence of venting generated turbulence is presented and discussed. The scale of enclosure and the Bradley number are shown to be the main parameters influencing the turbulence generated during venting. This correlation is a part of the innovative vent sizing technology that is based on two correlations, which are valid for various combustible mixtures and enclosures of arbitrary volume and strength. The conservative form of the universal correlation for vented gaseous deflagrations is presented for the first time. The result of a comparison between the suggested conservative vent sizing formulas, experimental data and predictions by the empirical vent sizing technique of NFPA 68 standard (Edition 1998) is given. The influence of turbulence generated during venting on vent sizing of enclosures with inertial vent covers is analysed and equation for scaling of upper limit for vent cover inertia is suggested. The upper limits for vent cover inertia are estimated for enclosures of different volume from 0.1 to 1000 m^3, which can withstand the same maximum overpressure of 30 kPa and have the same vent cover release overpressure of 3 kPa. Results have demonstrated that inertial vent covers have 100% "efficiency", if inertia is below an upper limit calculated by the suggested equation, even the absolute value of inertia is much higher than the level that has been accepted so far.

INTRODUCTION

As a part of the new ATEX Directives, manufacturers of venting devices have to provide vent efficiency data, including vent inertia effects [1-2]. Although the effect of turbulence has been generally acknowledged as being a major factor in the development of gas explosions, no quantitative measurements have been attempted to assess the extent of this effect in venting experiments with inertial vent covers until today.

Butlin concluded in 1975 that turbulence should be studied in future work [3]. In 1978 Anthony underlined again that the production of an adequate mathematical model for vented deflagration would depend on resolving the problem of turbulence [4].

Some models, as those for dust explosions [5], assume that the flame propagates throughout the entire event at a constant effective burning velocity. This is probably a fair enough approximation in dust explosions, where turbulence generally dominates the combustion process. However, it is not true for situations involving gas mixtures, where the venting process itself is known to cause the flame to accelerate [5]. Governing equations for turbulent vented gaseous deflagrations were derived from the first principles in paper [6]. The inverse problem method for vented gaseous deflagrations has been developed [7] and efficiently used over the years of research allowing to gather unique data on venting generated turbulence. For example, an analogue to the Le Chatelier-Brown principle for vented gaseous deflagrations [7] was revealed by this method. On the way to an innovative performance-based vent sizing technology a generalization of international experimental data was performed for vented gaseous deflagrations and the universal correlation was revealed for the first time in 1995 [8] followed by the closure of this fundamentally new vent sizing approach with the correlation for venting generated turbulence, which was presented for the first time two years later in 1997 [9]. Two of our previous articles were devoted to the problem of inertial vent covers in explosion protection [10-11]. Recently our original correlations for vent sizing were developed further to include experimental data on fast burning mixtures, such as near stoichiometric and rich hydrogen-air mixtures, and test data on elevated initial pressures [12-15].

There are some statements on inertia effects in early publications. For room-size enclosures in high turbulence tests with specified fasteners inertial effects appear to be evident with panels weighing 6 kg/m^2 or more and the data obtained suggest that the influence of inertial effects on the release pressure cannot be ignored for panels weighing more than about 10 kg/m^2 [16]. A recent paper [1] states that above the 60-m^3 vessel volume, the effect of panel inertia up to 10 kg/m^2 can be taken to be negligible, but below there is uncertainty. Other sources suggest similar values, for example Cooper [2] states that, as the volumes increase beyond 100 m^3, doors with a mass of less than 20 kg/m^2 could be employed with little or no penalty on the predicted reduced pressure. However, there are still questions: do these conclusions still hold for near-stoichiometric hydrogen-air and very lean/rich hydrocarbon-air mixtures, and what is the penalty, if any, for higher inertia? To neglect the influence of vent cover inertia Bartknecht [17] suggests a mass of less then 10 kg/m^2, whereas NFPA 68 suggests approximately 12 kg/m^2. In the UK, values of up to 25 kg/m^2 have been acceptable in the past, with some vents being more than 40 kg/m^2 [2]. The Russian standard SNiP II-90-81allows the inertia of relief panel of 120 kg/m^2! Can the inertia values given above be applied to any enclosure volume, vent area and combustible mixture?

The problem of scaling for vented gaseous deflagrations with inertial vent covers does not seem to have received a great deal of attention. Most of the works have been done on too small a scale to be applicable to deflagrations in large-scale enclosures, including buildings. Research should therefore include derivation of the scaling laws [4]. That is the main objective of this paper.

VENTING GENERATED TURBULENCE

It is well known today that vent opening will facilitate the distortion of flame front due to reasons of different physical nature. Numerous types of flame front instabilities, its cellular or fractal structure development and large-scale flame front–flow interactions are some of these reasons. As a result, the burning velocity in vented vessel is known to exceed its value for laminar spherical flame in up to 100 times, depending on conditions. The *turbulence factor* is a widely accepted concept that characterises the augmentation of burning velocity or, what is more correct, the flame front area with respect to the ideal case of laminar spherical flame propagation. Until 1995 the data on the turbulence factor obtained by different authors were not correlated [8, 18]. The main barrier was the use of different models, some of which have been built on unacceptably rough assumptions.

It is clear that the turbulence factor is not constant in the course of vented deflagration. The turbulence factor increases with the vent opening when combustion in a closed enclosure proceeds to deflagration in the vented one. It can grow up or slow down in course of vented deflagration depending on conditions. The turbulence factor can decrease due to flame laminarisation close to walls, flame extinction, etc. Nevertheless, in our approach we use the constant turbulence factors – one before venting, χ_0, and another one after the vent cover is released, χ. This is a simplification. However, it coincides with the conclusion by Swift et al. [19], who attempted to employ a variable turbulence factor in their analysis: "it seems best to employ a constant turbulence correction factor and gain the corresponding simplicity, rather than to carry more elaborate equations through a train of numerical computations whose accuracy is also limited to only a narrow range of experimental conditions".

The attempts to produce any reasonable correlations for venting generated turbulence have failed for another reason as well – due to a neglect of the role of the generalised discharge co-efficient, μ, which is dependent on vented deflagration conditions. This fact of discharge coef-ficient dependence on conditions was recognised already about 20 years ago by various au-thors. It has been demonstrated in a series of studies that reduced explosion pressure corre-lates with the *deflagration-outflow interaction (DOI) number*, that is the ratio of the turbu-lence factor, χ, to the discharge coefficient, μ, rather than with the turbulence factor alone. Tufano et al. [20] paid particular attention to this issue. They have recommended the follow-ing correlation for the DOI number (*effective turbulence factor* in their terminology)

$$\chi / \mu = 0.51 \cdot W_C^{0.6} \cdot \exp(-0.27 / \pi_v^3), \tag{1}$$

where the venting parameter is

$$W_C = \frac{\mu F A}{V} \frac{c_{ui}}{S_{ui}} \sqrt{\frac{2}{\gamma - 1}}, \tag{2}$$

that is close to our Bradley number (see equation (4)).

We have processed experimental data on vented gaseous deflagration in a wider range of conditions than in [20] and have obtained the correlation for venting generated turbulence in the form [15, 25]

$$\chi / \mu = \alpha \cdot \left[\frac{(1 + 10 \cdot V_\#^{1/3}) \cdot (1 + 0.5 \cdot Br^\beta)}{1 + \pi_v} \right]^{0.4} \cdot \pi_{i\#}^{0.6}, \tag{3}$$

where the empirical coefficients α and β are equal for hydrocarbon-air mixtures to α=1.75 and β=0.5 and for hydrogen-air mixtures to α=1.00 and β=0.8 and the *Bradley number* is

$$Br = \frac{F}{V^{2/3}} \cdot \frac{c_{ui}}{S_{ui}(E_i - 1)}. \tag{4}$$

Correlations (1) and (3) express different dependence of the turbulence level, which is measured in our papers by the value of the DOI number, on enclosure scale. The turbulence will increase with volume/scale according to our correlation (3) and will not change with scale in the previous correlation (1) if the Bradley number (or W_c) is constant. It has been shown previously [14] that our result (3) agrees with the conclusions of Gouldin [21] who used the fractals theory in turbulent flames modelling. Both our results of direct processing of large amount of experiments and the fractal-based approach yield the power dependence of the turbulence factor on enclosure scale with the exponent equal to about 0.4. In contrast to the earlier correlation (1), we have revealed dependence not only on the Bradley number (*venting parameter* in terminology of [20]) and the vent opening pressure but on the *enclosure scale*, $V^{1/3}$, too. This finding allowed us to improve the vent sizing technology drastically.

The influence of the vent cover release pressure on the level of turbulence is different in the correlations (1) and (3) as well. However, the size of variation of this parameter and hence its influence on the DOI number is not so important as for two other arguments - enclosure scale and the Bradley number. Since the influence of the vent release pressure on the venting generated turbulence can not be revealed unambiguously from the existing experimental data, we will leave discussion on this issue for the future.

A reasonable compliance of the DOI numbers obtained directly from processing of the data of 44 experiments in enclosures, of various volumes up to 8087 m^3 and initial pressures up to 0.7 MPa, with the DOI numbers calculated by the correlation (3) is demonstrated in Fig. 1. Noticeable experimental data scattering can be seen at high level of turbulence for large-scale experiments in "segment" form 4000 m³ enclosure [23] and Monsanto real explosion in 8087 m³ building [24].

The dependence of the DOI number on enclosure volume is presented in Fig. 2 for a series of the Bradley number 0.3, 3, 30, 330 and dimensionless vent opening pressure π_v=1.01 for both hydrocarbon-air and hydrogen-air mixtures. The turbulence level grows with volume of enclosure. The higher the Bradley number the higher the DOI number for a given volume of enclosure. The influence of the Bradley number is more significant for hydrogen-air mixtures.

The DOI numbers have been obtained recently [15] by processing experimental data on vented 4.8% propane-air deflagrations in a vessel of 0.65 m³ volume [22] at atmospheric and elevated pressures up to 0.7 MPa with central ignition. It is easy to see in Fig. 3 that the suggested correlation between the DOI number and the initial pressure is reasonable. The turbulence level for vented deflagration in conditions of experiments [22] increased from 4-6 at initial atmospheric pressure to 15-20 at initial pressure 7 atmospheres. Hence the increase of initial pressure from 1 to 7 atmospheres leads to about four-fold increase of the turbulence level. It has been found that there is only 20% increase of the turbulence factor for the stage of deflagration in closed vessel for the same increase of initial pressure [25]. This result demonstrates explicitly that it is venting that is responsible for a substantial increase in the turbulence level, but not just an elevated initial pressure itself.

The correlation (3) suggested fits the experimental data regardless of the location of ignition source relatively to a vent (see Fig. 4).

CONSERVATIVE VENT SIZING

The universal correlation for vented gaseous deflagrations was obtained previously by the best fit to experimental data. However, explosion safety practitioners are used to employ techniques that are conservative from a practical point of view rather than accurate from a mathematical point of view. The conservative form of the universal correlation has been developed in this paper

$$\frac{\pi_{red}}{\pi_v^{2.5}} = 5.65 \cdot Br_t^{-2.5} (\frac{\pi_{red}}{\pi_v^{2.5}} \leq 1; Br_t \geq 2) \quad \text{and} \quad \frac{\pi_{red}}{\pi_v^{2.5}} = 7.9 - 5.8 \cdot Br_t^{0.25} (\frac{\pi_{red}}{\pi_v^{2.5}} > 1; Br_t < 2), \quad (5)$$

where the turbulent Bradley number Br_t is proportional to the ratio of the Bradley number and the DOI number. The exact proportion coefficient is given in the following formula:

$$Br_t = \frac{\sqrt{E_i/\gamma_u}}{\sqrt[3]{36\pi_0}} \cdot \frac{Br}{\chi/\mu}. \quad (6)$$

The correlation estimate of the DOI number in the form (3) has been employed to design the correlation (5) and hence has to be used along with it in vent sizing. The essence of the conservative approach is to "cover" all experimental points on the graph from the top. Two curves (5) cover from the top all the processed up to date 139 tests, as shown in Fig. 5. All the data for the experimental points in Fig. 5 were taken directly from the tests processing excluding the values for the DOI numbers, which were calculated by the correlation (3) and then substituted to the turbulent Bradley number.

The correlations (3) and (5) form the base for the innovative performance-based vent sizing technology. This technology has been compared recently in our current study with the most wide spread in the world the NFPA 68 standard "Guide for venting of deflagrations". A detailed comparison between these two approaches is not the objective of this paper. However, it is useful to mention that in about 90% of cases the predictions of experimental results made using our innovative technology are more accurate. It is the demonstration that the physically sound theoretical approach can produce more robust engineering tool compared to the existing purely empirical approach.

SCALING OF VENT COVER INERTIA

The phenomenon of the double pressure peak in vented gaseous deflagration experiments has been well established since the beginning of research at 1950th, but it has not been explained on a satisfactory theoretical basis for a long time [3]. The principal works by Yao [26], Pasman et al. [27], Bradley and Mitcheson [28] proved theoretically the existence of a two-peak structure. The first theoretical work of the present author [6] in 1981, that laid the foundations for all the studies that followed, explained this phenomenon too. Later in 1986, a more complex four-peak pressure structure was revealed and investigated for cubic enclosures and very low vent release pressures [29]. Increasing the failure pressure of relief panels to 7.5 kPa was found to result in two pressure peaks becoming the dominant features of the observed pressure-time profiles [29]. Moreover, the relative ease, with which the fourth acoustically driven peak can be significantly reduced in magnitude or eliminated altogether, suggests that in most practical situations acoustically enhanced pressures will be of little or no importance [29, 30].

It seems that Cubbage and Simmonds [31] were the first who made the statement that inertia of the vent panel, at least over the range of conditions of their tests, had no effect on the second pressure peak. It was demonstrated then in 1978 by Zalosh [32], for tests in a 0.19-m³ vessel with the same vent area but different vent release pressures, that the second peak pressures were almost identical, even though the first peaks differed by a factor of 2.5. The phenomenon has been explained theoretically in our paper [11]. This result would be expected to be correct only in those cases where the vent cover is removed fully before the completion of deflagration inside enclosure. Recent experimental results on vented deflagration in a small-scale duct with ignition at rear wall have shown that the phenomenon of independence of the second pressure peak on the first one does not work always [33]. The case of central ignition in an enclosure with the ratio of the smallest to the largest sizes less than 1:3 will be considered further in this paper. We will employ the effect of independence of the second pressure peak on the vent cover release pressure in our further calculations.

In 1973 Cubbage and Marshall suggested a formula for the maximum explosion pressure at the first pressure peak that appears after the release of the inertial vent cover [34]

$$P_1 = P_v + 0.023 \cdot S_u^2 \cdot K \cdot w / V^{1/3}.$$ (7)

Equation (7) is based on experiments in chambers of volumes up to 30 m³ using a variety of fuel gases to maximize the range of burning velocity. Unlike the Cubbage and Simmonds's formula for freely lying horizontal relief panels [31], this latter correlation was devised from the experiments with relief panels that were positively fixed and had to be physically broken by the overpressure in order to create an open vent (P_v is larger than about 2 kPa). The fact that the overpressure is proportional to the square S_u^2 of the burning velocity, and not to S_u, leads to some overestimation of the explosion pressure for mixtures with $S_u > 0.5$ m/s. On the basis of experiments with such mixtures, British Gas [35] recommended that the coefficient in (7) should be reduced from 0.023 to 0.007. There is even an opinion that the equation (7) can be applied with confidence to empty rooms of volumes up to 200-300 m³ [36].

Let us consider enclosures able to withstand internal overpressure not more than 1 bar. It means that the first of two equations (5) can be used to calculate the second pressure peak. Hence, for initial atmospheric pressure we can write

$$P_2 = 1 + 5.65 \cdot P_v^{2.5} \cdot Br_t^{-2.5} (Br_t \geq 2).$$ (8)

For the overpressure at the second peak to be less than 1 bar the turbulent Bradley number has to be equal to 2 or greater.

Russian scientists Korotkikh and Baratov concluded more than 20 years ago that the cause of building destruction by internal gaseous deflagration is in most cases not the insufficient vent area but the excessive inertia of removing elements [37]. Since that time there has been no suggestions of a reasonable relationship that would calculate the upper limit of the cover inertia dependent on the enclosure volume, the vent size, the mixture characteristics and the venting generated turbulence.

It can be stated that for a cost-efficiently designed explosion protection system, when the vent area is equal to its lower limit and the inertia may be equal to its upper limit, the first pressure peak value has to be equal to or less than the second peak value. The upper limit for the inertia of a vent cover can be derived from this assumption after simple calculations with equations (7) and (8) and presented in the form

$$w \le \frac{V^{1/3} \cdot (F/A_{cs})}{0.023 \cdot S_u^2 \cdot \chi^2} \cdot \left[1 + P_v \left(\frac{5.65 \cdot (36 \cdot \pi_o)^{5/6}}{Br^{2.5} \cdot (E_i/\gamma_u)^{5/4}} \cdot (\chi/\mu)^{2.5} \cdot P_v^{1.5} - 1 \right) \right], \tag{9}$$

where the burning velocity, S_u, has been multiplied on the turbulence factor, χ, as a conservative measure.

Let us calculate the upper limits for the vent cover inertia of enclosures of different volume of 0.1, 10, 100, and 1000 m^3 for the following model conditions and at the assumption that formula (7) is valid for cases under consideration. Let us suggest for simplicity that enclosures have a cubical form, and a relief panel is mounted in one side only and has an area enough to ensure the reduced pressure 30 kPa. Let us assume further that for all enclosures the vent cover release pressure is equal to P_v=1.03 bar and near-stoichiometric propane-air mixture is used as a fuel (S_u=0.31 m/s; E_i=7.9; γ_u=1.365; c_{ui}=335 m/s). These values of reduced pressure and vent release pressure have been used to determine the value of the turbulent Bradley number Br_f=3.4 by the first of the two equations of the universal correlation (5). The turbulent Bradley number is the same for all cases. The DOI numbers were calculated by the correlation (3). The values for the turbulence factor were calculated from the DOI numbers with a characteristic value of the discharge coefficient μ=0.6 for all enclosures. The values of the vent areas F, and hence the respective ratios F/A_{cs}, were calculated by employment of the correlations (5) and (3) of the conservative vent sizing technology. General initial and intermediate data and the results of calculation of the upper limit of the vent cover inertia for different enclosures are given in Table 1.

Table 1. General initial, intermediate data and upper limits for vent cover inertia.

V, m^3	F, m^2	F/A_{cs}	Br	χ/μ	χ	w, kg/m^2
0.1	0.04	0.20	31	4.5	2.7	< 0.31
10	1.76	0.38	59	8.6	5.2	< 16
100	11.62	0.54	84	12.3	7.4	< 113
1000	77.70	0.78	122	17.7	10.6	< 782

It is easy to see that the upper limits of the vent cover inertia depend significantly on the enclosure volumes. Nevertheless all vent covers are of 100% "efficiency". The same material can be "heavy" for small-scale enclosure and "light" for large-scale ones. For example, the density of glass is about 2470–2560 kg/m^3 and hence the inertia of panes with thickness in the range of 2–5 mm constitutes 5–13 kg/m^2. Such inertia practically has no influence on the value of the first pressure peak in empty room-size enclosures and enclosures of bigger volume without initial turbulence. However, glass is unacceptable for use as a vent cover for enclosures with volume of about 0.1 m^3 under the conditions considered in this paper. On the other hand, we have obtained that the upper limit of the inertia for the vent covers in large-scale enclosures is about 800 kg/m^2 even if the estimate is conservative. This value is well above those from 0.5 to 20 kg/m^2 that are under discussions for implementation into international standards.

CONCLUSIONS
The correlation for venting generated turbulence, i.e. the DOI number, is presented and discussed in detail. It is an essential part of the innovative performance-based vent sizing technology, which predicts experimental data on vented gaseous deflagrations with better accuracy than other vent sizing techniques, including the NFPA 68 standard. The conservative form of the universal correlation for vented gaseous deflagrations is presented for the first time.

The issue of scaling of vent cover inertia is analysed. The equation to calculate the upper limit for inertia of vent cover is suggested for the first time. It takes into account the dependence of the venting generated turbulence on the conditions of vented gaseous deflagration, such as the scale of enclosure and the Bradley number. Conservative estimations have shown that the upper limit for vent cover inertia is reaching 113 kg/m^2 for 100 m^3 enclosure and 782 kg/m^2 for 1000 m^3 enclosure (the case of propane-air mixture and reduced pressure of 30 kPa is considered). This is substantially higher than the values under consideration for implementation into international standards. The equation suggested has to be verified further against experimental data and can be used in the future as a part of performance-based vent sizing technology.

NOMENCLATURE
A characteristic enclosure size, m
A_{cs} cross section area of enclosure which is parallel to a wall with relief panel, m^2
Br Bradley number
Br_t turbulent Bradley number
c_{ui} speed of sound at initial conditions of deflagration, m/s
E_i combustion products expansion coefficient at initial conditions
F vent area, m^2
K vent area coefficient (ratio of the area of enclosure cross section to the area of relief)
P_1, P_2 values of the first and the second pressure peaks, bar abs.
P_i initial pressure, bar abs. = 10^5 Pa
P_{max} maximum explosion pressure at the second pressure peak, bar abs. = 10^5 Pa
P_{red} reduced pressure, bar gauge = 10^5 Pa, $P_{red} = (P_{max} - P_i)$
P_{stat} vent closure release pressure used in the NFPA 68, bar gauge = 10^5 Pa, $P_{stat} = P_v - P_i$
P_v vent closure release pressure, bar abs. = 10^5 Pa
S_u laminar burning velocity, m/s
S_{ui} burning velocity at initial conditions, m/s
V enclosure volume, m^3
$V_{\#}$ dimensionless volume (numerically equal to enclosure volume in m^3), $V_{\#} = V / V_{1m^3}$
w inertia of vent cover, kg/m^2
W_C venting parameter by Crescitelli et al.
Greek
α, β empirical coefficients

γ_u, γ specific heats ratio for unburned mixture

μ generalized discharge coefficient

π_{red} dimensionless maximum explosion overpressure (reduced pressure), $\pi_{red} = P_{red} / P_i$

π_v dimensionless vent closure release pressure, $\pi_v = P_v / P_i = (P_{stat} / P_i + 1)$

$\pi_{i\#}$ dimensionless initial pressure, $\pi_{i\#} = (P_i / 1\,bar)$

π_0 "pi" number, $\pi_0 = 3.14$

χ turbulence factor after vent opening

χ_0 turbulence factor before vent opening

χ/μ deflagration-outflow interaction number (the DOI number)

χ / μ_{exp} the DOI number, determined by processing experimental data

REFERENCES

1. Lunn, G.A., Holbrow, P. and Brookes, D.E., 2000, Some practical solutions in dust explosion protection, Presented at the *Third International Seminar on Fire and Explosion Hazards.* 10th-14th April 2000, Lake Windermere, UK.

2. Cooper, S., 1998, Explosion venting – the predicted effects of inertia, *Proceedings of Institution of Chemical Engineers*, Symposium Series No. 114, 305-309.

3. Butlin, R.N., 1975, A review of information on experiments concerning the venting of gas explosions in buildings, *Fire Research Note No. 1026*, 19 p.

4. Anthony, E.J., 1977/78, The use of venting formulae in the design and protection of building and industrial plant from damage by gas or vapour explosions, *Journal of Hazardous Materials*, 2: 23-49.

5. Tamanini, F., 1996, Modeling of panel inertia effects in vented dust explosions, *Process safety Progress,* 15: 247-257.

6. Molkov, V.V. and Nekrasov, V.P., 1981, Dynamics of Gaseous Combustion in a Vented Constant Volume Vessel, *Combustion, Explosion and Shock Waves*, 17: 363-369.

7. Molkov, V.V., Baratov, A.N. and Korolchenko, A.Ya., 1993, Dynamics of Gas Explosions in Vented Vessels: A Critical Review and Progress, *Progress in Astronautics and Aeronautics,* 154: 117-131.

8. Molkov, V.V., 1995, Theoretical Generalization of International Experimental Data on Vented Explosion Dynamics, *Proceedings of the First International Seminar on Fire-and-Explosion Hazard of Substances and Venting of Deflagrations,* 17-21 July 1995, Moscow - Russia, 166-181.

9. Molkov, V.V., 1997, Scaling of Turbulent Vented Deflagrations, *Proceedings of the Second International Seminar on Fire-and-Explosion Hazard of Substances and Venting of Deflagrations,* 10-15 August 1997, Moscow - Russia, 445-456.

10. Molkov, V.V., Nikitenko, V.M., Filippov, A.V. and Korolchenko, A.Ya., 1993, Dynamics of Gas Explosion in a Vented Vessel with Inertial Vent Covers, *Proceedings of Joint Meeting of the Russian and Japanese Sections of The Combustion Institute,* Chernogolovka - Moscow Region, 2-5 October 1993, 183-185.

11. Molkov, V.V., 1999, Explosions in Buildings: Modelling and Interpretation of Real Accidents, *Fire Safety Journal,* 33: 45-56.

12. Molkov, V.V., 1999, Explosion Safety Engineering: NFPA 68 and Improved Vent Sizing Technology, *Proceedings of the 8th International Conference INTERFLAM'99 Fire Science and Engineering,* 29 June – 1 July 1999, Edinburgh, Scotland, 1129-1134.

13. Molkov, V.V., Dobashi, R., Suzuki, M. and Hirano, T., 1999, Modeling of Vented Hydrogen-Air Deflagrations and Correlations for Vent Sizing, *Journal of Loss Prevention in the Process Industries,* 12: 147-156.

14. Molkov, V.V., Dobashi, R., Suzuki, M. and Hirano, T., 2000, Venting of Deflagrations: Hydrocarbon-Air and Hydrogen-Air Systems, *Journal of Loss Prevention in the Process Industries,* 13: 397-409.

15. Molkov, V.V., 2000, Unified Correlations for Vent Sizing of Enclosures against Gaseous Deflagrations at Atmospheric and Elevated Pressures, *Proceedings of the Third International Symposium on Hazards, Prevention, and Mitigation of Industrial Explosions,* 23-27 October 2000, Tsukuba, Japan, 289-295.

16. Howard, W.B. and Karabinis, A.H., 1982, Tests of explosion venting of buildings, *Plant/Operations Progress,* 1: 51-65.

17. Bartknecht, W., 1978, Explosionen. Springer-Verlag, Berlin, Heidelberg, New York.

18. Zalosh, R.G., 1995, Review of Gas Deflagration Venting Models, *Proceedings of the First International Seminar on Fire-and-Explosion Hazard of Substances and Venting of Deflagrations,* 17-21 July 1995, Moscow - Russia, 79-84.

19. Epstein, M., Swift, I. and Fauske, H.K., 1986, Estimation of Peak Pressure for Sonic-Vented Hydrocarbon Explosions in Spherical Vessels, *Combustion and Flame,* 66: 1-8.

20. Tufano, V., Crescitelli, S. and Russo, G., 1981, On the design of venting systems against gaseous explosions, *Journal of Occupational Accidents,* 3: 143-152.

21. Gouldin, F.C., 1987, An Application of Fractals to Modeling Premixed Turbulent Flames, *Combustion and Flame,* 68: 249-266.

22. Pegg, M.J., Amyotte, P.R. and Chippett, S., 1992, Confined and Vented Deflagrations of Propane / Air Mixtures at Initially Elevated Pressures, *Proceedings of the Seventh International Symposium on Loss Prevention and Safety Promotion in the Process Industries,* Toormina, Italy, 4-8 May, 110/1-110/14.

23. Harrison, A.J., and Eyre, J.A., 1987, The Effect of Obstacle Arrays on the Combustion of Large Premixed Gas/Air Clouds, *Combustion Science and Technology,* 52: 121-137.

24. Howard, W.N., 1972, Interpretation of a Building Explosion Accident, *Loss Prevention,* 6: 68-73.

25. Molkov, V.V., 2000, Explosion Safety engineering: Design of Venting Areas for Enclosures at Atmospheric and Elevated Pressures, *FABIG Newsletter,* Issue No.27, 12-16.

26. Yao, C., 1974, Explosion Venting of Low-Strength Equipment and Structures, *Loss Prevention,* 8: 1-9.

27. Pasman, H.J., Groothuisen, Th.M. and Gooijer, P.H., 1974, Design of Pressure Relief Vents, In *Loss Prevention and Safety Promotion in the Process Industries,* Ed. Buschman C.H., New-York, 185-189.

28. Bradley, D. and Mitcheson A., 1978, The Venting of Gaseous Explosions in Spherical Vessels, *Combustion and Flame,* 32: 221-236 and 237-255.

29. Cooper, M.G., Fairweather, M. and Tite, J.P., 1986, On the Mechanisms of Pressure Generation in Vented Explosions, *Combustion and Flame,* 65: 1-14.

30. van Wingerden, C.J.M., and Zeeuwen, J.P., 1983, On the role of acoustically driven flame instabilities in vented gas explosions and their elimination, *Combustion and Flame,* 51: 109-111.

31. Cubbage, P.A. and Simmonds, W.A., 1955, A investigation of explosion reliefs for industrial drying ovens. I – Top reliefs in box ovens. *The Gas Council Research Communication GC23,* 46 p.

32. Zalosh, R.G., 1978, Gas Explosion Tests in Room-Size Vented Enclosures, *AIChE Loss Prevention Symposium,* 13: 98-110.

33. Ibrahim, S.S. and Masri, A.R., 2001, The effects of obstructions on overpressure resulting from premixed flame deflagration, *Journal of Loss Prevention in the Process Industries,* 14: 213–221.

34. Cubbage, P.A. and Marshall, M.R., 1973, Pressures generated by explosions of gas-air mixtures in vented enclosures. *Inst. Gas Engineers Communication*, No. 926.

35. British Gas, 1990, Review of the applicability of predictive methods to gas explosions in offshore modules. London: Department of Energy. 175 p., Offshore Technology Report OTH 89 312, ISBN 0-11-413314-X.

36. Lautkaski, R., 1997, Understanding vented gas explosions. Technical Research Centre of Finland, *VTT Research Notes 1812*, 129 p.

37. Korotkikh, N.I. and Baratov, A.N., 1978, Vent area calculation for enclosures in case of internal gaseous deflagration, *Flammability of Substances and Chemical Fire Extinguishing Agents*, Transactions of VNIIPO, Issue 5, pp.3-15 (in Russian).

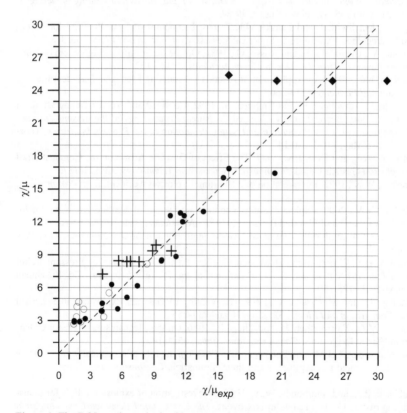

Figure 1. The DOI numbers obtained by processing experimental data, χ/μ_{exp}, and determined by correlation (3), χ/μ, for enclosures of different volume: black circles - 0.02-1.00 m^3 (including experiments at elevated initial pressures up to 7 bar [22]); white circles – 2-11 m^3; crosses – 30-50 m^3; diamonds – 4000-8087 m^3.

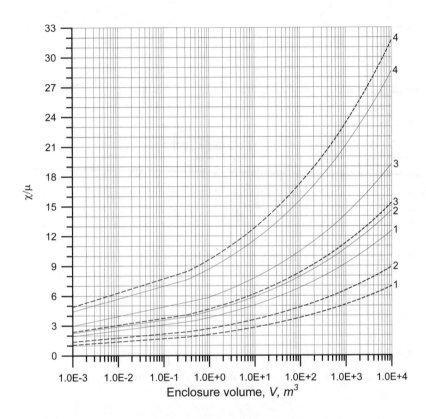

Figure 2. The dependence of the DOI numbers on enclosure volume for hydrocarbon-air (solid lines) and hydrogen-air (dashed lines) mixtures for dimensionless vent cover release pressure $\pi_v = 1.01$ and the Bradley number 0.3 (curves 1), 3 (curves 2), 30 (curves 3) and 330 (curves 4).

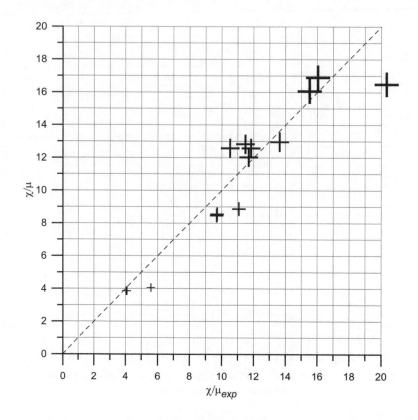

Figure 3. The DOI numbers obtained by processing experimental data [22] at atmospheric and elevated pressures, χ/μ_{exp}, and determined by correlation (3), χ/μ: four series of tests with initial pressures 1, 3, 5 and 7 bar (the higher initial pressure the bigger cross size on the graph).

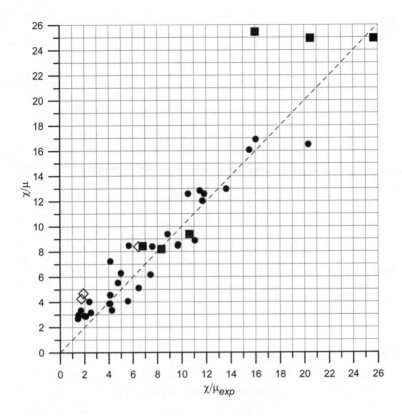

Figure 4. The DOI numbers obtained by processing experimental data, χ/μ_{exp}, and determined by correlation (3), χ/μ, for different locations of ignition source: black circles – centre; black squares – rear wall; white diamonds – near the vent.

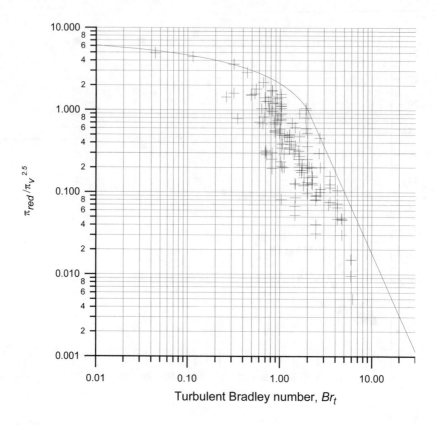

Figure 5. The conservative form of the universal correlation (solid curve) and 139 experimental points (crosses).

THE RELIABILITY AND ACCURACY OF REMNANT LIFE PREDICTIONS IN HIGH PRESSURE STEAM PLANT

Ian Chambers
Safety and Reliability Division, Mott MacDonald

Studies have been carried out to show how failure probabilities can be calculated from plant measurements, to set confidence limits on predictions of time-to-failure for components under varying load or operating conditions.

The studies concentrate on creep damage in steam pipework, but the method developed can be generalised to a wide range of situations, because it relies only on general principles of measurement, rather than the specific technique or application. It uses numerical simulations to show how the reliability of time-to-failure predictions depends on the characteristics of measurements taken on plant, such as frequency of testing, accuracy of measurement technique, and number of samples taken at each inspection.

Keywords: Failure, probability, pipework, simulation, prediction

INTRODUCTION

This paper investigates what can be done to optimise predictions of the safe life of ageing plant, where the predictions are based on measurements characterising the current state of the plant and their historical trends. Taking a simple physical situation as a test case, it demonstrates how some simple simulation work can shed useful light on how best to concentrate finite resources on inspection using an approach that can be readily generalised to other forms of plant ageing.

The original work dealt specifically with high pressure, high temperature steam pipework, subjected to regular inspection, whose failure would cause significant financial loss to its operators and might pose a hazard to personnel. On the other hand, replacement of ageing pipework also involved a significant cost penalty, both in terms of the cost of the new component and in plant downtime. Over the years, a variety of techniques and design codes have been developed to give conservative predictions of a component's remaining life, but the simulation work described here goes beyond these to improve estimates of the actual remnant life, and so get maximum use (and therefore financial return) from it.

Such a situation is familiar to operators of many different types of plant, as they seek to optimise their inspection and maintenance strategies, and it leads to a number of questions concerning what can be done to improve the accuracy of the predictions of how much of a component's safe life still remains. Can the predictions be improved by making inspections more frequently? Would taking more measurements at each inspection have the same effect? What benefit would an improved measurement technique bring (to set against its development and implementation cost)? To try to answer these questions, safe life predictions have been simulated using a simple mathematical model, in which the frequency of inspection, number of measurements per inspection, and a range of other important parameters could be varied, and the effectiveness of the predictions could be quantified and compared. In this context, assessing effectiveness takes account of the undesirable instances where a component is marked for replacement prematurely, so incurring a cost penalty which would be avoidable with a more effective safe life prediction. The model is based on an idealised physical model of creep ageing of steam pipework, and the simulation work first investigates the effectiveness of different inspection and measurement strategies under ideal conditions of well-defined material properties and material behaviour, before going on to simulate uncertainties in both these parameters.

THE PHYSICAL MODEL: CREEP DAMAGE IN STEAM PIPEWORK

Creep is the gradual stretching of a piece of metal under the influence of an external load, even though the stress the load creates in the metal is below the material's yield stress. It is a relatively slow process, but the rate of growth is generally more pronounced at high temperatures and varies over the life of a component, as well as having its obvious dependence on the magnitude of the applied load [1].

Creep's variation over a component's lifetime is characterised by three distinct phases. The first, known as primary creep, occurs at the start of a component's life, is usually of relatively short duration and poses little risk of component failure, as the fresh metal of a new component is very likely to have high integrity, despite the fact that the strain rate is relatively high in this phase.

Following this, a component usually settles down into the secondary creep phase, a long period when the strain rate is considerably slower and almost constant for a given set of operating conditions, representing the great majority of the component's useful life. During this phase, however, component strain will be accumulating more rapidly at stress-raising features, via a variety of mechanisms, as well as slowly reducing the pipe's thickness and strength.

Eventually the accumulation of creep damage increases to such an extent that the component's ability to withstand the loads applied to it is significantly compromised, and the creep rate increases again. In this tertiary creep phase, the risk of the component failing in service is usually so high that it is deemed to have reached the end of its useful life. Inspections therefore have the aim of detecting the onset of tertiary creep, characterised by an acceleration of the creep growth rate after a long stable period of steady growth.

THE MATHEMATICAL MODEL: SIMULATION OF CREEP AND CREEP RATE

INSPECTION INTERVAL AND MEASUREMENT CHARACTERISTICS

Eqn. 1 shows the equation used to simulate the under-lying creep rate, R_{creep}, varying as a function of time, t,

$$R_{creep}(t) = R_{const}\left[1 + 0.1e^{\alpha(t-\tau)}\right] \qquad (1)$$

where $R_{const} =$ a constant, which defines the secondary creep rate,

      α =   a constant defining how quickly the creep rate increases when tertiary creep sets in,

and τ =   the time at which tertiary creep sets in.

(The equation, developed for this work, is a simple mimic of the typical strain rate behaviour, and is not intended as a model of the actual physical processes involved)

The process of taking measurements on creep-affected pipework was simulated by defining the pipe's actual creep strain history, based on Eqn.1. Measurements of the creep strain were simulated by generating a set of random numbers at regular intervals along the strain history (representing regular inspections). The measurements were taken from a population normally-distributed about the true underlying strain rate, whose standard deviation defined the accuracy with which a set of such measurements could be made. This allowed the effects of different inspection intervals, different levels of measurement accuracy, and different numbers of measurements per inspection to be investigated. In practice it is often found that when taking plant measurements some inspection staff produce much more tightly grouped sets of measurements than do others. This was simulated by allowing the standard deviation of the measurements to vary from inspection to inspection.

As shown in Fig. 1, the model produces an almost constant creep rate early on (representing secondary creep), followed by a very rapid increase, due to the exponential term in the bracket expression representing tertiary creep. In practice operating conditions will vary during a plant's life, subjecting the steam plant to a range of different temperatures and pressures, and so imposing a fluctuation on the creep rate. This was represented in some of the simulations by allowing the mean secondary creep rate to vary irregularly over time, partially masking the onset of tertiary creep. Note that creep strain is essentially the fractional change in the component's size, and is therefore dimensionless.

Life estimates of creep-affected pipework, are often made by using the creep rate in the following equation for the total component life [2],

$$t_{comp} = \frac{\varepsilon_R - 0.01}{\lambda \varepsilon'} \tag{2}$$

where $\quad$ t_{comp} is the component's life (in hours),
$\quad\quad\quad\quad$ ε' is the measured creep strain rate,
and $\quad\quad\quad$ ε_R and λ are material constants (the uniaxial ductility and a correction factor for multiaxial effects)

The expression is derived from the assumption that the creep strain at failure is the creep strain rate multiplied by the component's life. The constant 0.01 allows for the short primary creep phase when creep is relatively rapid. In practice, up-to-date creep rate data are used in the expression, which indicates the onset of tertiary creep when successive predicted values of t_{comp} show a trend to reduce markedly.

Results of the simulation work with Eqn.1 were used to investigate the accuracy and reliability of Eqn.2 under different inspection strategies.

FAILURE CRITERIA: DETECTING TERTIARY CREEP AND DEFINING END-OF-LIFE

Calculating the Creep Rate

Two pieces of information are required to establish whether creep has started to accelerate into the tertiary phase: a good estimate of the secondary creep rate (assumed constant for a given set of operating conditions), and an indication of the current trend.

The long-term average creep rate was calculated using a least squares fit, including all the data available up to the time of measurement (Fig. 2). So after two inspections the creep rate was simply based on two data points (the means of the measurements taken at each inspection). After three inspections, the rate was based on a least squares fit to three data points, and so on. As more data points were included in the fit, the fluctuations due to measurement inaccuracies tended to be smoothed out. This fitted long-term average was taken to be the best estimate of the secondary creep rate.

Least squares fitting was also used to calculate the current trend in the creep rate, following each inspection. However, in this case the number of previous data points included in the fitting process affects the method's ability to detect and follow trends. Fits based on small quantities of data are more susceptible to error and fluctuation than fits using many data points. When fitting to a small number of points each data point makes a relatively large contribution to the fit, and so points where the error is large tend to contaminate the overall result. Fits based on larger numbers of points fluctuate less, but when tertiary creep sets in, its presence is masked by the influence of earlier data points, from the phase of secondary creep. Therefore a longer interval elapses between the onset of tertiary creep and its unambiguous appearance in the fitted creep rate calculations.

Defining End-of-Life

The artificial data were used to investigate how easily the onset of tertiary creep could be resolved from the general scatter of measurements. Scatter tends to mask trends in the data, and to introduce spurious fluctuations into the calculated creep rate, which can give the false appearance of tertiary creep. Studies were carried out to establish the effect of measurement accuracy, inspection interval, etc. on the detectability of tertiary creep.

THE MOST IMPORTANT MEASUREMENT CHARACTERISTICS

Frequent measurements ought to indicate when failure is imminent, and prevent in-service failures, but this has to be set against the cost and operational penalties of carrying out inspections, and the possibility that measurement errors will lead to the component being replaced prematurely. For an optimum balance to be struck, it is necessary to know how the probability of failure varies with inspection interval.

Factors which affect the measurement accuracy also affect the predictions of failure probability, as does the criterion chosen to indicate that failure is imminent. The importance of different measurement characteristics was investigated using the artificial data described previously. In each case, a series of twenty simulations were produced, to examine how detection of tertiary creep depends on each of the measurement characteristics.

A BASE CASE FOR COMPARISONS

First of all a set of artificial measurements were generated that were typical of the measurements taken in practice from plain pipework, using the characteristics shown in Table 1.

An example of a set of measurements based on this definition is shown in Fig. 1 and Fig. 2 shows the corresponding creep rates, along with the best estimate secondary creep rate and the criterion used to detect tertiary creep. In this case the measured creep rate was based on just the two most recent sets of measurements, so that increasing creep rate can be detected with minimum delay. Even so, tertiary creep was not detected until three inspection intervals after its onset. During this time the actual creep rate had increased nearly seven-fold, so there is a clear risk that the component would fail before tertiary creep could be detected.

Table 1   Typical Data Describing Creep of Plain Pipework, and Measurements Made During the Pipe's Life: *The inspection interval has been normalised to 1.0 to ease comparisons with other inspection intervals. The natural scatter of the data sometimes leads to negative measured creep rates, but these were excluded from creep rate calculations, as would probably be done in practice.*

Characteristic	Value
True secondary creep strain rate	4×10^{-4} per inspection interval
Inspection interval	Normalised to 1
Maximum allowed standard deviation of measurements	10^{-3}
No. of measurements per inspection	4
Censor out negative creep rates?	Yes
Criterion for onset of tertiary creep	Doubling of creep rate

There is also one spurious indication of tertiary creep in Fig. 2, where the criterion is satisfied early on, although tertiary creep has not actually begun. In practice, however, indications of failure so early in life can usually be recognised as spurious and discarded. Therefore, in this case the indication was ignored. In general, any spurious indications occurring in the first quarter of life were ignored on the same grounds.

Out of twenty simulations, all sharing the measurement characteristics in the table above, all but one resulted in detection of tertiary creep within three inspection intervals of its start. The probability of detection within three intervals is therefore 95%. However, thirteen simulations resulted in spurious detection, so the reliable detection of genuine tertiary creep is offset by 65% probability of premature retirement from service.

SENSITIVITY STUDIES

Inspection Interval

More frequent inspections might be expected to improve the reliability and promptness with which tertiary creep can be detected, but in fact detection of accelerating creep was found to occur at the same time as in the base case. Furthermore there was considerable scatter in the measurements which would probably have led to spurious indications of tertiary creep. The data would have to be subjected to careful interpretation to determine whether the increase in creep rate were genuine or just an artefact of the measurement inaccuracies.

On average, halving the inspection interval did lead to earlier detection of tertiary creep, but spurious detection becomes so frequent as to mask the true result. In practice the criterion for tertiary creep detection would have to be relaxed, further inspections would be necessary, and overall there would be little or no benefit from the extra effort expended. Relaxing the detection criterion from a factor of two increase in creep rate to a factor of four restored the frequency of spurious detection of tertiary creep to a value comparable to that found in the base case, but the time taken to detect tertiary creep deteriorated back to the base case value.

Measurement Accuracy

Accuracy was represented in the artificially-generated data by the measurements' standard deviation; small standard deviation corresponded to high accuracy. The measurements were allowed to fall on a normal distribution, whose mean was the true creep strain at that time, so the mean of a large number of measurements would tend towards the true strain value.

The base case, in Fig. 1, used a standard deviation on the creep strain measurements of up to 1×10^{-3}, which is a fifth of the strain at the onset of tertiary creep. To see what effect improved accuracy would have, the allowed standard deviation of the measurements was reduced to 3×10^{-4}. Improving the accuracy of the measurements decreased the scatter, and made the onset of tertiary creep easier to detect. In this case, the failure criterion could be tightened, allowing detection of tertiary creep two inspections after its onset, compared with three in the base case.

Number of Measurements at Each Inspection

The base case assumed that four measurements were taken at each inspection, their mean being the best estimate of the creep at that time. A set of twenty simulations were carried out assuming twelve measurements per inspection. This is an increase of a factor of three compared with the base case, and allows direct comparison with the results of the previous section, where the measurement accuracy was improved by a factor of three. As might be expected, tertiary creep was detected with similar promptness and reliability to the case with improved accuracy.

Overall, spurious detection was much more common in this case than the previous one, where the accuracy of the measurements was improved. Nonetheless, there is a clear benefit from increasing the number of measurements, compared with the base case.

THE EFFECTS OF PROCESSING THE MEASUREMENT DATA

USING MORE DATA POINTS TO IDENTIFY THE TREND

As well as the characteristics of the measurements, detecting trends in the data and determining end-of-life depend on how the data are processed. Investigating the effect of inspection interval showed spurious detection became much more likely if the interval were short. However, this was based on a very simple calculation of the creep rate, using just the most recent measurement and the one before it. Smoother trends result from using more data points to determine the recent behaviour, at the penalty of longer delays in spotting the onset of tertiary creep.

To see how the additional data point affects the reliability of the measurements, a set of twenty simulations were carried out. Compared with two-point fitting, the results showed a small improvement. They were also a little better than those produced by the base case, but the overall difference was not very great, and may well not justify the extra expense and effort involved.

QUANTIFYING THE UNCERTAINTY

Uncertainty in the Measure Creep rate

Since in practice it is not possible to determine the under-lying creep rate exactly, a least squares fit through all the measured data must be used as the best estimate of the true rate. Clearly, this changes over the life of the component, as more and more inspections are carried out, and an increasing number of data points go into the least squares fit.

Quantifying the uncertainty associated with this procedure involves quantifying the degree of scatter about the least squares fit. The simplest way of doing this is to calculate the difference between each creep rate measurement and the long-term best estimate. A reasonable approximation of the best estimate's accuracy after n measurements can then be found from the root mean square of all these individual differences, that is,

$$\delta_{RMS}(n) = \sqrt{\frac{\sum_{i=1}^{n}\left[\varepsilon'(i) - \varepsilon''(i)\right]^2}{n}} \qquad (3)$$

where $\delta_{RMS}(n)$ is the root mean square error after n measurements,
        $\varepsilon'(i)$ is the best estimate of the long-term creep rate after i measurements,
and $\varepsilon''(i)$ is the best estimate of the instantaneous creep rate at the ith measurement.

This expression can then be used as an estimate of the range of values for creep rate. After n inspections, the long-term creep rate is estimated to be $\varepsilon'(n) \pm \delta_{RMS}(n)$, which can serve as a means of calculating the probability of obtaining a creep rate within that range. In the examples given above, where the measurements were assumed to be normally-distributed about the mean, so it would be reasonable to assume the creep rate is normally-distributed about $\varepsilon'(n)$, with standard deviation $\delta_{RMS}(n)$.

Uncertainty in the Component Life Prediction

Measured creep rates are used in Eqn. 2 to predict component life. Having established the uncertainty in the creep rate, this can be fed into Eqn. 2 to estimate the uncertainty in the component life prediction, which can be shown as error bars on a graph of predicted component life, Fig. 3.

It is a relatively simple matter to apply the same approach to other uncertainties that arise in Eqn. 2, such as the range of possible values for the material constants. The end result is a clear visual indication of the reliability of all the life estimates that have been made (from the length of the error bars), and note how the error bars shrink and life predictions depart from the long term average as the end of the component's life approaches.

DISCUSSION

On the basis of the simulations presented here, the most effective means of improving predictions of in-service failure is to improve the accuracy of the technique used to characterise the damage state of the plant. In many cases this will be easier said than done, but the simulations give a basis for determining whether the costs of developing or procuring a more accurate system would be cost-beneficial, compared with the outage and inspection time involved with some of the other alternatives.

This message is reinforced by comparing two of the other studies: it was considerably more beneficial to collect a relatively large number of measurements at a few, widely-spaced inspections, than to take frequent inspections consisting of a small number of measurements each. Using this knowledge, the most cost-effective inspection strategies for a piece of plant can be drawn up.

An important point to bring out from the study is that the principles can be applied to a much wider range of situations than the simple case of creep in steam pipework. As long as a reasonable physical model of the underlying damage process is available, mathematical simulations of the measurement process can be carried out, to guide and inform the development of inspection strategies. The simulations were performed with readily available and inexpensive mathematical modelling software, and provide considerable flexibility, such as allowing for operator-to-operator variations, and comparing different means of fitting and analysing the data once it has been collected. The main difficulty in setting up the simulations is to ensure that all the important factors affecting accuracy have been taken into account. To some extent this can be eased during development by carrying out some scoping calculations with the model, to rank the factors according to their importance, which helps determine the appropriate level of detail in modelling them.

CONCLUSIONS

The main feature of the results of this study into the effectiveness of different measurement strategies is that a small number of good quality, reliable measurements may well prove more useful than a large group of poor ones. This was evident from the relatively small improvement obtained from reducing the inspection interval and the relatively high benefit from improving the accuracy of the measurement technique.

The study also makes evident the need for a pre-defined inspection strategy, based on a knowledge of how inspection data can be best used, which will allow operators to get the most from their inspection efforts.

REFERENCES

1. Iron and Steel Standards Policy Committee ISE/73
   Guidance on Methodology for the Assessment of Stress-Rupture Data Part 1:
   Procedure for the Derivation of Strength Values
   PD 6605 : 1997 (Final Draft)

2. Clews J A, Barraclough D R, Browne R J, Cane B, Hepworth J K, Phillips J, and
   Plastow B, 1985,
   Creeplife Assessment of Boiler Pressure Parts Using Strain Data
   CEGB

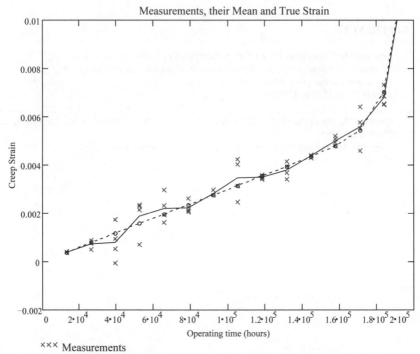

Fig. 1   Example of Artificial Measurements Generated from Base Case Data: *Initially the up-turn in the creep rate late in life is masked by scatter in the data.   If strains of the order of 0.005 are sufficient to cause failure, there is significant probability of failure between the last two inspections.*

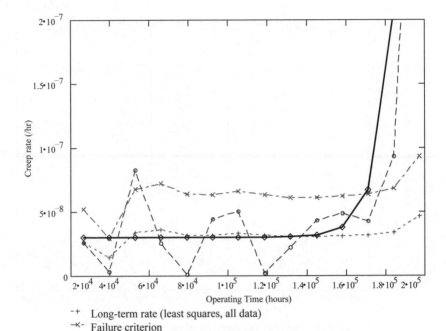

Fig. 2 The Actual and Measured Creep Rates from the Base Case: *The measured rate follows the actual rate with only a short time lag, although there is considerable fluctuation due to scatter in the data. The two near-horizontal lines represent the best estimate of the secondary creep rate (lower line) and the criterion chosen to remove the component from service, i.e. creep rate accelerates to double the secondary creep rate.*

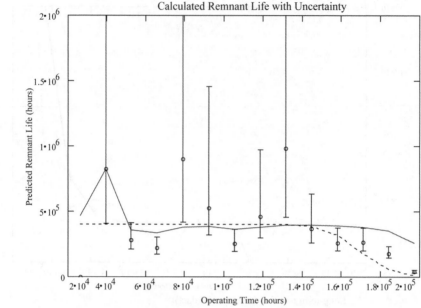

Long-term best estimate based on all measurements
One standard deviation confidence limits

∘∘∘ Instantaneous best-estimate, based on 3 most recent points
-- Using true creep rate and mean material properties

Fig. 3 Predicted Component Life, with One Standard Deviation Confidence Limits, from the Base Case: *The confidence limits are based on the scatter of the creep rate data, assuming that material properties are fixed. The best-estimate and standard deviation were based on a least squares fit using the three most-recent inspection, which was found to be a good compromise between accuracy and number of inspections required to detect imminent failure.*

PREPARATION OF A PHARMACEUTICAL INTERMEDIATE : AN EXAMPLE OF HOW INHERENT SAFETY CAN BE MAXIMISED DURING THE EARLY STAGES OF PROCESS DEVELOPMENT

S Hallam and P Wilkinson

Process Safety Group, AstraZeneca, Macclesfield, Cheshire, SK10 2NA

An inherently safe process has been defined as one which by virtue of its design will not generate a hazard if a fault occurs. Whilst inherent safety has traditionally been pursued by working with the principles of substitution, minimisation, attenuation and simplification [1], it is often very difficult, if not impossible, to make all processes inherently safe. In this situation the goal then becomes one of making the process as inherently safe as possible. The purpose of this paper is to show, by reference to the synthesis of a pharmaceutical intermediate, how it is possible to make very significant increases in the level of inherent safety within a process providing thermal stability and kinetic data is available.

Keywords: Inherent Safety

INTRODUCTION

It would obviously make life much simpler if every chemical process was inherently safe, ie no matter what went wrong, there would be no hazard. In reality this would be impossible to achieve and we are in fact often faced with the task of making processes as inherently safe as possible.

Within AstraZeneca, a potential new drug comes into Process Research and Development Department (PR&D) usually only after having been made on a very small scale. The process will not have been designed for plant scale operation but rather to produce material for initial screening tests, ie toxicological, efficacy etc. The development of the compound passes to a team of chemists whose aim is to devise a synthesis that is appropriate to the scale of manufacture. The initial campaign is usually carried out within the Large Scale Laboratory (LSL), which is equipped with glass reactors. Subsequent campaigns, where an increasing quantity of material is required, are usually carried out in conventional multi-purpose chemical plant.

When a compound first comes into PR&D a meeting is held between representatives of the Development, LSL and Process Safety teams, the purpose of which is to try and identify any potential problems before any significant development work is carried out. The following is an example of how beneficial this procedure can be in increasing the inherent safety factor within a chemical process.

OUTLINE OF PROCESS

The process under investigation involved the formation of hydroxylamine free base by the addition of aqueous sodium hydroxide to a mixture of hydroxylamine hydrochloride and water at ambient temperature. The batch temperature was then increased to 50°C and reagent X added. After acidifying with hydrochloric acid the batch is concentrated via distillation, the product isolated as a solid and finally dried. A more detailed description is given below.

1. Hydroxylamine hydrochloride and water are charged to the reactor.

2. Aqueous sodium hydroxide is added in a controlled manner, the batch temperature being maintained at 20°C.

3. On completion of the addition the batch temperature is raised to 50°C.

4. A solution of reagent X is added in a controlled manner.

5. On completion of the addition the batch is stirred for a further 2 hours at 50°C before cooling back to 20°C.

6. Hydrochloric acid is added to adjust the batch pH to 3.

7. The batch is concentrated by distilling under vacuum at a maximum batch temperature of 30°C.

8. The residue is extracted with toluene and re-distilled under vacuum at a maximum batch temperature of 34°C.

9. Cyclohexane is added and the product filtered off and dried.

FORMATION OF HYDROXYLAMINE FREE BASE

The literature contains many references to incidents involving hydroxylamine free base [2], including two recent incidents at Concept Chemicals in Allentown, Pennsylvania [3], and at Nissin Chemical in Japan [4]. In these two incidents nine people were killed and at least thirty eight were injured. The hazardous nature of hydroxylamine free base, which was highlighted at the initial meeting between development, production and safety representatives, resulted in a decision to evaluate, at the earliest opportunity, the kinetics of the reaction as well as the thermal stability of the various mixtures generated in the process.

The addition of aqueous sodium hydroxide was carried out in a power compensation calorimeter. The addition was exothermic, the overall heat of reaction being determined as - 11 kcal/mol hydroxylamine hydrochloride. Subsequent calculation indicated that the associated adiabatic temperature rise was 30K. Heat was evolved immediately on starting the addition, a maximum power output equivalent to 34 watts / mol hydroxylamine hydrochloride being recorded after 4 minutes, before falling gradually back to 13 watts / mol hydroxylamine hydrochloride by the end of the addition. On completion of the addition the power output fell quickly back to the baseline indicating no significant accumulation. It was therefore possible to conclude that the heat of reaction was controllable via the rate of addition and that the process could be operated safely on a large scale. Unfortunately even though the heat of reaction would not give rise to any hazard a thermal stability test (Carius tube) carried out on a sample of the batch after the addition of sodium hydroxide had been completed, showed the presence of a large exotherm from 58°C. It should be noted that all the thermal stability tests reported in this paper were carried out in the presence of very small quantities of mild steel, cast iron and stainless steel. This is done in order to simulate the presence of materials of construction.

This test is only used for screening and requires the incorporation of a scale factor if the onset temperature is to be related to operation on the plant scale. Application of the scale factor gave a potential plant onset temperature of below ambient and as the process called for the batch to be heated to 50°C there was obviously a potentially serious problem. In order to accurately determine the decomposition onset temperature under adiabatic conditions a Dewar experiment was carried out. This showed clearly that the hydroxylamine free base reaction mixture did self-heat from ambient temperature, the batch temperature reaching reflux after just over 15 hours, with approximately 5% of the batch being distilled from the reactor. It was therefore recommended that the batch temperature was not raised to 50°C following the addition of sodium hydroxide.

The adiabatic Dewar experiment clearly showed that the hydroxylamine free base reaction mixture would self heat from ambient temperature to reflux in the absence of cooling. Ejection of material and / or overpressurisation of the reactor was also a possibility. Consequently even though the batch was no longer going to be heated to 50°C, the consequences of loss of cooling at 20°C still needed to be addressed. The obvious way forward was simply to increase the heat capacity of the batch and the decision was taken to increase the initial water charge by 60%. A second adiabatic Dewar experiment carried out on the more dilute process still showed that the batch would self heat from ambient temperature but importantly that the rate of temperature rise was much slower, ie 25 hours to reach 96°C and that reflux would not be attained.

ADDITION OF REAGENT X

Discussions with the development chemists confirmed that reaction of the hydroxylamine free base with reagent X did not go to completion at ambient temperature and that it was necessary to increase the batch temperature to 50°C. They were also able to confirm that the reaction proceeded in two steps, an initial condensation followed by a cyclisation. It was therefore decided to carry out the addition of reagent X at 20°C and then, following subsequent thermal stability testing, to decide what processing conditions were most appropriate.

The addition of reagent X was carried out in a power compensation calorimeter and shown to be exothermic. The overall heat of reaction was determined as -29 kcal/mol hydroxylamine hydrochloride, the associated adiabatic temperature rise being calculated as 55K. Heat was evolved immediately on starting the addition, a maximum power output equivalent to 28 watts / mol hydroxylamine hydrochloride being recorded after 3 minutes. The power output then remained fairly constant at around 21 watts / mol hydroxylamine hydrochloride for the remainder of the addition before falling quickly back to zero on completion of the addition, ie no accumulation. Analysis of the batch however confirmed that the reaction had not gone to completion and that only the initial condensation had taken place.

A thermal stability test carried out on a sample of the batch after the addition of reagent X showed the presence of an initial exotherm from 61°C with a second from 152°C. Subsequent thermal stability testing of the batch after heating to 50°C showed that the exotherm at 61°C was no longer present. Analysis of the reaction mixtures both before and after heating to 50°C clearly showed that the exotherm seen from 61°C was associated with the cyclisation. The heat evolution associated with the cyclisation was not excessive and a gradual warming of the batch following addition of reagent X was acceptable from a chemical reaction hazard standpoint.

WORK-UP AND ISOLATION

In the originally submitted process the work-up involved the addition of hydrochloric acid followed by a distillation and isolation procedure that resulted in the final product being isolated as a solid. The addition of the hydrochloric acid was evaluated by power compensation calorimetry and shown to be exothermic. The overall heat of reaction was determined as -8 kcal/mol hydroxylamine hydrochloride, the adiabatic temperature rise being calculated as 14K. The heat was evolved immediately on starting the addition, ie no delayed onset and there was no significant accumulation on completion of the addition. It was therefore concluded that the heat was controllable via the rate of addition and that as thermal stability testing of the batch showed no exothermic activity at anywhere near the proposed operating temperatures, that this stage of processing would be free from chemical reaction hazard.

A thermal stability test (Carius tube) carried out on a sample of the final product showed the presence of an endotherm associated with melting from 59°C, followed by a very large exotherm from around 110°C. It is very difficult to determine the onset temperature when an endotherm runs directly into an exotherm and further larger scale stability work would have been necessary in order to determine safe operating and drying temperatures. Another potential problem was that the rate of pressure rise was too fast for the standard equipment to record. Further testing using a modified Carius tube high rate apparatus did confirm that the compound would not be classifiable as an explosive but the exotherm associated with its decomposition was certainly large and fast enough to cause structural damage if accessed.

Subsequent discussions with the development chemists centred around ways of avoiding the isolation of the final product as a solid. It was agreed that the most appropriate way forward was to try and devise a work-up where the final product was obtained as a solution which could then be telescoped into the next stage of the synthesis. Continued process development resulted in a work-up where the batch, after the addition of hydrochloric acid, was extracted with butyronitrile, washed and then concentrated to approximately 9%w/w.

Thermal stability testing (Carius tube) of the solution after extraction into butyronitrile and after distilling to the desired concentration showed the presence of exotherms from 162°C and 166°C, which even after making an allowance for scale, were still well in excess of the proposed 60°C distillation service temperature.

SUMMARY OF CHANGES

1. The amount of water used during the formation of hydroxylamine free base has been increased

2. The batch temperature is not increased to 50°C after the addition of sodium hydroxide.

3. Reagent X is added at 20°C and then the batch temperature is raised to 50°C.

4. The product is not isolated as a solid, rather it is obtained as a solution which is telescoped into the next stage.

CONCLUSIONS

The initially submitted process could not have been operated safely on the plant scale.

The modified process was evaluated by the development chemists and shown to be acceptable both from a product quality and yield standpoint.

This paper illustrates both the need for process development chemists to be aware of the potential hazards that could be associated with their processes and the advantages that can be gained from the early involvement of Process Safety Groups, both in terms of inherently safer processes and the reduction in abortive effort.

REFERENCES

1. Designing and Operating Safe Chemical Reaction Processes, Health and Safety Executive.
2. Bretherick, Handbook of Reactive Chemical Hazards.
3. Incident at Allentown, PA, United States, Chemical Incident Reports Centre.
4. Incident at Ojima, Japan, Chemical Incidents Reports Centre.

AVOIDING EXPLOSIONS BY MEANS OF INERTING SYSTEMS

Barry J. Cunliffe
Chilworth Technology Limited

The paper discusses the production of a new safety manual on Inerting of potentially flammable atmospheres. The manual was produced for a third party company following a serious explosion at one of their sites. No one was injured, but the failure of the Inerting system led to an explosion heard five kilometres away. The main approach of the new manual is on the management of Inerting systems, as well as design, installation and maintenance.

Keywords: explosion, fire, inert, Inerting, flammable, process, safety, incident, management, process safety management.

INTRODUCTION

It is often the case that an explosion occurs for a readily foreseeable reason. What is often not the case, however, is that a series of bizarre events occur, leading to an explosion, which, though foreseeable with hindsight, may not have been given credence from the unusual series of events necessary that preceded it.

After an explosion had occurred in a major company, and Chilworth Technology had investigated it, a series of failures was found leading back to the most basic design of the process. The pharmaceutical company had a means for drying powders inside a drying 'oven', and the drying process consisted of ensuring that all water and solvents present were evaporated and extracted to atmosphere, under an inert gas blanket.

When the explosion occurred, it was heard five kilometres away, but, fortunately, no one was injured.

This paper is not on the cause of the incident, nor on why failures occurred in the installation concerned. What it is concerning, is the lack of suitable guidance preceding their explosion on one particular aspect of safety. That is the topic of Inerting. It was the Inerting system that failed, and had several defects in it, which had accumulated over the years after initial installation, culminating in the explosion.

Whilst, prior to the incident, there were five documents in general use on the topic of Inerting, there was not one which covered the topic of management of an Inerting system, nor which covered maintenance of an Inerting system. Therefore Chilworth Technology, in conjunction with the company concerned, devised a Design Concept to cover such issues for future use by the company.

EXISTING GUIDANCE

There are several existing guidance documents on Inerting. These are:

1.   Factory Mutual. Property Loss Prevention Data Sheets. 7-59. 1977, revised
      1998. Inerting and Purging of Tanks, Process Vessels and Equipment.

2.   VDI   2263   Part   2,   1992.   Dust   Fires   and   Dust   Explosions:
      Hazards – Assessment – Protective Measures.

3.   Guide to Dust Explosion Prevention and Protection. Part 2 – Ignition Prevention,
      Containment, Inerting, Suppression and Isolation. C. Schofield and J. A. Abbott.
      Institution of Chemical Engineers.

4.   NFPA 69, 1997. Standard on Explosion Prevention Systems

5.   ESCIS Booklet 3, 1994. Inerting. Methods and Measures for the Avoidance of
      Ignitable Substance-Air Mixtures in Chemical Production Equipment and Plants.

These all cover the establishment of inert atmospheres adequately, so no detailed calculations
are given in this paper. Reference to the above documents is recommended.
However, what none of them cover is the Management of Inerting systems.

After the explosion, Chilworth Technology attempted to combine the existing
documentation with existing knowledge of safety management systems. This produced a
Design Concept, which could then be applied to new or existing Inerting systems to determine
whether they are managed appropriately.

What the guidelines tried to produce was a logical means of ensuring that the Inerting
system for any hazardous process is designed, installed, maintained and MANAGED to an
acceptable level of safety.

The Design Concept, as with all guidance, is open to interpretation and is not rigid.
Chilworth Technology personnel created it, and the information it contains is, generally, in
the knowledge of Chilworth Technology, even though the company concerned published the
document internally. Chilworth Technology cannot offer sight of the document, as it is not
their property. However, the following aspects of the lecture will cover how the topic of
Inerting is assessed from design, through to commissioning and maintenance, and includes
comments on the management of the system. The overall aim is to try to ensure such a major
incident does not occur in another company, due to lack of knowledge of the Design Concept.

The Design Concept is intended to ensure that all aspects of design and management are
covered, and define certain terms in association with Inerting. This means that certain items,
such as Critical Safety Items, are defined, with respect to Inerting. When an item is a Critical
Safety Item, it must be suitably assessed to ensure that the Level of Integrity of the item is
capable of ensuring that a suitable Basis of Safety exists.

INERT GASES

The guidelines cover different types of gases used for Inerting. Carbon dioxide, nitrogen, noble gases, steam and flue gases, are all types of gases that can be used for Inerting.

The type of gas used should be determined by taking into account the following factors:

Cost;
Availability;
Reliability of supply;
Effects of contamination of product by inert gas, and
Effectiveness in reducing explosibility.

OPERATIONAL OXYGEN LEVEL DETERMINATION

There are four stages to be taken into account when considering oxygen levels in an inerted atmosphere. These are:

Limiting oxygen concentration;

Maximum permissible oxygen concentration;

First alarm level, and

Normal operating conditions.

The Limiting Oxygen Concentration (LOC) is the level applicable at the operating temperature and pressure. The value determined in/by the laboratory may not be directly applicable if the operating temperature or pressure is different, or if the experimental gas was different – obvious, but sometimes overlooked.

But this level has no safety margins, and is therefore a level at which any increase in oxygen leads to a flammable atmosphere.

Hence, a lower value, known as the Maximum Permissible Oxygen Concentration (MPOC) is used to obtain a safety margin. This is the safety shutdown level, and if the oxygen level is monitored and allowed to reach this level, the plant should shut down in a safe condition.

The MPOC is generally accepted as being two percentage points below the LOC, but this depends on factors such as how quickly the oxygen concentration can rise in case of failure of the Inerting system.

Below the MPOC is the maximum set point - normal alarm level. This is a level at which plant alarms sound, and which the operator can take reasonable action to try to recover the situation, prior to the oxygen level reaching plant shutdown. This should be set at a suitable level below the MPOC, and would depend upon the sensitivity of the equipment used to detect the oxygen levels.

Below the maximum set point is the set point – normal operating conditions. This is the level to which the plant is normally controlled.

It is apparent that if the LOC is not known for the chemical being inerted, then the MPOC cannot be set. If the MPOC cannot be set, then the normal operating conditions cannot be fully listed. Hence, for any plant relying on Inerting as a Basis of Safety, the LOC, MPOC, Maximum Set Point and Normal Operating Conditions must be listed and recorded. It is only when the plant is operated outside these figures, or with materials irrelevant to the recorded figures, that incidents can occur.

In other words, we start to see the beginnings of the requirements for managing the Inerting systems.

METHODS OF INERTING

The method of *Inerting* chosen will depend upon several factors, as follows:

1.   The process itself, continuous or batch (or simple storage);

2.   The design pressure of the equipment, i.e. its suitability to withstand pressure or vacuum;

3.   The financial implications of the various types of *Inerting*: demand, price, type of generation, constant flow or intermittent flow, etc.

4.   Health and ecological considerations.

In addition, there are several different types of inert gases available, for instance carbon dioxide and nitrogen, which are the usual gases, but also on-site exothermic gas generators, endothermic gas generators, noble gases, steam and flue gases from boilers, furnaces etc.

They all have different characteristics, but the choice of inert gas is usually led by (a) availability of supply, and (b) the phrase 'everyone uses nitrogen'.

It is usual to use nitrogen, but it must be realised it is not the only gas available, and others may be more obscure, but, for given functions, may be more desirable.

The purpose of the choice of inert gas is to satisfactorily ensure that the concentration of oxygen in the atmosphere never reaches the level at which an explosion can be supported. In order to ensure this aim is achieved, the Inerting system must be appropriately designed.

DESIGN

The atmosphere in the plant item should never reach a higher level than the MPOC. This concentration is determined by applying several safety factors to the LOC.

However, before the MPOC can be calculated, the LOC must be determined. This can be from such sources as Material Safety Data Sheet (MSDS) Lists, from the lists given at the end of the manual, or from test data. Tests should be carried out by laboratories experienced in this field, such as Chilworth Technology.

The method for determining the MPOC takes into account the following factors. (An example of MPOC determination is given in section 4.1.)

a)   A correction for any difference in temperature and pressure for the determined value of the LOC and the operating conditions.

b)   A margin which will allow for oxygen concentrations, safety measurement delays, instrument errors and lags, and alarm delays. It is usual to subtract a figure of 2 percentage points to give this margin, although occasionally this margin may need to be increased.

The MPOC can be considered an automatic shut down level. Below this are two other levels, 'first alarm level' and 'normal operating conditions'. These are determined from the following:

c)   A margin to ensure spurious (false) alarms do not occur – this would depend on the reliability and time lag in the instrumentation utilised.

d)   Where the Limiting Oxygen Concentration is below 5 per cent, and the plant is continuously monitored, the plant shall not operate at any level higher than 60 % of that Limiting Oxygen Concentration.

e)   Where the plant is NOT continuously monitored, the plant shall not operate at any level higher than 60 % of that Limiting Oxygen Concentration. If the Limiting Oxygen Concentration is below 5 per cent, the plant shall not operate above 40 % of that Limiting Oxygen Concentration.

Therefore, if a plant uses a continuously sampling oxygen analyser, (a), (b) and (c), above, hold. If the Limiting Oxygen Concentration of the material is below 5 %, then (d) has an effect and the set point must be less than 60 % of the Limiting Oxygen Concentration.

If a plant does not use a continuously-sampling analyser, or does not use an analyser at all, then (a), (b) and (c) hold in conjunction with a limit on the operating level of no higher than 60 % of the Limiting Oxygen Concentration. If the Limiting Oxygen Concentration is below 5 %, then (e) applies and the plant cannot have an operating level greater than 40 % of the Limiting Oxygen Concentration.

Hence, the four levels of oxygen concentration applicable to each inerted atmosphere should be recorded for every system that relies on inert gas Inerting as its Basis of Safety.

If the LOC for any of the flammable materials in the plant is not known, then the above cannot be completed correctly. Thus, the Limiting Oxygen Concentration must be known for every flammable material for which Inerting is to be the Basis of Safety.

In the case of flammable gases or vapours and dusts occurring together, the lowest Limiting Oxygen Concentration should be used, if no specific data for the hybrid mixture have been determined. The Limiting Oxygen Concentration of the flammable hybrid mixture will not be lower than the lowest value.

There are several ways of designing a process to operate with an inert atmosphere in them. But, however they are designed, all such plants should have a suitable way of ensuring the inert atmosphere is present prior to the flammable material being introduced.

A brief summary of each is as follows.

PRESSURE-SWING INERTING

In this method, the plant atmosphere is pressurised with inert gas, and then depressurised. This continues for a calculated number of cycles, whereby the oxygen concentration will have been reduced to a known concentration.

FLOW-THROUGH INERTING

Flow through Inerting is undertaken when the plant cannot stand increased pressure. In this case, inert gas is allowed to pass through the plant, displacing oxygen (air) in its path. This method, like above, can give calculable results, but on the often incorrect assumption that perfect mixing is taking place throughout the plant, and that there are no dead spots.

Whilst a pipeline can be adequately purged with flow-through Inerting, the same cannot always be said for industrial plant. If the system is complex, involving side branches through which adequate circulation cannot be established, this method may be impractical and one of the other methods may be more suitable.

VACUUM PURGING.

This method is useful if the plant to be inerted can withstand a vacuum. The plant pressure is reduced to a low internal pressure, and then the vacuum is broken with an inert gas. If necessary, the vacuum/break cycle can be repeated a number of times to reach the desired oxygen concentration.

SIPHON PURGING.

This is similar to vacuum Purging. However, the plant (more appropriately a storage tank) is filled with an inert liquid (say water), then as the liquid is drained out of the tank, inert gas is allowed to replace it.

The benefit of this method is that the required volume of inert gas is exactly equal to that of the vessel being inerted. It also requires only one cycle.

Whilst the above is a suitable method for Inerting vessels that have an outlet at high level, it is obviously not suitable for any item of equipment where air might be trapped inside a void. Additionally, it may not be suitable where the vapour pressure of the inert liquid is high enough to prevent all the vapour space being replaced by inert gas.

The important point to be made is that the flow dynamics have to be checked if dead spaces can occur.

RECORDING

For each plant one of the above methods should be documented as the Inerting method. The operational parameters should be recorded; e.g. length of time of purge, or number of pressure (or vacuum) /relief cycles. This, again, becomes a part of the documented Basis of Safety for the plant.

It would be useful at this stage to also include any calculations undertaken to show how the time or number of cycles was determined. Then, in the future, operational changes can readily be recalculated.

VERIFICATION

Once an inert atmosphere has been established, its presence needs to be verified before any flammable materials are admitted. There is the possibility of stratification with flow through Inerting, and air ingress with all methods of creating the inert atmosphere. Hence, the *Basis of Safety* has to be assured before flammable materials can be admitted. In fact, the admittance of the flammable materials can, in itself, allow air into the plant.

This may be due, for instance, to air being added with powders (bulk powders can contain up to 50 % of their volume as air), or air being pumped in from a nearly-empty drum.

Air can also access the plant if the inert atmosphere fails or is displaced, for whatever reason. These could be because of:

- Convection
- Density differences – air to inert gas
- Diffusion
- Manholes and other charging operations
- Leaks
- Negative operating pressure compared to ambient (i.e. operating under vacuum)
- Temperature
- Operating errors
- Pumping air, not liquid, when the tank is virtually empty
- Air entering when discharging liquids from the plant.

There are several methods of undertaking verification. The preferable one being, simply, measuring the oxygen concentration within the plant. Another is by ensuring inert gas keeps flowing into the plant, or the plant remains under a positive pressure. A few are discussed below.

OXYGEN ANALYSIS

In general, if an oxygen analyser is used, the oxygen concentration can be monitored continuously, cyclically or at random. If the system is totally self-contained, or is operating under slight negative pressure, then continuous monitoring is required. Conversely, monitoring at random assumes good working knowledge of the plant, and what the likely failure scenarios are. This information may have been obtained by continuous monitoring over a period of time, before the conscious decision was taken to reduce the sampling intervals.

The requirement for continuous monitoring on systems working under negative pressure applies only to those systems that rely on Inerting as a Basis of Safety. If a system is operating under near full vacuum, the Basis of Safety is then the presence of the vacuum, not inert gas Inerting.

The oxygen analyser should preferably sample from multiple parts of the plant. These points should not be close to an inert gas inlet, or to an outlet. In the former situation, this is to prevent sampling the inert gas, and not the actual contents. In the latter case this is because there is the chance of the flow-through gas bypassing most of the plant, and exiting directly through the vent.

The oxygen analyser must be capable of giving an alarm in the event of lack of flow into the analyser, reduced flow, or any other parameter that could indicate potential problems. If the situation becomes unsafe, and there is the possibility of the oxygen level increasing beyond the safe operational envelope (i.e. the MPOC), the plant should go to immediate automatic shutdown.

It may be difficult to determine what the possible alarm situations could be, and what effect they could have on the integrity of the plant. It is therefore useful at this stage for a competent Instrument Engineer to draw up a Cause and Effect Table. This is a table of identifiable failures of the instrument, and the outputs (or lack of them) that would result. As an example, power failure to the instrument may cause the visual gauge to drop to Zero. This would then indicate a situation in which there was no oxygen in the plant, and hence the plant was safe. This is obviously not the case, so appropriate alarms would be necessary to identify these situations.

Whatever system is used it must:

- be capable of analysing a representative sample of the contents of the plant;

- responding to alterations in the oxygen content of the plant with reasonable rapidity;

- be capable of raising a first-stage alarm;

- be capable of causing an emergency shut down automatically, or, at the very least, raising an alarm which instigates a shut down procedure;

- be repeatable and verifiable;

- be installed in accordance with the manufacturer's instructions;

- be maintained in accordance with the manufacturer's instructions;

- not be altered in any way without the manufacturer's agreement, or a suitable Management of Change procedure being carried out;

- not be capable of indicating a fault condition that is not readily detectable by alarms, indicators etc., e.g. zero or full scale deflection.

PRESSURE INDICATION

Whilst pressure indication on the plant can assure the operator that the plant is operating at too high a pressure to allow air in, it does not confirm that the atmosphere inside is actually inerted. Nor does it ensure that air is not admitted through powder admission or manhole activities etc. Pressure indication alone is therefore not considered to be suitable as verification.

VACUUM INDICATION

As was stated earlier, any system that operates under negative pressure should have the oxygen content monitored constantly. This is to ensure that leaks of air into the system do not occur without being readily detected.

This requirement does not extend to those systems that are operating at less than 100 mbar absolute. At this pressure, an explosion would not increase the system pressure greater than ambient. Also, any system that operates below 50 mbar absolute is incapable of supporting an explosion.

Hence, a system that operates below 100 mbar absolute has the presence of the vacuum as its Basis of Safety, and does not use Inerting as a means of explosion prevention. Thus the requirement for the constant analysis of oxygen is removed.

Failure of the vacuum system could easily lead to a dangerous situation, hence, this needs special consideration as a Safety Critical Item, but this is beyond this paper.

FLOW INDICATION

The flow of inert gas into the plant could be indicative of maintenance of a suitable inert atmosphere. However, the following points would also need to be addressed.

• Is there the possibility of the inert gas leaking from the supply pipe, but beyond the meter? This would show inert gas flowing into the plant, when actually it was leaking to atmosphere. If this is a possibility, this system in conjunction with pressure indication could suffice.

• Is the inert gas fed into suitable inlet locations? Admitting inert gas at the incorrect locations may lead to a false sense of security. The inert gas feed must be capable of maintaining a suitable sweep of any air admitted into the system, for instance at powder addition locations.

TIME

The parameter of time can be used, for instance, once the purge duration has been calculated, a valve can be opened for a set period of time. This will then allow the calculated amount of inert gas through, which will then inert the atmosphere as calculated.

Obviously, this will not always be the case, and no system is perfect. Therefore the system of Inerting has to be suitably managed.

MANAGEMENT

The purpose of the manual is to try to establish safe operational parameters for the Inerting system under consideration. In order to be 'safe', it is essential that the numbers of levels of safety are commensurate with the risk and the consequences of an incident.

Whilst the greater the levels of safety that are provided, the safer the system is, it can still be perfectly justified to allow a single Safety Critical Item to manage the safety of a large, dangerous, process. However, this is only if the Level of Integrity of that item is suitable.

It is more than likely to be common place that extra levels of safety are required to supplement any Safety Critical Items identified. Similarly, the extra costs incurred in ensuring that the integrity of any remaining Safety Critical Item is suitable, are liable to be prohibitively expensive compared to duplication or triplication of the item.

When Low Probability High Consequence events are considered, it is unlikely that any Safety Critical Items can be tolerated at all. In fact, it is probable that the items under consideration should be duplicated, or even triplicated by equipment that is not subject to Common Mode Failure. Hence, it would not be necessary to examine the hazardous situations caused by failure of a single item, but rather, to consider the implications of failure of any common denominators in the control or operational systems involved.

NOTE. The guideline comments on two independent means of identifying the presence of an inert atmosphere, and two independent means of ensuring it is present at all times a potentially-flammable atmosphere is present. However, when referring to redundancy, this is applied to each of the parameters, and not to the number of parameters chosen. Thus each of two independent means may, in themselves, be triplicated, if necessary.

But this analysis only supports the philosophy behind the manual. A low risk low consequence system can have one or more Safety Critical Items throughout the process; a high-risk high consequence system cannot have any Safety Critical Items. In between, the process must be subject to a standard risk assessment.

Maintenance becomes a crucial part of the Basis of Safety when two or more systems are installed to prevent either being a Safety Critical Item. For, if one of the items fail, the other, by definition, then becomes a Safety Critical Item. Hence, whilst there is a back up, neither can be called safety critical, but if maintenance of one lapses, the integrity of the other becomes more crucial.

CHANGE

The operational parameters, settings and alarm levels should not be changed without a full Change Assessment. This should cover the implications for start-up, shutdown, normal, abnormal and emergency operations. It may be suitable to re-visit the Hazard and Operability Study, or other documentation.

The above paragraph also applies when there is a change to any of the chemicals and equipment used in the plant. For instance, a replacement solvent, a different grade of material, etc.

Change is defined as any 'changes to process chemicals, technology, equipment, and procedures, and changes to facilities that affect a highly hazardous process.' There should be adequate procedures to address the principle of change, and the following should be given adequate consideration:

- the technical basis for change;
- impact of change on safety and health;
- modifications to operating procedures;
- necessary time period for the change; and
- authorisation requirements for the proposed change.

If the change results in modifications to Standard Operating Procedures (SOPs), Piping and Instrumentation Diagrams (P&IDs) or any other Process Safety Management (PSM) information associated with the highly hazardous process, this information must be updated accordingly. All employees who may be affected by a change in the process must be informed of, and trained on, the change before start-up. This requirement includes contractors.

BASIS OF SAFETY FILE

All the documentation produced by the above should be kept in, for example, a Basis of Safety File for the plant concerned. Then, in the future, the method of establishment and maintenance of the Basis of Safety will be readily to hand.

This file (or other such documentation) should contain the following information:

1. Material being protected;
2. Limiting Oxygen Concentration;
3. Maximum Permissible Oxygen Concentration;
4. Process Safety Matrix category;
5. System shut down alarm setting;
6. Operational alarm setting;
7. Method of Inerting;
8. Time (or volumetric) purge parameter;
9. Pressure of vacuum levels;
10. Number of pressure or vacuum cycles;
11. Verification system utilised;
12. Verification measurement parameter;
13. Maintenance schedule for measuring equipment;
14. Manufacturer's recommended spares holding for the same;
15. Manufacturer's operating instructions for the measuring equipment;
16. Trip schedule;
17. List of any Safety Critical Items;

18.   HAZOP, Computer Hazard and Operability Studies (CHAZOP) and Hazard Analysis (HAZAN) undertaken on the system, as appropriate;
19.   An appropriate flow diagram;
20.   Piping and Instrumentation Diagram;
21.   List of ignition sources identified and methods of control;
22.   Brief justification for the Level of Integrity afforded by the control system;
23.   A statement justifying the decisions made in arriving at the Level of Integrity afforded the control system. This is recommended for all cases, but is considered mandatory for all systems which have a Safety Critical Item that creates the inerted atmosphere, or have a Safety Critical Item confirm its presence.

PROCEDURES

Once the Inerting system has been designed, installed and verified, it is possible for it to operate unsupervised. However, the Inerting system has been designed and installed as the sole Basis of Safety, and cannot be allowed to deteriorate.

The duty of management in this situation is to ensure that the system continues to operate within the boundaries that were determined when it was originally installed. Any modifications to the system should go through a Management of Change Procedure, which should compare the proposed modifications with the Basis of Safety File. This will establish whether it is foreseeable that the Basis of Safety can be negated by the proposed changes.

Similarly, if it is decided that maintenance intervals should be lengthened, then the equipment will not receive the same amount of preventive maintenance that the Basis of Safety depends on. This again would need formal managerial review and consideration.

Hence, it is suggested that, if they do not already exist, the following systems for the management and maintenance of Inerting systems be established.

1.   Management of Change Procedure.
2.   HAZOP, CHAZOP and HAZAN of systems.
3.   Permit to Work and Vessel Entry procedures;
4.   A procedure for identifying repetitive failure of Safety Critical Items.
5.   A procedure to ensure that regular calibration occurs for all instrumentation on which establishment of the inert atmosphere depends and on which verification of the establishment of the inert atmosphere depends. Also, procedures should exist for instrument technicians to draw attention to any deviation from 'normal' readings.
6.   A system for obtaining the Limiting Oxygen Concentration of any new materials to be processed. A written procedure should exist for determining what the Maximum Permissible Oxygen Concentration, alarm level and operating level should be for that new material, and for ensuring it is implemented.
7.   A system to provide full traceability of all change of operational parameters (which would usually not be considered in a Management of Change analysis).
8.   The SOPs should include the principles of control and verification of the inert atmosphere.
9.   Control and alarm settings should be recorded in the trip schedule, a copy of which is retained in the Basis of Safety file.

10.   Procedures should be established for validation of the inert atmosphere during pre-commissioning, possibly via independent (possibly manual) sample checks to ensure that the control settings (i.e. time, flow, pressure and oxygen levels) are correct to ensure a safe oxygen level is achieved.

11.   Maintenance procedures for Safety Critical Items should ensure that such work is carried out on a mandatory basis.

12.   Procedures should exist to ensure that breakdown of Safety Critical Items is monitored as a high priority, and necessary actions are then taken to ensure the integrity of the Inerting system is maintained at all times.

13.   Procedures should be set up to ensure that re-validation and calibration of the control instrumentation is carried out at defined, predetermined intervals.

14.   A procedure should ensure that testing of the inerted system includes the entire system, as well as individual unit operations.

15.   A procedure should ensure that the Basis of Safety file, and its contents, is reviewed in the light of new information or new Standards.

The requirements for the design and installation of Inerting systems are contained within the manual. However, management of the system, once installed, is outside the scope of this document. Nevertheless, there should be systems for identification of unsafe conditions, potentially unsafe conditions and unusual conditions. The systems should then ensure that these conditions are drawn to the attention of an appropriate person, who can ascertain whether action is required, or not. These systems are a part of the maintenance of the Basis of Safety, and should therefore be referred to in the Basis of Safety File.

If the structure of the document is followed, the design, assessment, maintenance and management of the Inerting systems should be to a standard that is as safe as is reasonably practicable.

The whole intention of the document is to ensure that the Basis of Safety is formally identified and managed. In essence the manual is attempting to follow the logic of:

a)   What is the Limiting Oxygen Concentration?

b)   How is the Inerting carried out to ensure that the oxygen level never exceeds the Limiting Oxygen Concentration of the materials being processed?

c)   How is the system managed?

Provided the above three points are addressed correctly, a flammable mixture should be prevented from forming, and the system will be running at a level of risk that is as low as is reasonably practicable.

ACKNOWLEDGEMENT

Acknowledgement is made to SmithKline Beecham for their assistance in the preparation of this paper.

NON-DESTRUCTIVE TESTING – LEARNING FROM THE PAST, MAXIMISING FUTURE BENEFITS.

Harry Bainbridge, Health & Safety Executive, Bootle
Bernard McGrath, AEA Technology plc, Risley

In 1997 the Health & Safety Executive instigated a programme to investigate the effectiveness of NDT as applied in industry. AEA Technology managed the Programme for the Assessment of NDT in Industry (PANI) on behalf of the HSE. Twenty operators participated in a round robin exercise to provide a snapshot of the capability and reliability of manual ultrasonic inspection methods currently used in industry. Test pieces which replicated key industrial components were produced containing artificial, service induced defects and these were mounted to simulate on-site access conditions. An ex-service boiler, which had been scrapped because it contained unacceptable defects, was also used as a test piece. The test pieces were sectioned to assist in the analysis of the effectiveness of the ultrasonic inspections. The results show a wide variation in the detection of the defects and in their sizing and positioning. The boiler was particularly challenging.

The presentation will describe how the round robin was planned in order to ensure results relevant to industry. The implementation of the round robin inspections, the details of the test pieces and the analysis of the results will also be discussed. This will provide the background information for a full understanding of the implications of the results which have led to a number of subsequent projects aimed at improving the quality of NDT. These projects have two aims: to add to the pool of data on the capability NDT techniques; to proactively communicate information on NDT capability issues. The progress of these projects will be reported and future benefits for industry highlighted.

Keywords: NDT, manual ultrasonics, reliability

INTRODUCTION

This paper presents the details of the Programme for the Assessment of Non-Destructive Testing (NDT) in Industry (PANI) which was managed on behalf of the Health & Safety Executive (HSE) by the Inspection Validation Centre (IVC), AEA Technology. The programme involved the investigation of current industrial ultrasonic methods for in-service inspection of typical industrial components. At the seminar to launch the PANI programme in June 1997, the HSE stated the objective as follows:
To examine the effectiveness of NDT in assessing the integrity of pressure plant by identifying the components and inspection methods of greatest concern and conducting a round robin exercise.

The reasons for investigating NDT were listed as:
a perceived lack of confidence from industry in NDT
doubts about the capabilities of NDT - the ability to prove 'fitness for purpose' by Engineering Critical Assessments (ECA)
lack of a benchmark or standard to judge these concerns
These reasons were supported by a number of examples of where NDT had failed to detect important defects and plant failures had occurred as a result. These examples involved a range of non-nuclear pressurised components.

There are a number of current trends in plant operation, which increases the importance put on the ability of the applied NDT technique to detect and size defects correctly in order to have confidence in its performance. Companies are looking to reduce costs by extending the life of pressurised plant, adopting risk based inspection, applying non-invasive techniques where possible and subjecting inspection to cost based analysis. In order to extend plant life,

life cycle analyses are being undertaken and decisions made on the periodicity of inspections. Risk based inspection techniques are being used to focus inspections on key areas of plant. The suitability and capability of the inspections subsequently performed on the key areas of plant are not always known. Non-invasive techniques allow inspections to be performed without opening up vessels or even taking them off line, but again the ability of the proposed technique to detect the defects of concern is not always known or evaluated. Inspections are being subjected to cost benefit analysis but if it is not known how good an inspection is for detecting defects then it is not possible to correctly assess its value.

In response to these industrial trends and in the light of uncertainties over the effectiveness of NDT, the HSE established the PANI project. The aims were to:
determine whether NDT is effective, reliable and repeatable;
eliminate doubts, fears and preconceptions by reducing the uncertainty;
to provide an estimate of NDT capability.
The results would also determine where improvements could be made.

PANI METHODOLOGY

In order to ensure that the programme provided both information and conclusions of direct relevance to industry a PANI Management Committee was set up. The principal industries for the PANI work were:
Steam raising plant using fossil fuels
Gas distribution and storage
Chemical production
Refineries
Oil production
The membership of the committee was taken from these industries and from other relevant organisations. Their remit was to advise the HSE and AEA Technology on the development, implementation and reporting of the PANI project with the purpose of ensuring that the project was aligned with the principal interests of the industries identified above.

An industry questionnaire was used to establish the NDT methods and components for a round robin exercise. The aims of the questionnaire were to gather information from plant owners and industrial inspection companies in order to identify the components and inspections for the round robin exercise. The topics covered by the questionnaire were: Components requiring inspection; Defects of concern; Materials; NDT Methods; Other Issues which covered access, environment etc.

A seminar was used to launch the programme and companies were invited to participate in the round robin. The test pieces manufactured for the round robin exercise were based on the information obtained from the industry questionnaire and were agreed by the Management Committee. The defect types and size ranges were also agreed but the Management Committee had no knowledge of the actual defects in the manufactured test pieces until the round robin inspections had been completed. At the half way stage of the round robin the interim results were considered by the Management Committee and actions agreed. Likewise, the final results were presented to the committee and actions relating to the analysis and presentation of the results, including the format of this report, were decided. At no stage during the project have the Management Committee had access to the results from individual operators.

DETAILS OF ROUND ROBIN

Based on the results of the questionnaire it was decided that the round robin exercise would look at manual ultrasonics applied to ferritic steel test pieces representative of the components identified above containing typical in-service cracking and erosion / corrosion defects.

Six test pieces were used for the round robin. Five were manufactured and one was an ex-service Cochran boiler. Five test pieces were manufactured containing artificial but realistic defects. The test pieces are summarised in Table 1.

The wall thickness ranged from 7 mm in the nozzle test pieces to 30 mm in the Tee piece. The material was carbon steel plate to BS4360 43A or equivalent and carbon steel pipe ST52. All the welds were manual metal arc with the exception of the upper vee on the longitudinal vessel weld which was a submerged arc weld. All the welds contained defects except for the pipe to pipe weld which was manufactured with deliberate mis-alignment. The types of weld defect are summarised in Table 2. The cracks were elliptical in shape and the lack of fusion defects were rectangular.

Table 1 Outline Details of the Manufactured Test Pieces

Test Piece Identification	Description
P1	Thin section set on nozzle with partial penetration weld.
P2	Thin section set through nozzle.
P3	Tee joint with unfused land in the middle of the weld.
P4	Longitudinal double vee vessel butt weld.
P5	Section of pipe and bend containing pipe to pipe, pipe to component and pipe to elbow welds.

In addition, two areas simulating wall thinning by erosion were inserted on the extrados of the pipe bend. Each of the defects in the manufactured test pieces was destructively examined to establish the actual morphology and height.

EX-SERVICE BOILER TEST PIECE

An ex-service Cochran Wee Chieftain Package Steam Boiler was also obtained for use as a round robin test piece. This boiler had been taken out of service because ultrasonic inspection had detected cracking in the front furnace tube to tube plate joint. The inspectors report recorded a maximum crack depth of 3-5 mm depth and 740 mm long about the Bottom Dead Centre position. The SAFed guidelines for the inspection of such boilers require 100% inspection of the internal welds such as the furnace tube to tube plate weld and 20% of the Shell to Tube Sheet welds. For the purposes of the round robin the inspections were restricted to 100% front furnace tube to tube plate joint and four areas of the front shell to tube plate weld meeting the 20% requirement. Following the inspection, two pieces were flame cut from the furnace tube of the boiler. These were taken about the 0 mm (Top Dead Centre) and the 800 mm (near Bottom Dead Centre) positions. These pieces were in turn cut at various positions to give the results described below. As the inspection results from the boiler shell to tube plate weld did not give a consensus on the position of any one defect, no sections were taken from this weld.

The objective of the PANI programme - " To examine the effectiveness of NDT in assessing the integrity of pressure plant..." - required that the inspections be performed in a realistic environment. Whilst no attempt was made to mimic the noise and dirt of many inspection environments, the test pieces were arranged so that the operators faced realistic access difficulties.

Table 2 Summary of Defects in Manufactured Test Pieces

Type of Defect		Total Number
Lack of Fusion		5
Rough Cracks		11
	Embedded (associated with unfused land)	6
	Far surface breaking	5
Smooth Cracks		7
	Near surface breaking	5
	Far surface breaking	2
Root Erosion Defect		2
Total		25

20 operators were offered by their companies for participation in the round robin. The years spent in NDT by the operators ranged from 5 to 25 with an average of 15. All operators held a PCN Level II qualification in ultrasonics. Eight of the operators held certificates in plate, pipe, nozzle and node categories whilst 5 held the critical sizing qualification. The ultrasonic procedures used by the operators were either a standard ultrasonic procedure, which had been produced by AEA Technology and approved by the Management Committee, or their own company procedures. All the procedures were basically the same, based on the now obsolete BS3923 Part 1, and used a sensitivity of 14 dB below a DAC (Distance Amplitude Curve) based on a 3 mm ∅ SDH (Side Drilled Hole).

RESULTS

The analysis of the results falls into two parts: the results obtained from the manufactured test pieces which contained known discrete defects which allowed for a general analysis of the performance of the operators in detecting the defects; the results from the boiler which can only be compared to discrete destructive analysis.

Although the round robin was principally aimed at the application of manual ultrasonics, it is common industry practice to apply magnetic particle inspection prior to any ultrasonic inspection. Five surface breaking smooth cracks in the manufactured test pieces were detectable with MPI. 72 MPI operator / defect interactions were achieved and only one failed to report a defect.

On the simple geometry of the vessel weld, test piece P4, the operators performed well giving the detection results shown in Table 3. The ultrasonic inspection of the set-on nozzle, test piece P1, was particularly challenging with the thin wall of 7 mm and an unfused land. The old British Standard gave a lower limit of 8 mm and so strictly speaking the procedure was not valid for this test piece. In the remaining test pieces there were 3 defects which could be said to be very difficult to detect with the techniques applied. So removing these 3 defects with the 4 defects in test piece P1 gives the operator performance shown in Figure 1 for the remaining 13 defects. The detectability of the individual defects in this reduced population is shown in Figure 2.

Table 3 Detection of Defects in Vessel Weld

Defect	Defect Height & Details	Signal Amplitude Above Recording Threshold	No of Operators Who Inspected Defect	No of Operators Who Detected Defect	Detection Frequency For Operators Who Inspected Defect (%)
2	3.0 mm vertical rough crack at weld root	18 dB	20	20	100
3	8.3 mm vertical rough crack at weld root	17 dB	20	20	100
4	3 mm LOSWF 55° tilt	25 dB	20	19	95

Looking at the total defect population of 20 defects, detectable by ultrasonics and not MPI, gives the ultrasonic operator detection rates listed in Table 4 and illustrated in Figure 3. The diagram gives data from 16 operators who were able to inspect most of the test pieces. One of the 16 did not inspect one test piece and his score is adjusted accordingly to give a percentage of the possible defects that he could have detected. The highest detection rate of 70% was achieved by three operators: this equates to the detection of 14 of the possible total of 20 defects. Conversely, the low detection rates of 30% and 35% equate to the detection of 6 and 7 of the 20 defects respectively.

Table 4 Operator Performance In Detecting Defects With Ultrasonics in Manufactured Test Pieces

No of Operators	No of Defects Inspected with Ultrasonics by these Operators	No of Defects Detected by these Operator	Percentage of Inspected Defects Detected. (%)
1	20	6	30
1	20	7	35
1	20	8	40
1	20	9	45
4	20	11	55
1	20	12	60
1	18	11	61
3	20	13	65
3	20	14	70

The detectability of individual defects in the 20 defect population is illustrated in Figure 4. Two defects were detected by all operators whilst at the other end of the scale three defects were only detected by single operators. False calls were few and appeared random.

Apart from the occasional measurement, the positioning of the defects and the length and height measurements show a spread typical of most studies using a variety of operators. A plot of measured height against actual defect height is shown in Figure 5. Note that a number of points on the plot are positioned on top of each other. The solid line is the best fit line obtained through regression analysis. This has a slope of 0.24 and an intercept of 2.7. The dashed lines above and below show the 95% limits. The ideal line would have a slope of 1 and an intercept of 0.

The results of the inspections of the vessel shell to tubeplate welds did not produce a common consensus of defect positions. However, the inspection of the furnace tube to tubeplate weld showed clearer evidence of the presence of defects. Of the 18 operators who inspected the furnace tube to tube plate weld, 11 reported a defect at the 800 mm (approximately Bottom Dead Centre) circumferential position, three reported unfused land only, one only reported defects at other circumferential locations and two were unable to make sense of the echoes from the weld geometry and therefore didn't report any indications. The final operator was only able to scan with the $0°$ probe and therefore only reported unfused land.

At the 0 mm (approximately Top Dead Centre) circumferential position the reports from five operators indicated that a defect might be present. This includes reporting an intermittent defect around the full circumference. The destructive analysis showed that there was weld undercut with associated minor cracking to a depth of 2 mm at the 800 mm region and only minor cracking less than 1 mm in the 0 mm region.

DISCUSSION

Overall it may be concluded that defects were not detected for the following factors:

- The defect had a low response or a response which was hard to distinguish amongst other geometric echoes.
- The defect was only short in length and therefore missed if there was any lapse in concentration or gaps in the scanning raster.
- Human Factors. This is manifested by a multitude of factors including loss of concentration, poor scanning, poor coupling and generally poor technique. Such effects arise from a variety of causes including poor motivation, poor training, adverse conditions for inspection, fatigue and so on.

The detection rates achieved in the round robin, 30 to 70%, appear poor compared to the results of the PISC III Action 7 inspections which showed detection rates of 67 to 96%. However, the latter were obtained on a test piece 600 by 500 by 100 mm with a double V weld prep. The defects were crack like, vertical and parallel to the weld centre line. They were 10 to 15 mm through wall and 20 to 30 mm long. They were therefore 'easier' than the PANI specimens where some of the defect lengths were small compared to the probe width, or distracting geometric echoes were sometimes present. If these differences are taken in to account, then the PANI results are consistent with the PISC III Action 7 results. These PANI results are in line with the NORDTEST conclusion that NDE may be very unreliable and the Finnish observation that detection in simple butt welds is good but that detection in pipe joints, fillet joints and stud welds is poor. The NIL-NDP detection rate of 50% is broadly consistent with the PANI results.

Although a number of the PANI defects were small and challenging, most were above or near to the allowable size for planar flaws in the ASME Section XI ISI code for volumetric examination of ferritic piping. In addition, all aspects of the design of the project, with the exception of the exact defect sizes, were controlled by the Management Committee to ensure that it was relevant to practices applied on site.

The inspections on all the test pieces have shown how important it is to know the possible defect types, positions and orientations in order to be able to reliably detect the defects of concern. Knowledge of the defect parameters allows the procedure to be tailored to the specific requirements of a particular inspection.

Further analysis of the location and size data from the manufactured test pieces by removing the defects detected by MPI and separating the defects by type - root, unfused land and others, does not provide any different information from that shown in the results section. These results are broadly consistent with the NIL-NDP results which showed an average length error of 8 mm with a standard deviation of 24 mm.

Figure 5, the plot of measured defect height against actual defect height shows what other studies have shown, in that small defects are oversized and larger defects are undersized. However, the slope of 0.24 is far removed from the ideal of 1 and compares poorly to data obtained during the Sizewell B validation process which gave best fit lines of slope 0.85 for operators who achieved certification and of slope 0.42 for all operators. The Sizewell B data was obtained on thicker section material and with larger defects. It is likely that the PANI results were skewed by the geometric echoes interfering with the sizing process and the bias towards smaller defects.

Three operators gave very similar results from P6 the boiler test piece, which in turn corresponded well with the destructive analysis results. One of the three had considerable experience of inspecting this type of boiler whilst the other two had experience of a range of components but not explicitly this type of boiler. No other characteristic such as age, years of experience or qualifications set these operators apart from the others.

The boiler was particularly difficult for the operators due to the geometry and the limited scanning surfaces. Better results are likely to have been achieved if the operators who had not inspected boilers before had received some training on the geometry and had gained familiarity through practice with the echoes both from the geometry and typical defects.

OVERALL CONCLUSION

The objective of the PANI programme was to obtain a snapshot of the current effectiveness of in-service NDT used for a range standard of key industrial plant components. The programme has identified shortcomings in the application of manual ultrasonics on industrial plant an it is recommended that personnel specifying inspections should not assume that the use of general procedures based on a National Standard will necessarily achieve their required level of reliability when applied by operators with general NDT qualifications. Ways of improving the reliability of application of manual ultrasonics should be considered, particularly when non-simple geometries are to be inspected and the structurally important defects are of a similar size to those in the PANI test pieces. These include the following:

- Use of specific training and practice specimens
- Use of inspection aids for scanning and data recording
- Use of improved procedures and techniques tailored to the specific geometry and defects
- In addition to the above measures aimed at improving the reliability of individual inspections, the use of multiple, independent inspections should be considered to reduce the effect of random human errors. This is particularly pertinent when complex geometries are involved.

THE IMPACT OF PANI

The results of the PANI project have generated a great deal of interest both within the NDT community and outside. There were two separate issues raised in response to the results: the first was to provide quantified information on the benefits to be obtained by adopting the various suggestions for improving the reliability of inspection whilst the second was to communicate the issues to be considered when buying in manual ultrasonics to the personnel on the periphery of NDT. The Health & Safety Executive have responded to these issues by supporting further projects. A document giving Best Practice guidelines has been produced and is available from the HSE web site. Already industry has responded to this best practice document, using them to assist in the procurement of NDT as a whole and using them as an audit tool for their own NDT procurement and application processes. A key detail of the document is the use of NDT operators within a recognised quality system and with technical support through access to a level III qualified person. Work on a Best Practice document for Surface Techniques, MPI and Dye penetrant, has just started.

A proposal for a further round robin exercise which will provide quantified improvements from the various ways of improving inspection reliability is currently under consideration.

PANI'S IMPLICATIONS ON STRUCTURAL INTEGRITY OF PRESSURISED PLANT

In an Engineering Critical Assessment (ECA) to establish continued fitness for purpose of pressurised components, one of the most important parameters is the dimension of the defect. The PANI project identified that defect detection rate was poor, and when detected, the sizing was inaccurate. These can have serious implications for the validity of an ECA of a component.

The worst detection rate of 26% was for the set on partial penetration nozzle, where operators found it difficult to distinguish between the lack of fusion and the defect. While the geometry of this component made the detection difficult, the external loading on this type of component can be difficult to evaluate, with site pipe fit-up, expansion loads, fatigue cycles etc. contributing to the overall lack of reliable information to confirm continued fitness for purpose.

The best detection rate of 98% was for the butt weld. Of the three defects found by ultrasonic inspection only, two were of 3 mm height, and the other was 8.3 mm high (one third of wall thickness). The three defects were all measured as being between 2 to 10 mm high. In the case of the two 3 mm high defects, only 5% of inspectors undersized one defect, and 16% undersized the other. In the case of the 8.3 mm high defect, 75% of the inspectors undersized it. While it is acknowledged that some inaccuracies will occur, this trend of undersizing the larger defect can have serious safety implications.

The above also calls into question the detection of failure mechanisms such as fatigue. Are the defects detected, and if so are they growing? In the case of a defect in the butt weld, the sizing scatter could disguise crack growth from 2 to 10 mm high if the inspection was carried out with manual ultrasonics at standard intervals.

As stated previously, the general trend in inspection of pressure plant is to extend the period between inspections, use Risk Based Inspection, or Non-Invasive Inspection. These changes to the inspection strategy should be based on the information gained from previous inspections. If the results of the PANI project are considered, the confidence in the results of previous inspections should be carefully evaluated before any major changes in inspection strategy takes place.

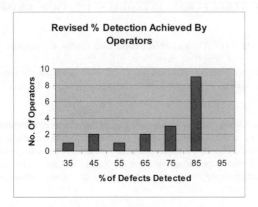

Figure 1 Operator Performance In Detecting Reduced Population of Defects With Ultrasonics In Manufactured Test Pieces

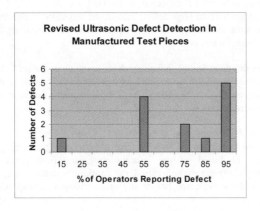

Figure 2 Detectability of Individual Defects In Selected Population of Defects in Manufactured Test Pieces

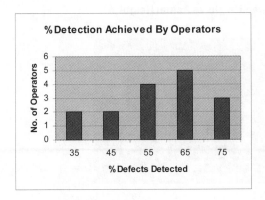

Figure 3 Operator Performance In Detecting All Defects With Ultrasonics In Manufactured Test Pieces

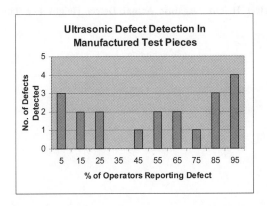

Figure 4 Detectability of All Individual Defects In Manufactured Test Pieces

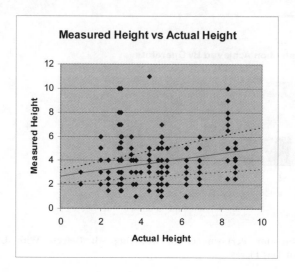

Figure 5 Plot of Measured Defect Height Against Actual Defect Height For The Manufactured Test Pieces

RAPID FIRE RISK ASSESSMENT

J. E. Gillett
34 Church Lane, Gawsworth, Macclesfield, Cheshire SKi 1 9QY

This paper describes the principles of "Rapid Fire Risk Assessment", explains how it is performed and how it could be developed as a diagnostic tool for fire safety improvement.
Keywords: Fire risk assessment, Pharmaceutical Industry, design tools

INTRODUCTION

All large multinational firms have premises world-wide that may be in many locations remote from the centre of the organisation. This diversity and separation makes corporate activities such as fire safety management difficult to control. A particular problem arises when attempting to plan and implement Fire Safety Audits.

Fire is one of the main risks to most facilities and to the business that they support. It is essential that adequate fire prevention and protection is provided at all locations and monitored by regular and effective fire safety auditing. It is particularly important to be able to identify sites where a fire could interrupt a key product supply chain and cause severe business interruption. Key sites such as these require priority for fire safety audits and fire prevention expertise.

Rapid Fire Risk assessment was developed for use in the international pharmaceutical industry, but is applicable to other industries. It was developed to set up fire safety audit programmes and to prioritise sites for fire safety audits. Since the local technical staff available to assess fire risks on some sites had little fire safety knowledge, a simple yet consistent fire risk assessment method was needed. The "Rapid Fire Risk Assessment" (RFRA) method was developed to meet this need[1].

TILE RFRA METHOD

RISK ASSESSMENT PRINCIPLES:
RFRA uses the risk assessment process described in Figure 1. The risk acceptability criterion is based on the principle that the greater the severity of the consequences, the less should be the likelihood of occurrence. By considering only order-of-magnitude differences, a scale of severity and a scale of likelihood can be used to define the boundary of acceptability for a range of identified hazards (Figure 2). This principle can be developed and simplified further as a 5 X 5 matrix with suitable numbers allocated to define acceptability limits (Figure 3).

RAPID FIRE RISK ASSESSMENT:
Rapid Fire Risk Assessment (RFRA) of a facility or premises involves six steps:
1. Divide the area into separate blocks, each of which could contain a fire.
(The boundaries of each block are defined either by natural separation or by suitable firewalls or barriers. A maximum of between six and en blocks is practical for most facilities. Complex facilities may require more sub-division.)
2. Inspect each block and identify a realistic fire scenario.
(The assessor is advised to identify several possible fire scenarios for each block ranging from a "Worst Case" to a "Typical Case" fire and to choose the most realistic scenario for

the RFRA. Alternatively each of the scenarios iden4fied can be assessed separately to decide a representative combination although this is more time-consuming)

3. Assess the scenario consequences using a simple scoring method *(Table 1):*

4. Assess the scenario likelihood of occurrence by a simple scoring method *(Table 2):*

5. Plot the consequences and likelihood on a risk-ranking matrix *(Table 3)* to determine the "RIFRA Mark" for the block being studied.

6. Use the "RIFRA Mark" to decide if the risk is "Acceptable", "Unacceptable" or "Unknown: Needs follow-up". *("Acceptable" implies that an audit is not thought to be necessary)*

It is important to record the six-step RERA process on auditable documents such as paper forms or electronic spreadsheets to analyse results and to identify areas for improvement. The RERA six-step method and documentation is explained in more detail in the following text.

RAPID FIRE RISK ASSESSMENT DOCUMENTATION:

The method and documentation developed to provide this is described as follows: -

1. Assess the Consequences:

The consequences of a fire in the area being assessed are in four categories of harm: -

Harm to people.

Harm to the environment.

Harm to buildings and equipment.

Harm to the product supply chain and business.

The severity of the consequences for each category of harm is assessed as either *"High"*, *"Normal"* or *"Low"* by using numerical guide values to aid the assessor's judgement. The guide values will depend on the company standards and will include values for loss of life and markets that are specific to the organisation. As a general guide to the overall monetary loss, a *"High"* loss would be above £10 Million of Net Present Value, a *"Normal"* from £1 - £10 Million, and a *"Low"* less than £1Million. The four factors in the assessment are then scored 3 for *"High"*, 2 for *"Normal"* and 1 for *"Low"*. The scores are added to give the total score for the overall consequences. Results are recorded on a form or spreadsheet (see Table 1).

The Block Consequences Total Score is then used to define whether the overall consequences are "Very Severe" (Score = 11 or 12), "Severe" (Score = 9 or 10), "Moderate" (Score = 8), "Slight"[1] (Score 6 or 7) or "Very Slight" (Score = 4 or5). The result is then ticked off on the vertical axis of the RFRA matrix in Table 3 to heap determine the block overall RFRA mark.

2. Assess the Likelihood:

The likelihood of a fire occurring in the selected area is more difficult to assess than the consequences. Also, human judgement of the likelihood of a hazard is notoriously unreliable. To overcome these problems, a step-by-step procedure is used, supported by suitable training using benchmark examples for guidance.

The likelihood of a significant fire depends on three simultaneous occurrences. A source of combustible material must be present *and* an effective source of ignition must be present *and* the fire must escalate. This is shown as a simple fault tree in Figure 4, where the probabilities of the key factors "Fire Load, "Ignition Source" and "Escalation" are combined to determine the overall likelihood of the block scenario.

Table 1. RFR.A Consequences assessment form:

BLOCK REF NO. _____ Assessors:_____ RFRA Date:_____

Block Description: _____

FACTOR:	High	Normal	Low	SCORE: H=3; N= 2; L = 1)
Harm to People:				.
Harm to the Environment				
Harm to Buildings and Equipment:				
Harm to Product and Business:				
			BLOCK CONSEQUENCES TOTAL SCORE:	

By ranking each of these factors *"High', "Normal"* or *"Low",* the overall likelihood can be assessed using a form similar to that shown in Table 2. An additional ranking *"Not sure"* (Scored as *"High"*) is also practical to cover atypical situations when the assessor needs expert assistance.

Table 2. RFRA Likelihood assessment form:

BLOCK REF.NO. _____ Assessors:_____ RFRA Date:_____

Block Description: _____

FACTOR:	High	Normal	Low	Not Sure	SCORE: (H = 3; N= 2; L 1)
Fire Load:					
Likelihood of Ignition					
Likelihood of Escalation					
BLOCK LIKELIHOOD TOTAL SCORE:	-	-	-	-	

As with the consequences, the rankings can then be scored and converted to an assessment of overall likelihood. The levels are "Very High" (Score = 8 or 9), "High" (Score = **7),** "Normal' (Score = 6), "Low" (Score = 5*)* or "Very Low" (Score = 3 or 4). The result is then ticked off on the horizontal axis of the RFRA matrix in Table 3 and with the consequences result on the vertical axis enables the assessor to determine the block overall RFRA mark.

However, most assessors would find it difficult to assess the three factors "Fire Load", "Ignition Source" and "Escalation" accurately in one step, so a further breakdown of each is provided to make it easier.

Fire Load:
The Fire Load is assessed in "Kilograms of Wood Equivalent" per square metre of floor area[2].

In the pharmaceutical industry, guidance values are provided for the assessor derived from typical pharmaceutical facilities data. Benchmark areas are visited during training to instil a visual impression sufficient to rank the loads as "High", "Normal" or "Low". The ranking "Not sure" is essential to cover the situations when the inexpert assessor encounters an atypical fire load and cannot obtain expert assistance over the telephone.

Likelihood of Ignition:

The likelihood of ignition is assessed by considering how the combustibles and sources of ignition are controlled when they are present. These are ranked using the form in Table 2.1.

Table 2.1. Likelihood of ignition assessment form:

BLOCK REF.NO. _____ Assessors: _____ RFRA Date: _____

Block Description: _____

Control of Combustibles:	Control of Ignition Sources:	LIKELIHOOD OF IGNITION
Uncontrolled	Uncontrolled Sources present	High
Uncontrolled	Well Controlled Sources	High
Uncontrolled	Sources rarely present	Normal
Well Controlled	Uncontrolled Sources present	High
Well Controlled	Well Controlled Sources	Normal
Well Controlled	Sources rarely present	Low
Combustibles rarely present	Uncontrolled Sources present	Normal
Combustibles rarely present	Well Controlled Sources	Low
Combustibles rarely present	Sources rarely present	Low

Likelihood of Escalation:

The burning rate of the materials present, the passive and active fire protection measures, the fire-fighting response time and the management of the combustible materials govern fire "Escalation". It is practical to assess an area for each of these factors separately. As a first step, fire escalation has already been subdivided in the simple fault tree (Figure 4) into "Rapid Burning" and "Safeguards Fail", but a further subdivision of the safeguards on a form is even more helpful *(See Table 2.2)*.

The form shown in Table 2.2 is used to assess the factors "Compartmentation", "Housekeeping", "Fire Detection" and "Fire-fighting Response Time as *"Good"* (Score = 1), *"Average"* (Score = 2) or *"Bad"* (Score = 3). The "Maximum Burning Rate" is weighted to score a *"Good"* or low rate = 1, an *"Average"* rate = 3 and a *"Bad"* or rapid burning rate = 9.

As previously, the scores for the factors are added and the total score is converted to enable an entry of *"High"*, *"Normal"* or *"Low"* in the "Likelihood of Escalation" row of the Overall Likelihood of Fire Table 2. The Block Escalation Score is translated into "Likelihood of Escalation" as follows: Block Escalation Score = 13 to 21 rates as *"High"*; 8 to 12 rates as *"Normal"*; 5 to 7 rates as *"Low"*.

Whereas 'Housekeeping' and 'Compartmentation' are relatively easy to assess, some explanation is required for the other factors as follows:

Maximum Burning Rate:

The maximum burning rate of a fire is governed by the configuration of the Fire Load[2]. To rank this factor, the assessor must consider how the combustibles are arranged. For example, combustible material stacked high so that fire can rapidly spread vertically will be rated *'Fast'* or *'Bad'*. A low roofed building that allows heat and fire to spread rapidly horizontally and affect adjacent combustibles would also be rated as *'Bad'*. The use of fireproof cabinets or

containers will minimise the burning rate, as will combustibles that are well separated from each other. (Compartmentation is assessed separately in the next row of Table 2.2). The RFRA marking for Maximum Burning Rate is weighted as follows:
Fast/Bad = 9,Average = 3, Low/Good = 1

Table 2.2. Likelihood of escalation assessment form:
BLOCK REF.NO._____Assessors:_____ RFRA Date._____

Block Description:_____

FACTOR:	Good	Average	Bad	SCORE:
Maximum Burning Rate: (Low = 1= Good Ave. = 3 = Average; Fast = 9 = Bad)				
Compartmentation: (Good = 1; Average = 2; Bad = 3)				
Housekeeping: (Good = 1; Average = 2; Bad = 3)				
Fire Detection: (Good = l; Average = 2; Bad = 3)				
Firefighting Response Time: Good = l; Average = 2; Bad = 3				
BLOCK ESCALATION SCORE:	-	-	-	

Fire Detection:
To rate as *'Good'* the correct type of automatic detection and alarm system must be in place in the block studied[3]. 24-hour attendance by vigilant staff will also rate as *'Good'*. No automatic fire detectors, no staff present and no regular surveillance would be rated as *'Bad'*.
Firefighting Response Time:
To rate as *'Good'* the appropriate automatic firefighting measures using sprinklers, deluge or foam systems must be in place in the block studied[3]. If the fire service can arrive in less than 5 minutes from fire discovery, this may also be rated as *'Good'*, although reliance on external fire service usually rates as *'Average'*, on the assumption of 10 minutes to respond. A response time of more than 15 minutes from discovery of fire rates as *'Bad'*.

3. Determine the Block Assessment (RIFRA Mark):
The foregoing explained how several key factors are used to assess the consequences and likelihood of a significant fire in the block. The results then provide the coordinates to define The block "RFRA Mark" in the matrix in Table 3.
The numbers in the matrix determine the final assessment of the block as "Acceptable", "Unacceptable" or "Unknown: Needs follow-up". The matrix numbers are weighted to ensure that a professional fire engineer always investigates events with very severe consequences. A mark of less than 5 is ranked as "Acceptable", marks of 5 or 6 require investigation and a mark of greater than 6 is "Unacceptable". An "Unacceptable" Fire Risk Assessment would initiate an immediate follow-up by a qualified fire engineer.
The results of the assessment are recorded on pre-printed forms or spreadsheets for use in subsequent investigations, for fire safety audits or for entry into a database. Rapid Fire Risk Assessment of each block is performed using the "Consequences" versus "Likelihood" matrix in Table 3 as follows.

Table 3. Rapid Fire Risk Assessment Matrix:

Consequences Severity:					
Very Severe	7	8	9	10	10
Severe	5	7	8	9	10
Moderate	3	5	7	8	9
Slight	2	4	5	7	8
Very Slight	1	2	3	5	6
	Very Low	Low	Normal	High	Very High

Likelihood of Occurrence

IMPLEMENTATION:
The forms and checklist tables described were thoroughly tested by experienced fire prevention staff and selected professional staff in a variety of different situations and premises. Several "Bench marks" of typical areas were defined for staff training purposes. A computerised database of RFRA results was developed to monitor the use of the method, to identify improvements, and to train new assessors. As the method was used more widely a significant body of data was collected. The database made it possible to identify anomalies and inconsistencies quickly so that results could be queried directly with the assessors. Although the methods used are not very precise, RFRA proved to be a useful and credible tool for deciding priorities for fire safety audits and site visits by a qualified and experienced fire engineer. RFRA also provided a useful pre-audit stage for a fire safety auditing protocol developed for use internationally.

RFRA EXAMPLE:

This example is based on the RFRA of a contract warehouse made by an experienced warehouse manager with some knowledge of fire safety engineering. He assessed the warehouse as a single block as follows:
Table 1. RFRA Consequences form:
"Harm to People" = *Normal*   Score = 2
"Harm to the Environment" = *Normal*   Score = 2
"Harm to Buildings and Equipment" = *Normal*   Score = 2
"Harm to Product and Business" = *High*   Score = 3
Block Consequences Total Score = 9 = *Severe*
Table 2. RFRA Likelihood Assessment Form:
"Fire Load" = *Normal*   Score = 2
Likelihood of Ignition = *Normal*   Score = 2
Likelihood of Escalation = *High*   Score = 3
Block Likelihood Total Score = 7 = *High*
Table 3. RFRA Assessment Matrix:
Locating *Severe* Consequences and *High* Likelihood on the RFRA Matrix Table 3, indicates Block RFRA Mark = 9

A Block RERA Mark of 9 is "Unacceptable" and requires that a qualified fire engineer should visit the warehouse immediately. It is now useful to refer to the supporting tables that the assessor completed to study how the Likelihood assessments were made: -

Table 2.1: Likelihood of Ignition Assessment Form:
Both The combustibles and the sources of ignition were considered to be "Well controlled".
From Table 2.1 this results in a "Normal" assessment for entry into Table 2. It would be
difficult to make changes to the warehouse to improve on this assessment except by excluding
all sources of ignition which would then result in a "Low" assessment for entry into Table 2.

Table 2.2: Likelihood of Escalation Assessment Form:

Maximum Burning Rate:
The warehouse contained combustibles that were stacked together vertically. This fire load
configuration was expected to result in an Average Maximum Burning Rate giving a score = 3.
(By relocating the combustibles so that they were not stacked together, and by not stacking them
vertically above each other, this arrangement could be considered to be "Good" with a score =
1)

Compartmentation:
There was no compartmentation in the warehouse. The assessor rated this as "Bad" giving a
score = 3. (The installation of partitions capable of resisting fire for >2hrs. could be considered
as "Good" compartmentation with a score = 1)

Housekeeping:
The assessor rated the housekeeping in the contract warehouse as "Bad" giving a score = 3.
(Improved training and management might possibly rate a "Good" assessment, but the
housekeeping might be due to an unacceptable contractor attitude that, at the best would only
rate an "Average" assessment with a score = 2)

Fire Detection:
No automatic fire detection was installed in the warehouse and the warehouse was unoccupied
for most of the time. The assessor rated this as "Bad" giving a Fire Detection Score = 3. (The
Fire Detection Score could be reduced to 1 if suitable fire detectors and alarm systems were
installed together with improvements to the security arrangements)

Firefighting Response Time:
No automatic firefighting systems were installed in the warehouse and the local fire officer
considered that access to the warehouse for firefighting appliances would be difficult. The
assessor rated this as "Bad" giving a score = 3. (The Firefighting Response Time Score could
be reduced to 1 if suitable automatic sprinkler systems were installed.)

Initial "Likelihood of Escalation" Assessment:
The assessor's initial scores were: 3 + 3 + 3 + 3 + 3 = 15. These scores resulted in a "High"
likelihood of escalation. (If all of the improvements suggested were made, the scores would
reduce to: 1 + 1 + 2 + 1 + 1 = 6 to give a new assessment as "Low" for the likelihood of
escalation)

ASSESSMENT OF IMPROVEMENTS IN WAREHOUSE FIRE SAFETY:
Because the warehouse was the only one available to supply markets in that country the local
materials manager was reluctant to alter stock and materials movements to reduce the potential
consequences of a fire before fire safety improvements had been considered.

The improvements to the Likelihood of Fire Escalation (suggested in brackets in the foregoing text) to gain a *Low* assessment would reduce the Block Likelihood Score in Table 2 from 7 to 5 which would then rate as *Low* for use in the RFRA Matrix in Table 3. Since the Consequences of a fire would remain *Severe* the Block RFRA Mark would then reduce from 9 to 7. Unfortunately this would still be "Unacceptable".

If additional measures were taken to exclude ignition sources from the warehouse, the Likelihood of Ignition would reduce to *Low* which would reduce the Block Likelihood Score in Table 2 to a value of 4 and give a *Very Low* rating for use in the RFRA Matrix in Table 3. The Block RFRA Mark would then be reduced to 5, which is at the boundary of acceptability using the RFRA criteria. It is thus essential for a qualified fire engineer to visit the contract warehouse and investigate whether the suggested improvements would be effective.

At this point the local materials manager was willing to consider how the Consequences of a fire could be reduced. As the largest contributor to the Consequences was "Harm to the Product and Business" it might be possible to locate some of the key items in different premises to reduce the rating from *High* to *Normal* even though this would not be a popular alternative. If containment could be provided for firefighting water, the "Harm to the Environment" might also be reduced from *Normal* to *Low*. Both of these measures would then reduce the Block Consequences Score from 9 to 7 to give a consequences severity rating as *Slight*. With *Slight* Severity and *Very Low* Likelihood in the Table 3 RFRA Matrix the Block RERA Mark would become 2 that would be "Acceptable". If only one of these two severity reduction measures was implemented, the severity rating would be *Moderate*. Assuming that the fire safety improvements were implemented this would result in a Block RFRA Mark of 3 which would also be "Acceptable".

There are several other alternatives that the reader may choose to study. These, together with those described above are then plotted on the Table 3 RFRA Matrix to decide which is the most "Acceptable". This exercise will demonstrate how RFRA can be a valuable tool for studying different fire safety alternatives from a range of options.

RFRA DATA COLLECTION AND ANALYSIS

PLANNING THE PROGRAMME:
The collection of RFRA data across an international business requires careful preparation and planning if it is to be successful. All operating units in the business must be contacted to explain the reasons for performing RFRA in order to gain commitment. Instructions and examples, similar to those in the preceding text, must be provided to explain how to perform RFRA locally. With careful preparation and planning, a worldwide RERA exercise for about two hundred locations was completed in less than two months.

METHOD OF DATA COLLECTION:
All operating units should use the same RFRA forms or spreadsheets described in Tables 1 to 3. These must be returned to a central co-ordinator for checking and entry into a computerised database. Alternatively, if there is a secure company e-mail system, results can be e-mailed.

ASSIGNING BLOCK BOUNDARIES:
Each site can be assessed as a single entity by dividing it into about 6 - 10 blocks and then averaging the RFRA marks over all of the blocks to get a site mark. This method does not work well for large sites, however. For large sites, it is wiser to divide the site into separate facilities and then sub-divide these into about six blocks. It is best to collect the RFRA marks

for each of the blocks studied as this identifies the hazardous areas more clearly. Assessors in some facilities may find it difficult to decide how many blocks to use for their facility.

On large sites as many as 40 blocks may be needed, on smaller sites that are mainly offices or warehouses, one or two blocks should prove adequate. The number of blocks chosen has a significant effect on the block marks. The optimum number of blocks is usually decided by iteration and experienced judgement.

INEXPERIENCED ASSESSORS:

In most cases, even with little fire safety knowledge, assessors are able to complete the RFRA forms without problems. Most problems can be resolved via the telephone or e-mail, and by reference to the database. As results flow in, any anomalous results can be queried immediately. Fire safety specialists always review the blocks rated as 'Unacceptable' and experience has revealed that about half of these may be overestimated. The RFRA method was designed to be conservative, so this should not be a cause for concern.

DATA STRUCTURE:

Each block record in the database needs about 20 fields to contribute to the RFRA overall mark. These fields together with the location data, assessor data, date, description and reference number, etc, give a total of about 30 fields. The data can be studied at different levels of detail to assess consistency and specific problem areas as described in the following examples.

TYPICAL RFRA RESULTS

The RFRA database information can be used to answer three main questions:-
1. Does the fire risk in the area need further study?
2. Where are the main areas of fire risk in the business?
3. What factors contribute to fire risk in specific areas?

In addition, the consistency of RFRA marking can be investigated across a wide range of assessors, countries and facilities, to seek potential improvements to the method and to define 'Benchmarks'. The range of RFRA marks across a typical international pharmaceutical business is shown in Table 6. The RFRA results in the table conform to the Pareto principle with about 10% of the blocks studied having 90% of the fire risk. It is simple to interrogate the database for further information to answer the three questions posed above. An analysis of the spread of "Consequence" and "Likelihood" scores is given in Tables 7 and Table 8.

The data can be analysed to study the distribution of the fire risk between blocks of different types to enable benchmarking and for comparing RFRA results. An analysis of the RFRA overall marks for the warehouses is shown in Table 9 as an example.

Table 6. RFRA Marks Distribution for a typical Pharmaceutical Business:

RFRA Overall Mark:	Number of Blocks with this RFRA Overall Mark:	Percentage of all blocks studied:
1	43	18
2	62	25
3	34	14
4	31	13
5	50	20.5
6	3	1
7	13	5
8	6	2.5
9	2	1
10	0	0
TOTAL:	244	100

Table 7. RFRA Overall Consequences for all Block Types:

Overall Consequences Score:	Number of Blocks with this Score:	Percentage of all Blocks studied:
4	32	13
5	58	24
6	54	22
7	52	21
8	38	16
9	8	3
10	2	1
TOTAL:	244	100

Table 8. RFRA Overall Likelihood for all Block Types:

Overall Likelihood Score:	Number of Blocks with this Score:	Percentage of all Blocks studied:
2	4	1.6
3	39	16
4	67	27
5	63	26
6	48	20
7	19	8
8	3	1
9	1	0.4
TOTAL:	244	100

Table 9. Summary of Typical RFRA Overall Marks for Warehouses:

RFRA Overall Mark for Warehouses:	Number of Records with this RFRA Mark:
1	2
2	10
3	3
4	9
5	9
6	0
7	5
8	3
TOTAL:	41

FURTHER DEVELOPMENT OF RFRA:

The six-step RFRA process described is relatively simple and easy to use for deciding fire safety audit priorities, but not very useful for diagnosis or facility design. However, by using the same principles of subdivision with lower levels of definition and extra data input, it is possible to improve the method. *(The subdivision principle has already been used in the case of "Likelihood of Escalation" by providing a lower level table of 5 contributory elements.)*
For example:
Assess "Housekeeping" at a lower level by ranking all of the factors considered to be significant contributors, such as "Cleaning Procedures", "Plant inspections", "Waste Materials Control", etc. Then suitably combine the marks for each element to determine a "Housekeeping" assessment of *"Good", "Average" or "Bad".*
The principle is illustrated in Figure 5.

CONCLUSIONS:

- RFRA is an effective way to decide if an area needs to be assessed by a fire engineer.
- RFRA can be performed by staff with only a basic understanding of fire safety and is useful for assessing facilities with no local fire engineering expertise.
- RFRA is a rather crude method, but the data can be stored and analysed in a database to gain an overview of the fire risk profile for a typical international business.
- RFRA can be developed further as a diagnostic tool

ACKNOWLEDGEMENTS

The author thanks Zeneca Pharmaceuticals for giving permission to publish the RFRA method and data and thanks his colleagues, particularly Sandy Black, Vic Orr, Steve Kershaw and David Edmundson, for their support in developing the method and database ideas.

REFERENCES:

1.Gillett, J.E.1994.*Rapid Fire Risk Assessment* "Fire Safety Engineering".Vol.1;No.6pp.18-21
2.Theobald, C.R. 1997. *Studies of fires in industrial buildings. Part 1.* Fire Prevention Science and Technology. Vol. 7; (September) pp. 4-14
3.NFPA 1995. *Fire Protection Handbook.* 17tEdn. Quincy, M.A. National Fire Protection Association. ISBN: 0-87765-378-X

Figure 1. The Risk Assessment Process

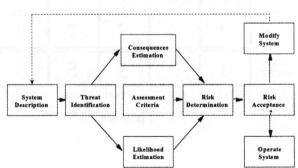

Figure 2. Risk Assessment Criteria

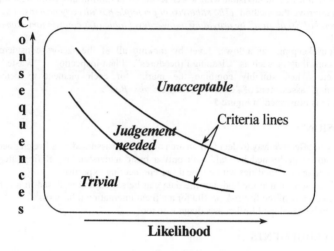

Figure 3. Fire Risk Assessment Criteria

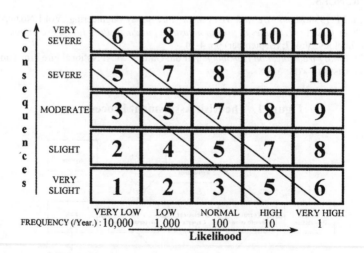

Figure 4. Fire Risk Assessment Fault Tree

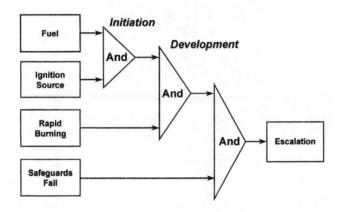

Figure 5. RFRA Development

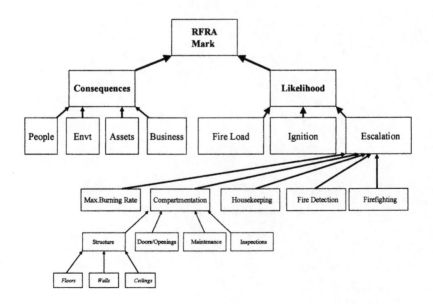

Figure 4. Life Risk Assessment Fault Tree

Figure 5. RAP Development

INTEGRATED RISK ASSESSMENT OF A PLANT HANDLING HAZARDOUS CHEMICALS

Lei Huang[a], Reginald B. H. Tan[a] and Malcolm L. Preston[b]
[a]Chemical and Process Engineering Centre, National University of Singapore
[b]ICI (UK)

In this paper, safety, health and environmental risks of a typical installation handling anhydrous hydrogen chloride were assessed in an integrated approach. A four-step procedure was used as risk assessment framework for this integrated risk assessment. The safety risk was presented as individual risk while Hazard Quotients were calculated for health and environmental risks. Some advantages of such an integrated approach were identified through the exercise. Difficulties were also encountered and discussed for causes and possible solutions.

Keywords: integrated risk assessment, safety, health, envrironment

INTRODUCTION

The integrated management of Safety, Health and Environment (SHE) has gained increasing priority within the chemical and process industry. The opportunities of integration arise from the common areas shared by SHE management systems. One such common management element is Risk Assessment. Chemical and process companies initiated risk-based process safety management decades ago. Environmental risk assessments[*] are often seen in major governmental development projects and redevelopment project of hazardous waste site. The health risk[**] of carcinogen in the environment is assessed in terms of incremental cancer occurrence caused by the carcinogen.

In the distinct realms of Safety, Health and Environment, risk assessment is currently employed in different degrees. Both qualitative and quantitative risk assessments are routinely employed in process safety management. Various risk assessment techniques are well developed for process safety applications, such as HAZAN, Fault Tree Analysis, Event Tree Analysis, dispersion modelling, etc. For environmental risk, the majority of risk assessments are carried out qualitatively as evident in most Environmental Impact Assessments. The rarity of detailed quantitative environmental risk assessments could be attributed to public apathy, the complexity of such assessments and a lack of suitable methods and data resources[1]. The risk of cancer caused by exposure to a health hazard is assessed quantitatively. On the other hand, the health risk of non-cancer effects are often assessed semi-quantitatively as hazard quotients based on the assumption of threshold limits.

These different forms of risk assessment possess similarities as well as incompatibilities. The similarities are inherent. The structure of the all risk assessments can be summarized in a four-step procedure: a source assessment, an exposure assessment, an effects assessment, and a summarizing risk characterization[2]. The first step, source assessment, is to identify and evaluate a potential hazard and or the route leading to an accident. In the exposure assessment, the receptors affected by an accident or exposed to a risk agent are chosen and the level of exposure determined. Effects assessment links the exposure levels to the extent of

---

[*] In modern environmental impact analysis, *environment* is often broadened to encompass the total surroundings of the proposed development in both physical and societal dimensions. In this paper, *environment* is restricted to the meaning of ecological surrounding; and *environmental risk* is interchangeable with *ecological risk*.

[**] In certain contexts, health risk caused by occupational and environmental exposure is termed environmental risk. Here, the *health risk* includes any risk posed to human health caused by prolonged exposure to the toxicant in any background media.

adverse effects. In risk characterization, the results of the above steps are summarized and compiled into an overall measure of the risk level.

The incompatibilities are often the results of differences in choices of receptors & end-points, exposure modes, exposure assessment techniques, underlying assumptions for effect assessment and risk characterization methods, etc. In both safety and health risk assessment, the receptors are, by default, human. The end-points, however, are often the level of exposure to cause acute health effect (such as 2nd degree burns and mortality) in safety risk assessment and the exposure level to cause chronic health effect (such as cancer) in health risk assessment. In environmental risk assessment, due to the vast number of species in a natural community, selection of receptors is often difficult and debatable[1]. The values of the management or stakeholders are of great influence here. The end-point selection of environmental risk assessment is also different from that of safety and health risk. Risk assessment of humans intends to protect the individual, while the environmental risk assessment typically seek to protect populations or communities of important species in the eco-system of interest[3]. Therefore, the end-points of environmental risk are often relevant to population dynamics, such as reproductive effects, development anomalies or behavioural changes affecting ability to survive. Acute exposure through inhalation, radiation and direct contact (overpressure, dermal exposure) are the main exposure modes in safety risk assessment. Chronic exposure through inhalation, radiation, dermal contact and ingestion are of equivalent importance in health and environmental risk assessment. Safety risk assessment uses consequence modelling almost exclusively for exposure assessment, while health and environmental risk assessment often use fate or transport models as well as field sampling and bioassay to assess the level of exposure. There is the assumption of a threshold exposure level, below which no adverse effect will occur, for safety and environmental hazards and non-cancer health hazards, but not for cancer-causing hazards. Safety risk can be characterized qualitatively or quantitatively and in terms of individual risk or societal risk. Environmental risk, however, is often characterized qualitatively or semi-quantitatively using Hazard Quotient (HQ). Health risk, on another hand, is often characterized quantitatively for cancer effect and semi-quantitatively for non-cancer effect.

The similarities indicate the opportunities for integrated risk assessment. At the same time, the incompatibilities pose obstacles to full integration. In addition, the incompatibilities render the comparison of the results of risk assessments in different forms difficult and prioritisation of risks among all SHE aspects impractical. In this paper, an attempt is made to assess the major SHE risks in a single risk assessment for the case of a typical semiconductor facility handling anhydrous hydrogen chloride. Efforts were directed to taking full advantage of the similarities and minimizing the incompatibilities.

Many governments have favoured risk-based controls over prescribed or performance-based controls. Some authorities, such as EPA, use risk assessment as base for regulatory decision-making. Following the trend, the Ministry of the Environment in Singapore has developed a unique set of land planning criteria for hazardous installations. The set of criteria are a hybrid of consequence-based and risk-based factors. It was used as a guideline in the risk characterization.

In the following sections, an integrated risk assessment is described according to the four-step procedure. Firstly, a typical anhydrous hydrogen chloride handling facility based in Singapore is described briefly, followed by hazard identification and scenario development. Secondly, transport modelling and exposure assessment are presented for the scenarios developed. Next, the acute and chronic health effects as well as ecotoxicology data of anhydrous hydrogen chloride are detailed. The final step is the characterization of SHE risks.

In the discussion, factors important to the comparability of the risk assessment results are discussed. The advantages and difficulties of such an integrated approach are also presented.

FACILITY DESCRIPTION AND HAZARD IDENTIFICATION

FACILITY DESCRIPTION AND CHARACTERIZATION

The semiconductor industry has been the fastest growing economic sector in Singapore over the past decades. The industry handles many hazardous chemicals, including but not restricted to anhydrous hydrogen chloride (HCl), trichlorosilane, nitric acid, hydrogen fluoride, phosgene and hydrogen, etc. These chemicals are highly flammable or toxic or both, and are present in various quantities. A survey of seven EPA RMP-regulated semiconductor facilities indicated that among the hazardous chemicals present, anhydrous hydrogen chloride and trichlorosilane are in the greatest quantities. In the silicon wafer preparation process, anhydrous hydrogen chloride is mainly used as a wafer-cleaning agent and trichlorosilane is used for deposition of silicon layer onto the wafer. Anhydrous hydrogen chloride was chosen for this study in the light of its clearly described process and well-defined release scenarios in the RMP reports, and the availability of well-documented toxicology studies.

Five of the seven facilities have tube trailers as on-site anhydrous hydrogen chloride storage. For these five facilities, the worst scenarios and the alternative scenarios of HCl release were all defined for releases from an HCl tube trailer. A typical HCl tube trailer is a combination of seven cylinders each containing 1360.8 kg liquefied anhydrous HCl under its own vapour pressure of 42 barg at 21 °C. Each cylinder has a length of 12.2 m and outside diameter of 55.88 cm. At one end of each cylinder, a safety device (usually rupture disk) is installed to prevent overpressure in case of exposure to elevated temperature. All operating valves and fittings are located at the other end of the cylinders and connected to the in-house process through transfer hose.

In this paper, a typical composite semiconductor facility handling anhydrous hydrogen chloride located in one of the industrial parks on Singapore main-island is considered. The nearest residential area is located 1.5 km away from the chosen site. Parks and industrial and commercial buildings surround the proposed site. Three meteorological conditions to be used in the transport modelling were derived from meteorology data provided by the Singapore Meteorological Service. An eight-point wind rose was used in the analysis. The data were tabulated below in Table 1.

Table 1   Meteorological Data

Meteorological Condition	Occurring Probability (%)
Stability Class F, 1m/s wind speed	10.6
Stability Class B, 2m/s wind speed	64.4
Stability Class C, 3m/s wind speed	25
Wind Direction	**Probability (%)**
East	19.49
North East	19.59
North	13.78
North West	12.85
West	13.67
South West	5.82
South	5.82
South East	9.00

SCENARIO DEVELOPMENT

With the focus on possible accidental releases within the installation fence line, two scenarios are defined considering both the likelihood and consequence. One is the failure of rupture disk at normal pressure. This scenario was reported as the worst credible release scenario by three of six RMP installations handling HCl tube trailer. The rupture disk was fitted with a 0.8 cm (5/16") orifice as reported in one of the RMP report. The release duration was assumed to be 30 min, which was the estimated time required to bring the release under control.

The other accidental release scenario was the leakage of HCl through the connecting hose. A hole of 2mm diameter was assumed and the condition was assumed to be under control after 20 minutes of release.

The release scenario for health and environmental risks was the emission of HCl from an elevated stack. The emission rates of five semiconductor installations were averaged to give 731 kg per year. The emission was assumed to be 24 hours per day and 365 days per year. The emission concentration of 200 mg/Nm^3 was set according to the National Standards of Concentration of Air Impurities of Singapore[4]. Without sufficient data, the stack parameters were arbitrary, with stack height of 10 m, stack diameter of 0.3 m and flue gas temperature of 303 K. Fugitive emission was also recorded in EPA Envirofacts Reports. The fugitive emission rate is much lower than point emission (about an order of magnitude). The difficulty of modelling fugitive emission prevented detailed assessment. In this paper, the facility was assumed to be well-ventilated and the workplace exposure level was controlled below PEL(Ceiling) of 5 ppm stipulated by Singapore Law[5].

EXPOSURE ASSESSMENT

RECEPTOR SELECTION

Safety Risk
The receptor in the case of safety risk is usually plant personnel and members of the general public in the vicinity of the hazardous installation. In some cases, the plant equipment and facilities are also considered as receptors. Since in this case, the toxicity of anhydrous HCl is the major hazard, corrosion damage to equipment is expected to be minor and therefore ignored.

Health Risk
According to exposure limit documentations, incidents of gastritis, chronic bronchitis, dermatitis, and photosensitization have been reported in individuals exposed to HCl occupationally[6,7]. However, by the concept of a threshold exposure level, the workers would be protected by strict adherence to the PEL(Ceiling) limit and therefore would not suffer any adverse health effect. Therefore, only chronic health risk arising from elevated stack release and affecting the general public is considered.

Environmental Risk
Singapore is a city-state with the main island 90% urbanized[8]. The 2879 hectares natural reserves (4% of the total land area) are mostly located at central and northern part of the island. There is very little natural eco-system around the industrial area. The prevalent form of wildlife in urban area is bird. The Common Myna (Acridotheres tristis) is a resident bird which frequents urban areas mainly feeding on seeds, insects or scavenging on waste food and rubbish. It nests in tree holes and roof eaves and roosts in large numbers often in trees close

to housing estates[9]. Although the common myna is not a threatened species in the local ecological system, it is chosen because its huge population and habit of visiting urban areas making it the most likely species to be affected by increased level of HCl in the atmosphere and an indicator of the deterioration of the environment quality.

EXPOSURE MODE

The primary exposure mode of anhydrous HCl is by inhalation. Once released, the liquefied anhydrous HCl would vaporize immediately and possibly form acid fumes. Skin contact with the acid fumes is a probable outcome to the on-site workers. With the assumption of adequate safety training and provision of personal protective equipment, the risk of dermal exposure can be minimized.

TRANSPORT MODELLING

There are various air dispersion modelling packages, which are able to handle dense gas dispersion as well as stack emission. One of such software package, TRACE™[18] was used for this exercise. The common exposure mode in all three kinds of risk allowed a considerable saving in transport modelling effort. The effect of rainfall was not considered in the transport modelling. However, it is predicted that rainfall will downwash the vapour cloud and reduce the impact of accidental release.

Accidental Releases

The accidental releases were modelled as dense gas dispersion. Peak concentrations and toxic dose were calculated for receptors located downwind over regular distance intervals for all three weather conditions.

Stack Emission

Continuous stack release was the model used for stack emission scenario. The receptors defined for the modelling were located downwind at regular distance intervals. At each downwind distance, the concentrations at 10m, 5m and 1m elevations were averaged to give an average atmospheric concentration.

EFFECT ASSESSMENT

EFFECTS OF ACUTE EXPOSURE

Inhalation of HCl vapour or fumes may cause irritation and a burning sensation in the throat, coughing and choking. High levels may cause inflammation and occasionally ulceration of the nose, throat or larynx, bronchitis, pneumonia, palpitations and headache. Higher concentrations may cause necrosis of the tracheal and bronchial epithelium, nasoseptal perforation, atelectasis, emphysema, damage to pulmonary blood vessels and lesions of the liver and other organs. Death may be due to laryngeal spasm, bronchopneumonia or pulmonary edema[6,7,10].

The assessment endpoint was set at a lethal dose, which would cause 3% fatality, as stipulated by the hazardous installation control rules. Probit equation is the most common expression of acute/lethal dose-response relationship in safety risk assessment. The CPD (Green Book) value of parameters in probit equations for lethality of hydrogen chloride are k_1=-6.7 (mg/m^3), k_2=1(mg/m^3), n=1(min)[11].

A second assessment endpoint, the IDLH level of the toxic gas, is also required by the hazardous installation control rules. In this case, the second endpoint is taken to be 50 ppm, the IDLH value of hydrogen chloride.

The possible chronic health effect resulting from acute exposure was not considered in this study. It was partly because the chronic health effect was not significant comparing to the acute effect[12] and partly because insufficient data was available to characterize the chronic health effects.

EFFECTS OF CHRONIC EXPOSURE

Repeated or prolonged exposure may cause erosion and discoloration of exposed teeth, chronic bronchitis, gastritis, dermatitis, and photosensitization[6,7,10]. Without suitable mathematical expression for the non-cancer chronic health effect of hydrogen chloride, a threshold exposure level was used as endpoint for this assessment. There are two possible values for the threshold exposure level. One is EPA Inhalation Reference Concentration, the other is Environmental Exposure Level.

The EPA has published an Inhalation Reference Concentration (R_fC) of 0.02 mg/m^3 for hydrogen chloride, based on a LOAEL (human equivalent concentration) of 6.1 mg/m^3, an uncertainty factor (UF) of 300 (3 for interspecies differences, 10 for intraspecies extrapolations, 10 for derivation of NOAEL from LOAEL), and a modifying factor (MF) of one[13]. The following equation was used for calculation of R_fC:

$$R_fC = NOAEL / (UF \bullet MF) \tag{1}$$

According to the EPA, the R_fC is an estimate (with uncertainty spanning perhaps an order of magnitude) of a daily exposure to the human population (including sensitive subgroups) that is likely to be without appreciable risk of deleterious effects during a lifetime. R_fCs are based on an assumption of lifetime exposure and may not be appropriately applied to less-than-lifetime exposure situations.

Another value, Environmental Exposure Level (EEL), could be derived from TLV or PEL value using the following equation[14]:

$$EEL = \frac{TLV \times D_{af} \times M_{af}}{S_f} \times 10^3 \tag{2}$$

where   EEL is expressed in μg/m^3
  TLV   = ACGIH-TLV or OSHA-PEL as 8-hr TWA, mg/m^3
  D_{af} = duration of exposure adjustment factor
       = working lifetime (80,000hr)/ biological lifetime for women (77.8yr)
       = 0.12
  M_{af} = magnitude of exposure adjustment factor
       = inhalation rate of adult/ inhalation rate of a 10-year-old child
       = 0.72
  S_f = safety factor, 10 to 1000

Since for hydrogen chloride, only TLV (Ceiling) value of 7 mg/m^3 (5 ppm) is available, a nominal value of 6 mg/m^3 was assummed as the TLV (TWA) value. With a safety factor of 10, the calculation gave an EEL value of 50 μg/m^3 or 0.05 mg/m^3 for HCl.

The assessment endpoint was set at the R_fC level since it was the lower (more conservative) one of the two candidates. It was assumed that if the atmospheric concentration was at or below the R_fC, no adverse effect was expected to occur.

ECOTOXICITY

The scarcity of ecotoxicity data is one of the major difficulties in environmental risk assessment. In this case, no ecotoxicity data were available for common myna with respect to environmental exposure to hydrogen chloride. Some derivation was necessary to obtain a suitable endpoint.

As mentioned before, the end-points of environmental risk are often relevant to population dynamics, such as reproductive effects, development anomalies or behavioural changes affecting ability to survive. The only reproductive and development studies of HCl were that of Pavlova's[13] on female rats. The chronic health data on rats were used to derive an endpoint for health effect. Although this is not the best approach for environment risk assessment, it was used as an estimate in order to complete a meaningful environmental risk assessment. The derivation was based on the same chronic rat inhalation study used for human R_fC and conducted in the similar manner. The rat LOAEL value was corrected to common myna equivalent value for gas respiratory effect in the extrathoracic and tracheobronchial regions as shown in the following equation[13]:

$$\text{LOAEL (common myna)} = \text{LOAEL (rat)} \times (\frac{IR_{rat}}{S_{rat}} / \frac{IR_{myna}}{S_{myna}}) \tag{3}$$

where $\text{LOAEL(rat)} = 2.5 \text{ mg/m}^3$
           IR is the inhalation rate of the respective species (m^3/day), and
           S is the surface area of extrathoracic and tracheobronchial region of the respective species (m^2).

In the derivation for human R_fC, inhalation rate for the test rat was 0.5 m^3/day[13]. The inhalation rate of common myna was calculated by the allometric equation suggested by EPA[15]:

$$IR = 0.00202 \text{ Wt}^{0.77} \tag{4}$$

where   IR   = inhalation rate (m^3/day)
           Wt   = body weight (g)

The body weight of common myna was taken as 110g[16]. The calculated inhalation rate was therefore 0.075 m^3/day. A factor of 2 to 3 was suggested by the EPA to account the higher metabolic rate of free-living birds. Therefore the inhalation rate of was corrected to 0.15 m^3/day.

There was no data available regarding the surface area of extrathoracic and tracheobronchial region of common myna. The ratio of S_{rat}/S_{myna} was assumed to be one.

The calculated value for LOAEL (common myna) was 8.33 mg/m^3. Applying the UF of 100, which included a factor of 10 for interspecies extrapolation, 10 for extrapolating from LOAEL to NOAEL, and the MF of 10 considering the inter-taxon extrapolation from mammal to avian, the reference concentration was 8.33×10^{-3} mg/m^3.

RISK CHARACTERIZATION

SAFETY RISK

The hybrid land-use planning control approach of Ministry of Environment of Singapore has been implemented since 1998. It combines the consequence-based and risk-based factors. Two types of zones are established around a hazardous installation: Hazard Zone and Risk

Zones. Hazard zone is determined based on the consequences of the worst credible accident scenario. No residential developments are permitted within the hazard zone. A set of risk zones is determined based on the individual risk calculated around the hazardous installation. Following criteria and guidelines for land use of risk zones are imposed (Table 2).

Table 2   Hazard & Risk Zones and Land Use Guidelines

Hazard/Risk Zone	Development Allowed
Hazard Zone · IDLH levels of toxic gas releases · 4 kW/m^2 of heat radiation from fires · 1 psi (6.9 kPa) blast overpressure from explosions	No residential developments
Risk Zone(Individual Risk, frequency/yr) · $5x10^{-5}* - 5x10^{-6}$ · $5x10^{-6} - 1x10^{-6}$ · Less than $1x10^{-6}$	Only industries Industries and commercial buildings Industries, commercial buildings and parks

* Note: No risk greater than $5x10^{-5}$ shall be allowed beyond installation fence line.

The frequencies for the two accidental release scenarios were estimated as $6x10^{-5}$ /yr for the rupture disk failure and $1x10^{-3}$ /yr for the connecting hose leakage based on historical data[11] and engineering judgment. Combining the information of accident frequency, dispersion modelling results and meteorological data, the individual risk was calculated. The results are summarized in Table 3.

Table 3   Hazard Zone and Individual Risk Zones

Zone	Max. distance from release point (m)
Hazard zone (IDLH)	5269
Risk Zones	
$\geq 5x10^{-5}$ /yr	273
$\geq 5x10^{-6}$ /yr	723
$\geq 1x10^{-6}$ /yr	814

Comparing the safety risk results with the land use guidelines, the risk was not acceptable. The nearest residential area was only 1.5 km away from the proposed site whilst the hazard zone in this case extended to 5.3 km. Also the individual risk of $5x10^{-5}$ /yr extended beyond the installation fence line, from which the nearest point to the tube trailer was 100m. The installation would not be permitted at the proposed site under the current rules of hazardous installation control.

To reduce the consequence of the release, several measures could be implemented. The tube trailer could be kept in an enclosed storage area with ventilation routed to a scrubber. Water spray/ water curtain could be installed around the tube trailer area. Other measures could be used to reduce the frequency of the accidental release. Administrative controls could be implemented to ensure more frequent inspections of connecting hose and rupture disk. The connecting hose could be replaced every half year to reduce the probability of developing leakage.

HEALTH RISK

Hazard Quotient (HQ) was used to characterize health risk in this analysis. Inhalation Health Hazard Quotient was defined by the following equation:

$$HQ = \frac{C_{air}}{R_f C} \tag{5}$$

where C_{air} = concentration of health hazard agent in atmosphere, mg/m^3

$R_f C$ = inhalation reference concentration, mg/m^3

Values of hazard quotient were calculated based on the results of stack emission modelling. The results were summarized in Table 4.

Table 4   Health Hazard Quotient at Various Downwind Distances

Downwind Distance	Hazard Quotient
30m	9.59
50m	3.46
70m	1.76
90m	1.88
100m	1.81
120m	3.61×10^{-1}
150m	1.30×10^{-8}
200m	1.30×10^{-8}

The high health risk was present within the installation boundary and the nearby industrial area. The general public would be exposed to insignificant health risk.

ENVIRONMENTAL RISK

Environmental Hazard Quotient was used as the risk measurement of environmental risk. The hazard quotient was calculated based on the predicted air concentrations of stack emission. The environmental hazard quotient is summarized in Table 5.

Table 5   Environmental Hazard Quotient at Various Downwind Distances

Downwind Distance	Hazard Quotient
30m	23
50m	8.30
70m	4.22
90m	4.52
100m	4.35
120m	8.67×10^{-1}
150m	3.11×10^{-8}
200m	3.11×10^{-8}

As in the case of the health risk, the environmental risk was also controlled and no great risk extended far beyond the fence line of the installation.

DISCUSSION

COMPARABILITY

It is often in the interest of management to compare the relative importance of different issues in order to set priorities and locate resources. Although ranking involves non-risk factors such as management goals, stakeholders' interest, perception of the general public and regulatory forces, etc, it is important to first understand how comparable the risks are. Some important factors that must be bared in mind when comparing risks of different contexts are: intentions of the risk assessment, risk representation and uncertainties associated with the risk estimates.

Intentions of the Risk Assessments
The intention of a risk assessment is very important as it directs the general approach of the assessment, and the selection of assessment endpoint and risk criteria. All three risk assessments were carried out to assess the impact of the installation to its surroundings. The primary concern was given to the health and well being of the general public. However, the objective was different in three risk assessments. Both health and environmental risk assessments employed the no effect level as the benchmark for exposure level. In other words, the risk assessment was intended to ensure that the general public and the ecosystem would not be adversely affected by the discharge of HCl. On the other hand, the safety risk assessment was carried out to maintain the balance between efficient land use and adequate protection of the general public against the hazardous installation. That is, the emphasis was a tolerable level of risk. Although, technically, a hazard quotient of 1 does not rule out the possibility of exposed receptor developing adverse effects, the difference in the intention must not be overlooked.

Risk Representation
Two types of risk measurement were used for the risk characterization in this case: individual risk and hazard quotient. Both risk measurements had a fixed consequence component, which were closely tied to the intention of the risk assessments: 3% fatality in the case of individual risk and no adverse effect in the case of hazard quotient. The likelihood component was represented quantitatively by the frequency in individual risk; while in health and environmental risk assessments, the probability of being affected by the HCl discharge was semi-quantitatively related to the magnitude of HQ.

Uncertainty
Risk assessments are subjected to various sources of uncertainty. Finkel has classified all uncertainties into four categories: decision rule uncertainty, model uncertainty, parameter uncertainty, and variability[17].

Decision rule uncertainty is present when management decisions must be made to balance different concerns in a single risk study. These decisions are often more of an exercise of management values and goals than scientific judgement. For safety risk, decision rule uncertainties are introduced when the risk assessor decides to select 3% fatality as the assessment endpoint, to choose individual risk as the measurement of risk, to accept the definitions of hazard and risk zones, and to exclude risk from transportation of the hydrogen chloride tube trailer, for instance. For health risk, the decisions of using R_fC as assessment endpoint, and exclusion of fugitive emission brought in uncertainties. During the environmental risk assessment, selection of exposure receptor & assessment endpoint, placing focus on stack emission only, and neglecting the existing HCl level in air were also sources of decision rule uncertainty.

Model uncertainty is a familiar source of uncertainty to risk assessors. The uncertainty is inherent since models are simplified realities. However, the uncertainty could be reduced by the proper selection of models and the advancement of the model. The transport modelling for all three risks were performed using the same commercial software package. The models involved were dense gas dispersion and continuous stack source dispersion. The uncertainty associated with the transport models was low judging from the extensive studies on the involved dispersion models and the fact that the software was widely accepted. High uncertainty was present in most dose-response models. The probit model used in safety risk assessment was known to be problematic at extreme ends of the dose-response curve. No dose-response model uncertainty was introduced in the health and environmental risk assessment, since no dose-response model was used.

Parameter uncertainty is caused by the inability to measure the needed parameters precisely or accurately. Meteorological data, dispersion coefficients and dose-response data are common sources of parameter uncertainty to the three risks. The first two sources were of same magnitude to all three risks. Dose-response data for acute health effect was in general more reliable than chronic health effect.

Variability uncertainty refers to the uncertainty caused by ignoring the variation in physical, chemical and biological processes. Statistical analysis could be employed to represent the variability with good certainty; however, failure to recognize the inherent variability in natural process or inadequate statistical analysis introduces uncertainty. In this case, the variability in weather condition was explicitly included in terms of probability. The variation in lethal dose of HCl took the form of probit equation. Uncertainty factor was used to account the variation in human NOAEL. Large variation in the response of different species to the exposure of HCl was expected. However, the variation could not be included in the assessment of environmental risk due to insufficient data; therefore variability uncertainty was high for the calculated environmental risk.

Overall, the uncertainty of safety and health risk results were of the same magnitude, and the uncertainty level of environmental risk was substantially higher. It must be known to the management that high uncertainty in the risk assessment often results in overly conservative risk estimates.

SOME LESSONS

The difficulties of assessing three types of risk in a single project were mainly in exposure and effect assessment phases, although in this particular case, the difficulty in exposure assessment phase was greatly reduced owing to a single exposure mode. The differences can be daunting. Transport of chemicals in different media requires different models, each having its own limitations. Modelling fate of chemicals in ecosystem is drastically different from that of transport modelling and requires expertise in ecology and biology. In addition, safety risk assessment often involves explosion and fire modelling, which is not encountered in health and environmental risk assessment.

Effect assessment in safety risk is relatively straight forward as dose-response data of heat radiation, explosion overpressure and toxicity of major chemical hazards have been published in many easy-to-use forms (e.g. probit equations). On the other hand, dose-response data for health and environmental risk assessments are scarce and expert judgment often required for parameter derivation and verification.

The benefits of conducting a combined risk assessment for safety, health and environment lie in the integration of closely related concerns. Effort was saved where the same information was needed to assess two or more risks. Examples of one-for-all procedures were facility & site characterization and exposure mode analysis. It is foreseeable that when two or even all three of the SHE risks were to be assessed for regulatory compliance purpose, an integrated risk assessment approach would increase the efficiency of such process.

Accident frequency estimation, an important step in safety risk assessment does not appear to have a proper place in the general four-step structure for risk assessment. It is mainly because the measurements of health risk (except cancer effect) and environmental risk do not include a quantitative expression for likelihood. A possible solution would be placing the frequency estimation in the first step --- hazard identification, since some techniques used in frequency estimation are also effective methods for hazard identification. It could be included as part of the scenario characterization.

CONCLUSION

Safety, health and environmental risk assessment with an integrated approach accords well with the principle of an integrated SHE management system. Such an approach has the advantages of resource saving and higher efficiency over individual risk assessments. Non-trivial difficulties in performing a truly integrated SHE risk assessment still persist. Challenges remain in several areas: the need for complete and ready-to-use databases; the need for a refined common risk assessment framework suitable for the chemical and process industry; and the need for a better risk presentation format for health and environmental risks.

REFERENCES

1. Crosby, G.D., 1998, *Environmental Toxicology and Chemistry*, Oxford University Press.
2. ACS, 1998, *Understanding Risk Analysis: a short guide for health, safety and environmental policy making*, American Chemical Society.
3. Rodier, D., Norton, S., 1992, *Framework for Ecological Risk Assessment*, U.S. Environmental Protection Agency, Risk Assessment Forum, EPA/630/R-92/001, Washington, DC.
4. Republic of Singapore, 2001, Environmental Pollution Control (Air Impurities) Regulations 2001, *Environmental Pollution Control Act 1999* (ACT 9 of 1999).
5. Republic of Singapore, 1996, The Factories (Permissible Exposure Levels of Toxic Substances) Order 1996, *The Factories Act*.
6. NLM, 1999, *Hazardous Substances Databank*, National Library of Medicine, U.S.
7. ACGIH, 1991, *Documentation of the Threshold Limit Values and Biological Exposure Indices*, 6th ed., American Conference of Governmental Industrial Hygienists, Ohio.
8. MITA, 2000, *Singapore Fact Sheets Series*, Ministry of Information and The Arts, Singapore.
9. Briffett, C., 1992, *A Guide to the Common Birds of Singapore*, Singapore Science Centre, Singapore.
10. Messer, 2000, *Anhydrous hydrogen chloride MSDS*, MG Industries.
11. Lees, F.P., 1996, *Loss Prevention in the Process Industries: Hazard identification, assessment and control*, 2nd ed, Butterworth-Heinemann, Oxford.

12. Machle, W., Kitzmiller, K.V., Scott, E.W., Treon, J.F., 1942, The Effect of the Inhalation of Hydrogen Chloride, *J Ind Hyg Toxicol*, 24: 222-225.

13. Office of Science and Technology, Oct 2000, *Integrated Risk Information System (IRIS) Database*, U.S. Environmental Protection Agency, Cincinnati, OH.

14. Daugherty, J., *1997, Assessment of Chemical Exposures: Calculation methods for environmental professionals*, Lewis Publishers, New York.

15. McVey, M., Norton, S. B., Nolt, C., Preston, R., Dec 1993, *Wildlife Exposure Factors Handbook*, U.S. Environmental Protection Agency, Office of Health and Environmental Assessment, Office of Research and Development, EPA/600/R-93/187, Washington, DC.

16. Forys, E.A., Allen, C.R., 1999, Biological Invasions and Deletions: community changes in south Florida, *Biological Conservation*, 87: 341-347.

17. Finkel, A.M., 1990, *Confronting Uncertainty in Risk Management: a guide for decision-makers*, Center for Risk Management, Resources for the Future, Washington, DC.

18. SAFER systems, 1992, *TRACE 8 User's Guide*, SAFER systems, LLC, Westlake Village, California, U.S.

LIST OF ABBREVIATION

HQ	Hazard Quotient
EPA	U.S. Environmental Protection Agency
RMP	Risk Management Plan
PEL	Permissible Exposure Level
TLV	Threshold Limit Value
CPD	Committee for the Prevention of Disasters
IDLH	Immediate Danger to Life and Health
$R_f C$	Reference Concentration
LOAEL	Lowest-Observed-Adverse-Effect Level
NOAEL	No-Observed-Effect Level
UF	Uncertainty Factor
MF	Modifying Factor
EEL	Environmental Exposure Level

NUMERICAL RISK ASSESSMENT AND LAND USE PLANNING

D A Carter, I L Hirst, S R Porter and R M Turner
Hazardous Installations Directorate, Health & Safety Executive,
Stanley Precinct, Bootle, Merseyside L20 3RA, UK

The proposed siting of new chemical Hazardous Installations, modifications to existing Hazardous Installations, and proposals for development within the vicinity of these installations, are assessed by the Hazardous Installations Directorate (HID) of the Health & Safety Executive. Numerical risk assessment methodology is utilised to enable advice to be given to Local Planning Authorities. The use of 'top down' Quantified Risk Assessment methodologies is well established in these circumstances. HID also uses simplified 'Risk Integral' techniques to enable decisions to be made on a consistent basis at low cost.

This paper describes the application of these numerical techniques with actual case studies which illustrate the methodologies and decision making criteria. The subsequent consideration and provision of risk reduction measures is also described with examples. The implications for the successful management of off-site risk are discussed.

Keywords: Hazardous installations, risk assessment, land use planning, numerical techniques

INTRODUCTION

Risks associated with major chemical accident hazards, though no different in many respects to all other health and safety risks, have the additional dimension of potentially resulting in a disaster, possibly involving members of the public. Though many aspects of societal concerns associated with major accidents are not amenable to analysis, the scale of the consequences and the associated likelihood are capable of numerical description and therefore provide a consistent though incomplete measure of risk.

Risk management is necessary both by industry and society to demonstrate that all reasonably practicable measures are taken to ensure the heath and safety of persons who may be affected, and the environment. This must include a decision making process which is appropriate, soundly based, open and transparent [1], so that all interested parties can participate and see that the objectives are achieved.

Successful management of these matters requires a systematic approach [2]:

Major Accident Prevention Policy (MAPP)

I

Organisation

I

Planning and implementation

I

Performance measurement

I

Review & audit

The Control of Major Accident Hazard Regulations 1999 (COMAH) implement the European Union (EU) Directive in the UK, and apply specifically to major chemical hazard sites. These requirements are in addition to the general requirements of the Health & Safety at Work etc Act 1974 and its associated Regulations, which include a requirement that employers are to conduct their undertaking in such a way as to ensure, so far as is reasonably practicable, that persons not in their employment who may be affected by work activities are not exposed to risks to their health and safety. Measures to reduce risk must be taken until the risk is broadly acceptable, or the cost, whether in money or effort, of further risk reduction, would be grossly disproportionate to the reduction in risk that would be achieved, in accordance with the principle of 'as low as reasonably practicable' (ALARP) [3]. Proposers of new hazardous installations need to show that adequate consideration has been given to the adoption of inherently safe technology.

RISK ASSESSMENT

Risk assessment is used to determine how the risks associated with an activity can be reduced to a level that is broadly acceptable. There are many possible methodologies which can be utilised [4]:

Qualitative risk assessment is the comprehensive identification and description of hazards from a specified activity, to people or the environment. The range of possible events may be represented by broad categories, with classification of the likelihood and consequences for comparison and the identification of priorities.

Semi-quantitative risk assessment is the systematic identification and analysis of hazards from a specified activity, and their representation by means of qualitative and quantitative descriptions of the frequency and extent of the consequences, to people or the environment. The assessment is informed by a representative selection of specific examples for comparison with standards.

Quantitative risk assessment is the application of methodology to produce a numerical representation of the frequency and extent of a specified level of exposure or harm, to specified people or the environment, from a specified activity. There is also a comparison of the results with specified criteria.

All assessments operate within a common framework:

Define scope

I

Perform hazard analysis

I

Perform risk estimation (with sensitivity and uncertainty analysis)

I

Compare with criteria

I

Consider of risk reduction measures

I

Report

DEFINITION OF SCOPE

- Risk from what? The system under scrutiny must be defined, including the circumstances in which it operates. Any relevant factors which are being excluded from consideration must be clearly stated.
- Risk to what? What are the objects of our concern?
- Risk of what? What are the measures of exposure and harm that we wish to assess?
- So what? Identification of the criteria against which to judge the outcome, including the basis for dealing with uncertainty.

HAZARD ANALYSIS

- Top down.

The possible hazardous events are identified in a general way and estimates of frequencies from knowledge of previous accidents and generic data sources are made. Dominating events

are selected for more detailed analysis. The consequences and likelihood of the outcomes are described.
- Cause and effect.

Causes of possibly hazardous conditions are identified by means of checklists and analysis techniques, including reports of accidents from similar activities. The results are available during the design, commissioning, operation, maintenance and modification operations for an activity and appropriate means of prevention, control and mitigation established. Abnormal conditions are postulated and appropriate control systems specified.
- Comparison.

Relevant standards and best practice for the operations are identified and the recommendations adopted.
- Continuous.

Data is collected and audits are carried out to establish the actual safety performance of the operation, and appropriate remedial measures are identified.

RISK ESTIMATION
- Selection of a representative set of events.

This is not an exact or trivial process and requires judgement and experience. Also variations in the ambient conditions need to be included (day, night, summer, winter, wind-speed, atmospheric stability) as appropriate.
- Ranking of events by severity and likelihood eg. in a matrix.

This gives an initial indication of the relative importance of the causes and where most effort may be needed to reduce sensitivity and uncertainty in the final results. Screening methods, based on cautious estimates, may be used to eliminate non-contributing events from further analysis. The greater the uncertainty of the likelihood of an event, the more weight may be given to the consequences. Where the consequences are uncertain a 'worst case' basis may be appropriate.
- Calculation of the event frequencies and conditional consequence probabilities to give numerical estimates.

COMPARISON WITH CRITERIA

The estimated levels of risk are considered in relation to the tolerability criteria.

If the level of risk either for the installation as a whole, or for the aspects of the installation under consideration, is shown by professional judgement and comparison with known standards and good practice to be 'broadly acceptable' (ie individual risks are <1 cpm and societal risks are negligible) then a simple statement to this effect is sufficient.

Numerical results (risk contours, F-N curves etc) can be compared with the tolerability criteria identified at an early stage [3]. The main contributing causes of risk can be confirmed. Where uncertainty is high and large safety factors or a 'worst case' basis has been adopted, a decision can only be reached if the criteria are not exceeded.

SENSITIVITY ANALYSIS
- Would being more thorough be worthwhile?

Particularly where certain events dominate part of the risk spectrum additional analysis of those events could well be appropriate and give a much improved representation of the main contributing factors. In other cases it may be appropriate to look for additional ways that risks may be realised. For example, it is common not to include high wind speed conditions in dispersion studies due to their relatively low frequency. However where positively buoyant conditions occur at the source (eg fires and other hot releases, containing toxic substances), the inclusion of high wind speeds (eg 10 metres per second or more) in the consequence modelling may result in much larger ground level concentrations and overall risks in the near field [5]. What were the initial assumptions? Are they still appropriate?

UNCERTAINTY ANALYSIS

- What I know I don't know, and what I don't know I don't know.

Uncertainties occur in the data used to set frequencies and probabilities, in the consequence models, and in the risk assessment methodology [6], particularly where important aspects of a problem have not been identified during the hazard analysis.

Where risks are estimated on a 'cautious' basis and that is satisfactory, or the criteria are not exceeded, then further uncertainty analysis is not necessary. However, where options are being considered of a different nature, eg whether to transport hazardous goods by road, rail or pipeline, then the uncertainties can be very important and possibly make the results of a quantified risk assessment unsuitable for decision making. The initial result of the analysis may be to identify where the greatest uncertainties exist and thereby justify research to improve our understanding.

The assessment of uncertainty also involves uncertainty. In many cases a simple estimate of the uncertainties and the use of qualitative judgement is as good as can be expected.

RISK REDUCTION MEASURES

- What could be done to reduce the consequences and frequency?

Simply relying on compliance with established codes may not be sufficient. In the case of major hazard installations the analysis for severe faults needs to review the design basis and look beyond that which is 'reasonably forseeable'.

Elimination, prevention, control and mitigation all need consideration before such risks can be judged to be properly controlled. Does the cost exceed the benefit? Is there gross disproportion? The reduction in risk should be estimated for each possible option.

Cost-benefit analysis can be used for difficult cases where the frequencies are low but the consequences are high. In more straightforward cases 'lines of defence' analysis can be used to assess options. 'Affordability' is not a legitimate consideration. Numerical results cannot justify non-compliance with statutory duties nor risks which are greater than following known standards and best practice, but may justify deviations from standards where risks are thereby reduced.

REPORT

- Describing the process and outcomes in a suitable way for the recipient.

Good documentation of the whole assessment process is critical. An 'audit trail' should be established at the beginning of the process. It is important that the information necessary for the decisions to be taken is presented in such a way that the decision makers will have confidence in their decision. In many cases an executive summary of one or two pages is most appropriate, with the supporting documentation available for reference. Direct discussion between the assessors and the decision makers throughout the risk assessment process can prevent unnecessary time and effort being expended on unimportant aspects.

Early identification of problems and their consideration can be of great importance. Where necessary the scope of the assessment can be modified accordingly. The assessment may need to be referred to long after the persons concerned have moved on to other work.

LAND USE PLANNING

For the last 15 years HSE has used quantitative risk assessment to assess the 'residual' risk from hazardous chemical installations [7]. That is the risk that remains to persons offsite after the risks at the installation have been made as low as is reasonably practicable. The maximum quantities of hazardous substances that the sites are entitled to have present are used as the basis for the assessments. The usual product of the methodologies are three concentric contours on a map of the area showing defined levels of individual risk to a hypothetical house resident who spends all of their time in or in the vicinity of their dwelling. The level of harm specified is exposure to the dangerous toxic load (DTL) [8] or equivalent for thermal radiation or blast overpressure, or worse.

Exposure of persons to the DTL would cause:

severe distress to all

a substantial fraction of the population requiring medical attention

some requiring hospital treatment

some (about 1%) fatalities

In some cases, where the risk is from a clearly defined and dominating hazard, such as a bulk storage tank at a small liquified petroleum gas (LPG) distribution site which on jet flame impingement could fail catastrophically within about 15 minutes resulting in a boiling liquid expanding vapour explosion (BLEVE) and a consequent fireball, the contours may be established on the basis of hazard range alone.These contours form the basis of HSE's advice to local planning authorities (LPAs).

A site may voluntarily agree to reduce off-site risks. An example is given in case study 1.

OBJECTIVES

Hazardous Substance Authorities (HSAs), which are generally the same locally elected government bodies as the LPAs, are required to consult HSE about the siting of new hazardous installations and modifications to existing hazardous installations, and LPAs are required to consult HSE about applications for development in the vicinity of existing hazardous installations. The objective of consultations between LPAs and HSE is to keep incompatible developments apart, and to this end HSE advises against the granting of planning permission for a significant development proposal in the vicinity of a hazardous installation [8].

PLANNING APPLICATIONS

Planning applications for developments in the vicinity of hazardous installations are first considered using a four category and three zone policy, making use of the risk contours previously mentioned, forming the 'consultation distance'.

Development proposals are placed into 4 broad categories:

Industrial (factories, offices, warehouses of limited size)

Retail and leisure (shopping and leisure developments of limited size)

Residential (housing and hotels)

Institutional or sensitive (hospitals, schools, accommodation for the elderly etc)

The three zones are:

Inner (where the risk, of a hypothetical house resident of being exposed to the DTL or greater, exceeds 10 chances per million (cpm) per annum)

Middle (where the risk is between 10 and 1 cpm)

Outer (where the risk is between 1 and 0.3 cpm)

In the inner zone only industrial and other very small developments are not advised against.

In the outer zone only institutional or sensitive developments and very large examples of certain other developments are advised against.

In the middle zone and in other cases of where the above policy does not result in a final answer the development proposal is considered on its merits. The main factors that are considered are:

The numbers of persons at the development and their sensitivity

The intensity of the development

The level of risk, taking into account the pattern of use of the development

These factors are all included in a parameter known as the scaled risk integral (SRI) [9]. For example, a proposal for 30 houses on a 1.2 Ha site at a risk of 1 cpm would result in a SRI of approximately 2500, which is used as the decision boundary value for 'significant' risk.

For developments involving sensitive populations (children, elderly etc) the number of persons is first multiplied by 2. For developments involving working populations those numbers are first divided by 4.

PROPOSALS FOR NEW HAZARDOUS INSTALLATIONS

A new hazardous chemical installation requires 'consent' from the HSA [10]. The HSA has to consult HSE for advice on the level of risk to the existing community and allow HSE to specify any 'conditions' that should be imposed over and above compliance with statutory requirements. A proposal for a new hazardous installation (HI) is first assessed to determine whether there are possibly incompatible developments within the likely consultation distance. These are existing populations which would automatically receive advice against if they were to be proposed following the existence of the HI (eg housing in the 'inner' zone or where the SRI exceeds 35,000).

If this is not the case then the 'case societal risk' for the proposal is estimated using another parameter called the approximate risk integral (ARI) [11]. The risk integral (RI) is defined as the integral under the curve of the cumulative frequency (F) times the number of fatalities (N) that may be expected among the local community from the hazardous installation. This formulation includes a substantial allowance for numerical risk aversion which we consider appropriate in these circumstances [11]. (NB The SRI is equal to the RI divided by the area of the single development proposal.)

The ARI uses a simplifying assumption that the plot of cumulative frequency F against N has a slope of approximately -1 on a log-log scale. The ARI is calculated from an assessment of only a single event at the installation. That is the 'worst case' type of event in terms of consequences and frequency. If the value of ARI does not exceed 10,000, and there are no 'incompatible' existing developments in the vicinity, then no further consideration of risks are considered necessary.

GENERIC RISK ASSESSMENT

In addition to compliance with the Health & Safety at Work Act [12] all hazardous chemical sites that come within the scope of the COMAH Regulations [13] also require hazardous substance consent from the HSA [10]. In all applications the maximum quantity of substance must be specified. Also the manner in which the substance is to be kept (buried/mounded/above ground, plus temperature and pressure information) is specified along with the maximum vessel capacity.

If a site chooses to apply for (or 'claim' in the case of existing inventories at the time of introduction of the Regulations) hazardous substance 'consent', but wishes to retain flexibility concerning the quantities of specific substances that may be present, then they may apply for consent for a category of substance (eg. 'toxic', 'very toxic', 'flammable', 'reacts violently with water' etc) where those substances are not specifically named in the schedule to the regulations. In this case HSE carries out a very simple generic assessment based on a 'worst case' exemplar substance for that category, and combines this with cautious frequency and consequence values to produce a conservative assessment. An example is given in case study 2.

Where unconditional consent would not be acceptable, possible 'conditions' are discussed with the site until the estimate of risk complies with the previously stated criteria. An example is given in case study 3.

CONCLUSIONS
Good risk assessment principles are universal, but risk criteria need to reflect the practical, social and cultural context in which they are to be applied.

Risk assessments only need to be 'fit for purpose' and simple screening methods are useful to ensure that the most effort is applied to the most difficult problems.

A QRA must be both reasonable and practicable. If the cost of the proposed improvement is of the same order as the cost of carrying out the analysis then professional judgement, supported by appropriate information, is the best basis for a decision. If adequate data or physical modelling is not available then much of the analysis has to be based on judgement in any case. It is on these occasions that wishful thinking can ruin an otherwise sound approach.

Though consistency in the application of QRA to major chemical hazards can be achieved by the strict application of standardised methodology, the significance of the results may be questionable in absolute terms. However the methodologies are now well established and provide good insight into the relative merits of risk reducing options.

ACKNOWLEDGEMENTS
The authors would like to thank colleagues in the HSE, particularly those in the Methodology and Standards Development Unit, and Dr Clive Nussey for their assistance in the preparation of this paper.
Nothing in this paper should be interpreted as a statement of HSE policy.

REFERENCES
1   "A Framework for Risk Related Decision Support", UK Offshore Operators Association, May 1999

2   "Successful Health & Safety Management", HSG65, 2nd Edition, HSE, 1997

3   "Reducing Risks, Protecting People", Discussion Document, HSE, 1999

4   "Preparing Safety Reports: Control of Major Accident Hazards Regulations 1999", HSG190, HSE, 1999

5   "Dispersion of Toxic Combustion Products from Large Fires", Carter D A, ChERD, 1989

6   "Guidelines for Quantitative Risk Assessment Uncertainty", UK Offshore Operators Association, March 2000

7   "The Application of Consequence Models in Risk Assessment: A Regulators View", Nussey C, Carter D A, Cassidy K, International Conference & Workshop on Modelling &

Mitigating the Consequences of Accidental Releases of Hazardous Materials, CCPS, New Orleans, September 1995

8 "Risk Criteria for Land-Use Planning in the Vicinity of Major Hazards", HSE, 1989

9 "The Scaled Risk Integral", Carter D A, Proceedings of the 8th International Symposium on Loss Prevention & Safety Promotion in the Process Industries, Antwerp, June Elsevier Science, 1995

10 "Planning Controls for Hazardous Substances", DETR Circular 04/2000

11 "A Worst Case Methodology for Risk Assessment of Major Accident Installations", Hirst I L, Carter D A, Process Safety Progress, Vol 19 No. 2, Summer 2000

12 The Health & Safety at Work etc Act 1974, and amendments.

13 "A Guide to the Control of Major Accident Hazards Regulations 1999", HSE, 1999

CASE STUDY 1: USE OF QRA TO DECIDE REASONABLY PRACTICABLE RISK REDUCTION MEASURES.

INTRODUCTION
This example is based on an sulphur trioxide/oleum production facility. The company decided to undertake a major refurbishment of the existing site at a cost of about £16M to reduce the risks to off-site populations as required by Section 3 of the HSW Act. This involved, among other things, relocation of the storage tanks, which in turn required a variation in the Company's hazardous substance consent to be granted by the LPA. HSE became involved when the Company and LPA sought advice.

RISK REDUCTION MEASURES (RRMS) PLANNED BY THE COMPANY
The Company had already designed a new plant to support its application, the purpose being to significantly reduce the risks from the manufacture, storage and tanker loading of sulphur trioxide and oleum.
 The main measures proposed by the Company were:
I. To replace existing SO3 tanks (3 by 65 te) by new double skinned tanks located inside a refurbished building to provide a modern secondary containment building.
II. To undertake all tanker loading indoors.
III. To reduce the number of operations involving 65% oleum
IV. To reduce the inventory of 30% oleum from two 1500 te tanks (single skinned, outdoors) to one 500 te tank (double skinned, indoors).
V. To replace of the converter for producing SO3, heat exchangers, absorption towers, and associated equipment.
 The Company employed consultants to assess the possible impact of the RRMs on its CD. Their QRA indicated that the contours defining the extremities of the inner, middle and outer zones would be reduced by about 40 to 50%.

HSE'S QRA TO SET A NEW CD AND CONSENT CONDITIONS
The Company decided that for operational flexibility it required three 100te tanks that would normally hold 65 te, but occasionally one may be full. In the event of an emergency the extra

capacity would enable the contents of a leaking tank to be transferred to another tank, thereby mitigating the incident.

The HSE QRA confirmed the significant reduction in risk levels and highlighted that the extent of the outer zone was influenced by the number of SO3 tanker loadings and the extent of the outdoor pipe work between the new production unit and the storage area. As a result of discussions with HSE the company agreed to:

- increase the height of the internal bunding around vessels to prevent overtopping in the case of catastrophic vessel failure;
- implement the Consent conditions at 4, 5 and 6 below.

Releases resulting from the loading of oleum into tankers were not significant. Credit was given for double walled vessels; vessel failure rates (catastrophic and limited failures) were reduced by a factor of 10. Mitigation provided by the building was modelled as described by Porter et al (17).

The QRA was based on over 120 scenarios covering:

- Liquid SO3 releases indoors (vessels, pipework and tanker loading)
- Gaseous SO3 releases outside (Converter vessel and pipework)
- 20% and 30% Oleum releases indoors (vessel, pipework and tanker loading)
- Various failures of oleum absorption tower leading to release of 35% oleum outside
- Outside pipework and plant failures leading to releases of 35% oleum
- Outside pipework failures leading to releases of 27% oleum.

The QRA enabled risk contours to be drawn for the new arrangements. The approximate extents of the risk contours from the centre of the storage area before and after improvements are shown in Table 1 below.

The main conditions placed on the Express Consent application were:

I.   SO3 and oleum to be stored in double-walled vessels.
II. No vessel to contain more than 100te
III. All vessels and loading operations to be located in a normally-closed building
IV. An automatic leak detection system to be installed in the building and interlocked with the outlet valves from the storage tanks so that they close 'automatically' in the event of a leak.
V.   In the event of a leak, the leak detection system should close down the ventilation of the building, but suction to the scrubber should be maintained.
VI. An automatic leak detection system to be installed outside, which automatically triggers the shutdown of pumps on the 250 mm dia oleum pipework conveying oleum and SO3 between the manufacturing plant and the storage tanks.

The measures agreed between HSE and the Company lead to the risk contours being reduced by 60% to 80%. The risks to off-site populations are now considered to be more compatible with the off-site developments.

Risk contour	Before RRMs	After RRMs originally proposed	After RRMs agreed with HSE
10 cpm	500	300	100
1 cpm	1,100	600	300
0.3 cpm	1,600	800	650

Table 1 Approximate extents (m) of the risk contours from the centre of the storage area before and after risk reduction measures (RRMs).

CASE STUDY 2: VARIATIONS TO AN INITIAL GENERIC CONSENT CLAIM (EXAMPLE)

An initial claim was made by a site for 500 te (Qn = 500) of toxic liquids (controlled quantity 50 te, Qt = 50) and 40 te of very toxic liquids (controlled quantity 5te) in a single vessel area (Nv = 1).

The worst case substance that could be stored is considered to be methyl chloroformate. The maximum vessel volume for toxic liquid was stated to be 40 m^3 (V = 40).

The installation is assessed on a 'worst case' basis.

The frequency of an event involving the maximum vessel volume is calculated from a formula:

$$F = 10 \times (Qn/Qt)^{1/2}/Nv \text{ cpm} \qquad ie = 10 \times (500/50)^{1/2} = 31.6$$

The radius of the resulting pool of liquid is also calculated from a formula:

$$R = 6.85 \times V^{0.44537} \text{ m} \qquad ie = 35.4 \text{ m}$$

The evaporation rates in D5 and F2 weather conditions are also parameterised:

$$M_{D5} = 9.73 \times 10^{-3} \times R^{1.9296} \text{ kg/s} \quad M_{F2} = 6.03 \times 10^{-3} \times R^{1.89} \text{ kg/s}$$
$$ie \ M_{D5} = 9.5 \text{ kg/s} \qquad and \qquad M_{F2} = 5.1 \text{ kg/s}$$

A similar procedure is followed for the very toxic liquid.

These source terms and frequencies were then entered into a simple passive dispersion and risk calculation model and the following risk contours were produced (Figure 1).

The worst case of using methyl chloroformate as the exemplar for toxic liquid would be unnecessary if the site were to accept a variation to the consent to limit the toxicity of the substance to 0.5 mg/m^3 LC 50 (Rat) and a boiling point of no less than 75 degC.

In this case the exemplar substance can be changed to propionitrile with the following result (Figure 2).

CASE STUDY 3: RISK REDUCTION MEASURES IDENTIFIED AS A RESULT OF AN EXPRESS CONSENT APPLICATION

The company involved produces water treatment chemicals. It recently applied for express hazardous substance consent for 20 te of very toxic substances, and 500 te of toxic substances, but did not specify particular substances. (When companies do not specify the substances that they will store HSE uses a generic assessment methodology based on exemplars for risk assessment purposes.).

The site has two outdoor storage tanks (40 m3 and 25 m3) for toxic liquids. In addition there are storage areas for packaged toxic and very toxic substances held in a covered warehouse, in open warehouse areas, and outside storage areas. There are three production areas, one of which has 7 reactors processing toxic substances. Blending processes take place in all three production areas in vessels containing toxic and very toxic substances.

RISK ASSESSMENT

When the generic methodology was applied to define the LUP zones, the resulting risk contours shown in Figure 3 were presented to the company. These risk contours were based solely on information in the express consent application. The 10 cpm contour was dictated by the quantity of toxic solids (hazards from warehouse fire plumes) the other contours were dictated by the quantity of toxic and very toxic liquids, using methyl chloroformate as the surrogate i.e. the hazards presented by evaporation from a pool following a 40m3 spill in D5 and F2 weather.

It can be seen from Figure 3 that there are a large number of houses in the middle zone (1 to 10 cpm). There is also a school and possibly other sensitive populations in the outer zone (1 to 0.3 cpm). The societal risks are therefore significant and HSE would have advised the local authority not to grant the hazardous substance consent. Some risk reduction measures were necessary to reduce the impact of the site on the local population. These would need to become the conditions of consent given at the end of this appendix.

Using condition (ii), the generic risk assessment was repeated using less toxic liquids as exemplars ie methyl iodide and propionitrile. The latter reduced the extents of the 1 and 0.3 cpm contours so that few houses were in the middle zone and the school was beyond the outer zone. The analysis also showed that catastrophic failure of reactors was potentially more hazardous than storage vessel failure owing to the releases being at elevated temperature (200 deg C) so that the entire reactor contents become airborne following loss of containment. Limits for the maximum quantities of materials in reactors (largest 12 te) were set by the application of ARI methodology.. The consequences of a 12 te release of propionitrile were therefore assessed and used to estimate the ARI. The wind direction that would give the worst consequences was used, giving at least 250 fatalities (LD50). The failure frequency was taken as 16 cpm, based on four 12 te reactors each with an estimated failure frequency of 4 cpm. This gives an ARI of 3,700,000 which is significantly greater than the criterion value for acceptable societal risks ie 10,000.

It is not reasonably practicable to reduce the reactor failure frequency by a factor of 400 in order to meet the criterion so, inherently safer methods must be considered ie reduce stored quantities, use less toxic substances etc. Reverse ARI calculations were therefore conducted. These showed that 2 te of propionitrile per reactor (failure frequency 7 x 4 = 28 cpm) give an ARI of 6000. (Condition (iii))

These results were discussed with the company. They agreed to accept some conditions on their Consents application provided they could store larger quantities of two named substances. Reverse ARI calculations suggest reactor quantity limits of 12 and 5 te respectively for these substances. The company also agreed to limit the very toxic consent to the substance currently present and similar substances. [The substance is a viscous liquid with very low vapour pressure at ambient temperature (vapour pressure less than 1 Pa at 20°C). It is classified as very toxic by inhalation because of tests undertaken with aerosols produced with the substance dissolved in water. On heating, decomposition begins before boiling. The company stores the substance in 200 l containers, and mixes it in blenders at ambient pressure. Provided that the substance is not pressurised, a significant off-site major hazard is not conceivable. (Condition (iv))

The site visit also enabled the warehouse RA to be updated. This and the changes agreed by the company results in the LUP zones shown in Fig 4 (LUP zones after the company agreed to adopt inherent safety measures).

HSE therefore advised the LPA that the express consent application, could be accepted provided that the following conditions are included in the consent:

i)   The hazardous substances shall not be kept or used other than in accordance with the consent application particulars, nor outside the areas marked for storage of the substances on the plan which formed part of the application.

ii)   No toxic substance shall be present on the site which has either a value for LC_{50} inhalation, rat, less than 0.5 mg l^{-1} 4hr^{-1} or a boiling point less than 75°C at ambient pressure.

iii)   No more than 2 t of toxic substances, along with up to 12 t of substance A or 5 t of substance B, shall be present in a reaction at above ambient pressure.

iv)   No substance classified as very toxic shall be present on site other than the named substance. The named substance shall not be used in reactions or blending, above ambient pressure, being subject only to vessel recirculation pumping and self-standing pumping from moveable storage containers into a vessel.

GLOSSARY

ARI   Approximate risk integral
CD   Consultation distance
CPM   Chances per million per annum
COMAH   The Control of Major Accident Hazard Regulations 1999
DTL   Dangerous toxic load
HID   Hazardous installations directorate
HSA   Hazardous substance authority
LPA   Local planning authority
MAPP   Major accident prevention policy
QRA   Quantified risk assessment
RI   Risk integral
RRM   Risk reduction measure
SRI   Scaled risk integral

FIGURES

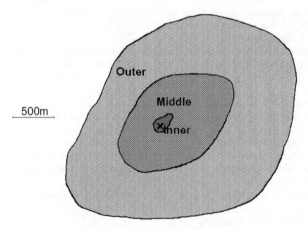

Figure 1: Land use planning zones: initial proposal

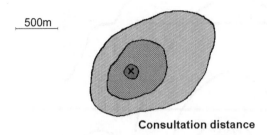

Consultation distance

Figure 2: Land use planning zones: with conditions

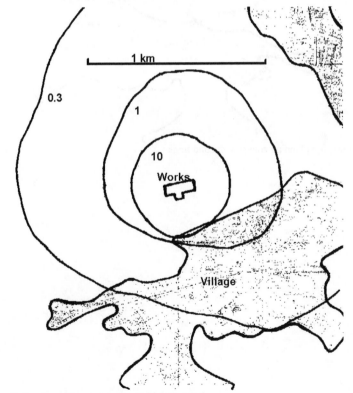

Figure 3: Land use planning zones: initial proposal

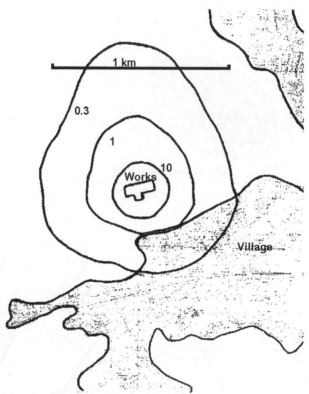

Figure 4: Land use planning zones: with conditions

GETTING FULL VALUE FROM HAZOP:
A PRACTICAL APPROACH TO THE ASSESSMENT OF RISKS
IDENTIFIED DURING STUDIES ON PROCESS PLANTS

G.C. Stevens, A. Verna and M. Marchi[a]

Arthur D Little, Science Park Cambridge CB4 4DW
[a]AgipPetroli, Via Laurentina 449, 00142 Rome, Italy

ABSTRACT

Busy plant managers working under time and budget pressures may be aware of the HAZOP technique but doubtful if it is suitable to apply to an existing operation let alone deliver a payout on the time and expense involved. This paper summarises an approach to HAZOP studies on operating plant which has delivered positive benefit cost for relatively little additional effort over and above that required for conducting the HAZOP itself.

INTRODUCTION

In the conventional approach, HAZOP studies are conducted during plant design and recommendations are incorporated prior to approval for construction. However, many process plants have been in operation for some time and have either undergone modification for debottlenecking or missed the HAZOP process altogether. In these cases it can be advantageous to conduct a HAZOP prior to major turnaround so that any recommendations to improve performance or safety can be incorporated along with other inspection and maintenance work.

Although Hazard and Operability Analysis (HAZOP) is a well-recognised method for hazard identification (ref 1) and is widely used in Process Hazard Assessment it suffers from practical difficulties. The method is known for its demand for intensive involvement from senior technical personnel from operations, maintenance, safety and process or project engineering taking these staff away from their day to day duties for the duration of the study which may be several weeks for a complex facility. This can make HAZOP a time-consuming and expensive exercise.

IMPLEMENTATION OF HAZOP RECOMMENDATIONS

The benefit for conducting a HAZOP study comes when the study recommendations are implemented and this is easier given a strong linkage to management processes for safety improvement, energy efficiency and investment appraisal. Without such linkage, HAZOP can reduce to a largely paper exercise serving as token compliance with external regulation or corporate standards.

When HAZOP is conducted as part of the design activities in a plant, the implementation of recommendations can be undertaken as part of the contractors overall scope. For example if HAZOP is undertaken on the P&IDs after design review prior to approval for construction, each recommendation can be addressed by the contractor in a close out report. This report may conclude there are good reasons that the recommendation be set aside or may incorporate it into updates of the drawings or draft manuals as appropriate.

For a plant, which is in service, implementation requires some other mechanism. It is important to recognise that there needs to be some plan to address each HAZOP recommendation because the HAZOP remains on file as 'discoverable' evidence in the event of an incident leading to legal action. It would not go well for a management team, which was shown in court to have ignored a recommendation pointing out a hazard, which subsequently lead to injury or loss.

The key to planning implementation activities is a sound method of prioritising HAZOP recommendations to recognise high risks in need of prompt attention. Once prioritised, recommendations need to be implemented as appropriate through operator action, unscheduled maintenance or turnaround as indicated in Figure 1:

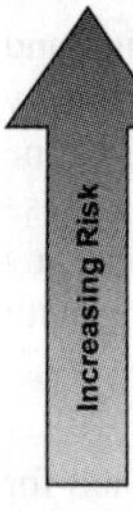

	Action	Purpose	Category
Increasing Risk	Immediate plant shut down	Urgent critical repairs to mitigate very high risk	Emergency work
	Precautionary operator action	Change to current operations to mitigate high risk	Changes to operating manual Revisions to operator training
	Switch to standby equipment or use of bypass	Repairs or modifications to mitigate high risk	Unscheduled Maintenance
	Use of planned turnaround	Repairs or modifications to mitigate medium risk	Scheduled maintenance

Figure 1: Relation between risk, urgency of action and category of action

Only in rare circumstances will an unacceptable risk be identified requiring immediate plant shutdown but such situations can occur.

The key requirements for the prioritisation method are that it should be reliable, practical, compatible with existing budgeting practices and cost effective to apply.

PRACTICAL APPROACH TO RISK PRIORITISATION

The output from a full recording HAZOP takes the form of a tabulated record of the discussion on each guideword - parameter combination. Where the discussion identifies a potential hazard that the team feels is not adequately addressed in the existing arrangements, a recommendation is made describing what the team feels is a practical and effective mitigation.

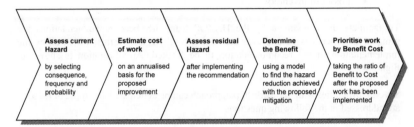

Figure 2: Sequence for prioritisation of HAZOP recommendation

To prioritise the recommendation the HAZOP team uses a matrix ranking approach in which the frequency of occurrence of the hazard, the probability the hazard will lead to a loss and the size of the loss are assessed. The assessment is carried out on the current situation and the situation after implementation of the recommendation. The cost of the mitigation is also estimated and the process is conducted stepwise in a workshop approach as illustrated in Figures 2 and 3.

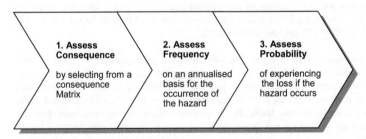

Figure 3: Sequence for assessment of hazard

The matrix approach is used for a number of categories of loss including:

- Property Loss
- Business Interruption
- Injury related losses to staff and third parties
- Environmental Liability
- Performance losses
- Losses of inventory

To facilitate the assessment by the HAZOP team members, recommendations are grouped by process issue and evaluated using Risk Register forms, which allow the implementation of the recommendation to be tracked. An illustration is shown in Figure 4.

Several difficulties with the workshop approach can be anticipated and some of these are addressed in the following questions.

IS GROUP ASSESSMENT ANY BETTER THAN GUESSING AT RANDOM?

The use of ranking matrices for risk prioritization has been practiced for some time (for example References 2 and 3). The HAZOP team carries out the assignment in a workshop session divided into groups who work together to assess each hazard using the ranking matrix. This process is facilitated by first grouping the recommendations into process issues which are categories of HAZOP recommendation which share a common operational or equipment aspect.

The extent to which two groups of experienced engineers working separately agree can be illustrated in Figure 5 which shows the assessment of 18 process issues which arose in the HAZOP of a 35 year old refinery plant.

In this assessment, five levels of risk were allocated to each of the 18 issues by two groups working independently. The diagram compares the actual differences between group assessment on the left and the pattern on the right, expected if the teams had chosen at random. The bars show the proportion of the process issues assessed at the same risk level by the two teams, the proportion differing by one risk level, two risk levels and so on up to 4 risk levels which represents complete disagreement on the ranking.

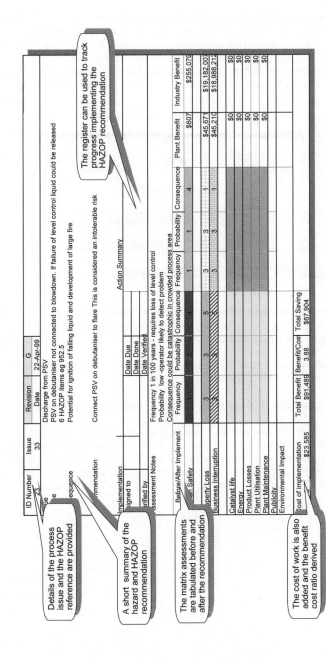

The register can be used to track progress implementing the HAZOP recommendation

Details of the process issue and the HAZOP reference are provided

A short summary of the hazard and HAZOP recommendation

The matrix assessments are tabulated before and after the recommendation

The cost of work is also added and the benefit cost ratio derived

ID Number	Issue	Revision				
23	33	G		Date	22-Apr-99	

Discharge from PSV
PSV on debutaniser not connected to blowdown. If failure of level control liquid could be released
6 HAZOP items eg 952.5
Potential for ignition of falling liquid and development of large fire

Connect PSV on debutaniser to flare This is considered an intolerable risk

Action Summary

	Date Due	
	Date Done	
	Date Verified	

Frequency 1 in 100 years - requires loss of level control
Probability low -operator likely to detect problem
Consequence could be catastrophic in crowded process area

Before/After Implement	Frequency	Probability	Consequence	Frequency	Probability	Consequence	Plant Benefit	Industry Benefit
Safety	1	3	4	1	1	4	$607	$255,079
Property Loss	3	3	5	3	3	1	$45,671	$19,182,000
Business Interruption	3	3	5	3	3	1	$45,210	$18,988,212
Catalyst life							$0	$0
Energy							$0	$0
Product Losses							$0	$0
Plant Utilisation							$0	$0
Plant Maintenance							$0	$0
Publicity								
Environmental Impact								

Cost of implementation	Total Benefit	Benefit/Cost	Total Saving
$23,585	$91,489	3.88	$67,904

Figure 4: Risk Register page to facilitate prioritisation of recommendation

The figure shows that the teams had no complete disagreements and differed by 3 risk levels on about 15% of the issues. 85% of the process issues were assessed either at the same risk level or an adjacent level. 45% of the issues were assessed using the same level of risk. Had they been selecting at random they would have chosen only 20% the same. The result shows that group assessment produces better convergence than random selection and it allows the workshop facilitator to concentrate on the few areas of divergence and so make progress more effectively.

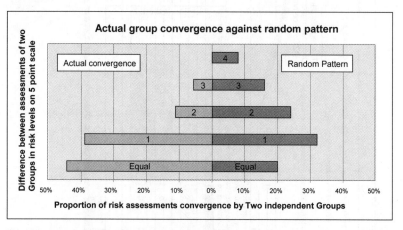

Figure 5: Performance of workshop groups against random selection

It is possible that the convergence of the group assessments is around the wrong risk level and this issue is tackled by the next question.

ARE RISK ASSESSMENTS BASED ON MATRIX ASSESSMENT REALISTIC?

One way to answer this question is to use industry loss histories to generate a Loss Expectation curve showing the size of loss that might occur in any time period for that category of plant plotted against the probability of its occurrence. The assessment of hazards by the HAZOP team using a ranking matrix can be used to simulate a Loss Profile for the plant in question which can be compared with the industry based Loss Expectation.

The illustration in Figure 6 shows three Loss Profiles. The red (dark) curve was derived from an accident database, which provided details of date of incidents and size of losses for a particular type of refinery plant. The brown (dashed) curve provides a similar set of data over a similar period for the same type of plant but this time from insurance claims. The similarity of the two curves drawn from completely different data sources offers some reassurance that the loss expectation is realistic.

On the same graph in yellow (light curve) is shown the industry loss expectation based on the assessment of the HAZOP recommendations of a modern plant in service six years. Firstly, the figure shows that the simulated loss profile is comparable in order of magnitude to the industry expectation and that, as would be expected, the modern plant benefiting from the recent know-how of the process licensor, has a loss expectation rather better than the average for plants of this type in the industry.

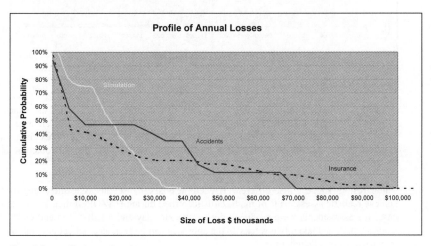

Figure 6: Loss profiles for a modern plant

A similar set of results can be compared, this time for a different plant type assessed by a different group in a different refinery. The curves are shown in Figure 7.

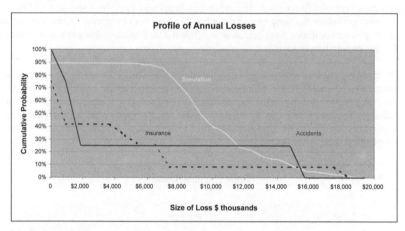

Figure 7: Loss profiles from an old plant

Again the similarity of insurance derived and accident database curves provide assurance that the profile of loss is realistic. The simulated curve derived from the HAZOP team assessment again covers a similar order of magnitude but shows losses on average rather higher than expected in the industry on average. For a plant built over 35 years ago this outcome is not unexpected.

These results suggest that different HAZOP teams can use the assessment approach to achieve realistic assessments of the hazards identified during HAZOP of their plants. In both cases the assessments were produced during an extra day and a half at the end of HAZOP studies which had taken two weeks so the approach can be seen as practical and not to cause undue extension of study time.

The Loss Profile graph can also be used to show the impact of recommendations. The following curve shows the simulated curve "after the recommendations" superimposed on the loss profiles for accidents and insurance data.

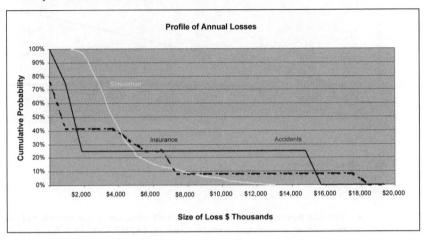

Figure 8: Loss profile for old plant after recommendations

Advocates of Quantified Risk Assessment (QRA), where specialists carry out detailed techniques such as fault tree analysis and consequence modeling, may feel that matrix assessment is too crude to give accurate results. This leads to the third question.

HOW CAN MATRIX ASSESSMENT PROVIDE AS RELIABLE RESULTS AS QRA?

To address this question, a number of moderate to severe risks identified in separate HAZOPs assessed separately by different HAZOP teams were examined by Fault Trees (to determine frequency) and consequence modeling (to determine effect distances for consequences such as pool fire, jet fire, dense cloud dispersion and explosion). Conventional criteria for 'dangerous dose' were used, including thermal radiation and explosion overpressure thresholds for fatal injury. The modeling was conducted using Arthur D Little software FaultEASE™ and Superchems™.

A correlation exercise was undertaken to compare the assessment of the HAZOP teams with the findings of the more systematic quantified risk analysis approach. The results for frequency assessment and consequence assessment are shown in Figures 8 and 9.

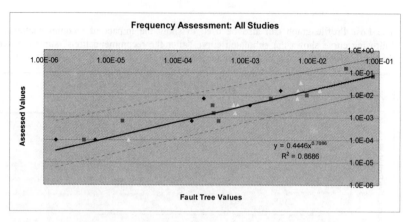

Figure 9: Frequency correlation

These graphs show:

- The data points as symbols. Three types are used, squares, diamonds and triangles representing assessments made by different HAZOP teams in different refineries.
- The best fit power correlation curve including the formula and value for R^2.
- The upper and lower ranges for the matrix assignments derived by taking the combination of lowest or highest values for frequency and probability from the ranges used by the teams.

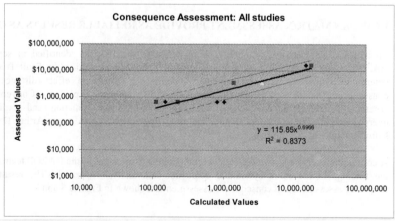

Figure 10: Consequence correlation

The result of the correlation exercises is to demonstrate that a reasonably strong relationship as indicated by values of R^2 over 0.8 exists between the results of detailed quantified risk assessment and the far more rapid matrix risk assessment.

Apart from other factors, the accuracy of the matrix assessment is limited by the range width of the matrices used for the assessment. As the correlation curves show all points lie in the band between the upper and lower matrix ranges used by the teams for their assessment.

DISCUSSION

The work reviewed in this paper shows that a workshop approach to assessment of hazards identified in HAZOP studies adds considerable value to the results of the work at comparatively little additional cost. Although the use of matrices for assessment seems crude and speculative, when used by groups of experienced engineers with appropriate facilitation, the method can produce consensus around realistic levels of risk. The results are shown to correlate reasonably with the results obtained with much more time consuming and expensive quantified risk analysis methods.

Coupling the approach with a Risk Register allows recommendations to be prioritised on a benefit-cost basis. In this way the economic benefit of risk avoidance or process improvement benefits offered by HAZOP recommendations can be assessed in relation to the costs of implementation and budgets available for activities such as unplanned maintenance or scheduled maintenance. When undertaken in advance of the planning for a major turnaround, the approach offers plant managers an effective way of identifying and prioritising plant modifications worth including in the scope of the turnaround contractor.

ACKNOWLEDGEMENT

We thank AgipPetroli for their support and encouragement during the studies described here and for their permission to publish the paper.

REFERENCES

1. Felix Redmill, Maurice Chudleigh and James Catmur: *System Safety HAZOP and Software HAZOP* Wiley (1999).
2. G.C Stevens*: Prioritisation of Safety related Plant Modifications* 7th International Symposium on Loss Prevention (May 1992).
3. G.C. Stevens and M Marchi: *A Benefit /Cost approach for prioritising expenditure during plant turnaround* 10th International Symposium on Loss Prevention and Safety Promotion in the Process Industries (June 2001).

TRIAL OF THE "HAZID" TOOL FOR COMPUTER-BASED HAZOP EMULATION ON A MEDIUM-SIZED INDUSTRIAL PLANT

S.A. McCoy and P.W.H. Chung

GRADIENTS Research Group, Department of Computer Science, Loughborough University, Loughborough, Leics. LE11 3TU.

The HAZID knowledge-based system was developed as part of the EC-funded "STOPHAZ" project, whose brief was to investigate the use of software tools for improving safety in chemical process plants. HAZID models the behaviour of a plant qualitatively, so that the potential hazards of equipment failures can be detected. The models in HAZID are based around the signed directed graph, and hazard identification is driven by a systematic HAZOP-style examination of the causes of all process variable deviations in the model. The potential causes are found by considering all possible fault propagation paths in the plant model being considered, using exhaustive graph search techniques.

This paper describes a trial of the HAZID software on the design information from a real medium-sized plant, which has been built and is currently in operation. The objectives were to demonstrate electronic transfer of plant design data from the client's CAD database system to HAZID, to present the results of the HAZID analysis in a structured form as a spreadsheet file, and to show that this type of search-oriented knowledge based system can perform well on a much larger test case plant than had previously been attempted.

The trial was successful in respect of each of these objectives, and also provided valuable information to guide future development of the system, which we hope will be made possible by increased interest from potential customers for the HAZID tool.

Keywords: Hazard Identification, HAZOP, Qualitative Modelling, Case Study, HAZID, Knowledge-Based System.

INTRODUCTION

The main purpose of this paper is to describe a case study in which a computer-based tool for HAZOP emulation, "HAZID", was used to identify hazards in a medium-sized continuous process plant design. The trial of the software involved extracting data electronically from a client's intelligent CAD system, analysing the plant design for hazards, and presenting the results in spreadsheet form.

Firstly, HAZOP is discussed, in order to set a background for the work done on computer emulation of this important technique. The HAZID tool is then introduced as a product of the STOPHAZ project. The tool, the models it uses and the HAZOP algorithm used to identify hazards, are outlined briefly, and some of the notable weaknesses of the tool are identified. After a description of the case study plant under examination, an account is given of the data transfer into HAZID, the production of results and the integration of the various software components. Finally, the results of the trial are briefly discussed, with an emphasis on what the future may hold for HAZID itself.

BACKGROUND

The Hazard and Operability (HAZOP) Study[1] occupies a dominant position in the broad spectrum of techniques used for the identification of process hazards. It has the advantages of being a highly methodical, systematic and effective way of examining all aspects of the detailed plant design; it is also widely known and recognised, with a distinctive reporting format which lends itself to documentation of the process. In view of the fact that submission of a safety case for many types of installation requires a fully documented hazard identification study to have been carried out, HAZOP is often indicated as the method of choice.

The principal difficulty with HAZOP is the time and expense involved – it demands the commitment of a number of technical specialists from multiple engineering disciplines, over an extended period of time, in order to examine a plant design in full. There is therefore a strong economic argument for developing computer-based tools to reduce the time and effort expended in these studies. In view of the fact that HAZOP is a highly creative process, it must be emphasised that the HAZOP team will not be made redundant by the development of improved software – the objective is merely to reduce the time spent by the team in the more routine activities related to HAZOP.

Aside from the obvious role that computers play in facilitating CAD and intelligent CAD (iCAD) systems, with the associated access to plant data which that implies, tools for the documentation and management of the HAZOP meetings have been successfully marketed for a number of years now. These provide help for the HAZOP team "secretary" and the team "leader" in their roles of recording discussions, actions and results of the meetings, and in following up the execution of those agreed actions.

A more ambitious goal is to model the behaviour of the plant under consideration and, by using simulation, predict the possible hazards which may arise in the plant. This approach seeks to emulate some of the reasoning which people do in a traditional HAZOP meeting. The types of simulation models required for this sort of application must allow non-steady states in the plant, as these are the states of interest for identification of hazardous scenarios. The models must also cover a wide variety of possible plant states in either normal or abnormal scenarios. Numerically precise values for process variables may not be a realistic or even desirable possibility in this case. For these reasons, qualitative reasoning techniques are often used.

The most common type of qualitative model used in this domain links process variables together with simple connections which specify a direct or reverse influence direction between disturbances of one variable and the next. Initiating faults in the plant are then linked to deviations in process variables and other deviations are linked to final hazards or consequences. By tracing the paths of propagation through the plant, it is possible to discover links between faults and consequences which may be remotely separated in the plant, via a sequence of deviations which mediate the propagation. The "signed directed graph" (SDG) is one representation for the qualitative linkages described here which has been used quite often in previous attempts to model chemical plants.[2,3,4] Other methods include so-called functional equations, decision tables, etc. A review of previous attempts to model plants in this way is given by Lees,[5] and in a previous paper on the HAZID tool.[6]

The most usual way of tackling plants which contain more than a couple of equipment items is to break down the plant into a number of "units", each of which is modelled by a "unit model". The units present are considered to be interconnected by some means – usually by virtue of process streams which flow between them.

THE STOPHAZ PROJECT AND HAZID SOFTWARE TOOL

The "STOPHAZ" Project (Software Tools for Operability and Hazard Studies) was funded by the European Commission (EC) as part of the ESPRIT Research Programme, between 1993 and 1996. Ten partner organisations took part in the project. These were: Aspentech, Bureau Veritas, Hyprotech, ICI Engineering, Intrasoft, Loughborough University, SfK, Snamprogetti, TXT and VTT. The objective of the project was to investigate novel software tools to improve chemical process safety. There were three main strands of this work:

- An engineering design "hyper-book" for design engineers to use in converting flowsheets to engineering line diagrams (ELDs).
- Tools to facilitate the refinement of plant operating procedures.
- Hazard identification by emulation of the HAZOP study method.

This last strand gave rise to the HAZID software package, a knowledge-based system using SDG models to model the behaviour of the process equipment in a plant. The aim of HAZID is to identify the hazards and their possible causes in a plant using a qualitative, SDG-based, model of the plant. It does this by emulating the procedure followed in a HAZOP study. That is, it examines the possible causes and consequences of variable deviations in the plant, finding links between remote events by fault propagation. The causes typically correspond to equipment failures and the consequences are the final hazardous events which may be caused in the scenario.

The most likely application for the current version of HAZID would be for a single process design engineer to use the tool as an aid to reviewing the plant design prior to a conventional HAZOP study. In this scenario, HAZID could provide a cost-effective way of identifying major safety concerns, for discussion in the study, or for fixing in advance of the HAZOP meetings. Because HAZID was first conceived as a HAZOP emulation tool, the level of detail required for the plant description consists of the types of equipment items which would be specified on an Engineering Line Diagram (ELD) or Piping and Instrumentation Diagram (P&ID). Therefore, the present library of models in HAZID is not well suited to evaluation of designs from earlier stages, such as conceptual design, Process Flow Diagrams (PFDs), etc. Nevertheless, further development of the model library could extend the use of essentially the same HAZID analysis program to earlier stages, facilitating its use as a tool to evaluate alternative conceptual designs, for example. We feel that once the safety analyses performed by tools such as HAZID become relatively easier (and therefore cheaper) to perform, there is scope for HAZOP-style examinations of process designs at many stages in the lifecycle.

ARCHITECTURE

As shown in Figure 1, HAZID is composed of a number of sub-systems, which each contribute to the functionality provided by the whole. Some of these are:

- A **Parser**, which reads files containing plant definitions or libraries of models used by HAZID, converting these into appropriate internal data structures.

- **Internal Plant Model** – This is the form in which the plant description is stored within HAZID. It consists of a list of equipment model instances, each with its own set of "slots" defining particular data concerning that unit.
- **Template and Equipment Models** – The equipment models used by HAZID are stored in an external library file and read in through the parser, into a list of unit models. Each unit model may make use of so-called "template" models, which define commonly re-used groups of SDG arcs in a more concise way. The template models are also read into HAZID from an external library file.
- **Fluid Model System** – During STOPHAZ, the HAZID system had access to physical properties calculations performed in external packages such as Aspentech Properties Plus, or Hyprotech HYSIM. Rules can be attached to the arcs in the SDG models of equipment to make them conditional on the properties of particular fluids in the plant. The interface to external packages is now inoperative because of the development of newer versions of the commercial software packages.
- **Link to External Database** – Access was also provided to a graphical tool for preparing outline plant description drawings during STOPHAZ. This link is no longer working, as it relies on a 16-bit Windows environment for operation of the underlying database.
- **Configuration Rules** – A number of rules for detecting poorly configured design features in a plant were also implemented in STOPHAZ. These are invoked whenever a plant model is examined using the HAZOP methodology, and add extra records to the HAZOP report which is produced.
- **HAZOP Algorithm and Report Generator** – This algorithm drives the examination of each deviation in the plant, filters the results of this work and feeds the refined results to the report generator. The result is a text file containing the deviations, causes and consequences for each unique scenario identified.

EQUIPMENT MODELS

Within HAZID, each equipment type is modelled by a unit model, which defines the arcs of an SDG representing the links between variables in that unit. Initial equipment failures are modelled as "faults" which cause specific deviations in those variables, and final hazards are modelled as "consequences" which may arise from specified deviations. In constructing a plant model, specified unit models are instantiated and connected together, forming a large, inter-connected SDG representing the structure of the whole plant.

This approach encourages the development of a smallish number of well-understood equipment models, each corresponding to a commonly used piece of equipment. In HAZID, these models are arranged into a hierarchy of equipment types, with more generic models near the root of the tree and more specialised models towards the leaves. Inheritance is conveniently used in this hierarchy to allow re-use of basic models in the definition of more specialised ones. A fuller description of the model system in HAZID, as well as the model hierarchy, is given elsewhere.[7]

Unit models are each provided with a number of slots giving information used in the definition of that equipment type. However, the main purpose is to define a set of SDG arcs giving the relations between process variables in the unit. The variables are always located at "ports" in the equipment item. There are three types of port: input ports, output ports and internal ports – each type may be associated with a number of process variables.

An additional level of flexibility is used in the models of HAZID, for groups of arcs which are commonly repeated in various unit models. The "template" feature allows such arcs to be grouped together and named, and for instances of the templates to be used in a variety of unit models.

A final element of the plant model is that of the process fluids. HAZID models allow for process fluids to be specified at every port in the plant, by giving a list of the chemical substances present and their compositions. Associated with each fluid is a pressure and temperature, and a flowrate for input and output ports. Usually, fluid data relating to a number of ports in upstream locations may be specified in this way, and HAZID will go through the plant propagating fluid information wherever appropriate to points downstream.

HAZOP ALGORITHM

The algorithm used by HAZID, to examine a plant model for hazards, is based on the overall procedure used for HAZOP studies of plant design drawings.

First of all, HAZID groups equipment items into "lines", in order to sort them all into an order for examination. It does this by tracing potential flow paths through the plant model, from inlets to major units or outlets, and from major units to outlets. Within each line, the first and last units are examined first, followed by the intermediate equipment items in order.

Once sorted, each unit from the overall list is then examined in order. All appropriate deviations of variables at each of the ports belonging to that unit are generated in turn. For each deviation, HAZID searches backwards through the SDG to find causes of that deviation, then looks forwards in the SDG to find any immediate consequences (hazards). Any immediate consequences of the deviations along the paths between the causes and the deviation under consideration, are also added. The results at this stage are a record of the deviation, its possible causes and associated consequences.

After producing these results for all units in the plant, HAZID filters them to remove repeated scenarios, deviations without any consequences, etc. It also makes use of rules involving properties of the process fluids at this stage, to eliminate scenarios which are in fact not feasible for the specific plant and scenario considered (e.g. flammability is a precondition for any hazard involving fire). The operation of this rule system (the "Fluid Model System") is described in an earlier paper.[8]

Finally, the filtered results are printed out to an output file in a format resembling a traditional HAZOP report table.

EVALUATION OF HAZID IN STOPHAZ

The evaluation of the HAZID tool is described in detail in a previous paper.[9] The main method used to inform the development of the models and the software in the STOPHAZ project was to look at the results produced by the tool when applied to case study plants. Results were criticised by experts in process safety and the HAZOP study technique, to provide pointers for improvement. A specific set of case study plants (called the "learning set") was collected together to facilitate this work. Another technique which seemed useful to elicit knowledge for improving specific equipment models, was to get a small group of process experts to meet as a "mini-HAZOP" study, in order to analyse a type of equipment item, and identify all the potential failures or hazards which could be associated with it.

In addition to this development work, later versions of the HAZID software were applied to previously unseen case studies (the "test set"), to evaluate their performance. The results produced were compared to those of conventional HAZOP studies on the same plants. Performance was quite variable, but it was found that HAZID could identify between 33% and 60% of the scenarios identified by the conventional HAZOP meeting.

POINTERS FOR IMPROVEMENT OF HAZID

A number of areas of work were identified for future improvement in HAZID, during STOPHAZ and afterwards. Many of these are documented elsewhere.[10] Some of the more important topics are:

- Automated access to electronic plant description data, as stored in iCAD systems. This is a priority to make use of the tool a realistic proposition in industry, where manual re-keying of process information is not a viable option.
- Acceptability of HAZID to users – There is a need to demonstrate that the HAZID system is a desirable and reliable tool which will save industry users time and money, whilst also helping them to eliminate hazards and improve their safety performance.
- Output reporting format – The text file produced by the STOPHAZ version of HAZID is not structured enough. There is a need to put output in a more structured format, to allow further processing of results by HAZID or other programs. Additionally, alternatives to the HAZOP table format may be considered, or a more interactive type of system could be devised for hazard identification.
- Robust identification of any protections and devices present, which may prevent a scenario from occurring. This requires some further development of the model systems in HAZID, to capture what alarms, trips, interlocks, etc., actually do in a plant.
- Separate configuration rules module – It may be appropriate to identify design glitches before the HAZOP emulation tool is invoked, rather than knitting these results into the fabric of the HAZID output report itself.
- Model quality and completeness – A more substantial investment in systematic improvement of the unit models is needed, to make the tool of more interest to industry.
- Flexible models – The model system as implemented for STOPHAZ does not allow units to have arbitrary numbers of ports and therefore makes the definition of specialised vessels, not already in the unit model library, rather difficult.
- Fluid Model System – Improvements are needed for this system, as well as a wider range of fluid rules for eliminating infeasible hazards from the results.
- Consequence evaluation/classification – These issues may be tackled in an attempt to focus attention on the most important hazards detected by the system.
- Richer model system – It may be possible to capture concepts such as state-dependent behaviour, using a richer representational scheme than the SDG. If this were the case, the range of scenarios which HAZID would be able to model would be greatly increased.

CASE STUDY

There were three main technical objectives in tackling a new demonstration of the capabilities of HAZID:

- To access the plant model from a real iCAD system containing the full set of plant data, in this case AspenZyqad.
- To demonstrate that HAZID could successfully examine such a large plant, as the case study plant was several times larger than previously examined case studies.
- To produce the same HAZOP-style results table in a more structured format than plain text. The format chosen, for this trial, was as a Microsoft Excel spreadsheet file.

The effect of successfully achieving these objectives would be to demonstrate HAZID's potential to a possible customer interested in further developing the tool. In any case, the experience would also outline where the priorities for further development of HAZID should lie. Therefore, it was judged very important to note any practical difficulties encountered in achieving these three goals.

THE TEST CASE PLANT

The plant examined during this case study trial (which took place in summer 2000) was a vent gas scrubber plant designed and operated by BNFL. It contains a packed bed scrubbing column and some other, fairly conventional, vessels and other equipment, processing aqueous streams.

In size, this plant is significantly larger than other plants previously examined by HAZID. When transferred into HAZID, the plant model of the scrubber plant contains a total of 558 plant items, pipes, valves and control valves. This compares to the 127 units in one of the larger "learning set" problems examined during the STOPHAZ project (a benzene production plant). When analysed by HAZID, 121 of the units in the scrubber plant are examined in detail, as compared to 29 units in the case of the benzene plant.

The fluids used in the scrubber plant are mainly water-based, which is something of a change from the previous test cases, which have often been petrochemical in nature.

All the data relating to the scrubber plant is present in BNFL's AspenZyqad database system. Interfaces to this data are provided through the company's CAD system (based on AutoCAD), and when the scrubber plant is displayed in the form of piping and instrumentation diagrams (P&IDs), it takes up 7 sheets. In this form, many of the streams between units cross boundaries between P&ID sheets.

DATA TRANSFER INTO HAZID

The plant description required by HAZID describes plant items in terms of "instances" of equipment models connected to one another using process stream connections. This connectivity model of the plant is augmented by various types of state information (e.g. the normal status of valves, operational status of pumps, etc.), information about the pressures, temperatures and fluid components present at various points around the plant, and information on maximum and minimum design temperatures and pressures for the equipment in the plant.

Using this information, in conjunction with equipment models stored in a library of unit models, HAZID can build up a representation of the plant in terms of a signed directed graph (SDG) model of all the variables in the plant.

The approach used to transfer data from the AspenZyqad database into HAZID is illustrated by Figure 2. Since the HAZID development team at Loughborough University did not have access to AspenZyqad software, the first step was for BNFL to dump the contents of their database into a file of a neutral, agreed format. This operation is supported by the software they use, so this step did not present any technical challenges to us. The second step is to take the file and read the data in it, extracting any information of use and discarding the rest, in order to compile the information needed to produce a HAZID format plant description file. After this data has been transferred, the job of analysing the plant for hazards using HAZID can begin.

The extraction of data was achieved using a program written in the computer language PERL (the script was called "conversion") to read the database file into a large table, from which relevant data could be extracted. Using these data, definitions of units could then be produced and written out into a new HAZID input file. PERL was chosen for this task because it is well-suited to text processing and allows rapid prototyping of a solution to the problem.

Every equipment item in the plant corresponds to an object in the database file, with a number of associated data fields. However, there are many objects in the file which do not correspond to equipment items, and so must be ignored. In any case, a subset of objects can be found in the file, corresponding to the plant items of interest to HAZID.

The process connectivity of the plant is defined in the database file in terms of PIPING-SYSTEM objects, which each define a FROM object and a TO object, and a list of objects which appear in between the two points. The objects usually correspond to equipment items in the plant, but may also include NODEs, which are points at which branches in the piping may occur. For major equipment items which may have many inlets and/or outlets, such as vessels or columns, the source or destination objects used are usually NOZZLEs, which are named objects associated with the large equipment item. It is important to map the NOZZLEs onto appropriate named ports in the HAZID unit models. Using this definition of connectivity (i.e. the PIPING-SYSTEMs) the "conversion" program pieces together how units in the plant are connected together.

The PIPING-SYSTEM objects also contain information about the temperature and pressure, and the type of fluids present. This information is also extracted from the data table, converted into appropriate measurement units where necessary, and inserted into the HAZID input file.

In larger equipment items, upper and lower design temperature and pressure limits are also provided. As HAZID can make use of this information in eliminating some hazards, the values are extracted wherever possible.

It is important to know the intended state of a valve, so that the HAZID model used can be adjusted appropriately. It is also important to know whether a pump is intended to be running normally, or on stand-by. Initially, there was no way of getting this information out of the database in a straightforward way. However, later, overlay objects were introduced for all valves which are intended to be normally closed, which made it possible to infer the default states of all valves in the plant. A similar arrangement is envisaged for the pumps problem, but so far this is accomplished using a look-up table giving the default states of each pump in the plant.

One important function of the "conversion" script is to map from names of equipment types in the AspenZyqad system to equivalent models in the HAZID library.

This is done using a look-up table in an external file, which is read in by the conversion program when it starts.

Equipment items with multiple input or output ports give rise to a similar problem. The nozzle connections in the AspenZyqad data must be mapped onto appropriate named ports belonging to the HAZID models used. Again, this is achieved so-far using a look-up table.

REPORT PRODUCTION IN SPREADSHEET FORM
In previous versions of HAZID, the main output format was a plain text report, containing results in four columns: deviation, causes, consequences and protections. It was felt that more structure was needed, so that these results could be post-processed by computer and/or displayed in a more versatile manner.

For this reason, an additional output from the HAZID analysis of a plant was introduced – to produce output as a Microsoft Excel spreadsheet file. Some modification of the core HAZID program code (in C++) was undertaken to make this happen.

Essentially the same information was presented in the new Excel report format, a sample of which is given as Figure 3.

SOFTWARE INTEGRATION
One additional benefit of this work was the development of a Visual Basic (VB) "wrapper" application, to launch the conversion and HAZID programs, and display the results produced by opening the results file in Microsoft Excel. This VB program was written quite quickly and has no impact on the performance of either the PERL script or the C++ program.

The VB wrapper provides a Graphical User Interface (GUI) to coordinate the execution of HAZID and the other components, while also allowing some of the configurable options in HAZID to be changed interactively. In avoiding the use of the text-based menu system of the central HAZID program, it presents a more "user-friendly" front-end to the system.

RESULTS OF TRIAL
The full analysis of the scrubber plant took 91 minutes and produced a 254KB spreadsheet file with 367 identified potential hazards. The time taken included: processing the intermediate data file, conducting a HAZOP-style examination of all the deviations in the plant model, filtering the results of the analysis and printing the filtered results to file. The hardware on which these results were produced was a mid-range desktop PC (Pentium P3, 600MHz, with 128MB of physical memory) running Microsoft NT4. The programs described here have also been successfully used in other 32-bit Windows environments.

HAZID is very demanding in its use of memory, because it makes use of a breadth-first search technique and has to store information about all the search paths it is considering. Therefore, virtual memory setup can be a problem in some versions of Windows.

During the trial of HAZID, a number of incremental improvements were made – to the database files containing the plant data and to the various parts of HAZID. Apart from the addition of the conversion program and the Excel output, the central HAZID program was enhanced by the addition of a new filter, which groups together similar causes of a scenario in the report, wherever those causes appear in similar equipment, so that the volume of the report can be reduced.

The input data was improved twice during the trial. Firstly, overlays were added to the valve objects in the file, which allowed the status of valves to be inferred by the conversion program. Then, some of the connectivity problems in the plant were fixed and sheet interconnectors (objects defining where a stream flows from one drawing onto another) were eliminated wherever possible from the database. Both these improvements meant that the file could be processed to produce a more accurate model of the actual plant design within HAZID.

Some of the above improvements had the effect of reducing the volume of the output files produced, by condensing repeated results or eliminating "nonsense" results. Some had the effect of connecting the plant units together more tightly and therefore increasing the time needed to search through the plant. The "headline" results given above relate only to the latest version of the data file, with all the new enhancements included.

The overall reaction of BNFL to the format of results produced by HAZID was positive. In meetings with the company, there has always been a great deal of interest in how HAZID could be further improved, to make it a genuinely useful tool for engineers at the design and safety verification stages of process design.

DISCUSSION AND FUTURE WORK

The new trial of HAZID has so far demonstrated that the electronic transfer of data, from a client database system into the format required by HAZID, is feasible. It has also shown that the search-based AI techniques deployed in HAZID are not defeated by the scale of problem posed in this, a medium-sized industrial plant design – and demonstrated this to a potential user of the tool. The results produced by the tool are now presented in a more attractive and structured format than before, which is certainly a valuable move. Perhaps most importantly, the experience of tackling this problem has identified some of the issues which need to be tackled more comprehensively in commercialising the HAZID software.

There is an important need for the databases of HAZID and the client CAD systems from which it draws its input to be harmonised. Thus, the names of models in the HAZID library should correspond in a predictable way with the names of objects in the intelligent CAD system. So far, this problem has been tackled by the use of a look-up table, which maps the type ("PARENT") of an object in the database file to a specific HAZID model name. In future, this may not be needed, as the two databases will use the same names to mean the same things.

The translation of connectivity in one database to the form that this information is expressed in HAZID input files, is an issue which needs to be addressed anew, for each client system HAZID is required to draw data from. Certainly, the standard method in AspenZyqad is unlikely to coincide with the method used in other environments.

How to deal with major units, in which there are multiple inputs or outputs, is another difficulty. At the moment, HAZID requires that all the ports belonging to an equipment model are defined (and named) in the unit model library, before that unit model can be used in a plant model. There is a need for further flexibility in the HAZID modelling language to support arbitrary numbers of ports, as well as a consistent approach to finding out how to model those ports, find out if they are carrying liquid or gas, what type of inlet or outlet fitting is used, etc.

In the HAZID trial described above, the issue of major units with many ports was tackled by defining a number of new generic models of vessels and tanks, which had large numbers of predefined inlets and outlet ports of various types. It then used a look-up table to allocate the particular nozzle seen in the intermediate data file to a named port belonging to the appropriate model. Clearly this is a poor solution in the longer term, and it imposes port names designed for a HAZID model onto the user of a CAD system in which the ports may be known by completely different names (e.g. C101-NOZZLE-5, etc.).

The fluid information which it was possible to glean from the client database in this case study was rather different from the type of data which was assumed by the earlier design of HAZID. In the BNFL plant, each PIPING-SYSTEM had an attribute (PIPE-DESC) which described the fluid type present – but the level of information given was in terms of a generic code, rather than a list of chemical species. The fluid information model used in HAZID has tended to assume that there would be information about all the chemical compounds present in a stream, giving their relative proportions, as well as the flowrate, temperature and pressure of the whole stream. This was just not the case in the scrubber plant, and might well not be the case in many other industrial case studies. Therefore, a review of the issue of how best (most flexibly?) to represent fluid information in the plant model may be required for further work on HAZID – with the over-riding priority that the information given must allow inference about safety and environmental hazards.

One of the main objectives of the trial was to renew awareness of the HAZID system, with a view to getting potential customers interested in further development of the functionality it offers. The trial has demonstrated once again, to us as developers and to BNFL as potential customers, that the tool is worthwhile developing and that the practical problems in commercialising it are realistically solvable.

The intention now is to get an interested group of potential user organisations together to fund further development of the system. Each member of such a consortium would pay a flat price to the development team, and in return would gain a licence to use the software produced for a certain number of years, as well as technical advice in how to make the best use of HAZID. The members of the consortium would be able to influence the development of an important piece of new software, as well as being able to use HAZID, almost from Day 1. The development team would benefit from valuable industry feedback and guidance to inform the development of HAZID, as well as having the opportunity to commercialise the tool when an appropriate level of functionality has been achieved.

CONCLUSIONS

This paper started by giving the rationale for developing model-based systems for hazard identification (such as HAZID) – namely, to save time and money in the verification of process plant safety, and particularly in making HAZOP studies more effective. The qualitative modelling system in HAZID, as it was developed for the STOPHAZ project, was then described in outline.

The main concern of the paper has been the trial of HAZID conducted in the summer of 2000, in conjunction with BNFL. The objectives of this trial were to achieve electronic transfer of plant data from an intelligent CAD system into the HAZID program, to analyse the plant as given and produce the results of the analysis in a structured format, as a spreadsheet file.

All these objectives were achieved, and HAZID demonstrated itself well able to handle the size of the case study plant (which is significantly larger than previously analysed plant models). The format of the output produced was also found to be acceptable to the client.

The trial gave rise to several improvements in the HAZID software and also in the information kept by BNFL in their database, although the intention of the trial was never to act as a test of the database system. A number of valuable pointers for further work on HAZID have also been identified, and are outlined in the "Discussion" section above.

On the whole, this trial (which was relatively small in scale, compared to the work done during the STOPHAZ project) has been a successful experience for us as developers. It has also succeeded in reviving the development of HAZID as an on-going concern – and we look forward to working with other partner organisations in furthering the cause of process hazard identification by computer.

ACKNOWLEDGEMENTS
The authors acknowledge the support of HAZID Technologies Ltd., and would also like to thank BNFL for their cooperation in ensuring the success of the trial described here.

REFERENCES
1. Chemical Industries Association Limited, 1977, A Guide to Hazard and Operability Studies, *published by Chemical Industry Safety and Health Council of the Chemical Industries Association.*

2. Chung, P.W.H., 1993, Qualitative analysis of process plant behaviour, *6th Int. Conf. Ind. Eng. Apps. AI, published by Gordon and Breach*, 277-283.

3. Vaidhyanathan, R., Venkatasubramanian, V. and Dyke, F.T., 1996, HAZOPExpert: An expert system for automating HAZOP analysis, *Proc. Safety Prog.*, 15:80-88.

4. Iri, M., Aoki, K., O'Shima, E. and Matsuyama, H., 1979, An algorithm for diagnosis of system failures in the chemical process, *Comp. Chem. Eng.*, 3:489-493.

5. Lees, F.P., 1996, Loss Prevention in the Process Industries (2nd edition), *published by Butterworth Heinemann.*

6. McCoy, S.A., Wakeman, S.J., Larkin, F.D., Jefferson, M.L., Chung, P.W.H., Rushton, A.G., Lees, F.P. and Heino, P.M., 1999, HAZID, A Computer Aid For Hazard Identification 1. The STOPHAZ Package and the HAZID Code: An Overview, the Issues and the Structure, *Trans. IChemE., Part B, (P.S.E.P.)*, 77: 317-327.

7. McCoy, S.A., Wakeman, S.J., Larkin, F.D., Chung, P.W.H., Rushton, A.G., and Lees, F.P., 1999, HAZID, A Computer Aid For Hazard Identification 2. Unit Model System, *Trans. IChemE., Part B, (P.S.E.P.)*, 77:328-334.

8. McCoy, S.A., Wakeman, S.J., Larkin, F.D., Chung, P.W.H., Rushton, A.G., Lees, F.P. and Heino, P.M., 1999, HAZID, A Computer Aid For Hazard Identification 3. The Fluid Model and Consequence Evaluation Systems, *Trans. IChemE., Part B, (P.S.E.P.)*, 77:335-353.

9. McCoy, S.A., Wakeman, S.J., Larkin, F.D., Chung, P.W.H., Rushton, A.G., and Lees, F.P., 2000, HAZID, A Computer Aid For Hazard Identification 4. Learning Set,

Main Study System, Output Quality and Validation Trials, *Trans. IChemE., Part B, (P.S.E.P.)*, 78: 91-119.
10. McCoy, S.A., Wakeman, S.J., Larkin, F.D., Chung, P.W.H., Rushton, A.G., and Lees, F.P., 2000, HAZID, A Computer Aid For Hazard Identification 5. Future Development Topics and Conclusions, *Trans. IChemE., Part B, (P.S.E.P.)*, 78: 120-142.

FIGURES

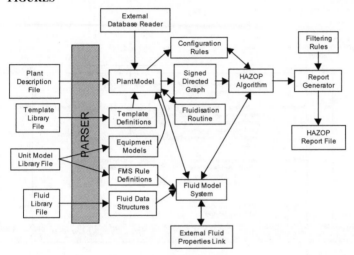

Figure 1: System Architecture of the HAZID Tool

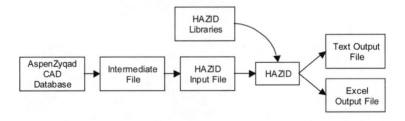

Figure 2: Data Transfer in the HAZID Case Study

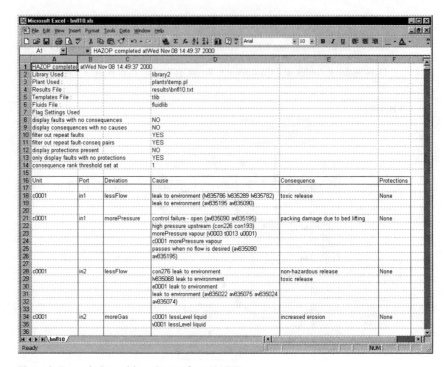

Figure 3: Example Spreadsheet Output from HAZID

MODELLING OF INDOOR RELEASES OF WATER REACTIVE TOXIC MATERIALS

Glenn Pettitt*, Gurinder Bains**, Tom Dutton**
*Environmental Resources Management, **Rhodia Consumer Specialties Limited

This paper presents a case study to demonstrate the modelling of indoor releases of water reactive toxic materials. The materials of concern were phosphorus trichloride and phosphorus oxychloride, both of which are classed as very toxic, but which produce toxic hydrogen chloride gas on reaction with water. To assess the risk from the storage and handling of phosphorus trichloride and oxychloride, it is required to determine the extent and nature of the toxic gas cloud produced. In the far field, this gas cloud will be hydrogen chloride, and thus the source terms are required for the rate of production of hydrogen chloride following a spill of phosphorus trichloride or oxychloride. The methodology used for this modelling is described using phosphorus trichloride as the example.

Keywords: water reactive materials, toxic gas cloud, phosphorus trichloride, phosphorus oxychloride, hydrogen chloride

INTRODUCTION

Where significant quantities of phosphorus trichloride (PCl_3) and phosphorus oxychloride ($POCl_3$) (or other water reactive materials) are stored and processed on a chemical plant, these may qualify the site to come under the UK COMAH Regulations. In the case of 'top-tier' sites, it is thus necessary to model the behaviour of such materials should a major accident occur, whereby the materials are released to the atmosphere.

PCl_3 and $POCl_3$ are classified as very toxic. They are liquids at normal temperature and pressure and if released from storage will form liquid pools on the ground. There boiling points are 75.5°C and 105°C respectively, and whilst there will be some vaporisation from a standing pool, the amount of vapour produced will not result in a large vapour cloud that would move downwind.

However, the materials are highly reactive with water. When they react with water, they give off heat and evolve toxic hydrogen chloride gas. The materials will react with the moisture in the atmosphere and in the worst case with precipitation. In such cases, a HCl cloud will form which may move downwind and have toxic effects at a greater range than the vapour cloud formed by the original spill.

For modelling purposes, it is required to have a 'release rate' of HCl as input to a consequence model. The modelling of the HCl 'release' following the reaction of PCl_3 with the moisture in the atmosphere is very complex and should take into account the relative humidity, temperature, and the size of the bunded area from which HCl will be emitted (or the size of the pool formed), among other parameters.

PCl_3 and $POCl_3$ are stored and handled at the Rhodia Oldbury site and formed a major part of the submission under the COMAH Regulations.

INTENT OF THIS PAPER

This paper is a case study on how PCl_3 and $POCl_3$ were modelled to obtain an estimate of their potential offsite impact should a major accident occur. The modelling described in this paper was for indoor releases of PCl_3 and $POCl_3$. Both materials are processed and stored onsite in process buildings, the materials being highly water reactive and thus the amount of water in the area is kept to a minimum.

The case study described below is for PCl₃ only. The modelling of POCl₃ releases used the same methodology.

It was not the intention of the model, and thus this paper, to provide a completely accurate method of modelling HCl releases following the reaction of PCl₃ and POCl₃ with water. Rather, it was the intention to produce a best estimate of HCl mass release rate that could be used as input to relevant dispersion models. Work has been carried out recently on a code for modelling spills of water reactive materials[1], and this is a useful reference source.

PHOSPHORUS TRICHLORIDE RELEASE RATES

The major hazardous events considered in this case study are given in Table 1, along with their corresponding mass flow rates and release durations. The mass flow rate from a hole (below the liquid level) is calculated using the Bernoulli equation:

$$m = C_d \, \rho \, A \, (2 \, ((P_i - P_a)/\rho + g \, h)))^{1/2} \qquad \text{(Equation 1)}$$

where:

m	= mass discharge rate, kg/s
C_d	= discharge coefficient (0.61)
ρ	= liquid density, kg/m³
A	= hole area, m²
P_i	= pressure at which the liquid is stored, Pa
P_a	= ambient pressure, Pa
g	= gravitational constant, m/s²
h	= static head of liquid, m

Only liquid releases of PCl₃ are considered in this case study, as these would have the most severe consequences. Vapour releases may also occur and HCl may be produced which would travel downwind, but the concentration of HCl would quickly disperse to below dangerous levels. This is because the pressure is relatively low where vapour is present, e.g. the distillation column is at 5 psig (0.35 barg), and this would soon reduce to atmospheric for a major failure. Hence, the mass flow rate of PCl₃ from the failure would be low. (For other studies, it may be the case that the PCl₃ in the vapour phase may be at high pressure and thus be released at a relatively high rate. Such a case would likely produce significant amounts of HCl as the PCl₃ would also be in the vapour phase following release.)

The liquid releases will form pools on the ground and the vaporisation from the release will be low, as the releases are at temperatures well below the boiling point of PCl₃.

TABLE 1   MAJOR ACCIDENT HAZARD EVENTS FOR PCL$_3$

Area	Event No.	Leak Size (mm)	Mass Flow Rate (kg/s)	Duration (s)
Lines to	PCl-1	12.5	1.1	890
storage or	PCl-2	25	4.2	240
reflux lines	PCl-3	50	17	60
Storage	PCl-4	12.5	1.1	3600
	PCl-5	25	4.2	3600
	PCl-6	50	17	3600
	PCl-7	rupture	150,000 kg	n/a
Burn down tank	PCl-8	12.5	1.1	3600
	PCl-9	25	4.2	3600
	PCl-10	50	17	1200
Lines to processes	PCl-11	12.5	2.7	1200
or loading	PCl-12	40	4.4	600
Tanker loading	PCl-13	12.5	2.7	300
	PCl-14	40	4.4	300
Head tank	PCl-15	12.5	0.8	3600
	PCl-16	25	3.0	3600
	PCl-17	50	12	1100
Drum filling	PCl-18	12.5	0.8	300
	PCl-19	25	3.0	300
Tanker	PCl-20	12.5	0.7	3600
	PCl-21	25	2.6	3600
	PCl-22	50	10	1760

DURATION OF EXPOSURE

As PCl$_3$ and HCl are toxic gases, one of the most important parameters is the time of exposure, in determining the potential toxic dose experienced by people. The magnitude of the hazard will be a function of the action taken (or not taken). These actions relate to the control and mitigation of major hazards in terms of quantifying the consequences. For example, in the case of failure of the loading hose, there is an emergency stop that will shut down the pump. This human interaction is taken into account in the failure events, where applicable.

It is important here to provide reasoning in the choice of durations used. The maximum duration used is 60 minutes. It is assumed that by this time people will have sought shelter, or they would have been overcome by the toxic cloud, although some calculations use a duration of exposure of 30 minutes. Hence, a maximum duration of exposure of 60 minutes tends to the side of conservatism.

For small leaks, although detection would likely be relatively quick in areas where there are HCl detectors (which are very reliable), there may still be a significant inventory left in the system downstream of any isolation valve that could be closed. Therefore, the release duration may still be significant.

The time to detection for larger leaks would be relatively quick, due to the array of detectors, and the fact that the leak would soon be noticed by onsite personnel. The leak may also be recorded by a process upset, e.g. loss of level in a reactor that would result in an alarm and trip of the process.

For leaks in the piping to downstream processes, e.g. $POCl_3$, and the loading area, the pressure would be reduced to the head of the storage tank by stopping the pumps. This would reduce the release rates significantly, in practice, particularly where the leak is at an elevated level above the head in the tank, e.g. at the loading arm. Furthermore, for major leaks in the piping or guillotine ruptures, the pump would not be able to maintain the flow rate, i.e. it would fall off its 'pump curve' and trip. Again, in this case the driving pressure would be the head in the storage tank. In these cases it is assumed that the release rate is the flow rate in the line, which is a reasonable assumption when taking into account pressure drops across control valves, etc.

For releases that can be isolated, this may be achieved by closing relevant isolation valves upstream of the leak. There are no remotely operated valves on the plant downstream of the reactors. If necessary an operator would put on special PPE in order to reach the appropriate isolation valve.

For both the tanker loading and the drum loading, an operator is always present. If there are signs of problems then the operator will shut down the process, e.g. by pushing the emergency stop button. In these cases a duration of 5 minutes is assumed.

CONSEQUENCE MODELLING OF PHOSPHORUS TRICHLORIDE RELEASES

DERIVATION OF HYDROGEN CHLORIDE SOURCE TERMS

For modelling purposes, it is required to have a 'release rate' of HCl as input to a consequence model. PCl_3 reacts with the moisture in the atmosphere or precipitation (in the worst case) to form HCl. This then forms a toxic vapour cloud that will be at dangerous concentration levels in the area of the spill and may still be at dangerous concentrations offsite.

The modelling of the HCl 'release' following the reaction of PCl_3 with the moisture in the atmosphere is very complex and should take into account the relative humidity, temperature, and the size of the bunded area from which HCl will be emitted (or the size of the pool formed), among other parameters.

MASS OF WATER FOR REACTION

One of the major rate determining parameters is the amount of water available for the reaction with PCl_3 to take place to form HCl.

The humidity in the air, in terms of unit mass of water /per unit mass of dry air can be found from a humidity-enthalpy diagram[2]. At atmospheric pressure, 10°C and 70% relative humidity, the humidity is 0.006 kg_{H2O}/kg_{air}. The density of air[3] is 1.2928 kg/m^3, hence the mass of water in 1 m^3 of air is 0.0078 kg.

For indoor process areas, it is assumed that the water available for reaction is the volume contained within the process building up to a height of 5 m, which is considered conservative, because the reaction will only take place at the boundary layer of the pool. It is also necessary to consider the number of air changes per hour and it is assumed that the mass of water available for reaction is the mass of the assumed volume up to 5 m, multiplied by the number of air changes per hour. For the process building and storage building, it is assumed that there are 12 air changes per hour. These buildings are relatively closed to the atmosphere. (Twelve air changes per hour is the number which is often used for offshore assessments where modules have grating or forced ventilation and thus this is considered conservative here.) For the loading area, this is open on one side, and thus 60 air changes per hour is assumed, i.e. one air change every minute. The mass of water available in the building over one hour is represented by the following equation:

$$m_w = H \rho_a \, l \, w \, h \, N_{ac} \qquad \text{(Equation 2)}$$

where:
m_w	= mass of water available in the building over one hour, kg
H	= humidity, kg_{H2O}/kg_{air}
ρ_a	= air density, kg/m^3
l	= length of building, m
w	= width of building, m
h	= height of building (up to 5 m), m
N_{ac}	= number of air changes per hour

The mass of water available in the buildings over one hour in each area is shown in Table 2.

POOL GROWTH

Another important parameter is the size of the pool formed, i.e. the surface area over which the reaction can taken place. The pool sizes will be restricted by either:

i. the size of the bunded area,
ii. the area of the building,
iii. other restrictions.

It is assumed that the maximum pool size that can be formed would be of 20 m in diameter, i.e. restrictions due to kerbing, etc. The size of the pool will also be determined by the volumetric release rate and the release duration, i.e. the volume released. It is assumed that the average pool height is 10 mm, which takes into account sumps, etc.

As stated above, a maximum duration of one hour is assumed (although the pool will have generally reached its maximum pool size by this time. Taking all the above into consideration, the pool sizes formed are listed below in Table 3.

TABLE 2   MASS OF WATER AVAILABLE IN EACH AREA OVER ONE HOUR

Area	Length (m)	Width (m)	Mass of Water to Height of 5 m (kg)	Number of Air Changes/Hour	Mass of Water Available in 1 hr (kg)
Process area	25	15	14.54	12	174.5
Storage area	25	15	14.54	12	174.5
Loading area	25	15	14.54	60	872.6

TABLE 3   POOL SURFACE AREAS FOR PCL$_3$ RELEASES

Area	Event No.	Volumetric Release Rate (m^3/s)	Duration (s)	Restricted Area (m^2)	Pool Area (m^2)
Lines to	PCl-1	0.00072	890	314	65
storage or	PCl-2	0.00265	240	314	65
reflux lines	PCl-3	0.01061	60	314	65
Storage	PCl-4	0.00072	3600	73	73
	PCl-5	0.00265	3600	73	73
	PCl-6	0.01061	3600	73	73
	PCl-7	n/a	n/a	73	73
Burn down tank	PCl-8	0.00072	3600	27	27
	PCl-9	0.00265	3600	27	27
	PCl-10	0.01061	1200	27	27
Lines to processes	PCl-11	0.00168	1200	314	202
or loading	PCl-12	0.00280	600	314	167
Tanker loading	PCl-13	0.00168	300	314	50
	PCl-14	0.00280	300	314	84
Head tank	PCl-15	0.00051	3600	314	183
	PCl-16	0.00188	3600	314	314
	PCl-17	0.00750	1100	314	314
Drum filling	PCl-18	0.00051	300	314	15
	PCl-19	0.00188	300	314	56
Tanker	PCl-20	0.00044	3600	314	158
	PCl-21	0.00162	3600	314	314
	PCl-22	0.00650	1760	314	314

For modelling the releases, the fraction of pool area per area of building is used, i.e.:

$$m_r = m_w A_p/A_b \qquad \text{(Equation 3)}$$

where: m_r = mass of water available for reaction over one hour, kg
          A_p = area of pool, m^2
          A_b = area of building, m^2

MASS FLOWRATE OF HCL PRODUCED

The mass of HCl produced is that which has been formed by the reaction of the water available. In the equation for the reaction shown below it can be seen that 1 mole of HCl is formed for 1 mole of water reacted.

$$PCl_3 + 3H_2O \rightarrow H_3PO_3 + 3HCl \qquad \text{(Equation 4)}$$

Thus, the amount of HCl formed in one hour is:

$$m_{HCl} = m_r\, MW_{HCl}/MW_{H2O} \qquad \text{(Equation 5)}$$

where: m_{HCl} = mass of HCl produced over one hour, kg
              MW_{HCl} = molecular weight of HCl, g/mol
              MW_{H2O} = molecular weight of H$_2$O, g/mol

Thus, the average release rate is this mass divided by the time taken for the release, taken as one hour. The release rates of HCl calculated are shown in Table 4.

DISPERSION MODELLING OF HYDROGEN CHLORIDE
The output of the HCl source term modelling is then used as input to a relevant gas dispersion model. This is not described in this paper.

TABLE 4   HCL SOURCE TERM OUTPUT FOR INPUT TO DISPERSION MODEL

Area	Event No.	Mass of Water for Reaction (kg)	HCl Produced in One Hour (kg)	HCl Release Rate (kg/s)	Duration of Exposure (s)
Lines to	PCl-1	30.3	60.9	0.017	3600
storage or	PCl-2	30.3	60.9	0.017	3600
reflux lines	PCl-3	30.3	60.9	0.017	3600
Storage	PCl-4	34.0	68.4	0.019	3600
	PCl-5	34.0	68.4	0.019	3600
	PCl-6	34.0	68.4	0.019	3600
	PCl-7	34.0	68.4	0.019	3600
Burn down tank	PCl-8	12.6	25.3	0.007	3600
	PCl-9	12.6	25.3	0.007	3600
	PCl-10	12.6	25.3	0.007	3600
Lines to processes	PCl-11	470.1	946.4	0.263	3600
or loading	PCl-12	388.6	782.4	0.217	3600
At loading	PCl-13	116.4	234.3	0.065	3600
	PCl-14	195.5	393.5	0.109	3600
Head tank	PCl-15	85.0	171.1	0.048	3600
	PCl-16	146.2	294.4	0.082	3600
	PCl-17	146.2	294.4	0.082	3600
Drum filling	PCl-18	7.1	14.2	0.004	3600
	PCl-19	26.2	52.8	0.015	3600
Tanker	PCl-20	368.0	740.8	0.206	3600
	PCl-21	731.1	1471.9	0.409	3600
	PCl-22	731.1	1471.9	0.409	3600

DISCUSSION

This case study is a demonstration of how indoor releases of water reactive materials were modelled. What was required in this particular case was input into a gas dispersion model of the rate of HCl formed following the reaction of PCl_3 and $POCl_3$ with the moisture in air.

It is important that the modelling of the released material takes into account the actual physical effects to which it is subjected. For example, in this case, dispersion modelling of a release of PCl_3 would not be representative of the problem. Certainly, the building that PCl_3 is released into would have very toxic vapours of PCl_3 within. However, these would soon disperse to concentration below dangerous levels. Thus, it is vital to model the reaction with water vapour where HCl gas is evolved.

However, modelling of such effects in the past has often tended to overpredict the amount of toxic gas liberated, as Kapias et al. point out[1]. An overprediction of the amount of HCl liberated per unit time in this case would overpredict the consequences of the toxic gas cloud produced. For example, if it was assumed that the continuous release of PCl_3 was all converted into HCl as it was released from containment, then a vast overprediction would occur.

Whilst the modelling described in this case study has made a number of assumptions, it was attempted to provide a more accurate representation of the amount of HCl produced for indoor releases. The rate determining step is actually the amount of water vapour available for reaction rather than the release rate of PCl_3. The model also takes into account the size of the pool produced by the release, i.e. the surface area available for reaction with the moisture in air. In this way, it can be seen that the 'release rate' of HCl for input into a dispersion model is only a fraction of the actual release rate of the PCl_3 originally released to the atmosphere.

Even though this 'release rate' is reduced significantly, the modelling still tends to the side of conservatism, particularly for the smaller release rates of PCl_3. It can be seen that the HCl 'release rate' is the same for say releases from storage, no matter the size of the leak from the storage tank. This is because it is assumed that the bunded area is immediately filled and thus the surface area over which the reaction with moisture in air takes place is always constant. In reality the liquid pool would grow to its limiting size[1] and there would also be the surface area of the liquid as it is released from the hole. This may be significant if there was aerosolisation of the released material, but the release velocity is not sufficient to cause such an effect.

In conclusion, although the model is not a completely accurate representation of the mechanisms involved in releases of water reactive materials, it does provide a more representative picture than if instantaneous conversion to the toxic gas (in this case HCl) is assumed. Such mechanisms are important for the source term effects if dispersion modelling of the toxic gas is to be conducted. If the off-site risk from a facility that stores and processes PCl_3 and $POCl_3$ is to be assessed, then it is important than more realistic modelling techniques are used, otherwise the off-site risk may be grossly overstated. To put it in perspective, the off-site risk from PCl_3 and $POCl_3$ is not significant compared to, say, chlorine, for similar inventories of material.

REFERENCES
1. Kapias, T., Griffiths, R.F., Stefanidis, C., 2000, REACTPOOL: a code implementing a new multi-compound tool model that accounts for chemical reactions and changing composition for spills of water reactive chemicals, *Journal of Hazardous Materials*, 2549: 1-18.
2. Coulson, J.M, Richardson, J.F., 1977, Chemical Engineering, Volume 1, Third Edition, p.370, Pergamon Press, Oxford.
3. Perry, R.H. Green, D., 1984, Chemical Engineers' Handbook, Sixth Edition, McGraw Hill, New York.

MOTIVATING EMPLOYEES FOR SAFETY SUCCESS

Thomas R. Krause * and Gordon Sellers [#]
* Behavioral Science Technology, Ojai CA, USA
[#] Behavioural Science Technology International, Bracknell RG12 1JB,
Gordon.Sellers@bstsolutions.com

This paper presents an examination of how to motivate employees for success in safety. That raises a two-fold issue: how to motivate employees; and how to apply that motivation for safety excellence. The difference between "motivation" and "motivation for success" lies in an organisation's ability to use motivation effectively. Enthusiasm alone is useless unless it can be harnessed and directed properly to improve safety. Motivating employees to be merely enthusiastic about safety is insufficient. We are interested in how to motivate employees to be SUCCESSFUL in safety. Frequently used methods include motivational speakers; slogans, posters and signs; discipline; gain sharing programmes; and contests, awards and incentives. However, building on the work of Herzberg and Deming, we find that the most powerful motivation for workers to be successful in safety comes from active engagement and participation in safety. When employees are given the opportunity to get involved in the improvement process, in real and meaningful ways, then that engagement becomes a tremendous source of motivation. Behaviour-based safety offers such opportunities.

Keywords: motivation, employees, behaviour, safety

WHAT IS MOTIVATION?
A working definition for motivation is:

A force that influences or causes a person to do something or act in a certain way.

So for the purposes of safety motivation the important question is:

How can an organization provide a "force that influences or causes" workers to be successful in the safety effort?

FREQUENTLY USED METHODS
Let us consider the common methods that many organisations frequently use to increase employee motivation for safety, and evaluate how successful each method is likely to be:

- Motivational speakers;
- Slogans, posters and signs;
- Discipline;
- Gain-sharing programmes; and
- Contests, awards and incentives

MOTIVATIONAL SPEAKERS
How many motivational speakers have you heard in your career, and what do you remember of what they said? The purpose of using motivational speakers for safety is to get the attention of workers, fire them up, cause them to feel good and give them energy for the effort. This method is effective in the short term, but loses its effect in a few weeks. The best motivational speakers are those that really do teach employees something that sticks with them rather than simply entertaining, amusing, or enthusing them with no real substance. The

best motivational speakers for safety are clearly the genuine article. The worst motivational speakers are those that are so transparently fake that we get a little sick listening to them. In any case, it is unrealistic to think that having a motivational speaker speak to a workforce will do anything in itself to improve safety at a facility.

SLOGANS, POSTERS AND SIGNS
Slogans, signs and posters are designed to motivate employees to do the things management would like them to do. How effective are they? Do these methods cause workers to do the things that the slogans exhort them to do?

Zero injuries
Safety first
Pay attention

It's hard to see how these methods have much to do with anything, other than making the people who put them up feel like they might have accomplished something.

DISCIPLINE
The use of discipline to motivate workers for safety success is a complex issue in today's workplace. It isn't just a matter of what the behavioural scientists tell us about the effect of punishment on behaviour. There are other factors present in the workplace that must be taken into account, things like morale, perceptions of what is "just and fair", and ongoing relations with the work force. Is it possible to use discipline to motivate workers to be successful in safety? We don't think it is. In fact, we think it is counterproductive. However, ironically, in our experience it is possible to de-motivate the worker for safety success by not applying the established discipline policy consistently. (Please note that this last statement does not mean that behaviour-based safety should use discipline as part of its employee-driven observation and feedback process, which we believe is always a mistake.)

GAIN-SHARING PROGRAMMES
Do gain-sharing programmes motivate employees for safety success? This is a difficult issue. For companies that do use gain-sharing programmes (which we believe are usually of marginal value at best) it is better to have safety represented in the programme than not. If safety is not represented, the company risks sending the message that safety isn't important enough to be considered. For these companies the important question is HOW to measure safety for gain-sharing. If they base gain-sharing on incident frequency rates the company is subject to all the problems that go along with incident-based incentive schemes (see below). A better method is to make gain-sharing contingent on an index of indicators that include 'upstream measures' of safety performance as well as statistically valid incident rates. This does not mean that gain-sharing is likely to truly motivate employees to be successful in safety. However, under certain circumstances, it is better to use gain-sharing for safety than to not use it.

CONTESTS, AWARDS AND INCENTIVES
Many companies use various types of safety incentives. Are they successful at motivating employees for safety success? Unfortunately, incentive programs are more often de-motivators than motivators. No company intends this to be the outcome. Nonetheless, it happens in hundreds of companies every year.

The incentives question is a complex one that we have written about extensively in other places[1]. Most companies that are serious about safety improvements have discovered that traditional safety incentives, in which tangible goods are contingent on incident rates, are more trouble than they are worth. These traditional incentives send a mixed message to the culture, create false feedback and set in motion expectations that are counter-productive, such as, "What will you give me next time?" The willingness of the worker to participate in the safety effort becomes contingent on the nature and size of the incentive.

Other companies make their incentive prizes contingent on worker performance of desired behaviours. This approach is an improvement over traditional incentives, but the approach also has aspects that are problematic. Workers are encouraged to "game" the system, and often become motivated for the wrong reasons. One company we worked with tried this type of incentive which they based on a baseball game theme to increase the frequency of its behavioural observations. They were "successful" in creating new observations, but the quality of observations declined dramatically during the same time period, as shown in Figure 1.

Even though they ended up with more observations, they taught their employees to make poor observations and this was detrimental to their real safety objectives.

Perhaps the biggest drawback to the use of incentives for safety is that they tend to drive injuries underground (Figure 2).

Employees know that reporting injuries can result in them losing a significant reward. It is only natural to try hard to keep this information private under those circumstances, which is a very poor outcome for the safety system.

MEANINGFUL INVOLVEMENT

Our experience, gained from working with hundreds of companies for the past 20 years, has shown that the most powerful motivation for workers to be successful in safety comes from **active engagement and participation in safety.** When employees are given the opportunity to get involved in the improvement process, in real and meaningful ways, then that engagement becomes a tremendous source of motivation. Interestingly, this experience is consistent with two of the most credible figures on the landscape in the last 20 years, Herzberg and Deming.

Herzberg[2] studied motivation very carefully in large numbers of companies across industries. His work was published in Harvard Business Review, originally in the 1970's and then again in 1987. It is considered a classic in management theory which, in our opinion, has not been surpassed since it was published. In this study Herzberg found that identifiable factors contribute to employee motivation, but interestingly, the factors that contribute to **dissatisfaction** are altogether different from those that contributed to **satisfaction**.

As Figure 3 shows, the factors that contributed to job satisfaction were achievement, recognition, the work itself, responsibility, advancement and growth. Herzberg referred to these factors as "Motivators." The factors that contributed to job dissatisfaction were company policy and administration, supervision and relations with supervisors, work conditions, salary, peer relations, personal life, subordinate relations, status and security. Herzberg referred to these factors as "Hygiene." In other words, workers could become "dissatisfied" from hygiene factors such as less money, poor relations with their bosses, etc. However, having more money and good relations with their bosses, etc., does not motivate workers, but makes them "not-dissatisfied" with their jobs. The things that contributed to worker job satisfaction were the motivation factors, such as achievement and recognition.

Herzberg put it this way:

"Motivation is based on growth needs...the ultimate reward in motivation is personal growth...Job enrichment remains the key to designing work that motivates employees."

What a long way this is from posters, motivational speakers and incentives!

W. Edwards Deming[3], the great pioneer in quality improvement, agrees with Herzberg on motivation. He sees that the natural pride that follows good work has a positive effect on the employee:

"If someone can make a contribution to the company, he feels important."

Deming even goes so far as to say the employee is entitled to this kind of job satisfaction:

"People are entitled to joy in work."

Clearly Deming sees that incentives, quotas and other attempts to manipulate workers into good performance are counter-productive:

"Forces of Destruction:

- *Grades in school.*
- *Merit System.*
- *Incentive pay.*
- *Business plans.*
- *Quotas."*

What motivates the employee is being part of the improvement process, being positively engaged:

"You can see from a flow diagram who depends on you and whom you can depend on. You can now take joy in work."

And of course Deming reminds us that this doesn't happen overnight:

"It does not happen all at once. There is no instant pudding."

CONCLUSION

It is not enough for workers to be enthusiastic about safety. Motivation methods that produce short-term enthusiasm for safety are often more trouble than they are worth. When employees are given the opportunity to get actively involved in the improvement process, in real and meaningful ways, then that engagement becomes a tremendous source of motivation. Behaviour-based safety offers such opportunities.

REFERENCES

1. Krause, T.R., 1998, Current Issues in Behavior-Based Safety, *Professional Safety*, 21: 247-261
2. Herzberg, F., 1987, One more time: How do you motivate employees?, *Harvard Business Review*, 65(5): 109-120
3. Deming, W.E., 1986, Out of Crisis, Boston: Massachusetts Institute of Technology.

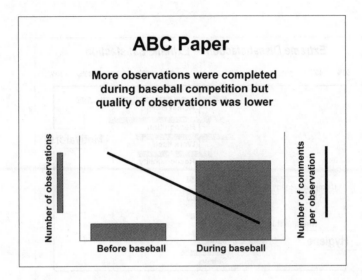

Figure 1. More observations were completed during an incentive programme, but the quality of observations fell

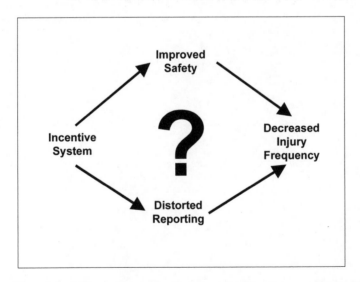

Figure 2. Incentive systems <u>can</u> lead to improved safety – but more often to distorted reporting

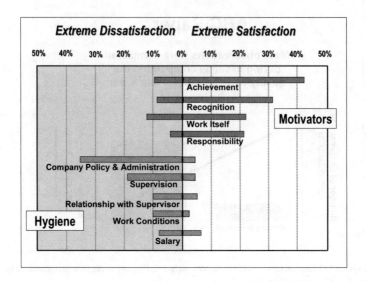

Figure 3. Hertzberg's analysis of Motivators and Hygiene Factors

ASSESSING THE SAFETY OF PROCESS OPERATION STAFFING ARRANGEMENTS

Helen Conlin
Entec UK
Philip Brabazon
University of Nottingham (formerly with Entec UK)

Demonstration is a core requirement of the UK Control of Major Accident Hazards (COMAH) Regulations and duty holders are required to demonstrate the adequacy of their safety arrangements including process operation staffing . The operation of a major hazard site must incorporate adequate safety and reliability (COMAH Schedule 4 3(b)). Process operation staffing and the technical measures available to operators have major impacts on the ability to control upsets, prevent major accidents and minimise disruption to production. A method has recently been developed by Entec on behalf of the Hazardous Installations Directorate (HID) of the Health and Safety Executive who have observed that a number of oil, gas and chemical sites are taking steps to reduce staffing levels in their operating teams. There is a concern that such reductions could impact the ability of a site to control abnormal and emergency conditions and may also have a negative effect on staff performance through an impact on workload, fatigue, etc. Although sites are often doing risk assessments on aspects of their staffing arrangements through task analysis and other existing techniques, problem areas are being overlooked. The aim of the project was to develop a structured assessment method which systematically covered all the relevant issues and would prevent potential problems in process operation staffing arrangements being missed. The method was developed through collaboration with industry and HSE and provides a systematic approach which structures people's thinking about the factors which need to be considered when assessing the safety of process operation staffing arrangements. The method is already being used on several sites in full studies. Some sites are using it to assess current staffing arrangements, some are using it to assess the impact of a planned organisational change.

Keywords: staffing arrangements, process operations, risk assessment

OVERVIEW OF ASSESSMENT METHOD

The method concentrates on the staffing requirements for responding to hazardous incidents. Specifically, it is concerned with how staffing arrangements affect the reliability and timeliness of <u>detecting</u> incidents, <u>diagnosing</u> them, and <u>recovering</u> to a safe state.

The method is designed to highlight when too few staff are being used to control a process. It is not designed to calculate a minimum or optimum number of staff. If a site finds that its staffing arrangements 'fail' the assessment, it is not necessarily the case that staff numbers must be increased. Other options may be available, such as improved control, detection, alarm or trip systems.

Assessment is in two parts. The first is a physical assessment of performance in a range of scenarios, the second is a ladder assessment of the management and cultural attributes underlying the control of operations. The overall assessment process is summarised in Figure 1.

The method assesses eleven elements which are comprised of:
- Technical factors: Physical assessment of the feasibility of dealing with each scenario in time.

- Individual factors (workload): Situational awareness; teamworking; alertness and fatigue (split into working pattern and health).

- Individual factors (knowledge and skills): Training and development; roles and responsibilities; willingness to act.

- Organisational factors: Management of operating procedures; management of change; continuous improvement of safety; management of safety.

PHYSICAL ASSESSMENT

The physical assessment tests the staffing arrangements against six 'principles':

1) There should be continuous supervision of the process by skilled operators, i.e. operators should be able gather information and intervene when required. This may take various forms and for example may be satisfactorily provided remote from the primary control area. There is a need throughout the physical assessment to demonstrate that staffing arrangements result in a residual risk which is as low as reasonably practicable.

2) Distractions which could hinder problem detection such as answering phones, talking to people in the control room, administration tasks and nuisance alarms should be minimised.

3) Additional information required for diagnosis and recovery should be accessible, correct and intelligible.

4) Communication links between the control room and field should be reliable. For example, back-up communication hardware that is not vulnerable to common cause failure, should be provided where necessary. Preventative maintenance routines and regular operation of back-up equipment are examples of arrangements to ensure reliability.

5) Staff required to assist in diagnosis and recovery should be available with sufficient time to attend when required.

6) Distractions which could hinder recovery of the plant to a safe state should be avoided and necessary but time consuming tasks, such as summoning emergency services or communicating with site security, should be allocated to non operating staff.

The assessment is in the form of specific questions, each requiring a yes/no answer. The questions are arranged in eight trees. An example tree is shown in Figure 2.

The physical assessment is completed for a range of scenarios. It is necessary to identify scenarios which could result in incidents with major hazard potential. There is no fixed rule on the number of scenarios that should or must be analysed - each plant or unit is different. Selection of scenarios is critical to the quality of the physical assessment and must include the worst case in terms of consequence and operator workload. The site's COMAH report, area HAZOP's or risk assessments plus incident reports can be used in scenario selection and the selected scenarios should be agreed amongst the assessment team prior to the study. It is recommended that scenarios representing the following are analysed:

- Worst case scenarios requiring implementation of the off-site emergency plan;

- Incidents which could escalate without intervention to contain the problem on site;

- Lesser incidents requiring action to prevent the process becoming unsafe.

It may be necessary to assess the scenarios at different times such as during the day and at night, during the week and at weekends, if staffing arrangements vary over these times. The scenario selection process needs to consider these factors when producing a list of representative scenarios as well as the range of inherent hazards and operating areas.

The scenarios must be defined in sufficient detail and historical data relevant to the selected scenarios used in the assessment. Evidence of reliability is required e.g. simulation exercises, equipment reliability data, incident reports.

LADDER ASSESSMENT

The individual and organisational factors are assessed using ladders (see Table 1 - note: the dotted line represents the boundary line between acceptable and unacceptable). There are eleven ladders in total.

Table 1: Example ladder (for training & development)

Grade	Description	Explanation of progression	Rationale supporting assessment
A	Process/procedure/staffing changes are assessed for the required changes to operator training and development programmes. Training and assessment is provided and the success of the change is reviewed after implementation.	The training and development system is dynamic and integrated into the management of change process.	
B	All operators receive simulator or desktop exercise training and assessment on major hazard scenarios on a regular basis as part of a structured training and development programme.	Operators get a regular opportunity to practice major hazard scenarios through physical walk through's or simulators or by desk-top talk throughs.	
C	There is a minimum requirement for a 'covering' operator in a particular role based on time per month spent in the covered role to ensure sufficient familiarity. Their training and development programmes incorporate this requirement.	It has been recognised that anyone covering roles must be competent and their skills kept up to date in all roles they are expected to cover.	
D	Each operator has a training and development plan to progress through structured, assessed skill steps combining work experience and paper based learning and training sessions. Training needs are identified and reviewed regularly and actions taken to fulfil needs.	The training and development needs are identified, provided and reviewed on an individual basis allowing operators to improve and extend their skills and understanding. It provides operators with a motivation to improve and continue to develop.	
W	All operators receive refresher training and assessment on major hazard scenario procedures on a regular, formal basis.	The need for formalised regular refresher training for major hazard scenarios has been recognised as essential when they are such infrequent events with severe consequences.	
X	New operators receive full, formal induction training followed by assessment on the process during normal operation and major hazard scenarios.	Full training and assessment for new operators, it is formalised and covers normal operation plus major hazard scenarios.	
Y	There is an initial run through of major hazard scenario procedures by peers.	Only an informal briefing on major hazard procedures is provided to new operators.	
Z	There is no evidence of a structured training and development programme for operators. Initial training is informally by peers.	Poor practice, staffing arrangements do not fulfil any of the rungs above.	

The assessment team for each ladder element should work through the guidance questions that accompany each ladder and use support material (e.g. procedures, job descriptions, incident reports) as evidence wherever possible.

ASSESSMENT OUTPUT

The method identifies areas of unacceptable risk in process operation staffing arrangements and provides target areas for improvement action. Typical output actions include:

- evaluate costs and benefits of improvement options identified;

- further investigation required, such as determine the reliability of equipment, further analysis of critical tasks, check assumptions about the behaviour of leaks;

- consult with a human factors expert on key judgements.

The output from the method is an action plan for each assessed element. The priority for improvement actions is:

1) Improvement actions required to ensure the reliability of the operations team being physically capable of detecting, diagnosing and recovering from scenarios.

2) Improvement actions required to move the staffing arrangements above the acceptable line on all ladder elements.

3) Improvement actions required to continuously improve the staffing arrangements towards best practice.

PRACTICAL APPLICATION

It is recommended the staffing assessment be managed similarly to other process safety assessments, such as HAZOP or risk assessments supporting a safety case.

It is recommended the assessment of a defined production area be co-ordinated and facilitated by one person who is technically capable and has experience of applying hazard identification and risk assessment methods. The role is similar to that of a HAZOP chairperson.

In addition it is recommended that the assessment team constitute:

- control room and field operators: experienced and inexperienced plus operators from different shift teams;

- operator first line management; if on shift, different shifts should be represented;

- staff who would assist during incidents, perhaps in giving technical advice to operators or with tasks such as answering phones;

- management or administration staff with knowledge of operating procedures, control system configuration, process behaviour, equipment and system reliability, and safety (including risk assessments and criteria).

Teams may require assistance from Human Factors specialists.

WHEN TO APPLY THE METHOD
Good practice is to apply the method in full and to review and reapply the method periodically. The method may be applied to existing arrangements, new arrangements plus changes to existing arrangements.

Changes in staffing arrangements (or other changes affecting the response to emergency or upset conditions) should be evaluated prior to implementation. Any change that could alter the rating from the method is considered to be a change in staffing arrangements. A guiding principle is that changes should not lead to a reduction in the assessment rating.

The procedure for analysing proposed changes is:
- produce an up-to-date baseline assessment of the existing arrangements;

- define the proposed change and evaluate it using the assessment method, modifying the plans until an equal or better rating is achieved;

- re-assess the arrangements at a suitable time after implementation (within six months).

New arrangements can be assessed by defining the roles and responsibilities of operators, line managers and support staff plus their skills and experience in similar detail to that required when assessing a planned change. Training and development programmes, work patterns, safety policy and other issues covered by the assessed elements need to be defined also. As when assessing a change the arrangements should be re-assessed at a suitable time after implementation (within six months).

HAZARDS AND CONTROLS ASSESSED
The selection of hazards and controls examined in the assessment method is informed by Human Factors research into process control operations and sociotechnical systems thinking – i.e. that operator performance is influenced by deeper organisational and management factors. These two perspectives can be seen in the set of ladders, which are split between ladders examining individual factors and ladders for organisational factors. However, in all ladders there is a management theme, emphasising the need to manage hazards.

Staffing has been treated as one of the contingent factors within the context of how organisations are designed for the demands of their operations. Hence it is intended to take account of sociotechnical factors (process hardware, control technology, human and organisational factors) and acknowledge there is no single 'ideal' organisational arrangement that must be adopted by all organisations. Therefore the method should give consideration to how organisations handle the trade-offs between staffing numbers and, for example, interface technologies, automation, communication arrangements, task allocations, team structure etc.

It is also intended the method indicates how 'comfortable' an organisation is in respect of its staffing arrangements : i.e. given its other organisational parameters and the operations it is engaged in, how close to 'unacceptable' is its staffing arrangements.

Human factors research highlights the abilities required of process control staff, and hence the hazards and controls required to:
- be able to take action, reliably and within the necessary time frame;

- be able to follow the condition of the process, anticipate its behaviour and hence select an appropriate control strategy (i.e. have high 'situation awareness');

- be in a fit state to monitor the process (i.e. be awake and attentive);

- be willing to take action as and when necessary;

- be able to take action, reliably and within the necessary time frame;

When working as a team:
- be able to collect and share critical information about the process and control actions, and

- be able to co-ordinate actions.

The physical assessment checks whether the staffing arrangements work in practice. Using the analogy of designing a marketable car, the first test is whether the new design can handle the stresses it will be under. Subjective issues such as whether it is attractive come later. The physical assessment is equivalent to the fundamental check.

THE FORMAT OF THE METHOD
The format of the assessment method is an amalgam of three forms:
- structured hazard assessment methods, such as HAZOP and fault / event tree analysis;

- walk- or talk- through methods;

- anchored rating scales.

These were selected as they are familiar to the chemical sector or are gaining favour. The techniques used in Human Factors research are too demanding in resources or in interpretation skills:
- simulation and real-time observational methods require costly facilities, are time consuming, difficult to interpret and can be disruptive;

- operator self-assessment questionnaires or diaries could be prone to bias due to organisational cultural factors (openness, blame culture etc.) when not used in confidential research. There could be scope for using such methods to tune operators into the issues in the lead up to the analysis using other methods;

- task decomposition methods, including link analysis, face problems in analysing scenarios with uncertainty, into which process upsets and emergency incidents would be grouped

RESULTS OF TRIALS
During development the method was tested in three case studies.

Several areas of unacceptable risk were identified using the method in the case studies and a range of actions for investigation suggested. The need for improvement actions was identified during the physical assessment and the ladder assessment stages. During the case studies, actions were identified which:

- would lead the staffing arrangements to pass the physical assessment (develop the physical ability to detect, diagnose and recover);

- would lead the staffing arrangements to pass the ladder assessments (produce an acceptable performance on individual and organisational factors);

- would further improve staffing arrangements ability to physically detect, diagnose and recover;

- would further improve the position of the staffing arrangements on the eleven ladders and progress them towards best practice.

Opportunities for improvement were identified in all three case studies which were accepted and welcomed by the sites.

There has been a further 'pilot study' at a site which plans a full study later in 2001. Plus the method has been applied in several full studies using the team assessment approach. At least four of these have assessed planned organisational changes plus several plant and hardware changes with an initial baseline assessment of the current arrangements followed by an assessment of the implications of the planned changes. The output from these full studies is a timetable summarising implementation of improvement actions and changes with appropriate review points.

EXAMPLE OF ASSESSMENT OUTPUT

SITE A

Site introduction
The site has operated since the 1930's although the plant and processes have been changed and upgraded and there have been several changes of ownership. There are several control rooms and operating units on site and approximately 500 people on site in total. Two operating areas were assessed, one comprising a single batch operated unit, the other comprising two continuous process units.

The site had been going through major equipment and organisational changes over the previous 18 months and were part way through these programmes at the time of assessment.

The major hazard for the site is toxic gas release, there are large quantities of two toxic gases on site.

It is surrounded by other major hazard sites and so has to be able to deal with an emergency which is caused by an off site event.

Batch operating area introduction
The control room monitors a batch dilution process. The control has been upgraded within the past 12 months to DCS, there are now level trips on all tanks, there are emergency stops on the plant but there is not one in the control room yet. The E-stop stops the main pump and recirculation pump which maintain flow of the hazardous liquid. Isolation valves have to be operated on the plant, there are no automated isolation valves.

There is one operator on shift to monitor variables in the control room and operate the process on plant. This operator is also responsible for loading tankers a few minutes up the road. He can hear process alarms anywhere on the plant and when loading a tanker. There is a shift supervisor who works from 8am to 4pm. The operations team for this unit are also responsible for the utilities plant which is about 5 minutes away. This unit has one operator present on shift and the same daytime supervisor is responsible for both units.

There is a team of ten operators who rotate around a five week shift cycle covering the batch chemical stores plant and the utilities plant.

Assessment results

The physical assessment was done for two scenarios within this operating area as part of a limited case study trial of the methodology and the results are summarised in Table 2 (completed trees not included). Both scenarios had occurred on site within the past 2 years, therefore incident reports were available plus the incidents were familiar to the operators interviewed.

Table 2 Summary table for physical assessment of Site A, batch

Scenario #	Scenario Description	Pass	Fail	Physical assessment #('s) failed on	Actions required
1	Flange leak of toxic gas, wind direction towards the road, at night		√	1, 2, 6	Trees 1 & 2: Implement man down alarm which contacts security if two audible alarms are not acknowledged by the operator after 15 seconds and 30 seconds, respectively (identified by area HAZOP). Need to ensure that failure rate of the man down alarm is as low as reasonably practical and of a similar order to safety critical plant items. (Otherwise need to consider other options). Additionally assess benefits of cameras to assist plant monitoring. Additionally the benefits of having a mimic of the chemical stores DCS screens in a nearby continuously manned control room could be assessed. Step 6: Implement E-stop in control room (identified by area HAZOP). Additionally, assess benefits of automated isolation valves plus assess benefits of cameras to assist plant monitoring
2	Damage to plastic pipe, toxic chemical dilution by contractor (on days)		√	6	Step 6: Implement E-stop in control room (identified by area HAZOP). Additionally, assess benefits of automated isolation valves plus assess benefits of cameras to assist plant monitoring Plus additional steps to ensure that contractors report incident to security if the operator is not in the control room, by placing a notice in the control room and incorporating as a question in the weekly audits of contractors working on site

Therefore several areas of unacceptable risk were identified from the physical assessment and some suggested improvement actions identified by discussion with the operator and SHE advisor. The problems arise due to the plant having a single operator for control room and plant operations. The suggested improvements above are technology based, an alternative is to make other operator(s) available for plant work. To ensure that an outside plant operator was always available to the chemical stores and that the chemical stores control room was continuously manned, there would need to be a dedicated outside operator to the area which may mean that the utility stores would need a dedicated outside plant operator.

Table 3 summarises Site A's performance on the ladder assessment elements and suggests improvement actions (completed ladders not included). As with the physical assessment, the ladder assessments were done as part of a limited case study trial of the methodology.

Table 3 Summary of ladder assessment for Site A's batch production area

Element	A	B	C	D	E	F	G	V	W	X	Y	Z	Action
Situational awareness		▨								▨			Evidence suggests that it is currently quite difficult for an operator to keep track of process conditions during upset or emergency conditions as they have to personally detect a toxic gas leak as there is only one person who could be in the CR, on plant or loading tankers. The actions suggested in the physical assessment apply to this element
Teamworking										▨			There is a plan in place for the operator to ask for assistance from an operator on the utility plant (if he is available) or to call in the next operator due in. Therefore the exact reasons and scenarios where the operator needs this assistance need identifying and assessing to ensure this arrangement does not introduce unacceptable risk to plant operation
Alertness & fatigue (work pattern)									▨				Although the 'man down' alarm, a suggested action for the physical assessment will alert security if the operator is incapacitated, there is currently no contact between the operator and other personnel on site outside daytime hours. There are several people on site at all times, including a shift supervisor for the main production units. The lone operator is likely to benefit from some interaction with others during a shift to combat fatigue. Assess benefits of introducing interaction with other parts of the site outside normal hours.
Alertness & fatigue (health)													Could introduce review and improvement of health monitoring control
Training & development											▨		New and existing operators would benefit from tabletop exercises on major scenarios. The site would like to do this but have a problem because the current shift system does not allow flexibility for people to be available for training and assessment. A structured training and development plan for each operator is suggested. There are plans for introducing a skill step system as part of a site re-organisation which will incorporate these aspects but this again depends on a change in shift system. Optional shift systems have been assessed but the changes need agreeing with the Unions
Roles & responsibilities									▨				Key requirement is a management control which ensures that core competencies required for the operations team are retained during any staff changes. Plus the need for operator training and development plans are the main actions required to progress up this ladder
Willingness			▨										A peer review of this ladder would be beneficial to ensure all agree about not being fearful of reprimand if they wrongly initiate recovery actions as long as they felt justified in doing so. The progression up this ladder requires the operators being involved in finding ways to reduce the costs of recovery actions which may not be applicable in this operating area as it does not really have costs associated with shutdown.
Management of operating procedures						▨							There are plans in place for the procedures to be audited and for a new management of change system which ensures procedures are kept updated and out of date procedures recalled. It is also planned for the procedure control system to be reviewed and continuously improved. When these are implemented the operating area will progress up this ladder. It may be beneficial to tell people when new operating procedures are put onto the system as the site already does for new quality and SHE documents.
Management of change		▨											The introduction of a review programme for changes would take the operating area up to the top of this ladder

Element	A	B	C	D	E	F	G	V	W	X	Y	Z	Action
Continuous improvement of safety							■						Key requirement is for the investigations from incidents/events to be used in the review of training needs and operating procedures. This can be done in conjunction with the improvements to the training and development element. This again requires on the operators being available for participation in training activities which the current shift system makes difficult. Additional improvements should be planned after this has been achieved
Management of safety			▨				▨						Operator involvement in continuous improvement teams which tackle quality, environmental and safety issues would progress the operating area up this ladder.

Note

CR = control room

OBSERVATIONS ON HOW THE METHOD COMPARES TO OTHER SAFETY APPRAISAL METHODS

Experience gained during the collaborative case studies suggests the method covers many issues which are not assessed by existing methods such as HAZOP and risk assessment. This particularly applies to the elements covered by the ladder assessments but also to the physical assessment as it is assessing the reality of process operation rather than a frozen P&ID or operating procedure. It also generates greater insights due to operators providing the majority of the assessment input which is often not the case with other methods.

For example an issue arising at one site was:

What would a contractor do if he had caused a toxic gas leak and went to the batch process control room to report it and the control room operator was not present (which is likely as he works alone and can be outside in the plant)?

At the site safety induction contractors are instructed to contact site security on detection of toxic gas. The physical assessment trees identified this as a critical action, since if a contractor tried to locate the operator instead the scenario could develop into an incident with off-site impact. Two contractors were quizzed on what they would do in that particular situation and correctly replied that they would contact security. However to ensure all contractors would act correctly the control room operator and site Health and Safety advisor involved in the assessment identified additional actions such as a reminder notice in the control room plus incorporating the situation as a question to ask contractors on the site weekly audits.

The assessment cross-validated findings from other hazard and risk assessment methods. For example, the physical assessment on a batch chemical dilution plant control room identified areas of unacceptable risk which had been identified during a recent area HAZOP. The problems were associated with lone working and how process alarms or a toxic gas leak would be detected during a night shift if the control room operator (who has no support team) is incapacitated.

One of the sites had recently been audited by a corporate team. This had covered matters including, auditing, emergency planning and response, management of personnel change, incident investigation, contractors, and training and performance. Consequently the audit had looked at some of the topics covered by the staffing assessment method, in particular it had overlapped with some of the ladder elements, but on a site wide basis. It did not overlap with the physical assessment approach. Some of the issues identified by the staffing assessment method had been picked up by the corporate audit, such as training and development. Of course the staffing assessment was focused on part of the site, while the audit was site wide. Nevertheless, the site Health and Safety Advisor commented that in comparison to the audit, the staffing assessment 'got inside people's heads' and both the ladders and physical assessment trees provided discrete measures to gauge themselves and set targets to aim for.

LESSONS AND FUTURE DEVELOPMENTS

LESSONS

From the experience and comments from the piloting case studies and full-scale application, there are grounds for concluding the method fulfils its objectives. Staffing in the process industries is, undoubtedly, a complex issue and determining whether staffing arrangements are safe is a non-trivial task. It is hoped the method allows organisations to make informed decisions about staffing arrangements, particularly when changing staffing arrangements.

Although the method was originally developed to assess staffing arrangements in control rooms, application experience during and since development has demonstrated that generally it is necessary to assess the entire shift operations team and the method easily lends itself to being applied in this way. Plus it may be (and has been) applied where the control room does not perform all detection, diagnosis and response to incidents.

FACILITATOR SKILLS
Although the role of facilitator is akin to the role of HAZOP chairperson, and parallels between the staffing assessment method and the HAZOP technique are apparent, experience to date suggests that there are significant differences between the two roles. People who are skilled in formal process HAZOP may be uncomfortable with steering the staffing assessment process due to the emphasis on Human Factors and management systems. It is recommended when appointing a facilitator that greater weight be given to skills in these areas than to skills in process engineering.

FUTURE USE OF THE ASSESSMENT METHOD
In addition to the tool being used to appraise the management of safety and support safety cases, it provides a ready means of comparing and benchmarking sites. Sharing of the scores poses no commercial risk, and it is unlikely revealing the reasoning behind the ratings will threaten intellectual property or process technology as the method is assessing fundamental human factors and hazard management principles.

One of the functions of the assessment method is to assess the effective implementation of an organisation's safety management system (SMS) in terms of policies, procedures and influence on culture at the operational level and should be used to introduce improvements to an organisation's SMS. It is anticipated that the assessment will sit within the SMS and form an integral part of an organisation's demonstration of safe operation along with technical safety assessments such as HAZOP, reliability assessments etc. The assessment should therefore be treated as a working document which is periodically reviewed to take account of 'drift' in working practices and plant performance. It should be noted that the approach is significantly different to management audits which tend to be very broad, compliance based and not human factors focussed.

FUTURE DEVELOPMENT OF THE ASSESSMENT METHOD
As the method is applied and experience gained it is foreseeable the elements will be reviewed and revised. Some of the elements deal with issues that could be broken down into sub-elements.

The method's framework structure allows it to be added to (new ladders or assessment trees) or modified (e.g. revision of the ladders or use of specialised assessment tools within elements such as task analysis). It is anticipated that expansion or amendment will come as experience of applying the method is accumulated and 'best practice' evolves.

SHOULD THE ASSESSMENT CALCULATE A SINGLE, OVERALL SCORE?
The question of weighting the elements is also a consideration. Among the differences between elements is that they deal with issues that have different time frames and the consequences of 'poor' scores from specific elements are likely to 'decay' the management of safety at different rates. The elements also differ in the degree of 'improvement' they can bring - a strong continuous improvement programme can raise the standard of safety management as a whole. How can weightings be devised to reflect these differences? It is our

perception that the understanding is insufficient to permit valid weights to be assigned. However, as data is gathered, analysis against safety records may reveal correlations.

From a more pragmatic perspective, the pitfalls of an aggregated score resulting in above average controls in some areas masking poor hazard management in others also made us omit an algorithm for combining the scores.

TRANSFER TO OTHER INDUSTRIES

The method has been developed for application in the major hazard process industries to assess the operations teams ability to cope with major incidents. Additionally it can be applied to other processes and medium scale incidents where there may be loss of containment but there is no off-site impact and also to operational problems with financial consequences. Essentially the methodology assesses the effectiveness of a defined group of people who have to respond to stimuli and carry out a defined series of tasks within a specified timescale. The feasibility of the tasks being physically completed is assessed plus the management and organisational controls in place which influence and shape the team's ongoing performance.

Other than the physical assessment trees, which have been formulated to suit the circumstances peculiar to the process industries, it is anticipated the issues addressed in the other elements are generic to many environments. The fundamental check of the physical assessment could be rebuilt from principles relevant to other industries. The ladder elements are applicable to a wide variety of situations although the detailed wording of preparatory questions and ladders may need tailoring for use in other industries.

This research and the work it describes were funded by the Health and Safety Executive (HSE). Its contents, including any opinions and/or conclusions expressed, are those of the authors alone and do not necessarily reflect HSE policy.
The full report is available in HSE's contract research report series Summer 2001.

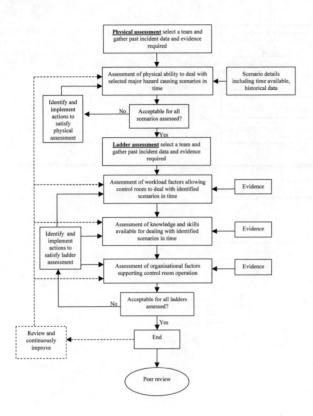

Figure 1: Flowchart of the staffing assessment process

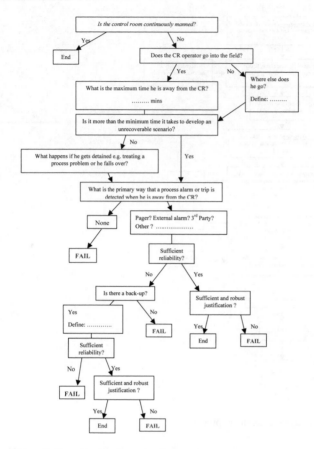

Figure 2: Example tree from physical assessment

FURTHER READING

1. Anderson P M, Smith A J, 1995, Human Factors in design of operational facilities - central and station control rooms, *Conference on railway engineering, Institution of Engineers Australia*, no 8, p105-108

2. Artman H, 1999, Situation awareness and co-operation within and between hierarchical units in dynamic making, *Ergonomics*, vol 42, no 11, p1404-1417

3. Ashleigh M, and Stanton N, 1996, A systems analysis of teamworking in control rooms: methodology considered, *Engineering psychology and cognitive ergonomics*, vol 2, p 33-38

4. Attwood D A, Nicolich M J, 1994, The effects of shift schedules on performance of control room operators: implications for a fitness-for-duty test, *Society of Petroleum Engineers of AIME*, vol 2, p485-492

5. Desaulniers D R, 1997, Stress in the control room: effects and solutions, *IEEE sixth annual human factors meeting*, IEEE

6. Defence Evaluation and Research Agency Centre for Human Sciences, 1999, Validation and development of a method for assessing the risks arising from mental fatigue, HSE Contract Research Report

7. Engineering Equipment and Materials Users Association, 1999, Alarm Systems, a guide to design, management and procurement, No. 191

8. Endsley M R, Kaber D B, 1999, Level of automation effects on performance, situation awareness and workload in a dynamic control task, *Ergonomics*, vol 42, no 3, p462-492

9. Entec, 2000, Development of a Business Excellence Model of Safety Culture, HSE Contract Research Report

10. Hallbert B P, Sebok A, Haugset K, Morisseau D S, Persensky J J,1995, Interim results of the study of control room crew staffing for advanced passive reactor plants. *In Proceedings of the 23rd water reactor safety meeting*

11. Hallbert B P, Sebok A, Morisseau D S, Persensky J J., 1997, The effects of advanced plant design features and control room staffing on operator and plant performance. *In Proceedings of the Sixth IEEE conference on Human Factors and Power Plants*, IEEE

12. Hogg D N, Follesø K, Strand-Volden F, Torralba B, 1995, Development of a situation awareness measure to evaluate advanced alarm systems in nuclear power plant control rooms, *Ergonomics*, vol 38, no 11, p2394-2413

13. Hollnagel E, 1994, Control room design and human reliability, Tunnel control and communication, 1st, p 37-46

14. HSE, Better alarm handling, March 2000, Chemical Sheet No. 6

15. HSE Books, 1999, Reducing error and influencing behaviour HSG48

16. Jensen R C, 1999, Alertness-support activities for control room operators in automated industrial plants, *Proceedings of the Human Factors and Ergonomics Society 43rd annual meeting*

17. Kecklund L J and Svenson O, 1997, Human errors and work performance in a nuclear power plant control room: associations with work-related factors and behavioural coping, *Reliability Engineering and System Safety* 56, 5-15

18. O'Hara J, Stubler W, and Kramer J, 1997, Human Factors considerations in control room modernisation: trends and personnel performance issues, *IEEE sixth annual human factors meeting*, IEEE

19. Paris C R, Salas E, Cannon-Bowers J A, 2000, Teamwork in multi-person systems: a review and analysis, *Ergonomics*, vol 43, no 8, p1052-1075

20. Plug E, van der Ploeg V B P, 1999, Re-design of a multi-operator control room based on workload analysis, *People in control: An international conference on human interfaces in control rooms, cockpits and command centres, 21-23 June 1999, Conference publications no 463*, IEE

21. Rosa R R, 1993, Performance and alertness on 8h and 12h rotating shifts as a natural gas utility, *Ergonomics*, vol 36, no 10, p1177-1193

22. Sebok A, 2000, Team Performance in process control: influences of interface design and staffing levels, *Ergonomics*, vol 43 No 8, p1210-1236

23. Vicente K J, Mumaw R J, and Roth E M, 1998, More about operator monitoring under normal operations: the role of workload regulation and the impact of control room technology, *Proceedings of the Human Factors and Ergonomics Society 42nd annual meeting*

MULTISKILLING: IMPLICATIONS FOR SAFE OPERATIONS

Dr Caroline Horbury & Michael Wright
Greenstreet Berman Ltd

Recent research funded by the Health and Safety Executive has produced a characterisation of "good practice" in the introduction of multi-skilling. The work was commissioned following the fire and explosion at the Texaco Refinery, where concerns were raised about the impact of multiskilling on the adequacy of the emergency response in the control room. The study included a review of published audits and of the causes of major accidents to identify the impact of multiskilling. The study reports on six case studies from high risk industry, including a rail control centre, nuclear power generation and chemical manufacture. A life cycle model was developed which provides practical advice to all those involved in the conception, planning and assessment, implementation and audit of multiskilling, and the ongoing skills maintenance and review. This paper covers research based on six industrial case studies, and describes the subsequent findings that will assist companies during the implementation of multiskilling. The practical guidelines and life cycle model provide a sound basis to aid companies undergoing these types of changes in terms of planning and implementing.

Multiskilling, organisational change, life cycle model.

INTRODUCTION

Multiskilling is part of a raft of changes that organisations may introduce with the aim of improving efficiency and competitiveness, reducing costs, improving quality, increasing production and so on. Research was commissioned by the Hazardous Installations Directorate of the Health and Safety Executive to:

- find evidence of the safety impacts of multiskilling;
- review previous accidents and incidents, as well as high profile audit reports to identify the role of multiskilling;
- give examples of how the health and safety aspects of multiskilling are managed in a number of case studies;
- develop management and implementation guidelines on empirical research;
- identify improvements to current HSE guidance.

This research on which this paper is based, will be published as a Contract Research Report by the HSE in Spring 2001.

DEFINITIONS OF MULTISKILLING

The Oil Industry Advisory Committee (HSC, 1998) define multiskilling as 'a way of working where the traditional divisions between work areas and separate disciplines are removed, and individuals are given responsibility for a range of different types of task.' Fundamentally we consider multiskilling as:

- increasing the range and scope of people's skills and competencies, and
- enabling and allowing them to carry out tasks previously or traditionally carried out by another function.

Organisations typically multiskill with the intent of removing functional barriers and increasing the flexibility of the workforce. Multiskilling can be either:

- Vertical multiskilling– where supervisory support tasks are learned by individuals;
- Horizontal multiskilling – where skills from another discipline are learned;
- Depth multiskilling – where more complex, specific skills within a trade are acquired.

Some organisations multiskill to ensure that incident management is adequate and appropriate. In these situations individuals are equipped with the skills, knowledge and expertise to competently handle an abnormal or emergency situation. This type of multiskilling is used in incident management scenarios, where it is imperative that there are appropriate skills to manage an incident or event at all times. This means that there must be flexibility within the team to ensure competent cover for lunch and other breaks, as well as for training and holidays. For incident management multiskilling can involve all forms of multiskilling.

ACCIDENTS & HSE AUDIT REPORTS – LESSONS FOR MULTISKILLING
A sample of major accident reports and public domain HSE Audit Reports were reviewed to identify if and how multiskilling contributed. The following accidents were reviewed where multiskilling had a role in the causation:

- Southall Rail Accident
- Fire at the Texaco Refinery
- Collision of mv Sand Kite with the Thames Flood Barrier
- Hickson and Welsh fire and explosion.

The review of these accidents indicates that the introduction of multiskilling has been associated with a number of serious safety problems. These problems relate to:

- workload problems arising from the reduction in staffing 'made possible' by multiskilling;
- the loss of coordination, error checking and supervision arising from deficient teamwork within multiskilled 'leaderless' teams;
- failure to support the introduction of multiskilling through appropriate staff training and performance monitoring.

Thus the problems arose from either the way in which multiskilling was implemented or by changes made possible by multiskilling, rather than by individuals committing errors in tasks previously carried out by other trades and disciplines.

HSE published audit reports on BNFL (2000) and British Energy (1999) and these provide insights into the impacts of multiskilling and the importance of the management process. The main concerns about BNFL were:

- the possibility of supervisory problems arising from vertical multiskilling;
- resource problems arising from staff reductions made possible by multiskilling;
- inadequate planning and assessment;
- a failure to support multiskilling through training etc.

The British Energy audit does take the point further by relating these types of problems to the integration of safety management into corporate decision-making, i.e. ensuring that corporate business plans make proper allowance for staffing and workload considerations.

The outcome of this review of accidents and audit reports suggests that the introduction of multiskilling per se does not create a risk. Rather it is the manner in which multiskilling is implemented.

POTENTIAL IMPACTS OF MULTISKILLING ON HEALTH AND SAFETY
Potential health and safety impacts of multiskilling from previous research, along with past incidents and audit reports include:

- the job scope exceeding the credible ability of an individual to learn and carry out tasks – leading to error and omission;
- failure to retrain staff adequately means they lack competence;
- overloaded staff can not manage workload so make errors and violations or omit tasks, especially during periods of high workload, emergent work and staff absence;
- vertical multiskilling in crisis management situations can lead to a loss of independent oversight.
- no one stands back to have an overview of an event during emergencies, which could lead to mindset and groupthink;
- insufficient exposure to a task to maintain adequate skills leads to error, lack of competent staff, and overload of those individuals who have maintained their skills.

CASE STUDIES: GOOD PRACTICE IN MULTISKILLING
The aim of the case studies was to identify how contemporary organisations have implemented multiskilling. Six case studies were carried out from the following industrial sectors:

- Nuclear;
- Major hazard/ chemical;
- Manufacturing;
- Rail.

Three case studies are described here in the form of examples of good practice.

RAIL COMPANY
This case study examined the control centre responsible for the control and monitoring of all rail operations on its network. Its role is to control and monitor all activities under normal, abnormal and emergency operating conditions. There are six posts in the Control Centre. Multiskilling was introduced as a means of providing cover within the team for lunch and other breaks on shift, without having too many under-utilised staff in the team. A number of changes have been introduced as a result of a recent incident and its subsequent investigation.
For multiskilling, this company uses the same processes of selection and training as those used initially to equip personnel with their primary skills. For example, those personnel recruited for higher ability posts with stringent selection criteria can be multiskilled in any task, whilst personnel in other posts will only be multiskilled in less complex tasks. The training provided is the same as that for originally learning the roles. Management formally assess an individual's competence by means of practically demonstrating the skills. Refresher courses are run, and all posts are re-certified every 3 years by means of an exam and practical assessment.
Their key safety concern is the competence of staff and handovers between posts on shift. Competence is assured by providing identical levels of training for the additional skill

and identical competency criteria, as for the single skill. Rigorous training, refreshers and re-certification are the chief mechanisms to achieve this, with competence being assured through on and off-the-job testing and demonstration of both skills and knowledge. As the multiskilled person provides cover for the team, crucial to the continued safety of the concession is the quality of this handover. This is recognised and a formal mechanism is used to ensure that handovers are properly carried out. During the survey the importance of handovers and the critical role of the log to document all issues was emphasised.

CHEMICAL PLANT CONTROL OPERATION

This case study studied multiskilling at a company that operates a main production site, and a number of unstaffed satellite sites. The company employs 80 people. In light of their high profile customers, continuity of supply and high quality products are their primary objectives. The majority of their staff are multiskilled, and the central control room on site monitors the process both on the main site and on the satellites.

The company originally started multiskilling about 20 years ago with the aim being to equip engineers with sufficient all-round skills to be able to address most of the issues arising at the satellite sites. Out of normal hours a single engineer is responsible for all on-site needs. Hence they need to be multiskilled to identify early indications from the control room, diagnose the problem, locate the problem and tackle it (either remotely or on site). The role of engineers has gradually evolved with the role being predominantly control room based with on-site activities being coordinated and carried out by multiskilled control room staff. Multiskilling is being pushed forward now within the main site to improve organisational efficiency and responsiveness, in part this is linked to the increase in organisational demands and a recruitment ban.

A matrix has been developed for all posts and roles on site. This is based on a task analysis of the different activities and the training and knowledge requirements to carry out these. All staff have a Training Needs Schedule where they are reviewed against the matrices relevant to their role every 12-18 months. This provides an opportunity for the management and workforce to identify training needs and skill gaps, as well as competence. The schedule lists the skills and knowledge required for each job and its constituent tasks. Training is typically on the job and supported by a log book, documenting practical experience. Competency decisions are made by management against a schedule and discussions held with the trainee about their confidence in their skills and abilities, as well as competence at executing them.

This company ensures that risk assessments are carried out for all activities, and through this ensures that only competent individuals carry out certain activities. Particular emphasis is placed on individuals understanding their personal competence limits, and they are encouraged to stand back and think about a job before undertaking it.

NUCLEAR POWER GENERATION

This case study examined multiskilling at a UK nuclear power station. Nuclear power generation is highly regulated in the UK and their activities are closely monitored and scrutinised by the Nuclear Installations Inspectorate. The multiskilling initiative was commenced in 1997.

The site employs approximately 800 people, and most staff are multiskilled to carry out radiological self monitoring. Furthermore most staff are cross-trained to carry out other tasks. The purpose of multiskilling was to:

- Streamline operational tasks; and
- Reduce the headcount.

The site recognised the importance of workforce ownership and involvement in nuclear power generation, to achieve this they:
- Ran a suggestion scheme to identify appropriate tasks
- The whole process was coordinated by a steering group who reviewed the appropriateness of multiskilling certain tasks;
- Negotiated with the trade unions and provided a monetary carrot to aid workforce buy-in.

Three distinct maintenance disciplines are maintained and follow the 80/20 rule to avoid the loss of core skills. The principle adopted is that only those jobs where less than 20% of the task is carried out by another discipline will be multiskilled. Training is thorough; an exam has to be passed following completion of formal training. Competency is then assessed following several weeks on the job, and involves observation and a decision is made jointly between the individual and their manager. The organisation has monitored the radiological cleanliness and contamination reports to ensure that health and safety has not suffered as a result of multiskilling.

MULTISKILLING LIFE CYCLE MODEL
Many of the issues which emerged from the case studies and the review of audit reports and major accidents, were linked to reduction in headcount, staff not being competent to carry out their requisite activities, an organisational culture which supported risk taking, and potentially 'macho' and 'can do' cultures. A life cycle is described which was developed based on information from the case studies, a review of accidents and audits, as well as published material to describe the features that need to be considered at each stage of the multiskilling life cycle. Due to the findings from the accident review and the case studies the life cycle model places particular emphasis on management of change, training and competence assurance. See Figure 1 for a representation of the life cycle model.

STARTING OUT
This is the point in time when the prospect of organisational change has just been recognised and the form of such changes is being conceived. The management objectives are to:
- recognise instances of multiskilling;
- identify the key risks and assess the importance of these;
- specify as a matter of policy / principle the need to ensure that health and safety requirements are considered during the multiskilling process, and;
- define safety criteria and factors to be taken into account during the multiskilling process.

PLANNING AND ASSESSMENT
The next step involves considering in detail the steps required prior to implementation. This stage is where decisions are being made on details of multiskilling such as:
- which individuals will be multiskilled;
- which tasks will be included in the remit of multiskilling;
- how will people be trained and supervised;
- how procedures and working practices are to be changed;
- staff headcount reductions.

The objectives of this stage in the life cycle is to:
- ensure that due account is taken of workload, competence, supervision and other factors when making specific decisions about multiskilling;

- ensure that suitable and sufficient risk assessments are completed, and;
- ensure changes are developed in a planned and systematic manner, including identification of all actions necessary to enable change to be made successfully.

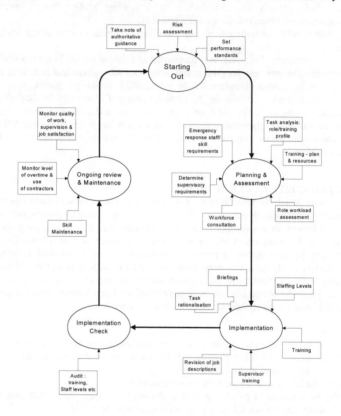

Figure 1: Multiskilling life cycle model

IMPLEMENTATION

This is where changes are implemented, and the detailed planning is turned into operational reality. Possible steps include staff being made redundant, retrained, new ways of working being introduced, and so on. The management objective is to:

- ensure implementation is properly resourced, scheduled and organised – so that planned changes are carried out effectively; and
- ensure flexibility is built in, so that unplanned changes can be dealt with, if training takes longer than originally anticipated the company can still operate.

IMPLEMENTATION CHECK

This is the stage following the implementation process, where changes have been completed, or are well underway. The objectives are to ensure planned training, supervision, etc has been carried out as intended and has achieved its required performance objectives. This stage provides an opportunity to modify implementation, and to take into consideration feedback and issues arising.

Ongoing skills maintenance & review - In the period following implementation it is important to:

- ensure that skills are maintained at both an organisational and individual level;
- detect any latent problems, and;
- seek opportunities to improve safety performance amongst multiskilled staff.

The lifecycle therefore provides a framework in which to consider multiskilling, as well as the different elements that need to be considered at the different stages.

CONCLUSIONS

The research found:

- the potential adverse impact of asking people to work outside of their limits is clear and recognised;
- that on the whole the case study companies recognised the importance of this and imposed clear boundaries on the extent of multiskilling;
- problems with multiskilling appeared to be linked to allied issues such as 'workload' and supervision. As such multiskilling guidelines should focus on the management of change issues and ensure that in 'business-driven' reorganisations that multiskilling is not overlooked.
- there is evidence to suggest that smaller firms can successfully multiskill and follow good practice guidelines;
- the risk controls adopted should be appropriate for task complexity, frequency, safety criticality etc.

On the whole the conclusions for this report is that multiskilling is typically introduced as part of a series of changes aimed at reducing costs within the organisation, and therefore care must be taken to ensure that safety is not overlooked. Previous incidents and audit reports show that safety can be jeopardised as a result of poorly implemented and managed multiskilling. However the case studies and life cycle show that if multiskilling is implemented systematically then it should not jeopardise safety.

ACKNOWLEDGEMENTS

This report and the work it describes was funded by the Health and Safety Executive (HSE). Its contents, including any opinions and/or conclusions expressed, are those of the authors alone and do not necessarily reflect HSE policy.

APPENDIX

Three aids are provided in the HSE multiskilling report, namely a:

- List of do's and don't of multiskilling;
- A characterisation of good and bad practice; and ;
- An Auditor's implementation checklist.

Some of the Do's and Don't are listed below, as is an example of the implementation checklist.

KEY DO'S AND DON'T OF MULTISKILLING

- Do develop and implement a company wide policy to the management of health and safety aspects of multiskilling;
- Do give staff a role in the planning and implementing change process;
- Do ensure you have an accurate estimate of peak and emergency workloads, as well as normal when determining how many posts can be eliminated by multiskilling;
- Do think about the necessary skills and experiences to ensure the relevant mix of expertise is still available within the company;
- Do ensure that staff competencies cover the full range of tasks within their remit by an appropriate mix of training, assessment and coaching, as well as refresher training;
- Do ensure that someone has the role of 'standing back' and taking the wider perspective, especially in emergency management;
- Do schedule hands-on experience, job rotation, refresher training and competence assessment;
- Don't ignore the valuable insights from those who actually do the work;
- Don't multiskill without considering the impact on succession management;
- Don't let the standard of health and safety management become the victim of local business/safety management haggling;
- Don't base resource estimates solely on 'normal' workloads;
- Don't forget that 'groupthink' and 'tunnel vision' can blind people to their mistakes, especially under stress & in emergencies;
- Don't ignore or forget the need for people to practice their skills.

EXAMPLES FROM CHECKLIST FOR IMPLEMENTING MULTISKILLING

This checklist is directed at those decisions and responsibilities that are likely to reside with management and the implementation team, in particular those responsible for planning and implementing organisational change.

1. Has the implementation team recognised which organisational and staffing changes entail the horizontal or vertical multiskilling of staff involved in safety significant work ?
2. Have staff been consulted by management on multiskilling proposals ?
3. Have criteria/guidelines been developed regarding the level of 'on-the-job' experience, refresher training etc required for people to remain qualified in each skill/task area ?
4. Have criteria and guidelines been developed regarding how individuals competence will be monitored and maintained ?

RECENT RAILWAY INDUSTRY ACCIDENTS : LEARNING POINTS FOR THE PROCESS INDUSTRIES

Christopher J. Beale, Ciba Specialty Chemicals, PO Box 38, Bradford, West Yorkshire. BD12 0JZ. UK.
MIChemE

Following a number of high profile accidents in the railway industry in recent years, there has been a large amount of public debate about rail safety. The lessons learnt from these accidents have raised issues which are applicable to the process industries, particularly regarding safety management, human factors, management of contractors and organisational structures. These issues contribute significantly to many process industry accidents. This paper reviews the press reports and published accident reports for some recent high profile accidents including the Channel Tunnel fire, the Kaprun fire, Southall, Paddington, Hatfield and Selby and identifies learning points which are relevant for preventing accidents in the process industry.

learning from accidents, engineering design, emergency response, COMAH

1. INTRODUCTION.

It is an unfortunate fact that many process industry accidents are similar to accidents that have happened historically in the industry or even within the same company. Recent process industry legislation, such as the Control Of Major Accident Hazards Regulations (COMAH, 1999), includes requirements for operators to learn from accidents on their sites and to review historic records of major accidents when identifying potential major accident hazard scenarios within their Safety Report.

Many early accident investigations focused on the specific technical or direct human causes of the accidents. As more knowledge has been obtained in the field, so more attention has been paid to the wider issues of safety management system failures which often lie at the root cause of accidents. This paper has therefore been produced to explore opportunities for learning from accidents in one industry (the rail industry) and applying the lessons to another industry (the process industry).

This will allow the databank of experience about the causes of major accidents affecting the industry to be widened. **Figure 1** illustrates the sources of this information for a typical multi-national company.

2. OBJECTIVES.

This paper reviews published accident and press reports about seven recent high profile accidents in the rail industry and identifies learning points for the major hazard process industries which can be used to avoid, prevent and minimise the impacts of major accidents to improve risk management.

The paper is structured in the following way :

- identification of the key similarities and differences between the two industries from a risk perspective.
- overview of the seven rail accidents that are reviewed in this paper.
- summary of key learning points in the following areas :
    - structural and organisational aspects.
    - safety management systems.
    - design aspects.
    - operational aspects.
    - hazard management.
    - emergency response and management.
- conclusions about how this information can be used practically in the process industry.

3. SIMILARITIES IN RISK DRIVERS BETWEEN THE TWO INDUSTRIES.

At first sight, the railway industry appears to have little in common with the process industry. A deeper investigation, however, reveals that many of the aspects of the two industries which influence major hazard risks are in fact similar. The similarities are general and do not apply to every rail or every process industry company. They include :

Accelerating pace of change in sector. Massive structural changes are occurring in both industries forcing the rail industry to adapt to the new regime which was created following rail privatisation and the process industry to adapt to constant pressure from the financial markets to restructure and improve efficiency.

Fragmentation of large organisations. The rail industry now operates as a complex web of different operating companies, infrastructure management companies, regulatory bodies and contractors. Large chemical companies have also often started to fragment, outsourcing activities which were once carried out in house such as engineering and maintenance, sharing sites with different operators and contracting out service provision such as energy supply, security and gases.

Increasing contractorisation. In order to improve efficiency, many activities which used to be considered to be core activities are now contracted out to specialist companies.

Loss of knowledge and experience. As companies restructure and outsource more activities, so many experienced and knowledgeable staff have been released from the industry.

Major hazard potential. Accidents in both industries have the potential to cause multi-fatality accidents.

High degree of regulation. Because of this major hazard potential, both industries have been tightly regulated and now have to produce detailed Safety Cases to demonstrate that risks within the operation are being managed in an acceptable manner.

Figure 1 : Sources Of Historical Experience About Major Accidents For A Typical Multi-national Company.

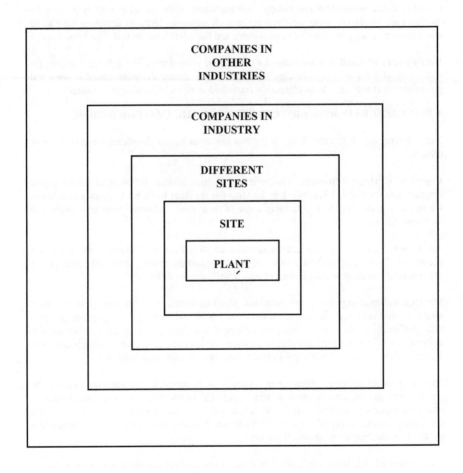

Degree of public scrutiny. When things go wrong in the industry, they tend to go wrong in a spectacular manner. Accidents therefore tend to be subject to a high degree of public, press and political scrutiny.

Use of complex automation technology. Advanced and costly control and safety systems are used and are constantly under development in each industry. Difficult decisions have to be made about balancing the costs of these systems and the safety benefits that flow from them.

Development of detailed management systems and procedures. As staff have to perform safety critical tasks in both industries, there has been a historic development of systems and procedures to enable risks to be effectively controlled across relatively large organisations.

4. DIFFERENCES IN RISK DRIVERS BETWEEN THE TWO INDUSTRIES.

The following key differences between the two industries have a significant effect on the risk drivers :

Degree of strategic influence. The centre of decision making for most of the front line companies in the UK rail industry is in the UK. On the other hand, many process companies are headquartered abroad, thus limiting some of their direct influence over investment and their operations.

Asset ownership. Chemical companies tend to own their core assets - the plant and equipment. Railway companies tend to lease their core assets - rolling stock. The priorities of the operating company and the leasing company will often be different.

Strategic national importance of company. If rail companies perform poorly, the knock-on effects of this poor performance are often experienced widely by a large population. This poor performance often has national importance. If a chemical company's production is affected, the effects are normally (but not always) experienced by a much smaller population. There is often, therefore, intense political pressure for a rail company to perform.

Degree of direct political interference. Because of the strategic national importance of the rail industry, the industry is often subject to political interference. This can destabilise or renew management, control investment levels and limit the capital investment priorities (depending on the levels of subsidy and length of franchise awarded). There is much less political interference in the chemical industry.

Populations at risk from accidents. By their nature, any rail accidents are likely to have a direct impact on members of the public as the public is directly at risk in most accidents. Chemical accidents may affect the public but are much more likely to affect employees.

Degree of control over external events. Chemical plants are bounded in limited geographic areas. Rail operations take place over long distances and wide areas. It is therefore much more difficult to control external events on the railways. External events are considered to be events which arise outside the boundary of the operation but cause effects inside the boundary eg. arson.

Availability of resource in an accident situation. Chemical sites are normally manned with teams of experienced people while potentially hazardous operations are taking place. Trains tend to be manned by one or two experienced people (driver / guard). There are therefore very limited immediately available resources for dealing with rail incidents. This is particularly important for accidents in remote areas.

Criticality of human error. Simple human errors (such as failure to see or interpret a signal) can directly cause major accidents on the railways. This problem is rarer in the process industries as it is often possible to deploy technological measures to prevent this condition.

Safety training for populations at risk. Most chemical sites have induction programmes for staff and visitors so that they are trained in how to behave if an accident occurred. This is rare in the rail industry. Populations at risk are therefore unaware of safety procedures and systems if an accident occurred.

Reliance on external emergency response. Many chemical plants have some degree of emergency response capability on site. If rail accidents occurred, great reliance is placed on the timely response of the emergency services.

5. OVERVIEW OF SOME RECENT RAIL ACCIDENTS.

This paper is based on published accident reports and press coverage related to the following seven recent high profile rail accidents :

- Watford South Junction, 8th August 1996.
- Channel Tunnel Fire, 18th November 1996.
- Southall, 19th September 1997.
- Ladbroke Grove, 5th October 1999.
- Hatfield, 17th October 2000.
- Kaprun (Austria), 11th November 2000.
- Selby, 28th February 2001.

The type and extent of information which has been published about these accidents varies. Detailed accident reports tend to be available for the earlier accidents with press coverage and interim accident reports available for the more recent accidents.

This section provides a brief overview of each of the seven accidents.

5.1 Watford South Junction, 8th August 1996.

A passenger train passed a signal at danger and collided with an empty coaching stock train. One passenger was killed, 69 passengers required hospital treatment and four train crew workers suffered injuries (HSE, 1998).

Key factors associated with the accident included :

- the risk of human errors causing SPADs (Signals Passed At Danger) and technological options for reducing these risks with Automatic Train Protection (ATP) systems.
- confusion caused to train drivers due to a speed restriction sign being placed in an inappropriate position and the ambiguity in the railway signalling standard which contributed to the problem.
- the shorter than normal safety margin for the signal that was passed at danger.

5.2 Channel Tunnel Fire, 18th November 1996.

A heavy goods vehicle (HGV) shuttle entered the long subsea tunnel on fire. The 31 passengers and 3 train crew on board were rescued but suffered from the effects of smoke inhalation (DETR, 1997). The fire was intense and caused extensive damage to the tunnel structure and severe disruption to a key European transport link.

The tunnel system was modern and extensive efforts had been made to incorporate safety into the system design from the outset. The fire was a serious test for the system which performed well when the fire occurred.

Key factors associated with the accident included :

- speculation in the press that the fire may have been started deliberately by staff in response to job losses (the cause of the fire is still subject to investigation by the French judicial review process).
- the reliability of the fire detection and fire safety systems and their robustness against common mode failures caused by fires.
- the emergency procedures for responding to incidents including fires and the adequacy of staff training for dealing with emergency situations.
- the adequacy of manning levels in the tunnel control centre for dealing with emergency and abnormal occurrences as well as routine operations.

5.3 Southall, 19th September 1997.

A high speed passenger train passed signals at danger on the approach to a busy London rail terminal and collided with a freight train. Seven passengers were killed and 160 people were injured in the accident (HSC, 2000).

Key factors associated with the accident included :

- the risk of human errors causing SPADs (Signals Passed At Danger) and technological options for reducing these risks with Automatic Train Protection (ATP) systems.
- operating trains knowing that safety critical systems were not functioning. Both the Automatic Warning System (AWS) and Automatic Train Protection (ATP) systems were known to not be working on the journey that lead to the accident.

- the efficiency of fault reporting and corrective maintenance systems so that failures could be quickly remedied and the problems caused by the fragmentation of the industry where different companies were responsible for the maintenance and operation of assets.
- the adequacy of emergency egress facilities from trains that have been involved in an accident.
- the lack of co-ordinated safety related research and development initiatives in the fragmented industry.

5.4 Ladbroke Grove, 5th October 1999.

A commuter train passed signals at danger on the approach to a busy London rail terminal and collided with a high speed passenger train. The collision ruptured fuel tanks and caused an intense fire in the wreckage of the trains. Thirty one passengers were killed and 227 people were treated in hospital following the accident (HSE, 2000).

Key factors associated with the accident included :

- the similarities in terms of causes and geographic location to the recent accident at Southall (see **Section 5.3**) and the delays in investigating the Southall accident.
- the SPAD occurred at a signal which had a history of SPADs and had one of the highest incidences of SPADs on the whole UK train network.
- the consequences of the accident were exacerbated by the intense fire that occurred in the wreckage immediately after the collision.

5.5 Hatfield, 17th October 2000.

A high speed passenger train was derailed when a section of damaged rail broke. Four passengers were killed and 70 people were injured, including four people who were seriously injured (HSE, 2001a). Large sections of the UK rail network were affected by subsequent track closures and speed limits as similar sections of track were investigated. This caused transport chaos in the UK and led to the resignation of the Chief Executive of the rail infrastructure company.

Key factors associated with the accident included :

- management and maintenance of the rail infrastructure and the systems for detecting and correcting fatigue cracks in rails.
- the long delays in responding to identified cracked rails.
- the fragmentation of the industry and resulting difficulties in completing essential work quickly when multiple independent organisations are involved, each with their own priorities and bureaucracies.

5.6 Kaprun (Austria), 11th November 2000.

A fire occurred in a train on a steep funicular railway serving one of Europe's main ski areas. 170 people were killed (Sunday Times, 2000).

Key factors associated with the accident included :

- identifying how a fire could start and spread in a train which was supposed to be fire resistant.
- the absence of fire fighting equipment (eg. fire extinguishers) inside the train or inside the tunnel, making it impossible to extinguish a fire.
- the absence of effective escape routes from the train and the tunnel as the train fitted tightly into a tunnel.
- difficulties in access for emergency services. A long steep walk was required into the tunnel and there were no helicopter landing sites close to the tunnel for evacuating casualties.
- the reasons that the fire doors at the ends of the tunnel were open when they should have been closed to prevent fire and smoke spread.
- the apparent absence of an emergency plan and poor operator training for dealing with an emergency.
- the reliance on unusual and specialist technology (funicular railways in mountain tunnels) with little or no provision for dealing with accidents.

5.7 Selby, 28th February 2001.

A road vehicle and trailer left the carriageway of the M62 motorway and slipped down a steep bank, coming to rest on a railway line. The vehicle was almost immediately hit by a high speed passenger train, causing the train to be derailed into the path of an oncoming freight train (HSE, 2001b). The two trains collided violently. Thirteen people were killed and 100 injured in the accident (Yorkshire Post, 2001).

Key factors associated with the accident included :

- the immediate cause of the accident was not within the control of the railway operating companies but was an interaction from a road transport accident.
- this appears to have been a freak and highly unlikely accident (although a detailed analysis of railway statistics would suggest that an accident of this type was reasonably foreseeable on the railway network).

6. LEARNING POINTS.

The example learning points which have been identified from the seven accidents have been grouped into the following six areas :

- structural and organisational aspects.
- safety management systems.
- design aspects.
- operational aspects.
- hazard management.
- emergency response and management.

6.1 Structural & Organisational Aspects.

These learning points have been obtained from a the Southall accident report and an analysis of press reports following the other accidents and include :

1. *Fragmentation of a business can cause problems with controlling critical safety aspects of the business.*

The Southall accident report identified at least three areas where the fragmentation of the industry had exacerbated safety problems for operating companies :

- the cause of defects and unreliability may be found to lie within the control of companies over which the operator has no formal or informal rights (section 16.13).
- no maintenance checks were carried out owing to differences between the operator and the contractor in interpreting a contract (section 16.14).
- the fragmented industry had been set up to run the railways in their existing state, but there was little incentive to explore research and development issues to the detriment of safety and the long term interests of the industry (section 16.19).

2. *Responsibilities must be clearly defined in fragmented organisations.*

Press reports following some of the accidents on the UK rail network have been very critical of the ambiguous responsibilities that different players in the industry have. This is of particular concern when these responsibilities concern safety critical tasks or operations.

3. *Redundancy programmes can cause skills shortages in an industry.*

Redundancy programmes tend to result in a loss of experienced staff from the industry. These staff tend to be familiar with working practices and safety procedures. If they are replaced with contractors or new workers, this corporate knowledge can be lost.

4. *Businesses can be difficult to manage when contractors are used extensively for critical tasks.*

One of the causes of the Hatfield derailment appears to have been the delay in correcting an identified problem with damaged rails. The response to this problem was bureaucratic and involved at least three organisations : one operating the infrastructure, one inspecting the rails and one laying the rails.

5. *Management must have adequate systems for managing safety critical operations.*

The Southall accident report identified problems with the identification of problems or deficiencies through the monitoring and audit processes which were in place. The following specific issues were raised :

- compliance with rules cannot be assumed without a positive system of monitoring. A different culture needs to be developed to get individuals to perform to the best of their abilities rather than simply delivering minimum service (section 16.10).

- potentially serious deficiencies may develop in detailed maintenance procedures which are not detected by conventional management procedures or audit (section 16.12).

6.2 Safety Management Systems.

These learning points have been obtained from a combination of published accident reports from the Watford South and Southall accidents and an analysis of press reports following the other accidents and include :

1. *Eliminate ambiguity in safety related standards wherever possible.*

The Watford South accident report recommended (#3) that signal standards should be unambiguous where possible as this will minimise the potential for operating systems which do not comply with the intent of the standard.

2. *Ensure that mechanisms exist for listening to the views of operators on the ground.*

Drivers using the section of track around Ladbroke Grove were aware that signal 109 had poor visibility. Mechanisms should be in place for listening to these views and dealing with any relevant issues. This increases the likelihood that the practical issues which are often overlooked by system designers and maintenance staff are addressed.

3. *Learn from previous accidents and incidents.*

Many of the accidents described in **Section 5** had similar causes. In particular, the Southall and Ladbroke Grove accidents were very similar. Signal 109 (where the Ladbroke Grove SPAD occurred) was known as one of the worst signals for SPADs in the whole of the UK. The accident might have been avoided if either a through investigation into the causes of SPADs had been carried out or the lessons from the Southall enquiry had been implemented.

4. *Prompt corrective action is required when safety critical defects have been identified.*

The defective rails which caused the Hatfield derailment were identified many months before the accident occurred but bureaucracy delayed the remedial work.

5. *Nothing should be allowed to delay the opening of an accident investigation.*

This was recommended in the Southall accident report (#80) because serious delays had been caused in the investigation process for legal reasons. This meant that the learning points could not be identified and implemented quickly after the accident.

6.3 Design Aspects.

These learning points have been obtained from a combination of the published Channel Tunnel fire accident report and an analysis of press reports following the other accidents and include :

1. *Fire detection system logic should provide an early indication of fire detection.*

The Channel Tunnel fire detection system logic included an 'unconfirmed fire' signal. This caused a delay in responding to a real fire and it was recommended that a simple logic should be employed (recommendation #1) so that any fires would be detected more quickly.

2. *Critical fire safety systems should be able to withstand the consequences of a fire.*

The Channel Tunnel fire report identified a number of areas where critical fire safety systems performed poorly in a real fire, often because of design deficiencies. These systems need to be robust against fire damage and include communications systems (recommendation #6), fire mains (recommendation #7) and power supplies (recommendation #4).

3. *Fires can occur in areas which are constructed of fire retardant materials.*

The Kaprun fire clearly showed that fires can still occur in systems which are constructed of fire retardant materials. Fire risks in these situations may be low but it is dangerous to assume that fires cannot happen in these systems.

4. *An acceptable basis of safety must be provided for unusual or non-standard technology.*

The Kaprun train used underground funicular technology. This is only used in a few places around the world. Comparatively little operating experience has been gained with these systems and each installation is likely to have it's individual design characteristics. Unfortunately, the design had totally inadequate provisions for emergency escape and rescue. Great care should therefore be taken when using unusual technology.

5. *Even complex automated protection systems will not guarantee that a system is safe.*

The passenger train which was involved in the Southall accident was equipped with a sophisticated ATP protection system. Unfortunately, the system had been isolated as it had been degrading the train's reliability. Complex and expensive safety systems will therefore reduce the likelihood of an accident if they are designed and maintained properly but cannot guarantee that an accident will not happen.

6.4 Operational Aspects.

These learning points have been obtained from a combination of published accident reports from the Channel Tunnel, Watford South and Southall accidents and an analysis of press reports following the other accidents and include :

1. *Procedures should not provide conflicting instructions to operators.*

The Watford South accident report recommended that a full audit of speed restrictions should be carried out to identify areas where conflicting information is provided to drivers (#6).

2. *Great care is required for managing situations where human errors are a significant contributor to risk.*

Press reports following the Ladbroke Grove accident highlighted two factors which may have contributed to the accident :

- the driver of the train which passed the signal at danger was relatively new to the job and may have been inexperienced.
- the government had been putting Train Operating Companies under intense pressure to improve punctuality in the months leading up to the accident. This pressure was invariably pushed straight down to the front line operators, the train drivers. This may have caused drivers to take additional risks to avoid delays, thus increasing SPAD risks. A direct conflict may have developed between punctuality (ie. production) and safety.

3. *Clear procedures and training should be provided for operators covering emergency situations.*

The Channel Tunnel accident report identified the following areas where staff training and procedures were inadequate for dealing with emergency situations :

- a structured emergency management training program should be implemented for all staff (#17).
- members of staff who are likely to observe fires or smoke should be given direct lines of communication with the control centre (#19).
- training should include familiarisation with breathing apparatus kits for all train crews (#22).
- operators should not be faced with an unmanageable increase in workload during an emergency. Alarm management systems should be used (#30).
- review control centre procedures to ensure that they are 'user friendly'. Allocate sufficient qualified personnel to complete their required tasks (#34).
- provide additional staffing to cope with abnormal / emergency situations (#36).

The Southall accident report also recommended that driver training should include operating in abnormal conditions (#4).

4. *An effective and simple near miss reporting system should be provided for front line operators.*

The Southall accident report made the following recommendations :

- drivers should be encouraged to report all actual or suspected faults through a formal incident / fault recording system (#6).
- fault reporting procedures should be made as simple and convenient as practically possible (#17).

5. *Manage operator daily and weekly workload in the light of current knowledge about human behaviour.*

The Southall accident report made the following recommendations :

- review driver's daily and weekly working hours in the light of current research into human behaviour (#9).
- regularly monitor the workload of all maintenance staff (#25).

6. *All safety equipment should be clearly designated and properly maintained.*

The Southall accident report made the following recommendations :

- all safety equipment should be clearly designated as to whether it is vital for the continued running of the train (#12).
- effort should be put into ensuring that safety related equipment does not fail in service through an appropriate system of replacement and maintenance (#31).

7. *Maintenance procedures should require an investigation of the historic failure record of components.*

The Southall accident report made the following recommendations :

- databases should ensure that faults are logged with a history of defects available to management and maintenance staff (#22).
- maintenance procedures should require checking the history of reported defects including repeat faults and ensuring that appropriate action is taken (#29).

8. *Paper based procedures must not become divorced from reality.*

This recommendation was made in the Southall accident report (#69).

9. *Over- optimising infrastructure can reduce safety levels.*

Press reports following some of these accidents have suggested that some of the efforts to improve operational efficiency may have contributed to unforeseen increases in risk levels on the railways. Areas of particular concern were :

- using the same rail lines for high speed passenger and heavy freight operations increases the risks of train collisions and the risk of damaging rails as freight trains are heavier and cause greater stress on the rails.
- running high speed and low speed trains on the same lines, especially where crossovers occur increases the risks of collisions.
- removed multiple lines causes greater congestion on the remaining lines.

6.5 Hazard Management.

These learning points have been obtained from an analysis of press reports following the accidents and include :

1. *External events can cause accidents.*

External events are difficult to manage because they are outside the immediate control of the operating company. Arson is suspected as the cause of the Channel Tunnel fire. The fire safety systems were sophisticated for detecting fires inside the tunnel and dealing with their consequences but they appear to have been deficient at preventing fires from being carried into the tunnel. The Selby rail crash was caused by a road vehicle accident. The railway companies had no direct influence over the design and operation of the adjacent motorway.

2. *Accidents can be caused maliciously.*

There are reports that the Channel Tunnel fire may have been started deliberately by disgruntled employees. Safety systems need to be robust against accidental and deliberate actions.

3. *Accidents can be caused by unforeseen interactions.*

The Ladbroke Grove collision was caused by a SPAD involving signal 109. It appears that the driver's view of the signal was obstructed for a number of reasons, including the presence of a recently constructed gantry to house equipment for the new Heathrow Express rail link. The designers of the new link and / or the organisation responsible for the signaling must have failed to detect this interaction or must have judged that the new gantry did not obscure the driver's vision.

4. *The consequences of accidents are often exaggerated by unforeseen interactions.*

The consequences of the Ladbroke Grove accident were exaggerated by the intense fire which followed the collision. Both trains contained fuel sources. A number of plausible ignition sources were also identified for the fire, including the overhead electric gantry,   The interaction of the gantry and the fuel tanks therefore had the potential for increasing the consequences of the accident.

5. *Uncontrollable and extremely unlikely combinations of events can occur.*

It is widely considered that the combination of events leading to the Selby train crash could reasonably be considered to be extremely unlikely and that the events were outside the control of the rail companies.

6. *Situations where simple human errors can lead to major accidents are very dangerous.*

SPADs have caused a number of the rail accidents that have been considered in this paper (Watford South, Southall and Ladbroke Grove). A simple (albeit unlikely) human error has therefore contributed significantly to these major disasters. The basis of safety against these accidents is therefore very dependent on avoidance of human error. Technological back-up systems do exist (eg. ATP) but are relatively expensive. Difficult decisions therefore have to be made about installing these protection systems.

6.6 Emergency Response & Management.

These learning points have been obtained from a combination of published accident reports from the Channel Tunnel and Southall accidents and an analysis of press reports following the Kaprun fire and include :

1. *Portable fire fighting equipment should be provided in areas where a fire risk exists.*

It has been reported that the Kaprun trains and tunnel were not equipped with any fire extinguishers. People inside the trains therefore had no means of extinguishing fires and preventing fire escalation. This suggests that the operating company considered that there was no risk of fire inside the tunnel despite the risk of arson, the combustible nature of the materials transported in the trains and the potential for mechanical friction.

2. *Staff must be given clear procedures and training explaining how to behave in emergency situations.*

It has been reported that the Kaprun tunnel doors were opened during the initial stages of the fire, causing the tunnel to act as a chimney, massively increasing the consequences of the fire. The correct course of action for dealing with a fire in the tunnel should have been incorporated into the tunnel operating procedures and all operators should have known how to deal with this type of incident.

The Channel Tunnel accident report recommended (#5) that procedures for radio use should be improved to avoid system and controller overload by improving radio discipline, making greater use of standard messages and using emergency call buttons.

3. *Emergency procedures should deal realistically with common mode failures.*

The Channel Tunnel accident report recommended (#11) that emergency procedures should address issues such as power loss, loss of communications and loss of firewater supply. If the procedures do not cater for such events, they could well be ineffective in an emergency situation.

4. *Ensure that there are clear procedures for alerting the emergency services in the event of an accident.*

The Channel Tunnel accident report recommended (#15) that this should be improved to ensure that the appropriate emergency services are alerted in a manner that avoids unnecessary delays when dealing with an incident which could escalate.

5. *Routes for evacuation should try to avoid distressing scenes.*

The Southall accident report recommended (#88) that this should be considered where practicable to avoid additional stress to evacuees and the emergency services.

6. *Ensure that practical evacuation routes exist in case accidents happen.*

The Southall accident report recommended (#44) that this should be incorporated in the design of railway vehicles to facilitate evacuation in an accident situation. Particular attention should be paid to egress routes, lighting and communication channels. These facilities were clearly inadequate in the Kaprun fire as the carriage doors were locked and the trains fitted very tightly inside the tunnels with no room for movement between the trains and the tunnel walls.

7. *Ensure that access is available for the emergency services to areas where accidents could occur.*

It was very difficult for the rescue teams to enter the Kaprun tunnel because the only access was via a long steep railway bridge. Helicopter access close to the tunnels was also impossible due to the surrounding terrain. This delayed the rescue teams. The problem would have been revealed if regular emergency drills had been carried out for the tunnel system.

7. CONCLUSIONS.

This paper has shown how useful information about avoiding, controlling and minimising the impacts of major accidents in one industry can be obtained by reviewing published accident reports from other industries. Specific examples of learning points have been produced, but these examples are not intended to be an exhaustive list.

Although the most efficient databank for learning from accidents will normally come from within the industry itself, companies may find it useful to review the reports of accidents in other industries to supplement their knowledge.

Table 1 summarises the areas where learning points have been identified in this paper.

8. REFERENCES.

(COMAH, 1999) 'The Control Of Major Accident Hazards Regulations', 1999.

(DETR, 1997) 'Inquiry into the fire on heavy goods vehicle shuttle 7539 on 18 November 1996', UK Department of the Environment, Transport and the Regions, published on internet http:///www.railways.detr.gov.uk/ctsa/18nov96/ctsa.htm, 29 July 1997.

(HSC, 2000) 'The Southall rail accident inquiry report', UK Health and Safety Commission, 2000. ISBN 0 7176 1757 2.

(HSE, 1998) 'Report into the railway accident at Watford South Junction on 8 August 1996', UK Health and Safety Executive, published on internet , http:///www.hse.gov.uk/railway/watford.htm, 21 May 1998.

(HSE, 2000) 'The train collision at Ladbroke Grove, 5 October 1999', UK Health and Safety Executive, 2000. ISBN 0 7176 1918 4.

(HSE, 2001a) 'Train derailment at Hatfield, 17 October 2000. Second HSE interim report', UK   Health   and   Safety   Executive,   published   on   internet   , http:///www.hse.gov.uk/railway/hatfield/interim2.htm, 23 January 2001.

(HSE, 2001b) 'Train collision at Great Heck near Selby, 28 February 2001. HSE interim report',   UK   Health   and   Safety   Executive,   published   on   internet   , http:///www.hse.gov.uk/railway/selby/interim.htm, 6 March 2001.

(Sunday Times, 2000) The Sunday Times, 12 November 2000.

(Yorkshire Post, 2001) The Yorkshire Post, 1 March 2001.

Table 1 : Summary Of Areas Where Learning Points Have Been Identified.

Structural & Operational Aspects	Safety Management Systems	Design Aspects
1. Industry fragmentation	1. Ambiguity in standards	1. Fire alarm system logic
2. Definition of responsibilities	2. Workforce involvement	2. Common mode failures
3. Redundancies and skills shortages	3. Learning from accidents	3. Unusual causes of fire
4. Management of contractors	4. Response to identified problems	4. Use of novel technology
5. Monitoring performance	5. Delays in accident investigations	5. Effectiveness of safety systems
Operational Aspects	**Hazard Management**	**Emergency Response And Management**
1. Conflicting information in procedures	1. External events	1. Provision of fire fighting equipment
2. Human errors	2. Malicious damage	2. Staff training for emergencies
3. Training for emergencies	3. Unforeseen interactions causing accidents	3. Emergency procedures and common mode failures
4. Need for near miss / fault reporting systems	4. Unforeseen interactions exacerbating accidents	4. Procedures for alerting the emergency services
5. Monitoring workload	5. Criticality of human errors	5. Practicality of evacuation routes
6. Designation of safety critical equipment		6. Access for emergency services
7. Maintenance procedures		
8. Realism of paper based procedures		
9. Production .v. safety conflicts		

PROMOTING PROCESS SAFETY IN THE FINNISH PROCESS INDUSTRY

A-M. Heikkilä
VTT Automation, Risk Management, P.O. Box 1306, FIN-33101 Tampere, Finland

A research programme to promote process safety is being prepared in Finland. The goal is to improve process safety by combining the expertise and resources of major companies, authorities and research institutes. One concern is with small and medium-sized enterprises. The aim is to reduce the number of accidents, and the losses caused by them, and to improve the working environment in the process industry. The programme will also generate material suitable for training employees. For the programme, a survey looking into the safety-related needs within the process industry was carried out. During the winter of 1998/99, 52 representatives from the process industry, various authorities and research institutes were interviewed. The identified needs dealt with, for instance, knowledge management, human and organisational performance, safety in process plant design and construction, and ensuring safety in multi-company sites and production networks. The results and conclusions of the survey are presented in this paper.

Keywords: safety-related needs, risk management, survey results, research programme

INTRODUCTION

In global markets the process industry needs to be efficient, flexible and reliable. Market shares and the prices of raw materials, as well as products, vary a lot in time, which means continuing changes in the process industry. To follow up the markets and to stay profitable, companies need to develop their operations and find new products and processes for the future. This means, for instance, outsourcing the operations that are out of the companies' areas of expertise, extending the utilisation of expert-nets, and increasing the use of new technologies, e.g. information technology. All of this also affects the operations of the company and its safety.

The Finnish process industry is quite heterogeneous in the sense of safety management. Some companies have done safety work for a long time while others are just starting to realise its importance. But the best Finnish companies are still behind the best ones in Europe when comparing the accident frequencies and the numbers of the lost working days. Some of the differences can be explained by the different ways used to collect the statistics, but it can not be the only reason. The situation demands closer co-operation between companies, researchers and authorities, and this was the goal of the work presented in this paper.

THE STRUCTURE OF THE SURVEY

In order to improve process safety in the Finnish process industry, the safety-related needs and problems first needed to be surveyed and analysed[1]. During the winter of 1998/99, VTT Automation interviewed 52 representatives from the process industry, various authorities and research institutes. The selected companies covered a broad section of the process industry and related services including, for instance, the chemical industry, the pulp and paper industry, the metal industry, the food industry, and also automation, and machinery and maintenance services. The interviews were mainly completed in groups, while some were done by interviewing one person at a time. The groups contained professionals from the areas of safety, production, maintenance, design, research, etc. In this way, the interview also promoted discussion within the company. The interviewees were asked about their company's goals and their identified needs, especially with regards to the following questions:

- How do you manage risks?
- Which risk management tools do you use?
- How does risk management affect your decision-making?
- How do you manage technical and organisational changes?
- How do you manage knowledge?
- How do you manage risks in multi-company sites and in production networks?
- How do you manage safety responsibilities in your production environment?
- What challenges do you see in the future with regard to process safety?
- Is safety a critical asset in the competition for market shares?

Based on the results of the interviews a workshop was held in October 1999. During the workshop, the 74 participants were divided into six groups, where they further discussed those problems and targets for development identified from the survey. These discussions formed the basis for the project ideas that were prepared in four groups during the spring of 2000[2]. The project ideas were presented in another workshop held in September 2000.

ANALYSES OF THE INTERVIEWS

The safety-related research and development needs in the Finnish process industry were determined on the basis of the interviews. Figure 1 outlines the demands created by the changes in the production environment and the continuous technical development. Similar demands were noted by several companies, and by the authorities. Solutions are most effectively found by combining the expertise and resources of major companies, authorities and research institutes in joint projects.

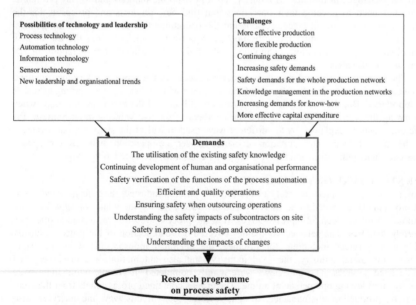

Figure 1. The safety-related research and development needs in Finnish process industry.

For some companies, safety is mentioned as a critical asset in the competition of market shares. Accidents or unsafe products are not good publicity in global markets. On the other hand, customers won't pay more for safety, which is perceived as a natural qualification of a product. But safety is also an economically critical asset. Accidents and breakdowns cause production breaks or may even shut down the factory. Also, the rebuilding of the good company image and new customer relations takes time and money.

SAFETY-RELATED NEEDS IN THE FINNISH PROCESS INDUSTRY

Analysis of the interviews revealed that most of the uncertainty and the identified needs fall into six groups (Figure 2). It was also noticed that some companies are much further advanced with regard to their perception of safety, and thus, the identified needs deal with every level from basic safety analysis to high-performance safety systems.

Figure 2. The grouping of the safety-related needs in the Finnish process industry.

KNOWLEDGE MANAGEMENT

There is lot of safety-related information available both within, and from outside the companies. The information contains, for instance, detailed knowledge about process solutions, chemical properties and malfunctions. The main problem concerns the efficient utilisation of that knowledge. It was generally felt that safety information is hard to find, but in reality people don't even know that the information exists and so they don't ask for it.

Inside companies, information about malfunctions, near-misses and even accidents almost certainly exists. Safety reports and the results of safety analyses also contain important data. But the problem is how to ensure the information flow between, for instance, shifts. Methods for collecting and arranging the information, in an easy to use form, are needed and better documentation procedures and guidance for the utilisation of the data would be good starting points.

Learning from errors is an effective way to promote safety. Databanks on accidents and other hazardous situations, for example, already exist[3,4,5,6]. Valuable safety-related information may also be found in the inspection reports made by authorities, e.g. according to the Seveso II Directive[7], and auditing reports made inside the company or by an outsider. But the utilisation of the data and the follow-up of the suggested actions require specific company procedures.

Communication problems and misunderstandings can lead to hazardous situations arising within companies. Terminological differences especially, for example, arise between employees and management, between shifts, and between process workers and safety professionals. A common routine for handling safety issues could even improve the communication within a company and therefore promote safety.

At the moment, many companies have similar systems in place for safety, environmental and quality management. This not only means extra work, but also increases the chance for misunderstandings. A way to combine safety, environmental and quality evaluations may prove to be beneficial. One solution might be the integration of these management systems – perhaps even also including economical aspects in the same system.

HUMAN AND ORGANISATIONAL PERFORMANCE

Human and organisational performance is an important part of many companies' policies, and safety management is needed on an everyday basis. A procedure for handling safety issues should exist within the steering committee and weekly meetings, and guidelines for these routines are required.

Safety targets should be determined together with the employees as part of safety management, and the evaluation and the follow-up of the results needs to be improved. While already quite good, positive evaluation methods are especially being sought, and the evaluation of any actions made to promote safety also still needs to be further developed. Currently, also the terminology used in the existing evaluation methods is not familiar to all the employees.

Many companies lack the means to ensure that the safety rules and instructions are obeyed. The employees often have their old ways of doing things, and these habits are not always the safest, but changing those old routines may be difficult. Obeying rules means that one understands their meaning, and it has been observed that an obvious risk to one's own life or health will encourage the obeying of rules – nobody would light a cigarette in a solvent store, but sawdust fires often start from burning cigarettes. It is also a matter of communication between the management and the employees. A positive attitude towards safety and safer routines is needed at all levels in the organisation. As a result of these needs, a project to model the safety performance in the companies – in order to find the most suitable practices for the Finnish process industry – has been started.

One concern is in the small and medium-sized enterprises, which often lack the knowledge, resources and money to create their own safety culture. Tools for them have been developed, such as the PK-RH Toolkit[8], but the implementation, acceptance, education in, and use of those tools requires time. Several SMEs may even be able to use, for example, a collective safety manager as a consultant. If so, more suitable tools for that collective safety manager need to be developed.

SAFETY IMPACTS OF AUTOMATION

In the production process, automation is used for both operational and safety purposes. Some experts in the process industry, however, have concerns about the reliability of automation systems during abnormal conditions. One reason might be that the structure of the automation systems is not familiar to those working at that production level. On the other hand, process automation has distanced the operators from the process itself, and so the operators do not necessarily recognise serious malfunctions in time or they do not know the correct actions to take when something goes wrong.

The reliability of automation systems in all situations demands good co-operation between the process and automation designers. Correct and detailed definitions are the basis of a reliable automation system, and the client is required to demonstrate an understanding of the process itself. The operators also need to understand how both the process and the automation systems function, and this creates even more demands on the system designers.

The safety and reliability of automation systems also depend on the components and the equipment used. For so-called economical reasons, the automation projects are often divided into smaller units which are then delivered by several different suppliers. This creates barriers between different system units which, without the proper supervision, can then also cause safety problems. For short-term economic reasons the system components are often bought where they are cheapest without guaranteeing that they work together as expected. This increases the uncertainty of the automation systems.

Projects dealing with, for example, too many alarms at the same time, more informative and functional screens for operators, and methods to evaluate the reliability and safety effects of automation systems are under preparation.

SAFETY IN PROCESS PLANT DESIGN AND CONSTRUCTION

The basis of process safety is created in the process development and design stages. Mistakes and safety defaults carried over from the process development and design often show up as problems in the production. To identify the risks in advance, safety evaluation methods such as reaction and compatibility matrices[9], the Dow Index[10], and Hazop studies[11] are used. Methods that show the client that the safety aspects have been integrated into the design could also be useful.

Safety aspects should be considered as early in the design process as possible. Modifications made in the early stages of process design are more effective and less costly than those required later in the process design, or even during construction or operation. The development of inherently safer processes and their evaluation methods were also considered to be important, and the process industry is especially interested in inherently safer process solutions for today's processes.

The current research and development needs in the process industry often concern batch processes and their safety issues. More details of fire and explosion risks are also needed, and some companies are especially interested in ensuring safety on pilot plants.

Experience is very important when designing and building process plants. Unfortunately, in many cases the desired information is not available during the design phase of the project. Systematic methods to collect and find the information needed in the different stages of process development and design projects, and recording the information in databases might be the solution, and some databases and methods are already under development.

MANAGEMENT OF CHANGES

Both technical and organisational changes occur rapidly in today's process industry. The changes put pressure on the safety management, and guidelines to manage those changes are needed.

Technical changes are mostly done on operating plants, and as minor changes are not always documented, dangerous situations may arise later during operation and maintenance. Systematic documentation practises could help prevent these types of incidents. Major technical changes need proper planning and safety considerations in advance. The need for technical changes obviously increases in ageing plants, and therefore it is especially important to recognise the critical pieces of equipment. Simple evaluation methods need to be developed.

Organisational changes need to be managed well in order to ensure that employees can adjust themselves to the new situation. Uncertainty amongst the employees may result in a hazardous situation arising due to a lapse in concentration. Especially the ways to implement these changes, however, need development. A step-by-step plan on how to carry out the changes, and document and inform about them, is needed. A lack of knowledge only causes uncertainty and rumours among the employees. Also, too often, there is no follow-up of changes and their results.

Changes often occur rather fast in the process industry and this creates demands on the education of the personnel. Many new technical issues need to be included in the training programmes at all levels and, unfortunately, this often means that fewer hours remain for safety, health and environmental issues. The lack of safety education also decreases the level of process safety in the industry. One goal of the forthcoming research programme, therefore, will be to affect the training programmes and to generate material suitable for the training of employees and graduates.

SAFETY IN MULTI-COMPANY SITES AND IN PRODUCTION NETWORKS
In the light of international competition, the process industry is concentrating on its main expertise areas. Many companies are now outsourcing, for example, the maintenance and the production of oxygen, steam and other goods. The workers coming from outside the factory, however, do not necessarily know the process at hand, and thus do not know the associated risks and how to behave in potentially dangerous situations. Also, several subcontractors with different safety protocols may be working on the site at the same time, making it an even more demanding task to manage safety.

In the process industry, it has become a recent trend to merge companies or sell parts of them. As a result there are often several independent units working on the same site. The workers from different companies may even use the same equipment, while the units themselves may have different ways to handle, for instance, the associated safety issues. It may even be that safety managers are not even located on the site. This raises questions about who is responsible and in charge of the safety issues. Several projects dealing with safety issues in production networks have been ongoing in Finland. While bigger companies have their own ways to ensure safety when using subcontractors, both the process industry and contractors would appreciate a uniform way of handling safety issues. There have even been discussions about safety passes or such an equivalent, while national tests for graduates of all educational levels have also been mentioned.

RESEARCH PROGRAMME ON PROCESS SAFETY
The results of the survey[1] during the winter of 1998/99, and the project planning[2] in the spring of 2000, clearly showed that a national research programme on process safety could be beneficial for all parties involved. This will be the first in-depth research programme covering the entire field of process safety. By combining the expertise and resources of the process industry, authorities and research institutes, the goal of the research programme will be effectively achieved. Small and medium-sized enterprises, which do not have sufficient knowledge and resources to manage safety issues by themselves, will also benefit.

The goal of the 3-year research programme is to reduce the number of accidents, and the losses caused by them, and to improve the working environment in the process industry. The concrete aims of the programme are to:

- achieve zero fatalities,
- halve the number of accidents,
- halve the number of accidental releases to the environment, and
- eliminate the added expenses due to accidents,

in the Finnish process industry.

The aims are meant to be achieved both in the individual companies participating in the programme, and in the process industry as a whole. The research programme also ensures that safety information and new inventions will reach the entire process industry.

At this point the safety-related needs have been surveyed from the process industry's point of view. To achieve the goal of this research programme the entire process safety field must be covered, and therefore the research field needs to be examined more scientifically. New themes in the programme could be, for instance, the bench-marking of Finnish companies, the management of acute environmental risks in the process industry, the risk evaluation of bio- and gene technology, and the wider use of information technology for ensuring safety.

CONCLUSIONS

During this work it was observed that the safety-related problems in many different fields of the process industry are quite the same, but the level of safety management differs between individual companies. Some have done safety work for decades while others are just beginning to realise the importance of safety management. At the same time, the safety-related problems are from the whole range of process safety – from human behaviour to technical solutions – and the solutions come from different fields of science.

To improve process safety in the Finnish process industry, the best way is to combine the expertise of the companies, researchers and authorities, like in a research programme. The best solutions can be found and tested for use in the entire process industry, and in the other fields of industry too. When problems are solved together all parties make savings with regards to the resources – and especially financially. To avoid repeating work, existing safety research must be investigated. For many of the safety issues that arose in this survey, solutions may also be found from outside Finland, but most of those would then probably need to be modified for the Finnish working environment. In any case, the main target is to improve process safety at all levels of the Finnish process industry.

ACKNOWLEDGEMENTS
The funding was provided by the Safety Technology Authority (TUKES), the National Technology Agency, the Ministry of Social Affairs and Health, the Work Environment Fund, and VTT Automation.

REFERENCES
1. Heikkilä, A-M., 1999, *The safety-related needs within the Finnish process industry* (in Finnish), VTT Automation, Tampere, 46p.
2. Heikkilä, A-M., 2000, *The safety-related needs within the Finnish process industry – the project preparation in workshops* (in Finnish), VTT Automation, Tampere, 38p.
3. Institution of Chemical Engineers, *The Accident Database*, http://www.icheme.org/shop/ (April 3, 2001).
4. American Institute of Chemical Engineers, *The CCPS Process Safety Incident Database*, http://www.aiche.org/ccps/lldb.htm (April 3, 2001).
5. Safety Technology Authority, *The VARO accident database* (in Finnish), http://www.tukes.fi/ (April 3, 2001).

6. Major Accident Hazards Bureau, *Major Accident Reporting System (MARS)*, http://mahbsrv.jrc.it/mars/ (April 3, 2001).
7. *Seveso II Directive*, 96/082/EEC.
8. *Risk Management for SME*, http://www.vtt.fi/rm/projects/pk-rh/eng/ (April 3, 2001).
9. Lees, F.P., 1996, *Loss Prevention in the Process Industries*, 2nd Ed., Butterworth-Heinemann, Oxford.
10. Dow Chemical Company, 1994, *DOW's Fire & Explosion Index Hazard Classification Guide*, 7th Ed., American Institute of Chemical Engineers, New York.
11. Kletz, T.A., 1999, *HAZOP and HAZAN - Identifying and Assessing Process Industry Hazards*, 4th Ed., IChemE, Rugby.

PROMOTING BEST PRACTICE IN BEHAVIOUR-BASED SAFETY

Dr. Mark Fleming: Assistant Professor, Saint Mary's University, Halifax, Nova Scotia, Canada.
and
Mr. Ronny Lardner, Director, Chartered Occupational Psychologist, The Keil Centre, Edinburgh

ABSTRACT

Promoting safe behaviour at work is a critical part of the management of health and safety, because behaviour turns systems and procedures into reality. Good systems on their own, do not ensure successful health and safety management, the level of success is determined by how organisations 'live' their systems. Behaviour based safety programmes aim to improve safety by promoting critical health and safety behaviours. There is evidence that these programmes are effective in improving safety, but only when they are implemented effectively. Four offshore case studies are presented to highlight how behaviour safety programmes can be implemented effectively. To date behaviour-based safety programmes focus on the behaviour of frontline employees and behaviours that prevent individual accidents as opposed to major hazards. A behavioural safety intervention strategy to promote any critical risk control behaviour including management behaviour is described.

INTRODUCTION

Over the past few years, there has been a dramatic increase in the use of behavioural safety programmes in the UK. They are now routinely used in a wide range of industry sectors, from construction to food processing. Behavioural safety techniques are based on a large body of psychological research into the factors that influence behaviour. This research has led to the development of a range of techniques to influence behaviour. Behaviour modification is the psychological term for these techniques. Within a health and safety context, behaviour modification techniques are used to increase the frequency of behaviours that enhance safety and decrease the frequency of unsafe behaviours.

The majority of behavioural safety programs concentrate on front-line employee behaviour, and do not take into account the behaviour of managers. Given the known impact of visible management behaviours on safety, it is important to investigate how behavioural safety techniques can be used to increase the frequency of safety critical management behaviours. .

This paper presents the results of two research projects supported by the Health and Safety Executive:-

1) a joint industry / HSE project[1], part of the UK offshore oil and gas industry's Step-Change in Safety Initiative, which (a) examined best practice in behaviour-based safety, including barriers and enablers to effective implementation and (b) documented four different types of offshore behaviour-based safety initiatives, each appropriate for different circumstances

2) an ongoing HSE-funded project which builds upon the first project, to describe strategies to promote critical behaviours that support health and safety management.

WHAT IS BEHAVIOURAL SAFETY?

Behavioural safety techniques improve safety by identifying and promoting critical safety behaviours.   Critical safety behaviours are promoted by altering the consequences of these behaviours to reduce or eliminate unsafe behaviours and to increase the frequency of safe behaviours.   Safety and risk control improves as the frequency of "at-risk" behaviour decreases and the frequency of safe behaviours increase.

Behavioural safety is also known by other terms, including

- behaviourally-based safety
- behaviour modification
- behavioural safety management systems
- safety observation systems.

HOW TO PROMOTE CRITICAL HEALTH AND SAFETY BEHAVIOURS

Behavioural modification is based on an ABC model of behaviour[2]. This model states that behaviour is triggered by a set of antecedents and the likelihood that a behaviour is repeated is dependant on the consequences following the behaviour. By examining any behaviour, it is possible to identify the antecedents and the consequences. For example, the behaviour of 'lifting receiver on a telephone when it rings' would reveal that sound of the telephone ringing is the antecedent and speaking to another person on the other end is a consequence. This ABC model of behaviour can be used to understand why people behave in a specific way and how to influence their behaviour.

Behavioural safety programmes typically seek to arrange antecedents (A) and consequences (C) around the behaviour to be changed (B) in such a way as to maximise the reduction of at–risk behaviour, and increase safe behaviour. By using this ABC model of behaviour change, at-risk behaviour is reduced or eliminated, accident rates drop and safety improves. For example, ABC analysis could be conducted to investigate why workers do not wear their ear defenders in noisy environments (see table 1).

Table 1 Example of an ABC analysis

Antecedents	Behaviour	Consequences
Ear defenders supplied by company	Wearing ear defenders in noisy environments	Reduces the likelihood of hearing loss in the future
Required by company to wear ear defenders in specific areas		Less likely to get into trouble with management for not wearing ear defenders
Knowledge of potential damage to hearing if ear defenders are not worn		Difficulty hearing their radio
Signs highlight areas where defenders are needed		Discomfort of wearing ear defenders
Noisy environment		
Peers do not wear ear defenders	Not wearing ear defenders in noisy environments	Impaired hearing in the future
		Avoid discomfort of wearing defenders
Knowledge that rules on wearing ear defenders are not enforced		Able to hear better in the noisy environment

Before the above analysis can be used to identify interventions to increase the use of ear defenders, it is necessary to understand that consequences can either increase or decrease the likelihood of behaviour being repeated and that some consequences have a greater impact on behaviour than others.

CHANGING BEHAVIOUR

The likelihood that a behaviour will be repeated is dependant on the consequences. If the consequences are reinforcing for the *individual* then they will repeat the behaviour. If they do not find the consequences reinforcing then they will not repeat the behaviour. Therefore, it is possible to change behaviour by altering the consequences. The frequency of a desired behaviour can be increased by providing consequences after the behaviour that an individual finds reinforcing. It is important to note that, it is what the individual finds reinforcing that drives their behaviour and that what people find reinforcing can sometimes seem counter intuitive. For example, sometimes disciplining children can reinforce the undesired behaviour, as the discipline is the only attention that they receive.

There are three main types of consequences that influence behaviour. These are positive reinforcement, negative reinforcement and punishment. Positive and negative reinforcement, increase the likelihood that a behaviour will be repeated, while punishment reduces the likelihood.

Table 2 Types of consequences*

Consequences that increase behaviour

Positive reinforcement	Negative reinforcement
Receive something that you want	Avoid something you do not want

Consequences that decrease behaviour

Punishment	Punishment
Receive something you do not want	Loose something you have or want

*Adapted from Daniels[3]

The above consequences can be used to separately or together to change behaviour. For example, the frequency of managers conducting site tours could be increased by:

Positive reinforcement: superiors praising manager after they conduct tours
Negative reinforcement: peers remove disapproval for not conducting tours
Punishment: managers' bonus is reduced if tours are not conducted.

There are three major factors that influence the impact that consequences have on behaviour change and these are described in the table 3 below.

Table 3: Factors influencing impact of consequences on behaviour

	Timeframe	Predictability	Significance
Large impact on behaviour	Soon	Certain	Important to individual
Limited impact on behaviour	Distant	Uncertain	Unimportant to individual

Consequences that have the greatest impact in determining an individual's behaviour occur soon after the behaviour, the individual is certain that they will occur and the consequences are important to the individual. Consequences that delayed or distant, that the individual is uncertain whether or not they will occur and are unimportant will have limited impact.

EFFECTIVENESS OF BEHAVIOURAL SAFETY PROGRAMMES

A large number of studies have been conducted to evaluate the effectiveness of behavioural modification programmes in improving workplace safety. These studies have focused on establishing (a) their ability to decrease accidents / injuries, (b) their ability to increase safe behaviour and (c) which components in a behavioural safety programme are most important in changing unsafe behaviour and reducing accidents and injuries.

A literature review[4] investigating the effectiveness of behaviour based safety programmes in reducing accident rates identified 33 published studies that reported accident data. Of these studies, 32 reported a reduction in injuries, although the reporting format varied. The level of improvement varied widely with one study reporting a 2% improvement with another reporting an 85% improvement. In addition, very few of the studies conducted statistical analysis to establish the significance of the change in accident rates. In spite of the limitations of these data presented in published studies, this review concluded that there was sufficient evidence to demonstrate that behavioural safety programmes improve safety when implemented effectively.

Strong research evidence exists from a range of industries on three continents that behaviour modification techniques can lead to safer behaviour[5]. A recent literature review[6] compiled for the UK HSE concluded that behavioural safety programmes are effective in altering employee behaviour. The review identified twelve methodologically sound research studies, which investigated the effectiveness of behavioural safety programmes in changing behaviour. All twelve studies demonstrated that behavioural safety programmes are effective at changing employee behaviour.

A number of research studies have been conducted to investigate the relative importance of the component parts (see Figure 1) of a behavioural safety programme, in order to establish how they can be optimally combined[6]. Use of a training-only component achieved mixed results, and where successful only modest improvements. The addition of graphical feedback, goal-setting and support from management and peers produced significant additional gains. Although theoretically and intuitively important, the added impact of immediate face-to-face feedback has not been systematically demonstrated. Management's commitment to supporting programme implementation was also identified as a critical success factor.

Figure 1: Behaviour based safety programme

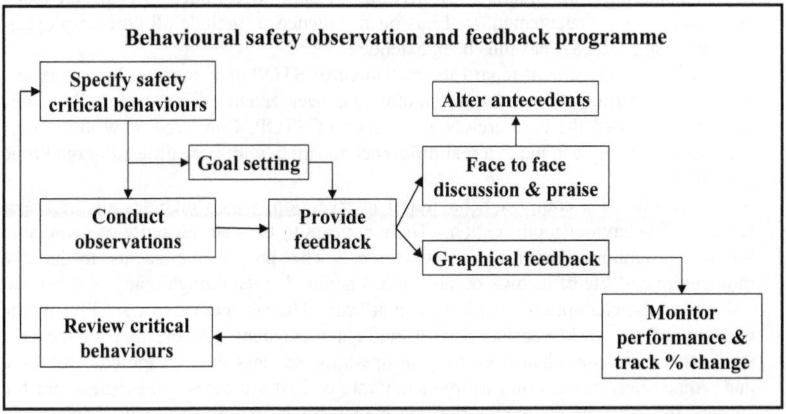

Behavioural safety observation and feedback programme

Since 1978, a large number of studies have been conducted to evaluate the effectiveness of behavioural modification programmes in improving workplace safety. The majority of these studies have concluded that behavioural safety interventions are effective.

OFFSHORE CASE STUDIES

Recently a joint oil industry and HSE funded study[1] was conducted to identify best practice in implementing behaviour modification programmes. Four case studies were carried out to provide information about the range of programmes currently being used in the UK Offshore Oil and Gas Industry. The project aimed to identify barriers and enablers associated with these behaviour modification programmes. The four programmes included: Time Out For Safety (TOFS), Advanced Safety Auditing (ASA), STOP and Care Plus.

Each case study involved interviewing both onshore and offshore managers and installation employees. The interview schedule was structured around the principle features of behaviour modification programmes identified by a literature review, to ensure that all the important features were discussed and the results could be placed in the context of a theoretical framework. The results of the interviews were analysed to produce an overall picture of the elements and features of effective behaviour modification programmes and the organisational requirements to increase the likelihood of success. Accident statistics were reviewed to assess the impact of these programmes on safety.

TOFS was developed by the drilling crew on the bp's Andrew platform, in response to some of the challenges they were facing. Over time, it has been adopted by the entire platform and more recently by other installations. TOFS is effective because it is designed to modify an important behaviour of frontline employees, namely stopping the job if they have any concerns. It is simple, as it does not require employees to complete forms, which also reduces anxiety about colleagues being reprimanded for their actions. The successful introduction of TOFS on the Andrew was partially due to the installation's high level of safety cultural maturity.

ASA has provided an additional means for management on bp's Miller platform to make a visible, tangible commitment to safety. They do this by conducting ASA's themselves, providing ASA training for most of their workforce, and opening up their own managerial work practices by inviting all staff to conduct an ASA on them. What began as a management tool has been widened to include all core employees, and ownership of ASA has thus been extended.

Conoco management regard the re-launch of STOP as a success. Managers and supervisors' participation in the programme has been enhanced, and they believe they have now enlisted the core crew's acceptance of STOP. Core crew now understand that via STOP they can make a real difference to safety with very little additional time and effort.

Care Plus is a complex behavioural intervention, which includes all the major features of behaviour modification. There appears to be a strong sense of ownership for the programme among the workforce. The programme seems to have a momentum and life of its own because it has endured, even though many of the initial volunteers and champions have left the platform. The acceptance of Care Plus by the majority of the workforce has been a major achievement. At the time of the case study, the programme had been fully in operation for less than 12 months, yet there had already been a reduction in frequency rate of first aid cases. The criteria for the success for this type of intervention are management commitment, trust between all staff and employees who are interested in safety and willing to take ownership of their own safety behaviour.

The four case studies included very different types of behaviour modification programmes. The case studies are representative of the type of programmes currently being used in the offshore oil industry. General conclusions that can be drawn from the four case studies are outlined below.

- All the interviewees were convinced that the behavioural intervention they were using was having a significant positive impact on safety.
- Only one of the four case studies could demonstrate a significant reduction in accident rates following the introduction of the programme.
- The success of all four programmes was dependent upon management support and commitment.
- Employee involvement in the process from the beginning increases the likelihood of success.
- Setting quotas for the number of observation cards to be submitted is likely to be counter productive and may lead to fictions cards being submitted.
- The success of programmes aimed at frontline employees requires a pre-existing level of trust between management and workers.
- It is important to control people's expectations for early reductions in accident statistics.
- The interpersonal skills (e.g. non-threatening questioning) of installation staff need to be developed in order for the behaviour modification programme to be effective. It is important to note that although some proprietary programmes do not include interpersonal skills training, employees still requires these skills to ensure programme effectiveness.

PROMOTING CRITICAL HEALTH AND SAFETY BEHAVIOURS THAT SUPPORT THE SMS

Current behavioural safety observation and feedback programmes only target a limited proportion (approximately 25%) of critical health and safety behaviours[7]. Health and safety can be dramatically improved, if behaviour modification is used to promote even a proportion of the remaining 75% of critical behaviours.

Figure 2 Health and safety behaviours categories

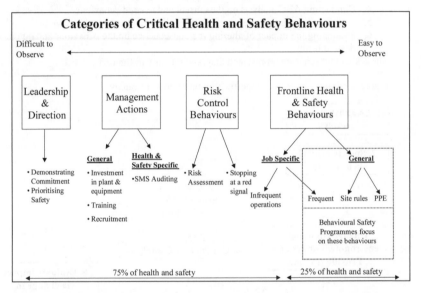

Figure 2 describes four main categories of critical health and safety behaviours, including: frontline health and safety behaviour, risk control behaviour, management actions and leadership and direction. The majority of behavioural safety programmes currently in use within the UK focus on general safety behaviours of frontline personnel including compliance with site rules and procedures (wearing light eye protection, adhering to speed limit) or frequent job specific activities such as correct manual handling behaviours.

Since there are no published examples of behaviour modification being used to promote the entire range of critical health and safety behaviours, it is necessary to develop an intervention from first principles.

DESIGNING A HEALTH AND SAFETY BEHAVIOUR MODIFICATION INTERVENTION

This section describes how to design a behaviour modification intervention to promote critical health and safety behaviour not included in current programmes. Initially the core elements of behaviour modification interventions are described, followed by a six-step guide to behavioural change. Finally, an example to illustrate how to used the six-step guide to promote critical health and safety behaviours is provided.

Behaviour modification interventions vary depending on the organisational setting, the target population and the behaviours to be changed. The core elements of behaviour modification form a six-step intervention process:

1. Establishing the desired result or output of the activity or the individuals under examination
2. Specifying critical behaviours that influence performance of the area to be improved
3. Ensuring that the individual(s) can perform the desired behaviour
4. Conducting ABC analysis on the current and desired behaviour
5. Altering the consequences immediately following the desired behaviour
6. Evaluating the impact of altering the consequence on the behaviour and on the desired result.

These six main steps are represented diagrammatically in figure 3.

Figure 3: Six-step behaviour modification intervention strategy.

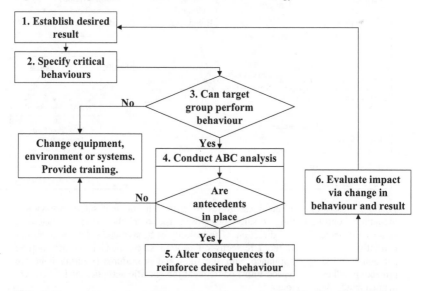

This six-step process can be used to analyse and promote any critical health and safety behaviour.

Establish the desired result

The first step in any behavioural change process is establishing the desired results or outputs from the group of individuals in question. It is important to be clear about what you are trying to achieve because if you do not know this, it is not possible to judge success. In the context of health and safety, an example of desired result is increased compliance with SMS procedures and rules, which would be demonstrated through improvements in independent SMS audit results.

Specify critical behaviour

Once the desired result is specified, then the behaviours necessary to achieve this result need to be established. When specifying the desired behaviours it is important to remember that behaviours are tangible and observable, they are not beliefs, attitudes or subjective[3]. These behaviours need to be defined precisely, statements like: 'demonstrates that they are committed to safety' are too general. It is necessary to specify the actual behaviours required to demonstrate commitment to safety. It may be necessary for organisations to investigate this topic further before they can specify the behaviours. One useful way of identifying critical behaviours is to examine what behaviours differentiate effective employees from those who are less effective in the area where improvements are sought.

These behaviours need to be stated as positive actions, as opposed to a lack of action e.g. 'adheres to all rules and procedures' instead of 'does not violate procedures'. Although this may seem like a difference of semantics, it is a critical difference, as it is possible to achieve the latter by doing nothing, which means it is not a behaviour. This pitfall can be avoided by applying the 'dead man test' developed by Dr. Lindsley, which states, "If a dead man can do it, it is not behaviour and you should not waste your time trying to produce it"[3]. Although this may seem like common sense, it is surprising how many common goals violate this rule. For example, a common safety goal is zero accidents, which violates the dead man test, as dead men never have accidents. It is important to specify behaviours that positively enhance safety, because it is possible for organisations to achieve zero accidents in the short term by reducing their levels of maintenance, yet the safety of the organisation may in fact be deteriorating drastically.

In addition to being positive actions, behaviours must be observable, measurable, and reliable. It is sometimes argued that many important behaviours are not observable, but this cannot be the case, as by definition all behaviours are observable, even if the behaviour is only observed by the actor. If it is not something that can be observed then it is not a behaviour. In situations where the actor is the observer, it is possible to use self-observation, combined with graphical presentation in public to encourage honest reporting.

Once something can be observed then it can be measured, even if a behaviour is not happening it can be measured, "the measure is zero"[3]. It is important that the behaviour can be measured reliably if behaviour change is going to occur. The most effective way of testing reliability is to compare the results of two observers who are observing the same behaviour. If they come up with the same result, then the behaviour is reliable. These three criteria (observability, measurability and reliability) can be achieved through detailed description of the specific critical behaviour.

Establish that the target group can perform the behaviour

The target individual or group must have control over the critical behaviour for a behavioural intervention to work. If the behaviour is not within their control, then it will not be possible for them to alter their behaviour. If they are not able to perform the behaviour then changes will be required to the environment, systems, equipment or the individual through training (see HSG48 for further details).

Conduct ABC analysis

ABC analysis is conducted on the desired behaviour and the current behaviour to identify the antecedents and consequences of the behaviour. If this analysis reveals that the antecedents for the desired behaviour are not in place then this will need to be addressed. These are necessary to enable the individual to perform the behaviour; therefore, all individuals that may be required to perform this behaviour will require these antecedents. For example, following a fatality an organisation mandated that all employees working above six feet had to wear a safety harness. In effect, this meant that all process operators would need to wear a safety harness on occasion, but they had not received training in how to use a safety harness. A subsequent incident revealed that process operators were not using the harness correctly and it was providing limited protection.

The analysis involves rating the consequences of the desired and undesired behaviour in terms of their timeframe, predictability and significance (as described above). An effective way of ensuring that the consequences for the individual are identified is to involve individuals who perform the behaviour in the analysis. The process of identifying consequences needs to be conducted in an open environment where participants can highlight negative consequences (punishments) for performing the desired behaviour.

Alter consequences to reinforce desired behaviour
The ABC analysis identifies the consequences that are driving the current behaviour, which highlights the areas requiring change. The intervention will involve providing more soon, certain and positive consequences for the desired behaviours or removing these consequences from the undesired behaviour. In reality, a mixture of both will be required.

Evaluate impact of intervention
Assessing the effectiveness of the programme requires establishing the level of behavioural change and change in the desired result following the intervention. In practice, this involves comparing the output and the behaviour of the target group following the intervention with the baseline measure to establish the degree of change.

USING BEHAVIOUR MODIFICATION TO PROMOTE MANAGEMENT BEHAVIOURS
The above outlined the six stages of a behaviour modification intervention. The following section illustrates how this six-step process can be used to promote any critical health and safety behaviour through an example of promoting management behaviours.

Step one: Define the desired result of the management activity
The desired result of effective safety leadership is a positive safety climate, indicated by at least 70% of employees perceiving that senior managers are committed to safety.

Step two: Specify the critical behaviours
Specifying the critical behaviours required for effective safety leadership involved reviewing the literature on safety leadership. The identification of company specific leadership behaviours could be established by holding discussion groups with employees and interviews with managers who are perceived to be committed to safety. The literature review identified behaviours that were consistently associated with effective safety leadership. One of these behaviours was selected for the current example. The critical behaviour is:

- Meeting with employees frequently to discuss safety issues.

Step three: Establish that the managers can perform the behaviours
Managers have control over their time and meet frequently with subordinates and therefore are able to meet with employees frequently to discuss safety issues. Pressures from other commitments sometimes make it difficult for managers to meet with staff frequently.

Step four: Conduct ABC analysis on the desired behaviours
The critical behaviour was analysed using the ABC process described above. The ABC analysis for meeting and not meeting with employees to discuss safety issues is presented in table 4 below.

Table 4: ABC analysis of meeting with employees frequently to discuss safety

Antecedents	Behaviour	Consequences	R/P	T	P	S
Awareness of the benefits of discussing safety with subordinates Holding safety discussions is a part of job	Meeting with employees frequently to discuss safety issues	Perceived by subordinates as committed to safety	R	D	U	U
		Recognition from senior management	R	D	U	I
		Increased workload	P	S	C	I
		Receive a list of problems to resolve	P	S	C	I
Other managers do not meet with staff to discuss safety	Not meeting with employees frequently to discuss safety issues	Continue working uninterrupted	R	S	C	I
		Avoid negative interactions with subordinates	R	S	C	I
		Perceived as not committed to safety	P	D	U	I

R/P =Reinforcement/ Punishment. T= Timeframe (Soon / Distant). P= Predictability (Certain/ Uncertain). S= Significance (Important/ Unimportant).

The ABC analysis in table 8 reveals that the antecedents are in place for the desired behaviour to occur.

The analysis of consequences indicates that the reinforcing consequences for meeting with staff to discuss safety issues are distant, uncertain and unimportant, while the punishments are soon, certain and important. In addition the reinforcing consequences for not meeting with employees are soon, certain and unimportant, while the punishment is distant and uncertain. It is therefore not surprising that managers do not meet with staff frequently to discuss safety. The frequency of the desired behaviour will be increased by providing more reinforcing consequences that are soon, certain and important and removing the punishments for the desired behaviour.

Step five: Alter the consequences
The ABC analysis of the critical behaviour revealed that this behaviour could be promoted by introducing additional consequences to reinforce the desired behaviour. An effective way of doing this is to introduce an observation and feedback programme to promote this behaviour.

Designing an observation and feedback programme targeted at managers, professional and technical staff presents a number of difficulties. For example, the relatively low number of managers within an organisation means that there is less opportunity to observe managers displaying these behaviours. Therefore, even if managers are meeting with subordinates frequently to discuss safety issues they may not be observed. It can also be difficult to observe managers behaviour as they can be conducted behind closed doors. It is unlikely that a random observation programme would be able to collect meaningful data on this behaviour and therefore it is unlikely to work. This suggests that a self-observation of the critical behaviours would be more effective.

Consultation with the target group of managers is required before introducing a self-observation and feedback programme. The consultation needs to explain the rationale behind observation and feedback, the theory underpinning behaviour modification and how the information collected will be used. Managers will also require training in how to conduct the observations and record their data.

Observation and feedback programmes require a list of clearly defined behavioural measures. The list of behavioural measures is drawn up in consultation with the target group of managers. The following is the list of behavioural measures to promote the critical behaviour.

- The number of interactions per week with frontline staff where safety is the main topic of conversation and the member of staff rates as positive. (Employee to complete card evaluating quality of interaction and submit it anonymously)
- The number of safety concerns raised by employees per week that are responded to, actions agreed and a completion date mutually agreed within 12 working hours.

Once the behavioural measure is agreed, a set of initial observations provides a baseline measure of current performance. The management team set a group target for each behavioural measure using the baseline results. Individual managers conduct self-observations, with confirmatory information drawn from frontline staff through their evaluation of discussions, safety concerns raised and safety suggestions made. Managers use an individual behavioural matrix to record their performance. The results are shared with the manager's team and the results for the management group are presented graphically to the entire workforce.

The managers also identify the consequences of the desired behaviour to ensure that they find them reinforcing. The consequences for performing the desired behaviours for the managers include praise from colleagues and superiors, positive feedback and success at reaching target.

Step six: Evaluate the impact of the intervention
The effectiveness of the programme in changing behaviour is evaluated by comparing results with the baseline measure to establish the degree of behavioural change. The effectiveness of the programme in improving the safety climate is measured by repeating the safety climate survey to identify the degree of change in employee perceptions.

CONCLUSIONS

Behaviour is a critical aspect of all activities conducted within every organisation. Therefore, the behaviour of all staff has a dramatic impact on safety. Behaviour modification techniques can be used to promote the effective use of risk control strategies and to analyse the at risk behaviours to ensure that the risk is minimised.

There is strong research evidence that behaviour modification is effective in changing a range behaviours within organisational settings. Within a safety context the research shows that behavioural safety programmes can alter frontline employees behaviour and reduce incident rates. Surprisingly there were a limited number of publications demonstrating the effectiveness of a behavioural intervention in promoting critical risk control behaviours or safety leadership behaviours.

In the absence of published description of interventions designed at promoting critical risk control behaviours, first principle were used to describe how behaviour modification could be used to promote these behaviours. The approaches described could be used to promote critical behaviours, such as managers ensuring that manpower levels are adequate for the workload or frontline staff monitoring the status of machinery to ensure it is functioning effectively.

It is widely accepted that human behaviour is a contributory factor in approximately 80% of accidents. This statistic has lead to confusion about how to improve health and safety at work, as many people have concluded that further improvements in safety will occur by changing the employees in some way to make them 'safer' or to make them adhere to safety rules and procedures. Perceiving the problem as a within the employee prevents the identification of effective solutions. Behavioural change is not brought about by changing the person, but by changing their environment. Further improvements in safety require changes systems and engineering that facilitate behavioural change. This document describes strategies to promote critical health and safety behaviours, implementing these strategies involves introducing new systems and or changing existing systems and engineering controls. The strategies described in this document will not change the employees, only their behaviour.

ACKNOWLEDGEMENTS

This paper is based on two research studies; one was funded by two oil companies (AMEC Process and Energy, bp Exploration and Production,) and the Offshore Safety Division of the UK Health and Safety Executive, the second was solely funded by HSE. The views presented here are those of the authors and should not be taken to represent the position or policy of the organisations involved or of the UK Health and Safety Executive.

REFERENCES

[1] Fleming, M. and Lardner, R. (2000) Behaviour modification programmes establishing best practice OTO Report 2000/047 HSE Books

[2] Arnold, J., Cooper, C. and Robertson, I. (1998). Work psychology: Understanding human behaviour in the workplace. Pearson Education. Harlow, England.

[3] Daniels, A. (1999) Bringing out the best in people. McGrawHill New York.

[4] Sulzer_Azaroff, B. and Austin, J. (2000). Does BBS Work? Professional Safety. American Society of Safety Engineers.

[5] Komaki, J et al (2000). A rich and rigorous examination of applied behaviour analysis research in the world of work. International Review of Industrial and Organisational Psychology, 15, 265-367.

[6] Fleming, M. and Lardner, R. (2000) Behaviour modification to improve safety OTO Report 2000/003 HSE Books

[7] Groeneweg, J. (2001). Moving from compliance to competence. Paper presented at the IIR Human Error conference in London 14 &15 June 2001.

AUTOIGNITION OF GASEOUS FUEL-AIR MIXTURES NEAR A HOT SURFACE

A.Ungut[1] and H. James[2]

[1] Shell Global Solutions, P.O. Box 1, Chester CH1 3SH, UK
[2] Health & Safety Executive, Grove House, Skerton Road, Manchester M16 0RB, UK
© Crown Copyright 2001. Reproduced with the permission of the Controller of Her Majesty's Stationery Office.

An experimental investigation of the hot surface autoignition temperatures for methane, natural gas, propane, and butane mixtures with air was conducted. A stainless steel cartridge heater was installed, with the exposed surface pointing downwards, within a thermally insulating ceramic plate, and heated up to 1000 °C in an enclosed volume of flammable fuel/air atmosphere. Exposed surface temperatures that caused autoignition in mixtures of varying stoichiometry were determined by slowly heating up the cartridge heater until combustion occurred. The measured hot surface temperatures, representing the most favourable conditions for ignition to occur near an exposed stainless steel surface, were found to be approximately 1.5-1.75 times higher than the reported minimum autoignition temperatures determined by standard test methods. These observations were used to validate a CFD based chemical kinetics modelling method. This validated model could form the basis of a predictive tool for general use.

INTRODUCTION

In many industrial applications the presence of heated surfaces, and pipework may present an ignition hazard if an accidental leakage of fuel or lubricants comes into contact with the hot surface. This is particularly important in onshore or offshore gas turbine power plants where the engine is sound-insulated in an acoustic-chamber, and the gaseous fuel under usually very high pressure is delivered through a complex network of pipes[1]. In the absence of adequate ventilation an accidental fuel leak may lead to the build-up of a combustible gas cloud near the gas turbine exhaust diffusers which operate at elevated temperatures (450-550 °C). Conditions which lead to spontaneous ignition are controlled by the balance of the heat generated by low temperature combustion reactions, rates of which are determined by the time history of the mixture temperature, and the heat losses from local hot spots to nearby surfaces. The type of the metal surface also affects the ignition phenomenon to a lesser extent. In practice, the buoyancy effects caused by the temperature differential near the hot surface induce a natural convection flow which makes the onset of spontaneous ignition dependent on the geometry. This may be sometimes referred to as the Damköhler number criterion[2], where a critical value of the ratio of a characteristic flow time to a characteristic chemical reaction time affects the onset of ignition. Because of the rather complex nature of this phenomenon risks associated with hot surface autoignition are poorly understood, and measures taken to minimise the risk are usually based on tabulated minimum autoignition temperatures which can be considerably lower than the actual hot surface autoignition values.

Standard test methods for determination of autoignition temperatures of liquid and gaseous fuels involve heating up of a known quantity of fuel in a uniformly heated 500 ml [3], or 200 ml test flasks[4]. These tests provide a quantitative description of the likelihood of autoignition for various fuels but the reported values have a limited range of applicability.

The standard test conditions correspond to near adiabatic conditions where heat losses from the reaction centres, and the effect of the buoyant convective flow are minimised. Thus, they provide a minimum ignition temperature for the fuel in question. It is also reported that the use of larger flasks reduces the autoignition temperature even further by restricting the heat losses [5]. Similar observations are also reported in [6]. A detailed study of the autoignition temperatures of methane, propane and methane/propane mixtures as a function of fuel concentration is also reported in a slightly different test apparatus [7]. We shall refer to the standard test measurement as minimum autoignition temperature (MAT) in this paper.

In realistic hazard scenarios both the buoyant flow, and the presence of hot metal surfaces which serve as a conductive heat sink for the reaction hot spots, reduce the likelihood of autoignition by increasing the minimum wall temperature to much higher values than the MAT. An API publication[8] has concluded that, based on the experimental results, ignition by a hot surface in the open air should not be assumed unless the surface temperature is about 200° C above the MAT. Recently, Smyth & Bryner[9] reported similar results in an experimental apparatus where a jet of fuel/air mixture impinged on a small heated surface.

The surface ignition temperatures of heated rods, pellets, and strips of metal sheets that cause ignition in fuel/ air mixtures have been an area of historical interest [10]. Detailed reviews of the subject are given in references [11], [12], and will not be repeated here. In general, reported hot surface ignition temperatures for methane and natural gas are higher than 1273 K , and the lowest ignition temperatures are observed for leaner mixtures (equivalence ratio of 0.7). For surfaces with small areas (<400 mm^2) the ignition temperature increases with decreasing surface area [13]. Catalytic surfaces such as platinum have been reported to have higher hot surface ignition temperatures than inert surfaces [14], [15] such as nickel and stainless steel. There is also an observed dependence on the orientation of the surface, mixture velocity and surface heating / cooling rates. Hot surface ignition temperatures for propane mixtures vary from 1073 to 1273 K for horizontal hot tubes, and vertical hot plates, respectively in tests reported by Kong et al. [7].The observed hot surface temperatures that cause ignition increase with increasing equivalence ratio for methane or hydrogen mixtures with air, and reverse is true for higher alkanes [11]. Similar observations were reported in [7] for measurements of MAT for methane and propane mixtures.

The purpose of this paper is to provide hot surface autoignition data for the most commonly used gaseous fuels such as methane, natural gas, propane, and butane in a systematic way covering a wide range of the mixture stoichiometries. The experimental data, representing a 'worst case' scenario of a typical industrial application, is intended to be used for assessing the spontaneous ignition hazards for exposed, clean, non-catalytic metal surfaces, such as stainless steel. The data is also to be used for the validation of a computational fluid dynamics (CFD) based hot surface autoignition model which will be published elsewhere[16]. This model involves the calculation of the buoyant gas flow over the heated plate using a commercial CFD code. The steady state streamlines calculated are used to provide temperature-time histories to a kinetics integration program which also simulates the heat losses to the wall from the reacting gas volume. As the surface temperature increases, the likelihood of autoignition is predicted along the streamlines.

The total exposed area of the heated metal surface should be large enough to provide sufficient residence time for the reactions to occur (Damköhler number criterion), the practical limit to the size of the surface is determined by the maximum surface temperature that could be attained despite the increasing radiation cooling. The cartridge heater chosen for this study has an exposed stainless steel surface of dimensions 0.025 m x 0.080 m, with a maximum attainable surface temperature of approximately 1300 K. In order to maximise the residence time of the gas pockets near the hot surface the heater is placed pointing downwards in a recess. This arrangement is considered to represent the most likely geometry for the occurrence of the spontaneous ignition ('worst case'). CFD simulation of the buoyant convective air flow near the experimental geometry indicated that the flow residence time is greater than approximately 1.5 s which is much longer than the chemical induction period of the mixtures investigated.

EXPERIMENT

The experimental apparatus consisted of an open-sided steel compartment of 0.6 m^3 volume (internal dimensions: length 1.0 m; depth 0.6 m; width 1.0 m). A vent was located in the roof of the compartment. Gases entered through a line at the base of the compartment fitted with an air mover to aid mixing. Gas sample points (protected by flame arrestors) were situated at the base of the compartment and within the roof vent. A ceramic board (0.48m x 0.48m) with a centrally located heated surface was suspended from the roof. The base of the compartment was water cooled. Fig. 1 shows the rig in more detail. The board was suspended from the roof by four rods and its height within the compartment could easily be adjusted. Thermocouples monitored the temperature of the heated surface and the gases at the surface of the plate and within the compartment.

The cartridge heater was installed into a recess within the thermally insulating ceramic block with a 0.7 mm diameter type 'K' thermocouple welded at the centre of the unexposed surface. Each leg of the thermocouple was welded separately by a capacitance discharge welder to the back of the heater, approximately 5 mm apart. Thus the stainless steel surface becomes part of the thermocouple junction and the thermocouple accurately and unambiguously measures the steel temperature. The thermocouple cable was extended out of and beyond the auto-ignition chamber into type 'K' connector blocks. These were used to transfer the thermocouple output signals into type 'V' compensating cable and to the data collection point. This thermocouple was linked to a Eurotherm controller which regulated the rate of temperature rise and to the data logger used to measure the temperature at which ignition occurred. Fig. 2 shows the details of the cartridge heater.

As the heater was located in the insulated block there was a temperature differential across the heater between the unexposed face with the thermocouple welded to it and the face exposed to the flammable gas atmosphere because of radiation losses. The validity of the autoignition data depended on knowing with a certain degree of confidence, the temperature of the exposed surface when the gas mixture ignited. Therefore, the exposed surface temperature needed to be calibrated in relation to the unexposed surface. To do this, three extra thermocouples were welded onto the exposed surface of the heater at approximately 25%, 50%, and 75% of the distance along its length. These were all connected into a Netdaq data logger together with the control thermocouple signal. With the data logger running the heater was put under load via the Eurotherm controller to rise at a rate of 33.3 °C. per minute. For mapping purposes, this was continued up to a maximum of 1050 °C. The heater was then set to decrease to room temperature at exactly the same rate. On examining the data, the average value of the temperature of the exposed surface was compared with the co-incidental value on the unexposed surface and a calibration   curve-fit expression was derived over the range in excess of 700 °C. Fig. 3 shows the variation of the exposed surface temperature as a function of the back surface temperature. The solid black line shows the centrally located thermocouple, and the dotted lines show the thermocouples positioned at the edges of the heated surface. The variation of the temperature across the length of the cartridge heater introduced an uncertainty in the measurement of the autoignition temperature and this is shown as error bars in the results. Because of the excessive thermal loading it was necessary to replace the cartridge heaters regularly, and repeat the calibration procedure described above. During the tests these extra thermocouples were removed from the exposed surface of the heater and the surface smoothed to eliminate the possibility of any 'hot spots'.

Four extra thermocouples were used to monitor the gas temperature inside the autoignition chamber. These were located inside the recess cavity, on the lower surface of the insulation block, in the volume between the insulation block and the cling-film wall, and inside the cable conduit above the heater. The details of the thermocouples, and the cartridge heater used in these tests are given in the appendix.

A suitable span gas was used to calibrate the analyser before each test. During the experiment, the open sides of the compartment were sealed with cling-film (held in place using magnetic strip) and the volume filled with the fuel/air mixture. The gaseous fuel and air used were supplied in standard gas cylinders. These were stored externally in gas bottle racks and piped directly into the lab. The pressure of the gases was controlled using regulators and the lines downstream were protected by pressure relief and non-return valves. The flow and mixing of the gases were controlled remotely through valves operated from within a control room. With the vent valve at the top of the chamber open, the fuel and the air were introduced in separate bursts into the chamber and mixing was achieved by relying on turbulent mixing within the chamber. The mixture was sampled from both the upper and the lower levels of the chamber to assess the homogeneity of the mixture, and when the desired gas concentration had been reached the gas supply and vent valves were closed.

In the event of the gases failing to ignite upon the hot surface a nitrogen purge was used to remove the flammable gas mixture from the rig and supply lines. As a back up to the nitrogen purge system the gases could also be safely removed from the compartment by a controlled ignition. For this purpose a spark plug, which could be triggered remotely from the control room, was situated in the roof of the compartment. All data produced was collected and digitised using transient recorders and stored on a PC for further analysis.

A TV camera was set up to monitor the conditions inside the chamber close to the surface of the heater. The heater was then powered up. The Eurotherm controller was set to increase the heater temperature by 33.3 °C. per minute. During the heating up period the contents of the chamber were sampled through the gas analyser to ensure the concentration was still within specification. The temperature rise continued until either ignition occurred or the temperature reached approximately 1150 °C at the back surface of the heater which corresponds to an average temperature of approximately 1000 °C at the exposed front surface. If ignition did not occur, the heater was set to cool down and the atmosphere within the chamber was purged with nitrogen.

RESULTS

Tests for butane, propane, natural gas, and methane mixtures with air were conducted with varying stoichiometries. Table 1 shows the details of the mixture compositions and the average, minimum, and maximum hot surface temperatures that caused the autoignition of the fuel air mixture. An artificial natural gas (NG) mixture similar to the Shell Gannet platform production gas composition (77.7% methane, 10.34% ethane, 6.67% propane, 2.9% butane, 0.74% pentane, 0.09% hexane, balance carbon dioxide) was used in this investigation. The ignition of the mixture was determined from the colour video recordings, and the response of the gas phase thermocouples to the arrival of the flame front. Fig. 4 shows a typical thermocouple measurement during the tests. A sharp spike on the temperature profiles of the gas phase thermocouples is related to the flame front arrival, and the occurrence of ignition is further confirmed by the colour video recording of the test. The temperature of the exposed surface of the cartridge heater was than determined from the calibration data.

Measured hot surface autoignition temperatures are shown in Figs. 5-7 as a plot of the surface temperature against the mixture stoichiometry for mixtures in air of butane, propane, natural gas, and methane respectively. Recent data published by Smyth & Bryner[3] is also shown for butane, propane, and methane mixtures for comparison. Although the method used to measure the hot surface ignition temperatures is very different their results agree well with the data from the current study, with the exception of methane where their measurements are unexplainably low for stoichiometric, and richer methane/air mixtures. In our methane tests, mixtures with stoichiometries greater than 0.8 failed to ignite within the maximum temperature range of the heater. Results agree with published data [7, 11] that the observed hot surface temperatures that cause ignition increase with increasing equivalence ratio for methane or hydrogen mixtures with air, and the reverse is true for higher alkanes.

DISCUSSION

A small number of repeat experiments for near stoichiometric butane/air mixtures show significant scatter of the hot surface autoignition temperatures (standard deviation of 42 °C). Although not representative of the tests with other mixtures this variation may be considered as typical for the present data. The average values of the hot surface ignition temperatures in Kelvin for a given mixture stoichiometry, normalised with the tabulated minimum autoignition temperatures, are plotted for all of the tests in Fig.8. This ratio varies between 1.5 to 1.75 depending on the mixture composition and stoichiometry which is in good agreement with the API recommendation[8].

Results are used to validate a CFD based model using detailed chemical kinetics calculations [16], details of which will be published elsewhere. The experimental geometry reported is modelled to simulate the convective buoyant flow near a heated surface, and the detailed chemical kinetics model was used to predict the gas phase self ignition. Fig. 9 shows the comparison of the predictions with the experimental results for the butane / air mixture (see Fig. 5). The empty circles show the average hot surface ignition temperature for each mixture stoichiometry investigated. The horizontal lines show the model predictions that failed to ignite, and the plus signs indicate predicted ignitions as a function of surface temperature, and mixture stoichiometry. The agreement between the model predictions and the experimental data is excellent [16] and the use of this methodology in accident investigations and hazard assessment will be potentially very valuable.

CONCLUSIONS

- In this study, autoignition in mixtures in air of methane, natural gas, propane, and butane near a hot stainless steel surface occurred at temperatures (in K) approximately 1.5-1.75 times higher than the minimum autoignition temperatures measured using the standard test method.

- Results are in good agreement with other published data, and represent a realistic accident geometry which can be modelled using the available computational fluid dynamics and chemical kinetics methods. The results also provided much needed validation data for the model.

- The experimental results reported here are specific to the experimental arrangement in this study, and should be used with care, taking into account the possible influence of other variables that could affect autoignition temperature.

Table 1 Details of the mixture compositions tested and the average, maximum, and minimum surface temperatures that ignited the fuel air mixture.

FUEL	STOICHIOMETRY	AVERAGE SURFACE TEMPERATURE (K)	MAXIMUM SURFACE TEMPERATURE (K)	MINIMUM SURFACE TEMPERATURE (K)
Butane	0.46	1264	1291	1249
	0.5	1107	1124	1093
	0.7	1089	1100	1078
	0.8	1099	1115	1085
	0.81	1091	1102	1080
	1.1	1096	1113	1082
	1.07	1013	1023	1003
	1.11	1070	1081	1059
	1.71	1097	1108	1086
Propane	0.71	1110	1123	1101
	1.1	1113	1126	1104
	1.57	1127	1141	1118
NG	0.5	1152	1168	1140
	0.51	1145	1160	1134
	0.6	1159	1175	1147
	0.71	1163	1180	1151
	0.71	1164	1181	1151
	1.1	1197	1217	1181
	1.15	1197	1217	1181
	1.15	1196	1216	1180
	1.3	1227	1250	1207
Methane	0.71	1209	1227	1209
	0.76	1223	1246	1204

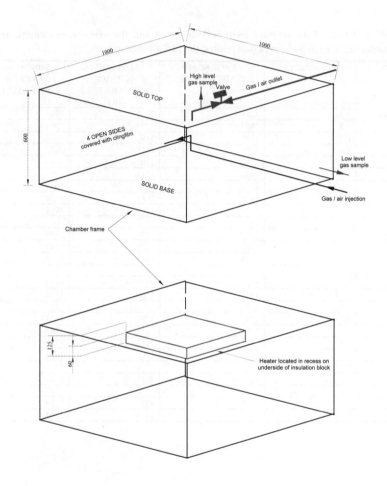

Figure 1 Details of the autoignition rig showing locations of services and the ceramic heater block. Units are in mm.

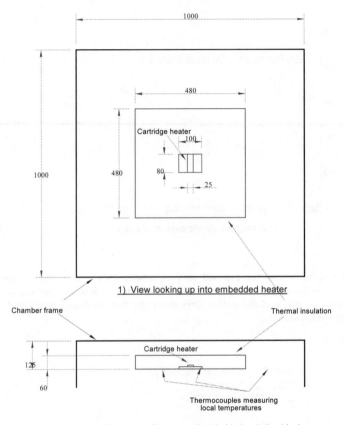

1) View looking up into embedded heater

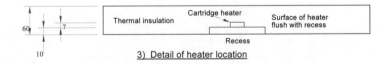

2) Elevation of heater embedded in insulation block

3) Detail of heater location

Figure 2 Details of the cartridge heater, and positioning of thermocouples. Units are in mm.

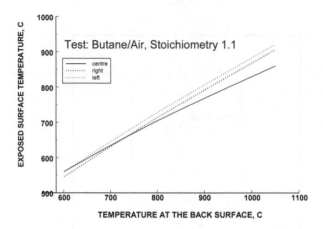

Figure 3 Calibration of the exposed surface temperature against the temperature measured at the back of the cartridge heater. The solid black line shows the centrally located thermocouple, and the dotted lines show the thermocouples positioned at the edges of the heated surface.

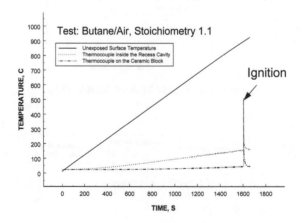

Figure 4 Thermocouple measurements that show the measured temperature behind the cartridge heater, and the gas phase temperature during a test.

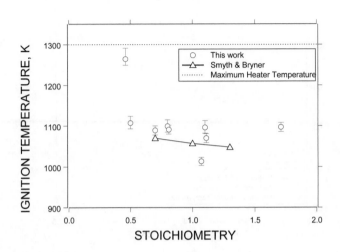

Figure 3 Hot surface ignition temperatures for butane air mixtures

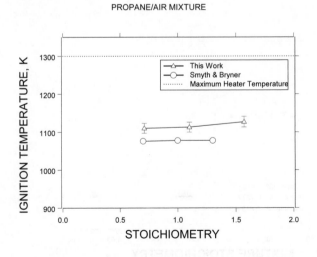

Figure 4 Hot surface ignition temperatures for propane air mixtures

NATURAL GAS AND METHANE MIXTURES WITH AIR

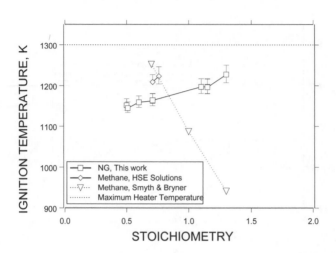

Figure 5 Hot surface ignition temperatures for methane and natural gas mixtures with air.

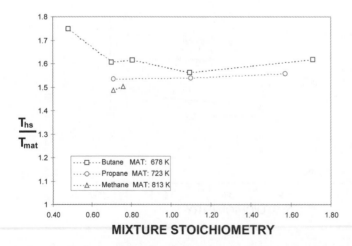

Figure 6 Ratio of the measured hot surface ignition temperatures(T_{hs}) to MAT (T_{mat}) measured by the standard method for all of the mixtures investigated.

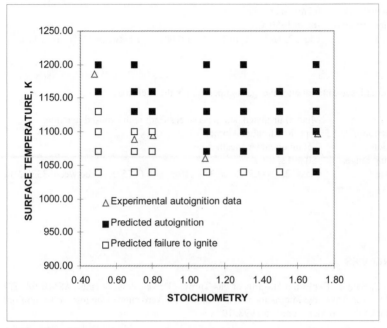

Figure 7 Comparison of the model predictions[16] with the experimental data. The experimental data points are the average hot surface autoignition temperatures for a given stoichiometry.

APPENDIX

Cartridge heater details

Type:	Hotwatt SR 16-5.
Construction:	Stainless steel sheath with magnesium oxide packing.
Dimensions:	7mm thick by 25mm wide by 127mm long
Power consumption:	Up to 500 Watts
Maximum continuous temperature:	650°C.

Thermocouples welded to the surface of the Cartridge heater

Thermocouple welded to the centre of the unexposed surface
Type: Solid wire
Construction: Type 'K' Chromel Alumel

Dimensions: 0.7mm diameter.
Measuring range: -80 to 1350°C.
Tolerance: Class 2, +/- 2.5°C to 333°C or 0.0075 x T between 333°C to 1200°C.

Thermocouples used to monitor the gas temperature in the enclosure

Type: Mineral insulated, stainless steel sheath with exposed junction.
Construction: Type 'K' Chromel Alumel
Dimensions: 0.5mm diameter sheath.
Measuring range: -80 to 1350°C.
Tolerance: Class 2, +/-2.5°C to 333°C or +/-0.0075 x T between 333°C to 1200oC.

REFERENCES

[1] R. C. Santon. Explosion Hazards at gas Turbine Driven Power Plants. ASME 98-GT-215 Presented at the International Gas Turbine and Aeroengine Congress & Exhibition, Stockholm, Sweden, June 2-5 1998. 1998.

[2] A. Hamins and P. Borthwick. Suppression of Ignition over a Heated Metal Surface. Combustion and Flame 112, 161-170. 1998.

[3] ASTM-E 659-78. Standard Test Method for Autoignition Temperatures of Liquid Chemicals, ASTM-E 659-78. American Society for Testing of Materials, Philadelphia, PA. 1978.

[4] British Standards Institute. A Method of Test for Ignition Temperature of Gasses and Vapours. BS 4056. 1966.

[5] T. J. Snee. Auto-Ignition, Slow Combustion and the Variation of Minimum Ignition Temperature with Vessel Size. Health & Safety Executive, Research & Laboratory Services Division , Buxton Loss Prevention Bulletin 081, 25-38. 1-6-1988.

[6] V. B. Kaesche-Krischer and H. Gg. Wagner. Brennstoff-Chemie 39, No.3/4, 33-43. 1958.

[7] D. Kong, R. K. Eckhoff and F. Alfert. Auto-ignition of CH4/air, C3H8/air. CH4/C3H8/air and CH4/CO2/air using a 1-Litre Ignition Bomb. Discussion of a Comprehensive Approach for Predicting Realistic Auto-ignition Temperatures. Journal of Hazardous Materials 40, No.1, 69-84. 1995.

[8] Ignition Risk of Hydrocarbon Vapors by Hot Surfaces in the Open Air. API PUBLICATION 2216, Second Edition, Jan 1991 . 1-1-1991.

[9] K. C. Smyth and N. P. Bryner. Short-Duration Autoignition Temperature Measurements For Hydrocarbon Fuels Near Heated Metal Surfaces. Combust Sci and Tech 126, 225-253. 1997.

[10] Bernard Lewis and Guenter von Elbe, In *Combustion Flames and Explosions of Gasses*. pp. 446-457, Academic Press, 1961.

[11] F. Powell. Ignition of Gases and Vapours by Hot Surfaces and Particles- A Review. 9.international symposium on the prevention of occupational accidents and diseases in the chemical industry, Lucerne, Switzerland, 5 Jun 1984 . 19684.

[12] N. M. Laurendeau and N. R. Caron. Review of Methane-Air Ignition by Hot Surfaces. 1980 Fall Meeting Western States Section / The Combustion Institute, Los Angeles, California . 1980.

[13] D. Rae, B. Singh and R. Danson. Safety Mines Res.Rept.No.224 . 1964.

[14] H. F. Coward and P. G. Guest. J.Am.Chem.Soc. 49, 2479. 1927.

[15] H. M. Kim, H. Enomoto, H. Kato, M. Tsue and M. Kono. A Study of the Ignition Mechanism of Methane-Air Mixtures by Inert and Catalytic Hot Surfaces. Combust Sci and Tech 128, 197-213. 1997.

[16] A. Üngüt. CFD Simulation and Detailed Chemical Modelling of Alkane Autoignition Near a Heated Metal Surface. Report submitted to UK-HSE . 2001.

A METHOD FOR ASSESSING THE CONSEQUENCES OF SMALL LEAKS IN ENCLOSURES

R.P Cleaver and P.S. Cumber

Advantica Technologies Ltd, Ashby Road, Loughborough, Leicestershire, LE11 3GR
© Crown Copyright 2001. Reproduced with the permission of the Controller of Her Majesty's Stationery Office.

Recently there has been interest in the possible consequences of a small leak of natural gas from high-pressure plant located in a confined volume. This paper describes a method for assessing the explosion hazards produced by such leaks. The method may be used for natural gas fired plant in turbine halls, for example. Of particular interest in this context is a method for assessing the consequences of the largest leak that is not detected by a gas detection system of a specified sensitivity.

The scenario that is analysed is a high-pressure release of natural gas into an enclosure. The natural gas mixes with the surrounding air and the gas concentration distribution in the enclosure increases towards a steady state determined by the leak mass flow rate, location and orientation, the volume and shape of the enclosure and the ventilation characteristics of the enclosure. If the enclosure has a gas detection system then it is possible that the leak could be detected and mitigating actions taken before the steady state conditions are reached. The flammable volume that is produced by such a small leak may never then reach the hypothetical steady state value that would be created if the leak had not been detected. In this work, the consequences of igniting the flammable volume that is produced by the leak, whether it is detected or not, are evaluated. The method that is used to assess the consequences includes mathematical models for the leak flow rate, the gas dispersion or accumulation and the pressure generation, should a flammable volume be ignited.

The method has been applied to a number of gas dispersion experiments carried out in enclosed volumes and has been found to give reasonable agreement with the data for the flammable volumes that are produced by the leaks. As an illustration of its application, the methodology is applied to two enclosures with different ventilation systems. In both cases, the predicted consequences of a small leak are evaluated and discussed.

KEYWORDS: Gas releases, Gas explosions, Small releases, consequence assessment

INTRODUCTION

This paper describes a method for assessing the explosion hazards produced by small leaks in natural gas handling plant situated within an enclosure, such as a gas turbine hall. Historical data demonstrates that small leakages from fittings or connections are more likely to occur than larger releases associated with the complete failure of a vessel or pipe-work. Hence, there is a need to assess the consequences of small releases, to ensure that the hazards that they pose are understood and are being controlled. Of particular interest is the possibility of the formation of a flammable mixture of gas and air in the immediate neighbourhood of a small release. Such an accumulation might be difficult to detect and so persist for a long time, posing a possible explosion hazard.

This paper provides an explanation of the methods that can be used to assess the explosion hazards produced by a natural gas release in an enclosure. Particular attention is paid to ensure that the methods can be used for the smaller, more credible releases. From a practical viewpoint, the individual methods have been linked in such a way that they can provide an estimate of the size of the largest release that just fails to trigger an alarm from a gas detector of a given sensitivity placed in the outlet from the enclosure or can be used to investigate the effects of different mitigation actions, such as isolation and blowdown of the gas supply pipe-work on gas detection.

A description of the separate models that are used to predict the leak flow rate, gas accumulation and overpressure generation, should any flammable cloud ignite, is given in the following Section and the way in which these individual models are combined to analyse a release inside an enclosure is explained. A comparison of the resulting method with experimental data is then provided, along with two examples of the application of the model. Finally, the paper ends with a discussion of the results of this work.

INDIVIDUAL MODELS
The separate models that are used to assess the consequences of small releases are discussed individually below.

LEAK FLOW RATE
The first step in assessing the consequences of a natural gas leak in an enclosure is the specification of the leak flow rate. The operating pressure of the gas handling equipment under consideration is known in most cases. The area through which the leakage occurs is more difficult to define. It is sensitive to the mode of failure, the type of equipment and the operating environment. Further, failure frequency databases rarely include detailed information on leak size to allow conclusions to be drawn

Nevertheless, guidance documents for hazardous area classification (HAC) often include information on what is viewed as a maximum 'credible' leak – that is, one that is likely to be experienced in the lifetime of a plant. The hazardous area classification recommendations for natural gas installations, IGE SR25[1], specifies a maximum credible leak area of 0.25 mm^2, for non-vibrating equipment with dry natural gas and 2.5 mm^2 for equipment operating in adverse environments (i.e. not clean or vibrating). The 1996 version of Institute of Petroleum Code of Practice for HAC, IP15[2], provides guidance for facilities used for the storage, transportation and processing of flammable liquids, and also includes guidance for equipment processing flammable gases. It specifies the extent of a 'hazard radius' around different types of equipment. The hazard radius is defined as the largest horizontal extent of the hazardous area generated by a leak when situated in an open area. The hazard radius defines the distance to a 'safe' gas concentration. Using correlations given by Birch et al[3], for natural gas concentration decay on the axis of a sonic natural gas free jet, the leak diameter or area that is associated with the hazard radius can be inferred once a 'safe' concentration and operating pressure are defined. Table 1 shows the values that have been deduced for the equipment listed in IP15. . These results are obtained assuming an unimpeded leak directed horizontally close to the ground and by taking a safe concentration of one half of the lower flammable limit for natural gas (2.5%) and an operating pressure of 100 bar.

Equipment	Hazard Radius (m)	Leak Diameter (mm)
Compressor	5[*]	2.6
Diaphragm Compressor	3	1.6
Flange	1.5[**]/3	0.78/1.6
Valve	1.5[**]/3	0.78/1.6
Instrument vent		
Diameter 6 mm	3	1.6
" 12 mm	7.5	3.9
" 25 mm	15	7.8

[*] - Compressors fuelled by natural gas
[**] - Flanges or valves broken infrequently (2 years or more), and there are no other factors, such as pressure or thermal shocks or excessive pipe loading.

Table 1 – Leak sizes inferred from the hazard radii specified in IP15.

The leak diameters inferred in this way cover a wider range than those defined in IGE SR25 for natural gas equipment (d_{leak}=0.6mm for non-vibrating equipment with dry natural gas or d_{leak}=1.8mm for adverse environments), but they are of a similar order. Recently, work has been carried out for the Institute of Petroleum to provide a risk based approach to HAC[4]. The resulting values recommended for hole size and their corresponding frequency of occurrence are summarised in Table 2. These values were recommended based on data from a number of sources[5-7].

Equipment	Category	Hole size	Frequency per year
Centrifugal pump	Seal failure single seal pump	Manufacturers data or: 0.1x shaft diameter 0.23 x shaft diameter	2.4E-2
"	Seal failure double seal pump	Manufacturers data or: 0.1x shaft diameter	1.5E-3
"	Minor	0.01 A[*]	1.5E-3
"	Major	0.1 A[*]	3.E-4
"	Rupture	A[*]	3.E-5
Centrifugal compressor	Small	7 mm	1.65E-2
"	Medium	22 mm	8.4E-4
"	Large	70 mm	1.03E-4
Flange	High Frequency	0.6 mm	1.E-2
"	Medium Frequency	2 mm	1.E-3
"	Low Frequency	6 mm	1.E-4
Valve	High Frequency	0.1 mm	1.E-2
"	Medium Frequency	2 mm	1.E-3
"	Low Frequency	0.1 D[**]	1.E-4

[*] A - Cross-sectional area of shaft
[**] D -Diameter of valve

Table 2 – Hole size and frequency data taken from an IP report[4] on HAC

The hole sizes in Table 2 include those that are up to two orders of magnitude larger than the leak diameters recommended in IGE SR25, or inferred from the hazard radii in IP15,[2]. However, if leaks with a frequency of greater than once in a hundred years are considered to be equivalent to those 'likely to be experienced in the lifetime of a plant', then some consensus in the range of leak sizes for HAC purposes is obtained – that is, releases in the range from about 0.1mm to 10 mm, with an average of about 1mm. It is noted that if the objective is a more complete assessment of the safety of some natural gas handling plant, then considering all modes of failure, including the wider range of leak sizes indicated in Table 2, may be more appropriate.

Once the leak area and stagnation pressure are known the gas mass flow rate can be calculated using an outflow model. Standard methods are available from engineering text books. For natural gas, models have been developed that use 'real gas' thermodynamics and solve conservation equations for mass and energy to calculate the mass flow rate either in a steady state or transient mode.

GAS ACCUMULATION IN THE ENCLOSURE

Once the leak size, location and orientation are specified, the gas accumulation in the enclosure can be estimated using a simple zonal approach, such as that given in Cleaver et al[8] for example. This model predicts whether the gas-air mixture is well mixed throughout the enclosure or, because the natural gas is lighter than air, forms a stratified layer from the enclosure ceiling. The model predicts the bulk gas concentration and the depth of the gas–air layer that the release creates, as a function of time. The term 'bulk' concentration is taken to refer to the concentration that would be measured within the layer, outside of the direct path of the natural gas jet issuing into the enclosure. The model has been extended more recently to incorporate the effects of natural or a forced ventilation system within the enclosure. For a naturally ventilated enclosure, the method balances the pressure in the enclosure with that on the four external walls, taking into account the external wind speed and direction, to calculate the elevation of the effective 'zero' or neutral pressure plane within the enclosure. Lighter than air mixture is assumed to flow out of all openings above the zero pressure level, to be replaced by an equal volume inflow of heavier air beneath it. A forced ventilation system is incorporated within the model by adjusting the level of the zero pressure plane so the total inflow and outflow are balanced. The predictions of this aspect of the model have been compared with experimental data for high pressure gas releases into otherwise empty enclosures of volume up to $216m^3$. Satisfactory agreement has been found for the 'bulk' concentration within the regions in which mixture accumulation took place for a variety of ventilation flows.

In cases in which the model predicts that the concentration everywhere in the bulk atmosphere exceeds the lower flammable limit for natural gas of 5%, the flammable volume is taken to be that of the enclosure. When the bulk concentration satisfies the inequalities,

$$2.5\% < <C> < 5\%,$$

the contribution to the flammable volume from the bulk atmosphere is taken to be,

$$V_{flam, AGRO} = \frac{<C> - 2.5}{2.5} V_{encl}$$

This is used as a pragmatic estimate to take account of the nonhomogeneity in the distribution of gas in the bulk atmosphere. Available experimental evidence on the behaviour of high-pressure gas releases in enclosures, obtained over a range of enclosure sizes and for a variety of size and direction of releases, suggests the above provides a cautious estimate of the contribution to the flammable volume from the bulk atmosphere (that is, tends to over-predict the volume).

LOCAL INFLAMMATORY INVENTORY

The gas concentration distribution immediately downstream of the gas leak can be calculated using a variety of mathematical models, ranging from empirical concentrations to advanced computational fluid dynamic codes. An empirical model has been used in this study, using correlations similar to those in Birch et al[3]. The model covers two jet configurations, a free jet and a jet impacting normally onto a flat surface. The model has been adapted for this study to calculate the local flammable volume taking account of the composition of the bulk atmosphere predicted by the gas accumulation model. That is, the concentration of gas arising directly from the jet is supplemented by the concentration of gas in the entrained mixture from the 'bulk' atmosphere in the enclosure to give a time dependent concentration in the vicinity of the release.

EXPLOSION OVERPRESSURE

Explosions can be produced by the ignition of a region of pre-mixed flammable gas inside an enclosure. To make an assessment of the 'worst case' consequences, the volume enclosed by the specified concentration level, predicted by the flammable inventory model, and the flammable volume in the bulk atmosphere inside the enclosure, predicted by the gas accumulation model, are added together. For the purposes of the 'worst case' assessment, the concentration in the flammable volume is assumed to be uniform and stoichiometric, and the overpressure following ignition is predicted using a confined volume explosion model,[9,10]. This model was developed and validated for those enclosures in which the congestion is typically in the form of a smaller number of large obstacles, as found in an onshore compressor cab, rather than a more homogeneous and extensive distribution of obstacles of all sizes, as may occur in offshore modules, for example. A different explosion model would have to be used in the latter case to take account of the rapid flame acceleration produced as a result of encountering repeated obstacles.

IMPLEMENTATION OF THE METHODOLOGY

The individual models described above are linked together, as shown in Figure 1. A flow chart showing how the models would be applied in practice is shown in Figure 2. The information necessary to use this method includes a specification of the leak (its location, orientation and size); the enclosure (its dimensions, vent area and location, estimate of congestion such as volume blockage and representative obstacle diameter); the ventilation system (the type, rate, opening area and location); the gas detection system (detection response and threshold values and location) and explosion relief panels or other potential perimeter openings (their size and weight, failure pressure and location).

By implementing the models in the way shown in Figure 2, an estimate of a representative 'worst case' value for the amount of flammable accumulation and the overpressure generated by any subsequent explosion can be obtained for a gas leak. The method can also be used to estimate the time at which a gas leak would be detected for a gas sensor located in the outlet of the ventilation system and to investigate the results of mitigating actions, such as isolation and blowdown of the gas supply. Further, by changing the threshold values used within the methodology to define the flammable volume, the method can be configured to provide a representative 'best estimate' values.

EVALUATION OF THE SMALL LEAK METHODOLOGY

The separate models that form the method have all been validated independently. However, an assessment of the performance of the composite method has not been given previously. In this section, the flammable volumes predicted by the method are compared with the measurements of Santon et al.,[11] and a programme of gas build-up experiments carried out in a representation of an offshore module[12].

Considering firstly the experiments of Santon et al, the experimental rig was a rectangular enclosure with dimensions 15m long by 2.5m wide by 2.5m high. The gas leak was introduced through a horizontal pipe orientated to be parallel with the major axis of the enclosure. The geometry of the enclosure is shown schematically in Figure 3. Downstream of the leak a number of different obstacles, such as a flat plate, were located across the middle of the enclosure to investigate how such obstructions modified the gas accumulation characteristics. Ventilation air was introduced at one end of the enclosure and the outlet for the ventilation air was located at the other end. In the experiments, the volume defined by the 2.5% contour was estimated for a range of gas leak mass flow rates, air ventilation rates and obstacle types downstream of the leak using a matrix of probes to detect the gas concentration. Table 3 shows a comparison of the methodology with the measurements of Santon et al.

Q_{air} $(m^3/$ sec$)$	m_{leak} (kg/ sec)	A_{vent} (m^2)	Obstacle type	V_{flam} $(m^3)^*$	
				Measured	Predicted
800	0.023	0.63	None	0.02	0.04
400	0.046	0.63	Small tray	0.25	0.6
400	0.046	0.63	Large tray	0.75	0.6

* - Volume defined by the 2.5% contour

Table 3 – Comparison of measured and predicted 'flammable' volume for the experiments of Santon et al.

A similar comparison of the flammable volume with a much larger database of experiments studying gas dispersion in an offshore module has been carried out. Experimental details and information on the measurements that were made can be found in Savvides et al[12]. The rig has a solid, impermeable roof and floor and Figure 4 illustrates the different arrangements of perimeter confinement that were used in the test programme. The releases that were studies in this test programme were much larger than those normally considered for HAC. Typical release rates were in the range of 5 kg/s to 10 kg/s, driven by an upstream pressure of typically 30 bar. However, the test rig that was used, being 28m long by 12m wide by 8m high, has a similar size to some of those of concern here and so the comparison is of interest, representing a test of the flammable volume estimates for larger releases.

The rig configurations A and C have two of the perimeter boundaries open to the atmosphere and are outside the limits of applicability of the gas accumulation model referred to in Section 2. Nevertheless, there were a number of experiments carried out in these configurations in which the release was directed towards an open boundary and significant accumulation did not occur. Comparison with experiments of this type carried out in lower wind speeds indicates that the dilution rates are consistent with the predictions of a model of the type discussed above.

The accumulation model would be expected to be more applicable for rig configuration B, in which the two short end walls were partially obstructed as well. The quality of the agreement in this case is dependent on the orientation of the gas release and the extent to which it interacts with the ventilation flow. The agreement was found to be reasonable for gas leaks co-flowing or normal to the direction of the ventilation flow prior to the release being initiated. However, when the gas leak was directed into the pre-existing ventilation air, the flammable volume is under-predicted for some of the experiments. This appears to be associated with the interaction of the natural ventilation flow in the rig with the large, release driven motions. However it is thought that the conservative assumptions in the method as a whole, such as assuming that the flammable volume is taken to be the volume enclosed by the 2.5% gas concentration contour and that the flammable volume is taken to be stoichiometric, mean that any overpressure would tend to be overpredicted, provided an appropriate explosion model were used.

APPLICATION OF SMALL LEAK METHODOLOGY
In this section, the method is applied to consider small releases in two different enclosures. The first case to be considered is inside a larger enclosure having a high ventilation rate and a gas detection system able to detect gas concentrations greater than 0.5% (10% of the LFL). The second is for a smaller enclosure, fitted with a less sensitive gas detection equipment, assumed to respond at a natural gas concentration of 1.25%.

LARGER ENCLOSURE
The dimensions of the enclosure are 14m long by 9.4m wide by 7m high. The ventilation rate under normal operation is taken to be 25 m/sec^3, equivalent to 98 air changes an hour. The enclosure is assumed to have a number of gas detection sensors located near the ceiling, set to detect gas concentrations in excess of 0.5%. The ventilation inlets and outlets are distributed around the perimeter of the enclosure, as defined in Table 4.

Outlets	Vent Location			Wall
	Elevation of bottom	Elevation of top	Width	
1	0	1	1	West
2	4	5	1	West
3	5.2	5.9	0.7	North
4	5.2	5.9	0.7	North
5	5.2	5.9	0.7	West
6	5.2	5.9	0.7	West
7	4.8	5.6	0.5	South
8	4.8	5.6	0.5	South
Inlet				
1	3.8	5	3	East

Table 4 – Details of the ventilation inlet and outlets in the enclosure

The explosion model represents the level of congestion in the enclosure by a volume blockage parameter and a blockage length. In the following calculations it is assumed that the internal volume blockage is 20% and the blockage length scale is 0.5m, typical values for those of compression facilities associated with gas transmission. Three scenarios have been considered, as follows. A leak of natural gas either during normal operation or when the ventilation system fails and a leak that is sufficiently small to be undetectable by the gas detection system when the ventilation system is operating.

The leak source assumed for scenario 1 and 2 has a diameter of 1.7mm and a drive pressure of 85 bar. For scenario 3, the leak volume flow rate is dependent on the ventilation rate and the threshold of the gas detection system and using the gas detection threshold of 0.5%, it follows that the leak flow rate is approximately $0.12 m^3$/sec. The results of using the methodology for the three scenarios are summarised in Table 5

d_{leak} (mm)	Q_{air} (m^3/sec)	t_{det} (min)	t_{steady} (min)	$<C>_{max}$ (%)	V_{flam}* (m^3)	O.P. (mbar)
1.7	25	-	3	0.16	0.14	less than 1
1.7	0	1.8	-	1.1**	0.70	less than 1
3.0	25	-	5	0.5	0.85	less than 1

* - Volume defined by the 2.5% contour
** - Volume defined after a further 2.5 minutes

Table 5 – Summary of results obtained for the small leak assessment

The calculations suggest that the representative small leak would be undetected when the ventilation supply is operating normally, as the gas detection threshold is not attained before steady state conditions are reached. Steady state conditions are calculated to occur after 3 minutes. The steady state bulk gas concentration is predicted to be 0.16%, with a corresponding flammable volume of 0.14 m^3, equivalent to 0.015% of the volume of the enclosure. The overpressure predicted is less than 1mbar, taking the volume defined by the 2.5% concentration contour to be at a stoichiometric concentration in the explosion calculation.

In the second scenario it is assumed the ventilation system fails or is not in operation at the time of the gas leakage. The gas accumulation model predicts that the gas detection threshold is reached after about 105 seconds. In practice, some mitigating action would be taken on gas detection (e.g. the gas leak would automatically be isolated or the air ventilation rate increased). However, the gas leak would continue for some time after it is detected. This is because the system will remain pressurised for some time, even if it is isolated and blown down. However, once the leak is isolated, the natural gas mass flow rate will tend to decay, albeit slowly initially, tending to reduce the flammable inventory in the jet and the bulk atmosphere. For the purposes of illustration, an estimate of the largest flammable volume produced by the leak is obtained by calculating the inventory that would have been produced had the leak continued at a constant rate for a further 2.5 minutes after it had been detected. At this time the predicted bulk gas concentration is 1.1%. The volume enclosed by the 2.5% contour is predicted to be 0.7 m^3. This gives some insight into the sensitivity of the flammable inventory to changes in the gas concentration in the bulk atmosphere at relatively low levels of gas concentrations. However, the predicted overpressure for scenario 2 is still less than 1 mbar.

In the third scenario, the gas leak is prescribed such that the gas concentration in the bulk atmosphere of the enclosure, assuming perfect mixing, is below the detection threshold. Under these circumstances, it is only the region immediately downstream of the gas leak that is contributing to the flammable volume. This scenario gives the largest flammable volume of 0.85m^3. However the predicted overpressure is still less than 1 mbar. The small overpressures predicted by the explosion model suggest that it is more plausible for the ignition of the flammable volume to have the characteristics of a flash-fire, followed by a jet fire, rather than an explosion followed by a fire.

The largest acceptable flammable volume in all three cases meet the criterion recommended in Santon et al[11] that less than 0.1% of the enclosure volume is filled by a given release.

SMALLER ENCLOSURE

The dimensions of the second enclosure are smaller and are taken to be 12.8m long by 5.6m wide and only 4.4m high. The rate of supply of ventilation air is assumed to be 6 m^3/sec, equivalent to 68 air changes an hour. Ventilation air is introduced through two vents with a combined flow area of 0.6 m^2. The ventilation air is assumed to leave the enclosure through a centrally located stack with a cross-sectional area of 0.9 m^2. A gas sensor with a detection threshold of 1.25% is assumed to be located in the stack. The release specification for the first two scenarios is taken to be the same as example 1, with a pressure of 85 bar and a leak diameter of 1.7mm.

The results of the gas accumulation and explosion calculations are summarised in Table 6.

d_{leak} (mm)	Q_{air} (m^3/sec)	t_{det} (min)	t_{steady} (min)	$<C>_{max}$ (%)	V_{flam}^* (m^3)	O.P. (mbar)
1.7	6	-	5	0.74	0.34	less than 1
1.7	0	1.6	-	2.9	50	90
2.3	6	-	6	1.2	1.6	3.3

* - Volume defined by the 2.5% contour

Table 6 – Summary of results in the older compressor cab small leak assessment

As in the first example, in scenario 2 (in which the ventilation system is assumed to fail or not to be operating when the release takes place), the release is assumed to continue for 2.5 minutes after the gas concentration remote from the gas leak is detected in the outlet. The largest flammable volume and overpressure occurs in scenario 2. For this scenario the bulk gas concentration 2.5 minutes after gas is detected is 2.9%, the flammable volume is 50m^3 and an overpressure of 90 mbar is predicted. Depending on the details of the construction of the enclosure, such a pressure may cause some structural damage. In this particular case, the safety criteria recommended in Santon et al[11] is violated, as the flammable volume is over 150 times larger than 0.1% of the enclosure volume. The largest 'non-detectable' leak in the third scenario is predicted to produce approximately steady conditions after approximately 6 minutes. The maximum flammable volume is calculated to be 1.6 m^3 and the corresponding maximum overpressure is 3 mbar. In this case the threshold criterion for the size of the flammable volume is just exceeded, although the overpressures that are calculated, assuming a stoichiometric mixture, are small.

DISCUSSION

A method for assessing the explosion hazard relating to small leaks in enclosures is described in this report. The method has been applied to a number of gas dispersion experiments and found to give reasonable agreement or overestimate the flammable volume except for cases in which a large release is directed against the ventilation stream. However the conservative assumptions in the methodology, such as the flammable volume is taken to be the volume enclosed by the 2.5% gas concentration contour and the flammable volume is taken to be stoichiometric, mean that the overpressure would tend to be overestimated in all cases by the methodology. Application of the method to a number of test cases demonstrates that its predictions are consistent with data in Santon et al[11]. However, because of the simplifying assumptions that have been made, the model may not be applicable in more complex cases, especially those in which large recirculating flows are produced by the release. There may be a need for a more sophisticated analysis of these cases.

As an illustration of the application of the method, it has been applied to two different types of enclosure. In both cases the consequences of a small leak are shown to be within typical design specifications for an enclosure provided the ventilation system is operational. In the second case, with a higher gas detection threshold and a smaller enclosure volume, the overpressure that is calculated in one case approached the design value for a typical compressor cab. The model could be used to investigate the effectiveness of possible mitigating actions for such a scenario, for example isolating the gas supply and/or reducing the inventory through blowdown, or to test the sensitivity of the consequences to changes in operating conditions, such as changing the ventilation flow. The capability to examine these factors would also be useful at the design stage for projects. The models may be used at this stage to compare alternative options and to identify a smaller number of cases for more detailed analysis, using experimental or more detailed modelling techniques

REFERENCES

1. "Hazardous Area Classification of Natural Gas Installations", IGE/SR/25, Communication 1665, Institute of Gas Engineers, 2000.
2. "Area Classification Code for Petroleum Installations, Model Code of Safe Practice, Part 15", Institute of Petroleum, London, March 1990.
3. A.D. Birch, D.R. Brown, M.G. Dodson and F. Swaffield, "The structure and concentration decay of high pressure jets of natural gas", Combustion Science and Technology, Vol. 36, pp. 249-261, 1984.
4. "A risk-based approach to hazardous area classification", Institute of Petroleum, London, November 1998.
5. Cox, Lees and Ang, "Classification of hazardous areas", IChemE, 1993.
6. Hydrocarbon leak and ignition database E&P forum Technica a.s. 1992.
7. Hydrocarbon leak and ignition database E&P forum Technica a.s. 1996.
8. R.P. Cleaver, P.F. Linden and M.R. Marshall, J. Haz. Mat. Vol 36, pp209-226, 1994.
9. M G Cooper and M.F. Fairweather, "Modelling explosions in confined volumes" Comb. Sci. and Technol. Vol 65, pp 1-14, 1985.
10. R.P. Cleaver and G.A. Shale, "Gas explosions in congested or confined volumes", International Conference and workshop on modelling the consequences of accidental releases of hazardous materials, San Francisco U.S.A., 1999.
11. R.C. Santon, C.J. Lea, M.J. Lewis, D.K. Pritchard, A.M. Thyer and Y Sinai, 2000, Studies into the role of ventilation and the consequences of leaks in gas turbine power plant acoustic enclosures and turbine halls, Hazards XV, The process, its safety, and the environment.
12. C. Savvides, V. Tam, R.P. Cleaver, S. Darby, G.Y. Buss, R.E. Britter and S. Connolly, "Gas dispersion in a congested, partially confined volume", International Conference and workshop on modelling the consequences of accidental releases of hazardous materials, San Francisco U.S.A., 1999.

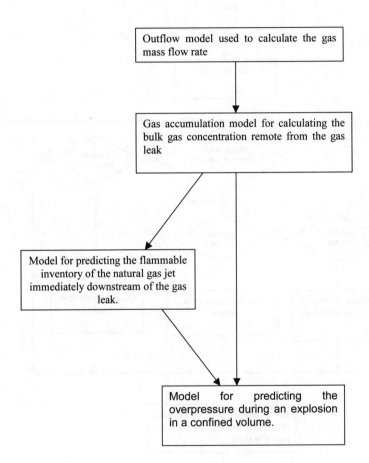

Figure 1 – Schematic diagram showing the linkage between models

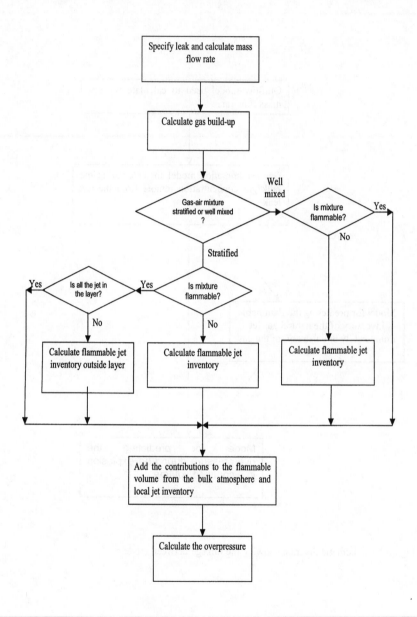

Figure 2 – Flow chart of how the models are applied to assess a small leak

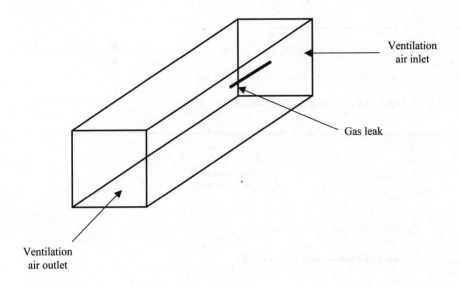

Figure 3 – A schematic diagram showing the experimental rig used by Santon et al[11].,.,

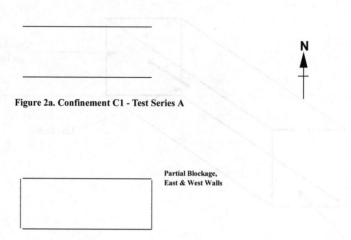

Figure 2a. Confinement C1 - Test Series A

**Partial Blockage,
East & West Walls**

Figure 2b. Confinement C2 - Test Series B

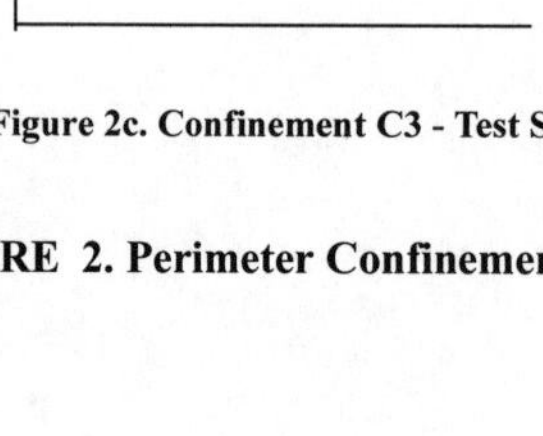

Figure 2c. Confinement C3 - Test Series C

FIGURE 2. Perimeter Confinement Arrangements

Figure 4 – Arrangements of perimeter confinement used in the dispersion experiments to investigate dispersion in an offshore module[12]

A STRUCTURED APPROACH TO INHERENT SHE IN PROCESS AND PRODUCT DEVELOPMENT

M K Fitzgerald, G R Ellis, M Mz Recaman[+]
ABB Eutech, Daresbury, Warrington UK. [+]Department of Chemical and Process Engineering, University of Sheffield, Sheffield UK[1].

The potential benefits of adopting Inherent SHE principles in process design have been recognised since the 1970s, following the pioneering work of Trevor Kletz and others. However, it has not proved so easy to realise these benefits in actual process design. Some reasons which have been put forward to account for this include cultural issues associated with the multidisciplinary nature of process development, and the lack of formal tools to support Inherent SHE ranking of process alternatives. This paper contains an introduction to a methodology which has been developed to facilitate the application of Inherent SHE principles throughout the design cycle, from initial identification of the need the develop a product, to equipment selection and preparation of a "base case" Process Flow Diagram.

Keywords: Decision-making, Inherent SHE, chemical process design, risk management.

INTRODUCTION

The increasing size and complexity of chemical plants in the 1960s and '70s, coupled with the occurrence of major accidents such as Flixborough, resulted in the development of such techniques as HAZOP (Hazard and Operability Studies), risk assessment and inherent safety as means to manage hazards and risks more effectively. By reducing the need for protective systems, it is widely believed that inherent safety can actually add commercial value to a project, unlike other tools which may simply provide a check that the design is "safe enough". However, although HAZOP and quantified risk assessment (QRA) are methods that are in common use today, the ideas of inherent safety (or, recognising the broader range of issues, Inherent SHE – Safety, Health and Environment) have not been so successfully adopted. Reasons given for this range from lack of awareness of the benefits to the lack of tools and methodologies to support assessment of process designs.

Principles such as *substitution, minimisation, moderation* and *simplification* are often used to capture the essence of the "inherently safer" (or "SHE-er") approach[1, 2]. Thus, for example, we would seek to substitute hazardous materials with less hazardous ones, minimise process inventories, moderate process conditions, and simplify processes and their operation. It is widely believed that the timely and effective use of these principles can make a process and plant cheaper to build and operate, as well as helping to improve safety, health and environmental performance. Research appears to confirm[3] that there is indeed a link between the inherent safety "score" associated with the reaction conditions, i.e. temperature, pressure and yield, and the total fixed investment associated with a plant. Recognising the range of benefits which can be gained from application of I-SHE principles, some companies, for example ICI[4], have made consideration of I-SHE a formal requirement. There is now also increasingly pressure from the regulators to consider I-SHE formally in the design process. In the UK, under the COMAH legislation, there is a requirement to demonstrate that a hierarchical approach to process design, including I-SHE, has been taken. In the USA, it is notable that the Worst Case Scenario element of Risk Management Programs (which are a requirement of the Clean Air Act) allows only the mitigating effects of passive measures to be considered – a clear driver for industry to adopt inherently safer processes.

---

[1] Now at Geon Polimeros Andinos, Cartagena, Colombia

Given the range of benefits which can be accrued from I-SHE, why have the ideas not had more impact ? Some of the factors necessary for the successful adoption of I-SHE have been identified by Mansfield[5]. These include[2]:

i)	*assuring management commitment and support, and their implications for training programmes, project organisation and other aspects of corporate activity*
ii)	*introducing and maintaining awareness of the I-SHE principles and applications among the chemists and design engineers*
iii)	*setting aside time in the development and design programme to identify and evaluate alternatives, recognising that this should save time later by reducing the need for changes*
iv)	*providing opportunities for chemists, designers and plant operators to discuss ideas at all stages in the development and design process*
v)	*actively encouraging lateral thinking and innovation*
vi)	*addressing S, H and E aspects on an integrated basis, to establish the trade-offs and conflicts these can bring.*

Many of the decisions determining the basic process and unit operations are taken early in a project, usually before formal Hazard Studies are initiated. It is therefore important that I-SHE issues are considered at these early stages where the basic SHE characteristics of the process are determined. In practice, it can be difficult to ensure this happens. In contrast to HAZOP, which is generally "owned" and driven by a project manager accountable for delivery of a physical asset, the ownership of and accountability for the early stages of product development can be less clear. In the absence of clear ownership there is the risk of a business becoming committed to a process which is not as attractive with regard to I-SHE as it might have been if the SHE aspects had been actively managed at the outset.

METHODOLOGY

We introduce in this paper a methodology which has been designed to facilitate application of I-SHE design principles throughout process selection and development. The methodology builds on ABB Eutech's involvement in the EU-funded "INSIDE" (Inherent SHE in Design) project[6], and other experience gained working with chemicals manufacturers, and dovetails with existing hazard study procedures including the ICI 6-stage methodology. The methodology which has been developed is a four-stage approach which allows the principles of I-SHE to be applied in a structured way throughout the design cycle from process selection through to equipment specification. By employing guide words and guide diagrams reminiscent of HAZOP, together with other supporting tools, a multi-disciplinary team meeting at key stages in the design cycle can assess processes in a cost-effective fashion to gain the benefits of I-SHE improvements. The approach can be applied to completely new plant, or to modification of existing plants and processes. The scope of application is however limited to projects where there is the potential to make changes to the basic chemistry, or where significant changes can be made to the Process Flow Diagram. In all cases, the depth of the study and the tools employed can be varied to suit the project.

---

[2] (Reprinted by special permission from Chemical Engineering (1996) copyright © 1996 by Chemical Week Associates., New York, NY 10038

STRUCTURE AND APPROACH

Process and product development is essentially a multi-disciplinary process in which accountabilities and responsibilities change as the project progresses from identification of a market and the need to develop a product for that market, to preparation of a "base case" process flow diagram (PFD). The ownership and focus of development move from marketing in the early stages through chemistry and process technology selection to detailed process design.

We distinguish four main phases in process selection and development, illustrated diagrammatically in Figure 1. Figure 1 also serves to emphasise that the greatest opportunities to incorporate I-SHE are at the early stages of the design cycle where there are fewer constraints – and less information available on which to base decisions. The four stages are outlined below.

Stage 1, Chemistry Route Screening
The purpose of activities at this stage is to:
- establish the business constraints and objectives of the project, in terms of timescale and cost, along with any SHE constraints on raw materials, intermediates or final product
- complete a preliminary screening of potential chemical routes so as to determine the most viable with regard to the project constraints and objectives, and nominate the most promising routes for further, more detailed, assessment

Stage 2, Chemistry Route Selection
A Chemistry Block Diagram is developed for each chemical transformation of interest. This shows flow rates along with all the reaction and separation stages, and is used to help the study team:
- determine the feasibility of the more promising chemistry routes from Stage 1, by ranking them in terms of waste generation
- select one or two routes for process design, taking into consideration cost and SHE benefits

Stage 3, Process Route Definition
A Process Block Diagram is developed and used to help the study team:
- consider the implication of proposed process conditions and inventory, with the aim of producing a process route optimised with regard to I-SHE

Stage 4, Process Route Development
A firm "base case" Process Flow Diagram is developed and used as the focus for study to:
- select appropriate equipment, taking into account opportunities to make the process more I-SHE

STUDY TEAM

The methodology requires that a team is established to guide process development throughout this cycle, but the make-up of the team will change to match the study's changing focus. Team members will include, at various stages, the Project Leader, Process Engineer, Development Chemist, SHE representative and a representative of the Business Manager. The Business Manager's role is to establish the business context and to help set the project constraints and objectives. The overall process is facilitated by a Study Leader, through a small number of focused meetings typically held at the start and end of each of the four stages. There is a strong emphasis on "off-line" activity, and the meeting overhead is small.

SUPPORTING TOOLS

Each stage of the Four-Step I-SHE Study Process is associated with a set of proformas and tools to support structured analysis of the options. Some of the tools are indicated in Figure 2, along with the stage with which they are associated. The relationship between Inherent SHE studies and Hazard Studies 1 and 2 of the ICI 6-stage Hazard Study Process is also shown. We note that Hazard Study 3 of the ICI process is the HAZOP study.

EXAMPLE – I-SHE EVALUATION TOOL

Use of one of the tools, the I-SHE Evaluation Tool is illustrated below. The I-SHE Evaluation Tool is used to help highlight opportunities for improvement with regard to I-SHE, and can be applied at Stages 2, 3 and 4. The relevant process diagram (chemistry block diagram, process block diagram and process flow diagram respectively) is subdivided into appropriate units, and I-SHE guidewords applied in a structured way using a guide diagram to provide appropriate prompts for potential improvements. Thus at Stage 2, for example, with the focus on the chemistry block diagram and opportunities for waste reduction or elimination, the guide diagram takes the form shown in Figure 3.

So, the main reaction and separation stages of a chemistry route are established, and each of these "blocks" assessed in turn for opportunities to make the process "I-SHEer". Thus the guidewords "Eliminate / Substitute", are applied to raw materials, solvents, and waste streams etc in turn. The guideword "Minimise" is then applied, and the process repeated for all guidewords, and all process chemistry blocks. The study technique is conceptually the same regardless of the stage of the process, but the focus for evaluation, along with the prompts can change. The output of the evaluation is recorded in the study meeting on a proforma which also provides for actions to be assigned and monitored.

A similar approach is adopted for the other assessment tools, which include I-SHE ranking tools to enable tradeoffs between S, H and E to be established, and others which support decision-making regarding relative advantages of routes having different SHE characteristics.

CONCLUSIONS

In order for Inherent SHE to have the greatest impact on process development, the principles must be applied early on. In general, once formal hazard studies have been started, it is too late for major conceptual changes to be made to chemical processes and we are generally faced with the challenge of risk reduction rather than risk elimination.

Application of the ideas presented in this paper has been seen to have a real impact on process development, leading to processes which have a lower SHE impact as a result of:

- inventory reduction
- use of different solvents
- reformulation of catalysts to less toxic form

The methodology which has been presented here has been trialed on table-top exercises and is both straightforward to use and time-efficient. Adoption of this approach to process evaluation helps generate a "level playing field" when comparing different process routes and clarifying SHE issues. Thus, for example, the different requirements of different processes for on-site storage and for waste treatment are brought out in an integrated assessment of total SHE impact, instead of the focus being primarily on the core process. Use of such an approach should also help encourage early formation of project teams and so drive better communication between disciplines - leading to less misdirected effort and the consequent need for re-work.

Precise legislative requirements for Inherent SHE study under COMAH remain to be clarified, but one further advantage of this proforma-based technique is that can be used to demonstrate that a structured process has been adopted to justify the selection of the preferred route and process design.

REFERENCES
1   Kletz, T., 1991, "Plant Design for Safety. A User-Friendly Approach", Hemisphere, ISBN 1-56032-068-0

2   Hendershot, D., 1997, "Inherently Safer Chemical Process Design", *J Loss Prev Process Ind*, Vol 10, No 3, pp.151-157

3   Edwards, D. W. and Lawrence, D., 1993, "Assessing the Inherent Safety of Chemical Process Routes: Is There a Relation Between Plant Costs and Inherent Safety ?", *Trans I Chem E*, Vol 71, Part B

4   Hawksley, J. L. and Preston, M. L., 1997, "Inherent SHE – 20 Years of Evolution", paper presented at Hazards XIII. I Chem E (NW) Symposium, held at UMIST, Manchester, UK, 22-24 April. I Chem E Symposium series No. 141, pp11-23

5   Mansfield, D. P., 1996, "Viewpoints on Implementing Inherent Safety", *Chemical Engineering*, March, pp 78-80

6   INSIDE Project, 1997, "The Inherent SHE Evaluation (INSET) Toolkit, Volumes I and II, Version 1, July 1997", Final Report from Contract No. EUSV-CT94-0416 under Major Hazards research programme of the European Commission, DG XII

Figure 1 – Inherent SHE Study Process

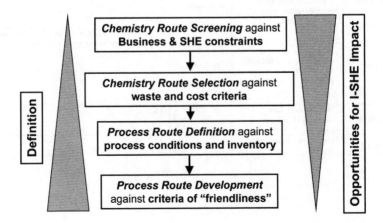

Figure 2 – Study Tools and Techniques, and Timing

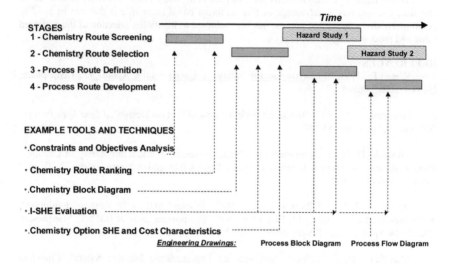

Figure 3 – Stage 2 Guide Diagram

Guide word	Meaning	Applied to	Prompts
Eliminate / Substitute	Remove the hazard or the material, or task creating it OR Substitute less hazardous materials and processes wherever possible	Raw materials Solvents Waste streams By-products Recycle streams Purge	*Is it possible to avoid a waste stream?* *Etc.*
Minimise	Minimise the amount of hazardous material that is in use or waste that is generated		*Is it possible to reduce the amount of waste produced, or to reduce the number of waste streams?* *Etc.*
Moderate	Moderate the process conditions of the hazardous materials		*Etc.*
Simplify	Simplify the process that is used		*Etc.*

HYDROGEN EXPLOSIONS - AN EXAMPLE OF HAZARD AVOIDANCE AND CONTROL

I.D. Kempsell, M.J. Wakem, M.P. Fairclough and J.M. Ingram[*]
British Nuclear Fuels plc
[*]Chemical Engineering Research Centre, South Bank Univ. London, SE1 0AA

Synopsis

Many nuclear chemical plants have to deal with hydrogen gas generation caused by reactions such as radiolysis of water. Because of the continuing major construction and decommissioning activities on the Sellafield site, guidance has been developed to build in safety as early as possible to ensure the safety of new plant and to continuously review existing plant. The guidance adopts the approach that prevention is better than complicated design. Therefore a hierarchy has been adopted that:

i) the design should be such that hazards are avoided

ii) the design should use passive features

iii) any failure or fault should produce no significant deviation

iv) the plant should be brought to a safe state by continuously available safety measures

v) administrative safety measures are an option only when there is no reasonable alternative

vi) finally mitigation is taken into account

The aim is to develop a design as close to the top of this list as possible, and to tailor assessment methods appropriate to the stage of design development. The application of these principles has been developed for the review of existing plant.

The guidance is supported by data and methods that may be required in making an assessment in detail (e.g. radiolysis generation rates, ventilation calculations, etc), and references further sources of information.

Keywords: hydrogen, explosion prevention

BACKGROUND

Hydrogen generation, and hence the need to assess and control hydrogen explosions hazards is common to almost all nuclear chemical processing and many waste storage activities

When the phrase "Hydrogen explosion" is used in connection with the nuclear industry peoples thoughts generally turn to well publicised incidents such as Three Mile Island or Chernobyl. At Three Mile Island an explosion of hydrogen, generated by the reaction of hot metal with steam, occurred during a severe loss of cooling accident in a nuclear reactor. This incident prompted a great deal of research into hydrogen explosions and models were developed to assist in severe accident analysis [1].

Although accidents such as TMI attract a lot of publicity, hydrogen is routinely generated at nuclear installations by other mechanisms such as radiolysis, corrosion, chemical degradation, and release from the disturbance of a bed of solids. It may also be used as a feed gas. Most of the above mechanisms for production of hydrogen are common to many industrial (and natural) processes. Radiolysis however is specific to the nuclear industry. Radiolytic hydrogen is encountered in a wide range of scenarios and is a potential hydrogen issue for many different processes and operations.

Incidents of hydrogen explosions

Given the extent of the potential for hydrogen generation at nuclear installations and in particular reprocessing plant there appears to have been few reported incidents of hydrogen explosions in recent years. This would indicate that what incidents there have been must have been minor i.e. resulting in neither serious injury nor a significant release of activity and that, in general, hazards are being identified and controlled effectively. It is however interesting to note that a significant proportion of the incidents reported related to the unforeseen generation of hydrogen, in storage flasks/waste drums, such as illustrated by the case history below [2].

The incident, involving a transport cask, occurred at the Point Beach Nuclear Power Plant on the 28th May 1996. A hydrogen explosion occurred during the welding of the shield lid on the multi-assembly sealed basket of a spent fuel storage cask. The root cause of the accident in this case was the failure of designers at several stages of the design process to identify a mechanism by which significant quantities of hydrogen could be produced within the flask. The process of transferring the spent fuel from the storage pond to the cask consisted of the following stages. The cask is first lowered into the spent fuel pool and loaded with spent fuel. It is then removed from the pool remaining mostly filled with pond water. The lid is then lowered into place and welded shut prior to the flask being drained of water, vacuum dried and filled with helium. An investigation into the root cause of the accident revealed that the hydrogen had been produced by an electrochemical reaction of the basket's zinc containing coating with the borated fuel pond water. The delay between putting the lid in place and welding was sufficient for a flammable atmosphere to form in the cask. The explosion was sufficient to lift the lid by about 3 inches but there was no damage to the cask, injury to workers or release of activity as a result of the explosion.

In contrast, outside of the nuclear industry, many of the incidents reported relate to explosive atmospheres formed by releases of large volumes of hydrogen from pressurised systems. An example of such an incident occurred at the Fuji Oil Sodegaura refinery, Japan in 1992 [3]. A large release of hydrogen occurred from a rupture on a feed/reactor effluent heat exchanger on the heavy oil indirect desulphurization unit as the plant was being started up after shutdown. After a few minutes, during which time personnel took measures to try and stop the leak, it exploded killing ten people and injuring seven. In this case the cause of the leak was traced back to a repair made to a gasket retainer on the heat exchanger. There have also been reported incidents of explosions inside vessels and pipelines. One such incident occurred in a pipeline for the transfer of CO_2 from an ammonia plant [4]. The gas in the pipeline normally contained 2-3% hydrogen and a trip system was installed to shut down the transfer process if the concentration exceeded 8%. When the explosion occurred the plant had been down and the line out of operation for six days. The line had also been purged with nitrogen and blinded. From the damage it was estimated that the pipeline must have contained more than 10-15 % hydrogen and 40% air. The cause of failure of the trip system was clearly identified. The trip required signals from two hydrogen analysers, sent via a printer, and one of these had been disabled whist re-configuring one of the analysers/printer for the monitoring of H_2 in N_2. It was not fully established why the nitrogen purge failed, how a sufficient volume of air to form an explosive mixture could have entered the pipeline or the exact source of ignition.

WHY IS THERE A NEED FOR GUIDANCE?

Hydrogen is a potential issue for many different types of plant and processes. All designers and assessors need to be able to identify that they have hydrogen issues, have guidance on how to assess the hazard, how to control it and know when to seek expert advice. In the past designers would have to seek information from a number of sources (e.g. radiolysis experts, corrosion experts, flammability experts etc.) in order to assess the hydrogen hazards and implement suitable explosion prevention and protection measures.

There is considerable guidance in the literature on design for hydrogen issues, and although in BNFL and the nuclear industry in general there have been very few reported incidents in recent years involving hydrogen. It is however:

1. important to remain vigilant
2. desirable to minimise reliance on designers and experts
3. important that hydrogen control and good design should be built into the design process as early as possible
4. important that decisions on hydrogen control should be integrated with other hazard elimination or reduction decisions, and
5. advantageous to 'demystify' the majority of hydrogen issues, making better designs more likely

The development of guidance has been a considerable undertaking. The exercise began by reviewing international standards and guides. There is a wealth of good literature spanning a large field including furnace design, ventilation design, explosion prevention and protection, overpressure calculations, explosion reliefs, etc. Given this background, it was decided to produce a 'route map' based guidance using basic principles to enable designers and reviewers of existing plants, to see the 'wood from the trees'.

This led to the development of hydrogen guidance within BNFL.

THE PRINCIPLES

All new plant should be designed, in order of preference, according to the following principles.

1. As far as reasonably practicable avoid the generation/use of hydrogen.
2. (a) If hydrogen generation cannot be eliminated measures must be taken to prevent the formation of flammable atmospheres. This can be achieved by various means

   - By control of the hydrogen concentration, or
   - By control of the oxygen concentration, or
   - By operation above the autoignition (AIT) temperature

2. (b) As a matter of good practice where there is potential for significant hydrogen generation/release, irrespective of any explosion prevention measures, it is required (so far as it is reasonably practicable) that:

- particularly if consequences of an explosion are high, vessels and pipework are designed to withstand hydrogen explosions.

- ignition sources should be eliminated.

Credit should however not (or need to be) taken for such measures in the safety case. Safety cases requiring credit to be taken for such measures are unlikely to be acceptable (see point 5 below). Safety cases should be based on the prevention of the formation of flammable atmospheres.

3. In the event of fault conditions the design should be such that the deviation away from normal operating conditions is slow and a flammable atmosphere is never formed.

 (a) Ideally the plant design should aim to be deterministically safe i.e. it should be physically impossible for significant volumes of flammable atmosphere to form e.g. by use of natural ventilation.
 (b) Only if a passive safety design is not possible should an active system be used to prevent flammable volumes forming.

4. Any design or process which gives a sudden release of a large volume of gas or allows one to accumulate should be avoided if possible.

5. Plant designs relying on the low consequence of an explosion (e.g. explosion containment) are generally unacceptable, as such an event is likely to be regarded as a loss of control of the process, and would lead to prolonged shutdown during investigation. For such a design to be acceptable it will be necessary to demonstrate why more preferred methods were not applicable.

In the case of existing plant the same principles should be applied if reasonably practicable. Nevertheless, there will be instances where this is not the case since the risk associated with modifying plant to fully meet the design principles could be greater than leaving it unchanged. In such cases modifications (if any) would be justified on a balance of risk.

The design principles and the acceptability of various methods for dealing with hydrogen explosions can be seen more clearly on the 'road maps' discussed below.

DETAILED GUIDANCE

The guidance is intended to ensure that the design principles are being applied throughout the design process from the earliest stages i.e. from the concept stage studies right through to HAZOP of the final design. There were two important considerations during development:

- The guidance should be comprehensive, covering as many scenarios where hydrogen hazards could arise as reasonably possible.
- Give simple guidance in a format that design and safety engineers, without a great deal of specialist knowledge of hydrogen issues, could use safely. This should allow them to assess the hydrogen hazard and produce safety cases in straightforward commonly encountered scenarios but instructing them to seek guidance from specialists in cases that could present problematic/difficult hydrogen issues.

The development of the guidance required extensive input from people both from within BNFL and externally across a range of disciplines with relevant experience/interests in hydrogen issues including inter alia CFD modellers, process engineers/designers, research scientists (e.g. corrosion experts, radiolysis experts), flammability & explosion experts. The finished guidance has also been reviewed by two external bodies. Fauske & Associates in the US, who have experience of hydrogen issues with similarities to those at Sellafied in US nuclear installations, and also the UK Health and Safety Laboratory, Buxton.

The guidance is given in the form of annotated roadmaps.

Prior to considering the individual road maps it is worth considering some potential means by which hydrogen may be generated which reflects the range of scenarios to which the guide is applicable.

Sources of hydrogen

The initial step in the design process is to identify and quantify all sources of hydrogen. Particularly at the conceptual stages consideration should be given to means by which it could be minimised or eliminated.

Radiolysis

Radiolytic hydrogen is produced through the absorption of ionising radiation by a range of materials. It may be encountered in connection with, for example, aqueous solutions containing radionuclides (with respect to re-processing the amount of hydrogen produced is often significantly reduced by the presence of high concentrations of nitrate ions), other hydrogen containing solutions (e.g. kerosene), contaminated materials such as plastics, radioactive waste encapsulated in concrete and fuel storage in ponds (i.e. radiolysis of water). The determination of the hydrogen generation rates for radiolysis is based on empirically derived $G(H_2)$ values which give the molecules of hydrogen produced per MeV of radiation absorbed for a specific material e.g. water and type of radiation e.g. α. It is usually possible to give bounding case values for $G(H_2)$ that can be used safely by non-experts.

Corrosion

The other most commonly encountered mechanism for hydrogen generation at BNFL installations is corrosion. Hydrogen from corrosion is less extensive in terms of the number of processes in which it occurs but is often more difficult to assess. The hydrogen generation rate can be affected by many factors such as the exposed surface area of metal (this will reduce significantly over time in the case of Magnox swarf in water), oxygenation of the solution, and pH (high pH reduces Magnox corrosion rates). In addition in might be necessary to also consider the possibility of galvanic coupling. Other impurities, particularly chloride will also enhance corrosion rates. Hydrogen generated by corrosion is typically an issue for waste (e.g. Magnox cladding from decanning fuel) and fuel storage in silos/ponds. There is considerable amount of ongoing research being conducted by BNFL into hydrogen generation from corrosion to identify different cases rather than using a single worst case hydrogen generation rate.

Release from disturbance of sludges

Where radioactive material is stored under water an amount of hydrogen (produced by for example radiolysis or corrosion) will remain trapped within the sludge bed. If the material needs to be recovered from the tanks, disturbance of the bed will cause some of the trapped hydrogen to be released. This can present an additional problem for decommissioning operations since it can sometimes be difficult to predict the holdup and the amount that will be released and the rate of release during disturbance of the sludge bed. Such cases will invariably require input from experts in, for example, soil mechanics. As detailed on the flow sheets processes should be designed to gradually disturb such beds to release hydrogen in a controlled manner, or the vessel ullage should be inerted when it can be demonstrated that simultaneous oxygen and hydrogen generataion is negligible.

Feed Material

A third significant source of hydrogen is its use as feed material for certain reprocessing operations. Very few BNFL processes use significant quantities of hydrogen as a feed. Some use 100% hydrogen as a process material, but the majority use an 'eversafe' hydrogen-in-argon mixture.

Reduction of water

The application of water to esatablished fires involving reactive metals could potentially result in a hydrogen explosion. This is not an issue for normal plant operations but is a consideration for emergency fire fighting procedure/systems.

FIGURE 1   SUMMARY OF EXPLOSION PREVENTION MEASURES (SHEET 0)

Figure 1 would mainly be used at the early stages of the design process, such as concept development, process selection and early flowsheeting. The ability to control any hydrogen hazard needs to be evaluated when considering the various process designs options for new plant/processes. The ability to control the hydrogen hazard could determine whether a particular design is viable at all.

There are a number of methods for dealing with hydrogen hazards given on the roadmaps. The most appropriate method is determined by too many different factors (not necessarily related to hydrogen hazards) to give definitive guidance on which is most applicable. It is however possible to offer guidance on how various options for the control of the hydrogen hazard relates to the hierarchy of the design principles as detailed above. This is the main function of Figure 1.

It can be seen that the boxes are joined by lines of different thickness. The thicker the line connecting the final box the more preferred the solution with regard to the control of hydrogen hazards.

For example:

box 0.5 – preferred path-ideally plant should be deterministically safe
box 0.10 – generally unacceptable – case based on low risk from explosion

If a less preferred solution is to be adopted it will be necessary to demonstrate why a more preferred solution was not applicable. The numbering of the boxes is intended to be used to form an auditable trail of this decision process.

The methods given on the roadmap for dealing with hydrogen hazards and their typical applications are described briefly below:

Control of the hydrogen concentration

In most cases explosions are prevented by maintaining sufficiently low hydrogen levels; <25% LFL for normal operation and <LFL under fault conditions (i.e. 1%(v/v) and 4%(v/v) at room temperature and pressure). This is normally accomplished for process vessels through forced ventilation, since natural ventilation or diffusion rates are often too small (especially to remain below 1%). In existing plant hydrogen is usually produced by mechanisms such as radiolysis of aqueous solutions and the release into the headspace of the vessel is slow and controlled. Existing process vessels typically have two independent air purges (from for example pneumercators which measure liquor levels by bubbling air into the vessels' liquors) and the hydrogen concentration in the vessels can be estimated from the hydrogen generation rate and purge flows. Hydrogen detectors are rarely fitted to vessels used in these circumstances, to minimise the amount of equipment requiring maintenance in radioactive areas. Fault conditions are revealed by other means e.g. the detection of low flow purge air flows, high liquor levels (and hence increased hydrogen generation), etc. The combined flows from a group of process vessels often have on-line H2 measurement for reassurance. There is no need to specify limits for operation above the UFL since (for hydrogen) they are, in effect, defined by setting limits on the oxygen concentration as detailed below.

Although forced ventilation is the most common method by which hydrogen concentrations are controlled, it is far from the only one. Other methods currently employed include:

Diffusion – Although diffusion is a slow process it can be a useful means of controlling hydrogen concentrations in storage drums/ sealed flasks/ packages in which the hydrogen generation rate is sufficiently small. For example for low level waste storage in drums it may often be possible to keep the hydrogen concentration in the drum below 1%(v/v) by fitting a filter to the drum through which hydrogen could diffuse. Another example is the storage of plutonium contaminated material in sealed polyethylene film through which hydrogen can diffuse.

Recombiners - Essentially these are noble metal catalysts (usually palladium) which promote the low temperature recombination of hydrogen produced in the ullages of enclosures/vessels with oxygen to form water. Their use has so far been restricted to fuel transport/storage flasks.

Natural Ventilation - Where hydrogen is released slowly into buildings of normal industrial design it may be possible to make a safety case based on generic data for the natural ventilation rates. In such cases a large safety margin would be applied to the predicted concentrations (i.e. an order of magnitude). It is however a useful as a tool for demonstrating that there is no credible explosion hazard in clear cut situations.

Buoyancy Driven Flow - Hydrogen is very much less dense than air and mixtures of small amounts of hydrogen with air will be significantly less dense than air alone. If a vessel containing a hydrogen air mixture has, for example, two vertical pipes attached to the top of it (open to atmosphere) a buoyancy driven flow will be established. Fresh air will flow into the vessel down one pipe and hydrogen/air mixture out of the other the pressure driving the flow being related to the difference in density of the air and hydrogen/air mixture and the height of the outlet pipe. In some simple well defined situations this can be a good passive method of controlling the hydrogen concentration.

Use of intrinsically safe fuel inert mixtures as feed

Although hydrogen issues are mainly associated with hydrogen produced as an unwanted by product of radiolysis and corrosion it is used as a reducing atmosphere in certain nuclear chemical processing operations. For a given temperature/pressure there is a critical amount of hydrogen in a given inert gas below which a flammable atmosphere cannot form when mixed with air (i.e. the hydrogen inert mixture can be regarded as non-flammable provided its composition is reliable). This is obviously preferable to operating with a high concentration of hydrogen (above the UFL/below LOC) particularly as many BNFL processes operate at sub-atmospheric pressure.

Control of the oxidant concentration

This is generally only considered where it is not possible to prevent explosions by control of the hydrogen concentration. Given the choice between forced ventilation with air and inerting it will normally be cheaper and easier to opt for ventilation particularly as radiolysis will often generate oxygen as well as hydrogen. There are however several scenarios where keeping the atmosphere below the Limiting Oxygen Concentration (<2% (v/v) oxygen for normal operation (the LOC minus 3% (From NFPA 69)) and < 5%(v/v) under fault conditions) would be considered:

1. If the process requires high concentrations of hydrogen.
2. Where a large volume of hydrogen could be suddenly released (e.g. from disturbance of sludge, and where the volume of oxygen co-released is negligible).
3. If the air ventilation rates required are particularly excessive. Even if hydrogen and oxygen are being released in stoichiometric proportions the required ventilation rate using inert gas will be lower (half the generation rate and double the limit for normal

operation at RTP (2%(v/v)), and therefore has the potential benefit of lower activity discharges to air.

Another means of controlling the oxygen concentration is the use of getters. These are essentially materials that slowly corrode and in doing so remove oxygen from the atmosphere. Their use, so far, has been restricted to fuel transport/storage flasks.

Operation above the Autoignition temperature

There are a limited number of processes which need to operate above the autoignition temperature (560°C). If this is the case it can be argued that the rate of oxidation will be sufficient to prevent a significant volume of pre-mixed flammable atmosphere from forming.

Low Risk from Explosion - Explosion Containment and Mitigation measures

For obvious reasons mitigation methods such as explosion venting, which would result in the release of material to the environment have always had extremely limited applicability to nuclear chemical processes. Less obvious is the restriction on the use of explosion containment. In principle explosion containment would be a valid means of controlling hydrogen explosion hazards. However in practice in order for a safety case based on explosion containment to be acceptable it is necessary to demonstrate that the vessel is not only designed to withstand the explosion now but is also designed to do so after, say 40 years of use. The undesirability of the use of explosion containment stems from both a requirement to prevent explosions in preference to minimising the consequences, as indicated by the design principles above, and the inevitable impracticalities of designing such vessels. In fact the majority of vessels constructed to BNFL standard pressure vessel design codes will withstand the deflagration of a stoichiometric hydrogen air mixture (initially at RTP).

FIGURES 2,3 DETAILED FLOWSHEETS – DESIGN/ASSESSMENT OF EXPLOSION PREVENTION MEASURES (SHEETS 5 AND 6)

These are primarily intended for use at later stages of the design process. There is also an additional set of similar flowsheets for the assessment of existing plant (i.e. for the production of Continued Operation Safety Reports). With existing plant the risk associated with modifying to meet the current explosion prevention standards could be greater than doing nothing i.e. a balance of risk argument would be permitted to justify not installing improvements, whereas new plant would need to meet current standards.

The flowsheets effectively set the explosion prevention standard. They would be used initially in taking the chosen conceptual design through to the production of plant flow diagrams and revisited again during hazard assessments of the detailed engineering designs.

These flowsheets give a standardised process for assessing the adequacy of explosion prevention measures. The required safety standards in terms of limits of hydrogen concentration etc. for safe operation under normal and fault conditions are built into the flow sheets. The flow sheets incorporate detailed annotations and highlight many potential problems/pitfalls.

Again the boxes are numbered in order to facilitate the production of an auditable trail, and the thicker lines indicate the preferred design which reflects the hierarchy of the design principles. For example, it can be seen how the design principles are incorporated into the road maps:

box 5.3 –   requirement to minimise hydrogen generation.
box 6.10 –   it is better that a fault would never result in a flammable atmosphere rather than making a case based on the fault being repaired in time.

It should be noted that the flow sheets intentionally do not give guidance on the required reliability of air purges etc as this is adequately covered by other BNFL standards/guidance.

General guidance

As mentioned in the design principles (and again on the road maps) there is a general requirement to eliminate, so far as is reasonably practicable, ignition sources wherever there is a potential for the release/generation of significant amounts of hydrogen. Credit should however not normally (or need to) be taken for such measures in safety assessments.

In the case of existing plant where it is necessary to take credit for the elimination of ignition sources to make a safety case, expert advice would have to be sought and the safety case will require technical peer review and a full audit trail of decisions.

Principal ignition sources include the following: Static sparks, sparks from electrical equipment, lightning, hot surfaces/particles (from frictional heating/impacts) and flames (e.g. from spontaneous ignition). With regard to nuclear chemical processing spontaneous ignition is known to be a potential problem with unusual chemicals such as uranium hydride, which can be generated in an atmosphere of damp hydrogen rich gas.

ASSESSMENT OF THE CONSEQUENCES OF EXPLOSIONS

The Guidance encourages explosion prevention. However, it is worth noting that he consequences of hydrogen within vessels/enclosures explosion would also normally be assessed to ensure compliance with quantified risk analysis techniques, as required by the Nuclear Installations Inspectorate.

CURRENT RESEARCH

BNFL is currently undertaking significant research for projects and for generic purposes. The principal generic research is in the following areas:

CFD modelling and validation programme and full size modelling of hydrogen dispersion in vessels from bubble release
- Determination of likely overpressures during deflagration

Detonation/deflagration transition of confined hydrogen/air mixtures
- The geometry of containment may be critical in determining the transition from deflagration to detonation. The safety issue is to determine the effect the geometry

of a containment may have on the transition from deflagration to detonation of an ignited hydrogen/air mixture

Hydrogen removal mechanisms

- Safety can be improved if methods could be developed for the safe removal of hydrogen using Recombiners or Getters. The current strategy is to develop Recombiners (catalysts that recombine hydrogen and oxygen) as an alternative to Getters (materials which remove oxygen).

ADVANTAGES OF THE ROADMAP APPROACH

Producing the guidance in the form of road maps has a number of significant advantages.

1. Guidance presented in this form can be interpreted far more easily than written text.
2. At the concept stage of the design process adopting this approach encourages designers to consider a range of solutions and not to opt for a particular path simply because that was how it was done last time.
3. Allows designers, without in depth knowledge of hydrogen issues, to identify hydrogen hazards and design in appropriate explosion prevention measures without recourse to experts in straightforward scenarios.
4. Provides a standardised framework for assessment of hydrogen hazards for a wide range of scenarios.
5. Numbered boxes simplify the production of an auditable trail of the decision process throughout all stages of the design/assessment.
6. The use of guidance in this way may be used as the basis for the development of an expert system.

REFERENCES

1. Lee J.H.S., Berman M., "Hydrogen Combustion and its Application to Nuclear Reactor Safety", Adv Heat Transfer, 29 59 (1997).

2. NRC Report No. 50-266/301-96005, "Point Beach Augmented Inspection Team Report", 1996

3. The High Pressure Gas Safety Inst. of Japan, "The Fuji Oil Sodegaura Refinery Accident", Loss Prevention Bulletin (116), pp9-14, 1993

4. J.O. Pande, R.G. Stokke, J. Tonheim, "Explosion of Hydrogen in a Pipeline for CO_2", Loss Prevention Bulletin (156), pp11-13, 2000

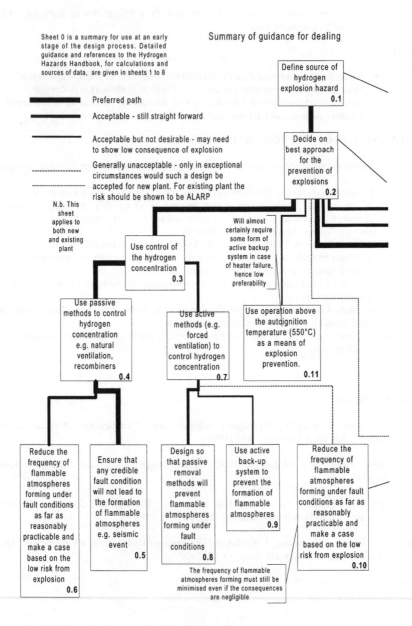

Sheet 0 is a summary for use at an early
stage of the design process. Detailed
guidance and references to the Hydrogen
Hazards Handbook, for calculations and
sources of data, are given in sheets 1 to 8

Summary of guidance for dealing

━━━━ Preferred path

──── Acceptable - still straight forward

──── Acceptable but not desirable - may need
to show low consequence of explosion

┄┄┄┄ Generally unacceptable - only in exceptional
⋯⋯⋯ circumstances would such a design be
accepted for new plant. For existing plant the
risk should be shown to be ALARP

N.b. This
sheet
applies to
both new
and existing
plant

**Define source of
hydrogen
explosion hazard**
0.1

**Decide on
best approach
for the
prevention of
explosions**
0.2

Will almost
certainly require
some form of
active backup
system in case
of heater failure,
hence low
preferability

**Use control of
the hydrogen
concentration**
0.3

**Use passive
methods to control
hydrogen
concentration
e.g. natural
ventilation,
recombiners**
0.4

**Use active
methods (e.g.
forced
ventilation) to
control hydrogen
concentration**
0.7

**Use operation above
the autoignition
temperature (550°C)
as a means of
explosion
prevention.**
0.11

**Reduce the
frequency of
flammable
atmospheres
forming under
fault conditions
as far as
reasonably
practicable and
make a case
based on the
low risk from
explosion**
0.6

**Ensure that
any credible
fault condition
will not lead to
the formation
of flammable
atmospheres
e.g. seismic
event**
0.5

**Design so
that passive
removal
methods will
prevent
flammable
atmospheres
forming under
fault
conditions**
0.8

**Use active
back-up
system to
prevent the
formation of
flammable
atmospheres**
0.9

**Reduce the
frequency of
flammable
atmospheres
forming under fault
conditions as far as
reasonably
practicable and
make a case
based on the low
risk from explosion**
0.10

The frequency of flammable
atmospheres forming must still be
minimised even if the consequences
are negligible

Figure 1   Summary of explosion prevention measures

With hydrogen hazards (Sheet 0)

Identify sources, quantify rate of generation/release, determine whether releases are sufficiently slow and controlled for the ullage of a vessel/enclosure to be considered perfectly mixed.

When designing new processes designs which could result in large uncontrolled releases of hydrogen will not be acceptable. Additionally new processes should be optimised to ensure that hydrogen generation is kept to a minimum, processes must not result in the accumulation of large amounts of waste which could at some point in time become the source of a hydrogen explosion hazard. Where there is a potential for hydrogen releases designs should attempt to eliminate sources of ignition even though little credit may be taken for it in safety assessments

The thicker lines only indicate which methods are more favoured/acceptable purely with regard to explosion prevention - It is only one factor in deciding the best approach for a specific case, in many cases there will be no option but to take a less preferred approach.

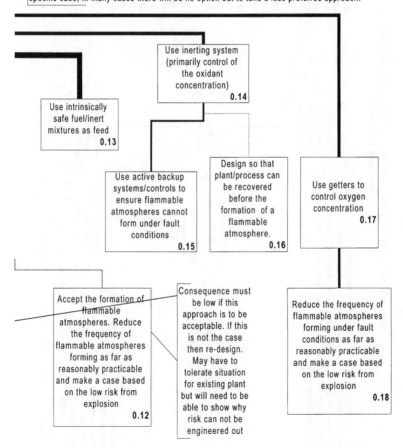

Selection of Explosion Prevention methodology for New Processes and Procedures (Sheet 5)

Elimination of sources of ignition is not an acceptable method of explosion prevention for hydrogen. Only in very specific cases can any credit be given for the elimination of ignition sources. Plant designs should still however avoid ignition sources and zoning principles be applied.

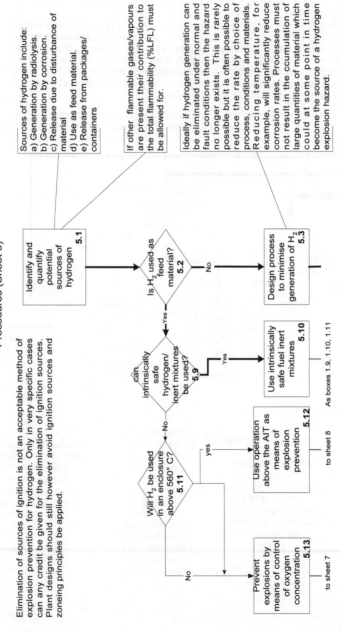

5.1 Identify and quantify potential sources of hydrogen

Sources of hydrogen include:
a) Generation by radiolysis.
b) Generation by corrosion.
c) Release due to disturbance of material
d) Use as feed material.
e) Release from packages/ containers

5.2 Is H_2 used as feed material?

If other flammable gases/vapours are present their contribution to the total flammability (%LFL) must be allowed for.

5.3 Design process to minimise generation of H_2

Ideally if hydrogen generation can be eliminated under normal and fault conditions then the hazard no longer exists. This is rarely possible but it is often possible to reduce the rate by choice of process, conditions and materials. Reducing temperature, for example, will significantly reduce corrosion rates. Processes must not result in the ccumulation of large quantities of material which could at some point in time become the source of a hydrogen explosion hazard.

Yes

No

5.9 can intrinsically safe hydrogen/ inert mixtures be used?

Yes

5.10 Use intrinsically safe fuel inert mixtures

As boxes 1.9, 1.10, 1.11

No

5.11 Will H_2 be used in an enclosure above 560° C?

yes

5.12 Use operation above the AIT as means of explosion prevention

to sheet 8

No

5.13 Prevent explosions by means of control of oxygen concentration

to sheet 7

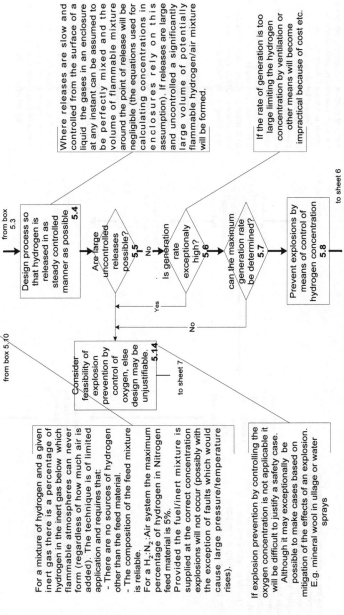

Where releases are slow and controlled from the surface of a liquid the gases in an enclosure at any instant can be assumed to be perfectly mixed and the volume of flammable mixture around the point of release will be negligible (the equations used for calculating concentrations in enclosures rely on this assumption). If releases are large and uncontrolled a significantly large volume of potentially flammable hydrogen/air mixture will be formed.

If the rate of generation is too large limiting the hydrogen concentration by ventilation or other means will become impractical because of cost etc.

from box 5.3

Design process so that hydrogen is released in as steady controlled manner as possible **5.4**

Are large uncontrolled releases possible? **5.5**

No

Is generation rate exceptionally high? **5.6**

Yes

No

can the maximum generation rate be determined? **5.7**

Prevent explosions by means of control of hydrogen concentration **5.8**

to sheet 6

from box 5.10

Consider feasibility of explosion prevention by control of oxygen, else design may be unjustifiable. **5.14**

to sheet 7

For a mixture of hydrogen and a given inert gas there is a percentage of hydrogen in the inert gas below which flammable atmospheres can never form (regardless of how much air is added). The technique is of limited application and requires that:
- There are no sources of hydrogen other than the feed material.
- The composition of the feed mixture is reliable.
For a $H_2:N_2:$Air system the maximum percentage of hydrogen in Nitrogen feed material is 5%.
Provided the fuel/inert mixture is supplied at the correct concentration explosions will not occur (possibly with the exception of faults which would cause large pressure/temperature rises).

If explosion prevention by controlling the oxygen concentration is not applicable it will be difficult to justify a safety case.
Although it may exceptionally be possible to make cases based on mitigation of the effects of an explosion.
E.g. mineral wool in ullage or water sprays

Figure 2   Detailed flow sheet for the design/assessment of explosion prevention measures

New Processes: Application of Explosion Prevention by Control of Hydrogen Concentration (Sheet 6)

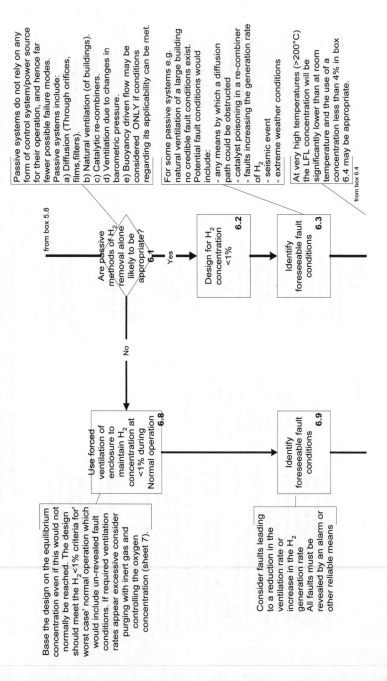

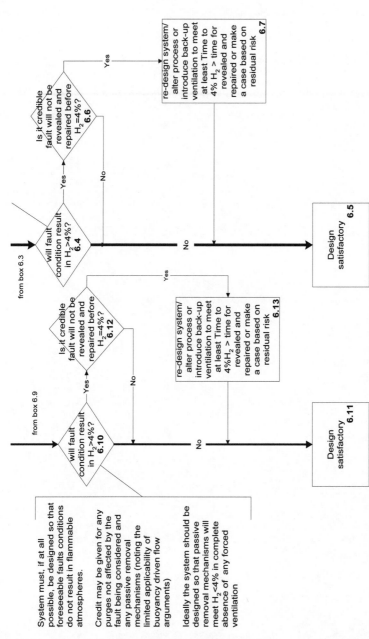

Figure 3   Detailed flow sheet for the design/assessment of explosion prevention measures

AIR INGRESS INTO NITROGEN INERTED VENT PIPES

P. Hooker, G.R. Astbury and G. Fauré[*]

Avecia Limited, P.O.Box 42, Blackley, Manchester M9 8ZS,

*Ecole des Mines d'Albi, Campus Jarlard, 81013 Albi, Cédex 09, France

Providing a continuous flow of nitrogen through a vent pipe can avoid the ingress of air back down the vent. In the event of the nitrogen flow stopping air will enter the vent pipe. This could result in the loss of the inert gas blanket within the vented vessel if the nitrogen flow was not re-established quickly enough. Knowledge of how quickly air enters the vent pipe would be useful in devising a suitable corrective action plan. This paper presents the results of a series of experiments in which pipes of 1", 2", 4" and 6" nominal bore were inerted with nitrogen, the nitrogen flow stopped and the ingress of air into the pipes measured. Comparison of the experimental results with a theoretical model revealed that the predictions of the model were of the same order of magnitude as the experimental results for many of the test conditions. However, it was apparent that transient effects became dominant in situations where the vent pipe volume is small compared to the volume of the vessel.

inert gas diffusion nitrogen oxygen concentration vent pipe

INTRODUCTION

Many chemical process operations involve the use of flammable materials. In many cases it is possible to avoid the occurrence of fires and explosions by implementing precautions to avoid potential ignition sources. However, in other processes there are inherent ignition sources, such as pyrophoric materials, that cannot be avoided. In such circumstances it is common practice to operate the process in an inert atmosphere, where oxygen is displaced by an inert gas to such an extent that the oxygen concentration is too low to support combustion. In many cases it is necessary to provide the vessel in which the inert atmosphere is established with an atmospheric vent, for example, if gases are liberated during the process. In order to prevent air diffusing back down the vent line a continuous flow of inert gas can be applied to the vent.

The flow of inert gas through the vent line will establish an equilibrium oxygen concentration profile along the length of the vent. The oxygen concentration profile has been studied previously by Husa[1,2] for a number of vent pipe diameters, employing various purge gas types and flow rates. The work of Husa indicated a logarithmic relationship between oxygen concentration and distance from the open end of the vent pipe under steady-state conditions. Recently reported work by the authors[3] has given evidence to support the relationship proposed by Husa. However, there is little practical information available on the rate of air ingress into vent pipes when the flow of inert gas stops. Earlier work by the authors had suggested that there was a power law relationship between the time taken for the oxygen concentration to increase to a particular value and the distance from open end of the pipe. Analysis by the authors of data generated by Tite, Greening and Sutton[4] had also indicated that there may be a power law relationship between these two parameters. The relationship determined by Husa has been used as the starting point in the development of a theoretical model of the relationship between the oxygen concentration, depth down the pipe and time. Experiments were carried out to measure these parameters for a number of pipes with different diameters. Nitrogen was used in the experiments since it is commonly employed as the inerting medium in industrial process plants.

THEORY

Husa's first paper gave the following equation to link the purge gas velocity, pipe diameter, purge gas molecular weight, oxygen concentration and distance down the pipe.

$$V = \frac{0.022}{h} \times \left(\frac{6}{X}\right)^{0.64} \times \left(\frac{28}{M}\right)^n \times \left(e^{0.16 \times D} - 0.96 \times e^{0.16 \times (D-M)}\right) \tag{1}$$

The above equation is in the form given Husa's paper, in which SI units are *not* used.

For a fixed pipe diameter, purge gas and oxygen concentration the equation can be expressed in the simplified form:

$$V = \frac{K}{h} \tag{2}$$

where K is a constant

If it is assumed that the purge velocity, V, represents the velocity at which oxygen will diffuse into the vent line at a given position, h, from the end of the vent pipe then it is possible to calculate the time taken for the oxygen concentration to reach the chosen value.

If the vent pipe is split into a series of small sections, each of height δh, it is reasonable to assume that the velocity within each section will be constant. The time taken to cross each section will then be given by:

$$\delta t = \frac{\delta h}{V(h)} \tag{3}$$

Substituting in for $V(h)$ from equation (2) gives:

$$\delta t = \frac{h}{K} \delta h \tag{4}$$

As δt tends to zero, then

$$dt = \frac{h}{K} dh \tag{5}$$

The total time taken for the chosen oxygen concentration to reach a depth, h, can be obtained by integrating the equation (5) with respect to h.

$$\int dt = \int \frac{h}{K} dh \tag{6}$$

Integrating equation (6) between 0 and h yields:

$$t = \frac{h^2}{2K} \tag{7}$$

Where:

$$K = 0.022 \times \left(\frac{6}{X}\right)^{0.64} \times \left(\frac{28}{M}\right)^{n} \times \left(e^{0.16 \times D} - 0.96 \times e^{0.16 \times (D-M)}\right) \qquad (8)$$

Equation (7) shows that for a particular pipe and purge gas the time taken for the oxygen concentration to reach a chosen value is dependant upon the square of the distance from the open end of the pipe.

The experiments conducted for this paper employed 2", 4" and 6" nominal bore pipes and nitrogen was used as the purge gas (ie $M = 28$). Therefore, equations (7) and (8) can be expressed in simpler forms.

For example, for the 2" pipe:

$$K = 0.022 \times \left(\frac{6}{X}\right)^{0.64} \times \left(\frac{28}{28}\right)^{n} \times \left(e^{0.16 \times 2} - 0.96 \times e^{0.16 \times (2-28)}\right) \qquad (9)$$

which simplifies to:

$$K = 0.0943 X^{-0.64} \qquad (10)$$

Therefore,

$$t_{2"} = \frac{h^2 X^{0.64}}{0.1886} \qquad (11)$$

Similarly for the 4" and 6" pipes:

$$t_{4"} = \frac{h^2 X^{0.64}}{0.2598} \qquad (12)$$

$$t_{6"} = \frac{h^2 X^{0.64}}{0.3578} \qquad (13)$$

As will be seen later in this paper, the predictions made using equations (11), (12) and (13) were compared with experimentally obtained results.

EXPERIMENTAL

EXPERIMENTAL TEST RIG

The experiments were carried out in the open air using 4 m long pipes. Pipes of 1", 2", 4" and 6" nominal bore were used. A vessel with a volume of approximately 70 litres was connected to the bottom of the vent pipe under investigation and the system sealed so that the only route for air to enter the system was through the top of the vent pipe. The experimental rig is shown in Figure 1.

The oxygen concentration within the vent pipe was measured using "Schools" Type Oxygen Probes and Model OT4 Oxygen Meters, both supplied by Walden Precision Apparatus Ltd., of Cambridgeshire, UK. The probes could be inserted into the vent pipes at any of nine pre-determined locations along the length of the pipe, the unused positions being sealed with plugs. The outputs from the oxygen meters were logged on a personal computer using the Orchestrator data logging package. The oxygen measuring system was calibrated across the range from 0 to 20.8% v/v oxygen before each experiment. Also, because the experiments were carried out over several hours, the probes were checked for drift at the end of each experiment. The upper limit was calibrated in fresh air and zero was set using oxygen-free nitrogen. The response time of the probe/meter system across the full calibrated range was less than 2 seconds.

The nitrogen used in the experiments was Oxygen-Free grade supplied by BOC and the flow rate to the pipes was measured using a Model 826-CE-NX-OV1-PV1-V1 mass flow meter supplied by Sierra Instruments Inc. of Monterey, USA. The flow meter was pre-calibrated using nitrogen by the manufacturer. As with the oxygen meters, the flow-meter output was logged using the Orchestrator data logging package. The nitrogen supply was connected to the bottom of the vessel via a pressure regulator and the flow meter.

In some experiments air was forced across the top of the pipe to simulate wind. A 300 mm diameter wind tunnel, incorporating flow straighteners, was placed across the top of the pipe and the air movement was achieved using a fume extractor. The fume extractor had a nominal air flow of 3740 m^3 hr^{-1} which resulted in a nominal average wind speed of 14.7 m s^{-1} (53 km hr^{-1}) through the wind tunnel.

A manometer was connected to the 1" diameter pipe during later experiments in order to investigate the transient effects that had been observed.

EXPERIMENTAL PROCEDURE

Once the oxygen probes had been calibrated, they were inserted into the pipe at the required locations. The vessel was then purged with nitrogen until the oxygen concentration profile within the vent pipe reached equilibrium conditions. The nitrogen flow was then stopped and air allowed to enter the vent. The oxygen concentration was recorded until the oxygen concentration at the probe position furthest from the open end had increased significantly, normally to a concentration of 10% v/v.

Experiments were performed using the 6", 4" and 2" diameter pipes under "wind" and "no-wind" conditions. The wind condition was achieved by providing a continuous flow of air across the top of the pipe, using the wind tunnel described above. For the no wind condition, an open topped box structure was placed around the top of the pipe in order to minimise the effect of the atmospheric air movement.

In order to investigate whether the volume of the vented vessel influenced the oxygen profile some experiments were carried out in which the vessel was removed from the 1" pipe.

The recorded oxygen concentration profiles were analysed in order to determine the time required for the oxygen concentration at various positions down the pipe to reach a chosen value. It was decided to carry out this analysis for three particular values of oxygen concentration. The values of 10%, 5% and 2% v/v were chosen since these would be representative of the typical range of interest in systems employing inert gas blankets.

RESULTS

EXPERIMENTS EMPLOYING THE LARGER DIAMETERS

In all experiments the oxygen concentration within the pipes increased once the nitrogen flow was stopped. For the 6" and 4" pipes the oxygen concentration was observed to increase steadily apart from when the probe was placed very close to the open end of the pipe. A typical example is shown in Figure 2. However, the change of oxygen concentration in the 2" pipe was more variable, and the oxygen concentration was seen to fluctuate considerably during experiments involving the 1" pipe. The transient effects observed for the 1" pipe are reported later.

The relationship between the time required to reach 2%, 5% and 10% v/v oxygen under nominal "no wind" conditions and the distance from the open end of the pipe, is shown graphically in figures 3, 4 and 5, respectively. Each graph shows data for the 6", 4" and 2" pipes.

Regression analysis of the data revealed that the time taken for the oxygen concentration to reach a particular value can be represented as a power law function of the depth, similar to equation (7) predicted by theory. This relationship can be expressed as:

$$t = \frac{h^b}{K'} \tag{14}$$

where K' is constant for a particular pipe diameter and oxygen concentration. The exponent, b, has a value between 1.7 and 2.4, with no apparent trend with respect to pipe diameter.

THE EFFECT OF WIND ON THE EXPERIMENTS USING THE LARGER PIPES

The application of a constant air flow across the open end of the pipe appeared to modify the rate at which air entered the pipe, when compared to the data obtained for the no-wind conditions. The effect was particularly noticeable for the 6" pipe where the time taken to reach a particular oxygen concentration was significantly reduced, to as little as 25% of the time observed for the no wind condition in some cases. The effect was less evident for the 2" and 4" pipes. Examples of the effect of wind are shown in figures 6, 7 and 8.

TRANSIENT EFFECTS OBSERVED FOR THE 1" PIPE

Soon after experimentation started on the 1" pipe, transient effects became evident. This behaviour, an example of which is shown in figure 9, exhibited the following characteristics. After a period in which the oxygen concentration appeared to rise reasonably smoothly, the oxygen concentration at the top probe position would increase rapidly, often reaching 21% v/v. After a short period, typically a few minutes, the oxygen concentration would decrease again and rejoin the "baseline". These "oxygen spikes" were seen to occur at the top probe position at intervals of about 10 - 15 minutes. Similar peaks were observed at lower probe positions later on in the experiments. When these transients were seen at more than one probe position, the upper probe position exhibited the increase in concentration first, followed by the middle probe position and finally the lowest position. At the end of the transient, the concentration recorded at the lowest probe position returned to the baseline first, followed by the middle probe and finally the upper probe. The transient effects were seen to be more prevalent under conditions of changing wind speed than when the pipe was guarded against wind or subjected to a continuous air flow.

In order to investigate the phenomenon, temperature and pressure measurements were carried out. The temperature measurements did not reveal any significant differences between the temperature of the ambient air surrounding the facility and the nitrogen within the test equipment. The application of a constant air flow across the open end of the pipe caused a small decrease in pressure within the pipe of less than 1 mbar.

Further experiments were carried out in which the vessel was disconnected from the 1" pipe, the bottom of the pipe was sealed and the pipe alone was purged with nitrogen. When the nitrogen flow was stopped the oxygen concentration increased steadily, as observed with the larger diameter pipes when they were connected to the vessel.

DISCUSSION

The experimental results suggest that there is a reasonable amount of evidence to support the use of a power law relationship between the distance from the end of the pipe and the time required for the oxygen concentration to reach a particular value. The exponent for the experimentally determined power law was reasonably close to the theoretical value of 2, as derived above. A comparison has been made of the time predicted by the theoretical model, using equations (11), (12) and (13), and the shortest times found by experiment, including the values found under wind conditions.

The predicted times are of the same order of magnitude as the experimentally determined times. However, there are a many occasions when the predicted time is longer than that found experimentally. A comparison of the predicted and experimental times to reach 2%, 5% and 10% v/v oxygen is given in Table 1.

Table 1. Comparison of predicted and experimental time to reach 2%, 5% and 10% v/v oxygen at a distance, h, down the pipe.

Pipe Size	Distance from open end of pipe (metres)	Predicted Time to Reach 2% v/v (minutes)	Exp'tal Time to Reach 2% v/v (minutes)	Predicted Time to Reach 5% v/v (minutes)	Exp'tal Time to Reach 5% v/v (minutes)	Predicted Time to Reach 10% v/v (minutes)	Exp'tal Time to Reach 10% v/v (minutes)
6"	0.95	0.7	0.2	1.3	0.3	2.0	0.7
6"	1.43	1.6	0.6	2.9	1.3	4.5	> Theory
6"	1.9	2.8	0.9	5.1	1.4	7.9	4.2
6"	2.3	4.1	2.0	7.4	3.6	16.1	11.1
6"	2.85	6.4	2.5	11.4	5.2	17.8	14.8
6"	3.3	8.5	4.0	15.3	7.3	23.9	17.2
6"	3.8	11.3	4.5	20.3	8.3	31.6	20.4
4"	0.95	1.0	0.3	1.8	0.9	2.7	> Theory
4"	1.43	2.2	1.1	4.0	2.7	6.2	> Theory
4"	1.9	3.9	2.8	7.0	6.7	10.9	> Theory
4"	2.3	5.7	4.1	10.3	9.6	16.0	> Theory
4"	2.85	8.7	8.2	15.7	> Theory	24.5	> Theory
4"	3.3	11.7	9.3	21.1	> Theory	32.9	> Theory
4"	3.8	15.6	9.3	28.0	> Theory	43.6	> Theory
2"	0.95	1.3	> Theory	2.4	> Theory	3.8	> Theory
2"	1.43	3.0	2.2	5.4	> Theory	8.3	> Theory
2"	1.9	5.4	> Theory	9.6	> Theory	15.0	> Theory
2"	2.3	7.8	> Theory	14.0	> Theory	21.6	> Theory
2"	2.85	12.0	> Theory	21.6	> Theory	33.7	> Theory
2"	3.8	21.3	20.2	38.1	> Theory	58.9	> Theory

From table 1 it can be seen that the theoretical predictions are worst for the 6" pipe, and best for the 2" pipe. It is possible that this is because turbulent mixing effects would be more prevalent in the 6" pipe, where the distance to diameter ratio is smaller, and less influential in the 2" pipe where the distance to diameter ratio is somewhat greater. Turbulent mixing effects at the open ends of vent pipes have been studied previously by Bryce and Fryer-Taylor[5].

Although the times predicted by the model can be shorter than those found experimentally, the model could be used to carry out an order of magnitude estimation, particularly if a suitable safety factor is applied.

TRANSIENT EFFECTS

The reason for the transient effects seen for the 1" pipe are not satisfactorily explained. The decrease in pressure in the pipe observed during the application of a continuous "wind" would only explain a movement of a column of gas a few centimetres in length, ie insufficient to explain the almost simultaneous increase in oxygen concentration at points within the pipe separated by about 1 metre.

Another potential reason for the transients could be bubbles of air, introduced by turbulent vortices caused by wind, flowing down the pipe in a plug-flow manner as discussed by Panchenko[6] However, the oxygen concentration at the top probe position was seen to increase before, and decrease after, that measured at the lower positions (see figure 9). Therefore, it appears that the transients are unlikely to be caused by Panchenko's bubble mechanism in this case.

What is evident is that the effect does not occur when there is no vessel attached to the bottom of the 1" pipe. During the experiments with the larger sized pipes, which were all connected to the same size vessel, no significant transient effects were seen with the 6" and 4" pipes. Although some transients were seen with the 2" pipe, these were significantly less than those observed for the 1" pipe. This suggests that the ratio of the total system volume to the vent pipe volume plays an important role in the occurrence of the transient effects. The ratios for the systems used in these experiments are given in Table 2.

The problem of transients was not reported by Tite, Greening and Sutton, but examination of their full scale system shows the ratio of total system volume to vent volume to be about 3. In our experiments with ratios of 3.2 and less no transients were noted. With larger ratios transients were noticed, the effect being greater for greater ratios.

The short term deviations exhibited during the experiments with the 1" pipe suggest that, in the event of nitrogen flow failure, a flammable atmosphere may form for short periods along the full length of the vent pipe. However, the behaviour of the baseline indicates that the oxygen concentration within the vented vessel is not increasing rapidly.

Table 2.   Volumes and volume ratios for systems used in the experiments

System Description	Vent Pipe Volume (litres)	Vessel Volume (litres)	Total System Volume (litres)	Ratio of Total Volume to Vent Pipe Volume
6" Pipe with Vessel	73.0	72.1	145.1	2.0
4" Pipe with Vessel	32.4	72.1	104.5	3.2
2" Pipe with Vessel	8.1	72.1	80.2	9.9
1" Pipe with Vessel	2.0	72.1	74.1	37.1
1" Pipe without Vessel	2.0	Nil	2.0	1.0

CONCLUSIONS

1. A theoretical model has been developed to predict the time required for the oxygen concentration to reach a chosen value at a particular distance from the open end of the pipe.

2. Experimental data indicates that the model can be used to carry out an order of magnitude estimate of the time required for the oxygen concentration to reach a chosen value at a particular distance from the open end of the pipe, although care would be needed and a suitable safety factor applied.

3. When the vent volume and vessel volume were similar the increase in oxygen concentration at a given point down the vent increased in a smooth manner and the model was in reasonable agreement with measured values.

4. Where the vessel volume is large compared to the volume of the vent pipe transient effects were seen to dominate, the oxygen concentration within the pipe increasing and decreasing rapidly. It appears that these transient effects are observed when the ratio of the total system volume to the vent pipe volume approaches a value of about 10.

5. The existence of transient increases in oxygen concentration could introduce the potential for an extensive, though short-lived, flammable region within a vent pipe servicing a vessel containing flammable vapours or gases.

6. Further work is required to investigate the rate of oxygen ingress into the process vessels that are connected to atmosphere via vent pipes.

ACKNOWLEDGEMENTS

The authors would like to thank the Directors of Avecia Limited for their permission to publish, and also to thank Mike Bailey of Syngenta for his help with setting up the data logging equipment.

NOMENCLATURE

V Velocity of inert gas through the vent pipe (feet per second)
h Distance from open end of vent (feet)
X Oxygen concentration (% v/v)
M Molecular weight of inert gas
D Internal diameter of vent pipe (inches)
n Exponent given in Husa's 1964 paper
t Time taken to reach a particular oxygen concentration (s)
K A constant derived from Husa's 1964 equation for constant pipe diameter and purge gas type.
b An experimentally determined exponent with values between 1.7 and 2.4
K' An experimentally determined constant

REFERENCES

1   Husa, H.W., 1964, Hydrocarbon Proc. And Petr. Ref., **43**, 179-82
2   Husa, H.W., 1977, "Purging Requirements of Large Diameter Stacks" (Presented at Fall 1977 Meeting API Fire/Safety Subcommittee, Sept 13-15 1977, San Francisco)
3   Astbury, G.R., and Hooker, P., 2000, IChemE Symposium Series No.147, 221-34
4   Tite, J.P., Greening, K., and Sutton, P., 1989, Chem. Eng. Res. Des., **67**, 373-80
5   Bryce, S.G., and Fryer-Taylor, R.E.J., 1994, J. Loss Prev. Proc. Ind., **7**, 249-55
6   Panchenko, V.I., 1993, Khemicheskoe i Neftyanoe Mashinostroenie, No 5, 5-7

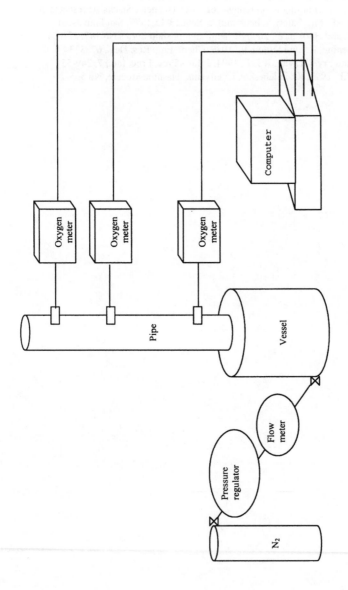

Figure 1.   Schematic of Experimental Arrangement

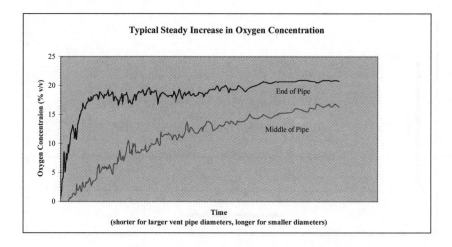

Figure 2.   Typical Increase in Oxygen Concentration After Stopping Nitrogen Flow in
Large Diameter Vent Pipes

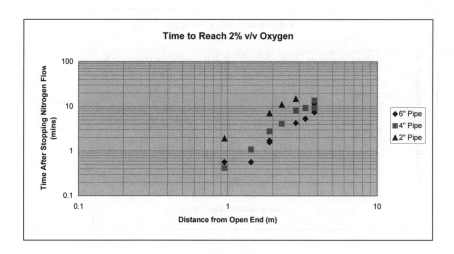

Figure 3   Time Taken to Reach 2% v/v Oxygen in 2", 4" and 6" Nominal Bore Pipes

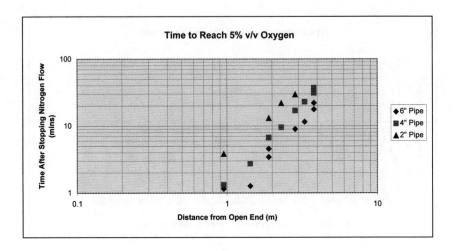

Figure 4   Time Taken to Reach 5% v/v Oxygen in 2", 4" and 6" Nominal Bore Pipes

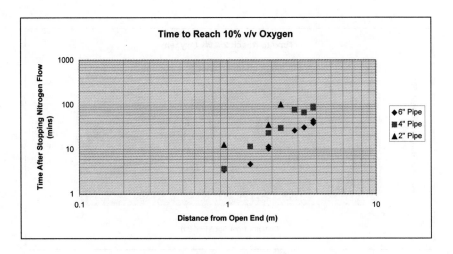

Figure 5   Time Taken to Reach 10% v/v Oxygen in 2", 4" and 6" Nominal Bore Pipes

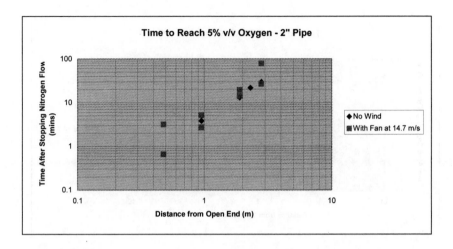

Figure 6.   Effect of Wind on 2" Nominal Bore Pipe

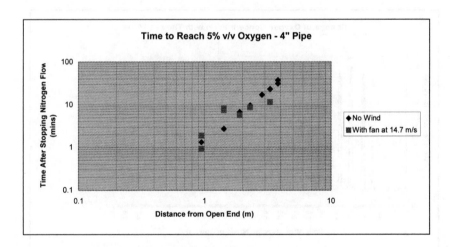

Figure 7.   Effect of Wind on 4" Nominal Bore Pipe

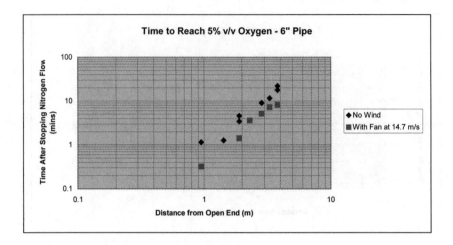

Figure 8.   Effect of Wind on 6" Nominal Bore Pipe

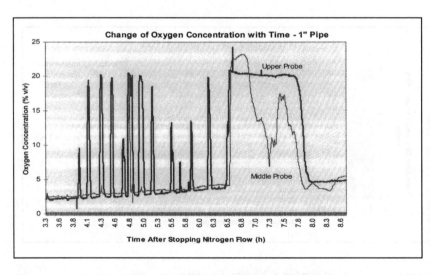

Figure 9.   Transient Effects Observed for the 1" Nominal Bore Pipe

RESPONSE OF A DOUBLE CANTILEVER FRAME SUPPORTED PIPELINE TO INTERNAL TRANSMITTED IMPULSIVE LOADS

A. D. Hallgarth and G. O. Thomas
Centre for Explosions Studies, Shock and Detonation Physics Group, Department of Physics,
University of Wales Aberystwyth, Aberystwyth, Ceredigion, Wales, SY23 3BZ, UK.

This paper presents experimental results of the response of a double cantilever frame supported pipeline to internal transmitted impulsive loads generated by the propagation of shock, detonation and blast waves, with both open and closed end flange configurations. Time resolved axial displacement responses of specially constructed supports were obtained. These showed the coupling of the impulsive loads transmitted into the longer time scale support oscillations. This paper also reports on the comparison between numerical simulations of the response of the pipeline supports with the experimental results obtained.

Keywords: impulsive, transient, loading, detonation, blast, shock, supports, pipeline

INTRODUCTION

Explosions in industry have been the subject of increasing levels of detailed investigation for nearly 50 years. During this period, factors that give rise to, and which control the development of explosions, have been investigated, and the majority of key parameters have been identified. However, advances in understanding the physical causes and predictions of explosions can usefully inform other disciplines of potential hazard scenarios and assess the associated risks in offshore and onshore process plant design and construction.

One area that has received little attention is the response of pipeline structures and supports to explosions. Small explosions could lead to local structural failure resulting in potential devastating escalation, if they formed critical elements of larger structures. Two escalation paths may arise. Direct failure of the pipe itself, or failure due to the subsequent failure of the pipe supports. The latter possibility is one that is considered far less frequently. Usually supports are designed to withstand the static weight of the pipe section and conventional loads associated with wind and seismic activity only, but not to loads associated with internal transient explosions. Currently there is a considerable amount of interest in the response of pipelines and associated structures to internal explosive loads. Interest has developed because of the distant possibilities, which exist of accidental explosions developing in plant pipeline systems.

The amount of material in the published literature on the mechanical response and failure of pipelines and support structures is very limited. Textbook style references such as Biggs[1] and explosion references such as Baker et al.[2] cover the fundamentals of external explosive loads and detailed analytical treatments of simple structures and response models. Brossard and co-workers[3, 4, 5] have reported several studies of the response and internal loading of pipelines by internal propagating pressure waves. More recently, Thomas and Oakley[6] reported the study of loading of GRP (Glass Reinforced Plastic) and Polyethylene pipes by internal detonations. These experiments were conducted using atmospheric ethylene - air in pipelines of internal diameters of 250mm and 300mm, and observed a catastrophic pipe failure in one particular case. Thomas and Oakley considered the motion and possible failure modes of the pipeline supports and noted their significance of the characteristic load duration to that of the natural resonant period of the coupled pipeline and supports. The response of PVC and stainless steel pipes to internal stoichiometric propane - air propagating detonation waves was studies by Brossard and Renard[7]. A model for the mechanical response of the pipe walls was created and tested against experimental results. Experimental results provide information of the dependence of the transverse and longitudinal strain on the pipe wall due to propagation of the detonation waves. The precursor effects, the oscillations and their frequencies and the end effects agree well with theory. However, the observed increase in the transverse strain behind the detonation front and its amplitude did not agree with predictions of the code. Klein and Wilming[8] investigated the response of a complex 'T' configuration piping system and connected supports to an internal oxy-acetylene detonation. Other variants were considered, including the speed of the detonation wave, three different pipe support designs, additional mass on the pipe bridges due to adjacent pipes and pipes as spring supported system without the mass of the supports. They used a simple explosion-propagating model, but made some sweeping assumptions regarding the nature of the loads.

EXAMPLES OF EXISTING PIPELINE SUPPORTS

Pipeline supports can be divided into two groups by their basic structural design. These include 'pipeline unclamped' and 'pipeline clamped' supports. Both groups actually support the static weight of the pipeline section, but only the 'pipeline clamped' group has the ability, if designed correctly, of being resistant to transmitted loads generated within the pipeline.

Examples of 'pipeline unclamped' supports include half-saddle and cradles. Half-saddles and cradles support the pipeline statically, but do not hold or clamp the pipeline to resist its axial motion. If the problem of transient impulsive loading occurs, there will be no resistance from the support and the pipeline is free to move in the direction of the loading.

Examples of 'pipeline clamped' supports include saddle clamps, beam, welds and I-rods. Saddle clamps work by clamping the pipeline circumferentially by means of two metal semicircular yoke bands. Saddle clamps are widely used, especially on larger diameter pipelines, as they offer excellent static mechanical support. They are often used in both horizontal and vertical pipe runs. Beam supports, which are constructed using a beam or girder perpendicular to the pipeline, are a very common method of supporting multiple parallel pipeline runs. The pipes are usually stabilised, usually with a U-bolt. This is a very attractive support method, due to its inexpensive and flexible nature for pipeline designers, where the U-bolts offer a greater inspection and maintainability to corrosion than saddles.

Adaptations that provide a solution to pipeline support corrosion include Welds and I-Rods. Weld supports involves direct welding or fixing of the support to the pipeline wall, in order to stop the amount of moisture being trapped in-between, which eventually causes corrosion. I-rods are a half semicircular yoke configuration on top, similar to half saddle clamps, and are joined to the bottom of a 'I' shaped girder section, made from a high strength thermoplastic material. These may be easily installed, either in a continuous length across the top of the pipe supports beams or as an integral part of a U–bolt assembly to replace saddle clamps.

Ideally, a pipeline support should be designed to withstand a range of loads transmitted from the pipeline, to which it is clamped. With all examples of clamped pipeline supports, if the support itself has a low elastic limit and easily extends into the plastic region under loading, the supports becomes potentially dangerous, if such a distant and rare event should occur.

EXPERIMENTAL DETAILS

The current experiments were conducted using a 4.3m, 150mm nominal bore, schedule 40 steel pipeline, comprising of a 1m driver section and 3.3m test section, supported by two specially designed supports as shown in Figure 1. Impulsive loads of varying strengths, which could be experienced in an accidental pipeline explosion scenario, were generated within the pipeline and transmitted to the supports. The generation of the impulsive loads were conducted by either shock, detonation and blast wave propagation. In the case of the shock and detonation wave experiments, the pipeline was closed at both ends. With blast wave experiments, both close and open-end flange configurations were considered. The 1m long driver section was attached to the 3.3m test section pipeline to act as either a detonation driver section for both blast and detonation wave experiments or as a high-pressure section for shock experiments.

For the shock wave experiments, the test section was filled with atmospheric air, while the driver section pressure was raised, by filling with compressed air, until the separating diaphragm burst. For detonation wave experiments, the driver section was filled with atmospheric stoichiometric acetylene – oxygen and the test section with atmospheric stoichiometric ethylene – air. For blast wave experiments, the test section was filled with atmospheric air, while the driver section was filled with atmospheric stoichiometric acetylene – oxygen. In the reactive experiments a slide valve was used to separate the test and driver sections. Ignition via a nominal 0.6J spark occurred immediately after opening the slide valve.

INSTRUMENTATION AND DATA COLLECTION
PCB piezo-electric pressure gauges, mounted in the pipeline wall and end flanges, were used to monitor the propagation of the pressure waves. To measure the axial displacement of the pipeline supports L.V.D.T. (Linear Variable Differential Transformers) sensors were used. The L.V.D.T sensors used were RPD type ACT1000 with a range of ± 25mm and were calibrated following the manufactures guidelines. The L.V.D.T. sensors were mounted in specially designed clamps/gimbals supports and the armature of the sensor was fixed to the stand by means of a steel rod and rose joint as shown in Figure 2.

For data acquisition, two 8 bit synchronised transient recording systems were used, to provide optimal sampling of both the pressure wave and pipeline support, which occur over different time scales. Synchronisation was obtained by duplicating reference gauges on both recording systems.

PIPELINE SUPPORT DESIGN CRITERIA AND VALIDATION
The pipeline used in these experiments was mechanically supported using specially designed supports by Wilfred Baker Engineering Ltd, shown schematically in Figure 2. The design criteria for each of these supports was to generate a realistic elastic displacement output to a load generated by a normal reflected stoichiometric ethylene – air detonation, giving a peak pressure of 40 – 45 atmospheres, subjected to a 150mm diameter end flange. Using the cantilever beam equation, the theoretical spring constant for this particular support design is 845N per mm. Adapting this into a theoretical frame cantilever supported pipeline configuration, gives a theoretical spring constant of 3381N per mm.

To experimentally measure the axial spring constant of a single pipeline support and the frame supported pipeline configuration for comparison and later numerical response simulations, both force and displacement measurements should be obtained. This was achieved by placing the pipeline system under static loading by means of a pulley system attached to a structurally static object. Loads were measured by placing an in-line mounted strain-gauge load cell. The load cell used was an Applied Measurements type DDE – 20000. Displacement was measured using the L.V.D.T. sensors described above. The axial spring constant of the single cantilever and double frame supported pipeline system can be seen in Figure 3 and 4, which gave a value of approximately and 860N per mm and 2500N per mm respectively. Therefore, the pipeline and support configuration used and shown schematically in Figure 1., has an experimental characteristic spring constant that is greater than the theoretical value for the two single combined cantilever supports and is less than the theoretical value for the frame supported pipeline configuration. The differences in the theoretical and experimentally measured spring constants are believed to be due to the pipeline supports not behaving with pure cantilever characteristics in this configuration. An additional factor to be considered is the weight of the pipeline, which will affect the spring constant of the entire pipeline and support configuration.

RESULTS

Typical short duration axial displacement response of the pipeline supports and associated end flange pressures can be viewed in Figures 5(a) – (d) for shock, detonation, blast closed end flange and blast open end flange experiments respectively. All show good correlation in both reproducibility and reliability. There is some scatter in the magnitude of the peak spike pressures from the detonation driver. This is due to the unpredictability associated with the deflagration to detonation transition. Pressures of the detonations may be seen to exceed stable values due to detonations tending to be overdriven in some cases. Positive axial displacement refers to the direction of the initial incident wave propagation into the test section (from left to right in Figure 1). It can be seen in Figure 5(a) that the response displacement of the pipeline supports is initiated from the start of the diaphragm burst – increasing due to the rarefaction waves travelling back into the high-pressure section. It can be observed that the reflected shock pressure on the test section end flanges doesn't have a distinctive effect on the short duration response of the pipeline supports.

The axial response profile of the supports from both the detonation and the blast closed end flange experiments is rather different to the response for either shock or blast open-end flange experiments. It can be observed that the same initial response, caused by the recoil load experienced by the ignition end flange, produces a displacement response in the opposite direction of the initial propagating wave. When either the detonation or blast wave meets the test section end flange, a reflected end flange load is created causing a displacement peak in the direction of the initial wave propagation. The bouncing waves within the pipeline transmitted to the supports create a high frequency response over this short time duration. The short duration axial displacement response of the blast open-end flange experiments with ignition end flange pressures can be seen in Figure 5(d). A single recoil load creates a sinusoidal damped oscillation response from the pipeline supports.

Figure 6. shows the long duration axial displacement response of the pipeline supports from shock, detonation and blast waves experiments, with both closed and open end flanges. The difference in long duration axial response of the pipeline supports from closed and open-end flange blast experiments can also be seen in Figure 6. Here it can be observed that with the closed end flange blast experiments, a high frequency response is initially produced from the bouncing decaying blast wave, which is travelling up and down the length of the pipeline. After the blast wave has decayed sufficiently, the natural frequency response of the pipeline system is adopted. The long duration axial response of the open-end blast wave experiment transmitted to the pipeline supports gives a decaying damped sinusoidal displacement history.

Figure 7. shows a slightly out of phase axial displacement response of the two supporting pipeline supports from a detonation wave experiment within the initial high frequency response of the system. This is thought to be the result of the elastic dilatation wave travelling through the steel pipeline wall at its acoustic speed. This develops a slight amount of stretch within the pipe wall, which in turn creates an out of phase axial response between the two supports.

RKM MODELLING

RKM (Runge-Kutta Method) SDOF (Single degree of Freedom) and MDOF (Multiple – degree of freedom) numerical simulation codes are simple elastic-plastic models using tri-linear spring constants. This numerical simulation uses a RKM subroutine to integrate the ordinary differential equations of motion. Using the measured frame supported pipeline configuration spring constant, mass of the system and empirical damping coefficient, the simulation can produce usful values for the axial displacement of the supports.

The RKM SDOF numerical simulation displacement output, using the ignition end wall load history from the blast open-end experiment is plotted against its displacement response for stoichiometric oxygen –acetylene and are shown in Figure 8. It can be seen that the RKM SDOF simulation output is in good agreement with the actual displacement associated with this open-end flange experiment.

Presently, the MDOF simulation can handle dual end flange load histories for closed end flange experiments, but doesn't replicate the initial high frequency response due to the interaction of the pipeline to the fluctuating impulsive loads within. The MDOF code does however simulate the pipe wall stretch causing the out of phase displacement response.

DISCUSSION AND CONCLUSION

The present study represents, what is believed to be a unique series of measurements of the dynamic response of pipeline mechanical supports in a double cantilever frame set-up to transmitted internal impulsive loads. These studies also demonstrate the feasibility of conducting detailed time resolved measurements of the response of pipeline supports to transmitted impulsive loads.

The pipeline supports designed by Wilfred Baker Engineering Ltd. have successfully met their design criteria. These supports, although is a frame configuration, have kept within the elastic region whilst withstanding transient impulsive loads from shocks, detonations and blast wave propagation within the pipeline that they support.

Closed end pipeline experiments, which exhibit large recoil and reflection end flange pressures, develop a high frequency axial displacement response initially. This is due to the internal interaction of the impulsive loads travelling up and down the pipeline colliding with the two end flanges. After the blast or shock wave has sufficiently decayed, normal harmonic oscillations at the systems natural resonant frequency is resumed.

Open-end flange pipeline experiments can be modelled using an equivalent elastic-plastic RKM SDOF numerical simulation. Presently, the elastic-plastic RKM MDOF simulation can handle duel inputted end flange load histories, as for the case of the detonation experiments. This initially high frequency displacement response from the interaction of the fluctuating impulsive loads within the pipeline cannot be modelled presently, but the simulation is giving sensible numerical results for the out of phase displacement between the two supports due to pipeline stretch.

The transient Von Neumann pressure spikes associated with the detonation generated experiments, vary in magnitude due to deflagration to detonation transition, and do not have an observable effect on the displacement response of the pipeline supports. Only the longer duration of the detonation load history affects the magnitude of the axial displacement response of the supports.

In all of the experiments conducted, the pipeline supports did not exceed their linear elastic proportional limit. However, the importance of the characteristic load duration to the natural period of the structure must be considered. In the present study, the duration of the internal impulsive loads were short in comparison to the natural period of the double cantilever frame supported pipeline configuration used. It is possible however that more deformation, or even failure of the supports may have occurred if a less severe, but longer duration explosion had been used. More damage might result in this case, even through the peak pressure would have been less than that observed in this study.

The overall conclusion from this work presented, is that when considering the potential hazards from internal transmitted impulsive loads, not only pipelines must be sufficiently robust to withstand these loads, but also the pipeline supports to withstand potential failure if the pipeline doesn't fail.

FUTURE RESEARCH OPTIONS
Intended future research will consist of a detailed experimental program using a variety of pipeline and support configurations subjected to impulsive internal transient loads form shock, detonation and blast wave propagation within the pipeline. Configurations will include a single supported pipeline, double frame supported pipeline and a double frame supported pipeline including a bend configuration, to investigate the two dimensional response from the waves travelling around a 90° 1.5 radius pipeline bend. Instrumentation will include, in addition to that described above, accelerometers attached to the supports and end flanges, and strain gauges fitted to the supports and pipeline walls to measure the travelling wall flexural waves, generated by the gaseous waves within the pipe.

In addition to this above experimental program, to extend and complete the range of structural response histories of pipelines and support configurations, experiments using load durations that would vary from quasi-static to the impulsive regime should be conducted. A method, which could enable this, is to use a range of flame velocities to induce a lower pressure, but longer duration load to the structure in question, than that of an impulsive load. Using a method like the one described, it could be possible to tune the load duration to the natural period, to develop the maximum displacement response from the pipeline and support configuration used.

Additional future work will be conducted on developing the MDOF numerical simulation code. Using this simulation as a basis, a more complicated two-dimensional simulation will be created, which will solve the loading associated for a bend configuration and the transmitted loads to the supports.

ACKNOWLEDGEMENTS
Many thanks are due to Mr. Gwyn Oakley, Mr. Paul Clarke and the members of the Shock and Detonation Wave Physics Group for their valuable contributions to experimental work reported in this paper. Thanks to Wilfred Baker Engineering Ltd for the initial design of the pipeline supports. The authors would also like to thank the University of Wales Aberystwyth electrical and mechanical workshops, without any of this work could have been completed.

REFERNCES
1. Biggs, J., 1964, Introduction to structural dynamics, McGraw Hill, London.
2. Baker, W., Cox, P. A., Westine, P. S., Kulesz, J. J., and Strehlow, R. A., 1986, Explosion Hazards and Evaluation, Elsevier, Amsterdam.
3. Brossard, J. et Charpentier de Coysevox, N., 1976, Effects d'un confinement souple sur la detonation des melange gazeux, Acta Astronautic, 3:971-981
4. Renard, J., Aminallah, M., Tronel, M. and Brossard, J., 1982, Rhologie d'un polymer a haute vitesse de defoemation: Tube parcouru par une onde de detonation, Extraitde 17e colloque annuel Group Francais de Rheologie, Tome Vi, 3:99-117
5. Brossard, J., Renard, J. and Aminallah, M., 1986, Shock waves in a gas filled flexible tube, Shock Waves and Shock Tubes, Stanford University Press, 595-600.
6. Thomas, G. O. and Oakley, G, L., 1998, The dynamic response and potential failure of pipes and supports subjected to internal explosions, 7th Annual Conference on Offshore Instillations, ERA.

7. Brossard, J. and Renard, J., 1981, Mechanical Effects of Gaseous Detonations on a flexible Confinement, AIAA, Prog. Astronaut. Aeronaut, 75:108-121

8. Klein, H. W. and Wilming, H., 1996, Dynamic behaviour of piping systems under dynamic load, Proc. ICPVT – Conf. ASME, 2:35-43

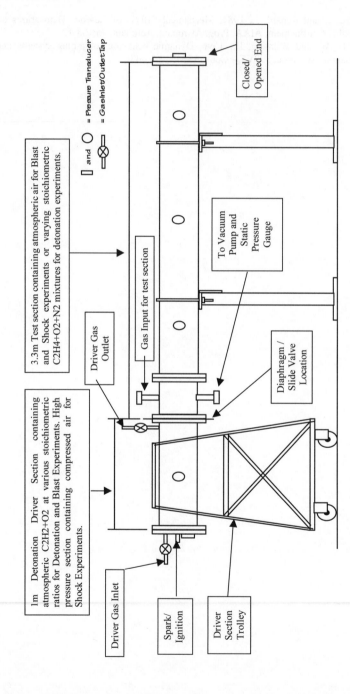

Figure 1. Schematic of pipeline layout showing supports and pipe instrumentation positions

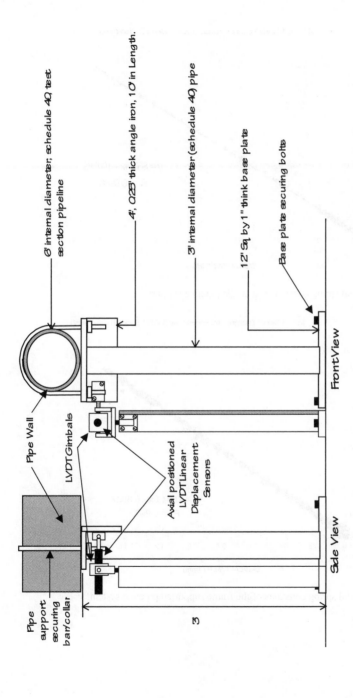

Figure 2. Schematic of supports and mounting arrangements for the (L.V.D.T.) linear displacement sensors.

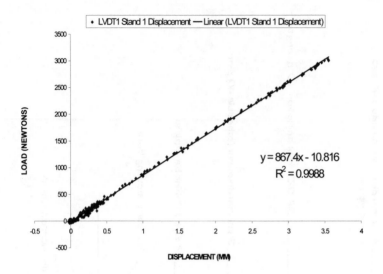

Figure 3. Axial spring constant of a single pipeline support.

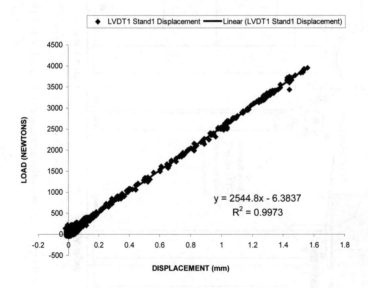

Figure 4. Axial spring constants of the frame supported pipeline system.

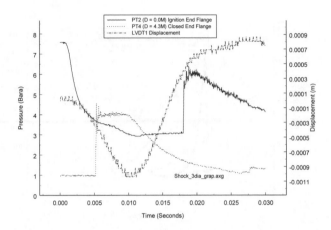

Figure 5(a). Typical shock wave experiment, showing the two end flange pressure histories and the short duration motion of the pipeline supports.

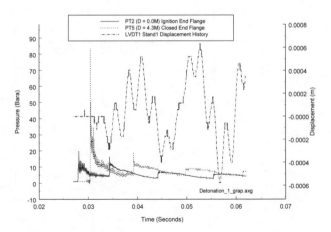

Figure 5(b). Typical detonation wave experiment, showing the two end flange pressure histories and the short duration motion of the pipeline supports.

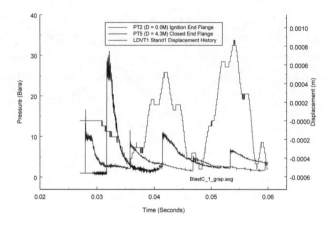

Figure 5(c). Typical closed end flange blast wave experiment, showing the two end flange pressure histories and the short duration motion of the pipeline supports.

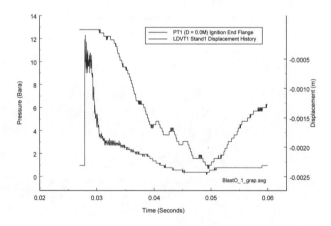

Figure 5(d). Typical open-end flange blast wave experiment, showing the two end flange pressure histories and the short duration motion of the pipeline supports.

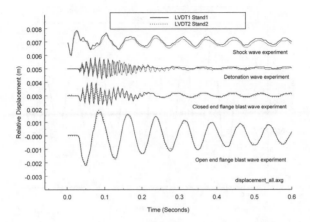

Figure 6. Comparison of the long duration support responses for the shock, detonation and blast wave experiments with both open and closed end flange configurations.

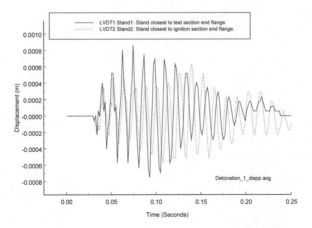

Figure 7. Comparison between axial displacement responses for the two pipeline supports subjected to a detonation experiment showing the out of phase response.

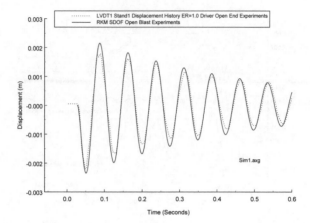

Figure 8. Comparison between RKM SDOF numerical simulation and the long duration response of the supports for an open-end blast wave experiment.

HAZARDS ASSOCIATED WITH ACCIDENTAL FIRES IN CLINICAL WASTE STORAGE

S.J. Kershaw

Haztech Consultants Ltd, Meridian House, Road One, Winsford Industrial Estate, Winsford CW7 3QG

Clinical waste and group D waste is incinerated throughout the United Kingdom in purpose built incinerators authorised under the Environmental Protection Act 1990, and conditions for incineration are detailed in SI No. 767 The Environmental Protection (prescribed Process and Substances) (Amendment) (Hazardous Waste Incineration) Regulations 1998.

Although generally incinerated upon delivery there is limited temporary storage on site awaiting incineration. The waste potentially contains biohazard material with pathogens present and active pharmaceutical products. There is a risk of fire in this stored material.

A simple theoretical model was developed to assess the contribution of the pathogens and group D pharmaceutically active waste to the toxicity of the fire plume from an accidental fire in the stored material. The method was applied to stored waste at an authorised incinerator site and the study showed the additional hazard of the pathogen biohazard and pharmaceutically active material to be negligible compared to the products of combustion of typical plastic packaging material.

The method could be used to screen other storage installations to indicate the additional risk posed by the type of storage and whether more rigorous fire modelling and or quantification of off site risk are warranted.

Key Words Products of combustion, Fire Risk, fire plume, accidental fire, clinical waste

INTRODUCTION

Clinical waste and group 'D' waste is incinerated in purpose built incinerators authorised under the Environmental Protection Act 1990, and conditions for incineration are detailed in SI No. 767 The Environmental Protection (prescribed Process and Substances) (Amendment) (Hazardous Waste Incineration) Regulations 1998.

The type of wastes accepted for incineration are groups A, B, C, D and E as defined by the Health and Services Advisory Committee HSAC [1]. These groups include sharps such as hypodermic needles, surgical tools and glass suitably contained in UN approved packaging. It also includes swabs, dressings and an extremely high proportion of plastic packaging material (up to 40%).

Group 'D' bulk prescription only medicines (POMs) suitably packaged on wooden pallets are also incinerated and these are generally from pharmaceutical companies. These materials are either out of specification, surplus or damaged material and need to be incinerated at a licensed site.

There is limited storage of this material at the incineration site and it is usually processed on the day of arrival. Following a licence application for an incineration site the site was asked to perform a risk assessment on the impact of an accidental fire in this stored material and particularly the potential effect of entrained group 'D' pharmaceutically active waste on the toxicity of the fire plume from an accidental fire.

LEGISLATIVE REGIME

The site has been issued with an authorisation licence under the Environmental Protection Act 1990.

The licence sets out parameters for releases to air from specified release points as part of the authorised process. The process is the incineration of waste in a purpose designed and built incinerator with monitoring and control.

The additional requirement in the authorisation to assess the impact of an accidental fire goes beyond the requirements of the authorised process in that it is requiring the assessment of potential accidents not associated with the process itself but in peripheral storage and their impact on the surrounding environment.

Calculation and determination of the potential impact of fire plumes from accidental fires has generally only been carried out on large warehouses which potentially come under the Control of Major Accident Hazard (COMAH) regulations[2]. The COMAH regulations are applicable where sufficient quantities of dangerous material are stored as defined by the threshold quantities in schedule 1 of the COMAH regulations i.e. they are deemed to have the potential to cause a Major Accident Hazard (MAH). The materials and quantities stored at the facility fall short of the threshold quantities in schedule 1 of the regulations. It could be argued that as such analysis and calculation of potential Major Accident Hazards is not required and the fact that the materials and quantities do not trigger the COMAH legislation that the storage is deemed to be low risk and unlikely to be capable of causing a Major Accident Hazard.

However, although not part of the Authorisation, aspects of the process that are not directly regulated by the authorisation are subject to a general condition implied by section 7(10) of the 1990 Act. It is incumbent on the licensee to comply with:

"(10) References to the Best Available Techniques Not Entailing Excessive Cost, in relation to a process, include (in addition to references to any technical means and technology) references to the number, qualifications, training and supervision of persons employed in the process and the design construction, lay-out and maintenance of the buildings in which it is carried on:"

It is therefore reasonable to require an assessment of the controls and measures put in place to prevent the occurrence of fire in the building in which the prescribed process is carried on and the potential impact of a fire occurring on the surrounding environment.

RISK ASSESSMENT

At the outset there is a need to determine the depth of risk assessment and whether to use a Qualitative Risk assessment. The value of this approach is that it is formal, documented and it may be all that is needed to make decisions on whether a risk is ALARP (As Low As Reasonably Practical) by comparing with standards and other operations that are generally accepted as tolerable risk. Decisions are effectively **'technology based'** - satisfactory risk control is achieved when relevant best or good practice is adopted or harm is not feasible. The alternative would be to use a Quantitative Risk Assessment technique with **'Equity based'** decision making criteria – in that people and environment have unconditional rights to certain levels of protection i.e. define the maximum level of risk. This would be In terms of a level of a numerically determined risk to which individuals on and off site should not be exposed.

Reviewing the toxicity of the material stored there were no materials which carried 'Risk Phrases','R' catagories or named substances that are noted in schedule 1 of the COMAH Regulations[2]. Some of the materials and active pharmaceuticals may have Control of Substances Hazardous to Health, COSHH assessments and occupational exposure limits determined. COSHH assessments are valuable for the safe handling of materials and protection of workers from long and short term exposure during normal use and operation and also abnormal exposure such as spill or other accidental loss of containment. However these COSHH assessments are of little help in assessing the risks associated with accident hazards such as large fires which can potentially release significant quantities of materials at temperatures and conditions that would not be expected in forseeable normal or forseeable abnormal use of the material.

In assessing the maximum quantities stored there are a number of storage zones as shown in Table 1.

Table 1. Material Storage

	PALLETS	WEIGHT	HC KJ/kg	Wood Equiv Kg
Zone 1				
Group D POMs	75	30000	25000	45,454.5
Waste on floor	50	20000	25000	30,303.0
Total Zone 1				75,757.6
Zone 2				
Waste on Mezzanine	50	20000	25000	30,303.0
Waste in pit		16000	17000	16,484.8
Total Zone 2				46,787.9

The maximum storage in zone 1 is 75,757 kg of wood equivalent material and in zone 2 46,788 kg. The heat of combustion for a kg of the waste in different locations was estimated and the weight of material in that area converted to a wood equivalent based on the typical heat of combustion of wood. Comparing this quantity of material to a small warehouse such with perhaps 1000 tonnes of plastic goods or foamed furniture the quantity of plastics and material for combustion is relatively small.

For the active pharmaceutical or pathogens to be a higher risk or hazard compared to a warehouse containing relatively common combustible commodities would need the contribution of the pathogen or pharmaceutical in the fire plume to be significantly more toxic or in greater abundance that the toxic species that are generated by the combustion of common combustible materials typically present in general warehousing and storage facilities.

Following this premise the following areas were considered

❑ Toxicology of fires in common combustible material

❑ Classification of materials stored on site in terms of toxicology for different wastes stored.

❑ Assessment of potential hazards associated with accidental fires in these different materials and comparison with Toxicology of fire in common combustible material. At this stage the hazard may be shown to be either significant and requiring more detailed analysis or the additional hazards associated with a fire involving the waste material compared to a normal fire to be negligible in which case further analysis would not be required.

TOXICOLOGY OF COMMON PRODUCTS OF COMBUSTION

The smoke generated by accidental fires in standard combustible material such as cellulosic material (wood, paper cardboard) and plastics that are used in packaging, construction and furniture contain a number of toxic species. These toxic species are generated from the combustion of the material and depend on the chemical formula and composition of the original material, the temperature of combustion and the level of oxygenation of the fire. Typical species in a fire plume and conversion from the elements in the original fuel are shown in table 2.

Table 2 – Typical Smoke Species for Standard Combustible Material

Material	Fire Species Conversion
Carbon (C)	Carbon Monoxide (CO)
Carbon (C)	Carbon Dioxide (CO_2)
Nitrogen (N)	Nitrogen Dioxide (NO_2)
Nitrogen (N) & Hydrogen (H)	Hydrogen Cyanide (HCN)
Chlorine (Cl) in plastics	Hydrogen Chloride (HCl)

These species in a fire plume are highly toxic in the concentrations found in domestic and industrial fires and are the main cause of fatality in the majority of accidental fire cases. This is a result of groups or individuals being either trapped in a building on fire or overcome while asleep in a dwelling or hotel, which is on fire, and they are unaware of the fire and risk to themselves. Over two thirds of fatalities are the result of smoke inhalation from UK fire statistics in 1987 [3] and this is typical for other years.

For fatality or serious injury to occur from normal domestic or industrial fires would generally require direct inhalation and an inability to escape the fire plume such as being trapped or incapacitated or unaware or the fire.

This assessment is aimed at determining the risk associated with the survival of pathogens and pharmaceutically active material in the fire plume. It is possible to assess all possible smoke species and compare the toxicity to the surviving material and all species generated from the products of combustion of the pharmaceutical material. However, the proportion of chlorine in the pharmaceutical material is reported to be extremely low in comparison with the packing material and plastics and the assessment is aimed at providing a quick reference to see whether the risk is greater than for normal combustible material.

Extensive investigations examining human fire fatalities with respect to exposure to toxic atmospheres have shown carbon monoxide to be the primary toxicant[4][5] . Hydrogen cyanide is also produced and is 300 times more toxic than carbon monoxide but as experience has shown the carbon monoxide usually predominates in terms of the toxicity of the fire plume because of its abundance. It would therefore be reasonable to assess the toxicity of entrained pharmaceutical or pathogen in comparison to carbon monoxide as an indication of the relative risk of an accidental fire involving the stored material. If a material were being stored with an extremely high proportion of nitrogen, nitrile or cyanide species then it would be prudent to review the HCN being produced. This is not the case in the pharmaceutical storage case.

The proportion of carbon converted to carbon monoxide in an accidental will depend on the level of oxygenation in the fire, which is a factor of the ventilation rate. In a confined fire the composition of the fire plume can range from negligible at the onset to over 10,000 ppm at flashover in a confined room. Studies on conversion factors by TNO laboratories[6] for a number of typically stored chemicals gave conversion factors of up to 9.7% of the carbon to carbon monoxide. Therefore a reasonable estimate would be to use 5% as a conversion factor.

TOXICOLOGY OF CLINICAL WASTE
This will include group A, B, C, and E wastes and arrives in yellow bags and UN approved packaging. The majority of this material may contain dressings, bedpans, organic matter, etc. which may have blood and body fluid contamination. There will be an amount of sharps that may have traces of prescription only medicines on them but this is negligible when considering the majority of this type of waste. The potential hazard associated with the waste is defined by its biohazard properties linked to pathogens that may be present in the body fluid contaminated material.

The main risk to an individual from this waste is transmission of a pathogen by direct contact with the bodily fluid and direct inhalation or transmission to the blood stream by accidental incision, puncture wound or direct contact with abraded skin [7]. As such the main risk is to the operators handling the material.

Products of combustion of the pathogen itself is not an issue, if it is combusted to produce products of combustion it will not have infectious properties. To remain a potential hazard the pathogen involved will need to be hazardous by airborne transmission and survive the fire plume and be breathed in sufficient dose to be infectious.

The typical bacterial pathogens found in clinical waste are not airborne pathogens and are inactivated at generally low temperatures. As an indication bed linen which is often contaminated with the same typical pathogens as in the waste is required to be washed at 80°C for 1 minute or 70°C for 3 minutes, there is also some light detergent used but this does not in itself have strong anti-bacterial properties. Laboratory testing with test pieces contaminated with heat resistant bacteria have shown this to be effective [7].

The centre line temperature of a developed fire plume is typically 600°C to 800°C and turbulent. For a pathogen to survive would need it to be introduced on a fine powder or in an aerosol which could be introduced at the very edges or top of the fire plume. The clinical waste is packaged in sealed bags and the pathogen is likely to be either on wet or dry dressings or swabs etc. To become airborne would require a fire to rupture the bag, the heat being sufficient to vaporise the water or body fluids sufficiently to carry off the pathogen. To vaporise water in a fire plume is likely to need temperatures in excess of 80°C resulting in a high probability of inactivation of the pathogen. Even if entrained it is then highly likely to be heated in the fire plume above a temperature where it would be destroyed. If the pathogen were on dry dressings or swabs it would require the destruction of the swab in the fire to micron sized particles containing a pathogen, to make it respirable, which would have an extremely high probability of destroying the pathogen. If large sections of material were lifted into the fire plume it would not pose a respirable carrier risk. Taking all these factors into account the risk of infection from accidental fires in clinical waste would appear to be remote.

This qualitative assessment cannot rule out 100% that there is absolutely no risk whatsoever of a pathogen surviving an accidental fire in the clinical waste in some combinations of unforeseen circumstances but in terms of infection and risk to people the risk is seen as vanishingly small compared to the accepted risks associated with handling this material on a day to day basis[7].

TOXICITY OF THE FIRE PLUME THE EFFECT OF ENTRAINED GROUP D WASTE

From work on agrochemical warehouse fires [8] the risks have been determined for survival fractions of the original material intact in the fire plume, products of total combustion and partial break down products of the material. In a fully developed well-oxygenated fire the majority of the material is completely combusted, there will be small and varying amounts of intermediate products depending on combustion conditions [9]. The majority will be completely combusted to the product species in Table 2. There will be a small proportion that is entrained in the fire plume. The building is a large open structure and it is unlikely that the fire would be ventilation controlled in its initial phase and so complete combustion would be more likely. Typical analysis and experimentation, [8], [9] have taken 10% of the original parent material to be seeded into the fire. This is a pessimistic assumption in this case.

Atkinson[9] indicates that in a well-ventilated fire the proportion of original material surviving the fire plume depends upon orientation and position of it in the flame. Where the material is introduced at the base of a flame there is almost total destruction of the parent material, where it is introduced towards the top of the flame there is a higher proportion surviving (up to 10%). The analogy is drawn that where there is racking of storage in a warehouse products on higher racks may be involved in the upper regions of a flame and there will be a shorter residence time in the flame and hence less of the original material will be destroyed. In terms of the storage at the site in question it is simply pallets one or two high, block stacked, there are no rack systems for storage and so any material introduced to the fire is likely to be introduced at or near the source of the fire or base of the flame and result in almost total destruction of the parent material. Even though this is the case it has been assumed that 5% of the parent material survives the fire.

POTENTIAL PRODUCTS OF COMBUSTION IN THE FIRE PLUME

The group D pharmaceutical waste is generally organic. There is a high proportion of plastic packing, wooden pallets and cellulosic/organic material. An initial assessment to provide an indication of the potential additional risk of pharmaceutical material seeded into the fire plume can be determined by the proportion of toxic species produced from the packing material and the proportion of the parent pharmaceutical seeded into the fire plume unchanged. The relative toxicity or potential dose can then be compared.

The proportions of packing and products vary. A reasonable estimate for the make up of a pallet of pharmaceutical would be:

Pallet Make Up

Plastic packing (PVC)	25%
Cellulosic packing, wooden pallet	10%
Pharmaceutical product	65%

It is assumed that all the PVC and cellulosic packing will be combusted and there will be 5 percent of the organic pharmaceutical product entrained into the fire plume. Although many pharmaceutical products that are stored and then incinerated are in preparations and contain excipients some are pure active ingredients in containers. To obtain a worst case the above 65% pharmaceutical product which makes up a pallet assumes it is 100% pure active ingredient.

Assuming 1kg of stored material there will be:

Make up in 1kg	kg
Plastic (PVC)	0.250
Cellulosic packing	0.100
Pharmaceutical product combusted	0.6175
Pharmaceutical product entrained in fire plume	0.0325

Where there are complex organic materials with chlorine and other species present there is always a potential for intermediate break down products to be formed in uncontrolled accidental fires. From past work on the risk of fire from an agrochemical warehouse it has been assumed that the toxicity of the surviving fraction is used to calculate risk[8] and so these intermediate species were discounted for this study. In this the case for a first estimate the products of combustion for organic pharmaceutical can be grouped with the cellulosic material

Fire Load Composition	kg
Plastic (PVC)	0.250
Cellulosic packing and pharmaceutical organic	0.7175
Pharmaceutical product entrained in fire plume	0.0325

A large proportion of the toxicity of the fire plume will be from the HCl produced from the PVC plastic and CO generated in the smoke plume. In addition there may be plastics other than PVC and there may also be bromine and nitrogen atoms associated with the other plastics and pharmaceuticals which could generate HBr, HCN and NOx. As we are really concerned with the toxicity and effect of the surviving fraction of pharmaceutical it is reasonable to assess the toxicity of the HCl and CO produced in a fire from 1kg as representative of the toxicity of the products of combustion compared to the pharmaceutical surviving unchanged in the fire plume. Further analysis may be valid if it is taken further.

Tables 3, 4, 5 and 6 are taken from a linked spreadsheet which calculates the proportion of species generated in the fire plume when 1kg of the stored material is burned. Table 3 is the input table. The weight of the different components per kg stored is put into Table 3 along with the numbers of atoms making up the material. The calculation of conversion is done in the subsequent tables with Table 6 sowing the weight of the products of combustion formed and pharmaceutical entrained unchanged per kg of stored material burned. Table 6 also converts the mass to a proportion relative to the amount of pharmaceutical entrained.

Table 3 Input of material per kg burned and atoms constituting the material

Material	State	C	H	O	N	S	Cl	F	Br	Mol Wt	Wt of Material per kg	Hc 10xe7 J/kg	Wood Equivlnt kg
		0		0	0	0	0	0	0	0	0	0	0
PVC	Packing	4	6	0	0	0	2	0	0	124.988	0.25	2.86	0.43
Cellulose/ organic	Comb solid	6	10	5						162.14	0.7175	1.65	0.72
Pharmaceutical surviving unchanged in fire plume											0.0325	0	0
Total											1		

Table 4 Atoms burned per kg

Material	State	C	H	O	N	S	Cl	F	Br	Mol Wt	Wt of Material in 1 kg
											0
PVC	Packing	0.10	0.01	0.00	0.00	0.00	0.14		0.00	0.00	124.988	0.25
Cellulose/organic	Comb solid	0.32	0.04	0.35	0.00	0.00	0.00		0.00	0.00	162.14	0.7175
											0
Total kg		0.41	0.06	0.35	0.00	0.00	0.14		0.00	0.00		0.9675
Check											0.9675

Table 5 Intermediate calculation

Element	Mass In fire plume Kg per kg burned
C	0.4150
Cl	0.1418
Pharm entrained	0.0325

Table 6 Products of combustion per kg burned

Products of Combustion	Product Kg per kg burned	Proportion relative to entrained Pharmaceutical
CO2	1.447552	44.54
CO	0.04839	1.49
HCl	0.146196	4.50
Pharmaceutical surviving unchanged in fire plume	0.0325	1.00

TOXICITY

Toxicity of airborne materials such as the products of combustion or airborne pharmaceuticals and pure gases is dependent on the concentration in the inhaled air and the duration of exposure. The concentration required to deliver a 'Dangerous Dose' to a human being is described as the 'Dangerous Toxic Load' (**DTL**). And is expressed as

$$C^n t = k \qquad (I)$$

where C is concentration (ppm), t is time of exposure (in 30 minutes) and n is a power function. This DTL is broadly equivalent to the LD_{1-5} which is the Lethal Dose expected to give a 1% to 5% fatality for the population exposed. For the carbon monoxide and HCl these are well defined and given in Table 7.

Table 7 – Typical Smoke Species

Material	Fire Species Conversion	*n* value	*k* (ppm^n.30min)
Carbon (C)	Carbon Monoxide (CO)	0.7	3,600
Chlorine (Cl) in plastics	Hydrogen Chloride (HCl)	1	23,730

The above data is well reported and is for inhalation risk. The data that is available for the pharmaceutical products are oral ingestion based in terms of LD50 for mice or rats. The effect of inhalation toxicity can be derived from such data to give an indication of the inhalation risk by following methods by Turner and Fairhurst[10] based on the LD_{50} concentration for the most sensitive species, assuming the LD_{1-5} for humans is ¼ the LD_{50} for the other species and assuming a 70kg individual and that the average volume of air breathed in 30 minutes is 0.625 m³.

From a review of all the pharmaceutical material likely to be stored and incinerated the most toxic pharmaceutical oral LD50 was 1,470mg/kg

Therefore the concentration in air required to give a **(DTL)** is:

$$Cmg/m3 \qquad = 1{,}470 \times 70/ (0.625 \times 4) \qquad\qquad (II)$$

$$= \mathbf{41{,}160 \ mg/m^3}$$

However this is in different units to data available for the products of combustion. Table 8 converts the concentration from DTL in ppm to give DTL in mg/m^3 .

Table 8

Species	k $(ppm^n.30min)$	Conc to give DTL ppm	Conc to give DTL mg/m3	Relative toxicity Of species
HCl	3,600	791.00	1,201	34.3
CO	23,730	933.81	1,088	37.8
Pharmaceutical			41,160	1

Table 8 shows the relative respirable toxicity of the products of combustion compared to the active ingredient in the pharmaceutical. However the relative toxicity in the smoke plume will depend on the proportion of each material in the plume. This is calculated in Table 9 from data in Table 6 and Table 8:

Table 9 Relative toxicity of products of combustion to pharmaceutical entrained.

Material in plume	Proportion in plume relative to entrained pharmaceutical	Relative toxicity Of species	Overall relative toxicity in plume
HCL	4.50	34.3	154
CO	1.49	37.8	56
Pharmaceutical	1.00	1	1

SUMMARY & CONCLUSIONS

The proportion of toxic products of combustion such as carbon monoxide and hydrogen chloride generated from the plastic packing and other combustible material would produce species in the fire plume which are between 56 and 154 times more toxic than the proportion of pharmaceutical entrained into the fire plume. As such the additional toxic risks of a fire from storing this group D material is low compared with the risks associated with general storage. As a result a formal fire review was carried out to ensure the fire prevention, detection and protection measures at the site were commensurate with those that would be expected for a similar sized installation storing normal combustible material. On a qualitative basis this would ensure the risk was satisfactorily controlled when relevant best or good practice is adopted.

The method of comparing the relative toxicity of the proportion of parent material entrained into the fire plume to that of the proportion of carbon monoxide or hydrogen chloride generated from the material and packaging could be used to indicate if a more rigorous assessment were needed. Caution would be required where materials containing high proportions of nitrogen, nitrile or cyanide species were being stored which could significantly increase the proportion of hydrogen cyanide generated.

(1)   Health and Services Advisory Committee, *Safe Disposal of Clinical Waste,* HSAC, 1999.

(2)   The Control of Major Accident Hazard (COMAH) regulations 1999

(3)   Fire Statistics United Kingdom 1987. 22- page 8 HMSO

(4)   Halpin, B.M. and Berl, W.G., "Human Fatalities from Unwanted Fires," Report NBS-GCR-79-168, U.S. National Bureau of standards, Washington, DC, 1978

(5)   Harland, W.A. and Woolley, W.E., "Fire Fatality Study," Building Research Establishment Information paper, University of Glasgow, IP18/79, Glasgow, Scotland.

(6)   Weger, D.d., et al., TNO Contribution to the CEC STEP Programme CT-90-0096"Major hazards arising from fires in warehouse and chemical stores",. 1995, TNO Institute of environmental science: Apeldoorn

(7)   Private communication with Dr. M Holiday, Freeman Laboratories (Pathology) Department of Microbiology, Freeman Hospital Newcastle Upon Tyne.

(8)   Atkinson, G.T. S.F. Jagger and P.G. Kirk. *The Assessment of Individual Risks from Fires in Warehouses containing Toxic Materials*. Health and Safety Executive Research Laboratory Services Division, Harpur Hill Buxton UK

(9)   Atkinson, G.T. S.F. Jagger. *Assessment of hazards from warehouse fires involving toxic materials*. Industrial fires. 1993. Apeldoorn The Netherlands: Commission of the European Communities Directorate General XII.

(10)   Turner, R.M. and S Fairhurst., Assessment of the toxicity of major hazard substances, , HSE, Specialist inspector report No 21, May 1989, HSE Information services.

BENCHMARKING EMERGENCY MANAGEMENT GOOD PRACTICE – THE EMPIRE STUDY

Jeremy Larken and Helen Shannon, OCTO Ltd.

Professor John Strutt and Brian Jones, Cranfield University

INTRODUCTION

During 2000, OCTO and Cranfield University undertook a benchmarking study on emergency management and emergency planning for the Health and Safety Executive. The result was the Empire benchmarking model – Emergency Management Performance Indicators and Risk Evaluation. Empire looks in depth at the quality of emergency preparedness on a major hazard site, relating standards of preparedness to site risks, and comparing also practices across major hazard industry. This paper describes briefly the structure of Empire. It goes on to describe how performance in emergency exercises was assessed and how, in detail, standards of performance in emergency exercises were related to training and exercise regimes. The purpose of the presentation is to describe how best to target effort to achieve maximum value from emergency management investment under COMAH.

THE EMPIRE APPROACH TO ASSESSING EMERGENCY PREPAREDNESS

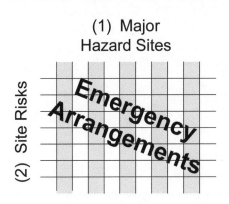

Empire stands for 'Emergency Management Performance Indicators And Risk Evaluation'. It is a database model of emergency preparedness which assesses:

- the effectiveness of the site's emergency preparedness as a comparison with other major hazard sites; and

- the effectiveness of the site's emergency preparedness in relation to the site risks.

Figure (1)   Empire assesses emergency arrangements wrt other major hazard sites and site risks

EMPIRE IS FOUNDED ON 3 KEY PRINCIPLES:

1. **Standards of performance are set by industry practitioners against agreed score criteria.** A key strength of Empire is that every value judgement in the study has been agreed with the industry participants concerned. This comprises in total some 2370 performance scores with associated rationale. To assist this process, 702 score criteria were developed for the project. All were derived from existing industry good practice and were agreed by industry collaborators to be appropriate. They have been applied consistently throughout the project.

2.   **Judgement on adequacy is made from two perspectives – good practice and site risks**. The first is a straightforward comparison with existing good practice; the second is a judgement in relation to the site risks. In order to achieve the second perspective a separate assessment was carried out to translate the site major hazards, based on COMAH safety case or equivalent, into the demands that the COMAH scenarios place on emergency response arrangements.

3.   **The measurement techniques should not 'lead' the results**. Given that the basis of data collection for this project is heavily reliant on expert judgement, great care has been taken to minimise subjectivity in both collection and interpretation of results. This was in part addressed in Principle 1. Secondly the Empire model as developed has no implicit value judgements of which components are 'good' or 'bad'. This point can best be explained once the overall structure of Empire is understood and is therefore addressed in more detail in the section on Maintaining Objectivity below.

Founded on Principles 1,2 and 3, Empire is a research tool. Used with circumspection, the large amount of data collected in the Empire model can be used to learn more about industry good practice and identify features which appear to contribute to good emergency response.

THE EMPIRE MODEL HAS THE FOLLOWING STRUCTURE.

It uses a balanced score-card approach to assess 82 indicators of emergency preparedness across 6 different emergency management perspectives and two exercise assessment perspectives:

▸   emergency philosophy

▸   emergency management structure

▸   emergency organisation

▸   emergency facilities

▸   emergency plans

▸   team preparedness

and

▸   qualitative assessment of performance in exercises

▸   quantitative assessment of performance in exercises

An evaluation of these perspectives can then be compared against the site environment and hazard characteristics, expressed as:

▸   The Site Incident Potential (SIP).

HOW DATA WAS COLLECTED

We invited and were delighted to receive the enthusiastic response of a number of experienced players across a good cross-section of major hazard industry. All the sites who took part had COMAH chemical hazards. Since the original research, more sites have joined in and the list of participants now comprises: Associated Octel; Avecia; AWE ; BHPP; BNFL Sellafield; BP; BNFL Thorp; ICI; IneosChlor; Pfizer; Scottish and Southern Energy; Shell; Urenco.

Each site shared with us its detailed emergency arrangements and subjected itself to an intensive and comprehensive assessment of its emergency preparedness. In addition to reviewing documents and conducting interviews with key personnel, we watched an exercise specifically offered by the company as a demonstration of emergency capability.

DERIVATION OF THE EMPIRE MODEL

The Empire framework was inspired and guided by several different research fields and concepts. These include the Balanced Score Card Approach (Kaplan, RS 1996), the Competence Maturity Method (CMM) (Carnegie Mellon, 2000) and to a lesser extent Business Process Analysis (BPA), and Quality Function Deployment (QFD). Some of this background research was already available at Cranfield University, through a parallel project on Design Safety Performance Indicator also funded by HSE (HSE/8890/3680).

The detailed structure of the Empire model was established through an iterative process starting with the COMAH regulations and a list of established good practice, contributed by OCTO. Each indicator was scored in detail, against parameters such as availability; effectiveness, alignment with strategy and company in-house capability. Contributions were then invited from industry collaborators to check for missing or superfluous elements. During the data-gathering process, the model was refined several times to reflect industry requirements. Finally, all the individual scores were ratified by the company concerned as a realistic representation of each element of its emergency preparedness.

The final structure is shown schematically in Figures 2 and 3 below:

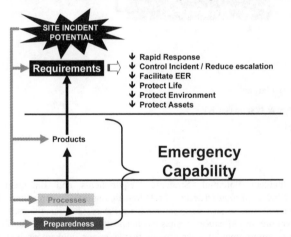

Figure (2)   Overview structure.

The Site Incident Potential (SIP) is a measure of difficulty for emergency management on site. It comprises an aggregation of the following elements:

▸ inventory in major hazard scenarios

▸ complexity of technology

▸ site population density

▸ diversity of hazards

- speed of scenario development
- level of off-site risk.

The SIP scale is calibrated to be compared directly with the emergency capability of the site.

The emergency management capability perspectives are illustrated in Figure 3.

At each stage this is assessed in the context of the strategic requirements of the site emergency arrangements, namely:

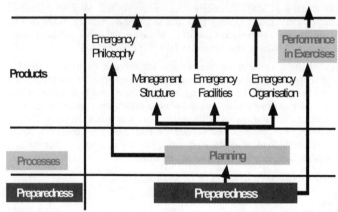

Figure (3)   Structure detail.

- initiate rapid response
- control incident / reduce escalation
- facilitate evacuation escape & rescue (EER)
- protect life (beyond EER)
- protect environment
- protect assets.

The links between Site Incident Potential, Strategic Requirements and Emergency Management Capability are achieved through a series of relationship matrices. Each matrix is as simple as possible, and easy to tune to site requirements if necessary. For most sites, the standard matrices served without modification. Sites with specific unusual factors, for instance particularly sensitive environmental risks, found that a minor adjustment better reflected its situation.

MAINTAINING OBJECTIVITY

Principle 3 of the Empire model is that the measurement technique should not 'lead' the results. In developing the overall structure of the model, each emergency perspective was sub-divided into a number of elements. The critieria for selection of these elements was that they should apply equally to each participant OR they should be based on some independent source, such as the COMAH regulations. Table 1 illustrates the basis for selecting elements of the team preparedness perspective.

Table (1)   Basis for selecting elements of the team preparedness perspective

Team Preparedness Element	Basis for Inclusion in Model
Selection of key staff for emergency duties	Guidance to Schedule 2 of COMAH Regulations 1999. Para 357 "arrangements for selecting and recruiting competent personnel".
Essential knowledge for key players in emergency response	Guidance to Schedule 2 of COMAH Regulations 1999. Para 370 "in order to find the necessary combination of theoretical and practical knowledge".
Emergency Management Competencies Addressed	Guidance to Schedule 2 of COMAH Regulations 1999. Para 357. Management of Health and Safety at Work Regulations 1999. Regulation 8 – "Nominate a sufficient number of competent persons to implement those procedures in so far as they relate to the evacuation from premises of persons at work in his undertaking." "A person shall be regarded as competent ... where he has sufficient training and experience or knowledge and other qualities to enable him properly to implement the evacuation procedures."….
Competence assurance / assessment for other key players	Guidance to Schedule 2 of COMAH Regulations 1999. Para 357.
Defined requirements for training exercises	Guidance to Schedule 2 of COMAH Regulations 1999. Para 357. "identifiying and meeting their training needs, monitoring their performance …." Schedule 5 "arrangements for training staff in the duties they will be expected to perform …". Guidance to COMAH Regulation 11, Para 227 "all relevant staff in all shifts in all the relevant organisations should be fully trained in their expected response in the event of an emergency."
Defined requirements for refresher training	As above.

A similar principle in selecting the relevant elements was applied for each perspective. For Management Structure, Organisation and Facilities the roles examined were a comprehensive set derived from all the industry participants. Emergency Philosophy and Emergency Plans were derived from the COMAH regulations and guidance, with contributions from industry. The two are closely related in that the Emergency Philosophy is primarily the justification of the approach taken in the Emergency Plan.

ASSESSING EMERGENCY EXERCISES – THREE METHODS

METHOD 1 - ASSESSMENT OF EMERGENCY MANAGEMENT TECHNIQUE

As the closest available analogue of reality, a part of the project was to observe how well each company performed in a demonstration exercise. The focus in exercise assessment was both the effectiveness of emergency management technique and the effectiveness of exercise response in saving life and otherwise mitigating consequences of the incident.

Those elements of emergency exercise performance examined at the exercise were:

▶ qualities and performance of emergency controller

▶ qualities and performance of deputy emergency controller, where present;

▶ discharge of mandates;

▶ information management;

▶ team performance;

▶ adequacy and use of resources;

▶ adequacy and use of facilities;

▶ performance outside procedural envelope;

▶ quality of the scenario

▶ review and learning process.

Detailed score criteria were prepared for each element and agreed with industry collaborators during the scoring process.

METHOD 2 - TPRC

A key determinant of performance was the success of the team in achieving sufficient response in a certain time, as illustrated by the Task Performance Resource Constraint (TPRC) model in Figure 4.

Figure (4)   TPRC Model.

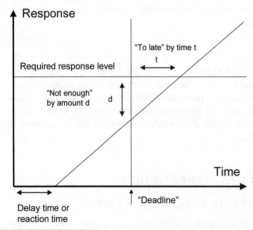

Emergency management can be viewed as a set of time and resource limited tasks performed by the team in managing an emergency incident. Each task has a goal or objective, a start, duration and end, plus one or more resources (including time itself) to support the task. The nature and amount of work to be carried out, the work rate, and the time and resources available and their rate of consumption are key factors. These can be related to the overall performance.

In the model, a distinction is drawn between the *time required* to complete a task, given the particular conditions (related to the nature of the task), and the *time available* to complete a task. The marshalling and application of resources and associated logistics will in general govern the latter. These points are explained below and illustrated in Figure 4 for the simple case of a single task.

Time Required

The nature of the task determines the amount of work necessary to complete the task. The required task duration depends both on the total amount of work required to achieve the task objective and the work rate or the rate of progress towards successful task completion. Take a simple routine task, with well-defined procedures, in which there is little or no special learning required, e.g. a person moving from position A to position B to muster. There will be little uncertainty in the time needed to undertake such a task. At the other extreme, a problem-solving task may be very complex, poorly defined, with no procedures or prior experience and demand a significant learning process to achieve the task objective. In this case there is likely to be a great deal of uncertainty both on how much work is required to achieve the objectives and on the rate of progress. Ultimately, full success in the task must be achievable.

Examples of tasks in this category are emergency management tasks that involve diagnosis of a complex problem. The task requirement in problem solving tasks can be equated to the level of information required, and the task completion rate to information gathering and knowledge accumulation rate.

Time Available

The speed of developments or rate of escalation will dominate the time available to complete emergency management tasks. If the task completion rate is insufficient, i.e. time required is greater than time available, then there will either be a short fall in the required performance or late completion of the task. These two modes of failure may result in very different consequences depending on the context.

A delay in the initiation of a task has a significant effect on the likelihood of successfully completing a task within the time available. The greater the delay, the greater the risk of a shortfall in performance or late completion. Hence the importance of a timely response.

An example plot is shown in Figure 5.

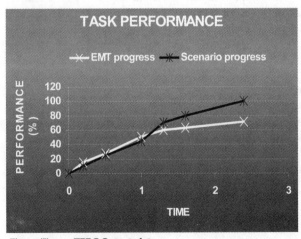

Figure (5)   TPRC Output plot.

Data gathering and the scenario

The scenario chosen for a TPRC analysis should be based on an emergency scenario identified in the safety case and for which technical information is available. The scenario could include management of:

» technical systems, e.g. shut-down systems, leak / release of hazardous materials possibly leading to fire

» personnel, e.g. mustering personnel, search and rescue of casualties

» external people, e.g. involving external assistance from emergency services,

» communications, e.g. informing personnel and public (if necessary) of incident and emergency management progress

The scenario selected for demonstration included a number of features that were "manageable" to test the skill of the emergency manager. Those emergencies which are so unmanageable that the only actions to be taken involve evacuation were avoided as scenario examples.

Typically, there was a minimum of 2 escalation points within the scenario to show management of changing circumstances. The emergency manager and team did not know in advance which emergency scenario has been selected for the exercise.

Preliminary data collection

Preliminary data collection established the objectives of the exercise and the extent to which it included elements of training and elements of assessment. A copy of the emergency scenario yielded the following information: the planned timings, the key inputs and the fixed escalation points.

It was then possible to develop a simple time-line for the scenario:

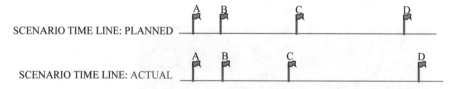

Figure (6)   Scenario timeline

Against this time-line we then monitored both the timing of the scenario and the timing of the emergency team responses throughout the exercise. Accurate time recording to a suitable accuracy took place by writing a time log based on direct observation, and was facilitated by use of a video camera with a time base.

At each defined escalation point we applied the TPRC model – collecting measurements as defined in Figure 4.

There are Inherent Limitations in Assessing Exercises

The following inherent limitations in assessing emergency exercises were taken into account:

» An emergency exercise usually tests only one scenario at a time.

» It is only a snap-shot of the performance of one team on a site.

» The time/event relationship is often compressed unrealistically (not necessarily a bad thing).

» Many of the mundane things that create serious difficulties in reality, e.g. the movement of people and resources, omitted actions and their real consequences, and all the associated communications and information intricacies, are difficult to simulate in exercises.

» It is not feasible, nor indeed generally helpful nor even safe, to attempt to reproduce the stress aspects of a serious emergency in an exercise (even if cautious insights may be gained from the different stress induced by the 'needle' of the occasion).

» Scenario writers tend to carry matters outside the procedural envelope in a misleading way, often as a consequence of their own inexperience; and

» Consciously or unconsciously, exercises can become the victims of stage management and wishful thinking.

It is important to approach these limitations in a constructive way. There are clear examples of exercise parameters which - with the most admirable of intentions - have over a period reduced a series of exercise demonstrations to a predictable ritual dance that is far removed from the reality of a serious emergency. It is important therefore always to analyse any exercise in the context of the site risk potential and the observed and needed emergency arrangements as a whole. Pre-study of this context together with an understanding of the prevailing background agenda should enable the exercise assessors to learn from what they witness through sensible filters and using a sound balance of indicators, and to make realistic and useful judgements thereby.

We showed earlier in Figure 5 the results of applying the model to the analysis of a scenario.

The dark line shows the progression of the scenario and the light line the actions of the emergency team. It can be seen that in the initial stages, the team were on top of the emergency, responding appropriately and in good time. Later on, the team fell behind as the emergency escalated. The critical end result here was that the team failed to rescue a casualty before unacceptable injuries were sustained.

METHOD 3 - RANKING

For various reasons it was not possible to undertake a full TPRC analysis for each emergency exercise demonstration. The principles of the technique could however be readily applied in a semi-numerical way by ranking the relative performance of emergency teams with each other. The ranking criteria used took a scale of 1 to 10 for two parameters – key objective achieved in terms of sufficient resources allocated, and key objective achieved in terms of resources deployed on time. These two measures were applied to the primary aim of the exercise, whether it be the saving of life on-site or the mitigation of consequences off-site or the protection of the environment.

Resources allocated

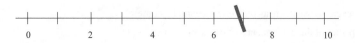

Resources on time

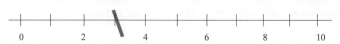

Figure (7)   Example of ranking methodology

SOME RESULTS FROM THE EMPIRE INVESTIGATION

COMPARING DIFFERENT METHODS OF ASSESSING EXERCISES

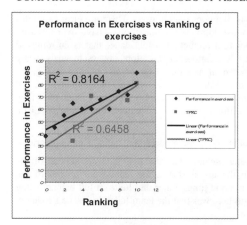

Figure 8 shows the relationships between the different means of assessing performance in exercises. In all graphs shown in this paper the R^2 value is NOT given with a view to demonstrating correlation but simply with a view to expressing the relative strength of the relationship between variables. In a study such as this, with largely empirical data, a value of ABS $[R^2]>0.5$ is considered significant. Only results with ABS $[R^2]>0.6$ are presented in this study as substantial positive indicators.

Figure (8)   Comparison of three methods of exercise assessment

Here it can be seen that the measurement of performance in exercises by two of the three techniques co-incide reasonably well. I.e. performance measured according to management technique co-incides with ranking of performance according to whether or not exercise objectives were met. The third measurement, the TPRC plot, shows an encouraging pattern, but is limited to 4 data points.

From these results we can start to conclude that overall achievement in emergency exercises is linked in some way to management performance. We now move on to examine these potential relationships in more detail.

INFORMATION MANAGEMENT IS AN ENABLER OF GOOD EMERGENCY MANAGEMENT TECHNIQUE

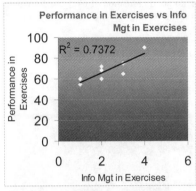
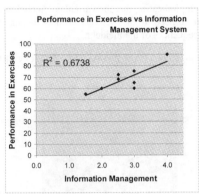

Figure (9)   Performance in exercises vs information management
Figure (10)   Performance in exercises vs information management system

From Figures 9 and 10 we can see that the information management system proved to be a key enabler of emergency management performance in exercises. A strong performance in information management was evidenced by the emergency manager being provided with the service of having information presented to him or her in a clearly expressed and readily accessible form. A clear and up-to-date display of both the current situation and a forward plan was in evidence throughout. Information management was not however the only determinant, as the relationship with the ranking in exercises metric demonstrates – Figure 11. The relationship here is much weaker, showing that there are other factors in play which have a bearing on achieving objectives.

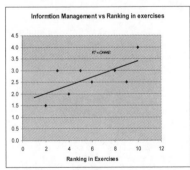
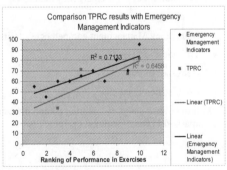

Figure (11)   Information management vs ranking in exercises
Figure (12)   Comparison of TPRC results with emergency management indicators

KEY INDICATORS OF EMERGENCY MANAGEMENT PERFORMANCE RELATE TO ACHIEVMENT IN EXERCISES

Figure 12 plots the average aggregate of a number of emergency management factors against achievement of exercise objectives, as measured both by ranking and by TPRC. The factors included are: performance of the Emergency Manager and Deputy (where relevant), information management in exercises, effectiveness of the emergency team in working together, and the suitability of the team's roles. An encouragingly strong relationship is shown, indicating that the variables selected can offer a good indication of likely performance with respect to the delivery of key resources for the saving of life and mitigation of consequences of the incident.

EFFECT OF TEAM PREPAREDNESS ON PERFORMANCE IN EXERCISES

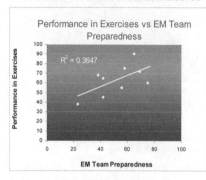
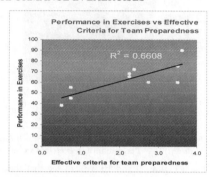

Figure (13)   Performance in exercises vs Emergency Management team preparedness
Figure (14)   Performance in exercises vs effective criteria for team preparedness

A surprising result is the very weak visual relationship between emergency team preparedness and performance in exercises as shown in Figure 13.

The constituent features of team preparedness scored here were:

▶ Selection process for emergency managers.

▶ Essential knowledge.

▶ Emergency Management competencies defined.

▶ Training exercises.

▶ Refresher training.

▶ Competence assurance.

On further analysis of this scoring protocol we can make a number of observations, which are summarised in the 2nd column of Table (2):

Table (2)   Comments on correlation of individual team preparedness elements with performance in exercises

Topic Scored (as shown in Figure 13)	Comment on results	Topic scored in Effective Criteria (as shown in Figure 14)
Selection process for emergency managers	There is a wide variation in approach.	No comparator
Essential knowledge	Would not expect this to correspond well to performance in a single exercise.	Command and Control training
Competencies defined and competence assurance	Established in about ½ the sample – wide range of results and no consistency of approach across sites.	Competence Assurance
Training exercises	Overall training in exercise did not relate well to the experts' observations of performance in exercises on the day of the assessment.	Professional coaching of team in training exercises
Refresher training	Wide ranging standards across the sample	No comparator
		Team continuity. i.e. team members are well practised with one-another and tend to exercise together.

Given that we would normally expect to find a relationship between team preparedness and performance, we tried an alternative approach to scoring team preparedness. In the first scoring protocol (column 1 of Table 2), we scored across a broad cross-section of preparedness features, covering the basics and also more advanced topics. In the second, (column 3 of Table 2) we selected and then scored team preparedness against a sub-set of more closely-targeted training features. These scores were subsequently tested and validated with industry participants. The aggregate results show a much closer relationship, as illustrated in Figure 14. Of the individual plots (not shown) the strongest relationships were observed for Team Continuity, Command and Control training, and Coaching in Exercises. That Command and Control proved to be the only subset of essential knowledge that was selected in the 'Effective Criteria' reflects not that it is the only relevant area of essential knowledge, but more that it is the only area that can reliably be demonstrated by watching an exercise. Most exercises can test only a very limited span of essential knowledge, and the remainder of essential knowledge is best assessed in ways that lie outside the scope of this study.

Since Command and Control is frequently misunderstood, a description as applied in this paper is offered here. As an aggregate term, Command and Control encompasses both the authority of an individual to take charge of a situation and the structured processes by which that authority is discharged. In the context of an industrial emergency the processes can include, although not exclusively, decision-making under pressure, information management, team management, structured communications and briefing. Team continuity is defined in Table 2. Coaching in Exercises refers simply to the process of having an independent and informed observer analysing the performance of the team and individuals and assisting them in critiquing their performance and identifying areas for improvement.

MANAGEMENT PERFORMANCE IN EXERCISES IS IMPROVED BY EXERCISING EFFECTIVELY

A strong relationship was observed between the type and nature of training exercises undertaken throughout the year and performance of the emergency management team in the demonstration exercise. (Figure 15.)

The features of the exercise regime which scored highly in this study were those which exercised all the basic processes on-site and then exercised and tested emergency management independently to a good standard before putting the whole together in large, demonstration exercises. Poor performances were evidenced where the exercise regime concentrated on putting too much together at a time and not addressing the basic elements first. For instance, where individual items such as personnel accounting systems or action monitoring or sourcing safety case reference material had not been addressed as an individual item except in large exercises, learning had not been consolidated and there was a tendency for exercises to simply re-inforce existing (and often bad) practice, instead of building up good practice. In all cases, contributors had some difficulty in demonstrating comprehensiveness of their exercise regime across all safety-case scenarios, work-teams, plants, and chemicals.

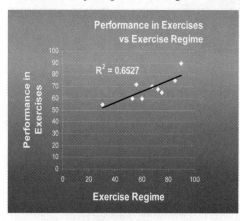

Figure (15)   Performance in exercises vs exercise regime

TESTING OF DATA RELATIONSHIPS

The data has been subjected to an extensive process of testing to establish if the correlation approach was suitable. Care was taken throughout the study to ensure that the data was selected so as not to 'lead' the results. Once gathered, many data relationships were plotted. Many failed to demonstrate any relationship. For instance Performance in Exercises did not relate to Emergency Philosophy. A similar result was obtained, in that performance in exercises did not relate to quality of emergency procedures (a variable related to Emergency Philosophy). In all cases of negative results identified, there was a satisfactory explanation. For instance, we would not expect a close relationship between performance in exercises and emergency philosophy. In the case of Philosophy vs Management Structure, there is no possible relationship from the way the data variables have been construed. This too is confirmed when we plot the results.

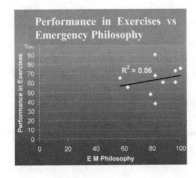

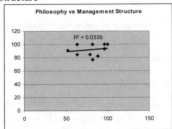

Figure (16)   Four graphs illustrating poor relationships

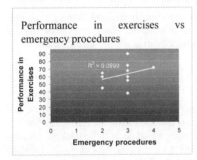

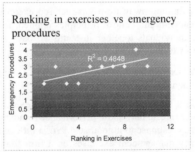

We recognise that the common factor in all of the value judgements is that of the researchers, primarily OCTO, specialists in emergency and crisis management. We have attempted to address this limitation on the data by assessing performance in exercises independently through ranking and TPRC techniques, which have been performed jointly with Cranfield University, and by having every data variable verified by industry practitioners. In our view these people represent some of the most experienced and knowledgeable individuals in major hazard industry emergency management and their value judgements have both independence and accuracy. To give a flavour of the quality of the verification process, between 10 and 20% of the individual element scores were debated between OCTO and the industry experts and in all cases agreement was reached. The rest were agreed without debate.

Such is the complexity and variation in the large number of data points collected – some 3000 to date, that it is impossible to adjust individual data points to give a particular result. The data sets have to be taken at face value and interpreted accordingly. It was concluded therefore that the graphs which showed a strong trend, as measured by the gradient of the line and the R^2 coefficient, could be interpreted as showing a relationship between the variables or their groupings.

CONCLUSIONS

All conclusions are based on the premise that performance in real emergencies correlates well to performance in realistic exercises.

1.   Performance of emergency response teams in saving life and mitigating the effect of an emergency is enhanced by effective emergency management.

Key areas on which to focus in assessing emergency management performance in exercises are: the performance of the emergency manager and deputy; the information management process; the effectiveness of the team in working together – the team dynamic; and, finally, the roles within the team and the suitability thereof.

2.   Information management is an enabler of good emergency management.

The skill of being able to display a clear and up-to-date picture of the current situation and forward plan plays a significant role in supporting the emergency management process.

3.   The training regime selected can be expected to have a significant bearing in subsequent performance in demonstration exercises.

Steering training away from unstructured exercises and towards targeted training exercises, with command and control principles applied, robust information management systems and keeping individuals together in teams all have a direct bearing on the effectiveness of the emergency team.

4.   The exercise regime selected can have a significant bearing on subsequent performance in demonstration exercises.

Establish a regime of simple, inexpensive exercises, with clear performance standards, and train and exercise until these performance standards are met. Build up the elements of on-site emergency response to a good standard; a little and often would seem to be the key. Overlay emergency management exercises on a firm foundation of basic skills and, again, build up these elements until they can be put together with confidence in large, demonstration exercises.

This research was funded by the Health and Safety Executive (HSE). The content of this paper, including any opinions and/or conclusions expressed, are those of the authors alone and do not necessarily reflect HSE policy.

BIBLIOGRAPHY

The final paper will carry a reference to the HSE research report on the empire model – currently being published – reference not yet available.

Carnegie Mellon Software Engineering Institute, 2000 *"Capability Maturity Modelling"* – From the Internet at: http://www.sei.cmu.edu/cmm/cmm.html

Health & Safety Executive, 1999 *"HSG191 – Emergency Planning for Major Accidents – Control of Major Accident Hazard Regulations 1999"* London, HMSO

Health & Safety Executive, 1999 *"L111 – A guide to the Control of Major Accident Hazard Regulations 1999 (COMAH)"* London, HMSO

Home Office, 1999 *"Standards for Civil Protection in England & Wales"* From the Internet at: http://www.homeoffice.gov.uk/epd

Home Office, 1999 *"The Exercise Planners Guide"* From the Internet at: http://www.homeoffice.gov.uk/epd

Home Office, 1998 *"Why exercise your disaster response?"* From the Internet at: http://www.homeoffice.gov.uk/epd

Home Office, 1997 *"Dealing with Disaster"* Ed. 3 London, Brodie Publishing

Kaplan, RS 1996 *"The Balanced Scorecard"* London, McGraw Hill Publishing.

Statutory Instrument No. 743, 1999 *"The Control of Major Accident Hazards Regulations 1999"* London, HMSO

Strutt J. E, Loa P. and Allsopp, K. 1997 *"Progress towards the development of a model for predicting human reliability"* in Quality and Reliability Engineering International, 13(6).

Strutt J.E, Lyons M, Allsopp K, Larken J, Værnes R.J 1998 *"Development of models and data for quantification human reliability on emergency management"* in Conference Proceedings of the Safety & Reliability Association Annual Conference.

EMERGENCY RESPONSE TRAINING USING NEW TECHNOLOGIES

Dr Panos Topalis, panos.topalis@dnv.com
Det Norske Veritas, Palace House, 3 Cathedral Street, London SE1 9DE

Emergency response management in the chemical industry is an important area which has the potential to benefit from recent technical progress in accident scenario modelling, artificial intelligence and other computing and education technologies. Emergency response training, in particular, is thought to be an area which is particularly suited to the use of new educational and software technologies. There has been some research and development work in this subject during the last few years with variable success. A review of relevant approaches and tools is presented with emphasis on emergency training. Is the current technology mature enough to provide useful help to the chemical industry? The industry is currently experimenting to find out more.

This paper introduces a international research project, aiming at improving training in serious technological emergencies resulting from chemical production and transportation. The new training approach makes use of a real-time expert system, dynamic consequence simulation, Geographical Display Systems and Multi-media within a client-server architecture. The integration of these features to create realistic interactive emergency scenarios is summarised.

The training methodology relies on a wide participation of users from the chemical industry. A user-requirement analysis was conducted with detailed questionnaires and interviews. The results of the analysis are presented, including functional requirements and the legal and institutional context. The emergency training methodology will be tested with customised training cases in five countries. An example of a training case is presented to illustrate the possible tool contents and the associated design process.

Emergency training, software, user requirements, artificial intelligence, distributed development, multi-media

INTRODUCTION

The use of simulation tools to assist emergency management and emergency training in the chemical industry started in the 1980s when some progress had been achieved in the area of consequence modelling and when graphical user interfaces and visualisation technology started being noticed. However, the first applications were not as interactive and user-friendly as we expect them to be today and it took some time before we could see applications which benefit from the advancements in the computing technology. Many software packages claim to be emergency management tools but this is a general term that may have different meanings and interpretations.

EMERGENCY PLANNING TOOLS

There are a number of consequence effect models, available publicly or commercially, which can assist with the development of an emergency plan. The commercial consequence analysis package PHAST (DNV, 2000) performs a wide range of effect calculations such as dispersion (Witlox and Holt, 1999)[29], fire and explosion. It also has the capability of graphically overlaying the effect zones on map images. Publicly available models such as HGSYSTEM (Witlox, 1993)[27] and SLAB (Ermac, 1989)[12] can also be used for dispersion calculation. All these tools are useful for the design of emergency plans in the chemical industry.

CAMEO (EPA, 2001)[12] is a publicly available software tool (through the Environmental Protection Agency) which is referred to as an emergency management tool but its main functionality is a consequence modelling. DISCOVER is a program developed by ICI in the early 1990s (Preston, 1994)[23]. This has been used mostly for dispersion calculations but it also has facilities for overlaying dispersion concentration contours over maps.

Development of emergency planning models was also reported recently. The SEVEX tool described by Dutrieux and Van Malder (2000)[11] emphasises compliance with the SEVESO II directive and appears to be an integrated consequence package. An interactive web-based planning and decision support system (HEVAN) has been described by Cameron (2000)[5].

EMERGENCY MANAGEMENT TOOLS

Some real time emergency management tools are described on the Internet or in the proceedings of specialist conferences:

The Riskware system (Fedra and Winkelbauer, 1999)[16] is a decision support software system which was progressively developed as part of European funded projects, especially the HITERM project (ESS, 2000)[15] and has been the starting point for the A-Team emergency training system. The Riskware system combines databases (hazardous installations, safety reports, hazardous substances, etc.) with an environmental Geographical Information System (GIS). All tools are embedded in a real-time expert system framework, which provides operational guidance and assists the emergency command and control tasks.

SAFER (SAFER Systems, 2001)[26] is known to provide a live link between consequence models and real time weather data to assist real time emergency management. CICERO is a program for Communication, Co-ordination and Control by α-COM and it is described by Ledger (1999)[18] and on the Internet (Cicero, 2000)[7]. Atlas OPS is distributed by Atkins and Partners Ltd and is presented by Atkins (1999)[2]. Another system is the Command Planning System (CPS) which is distributed by Fortek Computers and is described by Godliman (1999)[17].

Most of the above systems are described as Emergency Management systems but generally they could probably be used for Emergency Training.

EMERGENCY TRAINING TOOLS

Moeller-Holst (1988)[22] reports one of the earliest applications for emergency response training and planning based on expert system techniques. There are currently a number of computer systems which are referred to in the literature as emergency training systems:

The program TUTOR (Adamson, 2000)[1] was developed by the Defence Evaluation and Research Agency (DERA) in the UK and it has emergency training capabilities. The Minerva multi-media simulator training system was developed by the Metropolitan Police (Crego, 1999)[9]. The Emergency Simulation Program (ESP,2000)[14] is a Windows-based *authoring* system specially designed to create and present multi-media simulations for the training of emergency personnel. Bruhn Newtech's NBC-Analysis software (Bruhn Newtech, 2000)[4] takes hazardous input either manually from the user or directly from detectors.

Recently some multi-media and web-based training applications started appearing in the chemical industry literature. Goh et al (1998)[18] reported a safety improvement by a multi-media operator training system. Lee et al (2000)[19] developed evaluation algorithms for their operator training system.

EXISTING TOOLS AND THE A-TEAM PROJECT

The literature search indicated that there are a few computerised emergency management and emergency training tools, some of which are commercially available. We have not generally tested these tools, so we cannot make any judgement on their robustness or fitness for purpose. Some of these tools have been sold commercially and this is an indication that the industry and/or the emergency services are interested in and are prepared to experiment with these tools.

Some observations from our literature search:

- *Current practice.* The chemical industry still uses mostly conventional non-computerised systems for emergency training despite the growing interest in software tools

- *Consequence analysis packages.* Conventional consequence analysis programs are suitable for emergency planning (usually done by engineers or personnel with strong technical skills) but they need substantial customisation and a different graphical user interface if they are going to be used for emergency training

- *Control and command versus accident simulation.* Many emergency training packages are essentially 'control and command' training tools and they do not include any mathematical models of the accident. Sometimes the tools are used as one component of the emergency exercise while the rest of the exercise is done conventionally outside the software. Training in 'control and command' is obviously very important but it is thought that integration with simulation models would be a significant enhancement to the systems

- *Graphical user interface and model accuracy.* Most of the recent emergency training programs have focused on improving graphical users interfaces. Addition of multimedia capabilities is also given high priority. There appears to be little emphasis on improving the accuracy or realism of any attached consequence effect models.

- *Specialisation.* There are a number of tools that have focused on training of specific public services such as fire brigades or the police but they are probably less well adapted to the needs of the chemical industry. For example programs specialised to fire brigade training may not be very well suited to dealing with training for toxic gas dispersion incidents in the chemical industry.

- *Geographical Information Systems* (GIS) and electronic map systems are used to some extent for emergency response *planning* but these systems (GIS) are usually not integrated with emergency *training* systems. In general, it is not so common that emergency training systems make use of GIS.

- *Evaluation.* Evaluation in adult learning, especially in a work environment, is often a sensitive issue and sometimes it is not done properly to avoid emotional clashes. However since emergency response is a critical activity, evaluation of the trainees and the effectiveness of training are important. We are not aware of the evaluation included in the existing software systems and it seems that it is generally done outside the system. There is scope for research to improve evaluation within the software tools.

Our conclusion from the literature review is that modern computing technologies have provided significant potential for building useful emergency training software tools and there has been rapid progress during the last few years. There are some tools, which have interesting and useful features. On the other hand we have not found many systems which have all the important components necessary so that they would be accepted by the chemical industry. In this respect, the current computerised emergency training technology cannot yet be considered mature and there is scope for further research and development.

The A-Team project was defined with the aim of improving learning in the area of technological emergency response training. This aim would be achieved with the integration of artificial intelligence technologies and realistic consequence simulations. This would result in a system serving interactive multi-media content within a real time knowledge based system. The system would employ client-server architecture and would support easy access/

connection through Intranet/ Internet distributed systems.   A-Team is a multi-partner European project and includes testing of the training approach and the tool by five partners in different countries. DNV will be testing the system with emergency training in the chemical industry. Our tasks include:

- A user requirement analysis, which has focused mostly on UK chemical companies
- Contribution to the tool architecture and development, especially by providing well established consequence analysis models
- Developing a training case and testing the approach with chemical industry users

Further exploitation and industrial use of the results of this work, including methodology and tools, is strongly encouraged by the sponsors, as this will motivate production of tools, practical and useful to industry.

EMERGENCY RESPONSE TRAINING IN THE CHEMICAL INDUSTRY

INDUSTRY SURVEY

Selected companies and public organisations have been contacted in several European countries. DNV started the user requirement analysis with 8 companies, mostly in the UK, who expressed an interest in the emergency training tool. A very detailed questionnaire was sent to all participants and then interviews were conducted with almost all companies in order to clarify and finalise the questionnaires and to collect additional information. Exhibit 1 shows a sample page from the questionnaire filled partly during an interview, containing information on the current emergency organisation and practices. The questionnaires and interviews covered the following areas:

- General information on the company, the site, the chemical processes, the area and the environment
- Legal framework and interaction of the company with the competent authorities, the public agencies and the other stakeholders
- Current emergency organisation and training
- Definition of potential emergency training cases and trainee profiles
- Functional requirements i.e. what the software tool should do, contents of the training
- Non-functional requirements – constraints e.g. hardware and software constraints, educational requirements/ constraints.

Some of the results are summarised below.

LEGAL FRAMEWORK AND INTERACTIONS WITH OTHER STAKEHOLDERS

The COMAH regulations in the UK (COMAH, 1999)[8] is the implementation of the Seveso II Directive (Seveso II, 1996)[27] and this is the most important piece of legislation governing emergency planning and training in major hazardous installations in Europe. The main Seveso II requirement is that there should be an emergency plan and it should be tested at least every 3 years with the participation of external agencies, generally the fire brigade.

In England there are two relevant competent authorities: the Health and Safety Executive for safety issues and the Environment Agency for environmental issues. Emergencies have to be reported to these two authorities. The chemical company usually interacts with other stakeholders as follows:

- Fire Brigade
- Police
- Regional or local Emergency Planning Unit (EPU)
- Ambulance

- Regional Health Authority and Ambulance Trust
- Armed Forces (Terrorism, special branch etc)
- Neighbouring operating companies, which often participate in mutual aid schemes

EMERGENCY ORGANISATION AND CURRENT TRAINING METHODS

Most of the chemical companies in the UK (as well as in other European countries) have a similar organisational structure during emergency. This is shown in figure 1. The incident would first be notified to the incident controller (typically the shift supervisor) and his team. They would first attempt to control the incident at source at an operational level and then mitigate its immediate consequences. If the incident appears to be significant, the tactical team will be called so that they can direct and control the medium and longer-term effects. It can be seen that there can be a third level of emergency team (the crisis team) composed of the most senior people and having as objective to protect the company's reputation and take care of the longer term business interests of the company. If an external fire brigade is called, the fire commander needs to put his efforts together with the main controller to co-ordinate the response. It is usual that the fire brigade commander usually takes the initiative when there is a fire. However if there is a toxic gas dispersion, the fire brigade would leave the initiative to the plant manager/ main controller.

The survey also indicated that the following emergency training methods are commonly used:

1) Live exercises. These are major exercises, which try to mimic a major accident and its development in real time in the field. They typically require mobilisation of a large number of people to participate in the exercise on the same day. They involve the tactical management team, the at-the-scene incident control team, fire fighters etc. They can last from half a day to two days. They require prior preparation and organisation, sometimes several months in advance. They take place infrequently, at best every six months. They often involve external agencies. The fire brigade is the most common external agency. The exercise often involves the police, the ambulance service and the local or regional authority. Good descriptions of live exercises can be found in Ramsay et al (1995)[24] and Ramsay (1999)[25].

2) Regular drills. These field involve an accident scenario, typically a fire and the development of this scenario is followed to some extent but not to the same details as a major live exercise. Regular drills are organised by the safety manager or the shift supervisor or the emergency trainer and they involve a small number of people particularly the fire teams. Under the best circumstances they take place every week. They have a limited duration, say one hour. They don't involve external agencies.

3) Tabletop exercises. During a tabletop exercise, a major accident scenario is assumed and people sit around the table and play the roles they would have during an emergency. This is essentially a discussion of the participants' roles, responsibilities, and their actions under the circumstances of the accident. Tabletop exercises last about one to two hours. They are more frequent than the live exercises and they can take place a few times a year. They can involve external agencies but most of the time they do not.

4) Seminar training. This is normally lecture-based and typically: It includes basic knowledge on fires, hazardous chemicals, risks, case histories, emergency organisation and procedures. The emphasis is on problem identification and solution finding rather decision taking. Seminars are often introductory to other types of exercises such as live exercises.

5) Control post exercises. These exercises start again with a scenario while people (mostly team leaders and communications responsibles) are seated in their respective separate positions. People consider the various hazardous outcomes and practice communications.

REQUIREMENTS SPECIFICATION FOR A COMPUTERISED TRAINING SYSTEM

Table 1 shows the main observations of those who participated in the survey about weaknesses of the existing emergency training systems. The table has been used to compile some of the user requirements for the new computerised tool. A large number of user requirements came from the user's responses to the functionality questions and they are documented in a special report (McCracken et al, to be finalised, 2001)[21]. The most important requirements are summarised here:

System Architecture

The system will have a distributed architecture, at least during the development and testing phase to facilitate deployment and access. The main A-Team server (the real time expert system RTXPS) will run on its native Linux/ Unix while other components (the DNV models) will be running on Windows and communication will be through HTTP. User access will be primarily through web browsers.

Consequence Models

A-Team will run "live" all consequence models that can run reasonably fast i.e. all DNV models and most of the other models. The case-based reasoning technique will be used to display results from the slower models (CFD). For given model input data, this artificial intelligence technique allows selection of the best-matching results from a large database of pre-calculated results.

GIS

The system will use the existing RXTPS Graphics Display System to display and use maps.

Contours

The program will calculate concentration, radiation and explosion contours so that they can be overlaid over maps or site plans. It will be possible to plot contours at different time intervals in advance.

Communication

There will be some provision for allowing people to train in communications. This is likely to be through a system simulating communications.

Multimedia

The system will make use of multi-media elements such as photos, graphics, animations, symbolic objects and interactive links and text. It will be possible to play these elements as far as this information had been fed into the system. Access to the PC will be through the keyboard and mouse.

Links

The system will provide links to contact lists, site plans and operational posts and asset descriptions.

Table 1: Issues with Current Emergency Training and Possibilities of Improvement

Category	Issues identified by the Chemical Industry	Possible requirements for tool
General emergency training issues	• Training is not frequent enough. We cannot easily get all the relevant people together • There is a lack of real understanding of roles in a major emergency team	• Use tool to practice roles and responsibilities in emergencies
Live exercises	• They are inconvenient and costly. Result: They are not frequent enough. • Public emergency services are busy. They are not easily available for joint exercises	• Use software to practice more frequently. Simulate agencies
Regular fire drills	• Regular drills. As they cannot mimic actual emergency well, they cannot impose the same stress levels as a real emergency • The fire drills are repetitive and predictable and the trainees often lose interest	• Use tool for realistic mimicking of emergencies • Include multi-media in tool
Tabletop exercises	• They are not so realistic and not in real time	• Self-paced (seminar type) multimedia courses should be combined with emergency scenario practising
Seminar exercises	• They do not provide any real experience by themselves	
Some computerised exercises	• Lose effectiveness when computer tools are not customised to the company's scenarios	• Allow customisation of scenarios to company's processes
Main Controller (tactical team) issues	• Ineffective Communications with the other parties: incident control team, external agencies • Debriefing Documentation is not usually good enough to be used for improvement of emergency response	• Tool should allow main controller to practice communications • Tool should produce full debriefing documentation
Incident Controller (at-the-scene team) issues	• He cannot easily visualise development of unusual major accidents because he has not been sufficiently exposed to a realistic accident representation. • He has little experience in assessing a complex incident i.e. diagnosing what went wrong from the signs and symptoms and predicting what could happen next. He has difficulty in weighing up pros and cons of decisions and answering urgent questions such as: Should a major emergency be declared? Is it safe to go into the building? This is partly due to limited understanding of the escalation potential of the initial incident and little familiarity with risks and risk assessment • There are problems of interaction between the company fire teams and the production operators/ technicians	• Interface tool with realistic consequence models to allow visualisation of accident consequences • Tool should teach Incident controller elements of risk assessment. It should also allow practising decision taking under pressure • Practice communications

A-TEAM EMERGENCY TRAINING TOOL

Figure 2 shows the system architecture in more detail. The top boxes show the user access options. The primary access method is through a browser, which serves HTML, Java and possibly XML content. The main A-Team server is running under its native operating system UNIX/ Linux and is accessing the GIS and the real time expert system RTXPS. The use of HTTP and a browser, on the client side, has the big advantage of easy installation and easy updating. Figure 2 also shows that development of the other services (e.g. the DNV model service) can be initially running in different locations (e.g. London) far from the main server and under a different operating system i.e. Windows. When development is complete a decision will be taken if, for the purposes of the final distribution version, it is better to keep all components in the same box. Apart from the DNV model server there are two more servers:

- The DocCentre Multi-media and Course server. This manages an Oracle database which contains the multimedia material and the course management system
- The Case-based reasoning server, which accesses a database of CFD run results and selects the most appropriate results for user's input parameters.

TRAINEE PROFILES

The following groups of people were initially identified as candidate users of the emergency training tool:

1. *Operational* emergency response personnel who are employees of a chemical company. This may include: The incident controller (leader of the Incident Control Team) who is typically the plant shift supervisor, the fire team leader, a production technician or operator who assists with the initial control/ mitigation of incident, a fire fighter, other members of the emergency response team e.g. first aiders, security guards
2. Members of the *tactical* emergency response team, who are employees of a chemical company. This team includes a variety of roles but some of these roles could be assumed by the same person: Main Controller-leader of the team, assistant to the Main Controller, Technical Advisor-Engineer, SHE (Safety, Health and Environment) specialist, Communications responsible, Secretary-Record Keeper, Public Relations (PR) responsible, Human Relations (HR) responsible
3. *Public fire brigade* team leaders in chemical industry areas
4. *Police* officers dealing with emergencies in chemical industry areas
5. *Local/Regional authority* emergency response co-ordinators in chemical industry areas
6. *Ambulance* personnel in chemical industry areas

So far DNV has contacted mainly chemical industry potential users in categories (1.) and (2.) who have provided contributions to our user requirement analysis. However it is a possibility that people from the other categories will be considered, at a later stage, for using the training software tool. Public fire brigade officers (3.), police officers (4.) and regional authority emergency response co-ordinators (5.) are known to be users of similar software and are considered likely candidate users of A-Team.

Two trainee profiles have been selected for this initial phase of the A-Team tool are shown in Table 2. Both are team leader roles and there is some common knowledge that is included in both training cases. However there are some important differences:

- The Main controller is likely to have a good background education and knowledge and would think of both short term and long term issues and offsite consequences. The main controller represents the tactical team and would assume the most demanding role in his team.
- The Incident Controller is likely to have a very good practical knowledge and experience and would focus on short term and operational problems. The Incident Controller represents the people "at the scene" and has clearly the most demanding operational role.

Table 2: Trainee Profiles for a Test Case

Trainee Category	Primary job responsibilities	Roles in emergency situations	Relationship of role to other roles in emergency situations	Work practice
Main Controller (tactical)	Manager-Engineer	Emergency response control at a tactical level. Minimise consequence effects and offsite risk, including –short term and long term effects	Give advice/ recommendations to Incident Controller. Co-ordinates with external agencies	Management and /or technical experience
Incident Controller (operational)	Shift supervisor	Responsible for Incident Control at the scene. Mitigate consequences Address immediate hazards	Takes recommendations from tactical team (main controller) but maintains operational responsibility and control	Long practical experience. Some emergency response experience but only as a part time activity

TRAINING CASES AND POSSIBLE CONTENTS

The A-Team project considers 3 types of computerised emergency training:

1)   *Single-user, self-paced* (style similar to distance learning) for background information; this may include:

• basic safety knowledge such as hazardous materials, hazards, scenarios, consequences etc

• simple model simulations for illustration purposes only

• emergency response knowledge such as emergency response organisation and emergency procedures

• a briefing for the 2nd part of the training which is the real time scenario-driven exercise

• a simple evaluation test of the trainee's knowledge before and after the exercise. This is based mostly on automated multiple-choice questions.

The trainee can go through the first part in his own time and in his own way. The idea of this first part is to prepare the trainee for the second and most important scenario driven exercise. This first part allows the user to go back as he wishes or to request additional information if he finds it necessary. This type of training parallels the currently provided seminar training but it will be much more visual and interactive.

2)   *Single user,* scenario-driven emergency response exercise in real time. This is started with a hazardous initiating event, which is typically a release of a hazardous material. This includes a continuous dialogue between the system and the trainee, which is normally time-constrained i.e. the exercise runs generally in real time and the trainee has a limited time to respond or to take decisions. Under normal scenario-driven mode the user will not able to request additional information. On the other hand, the system avoids giving additional feedback or information so that the trainee does not deviate from his real time realistic scenario development.

The scenario-driven exercise initially takes place under trainer supervision, possibly within a small team of people. It logs the full scenario history in a file. The history is available for the debriefing session and is also used for the evaluation of the trainees. The evaluation is not initially completely automated and involves a discussion between the trainer and the trainee. The scenario driven exercise is intended to replace or to assist the conventional fire drills, tabletop exercises and live exercises.

3)   *Multi-user* (multiple actor input, one or several actor-specific views) *externally driven* real-time scenarios, primarily for simulated emergencies.

Our training is initially implementing training of types 1 and 2. Training of type 3 is considered particularly suitable for integrated multi-agency training and it is considered an important and useful enhancement of the tool.

CONCLUSION

This paper has provided a detailed review of recent advances of computer-based training in the technologically difficult domain of emergency response and it has also presented a new development in this area. Thanks to rapid progress in computing technology, including artificial intelligence, Geographical Information Systems, multimedia and visualisation techniques and advances in the area of consequence effect modelling, the components are now available to allow building of a useful emergency training simulator. The Chemical Industry needs to experiment a little more since this technology has the potential not only to cut training costs but also to bring an improvement in emergency training and ultimately an improvement in safety.

ACKNOWLEDGEMENTS

This work is partly funded by the European Commission, Information Society Technologies Programme IST-1999-10176, 5th Framework Research Programme. The author is solely responsible for the contents of this paper. This paper does not represent the opinion of the Commission or the opinion of Det Norske Veritas.

REFERENCES

1. Adamson J., 2000, The Use of Interactive Computer Simulations for Crisis Management. *Industrial Safety Management*, Vol.3, December 2000. http://www.bcd-modelling.com

2. Atkins T. , 1999, Atlas OPS, Atkins and Partners, *Joint HSE/ SIESO COMAH Workshop on Testing Emergency Plans* Emergency Planning College, Easingwold,25/26 March 1999.

3. Atlasops, 2000, In (http://www.atlasops.com)

4. Bruhn Newtech, 2000. Civil Emergency Products for Civil Emergency response. NBC-ANALYSIS Software. http://www.bruhn-newtech.com

5. Cameron I.T., 2000, An Interactive Web-Based Decision Support System for Hazardous Industry Land-Use Planning. *Computers and Chemical Engineering*, 24: 1057-1062. http://daisy.cheque.uq.edu.au/ hevan/

6. Champers T., St Tournis, 1999, The Essential Role of Modern Technologies in Emergency Response; Real World Cases. . In "SEVESO 2000 European Conference. *Risk Management in the European Union of 2000.* The Challenge of Implementing Council Directive "SEVESO II" November 10-12, 1999, Athens.

7. Cicero, 2000, In http://www.acicero.com

8. COMAH, 1999, Control of Major Accident Hazard regulations, UK.

9. Crego, J., 1996, Multi-agency major incident command training, using the MINERVA simulation system. *Fire magazine*, 18th October.(http://www.essenet.demon.co.uk)

10. DNV, 2000, PHAST 6.0 Manual. (http://www.dnv.com/software)

11. Dutrieux A. and van Malder G., 1999. The SEVESO EXpert System "SEVEX": An Integrated Approach for Off-Site Effects Analysis & Effective Emergency Planning. in "SEVESO 2000 European Conference. *Risk Management in the European Union of 2000.* The Challenge of Implementing Council Directive "SEVESO II" November 10-12, Athens.

12. EPA, 2000, In http://www.epa.gov/ceppo/cameo

13. Ermak, D.L., 1989, "User's Manual for SLAB: an atmospheric dispersion model for denser-than-air releases, Lawrence Livermore National Laboratory, Livermore, California.

14. ESP, 2000, http://www.intergate.bc.ca/business/strylght /ProductFeatures.html The Emergency Simulation Program.

15. ESS, 2000, http://www.ess.co.at/

16. Fedra, K. and Winkelbauer, L.,1999, A hybrid expert system, GIS and simulation modelling for environmental and technological risk management. In:*Env. Decision Support Systems and Artificial Intelligence*, Technical Report WS-99-07, pp 1-7, AAAI Press, Menlo Park, CA.

17. Godliman G., 1999, The Command Planning System. Fortek Computers Ltd. *Joint HSE/ SIESO COMAH Workshop on Testing Emergency Plans*, Emergency Planning College, Easingwold,25/26 March 1999.

18. Goh S., Chang B., Jeong I., Kwon Hyouk-Tae, Moon I., 1998, Safety Improvement by Multi-media Operator Education System. *Computers and Chemical Engineering*, 22: S531-S536.

19. Ledger C., 1999, CICERO, Crisis, Incident Control and Emergency Response Organiser. *Joint HSE/ SIESO COMAH Workshop on Testing Emergency Plans*, Emergency Planning College, Easingwold,25/26 March 1999. http://www.acicero.com

20. Lee S., Jeong I., Moon I., 2000, Development of Evaluation Algorithms for Operator Training System. *Computers and Chemical Engineering*, 24: 1517-1522.

21. McCracken J, 2001 et al, D01.1&D01.2 User Requirements and Functional requirements report

22. Moeller-Holst J., 1988, Decision Support System for Safety and Emergency Response Training / Planning based on Expert Systems Techniques. in *The Use of Expert Systems in Oil & Gas. User Applications for Practical Advantage* 12-13 April 1988.

23. Preston M.L., 1994, The Use of Computers in Emergency Response Planning. IChemE Symposium Series No 134. In *Hazards XII. European Advances in Process Safety*, UMIST, Manchester, 19-21 April 1994.

24. Ramsay C.G., Mayes T., Wallace D., 1995, Case Histories of High Reality Major Emergency Exercises. *Loss Prevention and Safety Promotion in the Process Industries*, Vol II: 753-764.

25. Ramsay C.G. , 1999. Protecting your Business: from Emergency Planning to Crisis Management. *Journal of Hazardous Materials* 65: 131-149.

26. SAFER Systems, 2001, http://www.safersystem.com/.

27. Seveso II, 1996, "Council Directive of 9th of December 1996 on the Control of Major Accident Hazards involving Dangerous Substances", European Council Directive 96/82/EC, Official Journal of the European Communities No L 10, pp 13-33.

28. Witlox, H.W.M., 1993, "Technical description of the heavy-gas-dispersion program HEGADAS", Report TNER.93.032, Thornton Research Centre, Shell Research, Chester, England (1993)

29. Witlox H.W. and Holt A., 1999, A unified model for jet, heavy and passive dispersion including droplet rainout and re-evaporation. *CCPS Conference on Vapour Cloud Modelling*, San Francisco.

Exhibit 1: Extract from a user questionnaire, with answers

4   Emergency Organisation and Training

4.1   *Do you have your own onsite emergency plan? Or do you share a plan with other companies in the area?*

▇   Company onsite emergency plan
☐   Onsite emergency plan shared with other companies/organisations
☐   Other, specify:

4.2   *What is the composition of your emergency response team? Please specify responsibilities of each team member.*

Incident Control Team
The purpose of the team is to provide the first response to the incident at the scene
The team is led by the Incident Controller who is typically the shift manager
It also includes 3 other members. There are 5 shifts of this team. The responsibilities of the team are:
• quick initial assessment of the incident and decision if a site emergency will be declared or not
• first response to the incident e.g. shutting isolation valves
• initial first aid
• initial security functions
• initial fire fighting

Major Emergency Control Team
The purpose of the Major Emergency Control Team is to provide tactical management of the emergency if a site emergency is declared.
The team is led by the Main Controller. This is typically a senior manager or director.
There are 7 shifts and each shift has 4 members, who are typically plant managers. The members of a shift must be accessible by telephone or pager and should be able to reach the site within 30 minutes. The team members have the following roles:
• SHE Advisor. He advises on technical matters of Safety, Health and the Environment (SHE)
• Communications Responsible. He deals with communications mainly with external agencies and other organisations. He speaks to silver-level (middle-rank) managers of the Police, fire brigade and ambulance He also communicates with the Incident Controller and provides information to the record keeper
• Record keeper

Crisis Control Team
This is a strategic crisis management team at a very senior level. It manages impacts on business image, operations and liabilities. It also liases with the Communications responsible of Major Emergency Control Team. It normally includes the following members:
• Site Director
• Human Relations (HR) Director
• Manager of the Regional SHE Group
• Public Relations (PR) responsible

4.3   *Does the Organisation conduct training on emergency issues?*   Yes ▇   No ☐

4.4   *Is that training carried out internally or is it conducted by an external organisation?*

There are both:
• Internal courses
• External courses (we used DNV for advice and Link Associates International)

4.5   *What are the topics and skills actually taught in the current training?*

A course typically includes 3 sections:
1) Lecture: The topics depend on the level. It may include case history, stress management principles, incident control principles, principles of command, dealing with the media and actions to take for the different types of incident
2) Pre-exercise briefing
3) Incident Exercise
Skills: It depends on the level. Can be fire fighting skills, decision making skills, and communication skills

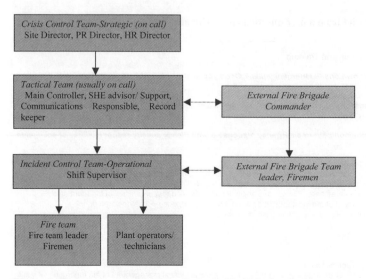

Figure 1: Emergency organisation of a typical british chemical company

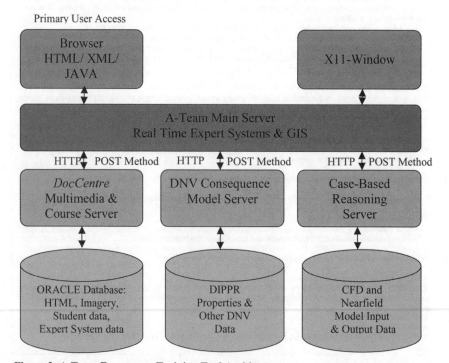

Figure 2: A-Team Emergency Training Tool Architecture

CONSEQUENCE ANALYSIS, EMERGENCY RESPONSE AND PLANNING FOR AN INTEGRATED RISK MANAGEMENT SYSTEM: SYSTEM DESIGN AND IMPLEMENTATION

Yong Ha Kim, Ku Hwoi Kim, D. Peter Shin and En Sup Yoon

Process Systems & Safety Lab., School of Chemical Engineering, Seoul National University, Seoul 151-742, Korea

In the multidisciplinary safety research with Korea Occupational Safety and Health Agency (KOSHA), we are developing, in the framework of a GIS-based, Integrated Risk Management System (IRMS), which is the wholly integrated system including Process information management, hazard identification, risk assessment, worst-case accident scenarios selection and emergency response planning. It is based on database system (of process information, layout, probability, etc.) and GIS of chemical plant complex in Korea, so its output can be expressed in both quantitatively and qualitatively and displayed on the digital map. In case of an emergency, escape routes for local residents and approach routes for fire engines and rescue teams are indicated for better control and management of the accident. In this paper, we emphasize the importance of integrated risk management by presenting on our experiences in designing and implementing the IRMS.

Keywords: Consequence Analysis, Integrated Risk Management System, Emergency Response Planning, Robust Accident Scenario Selection

INTRODUCTION

Despite on-going efforts with industrial accident prevention programs and improvements of occupational environments, according to an ILO report, about 2.5 million cases of accidents occur each year in the world involving about 335,000 casualties. Especially in the chemical industry, high concentration of sophisticated technical devices for handling, storage, shipping, and processing of many types of chemicals are used. These equipments have inherent dangers such as fire, explosion, leakage, etc. due to the nature of chemicals themselves. If such accidents happen, not only the workers engaged in the chemical industry but also the residents and the environment of surrounding area can be severely affected. Furthermore, the direct financial loss due to the damages to the equipments themselves can be serious. In addition, the situation could also affect the overall economy by affecting the supply of raw materials and other ways as a direct result of long equipment restoration period.

The Korean Government has been enforcing the Industrial Safety Management Act in accordance with the Industrial Safety and Hygiene Act since January 1996, in attempts to prevent major industrial accidents. Following the enforcement of this act, the safety of Korean petrochemical industries has shown a drastic improvement: significant reduction in fatality, injuries, near-misses, and emergency shutdowns of plants, and improved product quality and productivity as well. With this success and the implementation of Process Safety Management (PSM), which was introduced as a law in 1996, the Korea Occupational Safety and Health Agency (KOSHA) is building a GIS-based, Integrated Risk Management System (IRMS). There have been lots of research and studies on systematic finding of hazards, risk assessment, consequence analysis, mitigation measures, and emergency response concerning the characteristics of Korean industries, especially in hazard identification methodology. Integration of these safety technologies and techniques should elevate the overall safety control to a higher level.

In this multidisciplinary research with the KOSHA, our laboratory has been developing a new strategy for generation and selection of robust worst-case accident scenarios, to be used in the quantitative evaluation of risks at the plant sites, and designing and implementing the consequence analysis program. In this paper, we will discuss more on these two topics in the framework of IRMS. We will present on our experiences on designing and implementing these two programs and emphasize the importance of integrated risk management with discussions on the performance of the developed system.

IRMS: AN INTEGRATED SOLUTION

The IRMS is a tool for the prevention of major chemical accidents, which displays the risks on a map after calculating the risks quantitatively and identifying the risk level, and helps us to reduce potential risk and minimize possible losses[5]. The system has been designed to assimilate on-line and off-line data with geographical information with user-friendly access and interfaces. It consists of several main functions: display of petrochemical complex layout, display of equipment layout with related process information, zonation of the area in effective hazard with the estimation from the consequence analysis, and demographic analysis of the effected area, etc. It also provides risk contours using GIS technology. Figs. 1 and 2 show the structure and information flow of IRMS.

IRMS is composed of various integrated software elements. In terms of risk management, firstly potential hazards are found utilizing hazard analysis methods such as HAZOP and Checklist. For this, database which contains the previous accident information and the information of hazardous installations, such as capacity of equipment, hazardous material being handled, temperature, pressure and flammability, etc., is to be established. Secondly, we have to find the frequency and the size of consequence when the potential hazards are developed into actual incidents. For this we utilize ETA, FTA and consequence models enhanced by KOSHA. Thirdly, we calculate the risk which is a function of frequency and consequence ($R = F \times C$), and judge whether it is acceptable or not in comparison with the acceptable risk criteria.

The highlight of IRMS is to provide the risk contours using GIS technology. Data of hazardous installations and the result of consequence are also provided through computer screen. In this paper, we will present our part of work of major elements of IRMS such as accident scenario selection, GIS and consequence analysis.

REASONING ALGORITHM FOR ACCIDENT SCENARIO SELECTION

In this part of the study, we propose a new reasoning algorithm, through process partition and process component analysis, to improve the reliability of accident scenario selection[6]. Process elements are analyzed, and then the proposed strategy selects and generates the robust accident scenario of a worst case that is most likely to happen and should be foremost considered. The scenario reasoning scheme consists of three types of knowledge base and four reasoning algorithms (see Fig. 3): knowledge base (KB) of equipment property, material property, and process units; and four algorithms of macro decomposition, equipment screening, equipment behavior analysis, and accident scenario reasoning. Equipment property knowledge base is composed of equipment properties such as handling materials, operating condition, flow rate, safety devices, age, etc. (see Fig. 4). Material property knowledge base uses NFPA rating to describe toxicity, reactivity and flammability of process materials. Process unit knowledge base consists of topography and meteorological characteristics.

Accident scenarios are inferred according to the following steps: macro decomposition, micro decomposition using the equipment screening algorithm, equipment behaviour analysis, accident reasoning, and the effect analysis (see Fig. 5). In the macro decomposition, process units are selected according to their functions and the meteorological condition around the area. For the decomposition, the chemical plant is classified into the feed system, reaction system, separation system, storage system, and utility system. Meteorological characteristics and the surrounding condition are also considered: the main unit is defined, and meteorological characteristics and the topography of the selected unit are considered.

In the second step, we propose the Equipment Screening Algorithm (ESA) analyzing the process condition and selecting the process equipment with higher priority risk ranking. Equipment characteristics such as material property, flow rate, operating condition, capacity, safety devices, age, failure rate, accident history and repaired history are analyzed using ESA, which is a sequential reasoning method[4] (see Fig. 6). In case of material property, we use NFPA (National Fire Protection Association) code to confirm the flammability and toxicity; the criterion of this property is more than 3 NFPA rating. In the next stage, equipments of high flow rate or capacity or being operated in high pressure or temperature are determined. In the fourth stage, we decide whether the selected equipments have safety devices. In the final stage, we consider the age and accident history for individual equipment using the sequential screening method. The analyzed process elements are ranked and risk grades determined. According to the grades, risk assessment is performed. In the equipment analysis using the equipment behavior algorithm, the effect estimation for the selected equipment in the equipment-screening algorithm is accomplished: equipment with high severity is researched to find a detailed accident scenario. We use effect analysis method for the failure mode of the selected equipment to identify single equipment failure modes and each failure mode's potential effect on the system and the plant[1-3]. This mode describes how equipment fails and is determined by the system's response and cause to the equipment failure. In the scenario selection, we infer possible effects and the root cause depending on the failure mode of the equipment. Possible scenarios for each failure mode are so variable that risk rankings are assigned according to the potential hazard of material and the magnitude of the expected abnormal situation.

In the accident-reasoning algorithm, we infer the possible accident due to the equipment behavior and material property. For example, if the ultimate effect is valve breakage, we may infer that the possible accident is fire or explosion when material has a flammable property:

1) Valve leakage + toxic materials (Nh>2) $\Rightarrow$ personnel injury

2) No inlet flow + pump $\Rightarrow$ pump damage and malfunction

3) Downstream equipment breakage + flammable materials (Nf>3) $\Rightarrow$ fire or explosion

CONSEQUENCE ANALYSIS AND QUANTITATIVE RISK ASSESSMENT

In this part of the system, extents of damage due to plume, overpressure or heat leaks are displayed on the digital map. In case of an emergency, escape routes for local residents and approach routes for fire engines and rescue teams are indicated for better control and management of the accident.

The whole system being developed consists of (1) database of material property and approximation algorithm for chemicals, (2) geographic information and 2D maps on the surrounding area, (3) meteorological data processing module, (4) quantitative risk calculation module, (5) real-time consequence analysis, (6) models on the release and dispersion of mixed chemicals, (7) dispersion models on chemicals showing unusual behavior, (8) dispersion models for complex geography, (9) models on the effect of buildings and constructions to the dispersion, (10) dispersions inside the confined areas like buildings, and (11) Probit function-based estimation on the effect and the effected area. Fig. 7 shows how these modules are integrated to give the result of consequence analysis.

In our presentation at the conference, we will present on our experiences in designing and implementing the consequence analysis system, with comparison to commercial packages, and emphasize the importance of integrated risk management and discuss about the performance of the developed system.

DEVELOPMENT STATUS OF IRMS

From 1999, the phase three has been under implementation that includes GIS of five petrochemical complexes. The system is intended to manage hazardous installations more systematically and effectively and to reduce the number of accidents significantly, further minimizing production losses in the plant. Various modules of IRMS, which have been developed simultaneously, are being integrated into one package system with extensive field tests. All the elements are supposed to be built and ready for integration by Summer 2002 and will go to field tests. Integration of the components as one system of IRMS will be finished in the second half of 2002.

CONCLUSION

If the IRMS being constructed through methods overviewed in this paper is implemented and used for the risk management of petroleum chemical complexes in Korea, a substantial amount of benefits are expected in many areas. In the technological area, the degree of safety can be raised by employing a fast, effective analysis and systematic risk management which are made possible by the combination of separate safety management and technological factors. In the economical point of view, this IRMS can also help to prevent the loss of lives and properties by helping to make a notable decrease in the occurrences of accidents. In addition, effective operations of installations are possible using the established database and system, thereby decreasing the production loss at plants. However, since there are rapid developments in the fields of sensors, communication and information technologies, this system needs to be continually updated and maintained so that an even more effective risk management system can be established.

ACKNOWLEDGEMENTS

This work was supported in part by the National Research Lab Grant of the Ministry of Science & Technology of Korea and the Brain Korea 21 Program of the Ministry of Education of Korea.

REFERENCES

1. CCPS, 1989, *Guidelines for Technical Management of Chemical Process Safety*, CCPS of the AIChE.
2. CCPS, 1992, *Guidelines for Hazard Evaluation Procedures*, 2nd Ed., CCPS of the AIChE.
3. CCPS, 1997, *Guidelines for Integrating Process Safety Management, Environment, Safety, Health, and Quality*, CCPS of the AIChE.

4. Khan, F. I. and Abbasi, S. A., 1998, Techniques and Methodologies for Risk Analysis in Chemical Process Industries. *Journal of Loss Prevention in the Process Industries*, **11**(4), 261-277.

5. Kwon, H.-M., Lee, C.-K., Kang, S.-J., Pyeon, M.-W. and Moon, I., 2000, Establishment of GIS-based integrated risk management system (IRMS), *Proceedings of PSAM 5*, Nov. 27-Dec. 1, 2000, Osaka, Japan.

6. Kim, K. H., 2000, A New Strategy for The Development of Consequence Estimation Technique in Chemical Process, *Proceedings of PSAM 5*, Nov. 27-Dec. 1, 2000, Osaka, Japan.

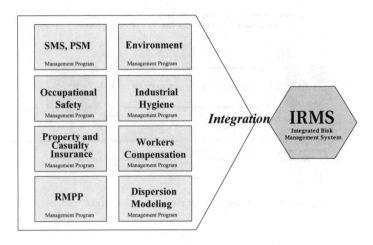

Fig. 1. Components consisting of the IRMS

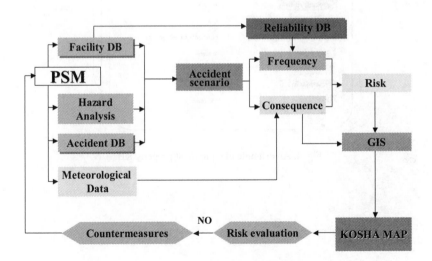

Fig. 2. Information flow in the IRMS

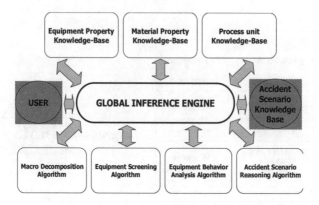

Fig. 3. Proposed framework for the accident scenario selection

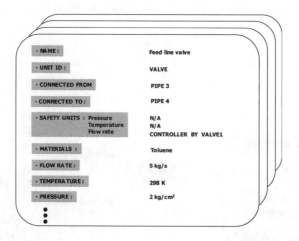

Fig. 4. An example of equipment property KB

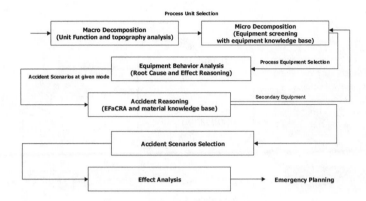

Fig. 5. Inference procedure of the proposed system

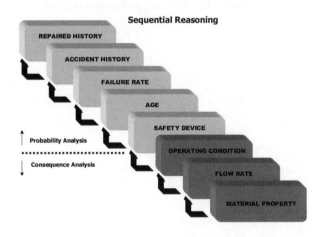

Fig. 6. Sequential reasoning of ESA

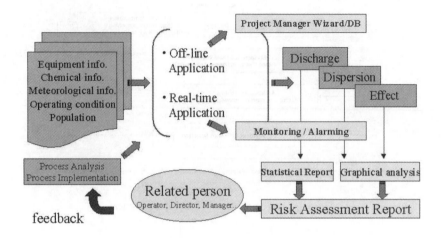

Fig. 7. Flowdigram of consequence analysis program

CONTROLLING AND DE-CONTAMINATING SITE WASTEWATER

Dr K J Patterson, Process Safety Manager and J Poppleton, Safety, Health, & Environment Manager

Hickson & Welch Limited, Wheldon Road, Castleford, West Yorkshire UK, WF10 2JT

The Castleford site of Hickson & Welch is situated astride the river Aire, just below its confluence with the River Calder. The site handles a wide range of toxic and corrosive organic chemicals, which have the potential to produce severe effects in the river, were they allowed to reach it. The protection of the river has assumed ever-greater importance during the last decade and the company has adopted a comprehensive strategy to protect the river from both accidental contamination and routine discharge.

The paper will describe the elements of the strategy, which includes action now completed, and the current programme of work. The completed strategies include: a site kerb, a low wall round the site which prevents accidental spillage and fire water from reaching the river; rigorous segregation of clean cooling water, which can be returned to the river, from process and rain water, which goes to the site effluent treatment plant; and site-wide renewal of the effluent collection system, bring it above ground into custom made piping systems.

Work in progress includes: the generation of a site storage register which is coupled to a storage risk assessment system – being developed with HSE – to assess potential risks from the storages onsite; a ground water survey to ensure that legacy pollution is understood; and work on the safe storage of drummed materials around the site.

At the centre of the strategy is a new best practice standard setting, wastewater Treatment Plant. This combines a Loprox®, wet oxidation plant using liquid oxygen at moderate temperature and pressure to detoxify otherwise hard to treat waste streams; and a Vitox® biological treatment plant, using an oxygen fed activated sludge. This holistic approach has enabled the site to treat most aqueous waste streams on site and to cease sending site effluent to the local municipal sewage treatment plant. The final treated stream is now discharged direct to river with consequent improvements in the quality of the site effluent stream. This has also enabled the local sewage treatment plant to improve its discharge. These two changes have contributed to a significant improvement in river quality.

The paper will describe these various initiatives in technical detail and indicate the site's vision for the future.

SITE DESCRIPTION

Hickson has been operating on its present site since 1915. Founded during the First World War it soon found its niche in the manipulation of aromatic organic chemicals, principally dye and pigment intermediate production. Through to the 1970s the company expanded on its present site, installing larger scale, more modern plant; introducing the production of optical brighteners ("Photines"); and building long-term alliances with other manufacturers for the custom manufacture of speciality chemicals. By the late 1980s Hickson & Welch employed over 1000 people at Castleford with large-scale nitration, hydrogenation and chlorination capacity; complemented by the custom manufacture of agrochemical intermediates and other speciality chemicals. The site also produced timber treatment chemicals for its sister company Hickson Timber Products.

Today the company is focused on contract manufacture but the site still handles large quantities of hazardous chemicals, is subject to the COMAH regulations and has 15 IPC authorisations. The expansion in the contract business means that over 30 new reaction stages were introduced during 2000, a rate which has continued into 2001. These changes have formed the backdrop to the improvement in the company's Responsible Care Performance.

The Hickson & Welch site lies on the north east outskirts of Castleford (a town of some 40,000 inhabitants) and within 1 Km of the town centre. Areas to the north and east are largely farmland and of relatively low population density. The surroundings of the site have changed substantially over recent years, from heavy industry to light industrial sites and a number of new housing developments. Coal mining and the associated engineering industries have all but disappeared from the locality. About 2 km to the north west of the company's site, the area of a former mine is to be redeveloped as an environmentally friendly 'Millennium Village' integrating housing and employment on a brownfield site.

A large and very important site of special scientific interest (SSSI) Fairburn Ings, a major wetland used by migrating birds and owned by the RSPB, lies approximately 1 Km to the northeast. Within 5 km of the site are a number of other SSSIs which harbour an array of sensitive flora. To the south and west lie the domestic and industrial conurbations of West Yorkshire.

The site has grown from an original 6 acres (just over 2 hectares) in 1915, to some 75 hectares today. It is essentially flat and has been assembled by acquisition of surrounding, mainly industrial land - some sections are the sites of other chemical companies acquired by Hickson & Welch. The rivers Aire and Calder join just west of the site and the resultant river runs through the centre of the site, with a canal running next to the site's northern perimeter. Manufacturing plant is situated on both sides of the river. Most of the site is developed, with significant areas used for on-site warehousing and outdoor storage. The site was no doubt chosen for its access to coal - both as fuel and as a source of raw materials - and to the river, used as a source of water, a convenient disposal point for wastes and as a transport route. Now, of course, protection of the river is a major management consideration.

The site and its surroundings can be seen in fig 1.

SITE HISTORY (PRE 1972, 1972 – 1992, POST 1992)

Over the period of its existence, the company's approach to water management has changed from being non-existent to a pro-active approach based upon the 'source – pathway – receptor' principle.

Prior to 1972, the river (just like most rivers in the industrial conurbations of the country) was used as a convenient disposal point for wastewaters, with only scant regard for resultant river quality. By the time the river reached Castleford having passed through industrial West Yorkshire, it was a polluted waterway with little perceived intrinsic value other than as a sewer and for the transport of goods. This attitude changed significantly in the early 1970's. The local authority proceeded with a major renovation of the local sewage treatment works and simultaneously, the company began its first major improvement of wastewater management.

1972 – 1992: FIRST STAGE EFFLUENT TREATMENT FACILITY

Instead of discharging (essentially) all wastewaters to the local river, the company began to collect them together for treatment at the local sewage treatment works. However, an assessment of the capabilities of that plant immediately identified that certain wastewaters were unsuitable for treatment by the local sewage treatment facilities and perversely these continued to be discharged directly to the river.

Given the variety of wastewaters and the range of processes they came from, primary consideration was given to controlling their pH and a neutralisation plant was installed (which is still operating). The plant built consisted of two neutralisation reactors in series, one utilising calcium lime and the second sulphuric acid. The product of this reaction was relatively insoluble calcium sulphate, which was separated in a gravity-settling tank. Calcium sulphate was drawn off the bottom of the settlement tank and filtered in a plate and frame press. Clarified liquid from the surface of the tank then passed to a flow-balancing tank prior to discharge via local sewers to the town's sewage works and ultimately to the river.

Also during the early 1970s, charging schemes were introduced which related disposal costs to the strength and volume of the wastewater. It became economically viable to install a system of pre-treatment to reduce chemical strength on site. The system installed was a high rate biological treatment plant based upon the ICI 'Flocor' system. In this system, wastewaters were deluged over a stacked plastic media on which biomass was allowed to accumulate. Air draught was induced below the packed media and a significant reduction in chemical strength was identified. The efficiency of the system was sufficient to reduce Biological Oxygen Demand (BOD) of the wastewater by approximately 50%. Unfortunately, the reduction in strength was as much as a result of volatile solvents being air-stripped as biological activity.

The site operated this effluent treatment plant from 1972. There were some modifications during the 1970s and 1980s but the basic processes were not reconsidered until the late 1980s. The original air-aspirated, biological treatment tower was extended by 50% to cope with the increase in the site's effluent. Wastewater from the on-site plant continued to be sent to the local Yorkshire Water sewage treatment plant, where it was further treated along with the local domestic and commercial effluent, before discharge to the River Aire. However, the quality of the ultimate outfall to river had room for significant improvement and, as noted above, some aqueous effluents could not be treated and were still being sent straight to river. Although these were licensed outfalls, by the late 1980s it was clear that the situation could not be allowed to continue and significant improvement was needed.

POST 1992: INTEGRATED POLLUTION CONTROL

The drivers for change increased radically with the introduction of Integrated Pollution Control (IPC) following the Environment Protection Act of 1990. The chemical industry was faced with having to identify its effects on the environment and more significantly introducing control measures to limit the effect of its operations. An assessment of the environmental effects and risks from each activity on the Castleford site was therefore undertaken. This led to an intensive programme of improvement, firstly to the process themselves and then to the waste streams, to ensure that the company's activities could be properly authorised under IPC.

Given this activity and the other activities that IPC was clearly going to require, the company realised that a significantly increased resource would be needed to manage and run its environmental programme. Initially the resource was targeted at the 18 (now 15) IPC applications/ authorisations (though significant external resource was also used to get these in place by the required date). Subsequently it was tasked with managing the environmental monitoring programme, running the existing effluent plant and managing the environmental improvement programme which was agreed with EA. Initially, the Environment Department operated separately, alongside the Health & Safety Department. By 1999 it was recognised the departments had sensibly identical goals and therefore the two departments were combined into one Safety, Health, & Environmental (SHE) Department. As would be expected, this department maintains a close relationship with other departments, particularly operations, and is also charged with maintaining good relations with the two regulators, EA and HSE.

The company's current Responsible Care programme is discussed further at the end of the article.

THE SITE ENVIRONMENTAL IMPROVEMENT PROGRAMME POST 1990

The programme of improvement initiated by the company from 1990 can be broken down into various aspects. Each of these is discussed below.

PROTECTION OF THE RIVER.

Water flows within the site can be broadly classified into two separate categories. The first is water used in chemical processing and which therefore is potentially heavily contaminated. The second water system uses water taken from the river, filtered and then pumped round the site to provide cooling. This can be returned to the river provided it is uncontaminated and only slightly warmer than the river itself.

DRAINS

In the period before 1972, all site drains passed directly to river, mixing cooling water, rainfall (potentially slightly contaminated), and contaminated process water. Little or no segregation of different classes of water was undertaken. Once the first on-site treatment facility was available consideration was given to process water collection. The first scheme saw the conversion of the discharge chambers, which were immediately adjacent to the river, to collection chambers. Contaminated wastewater was pumped overground from these collection chambers to the new treatment facility. This was only applied to those streams which were deemed suitable for treatment, though during the period from 1972 to 1992, progressively more streams were captured. Also, the feeds to the collection pits were generally still in the original underground drainage systems installed when the plants were first developed, which meant that some dated from the 1920s.

By 1990 then, the contaminated wastewater collection system was still mainly underground, with collection pits close to the site boundary - usually next to both the river and to the pits for the cooling water system. Plant drains were not part of the process plant and were considered solely as a civil engineering problem. Not surprisingly, after up to 70 years of constant use by process discharges containing everything from oleum to strong alkali, the drains were often in a poor condition.

From the early 1990s drains from individual plants have been renewed with the design and construction of the drains being based upon chemical engineering principles. Drains are now being constructed of material suitable for purpose (special steels, PTFE etc.), often with a double skin to prevent leakage to ground. Wherever possible, drains are mounted at or above surface level and are easily inspected and cleaned if necessary (see figure 2). This has the added advantage of reducing the potential for ground contamination. This is not a novel idea; it was used in the Ebbw Vale steel works from the early 1970s. The relative age of the idea perhaps shows that its more widespread adoption is overdue. The process water drains now go to new, well-lined but less deep collection pits, which have been constructed near to the centre of the site. These are continuously pumped overground to the effluent treatment plant. Each pit has been fitted with both a duty and a standby pump to ensure continuity of pumping. This arrangement draws water inwards to the site, away from the river and ensures that any leaks in the system are readily visible.

COOLING WATER

Water for cooling (and fire fighting) is drawn continuously from the river and distributed around the site in a dedicated system. The system is important to the safe operation of the site and relies on 3 river water pumps to provide a continuous flow. The site has a license to abstract up to 630 litres of water per second from the river which represents up to 10% of the river's flow at low (summer) flow. The system is kept rigorously separate from the process water system and considerable effort has been expended on-plant to ensure that it does not become contaminated, by covering tun dishes and removing open drains for example. Within buildings, cooling water collection systems are run approximately 1 metre above floor level to ensure that spillages etc. cannot enter the 'clean' water system. The collection systems are either enclosed or at very least covered.

Cooling water is returned to the river at a number of outfalls which are tightly controlled with continuous monitoring by the company and periodic monitoring by EA. The outfalls are monitored for various parameters including temperature, pH, and Total Organic Carbon (TOC). The outfalls are protected and can be closed if the continuous monitoring detects any significant deviation. The site's current consent allows the discharge to be no more than 10 ppm BOD different to the river, with no significant increase in prescribed micro-pollutants, and at no more than 28°C – essentially the discharge must be equivalent to the water upstream of the site. As we explain to the public, in terms of micro-pollutants this is equivalent to one eggcup full of petrol in an Olympic swimming pool. (Interestingly, as the cooling water is filtered to remove debris before distribution around the site, the outfall is usually cleaner than the upstream river.) Connected to the continuous monitors are sampling stations which will take grab samples in the event of any deviation. The monitoring stations were installed during 1994 at a cost of around £50,000 each (the site has 5 outfalls) and have been invaluable in ensuring a constant high quality discharge to the river.

The result of this effort can be seen in that over the last 4 years the site has not had to make a schedule 1 report to EA because of an excursion outside the consent limits, for the cooling water outfalls.

RAINFALL

Rainfall was traditionally mixed into the cooling water system to be returned to the river. However, with over 85 years of operation on the site, it is not possible to be sure that rainwater has not become contaminated. There is also the obvious possibility of material spilled on site roadways (for example) finding its way via the rainwater drains, into the river. Over the last decade the site's surface water drainage system has been progressively re-routed to the site effluent treatment system. As can be seen in figure 2 above, surface drainage is collected in the outer channel with process waters being carried in the inner pipe. This has clear cost and production implications - prior to the commissioning of the new ETP the site, had to curtail production in times of prolonged heavy rainfall.

SITE KERB

Given that the site lies astride a major river and in its flood plain, the major area of concern is the fate of material which escapes from storage, either bulk or packaged. The dangers are both from the material itself and from attempts to clean up after a spill, and the problem is compounded by the fate of firewater used on-site in time of emergency. Probably the most significant environmental incidents which have started on a chemical site but had consequences off the site are those due to contaminated firewater. The incidents at Sandoz in Basle, and two incidents in West Yorkshire – at Woodkirk in 1982 at Allied Colloids   in 1992 – are three obvious examples. Material lost from storage has reached a   number   of rivers with significant - if less headline catching - effects. Indeed material does not have to be chemically toxic to cause damage, milk releases have caused significant disruption to river systems. At Castleford although bulk HFL storages have been bunded for many years, toxic, corrosive and other materials have normally not been fully bunded Protection of the river had to be balanced against the high cost of bunding all 400 storages on site. Also, it was recognised that material can be lost during transfer to and from storage and that losses during movement around the site could not be discounted.

An alternative solution was sought, to complement the isolation of the site's drains from the river. The site has significant emergency tanks which can collect the main effluent flow for some time and the site is essentially level. The decision was taken to build a site kerb, about 350mm high, along the riverbank at all the vulnerable points. This kerb is constructed either from poured concrete or from "Trief" kerbs (the high rebated kerbs used where HGV turning damage is likely). The kerb means that it is virtually impossible for losses on site to reach the river, even in the worst cases. The kerb has proved its value. Not long after construction, a spillage of a non-toxic material would probably have reached the river had the kerb not been in place. This type of material would have had a very low priority for bunding but, like milk, it could have had a significant impact on the river.

The site kerb is of major advantage in the control of firewater run-off. Should large amounts of water need to be used on site for any purpose we can be certain that the run off will go to the effluent collection system. The network of surface drains allows water to go either direct to the on site effluent treatment facility or be diverted to the emergency tanks. If even this proved not to have enough capacity it would be possible, in extremis, to allow areas of the site to flood, giving an enormous volume of retention. Obviously, open channels have the potential to allow spread of fire via flammable materials floating on the surface run off and therefore the design of the drainage network includes fire break chambers at intervals to overcome this problem.

FLOODING

As the site lies in the flood plain of the River Aire, there is some potential for flooding during periods of heavy rainfall, indeed during 1979 part of the site was flooded at a time of very high river levels. The problems then were due to water backing up onto site through surface water drains and a "level imbalance" between the canal and the river due to the settings of the lock gates. The isolation of the site surface water drains from the river and building the site kerb have significantly changed the potential for flooding. Even in November 2000 when the river Aire reached record high levels in Castleford, the site was not significantly affected. The latest projections from the Environment Agency have however indicated that the present level of the kerb does not offer full protection against their calculations of the most extreme event (the 200-year flood) and work is currently progressing to raise the site kerb to the requisite level.

STORAGE OF CHEMICALS

Although the site kerb does provide ultimate protection of the river, it does not provide adequate protection for the environment on or off site. The site kerb has been complemented with a number of projects designed to provide better storage of all types of chemicals on site. As noted above, HFL storages have long been protected with bunds but drummed HFLs were for a long time not protected. A major HFL drum storage area has been constructed next to the main warehouse offering full containment for storage, loading and unloading together with shaded storage for heat sensitive materials. [As an indication of the significant costs involved in these projects, this area cost £330,000.] This area is not covered   and rainwater is collected in a sump for tankering to the site ETP. For drummed toxic material and material which reacts strongly with water, a former tanker cleaning shed has been converted to a toxic drum store, again fully bunded but dry. To complement the main HFL drum store, a number of bunded drum storage areas have been constructed at strategic locations around the site.

The bulk storages on site are of varying ages, some being over 40 years old. Many are bunded (fully or partially) and they have varying types of overfill protection, ranging from operator control to full level monitoring by the plant control system backed up by high and high-high protection interlocked to the feedlines to the storage. To assess the hazards the storages posed, a major exercise was undertaken to build a site storage register. This has proved to have a number of uses outside those originally envisaged, not least giving the site emergency controllers information on the contents of the 400 storages around site. (With increasing short-run contract manufacture, this can be very important as the use of storages now changes frequently.) The register is now being extended - in discussion with HSE - into a storage risk assessment system.

This has entailed building into the register weighting factors for the various hazards (content type, degree of bunding, overfill protection system, etc) the aim being to provide a guide to relative hazards posed to people and the environment by the various storages on site. In future the register will be used to assess the priorities for improvement and to provide a driver for future spending on storage protection.

PROTECTION OF THE EFFLUENT TREATMENT FACILITIES

All of the previous improvements have been designed to ensure that any potential contamination remains on site, and therefore is kept away from receiving waters, and to direct it to the site effluent treatment plant. However, this does transfer the risk to this facility. Given the importance of the ETP and the potential consequences of its failure, great thought was given to ensuring that it was adequately protected from damage. Primary protection was given by the installation of large, purpose-built emergency diversion tanks. Four such tanks were built each of 225 m^3 capacity. They are constructed of reinforced concrete and are lined with a resin liner to enable them to withstand the varying conditions to which they may be exposed. The tanks themselves are fully bunded to 110% of the capacity of any individual tank. Material may be diverted at any of four points within the primary treatment system:

1 Prior to reception
2 Immediately post neutralisation and prior to settlement of entrained solids
3 Post settlement of entrained solids
4 Post capacity buffering (in times of excessive flow).

Material diverted to these tanks is analysed prior to a decision on treatment, normally controlled flow back into the effluent treatment system.

A system of management control is also applied to all wastewater discharges to ensure, as far as is practicable, that all materials sent to the site ETP receives appropriate treatment. This results in an on-site 'licensing' system for discharge.

THE URBAN WASTE WATER TREATMENT DIRECTIVE AND THE LATEST EFFLUENT TREATMENT FACILITY

In the early 1990's a new driver for improvement appeared in the shape of the European Union's Urban Waste Water Treatment Directive (UWWTD). This directive meant that all discharges into controlled waters would have to reviewed. Any discharge   not meeting the required standards would need either to be diverted away from the controlled water or the discharge would need to be brought up to standard. With the whole of the contaminated wastewater from the site passing through the local sewage treatment plant, any alteration to their operation could have had significant effect on site activity. At the same time the charging regime for treatment for contaminated wastewater by the local operator (Yorkshire Water) was changing and it was clear that, having previously offered a relatively cheap disposal route, use of the local sewage treatment plant would become significantly more expensive. Discussion with the plant operator identified that three things would be required to give compliance with the UWWTD whilst continuing to use their facility:

1   A significant upgrading of the local sewage treatment plant,
2   A significant contribution to the funding requirement for the upgrade,
3   Potential restrictions on the nature and volume of discharges to the new plant.

Given the nature of the UWWTD - which is directed towards improving water quality - the improvements required for this wastewater treatment plant could be extended in future and this would almost certainly apply to the treatment facility even after the upgrading. Hickson & Welch therefore began an assessment of its future water treatment needs for the period from 2000 onwards (the activation date of the UWWTD).

Of particular concern in this area was the discharge from one small-scale treatment plant on site directly to river. This plant had been built as recently as 1993 and was a fully licensed discharge from a process which is fundamental to the site's processes. Discharge to the river had only been licensed following a significant research programme carried out at the Water Research Council into the potential environmental effects of the discharge. This research had identified that the discharge – even at the levels given above - had no significant effect on the river water quality. The discharge however suffered from two problems. Firstly the discharge was highly coloured and secondly it had a very high residual Chemical Oxygen Demand (COD) - of the order of 20,000 mg/l. The UWWTD requires discharges no higher than 125 mg/l (although action is taken at levels in excess of 250 mg/l). The discharge contains many conjugated benzenoid structures which are not amenable to biological degradation.

Studies were therefore instigated into potential technologies which would be able to overcome this particular problem. The range of technologies selected included:

1   Ozonation
2   Electrolysis
3   Oxidation with hypochlorite
4   Wet air oxidation
5   Oxidation with hydrogen peroxide
6   A variant of wet air oxidation utilising pure oxygen

Each of the techniques was evaluated over a period of some three years to establish effectiveness and economics. The evaluation was carried out both in our own on-site laboratories and at the laboratories of the developers of the techniques. Before acceptance of the results trials were always done with quite large samples of real effluent taken from the H&W effluent stream. Table 1 compares the results of the assessments.

Table 1 – Comparison of assessment results of treatment techniques

Technique	Colour destruction	COD destruction	Cost Index *
Ozonation	95 %	50 %	1.42
Electrolysis	95 %	50 %	1.29
Hypochlorite oxidation	90 %	35 %	1.18
Wet air oxidation	90 %	70 %	1.43
Peroxide oxidation	95 %	80 %	2.41
Variant wet air oxidation	95 %	80 %	1.00

* Cost index is the relative cost per tonne, with the cheapest technique given a value of 1.00

Following this assessment the two techniques with the highest quality output were subjected to large-scale trials to prove effectiveness. These trials confirmed the suitability of both techniques, however, as can be seen from the table, variant wet air oxidation was strongly favoured both technically and economically. The results of these trials convinced the company to go ahead with the building of a variant wet air oxidation plant to deal with this difficult to treat waste.

During subsequent discussions with suppliers of the chosen system and discussions with the local waste water treatment plant operator, it became clear that an option of a new plant to treat all of the sites wastewater should be considered. The plans were developed and refined over a period of two years and finally produced a combined plant, on the Hickson & Welch site, which would provide for treatment not only of the 'difficult' waste, but also the whole of the site's wastewater and allow discharge direct to river.

An aerial view of the plant is shown in Figure 3

This plant was subsequently built under an agreement with BOC under which BOC would build, own and maintain the facility and Hickson & Welch would operate the facility. This allowed Hickson to concentrate on the control of wastewater generation, treatment and quality of discharge to the river. The plant was constructed during 1998 and began commissioning in summer 1999 with treated wastewater discharge direct to river commencing in January 2000. The operation of the plant was described in "Process Engineering" at the time (Ref 1).

The plant retains the old neutralisation/ settling plant but dispensed with the Flocor unit. Wastewater is now treated in a BOC Vitox® oxygen based activated sludge treatment plant. The capacity of this unit is some 3,850 m³/day compared with the original plant capacity of 2,250 m³/day. The unit has two parallel streams each rated at up to 70% of full plant capacity to allow for essential maintenance. An integral part of the system was the provision of 2 further emergency storage tanks, each of 3,000 m³ capacity in addition to the existing emergency capacity (900 m³). Together these tanks give a total capacity of roundly 3 days normal wastewater flow and thus give greatly enhanced protection of the river.

The new facility also saw the introduction of a BOC Loprox® variant wet air oxidation plant, the first such facility in the UK and the first time in the world that these two technologies had been combined on the same site. The Loprox® unit has a capacity of 300 m³/day and is utilised to treat the more intractable wastewaters, discussed above, which were previously discharged to river at high COD strength. The plant has achieved greater than 85% destruction of COD in its first months of operation. Wastewater from the Loprox® unit is further treated in the Vitox® unit prior to discharge to river and the combined plant has proved to be very satisfactory.

One peculiarity of the Loprox® process is that in the reaction, organic nitrogen in the feed results in the formation of ammonia in the wastewater. This could have presented problems as assessment of the biological treatability of site wastewater suggested that nitrification would be so heavily inhibited as to be unattainable with the predicted product mix. The river Aire is at a transitional point in terms of its quality and there is ample evidence of a resurgent juvenile fish population. Ammonia discharges are highly toxic to young fish and would put this resurgence at peril. The design of the Loprox® plant was thus modified to include an ammonia stripping system, which would allow the extraction of the ammonia and produce a saleable by-product.

Experience of the operation of the new plant continues to be gained. To date the facility is producing a relatively high-grade discharge. One demonstration of this quality can be demonstrated by considering particular molecular species present in the discharge. The consent granted under IPC for the new facility requires the concentration of specific molecular species (chosen to be relevant to the Castleford site operation) to be within the levels achieved by the best 80% of the samples taken during the previous two years at the town's sewage treatment plant (adjusted for the dilution provided at that plant). All samples taken at the new discharge of the new plant have been significantly better than this consent. Figure 4 shows the mean values obtained for certain species compared with this consent value (note the logarithmic scale of this graph).

Overall, the strategies adopted by Hickson & Welch has enabled the site to transform its wastewater treatment. Whilst some work remains to be done, the site currently has a system in place which we believe makes it a UK, and probably European leader.

RESPONSIBLE CARE

This paper has concentrated on the technical side of the improvements the company has made. However the site's current performance could not have been achieved without the understanding, commitment and support of staff at all levels. The improvements are part of the company's commitment to Responsible Care, the chemical industry's commitment to excellence in its SHE performance.

The company's Responsible Care programme is led by the SHE department whose aims are to:

1   Increase focus and ownership of SHE issues within all operational departments and therefore increase commitment of all staff to SHE excellence.

2   Utilise core strengths that exist within departments to identify and carry through improvements which will improve SHE performance.

3   Utilise the SHE department's own strengths to provide advice, support, and assistance where it is needed

In order to progress this approach, one problem that had to be overcome was the attitude of staff towards environmental protection (and SHE performance in general). Geography (the nature of the surrounding work and social environment) and history (the company's traditional poor performance in SHE matters) conspired to push environment to the back of most people's minds.

Education and training have therefore been a major part of the site's SHE improvement programme. Increasing the awareness of all staff (and particularly those who actually operate process on an hour to hour basis) about their environmental responsibilities is absolutely vital in achieving compliance. Almost all deviations can in some measure be traced back to human error and operators must understand both their responsibilities and the potential consequences of their actions or inaction. The Environment Agency has recognised this fact and is insistent that operators are appraised of and understand the IPC authorisations for the processes which they are running.   EA's OPRA assessments are increasingly concentrating on management systems and training.

Training and management both require good communication. Training is of little use if the resulting effort is not properly directed and that requires a management process which sets and monitors SHE objectives.   Both objectives and monitoring must then be accurately conveyed to those expected to fulfil the plan. Over a period of time we have evolved, and indeed continue to evolve, a series of formal meetings, committees, and training programmes to carry out this function.

Amongst the principal elements of the routine Responsible Care programme are:

Management Committee	Monthly	Review performance/approve expenditure (SHE is the first agenda item)
SHEQ Committee	Monthly	Review performance/agree action jointly between management and union safety reps.
Senior Managers Meeting	Monthly	Reviews company performance, with SHE performance always as the first agenda item.
Operations Management Team	Weekly	Review and discuss issues, starting with SHE performance area by area.
Safety Briefing	Monthly	Communicates key issues formally to all staff - managers and technicians

The annual programme of SHE performance and improvement is agreed by both the site Management Committee and by the SHEQ Committee. Both groups are also encouraged to identify key issues for inclusion in the programme. This consensual approach ensures commitment by all sides and has been very important to the improvement seen on the site over the last 10 years.

Whilst this may seem a plethora of committees, it illustrates that environmental (and SHE) considerations figure at all operational and decision making levels. Equally, external debate and communication is strongly encouraged. The company seeks active liaison with the regulators and local authorities, is very active in the local Responsible Care cell, and has for many years hosted a local Liaison Committee. This committee has been very important in maintaining good relations with those who live around the plant through some difficult times for the company. The company also puts its performance in the public domain by publishing an annual Responsible Care Report identifying the company's key SHE performance indicators.   Finally, we actively communicate with local (and distant) groups such as educational establishments to ensure that we are aware of public opinion and concerns.

We strongly believe that this commitment to the Responsible Care programme has been essential to the current good site SHE performance.

FUTURE DRIVERS

The programme, both technical and people based, described above has allowed the environmental performance of Hickson & Welch to very markedly improve over the past decade. Indeed the Effluent treatment plant built in 1998/1999 won critical acclaim and was awarded the Water Section Award at the IChemE environmental awards ceremony in 2000. This award supplements that of the previous year when the company won the same award for the improvement in the site's performance for loss of VOCs to atmosphere (now less than 1% of the 1993 figure and to which the new ETP has contributed with now no loss of VOC from this plant).

The future will continue to present challenges as legislation is enacted. Already the Contaminated Land (England) Regulations 2000, The Groundwater Regulations (SI 1998 No. 2746), Pollution Prevention (England and Wales) Regulations 2000 and the Water Framework Directive proposed by the European Commission are affecting our medium term planning for environmental improvement. We believe and intend that the approach developed at Castleford will continue to form the basis of our future programme, ensuring not just compliance but continuing improvement in the performance of the site.

Ref 1 – Process Engineering - June 2000, P22/23

Figure 1: View of the site from the southwest showing the predominance of the river

Figure 2: Typical drain installation, showing the "pipe within a pipe" collection system.

Figure 3: The Vitox® & Loprox® facility at Castleford

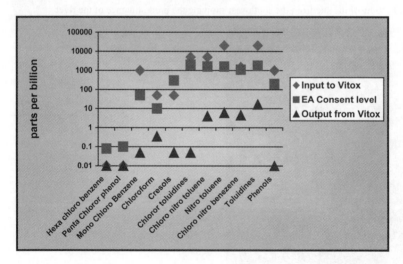

Figure 4: concentration of specific species in Vitox® effluent

TOWARDS A MATURE SAFETY CULTURE

Ronny Lardner, Chartered Occupational Psychologist, The Keil Centre Ltd,
Mark Fleming PhD, Assistant Professor, St Mary's University, Halifax, Canada
and
Phil Joyner, FIChemE , Asset Manager, bp

This paper describes a novel, solution focused approach to developing maturity of an organisation's safety culture, the Safety Culture Maturity™ Model. This method involves assessing current levels of safety culture maturity, and involving all members of the workforce in identifying practical and realistic actions which will move safety culture maturity to the next level. The paper describes how this approach was implemented at bp's Dalmeny and Hound Point Asset, the process involved and the outcomes achieved to date.

INTRODUCTION

In recent years, there has been an increasing recognition of the importance of organisational, cultural and behavioural aspects of safety management in high reliability industries. Investigations into major disasters such as Piper Alpha, Zeebrugge, Flixborough, Clapham Junction and Chernobyl have revealed that complex systems broke down disastrously, despite the adoption of the full range of engineering and technical safeguards, because people failed to do what they were supposed to do[1]. These were not simple, individual errors, but malpractices that corrupted large parts of the social system that makes organisations function.

Over the past 150 years the safety improvement has been largely focused on the technical aspects of engineering systems, and these efforts have been very successful. This success is evident in the low accidents rates found in the majority of safety-critical industries. However, it does appear that accident rates have now reached a plateau. As the frequency of technological failures in industry has diminished, the role of human error has become more apparent. Many safety experts now estimate that 80-90% of all industrial accidents are attributable to "human factors"[2]. It seems likely that the most effective way to reduce accident rates even further is to address the social and organisational factors which impact on safety[1]. Management has also come to realise that the general likelihood of an accident occurring in their plant depends not just on the actions of individual employees, but on the "safety culture" of their organisation, defined by the Confederation of British Industry[3] as "the way we do things around here".

An increasing number of studies have been carried out to investigate safety culture in high-hazard industries and a number of books have recently been published discussing the factors that underpin safety culture. An even greater number of 'tools' have been developed to measure safety climate or safety culture. In parallel, individual companies and industry groups have embarked upon a number of safety culture improvement initiatives, for example the Step-Change in Safety initiative in the UK offshore oil and gas industry.

This paper provides an overview of recent into safety climate and safety culture research, and describes a new method which overcomes a number of the difficulties encountered, namely the Safety Culture Maturity™ model[i]. The application of this model at bp's Dalmeny & Hound Point Asset is described, together with the benefits accrued to date.

---

[i] Safety Culture Maturity is a Trade Mark of The Keil Centre Ltd

SAFETY CULTURE - WHAT IS IT?

The term 'safety culture' appears to have arisen out of the report on the Chernobyl disaster in 1986, where the errors and violations of the operating procedures which contributed to the accident were cited as evidence of a poor safety culture at the planti. The identification of poor safety culture as a factor contributing to the accident led to a large number of studies investigating and attempting to measure safety culture in a variety of different high-hazard industries. Pidgeon[4] suggests that safety culture provides a useful heuristic for managing risk and safety in organisations. He suggests that safety culture can be grouped under three headings; 1) Norms and rules for dealing with risk; 2) Safety attitudes; 3) The capacity to reflect on safety practices - and that it provides a 'global characterisation of some of the common behavioural pre-conditions to disasters and accidents in high risk socio-technical systems'.

The Advisory Committee for Safety in Nuclear Installations[5] describes safety culture as 'the product of individual and group values, attitudes, perceptions, competencies, and patterns of behaviour that determine commitment to, and the style and proficiency of, an organisation's health and safety management. Organisations with a positive safety culture are characterised by communications founded on mutual trust, by shared perceptions of the importance of safety and by the efficacy of preventive measures'. Like other definitions of safety culture, it is broad-based and derived mostly from theory rather than empirical measurement. As a result, there is a danger safety culture definitions become a catch-all for social, psychological and human factor issues and the very broadness of the definition weakens its utility.

Most of the studies which have specifically attempted to measure safety culture concentrated on measuring 'safety attitudes' with positive attitudes to safety being considered to be the most important aspect of a 'good' safety culture. In the nuclear industry Lee et al[6] assessed attitudes to risk and safety among 5,295 employees at a large British nuclear reprocessing plant. They used focus groups as a forum for workers to air their views and discuss issues concerning risk and safety. Statements from these discussion groups provided the basis for a questionnaire of 172 items which was then distributed to all those working at the plant. Lee et al found major differences in the attitudes and perceptions of different occupational groups, according to supervisor status, type of shift worked (i.e. day or night workers), sex, age and experience. Different groups of workers clearly had different perceptions, beliefs and attitudes with respect to safety. It is interesting to note that these differences in risk perception and attitudes to safety were clearly linked with prior accident involvement.

While the term safety culture is relatively new, in many ways the studies that have attempted to measure it are very similar to studies of safety climate, which appear to have begun in the 1980's when Zohar[7] described what he called a 'climate for safety' in 20 Israeli industrial organisations. Zohar's measure of safety climate was a summary of perceptions that employees share about their work environment and more specifically, 'this climate [reflected] employees perceptions about the relative importance of safe conduct in their occupational behaviour' (p. 96). Data analysis reduced his 40 item questionnaire to eight dimensions; 1) Importance of safety training; 2) Effects of required work pace on safety; 3) Status of safety committee; 4) Status of safety officer; 5) Effects of safe conduct on promotion; 6) Level of risk at the work place; 7) Management attitudes to safety and 8) Effect of safe conduct on social status.

SAFETY CULTURE OR SAFETY CLIMATE?

There is perhaps a need to derive more specific definitions of 'safety culture' as distinct from 'safety climate'. What can we conclude from the research literature about safety culture and safety climate? First, there seems to be some degree of overlap in the definitions of the two concepts, however, those operating in the realms of 'safety culture' tend to talk in terms of the attitudes, beliefs, perceptions and values that employees share in relation to safety - a collective commitment to safety[8]. Those operating in the safety climate domain describe a set of perceptions and beliefs held by an individual and/ or a group about a particular entity.

Safety culture may therefore be defined in terms of underlying belief systems about safety which are partly determined by group values, norms and regulatory frameworks. Safety climate, on the other hand, refers to the state of a system in terms of perceptions of the current environment or prevailing conditions which impact upon safety. These can be related to the physical environment in which the system operates, the work environment and features of the work/management system. It could therefore be said that a site has a safety climate and employees share a safety culture. Whether termed safety culture or safety climate, it is clearly important to determine what beliefs or values predispose people to be involved in accidents and what perceived conditions can lead to unsafe behaviour.

THE NEED FOR A SAFETY CULTURE MATURITY MODEL

Due to the recognised links between a "good" safety culture and good safety performance, many organisations have attempted to measure or assess their existing safety culture, and thus identify strengths and areas for improvement.

In the UK offshore oil and gas industry, numerous safety culture and safety attitude surveys have been conducted, with varying degrees of success. They have been likened to "describing the water to a drowning man" – in other words, they may eloquently describe the nature of the problem, but offer little practical help or potential solutions. Moreover, such methods do not typically involve the main constituents of safety culture – the employees – in identifying specific, local actions necessary to improve safety culture.

It has also been observed that identical behavioural safety improvement initiatives have succeeded on one installation or site, but failed at a technically-similar site elsewhere in the same organisation. Why should this be so?

Research in the oil and gas industry has revealed that sites may differ in the *maturity* of their safety culture, despite being located in the same organisation. A safety improvement technique may fail if not matched to the maturity of a site's existing safety culture. Furthermore, as safety culture matures, further improvement does not necessarily involve "more of the same". The type of safety culture improvement method needed to support safety culture development differs as safety culture matures. This development concept can be compared with child development – the types of actions necessary to help an infant learn, develop and mature differ in nature to those appropriate for a young adult.

A number of limitations with safety attitude or safety climate surveys have also been identified. These include the time, cost and difficulty of using the results to identify clear actions to improve safety performance.

A recent joint Health and Safety Executive and oil industry-funded project to address some of these concerns led to the development of a Safety Culture Maturity™ Model (SCMM). The SCMM is based on the capability maturity model concept, initially developed by the Software Engineering Institute[9], as a mechanism to improve the way software is built and maintained. The SCMM aims to assist organisations in (a) establishing their current level of safety culture maturity and (b) identifying the actions required to improve their safety culture. It is proposed that companies or offshore installations in the early stages of developing their safety culture will require different improvement techniques from those with strong safety cultures.

The maturity model concept is new and therefore it was unclear if it could be effectively applied to safety culture improvement. An initial draft SCMM was developed based on safety culture research and maturity model literature. The components of the SCMM were based on the safety culture features listed in the Health and Safety Executive's human factors guidance document HS(G)48[10]. The initial model was tested by interviewing safety experts, operational managers, safety representatives and frontline staff about their company's safety culture development and the applicability of the SCMM. The led to the definition of a Safety Culture Maturity™ Model, with five levels of maturity (described below) and ten elements, namely:

- Visible management commitment
- Safety communication
- Productivity versus safety
- Learning organisation
- Health and safety resources
- Participation in safety
- Shared perceptions about safety
- Trust between management and front-line staff
- Industrial relations and job satisfaction
- Safety training.

SAFETY CULTURE MATURITY™ MODEL ASSUMPTIONS

Cultural or behavioural approaches to safety improvement are at their most effective when the technical and systems aspects of safety are performing adequately and the majority of accidents appear to be due to behavioural or cultural factors. The Safety Culture Maturity™ Model is therefore only of relevance to organisations that already fulfil a number of specific criteria. These include (a) an adequate Safety Management System, (b) technical failures are not causing the majority of accidents and (c) the company is compliant with health and safety law.

FIVE LEVELS OF SAFETY CULTURE MATURITY

The SCMM presented in Figure 1 overleaf is set out in a number of iterative stages. It is proposed that organisations progress sequentially through the five levels of maturity, by building on their strengths and removing the weaknesses of the previous level. It is therefore not advisable for an organisation to attempt to jump or skip a level.

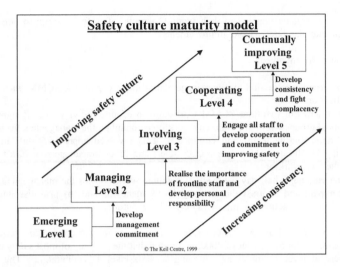

Figure 1: Safety culture maturity model

Note that the actions linking levels differ in their nature, and build upon the level of maturity established when moving to the previous level.

SAFETY CULTURE MATURITY DEVELOPMENT & IMPLEMENTATION – CASE STUDY

The Keil Centre has since developed the Safety Culture Maturity™ concept further and now provides an assessment tool to measure ten key elements of Safety Culture Maturity™. An interactive workshop process allows employees to identify current levels of Safety Culture Maturity™ and what needs to happen to move towards a more mature safety culture. The first application of this novel method was conducted in late 2000 at bp's Dalmeny and Hound Point asset.

bp's Grangemouth petrochemicals complex is one of their largest operating assets. It comprises an integrated crude oil stabilisation plant, oil refinery, chemicals plant and crude oil export terminal, and employs over 2000 people. bp's Forties Pipeline System transports 40% of oil output from North Sea offshore production platforms to bp Grangemouth for processing. The bulk of the crude oil is then pumped to bp's Dalmeny & Hound Point Asset on the Forth estuary, and onto crude oil tankers for export.

bp Dalmeny is regarded as having a relatively strong safety culture, and acceptable levels of safety performance. However, Dalmeny management are not complacent, and wished to identify realistic, practical actions that could be taken to further enhance their safety culture and performance. Dalmeny wished to focus particularly in the behavioural, human and organisational factors which influence health and safety, as they had experienced two recent incidents where unsafe behaviour was the most significant causal factor.

The Keil Centre used the Safety Culture Maturity™ Model to help senior managers plan and design a safety culture improvement initiative appropriate to their local needs and circumstances. The SCMM tool provided a systematic process to help senior managers understand key organisational and behavioural aspects of safety, prioritise areas for improvement, and plan how to make improvements.

At bp Dalmeny, this involved:-

- An initial orientation session for the management team, to explain the SCMM, its benefits and applications.
- Running a series of two-hour SCMM workshops to capture the views of all significant occupational groups within the Dalmeny workforce, including the management team, shift teams, fitters, marine teams and contractors. This involved approx 75 staff in total, comprising 50 BP staff (15 managers, 35 other) and 25 contractor personnel, a total of 75% of the total workforce.
- Thereafter running a half-day feedback & planning workshop for the management team, to (a) compare and contrast the maturity levels identified and (b) prioritise and plan tangible & realistic actions to improve safety culture maturity.

The assessment of Dalmeny Asset's safety culture maturity was conducted over a two-month period in the fourth quarter of 2000, and found that the maturity of most safety culture elements were at level 3 "involving", moving towards level 4 "cooperating". The safety culture was therefore relatively mature. Differences in levels of safety culture maturity were found between major occupational groups, with the craft and marine teams assessing the maturity to be at a lower level. This was an important finding, as it enabled tailoring of improvement actions to the needs and maturity of the group, rather than adopting a "one size fits all" approach.

All occupational groups were able to identify practical actions to improve the maturity of their safety culture.

Common themes identified, which required action, were:

- a desire for more two-way, face-to-face communication about safety between management and front-line staff, with less reliance on e-mail
- a need for a mechanism to engage all staff, including management, in observing unsafe acts and conditions, taking action to encourage safe behaviour and positive attitudes to safety, and giving a receiving prompt feedback
- an absence of an effective, user-friendly system for reporting near-misses and minor incidents
- lack of follow-up and close-out of safety issues raised, leaving people with the impression that nothing has happened, and demotivated from reporting their concerns again
- a wish for increased recognition for participation and involvement in safety.

Several Dalmeny staff commented that a behavioural safety program was required. It is likely that a well-designed and implemented program could successfully address many of these issues, whilst enhancing the maturity of the existing safety culture. Such a program should be designed for the Asset, include a near-miss reporting system, and be integrated with the existing safety management system.

A number of team-specific issues were also raised, which were examined and addressed by the relevant managers.

BENEFITS OBTAINED TO DATE

Three months after completing the project, Phil Joyner, the Asset Manager reviewed progress which had occurred. At an organisation level the following actions had taken place:

- Asset staff had designed and implemented their own simple near-miss reporting system, which had already resulted in the reporting & correction of unsafe conditions which had existed for a number of years. Approximately three near-miss reports were being submitted daily
- More face-to-face communication, both formal and informal, was taking place between management and shift teams
- Regular shift team leader meetings had been re-introduced to talk about process and safety improvements. These meetings had been livened up by asking guests to talk on specialist production or safety issues
- Shift safety teams, which had been dormant for a number of years, had been revitalised by the team members themselves who now realise that they can make a difference to safety and were taking ownership for important safety improvement actions.
- Safety issues which had been reported were now being consistently 'closed out'
- Increased recognition was being provided to members of staff who made a positive contribution to improving safety.

In addition, Phil has noticed some unexpected benefits of the Safety Culture Maturity™ workshops. The SCMM workshop process had been conceived as a means to assess levels of safety culture maturity, and identify improvement actions. It has become apparent that an additional educational benefit has been realised. Workshop participants have learned about the nature of safety culture, its main components, and how they can personally contribute to enhancing its maturity. Phil Joyner observed "people now possess a clearer understanding of the importance of their individual behaviour in improving safety performance, and demonstrate a greater willingness to take ownership of safety improvement actions".

CONCLUSION

The Safety Culture Maturity™ Model is a participatative, solution-focused safety culture assessment and improvement method, which has exceeded the expectations at the first site where it was trialled. Since then the process has been rolled out in bp's Bruce and Miller offshore production platforms, and will shortly be extended to bp's Forties Pipeline System business. The Safety Culture Maturity™ process has also been implemented in Singapore, Norway and with a group of Venezuelan managers. What makes it different from other safety culture assessment processes is that it has a strong focus on solutions, involves a high degree of workforce participation, and provides an opportunity for staff at all levels to learn more about key elements of safety culture, and their role in its development and maturity.

REFERENCES

[1] Lee, T.R. The role of attitudes in the safety culture and how to change them. Paper presented at The Conference on 'Understanding Risk Perception'. Aberdeen: Offshore Management Centre, The Robert Gordon University, 2nd February(1995).

[2] Hoyos, C.G. Occupational Safety: Progress in understanding the basic aspects of safe and unsafe behaviour. Applied Psychology: An International Review, 44 (3), 235-250 (1995).

[3] CBI: Developing a Safety Culture- Business for Safety. London: Confederation of British Industry (1990).

[4] Pidgeon, N. Safety culture and risk management in organisations. Journal of Cross-Cultural Psychology, vol 22, 129-140 (1991).

[5] ACSNI. Human Factors Study Group Third Report: Organising for Safety. London: HMSO (1993).

[6] Lee, T. MacDonald, S.M. & Coote, J.A. Perception of risk and attitudes to safety at a nuclear reprocessing plant. Paper presented at the Society for Risk Assessment (Europe) 4th Conference: Rome (October, 1993).

[7] Zohar, D. Safety climate in industrial organisations: theoretical and applied implications. Journal of Applied Psychology, 65 (1), 96-102 (1980).

[8] Mearns, K., Flin, R., Fleming, M. & Gordon, R. Human and Organisational Factors in Offshore Safety. HSE, OSD Report . Suffolk: HSE Books (1997).

[9] Paulk, M.C., Curtis, B., Chrissis, M.B. & Weber, C.V. (1993) Capability Maturity Model, Version 1.1. IEEE Software 10 (4) 18-27.

[10] HSC (1999) HSG48 Reducing error and influencing behaviour, Norwich HMSO

DEVELOPING A DATABASE TO ALLEVIATE THE PRESENCE OF MUTUAL MISCONCEPTIONS BETWEEN DESIGNERS AND OPERATORS OF PROCESS PLANTS

B.P.Das[1], P.W.H.Chung, J.S.Busby* and R.E.Hibbered*
Department of Computer Science, Loughborough University, Loughborough, UK.
* Department of Mechanical Engineering, University of Bath, Claverton Down, Bath, UK.

In this paper the development work concerning a novel system – *Mutual Misconception Database* is reported. The term *misconception* for this paper refers to the possession of an incorrect belief by the individual about some aspect of the complex system. Marine and process plant (off-shore and on-shore) accident case histories, which are available in public domain, are used in developing the system. It is based on the premise that mutual misconceptions occur between designers and operators. Prior to the commencement of this work, the authors could not locate any tools designed specifically for the identification of mutual misconceptions in accidents. This prompted the development of a mutual misconceptions database system, which should eventually assist in the elimination of the presence of these mutual misconceptions. In the body of this paper, the rationale that underlies the development of the database, the manner in which accidents were analysed, together with an example accident analysis including brief description of the database system are presented. Many interesting observations are made relating to misconceptions at appropriate places of the paper. The paper concluded with an examination of the potential uses of the database system that has been developed particularly as the starting point for the developing intelligent agenda-setting mechanisms that are integrated with other computer-based systems.

Keywords: Accident, Database, Design, Misconception, Mitigation, System

INTRODUCTION AND OVERVIEW OF THE PAPER

Researchers at Loughborough University and the University of Bath have begun a project to investigate the role of mutual misconceptions in marine and process plant (off-shore and on-shore) accidents. The project is based on the premise that mutual misconceptions occur between designers and operators. In other words, designers may have specific beliefs about the manner in which operators can and will behave, whilst operators possess beliefs about the behaviours that designers wish them to enact.

In this project, the term 'operators' does not simply refer to those individuals who are engaged in the manipulation of complex systems' user interfaces. It includes all other personnel involved in the operation of the complex system, such as maintenance personnel and managers. Further, the project does not constrain itself solely to investigation of errors that arise in the control room of a complex system. Rather, consideration is given to both the artefacts, such as storage vessels that comprise a complex system, and the procedures, such as permit-to-work systems, which dictate its operation.

This research hopes to identify the types of mutual misconceptions that arise and can suggest means by which to alleviate the occurrence of these misconceptions. It is also expected that a computer-based system can be developed which would promote the application of lessons learnt from previous accidents to novel situations and previously unused artefacts.

Prior to the development of such a system, it is necessary to identify and classify those misconceptions that have been found to contribute to accidents in complex systems. To

---

[1] Corresponding author. Email: B.P.Das@lboro.ac.uk

achieve this goal, a database has been developed, and it is this, which is the subject of this paper.

In order to provide insight into the development of this database, this paper is composed of a further five sections. The following section will introduce the rationale that underlies the development of the database. Following this, the manner in which accidents were analysed will be described, together with an example accident analysis. Consideration will then be given to the data that is considered to be significant in this analysis and that should inform the development of the database system. This database system will be described in the following section. The paper will conclude with an examination of the potential uses of the database system that has been developed.

THE NEED FOR A MUTUAL MISCONCEPTION DATABASE SYSTEM

In this paper, the term *misconception* refers to the possession of an incorrect belief by the individual about some aspect of the complex system. This may include misconceptions about those who design or operate the system, the environment in which the complex system can and should be used, the processes and activities enacted, and the properties of materials employed within the system. Such mutual misconceptions may arise from the manner in which the artefacts within the complex system communicate with the operator, the knowledge possessed by the operator, and the perceptions held of the dispositions of those responsible for the design and operation of the complex system.

The accident analyses conducted by (King, Hirst and Evans)[1] indicated the significant role of mutual misconceptions in accident causation. However, prior to the commencement of this project, there were no tools designed specifically for the identification of mutual misconceptions in accidents. This prompted the development of a mutual misconceptions database system, which should eventually assist in the elimination of the presence of these mutual misconceptions. It is envisaged that the database can form the basis for a tool that would assist designers in identifying potential sources of mutual misconceptions. This tool would provide strategies for reducing the presence of mutual misconceptions and would be used at crucial decision-processes during the design process.

THE CONDUCT OF ACCIDENT ANALYSES

Given that the aim of this project is to identify and classify the mutual misconceptions that underlie specific accidents, it is necessary to analyse specific accidents for their presence. It is impossible to predict *a-priori* when an accident will occur, therefore accident analysis can only be conducted retrospectively. Fortunately, researchers such as (Kletz)[2] have recognised this, and collated case-histories of accidents. Their intentions have been to identify the specific factors that contributed to a specific accident and remove them in some manner or mitigate their effects. These case histories form the foundation for the authors' database system.

Conduct of the causal analysis allows the identification of both the goals adopted by operators, and also the actions enacted to attain these goals. Causal analysis can identify those actions and goals that were inappropriate in relation to specific process plants. Further, an understanding of the reasons why the operators goals or actions were inappropriate can also identify the mutual misconceptions that arose from designers inappropriate beliefs about the manner in which the process plant would be used, or the manner in which it could be used.

Whilst identification of a root cause may provide a means to identify a specific inappropriate action from operators that the designer can avoid, the analysis of mutual misconceptions provides a means by which to understand why both designers and operators failed to consider the presence or consequences of specific actions. In the next section of the paper, attention will be given to the analysis procedure that was adopted for the identification of mutual misconceptions.

REQUIREMENTS FOR A MUTUAL MISCONCEPTIONS DATABASE SYSTEM

THE METHOD EMPLOYED FOR ANALYSIS

The mutual misconceptions database system relies upon a methodology that allows the identification of the mutual misconceptions that contributed to a specific accident. This procedure requires the identification of a specific outcome, and the immediate cause of this. Following from this it may be possible to further identify subsidiary causes that contributed to the immediate cause. The identification of subsidiary causes continues until the root causes presented within the case-history are identified, which may constitute either active errors, actions committed by operators, or latent errors, causal factors arising from decisions taken during the design of a particular process plant (Reason)[3]. Once root causes have been identified it is then possible to consider the mutual misconceptions that may have contributed to this specific accident. This data can then be included within the fields of the mutual misconceptions database system.

ILLUSTRATION OF THE MANNER IN WHICH ANALYSIS IS CONDUCTED

In order to illustrate the analysis procedure that has been used, an accident case-history available in the public domain, in (Kletz)[2] is first presented in Table 1. It looks at an *explosion* that took place in a process plant's batch reactor circulating system. Based on this case-history first of all an overall analysis is done as shown in Table 2. It leads to identify consequences of incident/accident and assists in finding answers to the subsequent question of "*Why*". Next causation analysis of all the consequences of incident/accident as identified from the previous stage is carried out which is briefly shown in Figure 1. It eventually leads to misconceptions held by an individual. The last part of the procedure develops the misconceptions in a concise manner as shown in Table 3.

There are six main misconceptions included in the causation of this accident, four of which arise from the beliefs held by the designer of the system, two of which arise from the operators beliefs. The first of these misconceptions was the designers' expectation that the operator would not make use of the system unless all alarms and instruments were operating in an appropriate manner. This presumed that the operator was able to identify the state of alarms and instruments, and that they would not be subject to external pressures that would encourage use of the system when it was in a non-functional state.

Another misconception held by the designer, was the expectation that the operator would heed all warning signs and would be able to conduct appropriate diagnosis of the state of the system. Further, the designer did not perceive any reason for providing a means to directly measure the physical properties of the system. The ability to directly measure the properties may have encouraged the operator to test their hypotheses about the state of instruments within the system. The last misconception held by the designer, was that explosion couldn't occur in a reactor because of their robust design. Probably the designer was not aware of an incident like this.

It is possible to identify two main misconceptions held by the operators of the plant. The management assume that it is unnecessary to monitor the state of key instruments within the system. In this case, the management appeared ignorant of the importance of ensuring that there are properly functioning instruments monitoring the performance of the system.

The operator demonstrates another misconception, which suggests ignorance of the consequences of their actions upon the state of the system. In this case it is apparent that the operator lacks strategies for effective diagnosis of system state or for simulating the consequences of their actions. Such actions may reflect a belief that the designer would provide a means to prevent them from conducting inadvisable actions, that the system would not fail in a catastrophic manner, or that the system had adequate defences to alleviate the consequences of inadvisable actions.

GENERAL CONCLUSIONS FROM THE ANALYSES

In this section, consideration is given to some of the conclusions that can be drawn from the analysis of these cases. In all we have studied 50 cases that are related to the operation of complex systems. These have been acquired from a number of sources including (Crowl and Louvar)[4], (Kletz)[2], the Marine Accident Investigation Board's Safety Digest amongst other sources. This study covers accidents that occurred with a variety of artefacts, failure modes, process operations and personnel. For example, artefacts examined included marine vessel auto-pilots, pipelines, reactors and valves amongst others. Process operations examined included preparation for maintenance, process control, amongst others. The analyses also included a variety of personnel including designers, managers, maintenance personnel, operators and supervisors.

Given the nature of the data presented in the case-histories analysed, it was difficult to find evidence of the actual psychological processes that underlie operator performance. For example, in the case-history presented in the previous section, the operator's decision to open the valve at the base of the reactor may have been simply because the operator forgot the appropriate procedure for the operation of this reactor. It may also have been the case that the operator lacked specific knowledge about the relationships between the components of the system and the dynamics of the reaction being controlled. However, these case-histories do allow the identification of the mutual misconceptions that could have potentially contributed to a specific accident. They allow us to identify what should have been known to ensure that these forms of accidents are not repeated.

In many of the case-histories that were studied, it was possible for the operator to overlook the recommended operating procedures. Related to this was the possession of inappropriate knowledge by operators, typically they appeared to lack an understanding of the relationships between the components of the system they were using, procedural models instead of structural models (Preece, Rogers, Sharp, Benyon, Holand and Carey)[5]. The nature of the system may also allow modelling of inappropriate behaviours by other personnel. That is an accident may not necessarily arise from the use of a non-recommended procedure, and this provides reinforcement for its use (Bandura)[6,7]. Further, there may be conflicting goals pursued by operators, safety goals being usurped by production goals (Reason)[3]. Indeed, there are many other psychological biases that may suggest means by which inappropriate behaviours are enacted, and by which mutual misconceptions develop.

The question arises as to why these mutual misconceptions should develop. It is possible that there are limitations to the degree to which designers can recall appropriate knowledge about the environment in which the artefact is to be used, possibly through lack of access to appropriate individuals (Katz and Khan)[8]. Further, both operators and designers may have differing expectations about the manner in which the others would perceive them. That is there may be projection of specific attitudes and values held by one group of individuals onto the other (Katz and Khan)[8]. The manner in which these mutual misconceptions arise is however addressed elsewhere.

DESCRIPTION OF THE MUTUAL MISCONCEPTIONS DATABASE SYSTEM

THE SYSTEM AND FUNCTIONS

Following analysis and collation of required information from accident reports, the Mutual misconception database system is developed using the Microsoft Access database management system. Currently the user interface of the Mutual misconception database system, (Figure 2) provides six menu options: (1) View case list (2) View case details (3) View Misconceptions (4) View reports (5) View notes (6) Quit the system.

The first menu option gives a choice of viewing accident cases by type of complex system involved, namely; (a) *Marine accidents* (b) *Offshore platform accidents* (c) *Process plant accidents*. For each category, it provides facilities to view full list of cases, the corresponding sources and the casual network of causation leading to primary consequences of an accident (Figure 3).

The second menu option of the system also gives the user a choice of viewing accident case details by type of complex system involved. For each category, the *source* of the case, the *narrative* containing brief description of the accident, the *causation* of the accident in the form of two dimensional *step* diagram linking consequences and corresponding causes can be viewed through this option (Figure 4). It also provides further facility to look into the corresponding misconceptions that were identified from the analysis of the case.

The third menu option of the system provides the facility of looking at the complete list of misconceptions associated with the subjects possessing those misconceptions, whether designer or operator. Each misconception is described in a short sentence. Again by clicking a particular misconception with a mouse pointer the user can view the *subject*, *object*, *description* relating to the misconception, *lessons learnt* from the incident and the *remedy* prescribed (Figure 5).

The fourth menu option of the system provides a formatted report of all the misconceptions available within the system. This report is generated automatically and is dynamic in nature. The user has the option of viewing them on the screen or to obtain a hard copy for detailed analysis. Finally, the fifth and sixth menu options allow the user to access a blank note pad facility and to exit the database system.

THE RESULT

Varieties of reports can be generated out of this system depending on user's requirements. A typical report containing list of misconceptions, the lessons learnt and remedy is given in Table 4.

CONCLUSIONS

This research has investigated the means by which to develop a database that provides data on a hitherto ignored contributor to accident causation in complex systems. It suggests a means by which to structure case-histories of accident causation that provides analyses that can be universally applied for a variety of design tasks.

The development of this database requires the involvement of individuals with appropriate expertise. In the case of this project, there is a need to gain the involvement of those with expertise in process operations, process plant design, psychology, and user-interface design. It is preferable that each case-history is analysed by as many members of the group as is possible. Such an approach allows the identification of ambiguities in the case-history and allows the identification of invalid conclusions.

The analyses that have been conducted suggest that in any accident there may be a number of mutual misconceptions operating. Further, the identity of the mutual misconceptions that caused different personnel to make errors may differ. This suggests a need to present specific remedies according to the different groups involved in the design and operation of complex systems. Further, it is recognised that identification of a specific mutual misconception does not in itself suggest any means by which to remedy it. Consequently, within the database, consideration has been given to the specific lessons that can be learned from specific case-histories and also to the remedies that these suggest.

It is expected that in the future, this type of database could provide a starting point for the development of intelligent agenda-setting mechanisms that are integrated with other computer-based systems. For example, it may be possible to integrate this type of database with computer-aided design tools and indicate to the designer where assumptions are based on an unrealistic view of the operator. Similarly, the database could be integrated with permit-to-work systems to ensure that operators are conducting work that does not assume an unrealistic model of the designer. However, such development is as yet only a future possibility, and relies upon further development upon the analyses that have been presented in this paper.

REFERENCES

1.   King, R., Hirst, R. and Evans, G., 1998, King's Safety In The Process Industries. Second Edition, Arnold: London, UK

2.   Kletz,T., 1998, *What Went Wrong? Case Histories of Process Plant Disasters.* Fourth Edition, Gulf Publishing Company: Houston, Texas, USA

3.   Reason, J., 1991, *Human Error.* Cambridge University Press: Cambridge, UK

4.   Crowl, D. A. and Louvar, J. F., 1990, *Chemical Process Safety Fundamentals with Applications.* Prentice Hall: New Jersey, USA

5.   Preece, J., Rogers, Y., Sharp, H., Benyon, D., Holland, S. and Carey, T., 1994, *Human-Computer Interaction.* Addison-Wesley: Harlow, UK

6.   Bandura, A., 1965, Influence of model's reinforcement contingencies on the acquisition on imitative responses. *Journal of Personality and Social Psychology*, **1**: 589-595

7.   Bandura, A., 1965, 'Vicarious processes: A case of no-trial learning' in L. Berkowitz (Ed.) *Advances in Experimental Social Psychology (Vol. 2)*, Academic Press: New York, USA

8.   Katz, D. and Khan, R.L., 1978, *The Social Psychology of Organizations (2nd. Edn.)*, Wiley: New York, USA

Table 1. Example accident case-history

(Kletz)[2] described an accident that took place in a batch reactor circulating system. This system consists of ethylene oxide feed pump, reactor, circulation pump, heat exchanger and catalyser forming a closed loop including associated control instruments such as pressure indicator, temperature indicators, flow indicator alarm and trip initiator. In short the material first flows through the reactor then through the circulation pump into the heat exchanger and finally into the catalyser from where it goes back to the reactor again.

The process starts with a batch of glycerol, which is placed in the reactor and then circulates through the heat exchanger and the catalyser. The heat exchanger of the system acts both as a heater and a cooler. At the beginning of the process, this heat exchanger acts as a heater, its role being to raise the temperature of the glycerol in the reactor to 115° Celsius. Once the glycerol reaches this temperature, ethylene oxide is then added to the reactor through the ethylene oxide feed pump. The reaction of the glycerol and the ethylene oxide is exothermic, and it is at this stage that the heat exchanger is used as a cooler to cool the reaction.

There are three conditions that has to be met before ethylene oxide could be added to the reactor. Firstly, the circulation pump must be running. Secondly, the temperature of the reactor's contents has to exceed 115° Celsius. If this condition is not met there would be no reaction between the glycerol and the ethylene oxide. Thirdly, temperature must be kept below 125° Celsius; else the reaction would be potentially explosive.

Although, the three conditions above identify three conditions that should ensure safe production using this batch reaction system, in this case-history an explosion did occur. In this case-history, the operator was confronted with a pressure indicator that showed rising pressure within the reactor, which indicated that there was no reaction between the ethylene oxide and the glycerol. On the basis of this indicator, the operator decided that the indicated temperature was reading too low, and so added more heat to encourage the start of the reaction. The trip setting was manually adjusted to allow this, and the indicated temperature was allowed to rise to 200° Celsius. However, the pressure reading indicated that the reaction had still not begun.

The operator then began to suspect that this theory about the state of the batch reactor could be wrong. At this point, the operator looked at other potential hypotheses to explain the present state of the reactor, and realised that a valve at the base of the reactor was shut. In order for the reaction to occur, the operator recalled that this valve needed to be opened, and so opened this valve. The resulting reaction from the two chemicals at a temperature that was in excess of 125° Celsius burst the reactor and released a plume of escaping gas. As a result two other operators were injured, one by flying reactor debris, the other by being blown off from the top of a tank truck.

Subsequent investigation indicated that at the time of accident key instruments were not kept in working order.

Table 2. Overall analysis of example accident case-history

Operation:
Operator started the addition of ethylene oxide in a reactor, so that the reaction with a batch of glycerol can take place.

What happened:
An explosion occurred in the reactor.

What is the immediate cause of accident:
Human error; Misdiagnosis of the state of the reactor.

How it happened:
  a. Increase in reactor pressure indicated that no reaction was taking place between the ethylene oxide and glycerol.
  b. Operator attempted to promote reaction by raising the temperature in the reactor by altering the trip setting.
  c. Opened the valve at the base of the reactor to promote reaction when the temperature of the reactor's contents was in excess of 125° Celsius.

What are the consequences of the accident:
  a. Explosion ruptures reactor.
  b. Gas ejected from reactor.
  c. Two men injured as a result of flying debris and escaping gas.

What are the causes of the accident:
  a. A pump was running with a closed suction valve, got hot and the heat affected the temperature measuring point of the reactor which was outside as well as close to the circulation pump.
  b. The operator opened the valve at the base of the reactor at wrong time.
  c. A violent uncontrolled reaction occurred as unreacted ethylene oxide together with glycerol passed through the heat exchanger and catalyser of the system.

Who are involved (direct):
An Operator

Who are involved (indirect):
The Designer of the system and the Manager of the plant.

Table 3. Misconceptions as developed from causation analysis of example accident case-history

By Designer:

1. The designer failed to foresee that if an alarm does not operate, the system must stop automatically, otherwise operator might attempt to operate the system manually.

2. The designer failed to foresee that operator could fail to heed warning sign and try his own remedial process through his own thought process, which might cause and fail to provide adequate safeguard.

3. The designer failed to foresee importance of direct measurement of physical properties of the system at the crucial points and consequently made no provision.

4. The designer failed to foresee that an explosion can happen around the reactor and failed to provide adequate explosion guard for flying debris, blown off by high-pressure burnt gas.

By Manager:

1. The manager failed to foresee the importance of keeping key instruments in working order and prevent operator to operate the system without them.

By Operator:

1. The operator failed to understand the severity of making wrong decision in adjusting interlock settings and the designer failed to prevent the operator in making such decision.

Table 4. List of misconceptions, the lessons learnt and remedy

fragment	291
description	The designer failed to foresee that an explosion can happen and failed to provide adequate explosion guard for flying debris which might be blown off by high pressure burnt gas.
misconception	explosion can not happen in a reactor
subject	designer
object	operator
lessons learnt	explosion can happen in a reactor and debris will scatter across the plant causing damage to equipment and plant personnel.
remedy	In order to contain debris flying all over the place of the plant and causing damage, a reactor must be provided with explosion guard or located outside the main plant in an explosion proof building.

Figure 1. Causation analysis of the example accident case-history

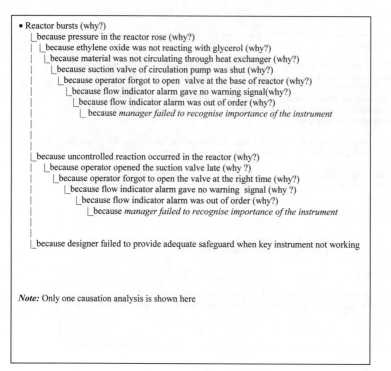

- Reactor bursts (why?)
  |_because pressure in the reactor rose (why?)
  | |_because ethylene oxide was not reacting with glycerol (why?)
  | |_because material was not circulating through heat exchanger (why?)
  | |_because suction valve of circulation pump was shut (why?)
  | |_because operator forgot to open valve at the base of reactor (why?)
  | |_because flow indicator alarm gave no warning signal(why?)
  | |_because flow indicator alarm was out of order (why?)
  | |_ because *manager failed to recognise importance of the instrument*
  |
  |
  |
  |_because uncontrolled reaction occurred in the reactor (why?)
  | |_because operator opened the suction valve late (why ?)
  | |_because operator forgot to open the valve at the right time (why?)
  | |_because flow indicator alarm gave no warning signal (why ?)
  | |_because flow indicator alarm was out of order (why?)
  | |_because *manager failed to recognise importance of the instrument*
  |
  |
  |_because designer failed to provide adequate safeguard when key instrument not working

Note: Only one causation analysis is shown here

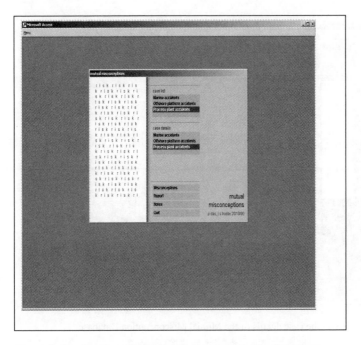

Figure 2. User Interface of the Mutual Misconception Database System

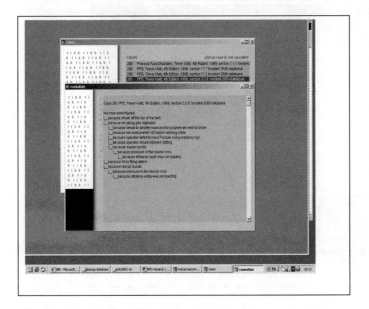

Figure 3. A view of the case list of the Mutual Misconception Database

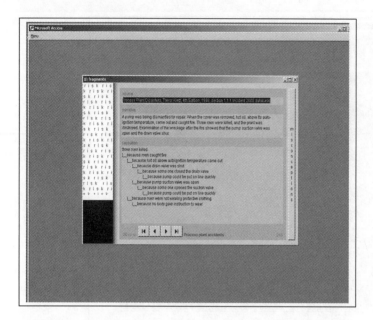

Figure 4. A view of the case details of the Mutual Misconception Database System

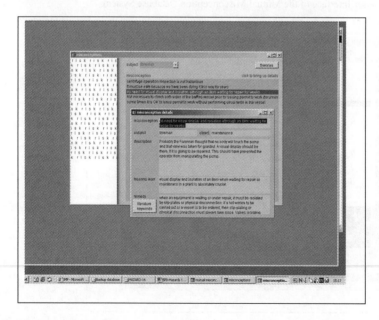

Figure 5. A view of the misconception details of the Mutual Misconception Database System

USE OF THE SAFETY CASE AS A TRAINING TOOL TO DISPERSE CORPORATE KNOWLEDGE

Nigel Cann
Australian Vinyls, Victoria, Australia.

Safety Case requirements are established in a number of jurisdictions around the world as a tool for authorities to assure themselves (and hence the community) that residual risks to the public adequately controlled. For a business to satisfy such requirements many years of effort are needed.

Australian Vinyls management saw the challenge of complying to Victoria's new OH&S (Major Hazard Facilities) Regulations 2000[1] as an opportunity to improve the business rather than a regulatory burden. Foremost in management's mind was the potential use of the Safety Case as a training tool to first capture, then disperse corporate knowledge about process safety fundamentals[2].

Keywords: Safety Case, corporate knowledge, Longford, Basis of Safety, Piper Alpha, safety training, Permit to Work,

INTRODUCTION

Victoria's OH&S (Major Hazard Facilities) Regulations 2000[1] were enacted by the Victorian Parliament following the explosion and fire at the Esso Gas Processing Plant at Longford[3] in which two people died, eight were injured and supply of natural gas to the whole state was cut for between 9 and 19 days[4].

The regulations call for a Safety Case to be prepared which must meet a number of requirements as part of a licensing regime for major hazard facilities. These requirements include:

- Summary of Safety Management System including demonstration of integration and comprehensiveness
- Method used to identify *ALL* hazards and potential major incidents
- Control Measures and a demonstration of their individual and collective adequacy
- General descriptions of:
  - activities
  - products
    - all dangerous goods
    - main units of process equipment
    - description of proposed changes
    - plans
- Weather information
- Emergency plans
- Signed statement from Chief Executive

Australian Vinyls (AV) agreed with the Victorian WorkCover Authority (VWA) to take part in an Exemplar program with the 140 ktpa Laverton PVC Resins Plant. AV's motivations for this were:

- To set ourselves in the best possible position to obtain a 5 year licence (the maximum available under the legislation)
- To have the Safety Case become a training tool, capturing information and wisdom

- To develop a process which could be integrated into our modification control system to ensure corporate knowledge is not forgotten
- To ensure the Safety Case was a working and living document owned by AV
- To influence Safety Case development in Victoria
- To develop our Safety Case process early on
- To release the key process engineering people for plant capacity increase design.
- To use the Laverton Plant due to its strong base of inherent process safety features
- To use learnings in the Safety Case for our nearby Altona Plant.

VISIT TO THE UNITED KINGDOM

As an Exemplar plant starting work before the legislation had come into law and before any guidance notes had been prepared, AV were unsure of what the end product would look like. The author undertook a visit to the United Kingdom to attend two conferences in late March and early April 2000. These were the **Safety Cases: Cross Industry Comparisons of Best Practice** and **HAZARDS XV**. These conferences and the contacts made were able to provide clarity of vision. The key points of this vision were:

- 100 pages maximum[5]
- To be clear and concise so that it could be read in a shift[5]
- Make use of graphics - Cause/Effect or "Bow-Tie" diagrams[6]
- Demonstration is key to the case so detail must be referenced outside[7]
- Make use of "sound engineering judgement"[8]
- Workforce involvement[8]
- A balance between qualitative and quantitative analysis required[8].
- The Safety Case must be complete to clearly demonstrate[7]
- Show our rationale[7]

This was even more critical as we found that VWA were not able to offer help in setting this vision. Our analysis suggested four causes for this:

- They did not know themselves where this was going
- They genuinely were developing and growing us
- They wanted to push the "bar" as high as they could and the highest point would be the one we set for ourselves
- Due to the licensing function of VWA there needed to be a distancing from a legal viewpoint

THE TRAINING ENVIRONMENT AT THE AUSTRALIAN VINYLS LAVERTON PLANT

Prior to July 2000 the plant operated 4 continuous shifts of operators working a nominal 40 hour roster including rostered overtime. During 1999, in Enterprise Bargaining Agreement (EBA) negotiations, this was changed to a 5 shift operation involving employment of 5 new operators and building in a formal training day every 5 weeks.

This provided the framework for future training structures at the plant and allowed the transfer of knowledge from a small expert base to all people on the plant[2]. Training packages have been developed around the arguments used in the Exemplar Safety Case to demonstrate the adequacy of Control Measures and which use the Safety Case document as a data source.

Further development of the training materials will take place as focus is placed on critical control measures using incidents (both local and international) as the hooks for learning.

TOOLS USED IN THE EXEMPLAR SAFETY CASE TO DEMONSTRATE ADEQUACY

The Exemplar Safety Case arguments have been developed around two key tools. The first that the plant has a well developed Basis of Safety (see figure 1). The second is the demonstration of links between hazards and control measures by the use of "Bow-Tie" diagrams[6].

BASIS OF SAFETY

The focus of our approach to safety is to prevent failure of critical controls and maintain the integrity of the detection systems and our emergency response capability. We do this through a concerted and sustained effort to create and maintain:

Operational Integrity This includes operator and maintainer skills, knowledge and understanding, procedures for normal and foreseeable activities, Permit to Work, contractor control, plant modification control, training. These systems form the core of the Safety Management System.

Process Integrity This includes control of vents, drains, backflow via utilities and other process interfaces with the environment, recipe control, overfill and overpressure protection, DCS integrity.

Plant Integrity This includes engineering standards for design, procurement and construction, pressure vessel, pipework and relief valve management, inspection, emergency power.

Response Integrity This includes systems to detect loss of containment, emergency plans, and various response mechanisms to mitigate the consequences and a culture of learning from unusual events.

Layout This includes the important features incorporated at the earliest stages of the design process that mitigate the effects of major incidents.

Siting This includes even earlier decisions that mitigate the consequential effects of a major incident on the local community.

This is summarised in figure 1, which shows these features acting as the barrier between the hazards of VCM, and the safe quality tons that we must produce to be a viable business.

BOW-TIE DIAGRAMS

Called a Bow-Tie diagram because of its shape, the diagram graphically conveys the relationship between hazards, control measures, and incidents. Figure 2 illustrates a generic Bow-Tie.

The causal (left hand) side of the Bow-Tie distinguishes the basic hazards from resultant hazards, and clearly identifies the control measures that are associated with a large number of hazards. Critical control measures are also highlighted on each Bow-Tie diagram.

The consequence (right hand) side of the Bow-Tie diagrams explains the possible consequences of each incident, and the control measures that prevent escalations.

Two different consequence diagrams were prepared for VCM, one for a liquid VCM release, and one for a vapour VCM release. In the Exemplar Safety Case, these have been "broken" off the Bow-Tie, and presented on separate sheets. This has been done so the diagrams can be read more easily.

Figure 3 illustrates a hazard scenario for the causal side of a loss of containment from a storage tank of VCM through a hole of greater than 150mm as prepared for the Exemplar Safety Case and figure 4 illustrates the consequence side of the resulting liquid VCM release.

THE TRAINING PROCESSES

BASIS OF SAFETY

The Basis of Safety training has been delivered using a lecture style format to provide an overview of the physical properties of VCM and its inherent dangers. This has then focussed on the Siting, Layout and Plant Integrity (refer to Figure 1) features used to control and mitigate the various hazards. These sessions were lead by the recognised expert on VCM and PVC process engineering and production with many years experience both in Australia and Europe.

BOW-TIES

The Exemplar Safety Case document was introduced to the site in a more interactive format[9]. The initial overview was provided in lecture style. Establishing the details of the case was worked through in small groups working on separate sections of the document and reporting back to the main group. This was followed by a group exercise at brainstorming hazards and control measures culminating in defining a single pathway on one Bow-Tie.

From this point individuals now have the skills to read through the Exemplar Safety Case document to understand the Control Measures they interact with every day and the hazards that are being controlled. And more specifically, understand the Bow-Ties and their use as a communication and demonstration tool clearly showing the links between individual hazards and the control measures that act as barriers leading to a major incident.

TRAINING IN HAZARDS AND CONTROLS

By the time this paper is presented the next stages of training will have been designed and some will have been delivered. A series of learning sessions are planned based around a group of control measures and hazards. These sessions will use case studies like Flixborough and Piper Alpha as well as local examples, and link back to appropriate Bow-Ties and to the Basis of Safety. The first of these is awareness training in Permits to Work.

PERMIT TO WORK

The Hazard Identification and Safety Assessment process undertaken for the Exemplar Safety Case produced for the Laverton Plant during 2000 highlighted the importance of the Permit to Work system in preventing Major Incidents occurring. In the 25 VCM related Major Incident scenarios developed, the Permit to Work system appears as a Critical Control Measure in 13 of them. As a result, a complete review of the Permit to Work system has been undertaken, after comparing our current systems with 7 different local and international standards, procedures and codes of practice[12-18]. This has resulted in the development of a new Permit to Work System.

Training in the new system has been broken down into three packages:
- Awareness Training
- User Training
- Authoriser Training

Awareness Training

AV has concluded that all personnel that undertake work on the plant must have an awareness of the Permit to Work system. This includes the operators who perform the isolations, the engineers who specify the work, the Shift Mangers that authorise the work, and the Management Team that counter authorise higher risk activities.

In the first stage of training a package has been designed to increase awareness and to provide understanding as to why such systems are necessary. The format prepared involves a number of different learning methods to reinforce the importance of the message over a three-hour period.

The Manufacturing Manager who is the line manager responsible for the system[10] introduces the first hour. This hour is centred around a Brian Appleton training video on the Piper Alpha disaster[11]. At the conclusion of the segment watched, the group is asked to brainstorm the lessons learnt. The Permit to Work issues are highlighted and retained for later use.

The second hour is lead by the then Plant Manger involved in an incident on the Laverton Plant in November 1998. A case study has been prepared of the incident and the group is broken into subgroups of 5 to 9 people to look at the case study and prepare issues as they see them. The subgroups are brought back together to summarise their findings which are once again retained for later use.

The third hour is lead by the Safety Case Manager who links the importance of the Permit to Work system to the prevention of Major Incidents. Changes coming with the new system are highlighted. A fitter then appears and asks the Shift Manager present in the training session to authorise a Permit to Work for removal of a piece of plant. Multiple copies of the Permit and associated Job Safety Analysis (JSA) are provided to the group and the Shift Manager leads the group to act as a collective Shift Manger to authorise the Permit to Work on site (including checking the isolations).

To summarise the session the group returns to the training room to review the permit they have completed against the things they learnt from the Piper Alpha video and the plant case study. And the session concludes with the final few minutes of the video that provides anecdotes of two survivors of the Piper Alpha disaster.

User and Authoriser Training

The training materials developed for those that use the Permit to Work System is designed to highlight the specific requirements and considerations that must be taken in planning a job, recognising hazards and planning specific controls to prevent injury and incidents.

The specifics of the training have yet to be designed and are not planned at the time of preparing this paper. However it will utilise similar techniques to those described in the previous section *and* require individual competency assessment.

Training for Authorisers is the same as that for users, with the additional requirement of an extensive verbal test of their working knowledge of the system and demonstration of their ability to discharge their responsibilities by use of worked examples in the field.

RESPONSES TO THE TRAINING PROGRAMME

OPERATORS

The Operators response was most favourable to those sessions that involved interaction and active participation. The operators give extra credence to the training when it involves interaction with the plant.

In particular the Awareness training on the Permit to Work System provided an overview of a system that they seldom interacted with (other than to perform isolations), and an understanding of the burden placed on Shift Managers.

However by far the biggest benefit was the realisation in the Operators minds that Safety was really the highest priority and that production *is to* be compromised if there are safety issues.

Criticisms reported included:
- A concern that individuals were identified in the local worked example during the discussions. This concern was not expressed by those involved who had all been involved in the development of the Case Study. (Also a briefing had been undertaken with the Industrial Chaplain should any issues arise).
- Use of check sheets by the work shop facilitator to see that the group had picked up all the points. One particular shift felt that this was poorly done. This process was modified for later groups and was no longer a concern.

MAINTAINERS AND ENGINEERS

This group interact with the Permit to Work system on a daily basis. As such they are more keenly interested in the changes proposed from the current system. For them the key benefit was that new starters now have a framework for learning about the Permit to Work System and were not required to learn it by absorbtion[19] or an unhappy event. They, like the operators, responded to interactive sessions, and walking around the plant more favourably than lectures.

PLANT MANAGEMENT

The most useful aspects for plant management were that out of the sessions changes occurred on the plant. As a result of the exercise of signing on a permit on the plant less than desirable equipment labelling was found which was corrected. Also problems with leaving some equipment spares isolated for extended periods were picked up.

THE REGULATOR

The Regulators Safety Case Officer has participated in a number of the training sessions to see how the Safety Case is being utilised and to see how well the critical hazards and control measures are understood by everybody on site. This has enabled the Regulator to see at first hand the benefits of Bow-Ties in particular. The key issue for the regulator was gaining an understanding of how we caught up with those people who missed the scheduled training sessions.

CONCLUSION

In preparing a Safety Case to meet regulatory requirements, Australian Vinyls has seen the opportunity to use the Safety Case as a tool that captures and retains vital corporate knowledge. This knowledge can be from initial design, incidents both within the company and outside it, and from the collective experience of those in the Organisation.

The "Bow-Tie" tool is a very useful means for communicating the knowledge about hazards that can lead to major incidents and the control measures undertaken to control the risks. Information in the Bow-Ties is shared via a series of learning sessions that focus on the Critical Control Measures and that can be designed to maximise the opportunities to learn.

REFERENCES

1. Occupational Health and Safety (Major Hazard Facilities) Regulations 2000, 2000, *Statutory Rule No. 50/2000*, Government Printer for the State of Victoria, http://www.dms.dpc.vic.gov.au/

2. Kletz T, 1993, *Lessons from Disaster: How organisations have no memory and accidents recur*, Institute of Chemical Engineers: 170-171

3. Government of Victoria, 1999, The Esso Longford Gas Plant Accident, *Report of the Longford Royal Commission*, Government Printer, State of Victoria

4. Boult K., Kenney G., and Pitlado R., 2000, Lessons learned from the Longford Royal Commission Investigation into the explosion and fire on 25 September 1998 at the Esso Gas Processing Plant, *Proceedings of Process Industry Incidents Conference, Orlando October 2000*, Center for Chemical Process Safety: American Institute of Chemical Engineers: 225-244

5. Rice S and Buchan A, 2000, A New Approach to Preparing Safety Cases for Existing Nuclear Plants, *Proceedings of Safety Cases: Cross Industry Comparisons of Best Practice Conference*, London March 2000:

6. Bellamy LJ, 2000, Best Practice Risk Tools for Onshore Sites with Dangerous Substances, *Proceedings of Safety Cases: Cross Industry Comparisons of Best Practice Conference*, London March 2000

7. Scott P, 2000 Charging into COMAH – A Regulator's Early Experience of Safety Reports, *Proceedings of HAZARDS XVI*, Manchester April 2000, Symposium Series No. 147, Institution of Chemical Engineers, UK: 505-516

8. Wilkinson P, 2000 Permissioning: The Case for Safety Cases, *Proceedings of Safety Cases: Cross Industry Comparisons of Best Practice Conference*, London March 2000

9. Kletz T, 1993, *Lessons from Disaster: How organisations have no memory and accidents recur*, Institute of Chemical Engineers: 167-169

10. Kletz T, 1994, *Learning from Accidents* ,(2nd Edition), Butterworth-Heinmann: 182

11. Appleton B, (video), 1991, *Learning from Accidents – The Piper Alpha Oil Platform Disaster – ICI International Management of Safety Course*, VEC International

12. *Guidelines for the Establishment and Operation of a Permit to Work System*, Australian Petroleum Exploration Association / Australian Institute of Petroleum

13. *Guidance on Permit to Work systems in the Petroleum Industry*, UK Oil Industry Advisory Committee / Health and Safety Executive, UK

14. *Occupational Health and Safety (Confined Space) Regulations (1996)*, 1996, *Statutory Rule No. 148/1996*, Government Printer for the State of Victoria, http://www.dms.dpc.vic.gov.au/

15. *National Code of Practice for the Safe Use of Vinyl Chloride*, 1993, National Occupational Health and Safety Commission, Australia.

16. *Chemical and Hazardous Installations Division Permit to Work systems pamphlet*, Health and Safety Executive, UK.

17. *Safety, Health and Environment Model Procedures* , Orica Pty Ltd, Australia.

18. *Geon Corporation Safety Standard*, USA

19. Kletz T, 1991, *An Engineers View of Human Error* ,(2nd Edition), Institute of Chemical Engineers: 137-139

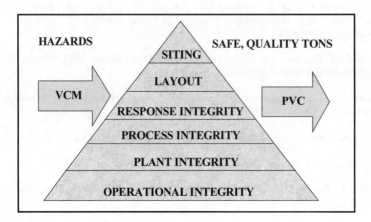

Figure 1. Basis of Safety

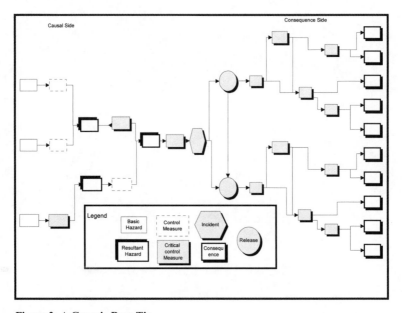

Figure 2: A Generic Bow-Tie

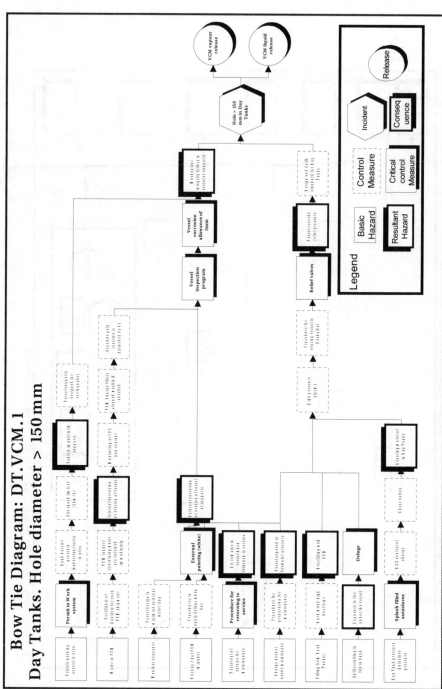

Figure 3: Causal Side of Loss of Containment from VCM Storage Tank from Hole > 150mm Diameter

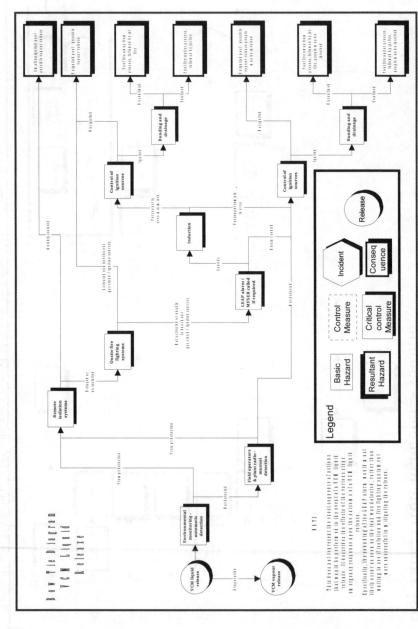

Figure 4: Consequence side from a Liquid VCM Loss of Containment

IEC 61508 – A PRACTICAL APPROACH TO ITS APPLICATION IN THE PROCESS INDUSTRY

Clive Charnock BEng CEng MIEE
AMEC Capital Projects, Jackson House, Sibson Road, Sale, Cheshire, M33 7XT

The new international standard IEC 61508 provides a generic framework for achieving functional safety through a risk reduction methodology. Because of the generic nature of the standard the challenge in the process industry has been to interpret these generic requirements in an appropriate manner. This paper explains why and how AMEC adopted and implemented the methodology and how it is being successfully applied in a practical manner on real projects

IEC 61508, risk-based, safety systems

INTRODUCTION

OVERVIEW OF THE STANDARD

IEC 61508 is an international standard for managing Functional Safety with regard to Electrical / Electronic / Programmable Electronic Safety Related Systems (referred to as E/E/PES). The standard has been in development for a number of years and the last of the seven parts were published in 2000. The standard is generic in nature and can be applied to a safety related application in any industry sector.

The standard defines a rational and consistent approach to achieving functional safety and uses the concept of the 'safety lifecycle' (from concept design, through hazard and risk analysis, specification, implementation, operation, maintenance to eventual de-commissioning) as a framework for addressing the phases to achieve functional safety in a systematic and auditable manner.

The standard is in seven parts. Parts 1, 2, 3 & 4 are normative and must be adhered to when claiming compliance with the standard. Parts 5, 6 & 7 are guidance documents providing suggestions for tools and approaches that may be used, if appropriate, to meet some of the requirements of the normative sections. This relationship between the individual parts is shown pictorially in Figure 1.

IEC 61508 is a "Basic Safety Publication" and is the basis for all sector-specific standards that are currently being developed. Due to the generic nature of IEC 61508 it can be difficult to interpret and sector-specific standards are being developed because:

- Each sector or industry having its own relevant and valuable experience that has built up over many years that needs to be captured;

- Each sector or industry has its own specific terminology and language.

The process industry sector specific standard IEC 61511 is currently in development, but will not be available for some time. Therefore, a detailed understanding of the generic standard IEC 61508 is currently required to achieve compliance.

WHY THE IEC 61508 METHODOLOGY WAS ADOPTED

AMEC are an established Engineering Contractor and have been involved in the Engineering, Procurement, Construction and Commissioning of many process plants / facilities that contain significant safety and environmental hazards.

Many chemical manufacturing companies now fall under the requirements of the Control of Major Accident Hazards (COMAH) Regulations. COMAH Regulations require submission of a report that identifies the major hazards and demonstrates the Safety Management Systems in place to mitigate those hazards. The methodology of demonstrable risk reduction through a formal risk management process is the same methodology that underpins IEC 61508. The resultant lifecycle documentation from a design, executed in accordance with the risk-based IEC 61508 methodology, would seamlessly integrate into a COMAH report.

It was also predicted that owner / operators would be citing compliance with the requirements of IEC 61508 in the technical sections of Request For Services documentation. This prediction has been vindicated as most enquiries now contain references to compliance with IEC 61508.

Compliance with the standard in the United Kingdom is NOT mandatory, but the view is that the standard represents current global best practice in achieving functional safety. Within the UK the Health and Safety At Work Act, 1974 places duties on employers, designers, suppliers, etc to provide safe equipment or plant that is 'so far as reasonably practicable', safe and without risk to health. Compliance with the standard would be a significant aid to demonstration of 'due diligence' in the delivery of a safe plant or facility.

AMEC have engineered many Safety Related Systems in the past using good engineering practice, Client engineering standards and guidance such as EEMUA Document Publication No. 160. Existing systems were in place, but were not risk-based and were difficult to audit through the lifecycle of engineering AMEC were involved in. Engineering safety related systems using the IEC 61508 risk-based approach offered the following significant advantages:

- Embracing current best practice to aid demonstration of 'Due Diligence' to mitigate legal risks;

- Understanding the implications of complying with IEC 61508 to aid mitigation of commercial risk;

- Minimising engineering, capital and operating costs on projects by utilising the risk-based approach;

- Demonstrating the capability to provide a marketing advantage.

Based on the above, the decision was made to adopt the IEC 61508 risk-based methodology into the engineering organisation, and is now being used successfully on all relevant projects.

HOW THE IEC 61508 METHODOLOGY WAS DEVELOPED

As outlined in the introduction IEC 61508 is a generic standard and as such it is a large and complex set of documents that introduces a whole new set of terminology and also presents concepts in a language that takes some level of interpretation when considering the process industry. These issues will be addressed, in many respects, when IEC 61511 is published, but the challenge was to be able to interpret the requirements of IEC 61508 to allow compliance with this base standard.

There have been many publications and articles that have discussed the standard and surrounding topics but there has, to date, been very little practical guidance as to the implementation of IEC 61508 on real process plant projects.

The key steps that were identified to lead to implementation of IEC 61508 within AMEC were:

- Initial knowledge gathering through attendance at specific IEC 61508 training courses, reviewing the standard and associated articles and papers;

- Modification of Engineering Group Procedures and Work Instructions to reflect the safety lifecycle. Identification of specific safety reviews and relationships with respect to other reviews, eg. HAZOP, Layout, Hazardous Area Classification, etc;

- Development of Design Guidelines that interpret the requirements of IEC 61508 and present the practical ideas and approach in terms engineers working on process plant projects will more easily recognise;

- Develop pro-forma documents for capturing and presenting information and data throughout the project lifecycle in a consistent format.

- Develop default tools and methodologies for hazard and risk analysis;

- Define default parameter calibrations for the selected Risk Graph and Hazardous Event Severity Matrix tools that reflect the ALARP (As Low As Reasonably Practicable) principle;

- Development of MS Excel based tools for calculations to support Integrity Level Assessment / Verification;

- Purchase failure rate data (FARADIP 3 and SINTEF data sources);

- Purchase of a tool for detail calculation of Common Cause Failure percentages (although IEC 61508 - Part 6, Appendix D contains a methodology for calculating Beta values);

- Provision of training for Engineers undertaking the work and development of a detailed competency assessment framework;

TYPICAL PROJECT EXECUTION

SCOPE DEFINITION

The scope for an individual project is normally defined by a project Basis of Design, which reflects the scope and boundaries of a project as a technical and commercial basis. The Basis of Design and covers the physical scope and the scope of responsibilities.

In most instances the physical scope of a project will generally be defined by a set of Process Flow Diagrams (PFDs) or Process & Instrumentation Diagrams (P&IDs).

Given an agreed physical scope, figure 2 illustrates the main steps in the project safety lifecycle that AMEC, in an Engineering, Procurement, Construction Management role, are involved in. The diagram is not definitive and the scope of responsibilities can change from project to project. Therefore, it is essential that the scope of responsibilities for all parties are clear and understood at the outset of the project.

Figure 2 also shows a simplified linear view of the process. In actual detail project execution the process can involve a number of iterative steps to achieve the final engineered and tested facility.

Examples of this iterative process are:

- An initial safety review identifying major hazards leading to a requirement for modification of the process design;

- A legitimate process design change (eg. Process expansion, De-bottlenecking, etc);

- A protective function requiring re-design if, through the integrity verification, the function does not comply with the target integrity level.

Even though the process of engineering is shown completing at Site Acceptance Test / Commissioning the design and engineering must take into account the requirements for ease of operation and facilitation of ongoing maintenance and proof testing.

This whole lifecycle approach is imperative as poorly designed systems, with respect to ongoing maintenance and testing, can lead to poor quality proof testing (limited coverage) and significant additional operational costs.

HAZARD IDENTIFICATION

Hazard identification is undertaken at the preliminary P&ID development stage. The study will take the form of a high level desktop review of the process to identify the major hazards associated with the process. This process utilises methodologies such as brainstorming, what-if scenarios, checklists, etc. These major hazards are assessed in a preliminary coarse Hazard Analysis. The first step in this process is to review if the risks are minimised / removed by modification of the process design to achieve a process that is inherently safer.

By having this review process as early as possible in the project lifecycle it allows the process design to be challenged in a more open-minded and effective manner as the impact of any resultant changes will be minimised.

Additionally, the issue that a detailed HAZOP study is undertaken when the P&IDs are effectively finalised. Therefore, the expectation is that the implementation of all protective functions have already been defined, leading to the requirement for an earlier Hazard Identification and Risk Analysis process.

HAZARD AND RISK ANALYSIS

Each of the hazards identified from the initial review are studied in more detail within a detailed Hazard and Risk Analysis process. The review process is undertaken by a mixed AMEC / Client team generally comprising of the following disciplines:

- Safety
- Process
- Control & Instrumentation
- Machinery specialists (as required, e.g. Incinerators or large compressors)

The default methodology for risk analysis is the Risk Graph, as this method allows a number of risk factors to be taken into account. Where there are significant hazards and a number of independent safety systems in place (eg. mechanical devices in addition to a Safety Related E/E/PES) the use of a Hazardous Event Severity Matrix is considered.

Within the risk analysis process environmental and commercial risks are considered in addition to safety risks and the most onerous of these risks defines the integrity level requirement of the protective function.

It is essential that prior to the commencement of Hazard and Risk Analysis that the risk parameters for safety / environmental / commercial risk are discussed, agreed and documented. The parameters must be such that the risk graph calibrations reflect the values and culture of the operating company in addition to meeting any statutory requirements for tolerable risk levels.

Everyone in the study team must also understand the terminology and concepts as defined within IEC 61508. The Equipment Under Control (EUC) is the plant or facility with its normal process control system (DCS or PLC / SCADA) but WITHOUT any Safety Related E/E/PES. The Equipment Under Control includes Other Technology (OT) protection systems such as pressure relief or other mechanical systems. External Risk Reduction Factors (ERRFs) are systems such as blast walls, containment bunds and plant operating procedures. The relationships between the above are shown diagrammatically in figure 3.

The process control system is used for the normal safe operation of the process plant. The control system is not designated as 'Safety Related' as the control system, in many cases, is the source of demand for a particular hazard. It could be possible, in certain cases, to claim that the control system can provide a layer of protection against a hazard. The implications of classifying a control system as 'Safety Related' normally leads to the more conservative approach of providing a separate, independent protective measure.

Within the Hazard and Risk Analysis process the plant is analysed, taking each individual hazard in turn and considering:

- What is the consequence of the hazard occurring based on the operating regime, physical features and layout of the plant (EUC) ?

- What conditions could cause the hazard to occur ?

- What is the frequency of occurrence of these conditions ?

- What measurements could be provided to detect the onset of the hazardous conditions ?

- What terminating devices could be provided prevent or mitigate the hazard ?

- Are the process dynamics such that an operator could manually detect and prevent the hazard from occurring ?

- Are there facilities and clear procedures to allow operators to detect a potential hazard and manually prevent it from occurring, or effectively evacuate the area ?

- If a protective function were provided what would be the effect of spurious tripping, and what target reliability needs to be achieved ?

By answering the above questions in the structured risk-based approach the requirement for a Safety Related E / E / PES can be determined for a particular hazard. The safety requirement is defined in terms of target Integrity Level (most onerous of Safety / Environmental / Commercial Integrity Levels) and functional operation (cause and effect). Figure 4 shows the Integrity Level Calculation Sheet, which is used to capture the information with respect to a particular hazard and forms the basis of the Safety Requirements Specification (SRS).

Where a target Integrity of SIL3, or above, is identified for a particular hazard the approach is to insist on re-examination of the process design to investigate if the risk can be reduced. If it not possible to effectively reduce the target Integrity Level then independent 3rd party assessment would be applied through the safety lifecycle for the particular hazard.

The Safety Lifecycle defined within IEC 61508 refers to a 'Safety Requirements Allocation' stage which is distinct from the Hazard and Risk Analysis. Theoretically, this is the stage where the decision is made as to what contribution is made to overall risk reduction by Other Technologies (OT), External Risk Reduction Factors (ERRFs) and Safety Related E/E/PES to achieve Functional Safety.

In practical situations the 'Safety Requirements Allocation' is an integrated part of the Hazard and Risk Analysis study process, for example:

-   The demand rate for a Reactor Overpressure hazard is reduced by a factor of a least 10 due to the pressure safety relief valve that is correctly sized for the particular case.

-   The consequence of reactor explosion due to overpressure is reduced by a factor of at least 10 due to the provision of a correctly design blast wall.

The above considerations are taken into account when assessing the resultant risk (and target Integrity Level for the Safety Related E/E/PES) and are identified / recorded on the Integrity Level Calculation sheets as Safety related Items.

SYSTEM REALISATION

The documentation resulting from the Hazard & Risk Analysis process forms the basis of the Safety Requirements Specification (SRS) which then requires realisation into an engineered system. The complete Safety Requirements Specification is not contained within a single comprehensive document, but rather within a coherent set of related documents that are developed through the engineering phase of the project. These documents provide an amplification / extension of the base requirements (target Integrity Level and functional requirements) to define the detailed realisation requirements, and include:

-   Safety System User Requirements Specification (performance criteria, reset requirements, maintenance overrides, communication links, Human Machine Interfaces, environment, etc);

-   Safety System Input / Output Schedules (including ranges & set-points);

-   Safety System Trip Matrix Definitions (including and sequential and timing requirements).

This collection of documents that form the Safety Requirements Specification is used as the basis for verification phase of the project, therefore, no unauthorised deviations from the approved specifications are allowed unless a formal change has been raised, reviewed, approved and implemented under strict revision control.

Where the consequences of spurious tripping of a Safety Related E/E/PES may cause significant commercial loss (eg production downtime or situations such as a product setting solid in a reactor vessel) or further downstream hazards there may be a requirement to achieve a specific Spurious Trip Rate target for the protective function. These situations require implementation of architectures (such as 2 out of 3 voting) which are robust to revealed failures.

Instrumentation and valves must be selected that are appropriate for the duty in terms of fouling, plugging and material compatibility.

Proof testing is an essential part of maintaining the integrity of Safety-Related systems and the design, where possible, is implemented to facilitate effectiveness and ease of proof testing, eg. Test pots for high level switches, isolate / vent valves for pressure instruments and facilities for by-passing or partial stroking of shut-off valves.

The internally developed Design Guides address these detailed realisation issues and provide practical advice for engineers during this phase of the lifecycle.

AMEC's engineering systems facilitate the very stringent requirements for the management of change through the safety lifecycle by employing engineering database tools that utilise the single point data entry paradigm. Therefore, a single instrument tag stored in the database is linked to the graphical representation on the P&ID, associated with an I/O definition and associated with a protective function. A Revision history tracking process is automated and operated down to individual tag level.

E / E / PES SAFETY RELATED SYSTEM VERIFICATION

To achieve functional safety the E / E / PES Safety Related System must perform specific actions with a certain degree of certainty to reduce the risks resulting from the EUC to an acceptable level. The system must be considered from the sensors through to the final terminating devices, ie. The 'Pipe to Pipe' concept.

Therefore, the verification process consist of two distinct parts:

Integrity Verification –   A defined level of certainty that a function will operate as required.

Functional Verification –   The function performs specific actions (eg. Close valve V1) when specific conditions (eg. Vessel V3 High Level) occur.

INTEGRITY LEVEL VERIFICATION

IEC 61508 defines four discrete levels for Safety Integrity Level (SIL 1 to SIL 4 - SIL 4 having the highest level of integrity). The Safety Integrity Level is expressed as a numerical range of values that are expressed as:

Probability Of Failure On Demand (PFD) – Low Demand Rate Systems

Probability of Failure Per Hour (PFH) – High Demand or Continuous Demand Systems

Applications within the Process Industry tend to mainly fall within the category of low demand systems.

The dangerous failure of a protective function can be caused by:

  - Random Hardware failures;
  - Systematic failures (software failures, design process failures, etc.)

Quantitative predictions of protective function PFD / PFH due to random hardware failures can be effectively calculated to assess performance. It is generally not possible to calculate PFD / PFH due to systematic failures using fully quantitative methods. Therefore, in the case of software based systems, it is necessary to ensure specific design methods / checking / review / test measures are undertaken for different target Integrity Levels.

To calculate the Integrity of a safety function, a block diagram of the complete function (from initiators to terminating devices needs to be defined). This block diagram is broken down into the three sub-system sections as shown in figure 5.

IEC 61508, Part 6 Has multiple tables to allow the user to look-up a PFD or PFH value for a sub-system. The multiple tables allow a selection of the following parameters:

Configuration:	One out of One (1oo1)
	One out of Two Voting (1oo2)
	Two out of Two Voting (2oo2)
	One out of Two Voting Reverting to One out of One (1oo2D)
	Two out of Three Voting (2oo3)
Proof Test Interval:	6 months, 12 months, 2 years & 10 years (Low demand)
	1 month, 3 months, 6 months and 12 months (High demand)
Failure rates:	0.1, 0.5, 1, 5, 10 & 50 failures per million hours
Diagnostic Coverage:	0%, 60%, 90% & 99%
Beta Values:	1%, 5% & 10%

The tables also assume that:

Mean Time To Repair: 8 hours

Dangerous Failures: 50% of total failures

Beta Values for Detected Failures = 0.5 x Beta value for undetected failures.

Failure Rate Data

The most accurate failure rate data for any operational plant would be data collected by the plant operator from maintenance records or incident reports. The problem is that many operational sites do not effectively collect historical data in a consistent format that could be used as a basis for use in calculations.

In most instances the default data sources utilised for analysis purposes are recognised data sources such as FARADIP 3 and SINTEF.

Extreme care must be exercised when making a judgement on percentage of failures to a dangerous mode. The duty and failure mode of the specific device in the context of the safety function must be clearly understood.

Diagnostic Coverage

There is little practical guidance for assessing diagnostic coverage for a sub-section, and again, careful engineering judgement must be exercised in understanding what facilities have been engineered into the sub-system to detect faults and make faults visible to the operator.

Beta Values

To make an accurate assessment of Common Cause Failure fractions it is necessary to not only have a detailed understanding of the complexity, environment and design features of the system, but an understanding of the safety culture of the organisations involved with respect to procedures, training and competency. The methodology used is an enhancement of the partial BETA model known as the BETAPLUS model.

Proof Test Interval

The proof test interval is agreed following discussions with the plant operator to understand the operating and maintenance regimes and experience with specific types of instrumentation and equipment. The normal approach would be to agree a short proof test interval in the first instance, and once satisfactory experience of the equipment is gained then the proof test interval can be review and increased given that the PFD / PFH figure for the complete safety function remains acceptable.

The tables may be acceptable as a 'first-pass' as the tabular results are based on specific assumptions that may not be applicable to the specific sub-system, and there are limited choices for other parameters that may not be suitable. Due to these limitations, Microsoft EXCEL tools have been developed by AMEC (based on reliability block diagram models) to allow the PFD or PFH to be calculated for a sub-system with specific values rather than pre-determined fixed value choices or coarse assumptions. An Figure 6 shows an example output.

A summary assessment sheet is set up such that the effective block can be modelled and the individual sub-system details added. The PFD or PFH for the complete safety function is calculated and compared against the numerical target value. The percentage contribution from each section is calculated to identify the dominant component that should be addressed if the target PFD or PFH is not met. An example output is shown in Figure 7.

Spurious Trip Rate

The summary assessment sheet contains a second sheet that calculates the spurious trip rate for the protective function and percentage contribution from each sub-system. Where applicable, the calculated spurious trip rate is compared with the target spurious trip rate as defined on the Integrity Level Calculation Sheet.

Hardware Integrity

In addition to meeting the requirement for compliance with a target PFD or PFH value the sub-system requires assessment of the hardware integrity. The sub-system hardware integrity is dependent upon the hardware diagnostic coverage and fault tolerance. Tables 2 & 3 within

IEC 61508 part 2 define the requirements for Type A and Type B sub-systems respectively. Type A systems are simple, well understood and proven in the field, whereas Type B systems are complex, with behaviour that cannot be not fully determined and is not proven in the field.

An example is a single trip valve sub-system that has the following attributes:

- Simple, well understood and proven operation in the field (Type A sub-system)
- No diagnostic coverage
- No fault tolerance (ie. A single fault could cause a dangerous failure)

Using Table 2 results in a sub-system hardware integrity that is applicable to SIL 1 applications. Regardless of the failure rate data or proof test interval the sub-system can only be applied in a safety function that has a target Integrity Level of SIL 1, eg. If the complete safety function had an input section rated at SIL 2, logic solver at SIL 3, and output section rated at SIL 1 then the complete safety function would be limited to SIL 1.

Terminology used within the industry such as a 'SIL 2 pressure transmitter' must be treated with caution, as the term is specific to the device in terms of the device having the hardware integrity applicable to SIL 2. Using this specific device within the sub-system of a complete safety function DOES NOT guarantee that the complete safety function will comply with the requirements appropriate to SIL 2.

FUNCTIONAL VERIFICATION

To ensure that all of the protective functions perform the necessary actions as defined within the Safety Requirements Specification (SRS) it is necessary undertake rigorous testing of the system. These tests are usually split into two phases, namely:

- Factory Acceptance Tests;
- Site Acceptance Tests.

The factory acceptance tests are carried out against a pre-approved test specification that reflects the Safety Requirements Specification (SRS).

The Site Acceptance Tests are performed at the pre-commissioning phase of the project and are normally the final proof tests undertaken prior to plant start-up. At this stage all installation checks have been made, the systems fully energised and instrumentation fully calibrated.

It is sensible to perform the Site Acceptance Tests utilising the actual proof test procedures that will be utilised during the operational lifetime of the plant. This approach has the benefit of validating the procedures prior to start-up. It is extremely important to agree early in the project lifecycle who will be responsible for the production of these procedures as it can be a significant task that needs to be well planned and carefully executed. Last minute development of these procedures can lead to shortcomings in the testing leading to a reduction of achieved integrity.

CONCLUSIONS

Adoption of the IEC 61508 has required a significant amount of work and commitment with the organisation going through a steep learning curve. The benefit of adopting the risk-based methodology is that it has driven the organisation to a more rigorous, consistent, auditable and holistic way of achieving functional safety.

By successfully delivering projects using the methodology AMEC have a detailed understanding of what is required and ensure that the necessary resources are taken into account, thus minimising risk to the project.

It has been noted in some cases on recent projects that application of the risk-based methodology has led to cases where a Safety Related E / E / PES, that previously would have been included (because of custom and practice or engineering judgement), has been found not to be required to achieve functional safety. By applying the methodology the number of Safety Related E / E / PESs can be reduced, allowing savings in capital, operating and maintenance costs that are achieved through the lifetime of the plant. This general reduction of the number of protective functions allows resources and effort to be concentrated on the legitimate protective functions, which will reap benefits in terms of maintaining functional safety through the complete lifecycle of the plant.

FUTURE PLANS

The plans for the future are to gain formal recognition of AMEC's ability to conform with the requirements of IEC 61508. The Conformity Assessment for Safety Systems (CASS) Scheme is an initiative recently launched in the UK and provides a common framework for companies involved in the Safety Lifecycle to demonstrate compliance with IEC 61508. The intention is to demonstrate compliance at management system level through what is known as a "Functional Capability Safety Assessment" (FSCA), which requires an audit process through a UKAS accredited assessment company.

REFERENCES

IEC 61508   Functional Safety of Electrical / Electronic / Programmable Electronic
                       Safety-Related Systems – Parts 1 – 7.

IEC 61511 (Draft)   Functional Safety: Safety Instrumented Systems for the Process
                       Industry Sector – Parts 1 – 3.

EEMUA   Publication 160. Safety Related Systems for the Process Industries.

FARADIP.THREE   Failure Rate and Failure Mode Databank and Failure Mode and Effect
                       Analysis Package. Technis, Tonbridge, Kent UK.

BETAPLUS   Common Cause Failure (Partial Beta model) Analysis Package.
                       Technis, Tonbridge, Kent UK.

SINTEF   Industrial Management Safety and Reliability.
                       Reliability Data for Control and Safety Systems. 1998 Edition.

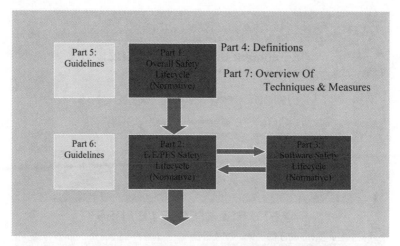

Figure 1 – Relationship Between The Seven Sections of The IEC 61508 Standard

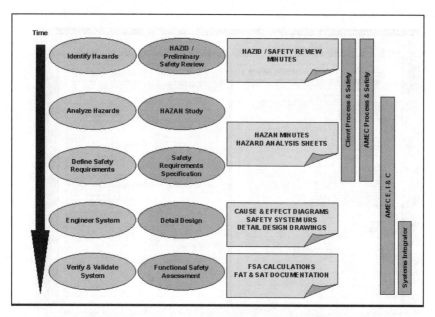

Figure 2 – Simplified View of The Safety Lifecycle Applicable to Design & Engineering

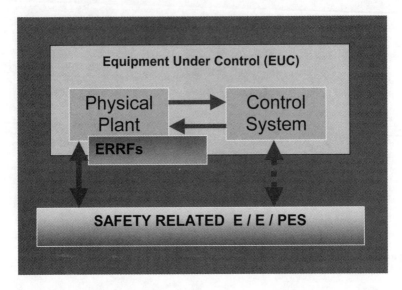

Figure 3 – Diagram of a Process Plant Entity

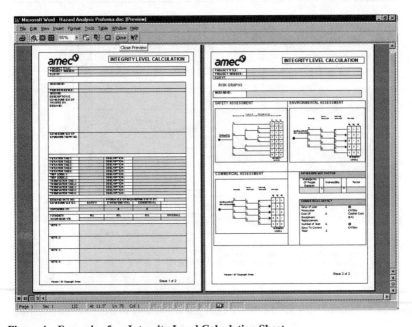

Figure 4 – Example of an Integrity Level Calculation Sheet

$$PFD_{FUNCTION} = \Sigma PFD_{IS} + \Sigma PFD_{LS} + \Sigma PFD_{OS}$$

Figure 5 – Block Diagram Representing Sub-systems and Contribution to total PFD

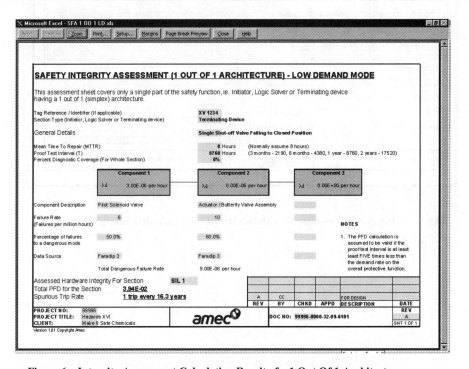

Figure 6 – Integrity Assessment Calculation Result of a 1 Out Of 1 Architecture

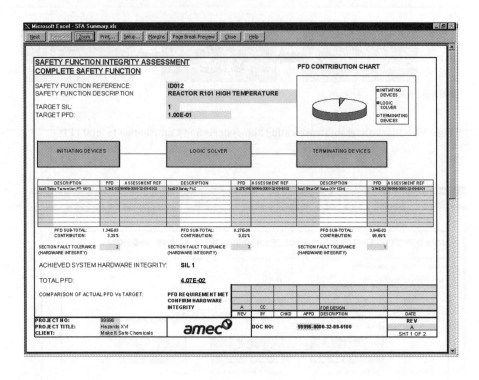

Figure 7 – Integrity Assessment Calculation Result for a Complete Safety Function

DISTRIBUTED COGNITION AND HUMAN FACTORS FAILURES IN OPERATING AND DESIGN PROCESSES

J S Busby and E J Hughes
Department of Mechanical Engineering, University of Bath, Bath BA7 2AY

J V Sharp and J E Strutt
School of Industrial and Manufacturing Science, Cranfield University, Bedford MK43 0AL

E Terry
Sauf Consulting Ltd, 30 Observatory Road, London SW14 7QD

The principle of distributed cognition provides a promising framework for understanding the way that human problem solvers rely on the environment to accomplish their tasks. People rely on cues they receive from human co-workers, they make inferences from the appearance of the artefacts they work with, and they draw on organisational culture to work out what is expected of them. This distribution of cognition is vulnerable to particular kinds of failure, however, and such failure can occur both in the design of an installation and its subsequent operation. The purpose of this project is to use the distributed cognition principle *both* to help the designers of offshore installations reason about human factors connected with their designs *and* to help the same designers reason about how they should work effectively in collaboration with human factors specialists. We also wish to find out how such aspects of the designers' environment as safety regulation and safety management systems influence this distributed cognition. The aim is to develop two main products: a workbook for offshore design organisations to help them anticipate human factors failures, and a guidebook for regulatory organisations and senior industrialists on how the safety environment influences failures and limitations in designers' thinking.

Keywords: human factors, human error, engineering design

INTRODUCTION

In one of our recent studies[1], we analysed a case in which a maintenance engineer was killed when he used a beam inside a vessel in order to suspend a hoist. The designers might have forestalled the accident if they had been able to predict this kind of behaviour at the accident site. They might also have forestalled the accident if they had realised there were certain cues that indicated they should consult human factors specialists during the engineering process. Furthermore, it is possible that with a more influential safety management system, a more influential professional culture and more influential regulation the designers would have actively sought such cues instead of responding only to those brought to their attention. The lessons of accidents such as this are therefore that:

- designers need a model to help them reason about failures in the process of operating the equipment they design;
- design organisations need a model to help them reason about failures in their engineering processes;
- regulators, professional institutions and managers need an understanding of how the regulatory, professional and managerial environment influences designers' reasoning about failures.

The principle of distributed cognition provides an organising principle that, potentially, can provide a consistent way of tackling these needs. This principle is that an individual's learning and problem solving is explained in terms of his or her environment and the tools, people and procedures that the individual works with. What you do and what you learn do not arise from mental processing alone but mental processing in conjunction with this environment. Similarly, when you fail the failure is not simply a limitation of human information processing but a joint limitation of human information processing and the features of the environment at the time. If, for instance, a fitter installs a check valve the wrong way round we should look at what characteristics of the valve, what features of the fitter's particular experience, and what assumptions made in the prevailing culture gave rise to the fitter's erroneous model of the valve's required orientation.

There are both weak and strong views of distributed cognition[2] - the weak view saying that there are both 'solo' and distributed cognitions, the strong view that all cognitions are distributed in some way or other. In both views, however, expertise and intelligent behaviour is seen as a characteristic not of individuals but individuals interacting with a technology[3, 4]. Applications of this idea have been mainly in real-time tasks where the environment provides much of the pacing and the human participants have little time to reflect on their current actions. Recent examples include, for instance, air traffic control[5]. Our own recent work has tried to apply the principle to understanding design processes, both where they succeed[6] and where they fail[1]. Distributed cognition is related to the ideas of situated cognition[7] and external cognition[8] - both of which again emphasise the role of a person's environment in that person's beliefs about the world and problem solving within it.

The idea in this project has been to apply this principle to understand failure in two processes - operating a piece of equipment or system, and designing it. Ultimately, we want designers to reason effectively about both how they contribute to operating failures and how the design process itself can fail. Also, we want them to reason about both kinds of failure in the same basic way because we want them to understand operators' failures as being of the same kind as their own failures. Designers sometimes make mistakes when they are under time pressure and take short cuts with CAD tools, and typically blame the CAD tool for providing too little feedback on the consequences of certain actions (like turning layers off). They need to see the operator of the plant they are designing also as a person under time pressure looking for short cuts in the operation of the plant who will make mistakes when the plant provides too little feedback on the consequences of the operator's actions.

Figure 1 shows the scope of the project. It shows distributed cognition in both design and operating processes, and shows how we would like to model this distributed cognition and the way the environment influences it.

OBJECTIVES

The gist of the project is to analyse past failures, use these to develop distributed cognition models of failure, and build these models into practical tools. In more detail, the specific objectives have been as follows:

- To investigate how distributed cognition failures contribute to accidents in the process of operating offshore installations.
- To investigate how distributed cognition failures contribute to shortcomings in the process of designing offshore installations.

- To investigate how the regulatory, professional and organisational environment influences these failures.
- To develop models and workbooks that guide and support the design organisation.
- To develop models and guidebooks for the Health and Safety Executive (HSE) that help staff involved in inspection, audit and policy development.

Our intention is that there should be a number of benefits:

- One of the main difficulties that designers have in thinking about human factors is their lack of a general model that helps them enumerate potential problems systematically. This work ought to provide such a model.
- Similarly, one of the main obstacles in all collaborative work - but particularly collaboration involving a technical discipline and a social discipline - is the lack of a model that helps each discipline ask the right questions and send the right cues to the other discipline. Again this work ought to provide such a model.
- Because accidents are relatively infrequent, it is very hard to be confident that one organisation's historical experience is enough to help it predict and prevent future accidents. Having a model gives some assurance that there are not large gaps in an organisation's understanding of how things can go wrong.
- A model of this kind would also help reveal any limitations and gaps in current HSE guidance on incorporating human factors in the offshore design process. In particular, by understanding both the manner in which cognition is distributed, and how this is affected by such factors as regulation and knowledge of regulation, we hope that it will become clearer how to influence designers' thinking.

METHOD

INVESTIGATING FAILURES IN THE OPERATING PROCESS

This has involved three main steps:

1. Building a case base of past accidents and incidents.
2. Identifying the distributed cognition that has failed through the analysis of these cases.
3. Developing classifications of these failures.

The cases have been obtained from two main datasets. The first is a fairly diverse collection of public domain investigative reports, particularly the Marine Accident Investigation Branch (MAIB) digests, the HSE's UK Continental Shelf Risk Review and proceedings of public enquiries into offshore disasters. The second dataset is the HSE's incident and early day report database. The analysis of each case has involved asking two main questions:

1. In what ways was information processing distributed? (For example, did design and installation engineers both have to have certain bits of consistent knowledge in order for a valve to be installed correctly?)
2. In what ways did this distribution fail? (For example, did the installation engineer draw on a memory of a previous valve instead of examining the new valve when determining the correct orientation or fitting?)

The next step has been to look for general patterns of failure and develop a classification. This is the stage that we have reached at the time of writing, described briefly below in the Results section.

INVESTIGATING FAILURES IN THE DESIGN PROCESS

This part of the work involves failure in the design process, rather than accidents in the operating process, and at the time of writing is not yet underway. Failures of the design process, such as in the collaboration between designers and human factors specialists, are naturally harder to obtain because they do not usually reach the public domain. Our intention is to draw on three main sources of cases. The first is a study of error in the design process that we conducted recently with several design organisations. This yielded a database of about 100 cases. The second source is a set of experts from different disciplines, in our own institutions, who have been involved in consulting with firms on failures of various kinds. This includes a reliability engineer, a regulatory expert, an organisational sociologist and a psychologist specialising in ergonomics. The plan is to run elicitation exercises with them in order to draw as systematically as possible on their experience in this and related industries of failures, breakdowns and limitations in the design process which have introduced hazards in the equipment being designed. The third source is a group of engineering designers in an offshore installation design organisation. Our intention is to get designers' observations of how the design process has failed - especially in the collaboration among different disciplines, especially in the involvement of human factors specialists.

As with the accident case analysis, the plan is to identify in these cases the nature of the distributed cognition and the modes by which it failed - and build a classification of these.

INVESTIGATING THE ENVIRONMENTAL INFLUENCES

The third part of the work concerns external influences, especially the managerial and regulatory environment. This has not yet started.

RESULTS

The work has at the time of writing been underway for four months and, accordingly, only the first main element has been tackled: failures in distributed cognition during the operating process. In the rest of this section we have described some of the general patterns that have been identified.

RELIANCE ON CULTURAL ARTEFACTS

In one case of an offshore platform capsize, the designers had relied on existing compartmentalisation standards that seemed to have been inappropriate to a structure of this kind. This led them to overlook the possibility of partial capsizing (which eventually became a full capsize). One consequence of the failure to anticipate a partial capsize in a semi-stable condition was that the lifeboat davits would not allow a launch in this condition.

The designers' problem solving was effectively distributed since they were relying on partial solutions provided by engineering standards. This distribution failed because there was no apparent inspection of the standards to test their applicability to the idiosyncrasies of this application. More generally, standards are 'cultural artefacts': things developed historically that get passed down to future engineers. This case provided an example of how using cultural artefacts can lead to failure because the conditions in which they are developed are not usually identical with those in which they are subsequently applied. A culture, typically, does not keep up with a technology.

RELIANCE ON CULTURAL ASSUMPTIONS

Another contributor to the same accident was that the designers extrapolated marine practice (developed for ships) to this installation and thereby underestimated wave loading. As with the reliance on inapplicable standards, the problem solving was effectively distributed: it was not just in the designers' heads but also in the assumptions they had carried over from previous practice. Instead of examining wave loading *ab initio* they relied on previous practice to short-cut this process. Again the failure was in using something handed down in their particular culture, although this time it was not an artefact but an assumption. So this case provided an example of how an inappropriate reliance on cultural assumptions, perhaps through ignorance of their limiting conditions, can lead to failure. Cultures are obviously powerful ways of transmitting customs and practices to people in an organisation or industry, and often serve to disseminate important lessons from experience. But cultural assumptions are typically tacit, not explicit, and typically lack analytical underpinnings.

INSENSITIVITY TO ANOMALIES OF TASK DECOMPOSITION

Yet another contributor to this same capsize was that the design was modified to add a fitting to the main structure. This subsequent design step effectively violated the assumptions made in the earlier stress analysis, and the violation went unnoticed. The need to repeat the analysis also seemed to go unnoticed. Thus the design process was distributed over time, with the main structural design task being separated from a modification task, and the anomalies that arose from this were not noticed. It is perhaps quite common for failures to arise from modification, because successful modification relies on making the right inferences about the rationale of the original design - and this rationale is often obscure. But similar problems arise whenever the design task is decomposed in some way - perhaps between different individuals rather than different times. There are usually subtle inter-dependencies between decisions made in the sub-tasks, and there is no guarantee the designers involved in all the sub-tasks will be aware of these. Thus the people who design modifications may be unaware they are violating assumptions made by the designer of an original device; and the people who design, say, vessels may be unaware they are violating assumptions made by the structural designer. Obviously, wise designers will consult others in case they are violating their assumptions, but the evidence is that not all designers are wise - and in particular some are unwise about the anomalies that accompany task decomposition.

DILEMMA OF SPECIFYING BOUNDARY CONDITIONS

In one accident, in which there was a sub-sea explosion, a gas release and a subsequent fire, a hose failure was implicated. These hoses had probably exceeded their useful lives, although service lives were not specified so they had not been changed. The information processing associated with working out whether a piece of equipment is beyond its safe life is naturally distributed between designers and operators. Designers understand what is needed for the equipment to achieve functional performance. Operators have local knowledge of the service environment and pattern of use, and can often make repeated observations of the state of the equipment. This distribution, however, is naturally vulnerable to failure in certain ways. If the designer decides service life should *not* be specified to operators because the responsibility must rest with the operator to monitor an equipment's state the designer is also making assumptions about what operators can reasonably do. Either they may not easily be able to do the monitoring, or they may give it too low a priority for it to receive any resources. The designer may typically be unaware of all the other tasks the operators have to perform. On the other hand, specifying service life usually means making certain assumptions about how the equipment is treated and the environment it operates in - of which designers may be uncertain.

It may encourage operators to think they need not monitor something if all they need to do is replace it at a fixed interval, and it relieves them of making judgements about a device's condition. So, either way, whether the designer specifies service life or not, there appears to be no foolproof strategy for avoiding failure. The argument could perhaps be extended to specifying boundary conditions of any kind. Designers understand how something performs more profoundly than operators, yet the operators know the local conditions in which something is having to perform. Neither on their own can fully be aware of when something is going to fail. Yet there is often no possibility of a continual dialogue between them.

INCONSISTENCY IN INSTALLATION MODELS

In another accident, a blow-out occurred and led to a heavy spill because both a shutdown valve and a blow-out preventor were incorrectly installed. Obviously when one person or organisation designs something that another person installs there is distributed information processing and there is redundancy - two mental models of the same entity in two people's minds. The models obviously need to be consistent. There are different ways of achieving consistency, for example by writing installation manuals, but all seem to have limited power. Even when designers can physically foolproof a device there is no guarantee of consistent models. We have come across cases where people have defeated foolproofing on both electronic and hydraulic equipment by physically destroying the features that provided the foolproofing. This shows how strong mental models can be in certain cases, and how resistant they are to cues which contradict them. As with the other failure modes we have described here, there is no obvious, guaranteed remedy. But the message to, say, designers is that one of their prime objectives should be to bring the user's mental models into line with their own, and it makes sense to use a variety of means to do this since none on their own is foolproof.

INCONSISTENCY IN CHOICE MODELS

In a different accident there was a gas leak from a wellhead because of corrosion of tubing below a sub-surface safety valve. A chrome connection should have been fitted but was not. So, as in the previous paragraph, the information held by designer and installer needed to be consistent and turned out not to be. Here this replicated information was not an installation orientation but a choice of material. We do not know from the accident investigation why the installer made the wrong choice, and there could have been incentives to make the wrong choice - for example saving money, or saving time (if only non-chrome connections were available to hand). It could be the case, therefore, *not* that an installer was ignorant but that he or she gambled that failure would not occur. The motivation for the gamble was an easier task. The problem was that the gamble was ill informed - since the installer was unlikely to have had good knowledge of the probability of failure. Designers would, we think, have been able to make better probability judgements. Since operators are almost always under some kind of pressure they are almost bound to gamble. So arguably the distributed cognition problem is how to get the designers' superior knowledge of the failure odds to the operator so that the operator can make informed gambles.

DISCUSSION

GENERAL INSIGHTS

We do not feel there was anything new in our diagnoses of specific accidents, and of course we relied on other people's investigations for our data. But we do believe that the principle of distributed cognition revealed important patterns. It illustrates, for example, the importance of 'culture' - the customs, practices, assumptions and tools that provide the background to engineering - and the ways in which it can fail and then cause accidents. The development of engineering knowledge has some interesting aspects[9] which contribute both to the power of engineering and to its vulnerability. We could see, in our analyses, how the practices that led to accidents could - in only slightly different circumstances - have been seen as considerable successes. For example, carrying across a practice from one domain into another has been responsible, in part, for some major disasters like the failure of the oil platform the *Alexander Kielland*. Yet the same act of carrying across a practice from one domain to another has been seen as a considerable creative leap in some well-known product designs[6]. We need to see failure and success as radically different outcomes which can arise from virtually the same practices, we need to be attuned to exactly what makes the difference - and we need to avoid dividing up the world into people and processes that fail and people and processes that succeed.

PRACTICAL IMPLICATIONS

The development of the main practical output of this project has not yet begun, so we have not properly examined the practical implications. Moreover, looking at the failure modes we described in the Results it is hard to formulate realistic general rules or practices that would dependably avoid such accidents. Our belief is that there are no systems or tools that would always prevent these kinds of failure. But one thing that might help is for designers to have in mind these general failure modes so that they are sensitive to the possibility of them occurring. This is really the premise for the second part of our programme in which we try to develop practical tools and practical guidance on the basis of the results. These are likely to involve asking the same questions that we did in specific cases - how is information processing distributed and how does this distribution fail?

One of the difficulties with acting on our analysis, however, is that what we have identified as being the cause of failure is often also the source of productive effort. People can accomplish things in reasonable timescales because they do not have to comprehensively re-invent and re-analyse, but can draw on partial solutions given by their cultures or their environments. If you criticise someone because they do not examine the assumptions underlying their use of a standard or an existing design you have to say where the additional time needed for this examination is going to come from. Therefore the recommendation should be *not* that people avoid the sources of failure described in the Results (like 'cultural artefacts') but that they are mindful of the ways in which failure can ensue. Arguably, from the standpoint of safety, it is better to analyse exhaustively whether a particular device suits a particular application than it is to simply follow the last design that used this device. But if this is impossible then a second best situation is to follow the last design but examine 1) what conditions would make the device fail, 2) ask whether any of these conditions are more likely in the new application than the old.

LIMITATIONS OF THE WORK

There are some obvious limitations to do with the data we relied on (other people's accident reports), and because we are at an early stage of the work we have not worked out the practical implications properly. But there are also some fundamental limitations in the analysis we conducted. In particular, there is usually the possibility of explaining people's wrong decision making both from a cognitive standpoint (where they have inappropriate beliefs) and a motivational one (where they have inappropriate motivations or incentives). For example, the installer who used a plain steel fitting instead of a chrome one may have been ignorant of the corrosive fluid or may have gambled that the fitting would not fail in his lifetime. Even when one is observing someone in the process of making an error it can be very hard to determine which of these two kinds of diagnosis is the better - the cognitive or the motivational. This means that our analyses of particular cases are always going to be debatable. But since the purpose of the work is to influence people in the future what matters is what *could* happen. And if we can argue that failures in distributed cognition could happen, and could cause accidents, our results should have some usefulness.

ACKNOWLEDGEMENTS
Many thanks are due to Bob Miles of the HSE for facilitating this work, which is being funded by the HSE under contract D3916.

REFERENCES

1.   Busby J.S., 2001, Error and distributed cognition in design, *Design Studies* 22: 233-245.
2.   Salomon G., 1993, Editor's introduction. In Salomon G (ed). *Distributed Cognitions: Psychological and Educational Considerations,* Cambridge University Press, Cambridge UK, xi-xxi.
3.   Hutchins E., 1995, *Cognition in the Wild*, The MIT Press, Cambridge MA, p.155.
4.   Norman D.A., 1993, *Things That Make Us Smart. Defending Human Attributes in the Age of the Machine,* Addison-Wesley, Reading MA, p.146.
5.   Marti P., 2000, The choice of the unit of analysis for modelling real work settings, *Cognition, Technology and Work*, 2: 62-74.
6.   Busby J.S., 2001, Practices in design concept selection as distributed cognition, *Cognition, Technology and Work*: forthcoming.
7.   Lave J., 1988, *Cognition in Practice*, Cambridge University Press, Cambridge UK.
8.   Scaife M. and Rogers Y., 1996, External cognition: how do graphical representations work? *International Journal of Human-Computer Studies,* 45: 185-213.
9.   Blockley D.I. and Henderson J.R., 1980, Structural failures and the growth of engineering knowledge, *Proc. Institution Civil Engineers Part 1*, 68: 719-728.

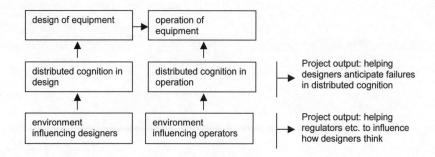

Figure 1: Scope of the project

REFINERY FIRE INCIDENT:
A CASE STUDY OF A MULTIPLE FATALITY INCIDENT AT THE
TOSCO AVON REFINERY, MARTINEZ, CALIFORNIA[1]

Donald Holmstrom, Stephen Selk, Stephen Wallace, and Isadore Rosenthal, U.S. Chemical Safety and Hazard Investigation Board, 2175 K St., N.W., Suite 400, Washington, D.C. 20037

On February 23, 1999, a fire occurred at the Tosco Avon Refinery in Martinez, California. Workers were attempting to replace piping attached to a 150-foot-tall crude fractionator while the process unit was in operation. The piping, which had developed a pinhole leak, contained flammable naphtha liquid that was not successfully drained or isolated during the thirteen-day period before the removal work began. During the removal of the piping, naphtha was released onto the hot fractionator tower where it ignited. Four workers were killed and one sustained serious injuries. The U.S. Chemical Safety and Hazard Investigation Board (CSB) initiated an incident investigation.

The CSB examined the following safety issues in the Tosco case:

    1. Control of hazardous nonroutine maintenance
    2. Management oversight and accountability
    3. Management of change
    4. Corrosion control program

This paper summarizes the results of the investigation, including a review of the incident, causes identified by CSB, and recommendations to prevent future similar incidents.

Keywords: oversight and accountability, management of change, corrosion, maintenance.

INTRODUCTION

On February 23, 1999, a fire occurred in the crude unit at Tosco Corporation's Avon oil refinery in Martinez, California. Workers were attempting to replace piping attached to a 150-foot-tall fractionator[2] tower while the process unit was in operation. During removal of the piping, naphtha[3] was released onto the hot fractionator and ignited. The flames engulfed five workers located at different heights on the tower. Four men were killed, and one sustained serious injuries.

Ultramar Diamond Shamrock Corporation (UDS) purchased the facility in September 2000 and renamed it the Golden Eagle refinery.

Because of the serious nature of this incident, and the fact that another fatality had occurred at the Avon facility in 1997, the U.S. Chemical Safety and Hazard Investigation Board (CSB) initiated an investigation to determine the root and contributing causes of the incident and to issue recommendations to help prevent similar occurrences.

INCIDENT

On February 10, 1999, a pinhole leak was discovered in the crude unit on the inside of the top elbow of the naphtha piping, near where it was attached to the fractionator (Figure 1) at 112 feet above grade.[4] Tosco personnel responded immediately, closing four valves in an attempt to isolate the piping. The unit remained in operation.

Subsequent inspection of the naphtha piping showed that it was extensively thinned and corroded. A decision was made to replace a large section of the naphtha line.[5] Over the 13 days between the discovery of the leak and the fire, workers made numerous unsuccessful attempts to isolate and drain the naphtha piping. The pinhole leak reoccurred three times, and the isolation valves were retightened in unsuccessful efforts to isolate the piping. Nonetheless, Tosco supervisors proceeded with scheduling the line replacement while the unit was in operation.

On the day of the incident, the piping contained approximately 90 gallons of naphtha, which was being pressurized from the running process unit through a leaking isolation valve. A work permit authorized maintenance employees to drain and remove the piping. After several unsuccessful attempts to drain the line, a Tosco maintenance supervisor directed workers to make two cuts into the piping using a pneumatic saw[6]. After a second cut began to leak naphtha, the supervisor directed the workers to open a flange[7] to drain the line. As the line was being drained, naphtha was suddenly released from the open end of the piping that had been cut first. The naphtha ignited, most likely from contacting the nearby hot surfaces of the fractionator, and quickly engulfed the tower structure and personnel.

KEY FINDINGS

1. The removal of the naphtha piping with the process unit in operation involved significant hazards. This nonroutine[8] work required removing 100 feet of 6-inch pipe containing naphtha, a highly flammable liquid. Workers conducting the removal were positioned as high as 112 feet above ground, with limited means of escape. The hot process unit provided multiple sources of ignition, some as close as 3 feet from the pipe removal work. One isolation valve could not be fully closed, which indicated possible plugging.

   On three occasions prior to the incident, the naphtha pipe resumed leaking from the original pinhole and felt warm to the touch, indicating that one or more isolation valves were leaking. Numerous attempts to drain the piping were unsuccessful; a failed attempt to ream out the drain lines and the removal of a small section of pipe confirmed that the line was extensively plugged. On seven occasions, the downstream naphtha stripper vessel filled–indicating probable isolation valve leakage.

2. The naphtha pipe that was cut open during the repair work was known by workers and the maintenance supervisor to contain flammable liquid. Although Tosco procedures required piping to be drained, depressured, and flushed prior to opening[9] this was not accomplished because extensive plugging prevented removal of the naphtha. The procedures did not specify an alternative course of action if safety preconditions, such as draining, could not be met. Although the hot process equipment was close to the removal work, Tosco's procedures and safe work permit did not identify ignition sources as a potential hazard. The permit also failed to identify the presence of hazardous amounts of benzene in the naphtha.

3. The naphtha stripper vessel level control bypass valve was leaking, which prevented isolation of the line from the operating process unit. As a result, the running unit pressurized the naphtha piping. Excessive levels of corrosive material and water in the naphtha line and operation of the bypass valve in the partially open position for prolonged periods led to erosion/corrosion of the valve seat and disk. Excessive levels of corrosives and water also plugged the piping and led to the initial leak.

4. Tosco's job planning procedures did not require a formal evaluation of the hazards of replacing the naphtha piping. The pipe repair work was classified as low risk maintenance. Despite serious hazards caused by the inability to drain and isolate the

line–known to supervisors and workers during the week prior to the incident–the low risk classification was not reevaluated, nor did management formulate a plan to control the known hazards.

5. Tosco's permit for the hazardous nonroutine work was authorized solely by a unit operator on the day of the incident. Operations supervisors were not involved in inspecting the job site or reviewing the permit.

6. Operations supervisors and refinery safety personnel were seldom present in the unit to oversee work activities. On the morning of the incident, prior to the fire, one operations supervisor briefly visited the unit, but he did not oversee the work in progress and no safety personnel visited the unit. The maintenance supervisor was the only management representative present during the piping removal work.

   The U.S. Environmental Protection Agency (EPA) similarly determined that a lack of operations supervisory oversight during safety critical activities was one of the causes of a previous Avon refinery incident, a 1997 explosion and fire at the hydrocracker, which resulted in one fatality (USEPA, 1998; pp. viii, 65). [10]

7. In the 3 years prior to the incident, neither Tosco's corporate safety group nor Avon facility management conducted documented audits of the refinery's line breaking,[11] lockout/tagout,[12] or blinding[13] procedures and practices.

8. Tosco did not perform a management of change (MOC)[14] review to examine potential hazards related to process changes, including operating the crude desalter[15] beyond its design parameters, excessive water in the crude feedstock,[16] and prolonged operation of the bypass valve in the partially open position. Tosco memos and incident reports revealed that management recognized these operational problems and the increased rate of corrosion. However, corrective actions were not implemented in time to prevent plugging and excessive corrosion in the naphtha piping.

ROOT CAUSES

1. **Tosco Avon refinery's maintenance management system did not recognize or control serious hazards posed by performing nonroutine repair work while the crude processing unit remained in operation.**

   - Tosco Avon management did not recognize the hazards presented by sources of ignition, valve leakage, line plugging, and inability to drain the naphtha piping. Management did not conduct a hazard evaluation[17] of the piping repair during the job planning stage. This allowed the execution of the job without proper control of hazards.

   - Management did not have a planning and authorization process to ensure that the job received appropriate management and safety personnel review and approval. The involvement of a multidisciplinary team in job planning and execution, along with the participation of higher level management, would have likely ensured that the process unit was shut down to safely make repairs once it was known that the naphtha piping could not be drained or isolated.

   - Tosco did not ensure that supervisory and safety personnel maintained a sufficient presence in the unit during the execution of this job. Tosco's reliance on individual workers to detect and stop unsafe work was an ineffective substitute for management oversight of hazardous work activities.

   - Tosco's procedures and work permit program did not require that sources of ignition be controlled prior to opening equipment that might contain flammables, nor did it specify what actions should be taken when safety requirements such as draining could not be accomplished.

2. **Tosco's safety management oversight system did not detect or correct serious deficiencies in the execution of maintenance and review of process changes at its Avon refinery.**
   Neither the parent Tosco Corporation nor the Avon facility management audited the refinery's line breaking, lockout/tagout, or blinding procedures in the 3 years prior to the incident. Periodic audits would have likely detected and corrected the pattern of serious deviations from safe work practices governing repair work and operational changes in process units. These deviations included practices such as:
   - Opening of piping containing flammable liquids prior to draining
   - Transfer of flammable liquids to open containers
   - Inconsistent use of blind lists
   - Lack of supervisory oversight of hazardous work activities
   - Inconsistent use of MOC reviews for process changes.

CONTRIBUTING CAUSES

1. **Tosco Avon refinery management did not conduct an MOC review of operational changes that led to excessive corrosion rates in the naphtha piping.**

   Management did not consider the safety implications of process changes prior to their implementation, such as:
   - Running the crude desalter beyond its design parameters.
   - Excessive water in the crude feed.

- Prolonged operation of the naphtha stripper level control bypass valve in the partially open position.

These changes led to excessive corrosion rates in the naphtha piping and bypass valve, which prevented isolation and draining of the naphtha pipe.

2. The crude unit corrosion control program was inadequate.

Although Avon refinery management was aware that operational problems would increase corrosion rates in the naphtha line, they did not take timely corrective actions to prevent plugging and excessive corrosion in the piping.

RECOMMENDATIONS

Tosco Corporation:

Conduct periodic safety audits of your oil refinery facilities in light of the findings of this report. At a minimum, ensure that:

- Audits assess the following:

  - Safe conduct of hazardous nonroutine maintenance
  - Management oversight and accountability for safety
  - Management of change program
  - Corrosion control program.

- Audits are documented in a written report that contains findings and recommendations and is shared with the workforce at the facility.

- Audit recommendations are tracked and implemented.

Ultramar Diamond Shamrock Golden Eagle Refinery

1. Implement a program to ensure the safe conduct of hazardous nonroutine maintenance. At a minimum, require that:

    - A written hazard evaluation is performed by a multidisciplinary team and, where feasible, conducted during the job planning process prior to the day of job execution.

    - Work authorizations for jobs with higher levels of hazards receive higher levels of management review, approval, and oversight.

    - A written decision-making protocol is used to determine when it is necessary to shut down a process unit to safely conduct repairs.

    - Management and safety personnel are present at the job site at a frequency sufficient to ensure the safe conduct of work.

    - Procedures and permits identify the specific hazards present and specify a course of action to be taken if safety requirements–such as controlling ignition sources, draining flammables, and verifying isolation–are not met.

    - The program is periodically audited, generates written findings and recommendations, and implements corrective actions.

2. Ensure that MOC reviews are conducted for changes in operating conditions, such as altering feedstock composition, increasing process unit throughput, or prolonged diversion of process flow through manual bypass valves.
3. Ensure that your corrosion management program effectively controls corrosion rates prior to the loss of containment or plugging of process equipment, which may affect safety.

American Petroleum Institute (API)
Paper, Allied-Industrial, Chemical & Energy Workers International Union (PACE)
National Petrochemical & Refiners Association (NPRA)

Communicate the findings of this report to your membership.

REFERENCES

[1] This paper is the Executive Summary of the U.S. Chemical Safety and Hazard Investigation Board's Investigation Report of the February 23, 1999, Tosco Avon Refinery fire incident (Report No. 99-014-I-CA, Issue Date: March 2001). The full report is available on the World Wide Web at http://www.chemsafety.gov/.

[2] A fractionator is an oil refinery processing vessel that separates preheated hydrocarbon mixtures into various components based on boiling point. The separated components are referred to as fractions or cuts. Inside the fractionator, some trays draw off the fractions as liquid hydrocarbon products (such as naphtha), and piping transports them to storage or for further processing.

[3] Petroleum naphtha is a highly flammable mixture of liquid hydrocarbons drawn off as a cut from the fractionator tower.

[4] "Above grade" refers to the vertical distance from ground level at the point upon which equipment rests.

[5] The term "naphtha line" is synonymous with naphtha piping. "Naphtha draw line" was also used at the facility to refer to the naphtha piping. The draw line takes or "draws" naphtha product from the 38th tray of the fractionator, where it flows through a level control valve to the naphtha stripper vessel.

[6] A pneumatic saw is a cutting device that is energized by air pressure rather than electrical energy

[7] A flange is a rim on the end of a section of piping or equipment used for attachment to other piping and equipment.

[8] The Center for Chemical Process Safety (CCPS) defines "nonroutine work" as unscheduled maintenance work that necessitates immediate repair and may introduce additional hazards (CCPS, 1995b; p. 212). One example is "breakdown maintenance," where equipment is operated until it fails. In this incident, the February 10 naphtha draw line leak is an example of breakdown maintenance.

[9] Tosco Avon Safety Procedure S-5, Safety Orders, Departmental Safe Work Permits, October 19, 1998.

[10] The EPA report states: "Supervision was not present at the unit even though there had been a succession of operating problems just prior to the final temperature excursion that led to the explosion and fire."

[11] "Line breaking" refers to equipment opening.

[12] "Lockout/tagout" refers to a program to control hazardous energy during the servicing and maintenance of machinery and equipment. Lockout refers to the placement of a locking mechanism on an energy isolating device, such as a valve, so that the equipment cannot be operated until the mechanism is removed. Tagout refers to the secure placement of a tag on an energy-isolating device to indicate that the equipment cannot be operated until the tag is removed.

[13] A blind is a piping component consisting of a solid metal plate inserted to secure isolation.

[14] Management of change is a systematic method for reviewing the safety implications of modifications to process facilities, process material, organizations, and standard operating practices.

[15] The desalter vessel removes inorganic salts, water, and suspended solids to reduce corrosion, plugging, and fouling of piping and equipment.

[16] Feedstock is material of varying constituents that is processed in a refinery.

[17] A hazard evaluation is a formal analytical tool used to identify and examine potential hazards connected with a process or activity (CCPS, 1992; p. 7).

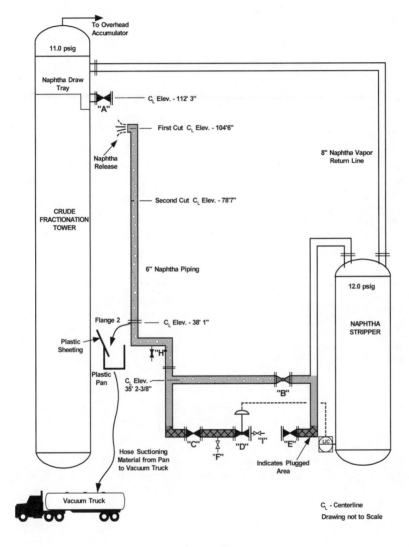

Figure 1

THERMAL OXIDISER FIRE & EXPLOSION HAZARDS

M Iqbal Essa MIChemE
Health & Safety Executive, Grove House, Skerton Road, Manchester M16 0RB
Tony Ennis FIChemE
Haztech Consultants Ltd, Meridian House Business Centre, Road One, Winsford Industrial Estate, Winsford, Cheshire, CW7 3QG
© Crown Copyright 2001. Reproduced with the permission of the Controller of Her Majesty's Stationery Office.

Thermal Oxidisers by their very design operate on generating a flame or intense heat in their combustion chambers for the destruction of process waste or emissions containing VOCs. If process conditions upstream, where these emissions are generated, are not properly managed or controlled thermal oxidisers can pose a significant fire and explosion hazard.

This paper discusses the type of oxidiser available, fire and explosion hazards in the oxidiser and vent collection system, risk assessment and basis of safety. An overview of applicable legislation and guidance is attached and several case studies of incidents discussed. This paper includes an extensive bibliography.

INTRODUCTION

Ever increasing global public pressures have prompted many countries to introduce pollution control legislation to protect the environment. In the UK this has led to the introduction of the Environmental Pollution Act (EPA) 1990 (Ref 34).

In order to comply with EPA 90, many process and manufacturing industries are having to install "thermal oxidisers" (Incinerators or Afterburners) for the abatement of Volatile Organic Compounds (VOCs) and gases in their process waste streams before discharge to atmosphere. There are, of course, several other techniques besides thermal oxidation such as Substitution, Condensation, Adsorption, Liquid Scrubbing, Biological treatment and others. These are outside the scope of this paper. See reference 46 for advice on other treatment technologies.

Thermal Oxidisers by their very design operate on generating a flame or intense heat in their combustion chambers for the destruction of process waste or emissions containing VOCs. If process conditions upstream, where these emissions are generated, are not properly managed or controlled thermal oxidisers can pose a significant fire and explosion hazard.

Over the years, both in the UK and abroad, there have been a number of serious fire and explosion incidents involving thermal oxidisers because companies using them have failed to either properly manage or control their processes. A number of these incidents have resulted in fatalities and a significant loss to business. Some of incidents that have been investigated by the HSE are discussed later in this paper. In the USA, incidents have been reported which resulted in fatalities (Ref. 36). Other incident descriptions can be found in Refs 39, 40, 41, 42.

The aim of this paper is to ensure that those who operate thermal oxidiser plants and associated equipment manage and operate them safely and effectively to ensure that conditions leading to fire and explosion are prevented or at least minimised. This paper does not include other abatement systems associated with the destruction of domestic, communal, agricultural, and hospital waste, either as solids or volatile residue sludge.

In order to ensure uniformity in design, installation and operation of thermal oxidiser plant across Europe, a recent European standard has been published - EN 12753:1999 (Ref.28) entitled 'Thermal cleaning systems for exhaust gas from surface treatment equipment Safety requirements'.

DESIGN & SELECTION

Until the publication of EN 12753 there was no specific standard is available concerning thermal oxidiser design and associated safety. Reputable manufacturers of thermal oxidisers may, however, include recommendations contained in Refs. 9, 12, 13 and 14 into their design philosophy. The unit selected should be appropriate for the full range of foreseeable flows and compositions. Where more than one plant or process vent discharges into the vent header system extreme caution should be taken to ensure that the full range of potential operating conditions have been identified. The amount of time required for this exercise when retrofitting a thermal oxidiser to an existing plant should not be underestimated. Design of oxidisers and vent collection systems should be undertaken by suitably qualified persons.

Typical types of thermal oxidisers being used in the chemical and related industries are:
- "Simple" Thermal Oxidisers. These may be vertical (see figure 1) or horizontal units. Details of burners and fitments vary widely between manufacturers.
- Oxidisers for hazardous chemical waste streams. These are designed for a more complex mix of VOCs which require special treatment in order to ensure complete destruction. Typical features include staged air injection and chemical resistant refractories. (Figure 2)
- Regenerative thermal oxidisers consist of a number of beds filled with ceramic packing which are used in sequence with the bed that just come off line being used to pre-heat the incoming gases. Heat recovery of up to 90% is possible with this type of unit. Figure 4.
- Recuperative Catalytic Oxidisers operate at lower temperature and destroy VOCs by a catalytic reaction. Catalyst is carried on a ceramic matrix. It should be noted that the catalyst may be poisoned by certain chemicals hence application is limited. (Figure 5). Incoming gases are pre-heated in a separate exchanger and good heat recovery is possible.
- Regenerative Catalytic Oxidisers are similar to regenerative thermal oxidisers but using a catalyst. This type is particularly suitable for low VOC concentrations.
- Flameless Thermal Oxidisers may be used for streams containing halogenated or sulphonated materials which could poison catalysts. These may operate without support fuels at VOC concentrations ~50% - 60% of the LEL. Figure 3.
- Thermal Oxidiser with Integrated Rotor Concentration System may be used in situations where the VOC concentration is extremely low (<500ppm). The rotor section contains a Zeolite which acts as a molecular sieve to concentrate the VOCs up prior to the thermal oxidiser.
- Flares are often used in the petrochemical industry and are a very simple form of thermal oxidation generally used when the concentration of gases is above the LEL and not suitable where the by-products may be toxic or acidic.

HEAT RECOVERY

Heat recovery is not generally an economic option for smaller thermal oxidisers. Larger units can, however, successfully integrate heat recovery options which may significantly reduce operating costs and improve environmental benefits. It should be noted that heat recovery is more difficult for VOC streams containing halogens or sulphur since wet scrubbing is usually required to remove acidic combustion products. This entails cooling the gases to less than 70°C before wet scrubbing and then re-heating to prevent a visible plume.

FIRE & EXPLOSION HAZARDS

When considering fire and explosion hazards, thermal oxidisers should not be considered in isolation but as fully integrated system including upstream and downstream plants and equipment. There are three distinct areas where fire and explosion risks are foreseeable and demand appropriate measures to reduce these risks to acceptable levels. These are:
- Upstream process plant
- Vent collection system
- Thermal oxidiser

VENT COLLECTION SYSTEM
Vent pipes or ducts carrying the flammable waste stream to the thermal oxidiser for abatement are also susceptible to being involved in fire and explosion. This can occur if the solvent concentration conveyed via these vent pipes is not properly managed or monitored and there is an ignition source present.

There are many potential sources of ignition in a vent header system including:
- Flashback from thermal oxidiser
- Naked flames
- Electrostatic discharges
- Mechanical friction
- External hot work
- Impact sparks
- Pyrophoric materials
- Electrical apparatus
- External sources (e.g. lightning)

Appropriate measures should be taken to exclude all ignition sources wherever possible.

Control of VOC concentration in the vent header system is essential to prevent potential fires or explosions. Where the basis of safety is operation below the LEL then on no account should the solvent concentration in the vent collection system exceed 25% LEL unless a suitable concentration monitoring system is used, in which case the solvent concentration must not be allowed to exceed 50% LEL. Where solvent vapour concentration is kept above the UEL, the VOC should be delivered in an inert atmosphere (such as Nitrogen) whenever passing through the explosive range (UEL - LEL), as would be the case during start-up and shutdown.

THERMAL OXIDISER
Abnormal operating conditions in the thermal oxidiser can result in an explosion. These conditions can develop as a result of various deviations described below.

The consequences of an explosion occurring in the thermal oxidiser are potentially lethal due to explosion overpressure and missiles generated by failure of the casing. These may also lead to domino effects on adjacent plant. Small explosions may lead to damage either to the oxidiser shell or the ceramic lining or packing. It is also likely that after an explosion in an oxidiser a thorough HAZOP and re-design of the system would be needed to the satisfaction of the competent authority (HSE in the UK) prior to the system being allowed to re-start.

POTENTIAL MALFUNCTIONS
There are many potential malfunctions which may result in fire and explosion hazards in the thermal oxidiser and vent collection system. Typical of these are:
- Interruption to power supply
- Instrumentation problems
- Control system problems
- Mixing of vent streams
- Reduction in air flow rates
- Fluctuations in VOC flow rates
- Process deviations
- Bringing new vessels or processes on line

INTERRUPTION TO POWER SUPPLY

If power supply is interrupted either to one or more of the upstream plants, or to the thermal oxidiser itself, then a hazardous situation may result. VOCs could continue to be fed to the thermal oxidiser or the upstream process may become unstable, releasing increased amounts of VOCs into the vent headers. The thermal oxidiser system should be designed to fail safe in the event of a power failure occurring in all circumstances.

INSTRUMENTATION PROBLEMS

The absence or incorrect position of protection devices may lead to potentially hazardous concentrations being formed, for example due to:
-   Over-temperature or under-temperature
-   Failure of flow rate controls leading to excessive VOC loading
-   Interruption in the exhaust system or recirculation system
-   Maloperation of fans and / or dampers.

Instrumentation should be specified correctly for the duty and must be positioned correctly within the system to provide an accurate reading. It is essential to ensure that instruments continue to function correctly and that sensors are not blocked up or blinded by depositions.

CONTROL SYSTEM PROBLEMS

Failure or improper set up of the control system can result in the formation of a flammable mixture in the oxidiser. The control system must balance the combustion air and fuel gas requirements with the VOC. The supply of combustion air is normally controlled by monitoring the oxygen content in the flue gas. Temperature is controlled by altering the flow of fuel gas.

Control systems should conform to the requirements of Ref. 7 or one of the equivalent NFPA standards (See below). It should be noted that although many control systems supplied by oxidiser manufacturers are adequate for their duty, they may not meet the higher standards of integrity and reliability demanded by some sectors of the chemical industry. Further attention may, therefore, need to be paid to such items as trips and alarms at the design stage.

MIXING OF VENT STREAMS

For plants handling more than one vent stream, mixing of streams can present major hazards. All variations of flow and composition should be accounted for in the design of the thermal oxidiser and vent collection systems. Ref. 47.

It should also be noted that within the upstream and downstream plant all control systems should be fully and correctly integrated. If they are not, failure of any one or a combination could lead to rapid formation of a dangerous concentration of solvent vapours and thus an explosion. It is critical that a full HAZOP study is carried out on this aspect of operation. The amount of time required for this process should not be underestimated.

OTHER FACTORS CAUSING HIGH VOC CONCENTRATION TO THE OXIDISER

If condensates and combustible deposits are not removed regularly from the system they can evaporate or decompose to form a dangerous concentration leading to a fire or explosion. To avoid this, the upstream and downstream plant and equipment should be inspected and cleaned regularly. The frequency of inspections should be dependent on the severity of build-up and the risk this build-up could pose.

VENT HEADER SYSTEM

Hazardous mixtures could form in the vent collection system as a consequence of the following:

- Inadequate purging of the whole system including the upstream ductwork.
- Insufficient dilution and flow in the system.
- Blockages,
- Deposits causing imbalance in the ventilation fan and reducing efficiency
- Poor operation or failure of the exhaust ventilation system
- Vaporisation of condensates (particularly on start-up)

Any one of the following could create disturbances within the exhaust ventilation system:

- Changes in process pressure or temperature
- Bringing new vessels on line or taking vessels off-line
- Incorrect maintenance

POOR THERMAL OXIDATION

Conditions that could cause insufficient thermal oxidation may be attributed to one or a combination of the following:

- Insufficient oxygen content within the waste stream feed to the thermal oxidiser
- Too low a temperature within the combustion chamber of the thermal oxidiser
- Insufficient turbulence/mixing within the combustion chamber of the thermal oxidiser
- Reduced catalyst function due to ageing, poisoning or deposits
- Poor auxiliary fuel feed supply to the thermal oxidiser
- Poor selection and maintenance of the thermal oxidiser
- Poor circulation of the waste stream through the combustion chamber

HAZARDS CAUSED AS A CONSEQUENCE OF ADSORPTION

Hazardous conditions can develop if flammable substances adsorb unintentionally on to the surface of the catalyst due to the system being operated at a lower temperature than the desired temperature to secure efficient combustion. These can later desorb and could develop potentially hazardous conditions within the system. Rapid exothermic decomposition of the organic waste within the thermal oxidiser could also occur if undesirable conditions develop due to incorrect process conditions.

NOTE: If the thermal oxidiser is in its shutdown mode, it should not under any circumstances be used as a channel or duct for exhausting VOCs. Such a practice may cause the inner brickwork of the thermal oxidiser to absorb VOCs which be released upon start up and cause a serious fire or explosion with devastating effect on the thermal oxidiser and associated plant.

RISK ASSESSMENT

Employers are legally required to assess the risks in the workplace and take all reasonably practicable precautions to ensure the safety of workers and others who could be affected. In the risk assessment process employers should identify the potential hazards and determine the risks. Appropriate prevention or mitigation measures should then be taken to reduce the risk to an acceptable level.

The risk assessment process should include the impact on the whole system of all foreseeable fluctuations and maloperations in the upstream and downstream plant as well as the oxidiser. It should also include the operation of all instrumentation, controls and safety interlocks.

This risk assessment should be carried out in accordance with the guidance in Ref.16 by a suitably qualified leader and in the presence of key members of the design team and operations personnel.

It is essential that the personnel responsible for operating the thermal oxidiser and associated plants are fully aware of the potential risks and hazards involved in operating the system especially in terms of the fire and explosion hazards. Information from the risk assessment process should be cascaded down to operating personnel in order to raise their awareness and ensure that the plant is operated safely.

HAZOP (HAZARD & OPERABILITY STUDY)

Hazards may arise in a plant due to deviation from the normal operating parameters or conditions. Hence, a HAZOP Study approach, which is a structured and systematic technique for identifying hazards and operability problems throughout an entire facility, can be applied to determine critical parameters that could have a detrimental effect on the plant and the process.

The list of deviations should form part of the HAZOP study to determine and examine possible causes, possible consequences, with appropriate actions to minimise the risk of an incident. Typical aspects considered should include foreseeable changes in normal operation, equipment, and instrumentation, provision for failure of plant services, provision of maintenance, safety etc.. It is essential that HAZOP studies be led by a trained and experienced hazard study leader. The team should include the responsible process engineer, electrical and instrument engineer, mechanical engineer and plant representative. Other members may also be required at certain stages, in particular a representative or representatives of the thermal oxidiser manufacturer who should be fully conversant with the design, control, operation and limitations of the oxidiser.

A HAZOP or process hazard review should be carried out periodically (5 yearly intervals or sooner if required) to ensure that the safety and integrity of the system have not been compromised and that any changes in operating conditions have been taken into account. Again, this process should be carried out by an experienced hazard study leader.

MODIFICATION CONTROL

It is essential for the continued safe operation of the unit that some form of change control be exercised. This should include an element of HAZOP in order to ascertain that the proposed modification does not compromise the safety of the thermal oxidiser, the associated systems or the upstream plants.

Modification control should also extend to vent header systems and upstream plants and processes. These modifications should also be HAZOPed to ensure that no additional hazards or risks are introduced. Modifications should be fully detailed and traceable using a quality control system.

SAFETY DESIGN OF THERMAL OXIDISERS & VENT HEADERS

Many of the problems that occur with thermal oxidation systems are due to problems with, or maloperation of the upstream plant resulting in the formation of a flammable mixture in the vent headers. It is essential that the upstream plant, vent header system and thermal oxidiser are considered as a fully integrated system and not as isolated units.

A clear and tenable Basis of Safety for operation should be written for the system. For vent headers it is not generally sufficient to propose a basis of safety on the absence of ignition sources since there is always the chance of an external factor as discussed above. The Basis of Safety for vent header systems should, therefore, be operation outside the flammable region. The potential consequences of an ignition occurring in the header system mean that it is critical that a non-flammable mixture is maintained at all times. Design of the system should be carried out by a qualified and experienced engineering team.

THERMAL OXIDISER SAFETY

THERMAL OXIDISER OPERATION
Under no circumstance should the VOC concentration reaching the thermal oxidiser inlet be allowed to exceed 25% LEL unless continuous solvent vapour monitoring is provided upstream of the thermal oxidiser, where a maximum of 50% LEL is acceptable. Operation of the vent header system above these limits can result in flashback and severe explosion damage to the vent header system and connected equipment.

If, for any reason, the VOC concentration exceeds these limits then it is essential that appropriate emergency action is taken. In the first instance this should be to divert the waste stream to atmosphere. An interlock system should automatically shut down the process in this event. Only when the cause of the increased VOC concentration has been fully investigated and conditions rectified and made safe should the system be brought back into operation.

Due to their thermal inertia many oxidisers do not respond well to sudden changes in flows and compositions. The oxidiser should, therefore, be operated as far as possible under steady-state conditions. It should, however, be noted that flows and compositions can change rapidly, especially when vessels or processes are brought on line. Rapid changes in waste stream composition can lead to control system cycling or instability with consequent explosion hazard.

There are several codes and guidelines which are relevant to thermal oxidiser safety e.g. Refs 6, 7, 8, 9, 10, 11, 12, 13. Refs 27, 32 may also be useful. References 35, 37, 38 discuss the safety of vent collection and destruction systems.

FUEL TRAIN & THERMAL OXIDATION PROCESS CONTROLS
The thermal oxidiser fuel train and controls must be designed and constructed to recognised standards in terms of safety e.g. IM30 (Ref.7) and EN 954-1 (Ref. 15). Other codes such as NFPA 69 (Ref.26) also contain detailed recommendations which may be used by non-UK manufacturers. Most modern thermal oxidisers incorporate PLC control systems (known as Programmable Electronic Systems or PES) to control operation. Where necessary, hard-wired emergency shutdown systems should also be incorporated. Where such PES are used they should conform to the recommendations in Refs. 22, 23 and 24. Further guidance covering electrical equipment can be found in Refs 19, 20, 21.

EXPLOSION RELIEF & PROTECTION
It is possible to construct the oxidiser to withstand an explosion however this may be excessively expensive for larger units and hence is not usually the preferred method of protection.

Many thermal oxidisers are not fitted with explosion relief but rely instead on high integrity control and safety systems to reduce the risk of an explosion occurring to an acceptably low frequency. Some designs cannot be fitted with explosion relief for mechanical reasons. Often, this is due to the difficulty of maintaining a gas-tight seal on the explosion relief vent panel under the high temperatures within the unit. Explosion vents, where fitted, should be located such that they discharge to a safe location. Explosion relief should be considered for all thermal oxidisers if practicable. Guidance for the provision of explosion relief may be found in HS(G) 16 (Ref.32) and NFPA 68 (Ref.25). Further information is available concerning explosion relief in references 7, 31 and 32 with further information in Refs 17, 18.

VENT COLLECTION SYSTEM SAFETY
The consequences of an explosion in the vent collection system may include:
- Damage to, or destruction of the vent header
- Domino effects on adjacent plant and systems
- Injury / fatality to personnel

Many vent headers are relatively long and pass through areas where personnel or vulnerable plant are located thus giving a high risk of injury or domino effects in the event of a failure. Additional protection is, therefore, usually required such as:
- Flame Arresters
- Explosion Relief
- Explosion Suppression
- Fire Extinguishing system

EXPLOSION PROTECTION OF VENT HEADERS
Acceptable VOC concentrations in headers are discussed above. Even so, it is foreseeable for the VOC concentration to rise to dangerous level under upset or abnormal process conditions. It is at this time that the plant and its associated ductwork is most vulnerable to fire and explosion hazards with a high risk of ignition from the thermal oxidiser.

The most common form of secondary protection used is a flame arrester which should be placed in a position appropriate to the design. There are several designs of flame arrester available including flat plate, crimped metal and hydraulic. It is essential that the correct type and specification is used for any particular duty.

It should be noted that flame arresters are not 100% effective. Typical problems are:
- Blockage with particulates
- Polymerisation on arrester elements
- Burn back
- Overheating

Flame arresters are a complex subject and cannot be covered in detail within the scope of this paper but are covered in Refs 30, 31. Explosion relief is described in Ref 43. Tests of explosions in pipelines are discussed in Ref 44, 45.

VOC AND OXYGEN CONCENTRATION ANALYSERS
A total unburnt hydrocarbon (VOC) analyser should be provided where necessary as identified by the risk assessment. The analyser should be of a suitable design and provide continuous solvent vapour and VOC concentration monitoring. Analysers should meet the requirements set in Ref. 29.

A maximum safe concentration should be set for the system below the 50% LEL limit which should trigger a high alarm with a high level trip set above the alarm but below 50% LEL.

The monitor should initiate the shutdown and emergency diversion systems for the oxidiser. Shutdown valves and dampers should be of a fast-acting type since concentration can change very rapidly as a result of process deviations. An oxygen analyser should be used to establish that the oxygen concentration is less than 1% v/v and thus avert any possibility of forming an explosive atmosphere.

LEGAL REQUIREMENTS
There are several general legal requirements which cover the safety of the workplace and equipment e.g. Refs. 1, 2, 3, 4, 5. In particular the following are important:
- Health & Safety at Work Act 1974
- The Highly Flammable Liquids and Liquefied Petroleum Regulations 1972
- The Management of Health and Safety at Work Regulations 1992
- The Provision and Use of Work Equipment Regulations 1992

CASE HISTORIES
Over the years HSE has investigated a number of fire and explosion incidents involving thermal oxidiser plants. A few of these are given below.

CASE 1
A fire and explosion incident occurred at a chemical plant manufacturing and processing acrylic resin. Substantial damage was caused to the plant including the ethyl acrylate dump tank.

The company had installed a catalytic thermal oxidiser for the abatement of ethyl acrylate vapours (flash point 16°C) released in the process as waste. The temperature of the thermal oxidiser's catalyst outlet is temperature was between 350°C to 500°C. High temperature should have prompted an alarm and shutdown condition. The incident caused the temperature to rise to 640°C. A flame arrester, provided to prevent fire from propagating upstream, failed because it was not designed for flowing gas. No solvent vapour analyser was fitted..

Recommendations Included installation of VOC concentration monitoring, re-evaluation of the capacity of the thermal oxidiser against maximum VOC flows and regular inspection of flame arresters. Modifications to pipework connections were also required.

CASE 2
Two consecutive fire / explosion incidents occurred at a company engaged in recovering and cleaning oils for reuse in industry and the automotive trade. The first of the two incidents occurred inside the thermal oxidiser and the second occurred inside a room upstream where oil fumes were being generated by a process. Oil fumes were oxidised in a recuperative natural gas fired thermal oxidiser.

The oil fume feed was bifurcated. One line took fumes into the combustion chamber and the other was diverted to the base of the thermal oxidiser's exhaust stack in emergencies. The former of the two inlets was fitted with a flame arrester but the latter was not. It was this which caused the explosion to propagate back through the thermal oxidiser involving the upstream oil processing room. A number of other irregularities were noted and these included:
- Little or no knowledge of the hazards associated with the thermal oxidiser
- Absence of adequate temperature control in the oil processing room / storage
- Incorrect thermal oxidiser design

Recommendations included: reassessment of the design of the thermal oxidiser to meet process fluctuations and demands, provision of explosion relief to the thermal oxidiser and installation of effective monitoring and control of process oil storage temperatures etc.

CASE 3

A series of fires / explosions occurred, involving a large (approx. 21m x 5m x 9m high) three bed regenerative thermal oxidiser and its associated upstream duct, at a factory manufacturing aluminium cans for the soft drinks industry. The company had installed the oxidiser to abate hydrocarbon based solvent vapours generated during the curing of resin that had been applied to the aluminium sheets in preparation for the manufacture of cans.

There was a gas detection system with detectors at selected parts of the ductwork. The system had been set to alarm at 20% LEL with an arrangement to bypass to atmosphere via vent just upstream from the thermal oxidiser. The system was also arranged to afford an alarm and to shut down the curing ovens at 40% LEL.

The investigation revealed that a small fire occurred inside the feed duct leading to the thermal oxidiser and this caused other residual resinous waste that had settled inside the duct to vaporise and produce a dangerous concentration of VOCs. When this was introduced into the thermal oxidiser it caused an explosion. The duct had been provided with a water sprinkler system to quench fires. Explosion relief had been fitted to the inlet manifold connecting the duct to the thermal oxidiser and this worked but was inadequate to cope with the explosion pressure generated within the system.

Recommendations included: reduction of waste accumulation inside ducts, use of less volatile compounds in the process, provision of temperature activated sprinkler system.

CASE 4

An explosion occurred in a propane/air fired thermal oxidiser provided for the abatement of an effluent stream containing hydrogen, ammonia and pyridine. The oxidiser had an internal wet scrubber in its base. No definite cause of the explosion was established but it was postulated that blockages in the perforated plate on which the ceramic bed rested inside the thermal oxidiser may have caused sudden release of waste stream into the combustion chamber of the thermal oxidiser. It was also established that the company, following an initial HAZOP Study, had made a number of modifications to the thermal oxidiser system and the associated plant upstream without carrying through the implications to the rest of the system.

Recommendations included: a fresh HAZOP study on the whole system and measures to prevent blockages.

SUMMARY

Thermal oxidisers and vent collection systems can pose a significant fire and explosion hazard if not properly designed, operated and managed. This paper has highlighted some of the hazards and their potential solutions. A list of useful references is provided where valuable information on the applicable legislation, safety and design of thermal oxidisers and vent collection systems can be found. The latest standard EN 12753:1999 (Ref.28) provides valuable advice on these matters.

REFERENCES

1. Guide to the Health and Safety at Work etc. Act 1974. Guidance Booklet (L1) HSE 1990; ISBN 0 11 88555 7

2. Management of Health and Safety at Work Regulations 1992. Approved Code of Practice (L21) HSE 1992, ISBN 0 11 886330 4
3. Workplace (Health and Safety and Welfare Regulations) 1992 (L24) HSE Approved Code of Practice, ISBN 0 11 886333 9
4. Supply of Machinery (Safety) Regulations 1992, SI 1992/3073 HMSO 1992, ISBN 0110257197
5. Provision and Use of Work Equipment Regulations 1992, Guidance on Regulations (L22) HSE 1992, ISBN 0 11 886332 0
6. Industrial Thermoprocessing equipment EN 746
7. The use of gas in Industrial process plant, British Gas Code of Practice IM 30 1993
8. The Gas Safety Regulations 1972, SI 1972/1178 HMSO, ISBN 0 11 0211782
9. Automatic Gas Burners BS 5885 Parts 1 & 2
10. Automatic flue dampers for use with gas fired heating and water heating appliances British Gas Code of Practice IM 19 1983
11. Standards of training in safe gas installations, Approved Code of Practice (COP 20) HSE 1987, ISBN 0 11 883966 7
12. EN 746-1, Industrial Thermoprocessing equipment - Part 1: Common safety requirements for industrial Thermoprocessing equipment
13. EN 746-2, Industrial Thermoprocessing equipment - Part 2: Safety requirements for combustion and fuel handling systems
14. BS EN 292, Part 1 & 2, Safety of Machinery, basic concepts, general principles for design
15. EN 954-1, Safety of machinery - Safety related parts of control systems - Part 1: General principles and design
16. EN 1050 - Principles of Risk Assessment
17. EN 1127-1 (1998): Explosive atmospheres - Explosion Prevention and Protection - Part 1: Basic concepts and methodology
18. prEN 13478 : Safety of machinery - Fire prevention and Protection
19. prEN 50154 : Electrical Installations in potentially explosive atmospheres (other than mines)
20. EN 60079-10 : Electrical apparatus for explosive gas atmospheres - Part 10: Classification of hazardous areas
21. EN 60529-1 : Safety of machinery - Electrical equipment of machines - Part 1 : General Requirements
22. Programmable Electronic Systems (PES) in safety-related applications: Part 2 General technical guidelines HSE 1987, ISBN 883906 3
23. Use of Programmable Electronic Systems (PES) in safety-related applications in the gas industry IGE/SR/15, Institute of Gas Engineers, 1989, ISBN 1367 7850
24. ICE 61508-1 Functional safety of electrical/electronic/programmable electronic safety - related systems - Part 1 : General Requirements
25. NFPA 68 'Guide for Venting of Deflagrations 1998 Edition
26. NFPA 69 ' Standards on Explosion Prevention Systems 1997 Edition
27. HSC Publication: Safe operations of Ceramic Kilns, ISBN 0 7176 0630 9
28. prEN 12753:1999 (final draft) - 'Thermal Cleaning Systems for exhaust gas from surface treatment equipment Safety requirements
29. EN 1539: 2000 - 'Dryers and Ovens, in flammable substances are released - Safety requirements'
30. HS(G) 158, Flame Arresters - (Preventing the spread of fires and explosions in equipment that contains flammable gases and vapours, ISBN 0-7176-1191-4
31. HS(G)11 'Flame Arrestors and Explosion Reliefs'; HSE Publications

32. HS(G)16 "Evaporating and Other Ovens"; HSE Publications
33. HSE 5 Steps to Risk assessment IND(G) 163 L (also available in priced packs ISBN 0 11 025849 5)
34. Environmental Protection Act 1990 (EPA 90), HMSO Publications
35. Nichols FP; Design of Vent Collection and Destruction Systems; 2nd Int Symp Runaway Reactions, 11-13 March 1998, New Orleans, pp655-676
36. Ready DF, Schwab RF; Incinerator problems and how to prevent them; 14th Loss Prev Symp; Vol 14, pp66-72, 1981
37. Leite OC; Operating thermal incinerators safely; Chem Eng; June 98, pp131-136
38. Clark DG, Sylvester RW; Ensure Process Vent Collection System Safety; CEP; pp65-77, Jan 96
39. Thomas I, a)Coode Island- vapour recovery to blame? b) Blast rocks chemical store c)Coode riposte; TCE; 31 Oct pp17-18; 12 Sept pp14, 12 Dec; pp5 1991
40. Fishwick A; Three flare stack incidents; Loss Prev Bull No.142, 1998
41. Desai VM; Flare deflagration incident at Rohm & Haas; Process Safety Prog; Vol.15, No.3, pp166-167, 1996
42. Anon; Incinerator overheats; Loss Prev Bull; No.130, p7 1996
43. Senecal JA, Garzia HW; Explosion protection of pipe systems conveying dusts or flammable gases; Process Safety Prog; Vol.16, No.1, Spring 97, pp50-53
44. Henderson E; Combustible gas mixtures in pipe lines; Proc Pacific Coast Gas Association; Vol.32, pp98-111, 1941
45. Rogowski ZW, Rasbash DJ; Relief of explosions in propane-air mixtures moving in a straight unobstructed duct; 2nd Symp Chem Proc Haz (Hazards II), Manchester 2-4 April 1963, pp21-28
46. AIChE; Reducing and controlling volatile organic compounds; Center for Waste Reduction Technologies, AIChE
47. Hunt PJ; VOC abatement & vent collection systems; Hazards XIV "Cost Effective Safety"

FIGURES

Figure 1: Simple Vertical Thermal Oxidiser

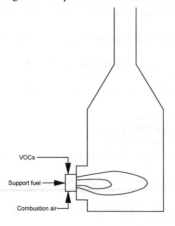

Figure 2: Thermal Oxidiser with Staged Air Injection

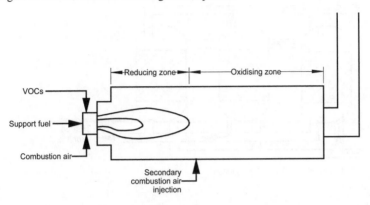

Figure 3: Flameless Thermal Oxidiser

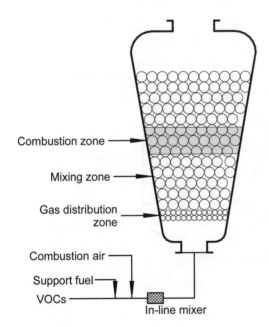

Figure 4: Regenerative Catalytic Oxidiser

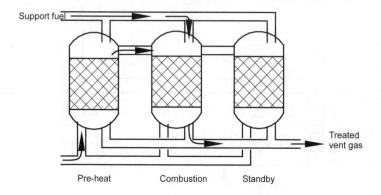

Pre-heat   Combustion   Standby

Figure 5: Recuperative Catalytic Oxidiser

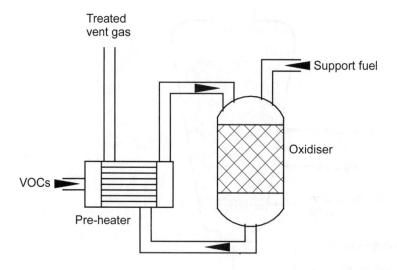

ANALYSING THE PAST, PLANNING THE FUTURE, FOR THE HAZARD OF MANAGEMENT

R. B. Ward
Visiting Fellow, School of Chemical Engineering, University of New South Wales, Sydney

One may readily accept that the hazards of work situations are related to the management, and the management systems, which supervise and control those work situations. This author has anecdotal data which shows that "everyone knows" there is a relationship between those two factors, work hazards and management, so although the knowledge exists, in practice, in industry, many ways are found to avoid making the connection. The author's research into the chemical industry identified the connection, an identity which has been strengthened by many accident investigations performed through the last ten years and by a serious incident in Australia, all during the last few years. This presents the author's research to show the connection between hazards and management, uses accident investigations to confirm that connection, and uses a brief description of the incident further to demonstrate the connection.

INTRODUCTION

Management, on one hand, has been recognised by many writers as an art. On another hand, there are many who have written about management as a science. The proportioning of the two schools of thought may lean either way, and as with many such conclusions with divided schools of thought the truth is quite likely to exist somewhere between the two, showing management is a mixture of art and science.

The hazards of work situations differ in a somewhat similar and perhaps equal manner. There are hazards which may lead to accidents occurring relatively frequently and may harm only one person or a few, ranging from minor injuries to fatalities, and there are accidents which occur very seldom but may cause loss of many lives and considerable property damage.

Where does management fit into that spectrum? A reasonable answer suggests that management should act to prevent accidents from occurring by minimizing hazards, and one may be sure most management bodies act in that manner. But we have had, in Australia, some cases which have shown management has acted in ways which have increased hazards, and in some of those cases serious accidents have occurred.

The conclusion which this author draws from research on the relationship between hazards and management practices in the chemical industry, from accident cases investigated, and from a major chemical disaster, is the management of a company can itself be a hazard. And, of course, no-one in the organisation can control management behaviour, the iron curtains between management and employees, and between management and the world around it means no-one outside knows and can control management behaviour, and a management heading in that hazard direction doesn't control itself.

THE RESEARCH (FROM THE PAST)

This section is a summary of the author's doctoral project and its results[1]. The foundation of that can be seen in the author's employment history, which was in a variety of chemical firms, some using batch processes and some continuous processes. Reflection on what had been seen in these companies led to a personal conviction that there were differences between the management systems. At that stage, however, there was no idea of what constituted the "systems", the differences, or the firms' hazards.

From that the project began with the thought that there must be a relationship between the way a management behaves and what and how the company produces its goods. Towards the end of the work, as measures of variables progressed, it became obvious that what was being measured about management was not behaviour but practices, a fine distinction, perhaps, but brought about because the investigation looked at procedures, protocols, actions, what the management system actually did, rather than any possible motivating factors behind the action.

A tentative hypothesis was formed and as work progressed was extended into two parts:

Identification of relevant chemical industry elements will enable companies to be ranked on a hazard-scale for each of those elements and for an overall hazard-rating. The individual hazard-ratings will present a 'hazard-profile' for each company.

Identification of the elements will lead to producing an ideal model of the industry and its management. Comparison of the overall ranking and the profile of each company with the ideal model will indicate the probability of a major disaster.

A major feature of the approach taken in the research was the recognition that the physical items which form a production unit, the materials which flow through it, the processes which convert input to output, the people who work in the factory, and the management who control whatever happens, are not independent of each other. They are "elements" of a complete *system.* The "traditional" view of a chemical production unit can be described in the following which itemises the elements in a chemical production unit and how they fit with occupations in the industry:

the physical equipment items, generally the concern of mechanical engineers,
the materials, generally the concern of chemists,
the processes, generally the concern of chemical engineers,
the workers, generally the concern of industrial psychologists,
the management, generally the concern of itself and management scientists,

that is, each element, each with an individual discipline, is *usually* compartmentalised in and by its speciality.

The view taken here was that all those elements of a chemical production unit or factory form a "system". In such a system each element interacts with the others[2]. If the contribution of one element to system results is below whatever standard is required of it, then the overall standard of the entire system will be reduced. In the system of a chemical production unit quantity and quality are determined by the interaction of the five elements listed above.

The approach taken, therefore, in the overview and research investigation was to consider the above five elements within the chemical industry, their relationship to each other, and the interactions between them, with the aim of forming and testing a model representing management and technical safety in a chemical manufacturing firm.

The above led to a review of models found in the literature, the Sociotechnical Pyramid by Technica (showing five "tiers" of components or elements leading to an accident)[3], the Tweeddale Safety Balance Model (which displays the various elements of technical or process safety as a three-dimensional structure, rather like a "mobile" room decoration)[4], and the Bignall-Fortune Formal System Paradigm (how an organisation is influenced by the wider external system, and how the organization operates internally, for example, to monitor performance and to make decisions)[3]

With the background established for developing a model to suit this research the author examined several alternatives. The proposed model would show the elements which make the industry hazardous and the elements which militate against those hazards, in a sequence which is consistent with their relationship to each other. The selected starting point for the model was whatever causes the inherent hazard in the industry.

The primary hazard in the chemical industry resides in the materials, because materials are a hazard even if only in storage, with no processing or other activity being performed. The raw materials, the intermediates, and the finished products present the primary independent hazard element.

Processes were considered next. They present an inherent hazard, secondary to materials because they act on the materials and cannot be caused to occur without the materials. They were therefore positioned next to materials as another inherent hazard and the second element to be put into the model.

Having determined the sequential ranking of the inherent hazards the relationship of other elements which should compensate or balance the inherent hazards was considered.

The technology was taken as the third element. This position in the model was selected because the technology has a relationship with the processes and with management, but is related more closely to processes than to management. Technology was not ranked ahead of materials and processes as it is not an inherent hazard. It is an external or subsidiary hazard. Its effect may be compensatory (that is, to counteract the hazards inherent in materials and processes) or contributory (that is, to exacerbate the inherent hazards in some manner).

Another reason for this third ranking for technology was one of the interactions considered between elements. This was that technology affects processes more directly than materials, and acts on materials through processes. Technology should reduce the hazard inherent in materials by controlling processes. Thus, an appropriate level of technology, as the third element, would help to balance inherent hazards by interaction with processes. Similarly, an inappropriate level could actually reinforce or even magnify inherent hazards, also by interaction with processes.

The next element taken, as the fourth item, was the human presence element. This was ranked next to technology. The reasoning was that human presence is related to technology through the definition of technology (system design, operation and maintenance as well as hardware), which implies that some human activities are components of the technology. Any action by human presence on the inherent hazards, processes or materials, would be through the technology. Also, as with the ranking of the third element (the technology) one of the interactions considered between variables was that although an appropriate level of human presence, as the fourth element, would help to balance inherent hazards through the technology element,an inappropriate level could actually reinforce or even magnify inherent hazards by action through the technology element.

Management was the final, fifth, element to be included in the model. The logical position for management is next after human presence, with which it has a stronger relationship than with the other elements. Human presence is related to management, for although management is a set of functions all those functions are performed by people, hence the relationship with human presence. Management also relates to technology, because management has a role in making decisions which select the level and type of technology; however, this relationship occurs through the human presence element.

While management is considered to be the most effective element to compensate for the inherent hazards, by making corrections for any hazard increase from technology or human presence, management can only perform that compensating role via the human presence element and the technology element, in series. Management may also increase hazard, if incorrect or inappropriate.

The five elements of the proposed model (from highest probability of hazard-causing to highest ability for hazard compensating) are: materials, processes, technology, human presence, and management, all as previously defined. In sequence:

a fundamental, primary, inherent hazard element (materials),

a secondary inherent hazard element (processes),

a tertiary, subsidiary, element (technology) which is closer to the processes element than to the materials element, and not as close to the management element as to the human presence element, and which may increase or decrease total hazard, depending on its features,

a second tertiary, subsidiary, element (human presence) which is closer to the management element than to the processes element, but is close to the technology element, and which may also increase or decrease hazard, depending on how it is used, and

a final tertiary, subsidiary, element (management) which acts on the technology element through the human presence element.

To sum up, a physical system (of materials and processes) with high inherent hazards will be less "forgiving" towards technology, human, and management inadequacies and errors than one which has low inherent hazards. Vice versa, a physical system with low inherent hazards will be more "forgiving" towards technology, human, and management inadequacies and errors than one which has high inherent hazards.

For convenience, the five elements for the model were identified by initial letters, and sequenced, as follows:

Materials (Chemical materials)	= C
Processes	= P
Technology (system design, operation, and maintenance)	= T
Human presence	= H
Management	= M

Five models using the above five elements were developed by the author. The first was based on the fault tree, which seemed to be an obvious approach, but when constructed and examined it proved to be unsuitable. An event tree model was then constructed, but also proved to be unsuitable. A flow-chart type model was constructed to show a relationship between hazards, technology, and management style, and the results of their interactions. but this also failed to give the require picture. All three thus far did little to show how the various elements can be varied in magnitude.

The fourth model was titled "The Engineering Model" and pictures a beam, balanced on a fulcrum, with "loads" or "weights" bearing on it in various positions. The implications of this model may be explained as follows: given that the inherent hazards from the materials and processes are a certain "weight" on the left-hand end of the beam, then technology, human presence, and management must be of a certain "weight" to maintain the balance, given that they occupy certain "positions" along the balance lever.

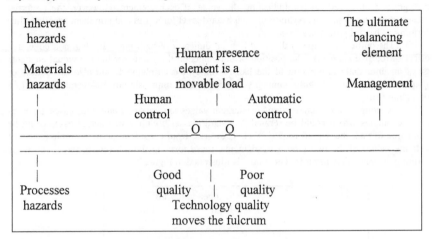

FIGURE 1
AN "ENGINEERING MODEL" OF HAZARD ELEMENTS

If either the materials or processes elements become "heavier" because their hazard contribution has increased then the technology (design, operations and maintenance systems) must be "shifted" to maintain the balance, or human presence must be "moved" (such as by having automatic systems replace human presence), or, finally, make the management system "heavier". Any of those response-actions would restore "balance".

This model appeals to the engineering mind-set because it is both "pictorial" and "functional". It can also be said to have built-in limitations. If hazards increase the human element can only be moved as far as its limiting position in the automatic direction (the limit, not yet achieved, would be total artificial intelligence), and the quality of the technology equally has a limiting value. When those limits are reached, and a balancing condition has not been reached, the only further possible action is to make management "heavier". The model also illustrates the relative fragility of the concept of technical safety by demonstrating the effect of a small increase of "weight" on the left, increasing materials or processes hazard, or the effect of reducing the "weight" of management by a small quantity, or of shifting human presence or technology in the wrong direction by a few millimetres. Any of those actions can be pictured as causing a slow tilting of the beam, until the movement reaches a critical point and the whole system overbalances into a state of hazard consumation.

However, this model only shows an overall, general, picture of the industry, and not an easily-interpretable statement of any particular firm's overall hazard level.

The fifth model, "The Profile Model", resulted from the search for a model which would provide such an easily interpretable statement of a particular company's overall hazard level, and was formed by considering the sequence of and possible interactions between the five elements.

The profile model was conceived on a two-axes framework, with a "hazard ranking" on the "y" axis (length proportional to hazard, according to some arbitrary convenient scale) and the five elements distributed equally-spaced along the "x" axis. This could be shown as a histogram, with a vertical bar indicating the value of each element. However, the preferred presentation was to plot the position of each hazard level for a firm and join these together, thus forming a "hazard profile".

The outline or shape of this profile is an indicator of both the individual and collective effect of the five elements. The position of the points on the y-axis for the individual elements gives an immediate impression of the hazard-value of each element, and also the outline or shape of the line through these points gives an immediate impression of the overall hazard, of a particular firm.

Although many combinations of element values are possible, only four cases appeared to be examples which could be termed "standard classes", with which actual cases could be compared to rank the overall hazard level. They arise from consideration of a simple matrix of extreme values of the two groups of elements, those forming the inherent hazards, and those forming the subsidiary hazards. The model is illustrated in Figure 2.

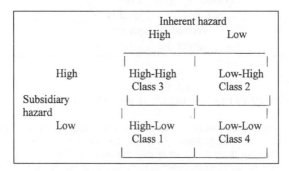

FIGURE 2
MATRIX OF ELEMENTS AND EXTREME VALUES

From this matrix, the four standard classes of profile are: High-Low (Class 1), Low-High (Class 2), High-High (Class 3), and Low-Low (Class 4).

The four "standard classes" of the profile model reflect, in general, the four possible distributions of scores on each of the five elements (chemicals, processes, technology, human presence, and management) discussed up to this point, following which a method for measuring these elements was devised and produced as a questionnaire.

The firms which operate major facilities such as oil refineries are in the Class 1 category, with (rather obviously) high-hazard materials and processes and low-hazard management (that is, management which by its nature presents a low hazard). Many small batch process firms were found to have low-hazard materials and processes and management systems which presented a relatively high-hazard, but with the low-level inherent hazards there was no need for higher-level management systems.

Ninety companies were contacted with a request that they might reply to a questionnaire which would quantify their element values. Thirty-one replied and the results were:

Class 4 (Low hazard materials + Low hazard management) : 22.
Class 1 (High hazard materials + Low hazard management): 4.
Class 4/Class 1 (Mixed low-low and high-low) : 3.
Class 2 (Low hazard materials + High hazard management) : 1.
Class 3 (High hazard materials + High hazard management): 1.

Of the above only one plant was a cause for concern: the one Class 3, which had no low hazard management to balance the high hazard materials and other elements. Several years later that factory was destroyed by fire.

DISCUSSION FROM THE RESEARCH

The chemical industry in the Sydney region is made up of a few very large firms and a large number of smaller ones. The concentration of the industry into the large firms is increased when one recognises that some of the smaller firms are part of a larger company group, even though they are operated under an independent name.

There is a large gap between the large number of small firms and the small number of large firms and several differences have been made apparent. The smaller firms tend to use less hazardous materials and less hazardous processes than large firms.

The smaller firms tend to use lower-level technology (which, by the definition which has been used, included some aspects of management) than large firms, to use people more to monitor and control the processes, and to have fewer tertiary-trained people in the higher levels of organisation, than large firms. Finally, the smaller firms tend to be less well organised at the management level than the large firms.

The impression one might obtain from the comments above is that small firms are high-risk enterprises, poorly managed, and capable of causing chemical disasters with great ease. However, when the whole 'system picture' is taken (for example, using the hazard profile) by considering *all* the elements, it does appear that most of the small firms are as 'safe' as large firms because they have less hazardous materials and processes. Or, phrasing that the other way around, the large firms which have the more hazardous materials and processes are as safe' as the small firms because they have higher-level management elements.

Hence, although simple comparative words have been used occasionally in the above, the lower-level (high-value) technology, automation, and management is not necessarily 'bad'. The results suggest very strongly that the level of these elements needed in any situation depends on the level of the inherent hazards. The companies investigated were ranked on a hazard-scale for each of the elements, using values of the elements in the hazard profile model, and the hazard profile of each company surveyed was presented. The profile of each company surveyed was compared with the standard cases. The comparison has indicated whether the company is acceptable on the hazard rating, and whether there is any conceivable probability of a disaster (bearing in mind that *any* 'probability' may be far from a certainty).

Comparison of sets of hazard profiles indicated a value of each element which *could* be taken as a safe limit or criterion, under specified conditions, an unexpected result. However, combination of these values of the elements into an overall hazard-rating, stated as one number, was rejected as not feasible at this time. Use of the hazard profile, as a whole, is the only form of hazard rating seen to be useful at this time.

CONCLUSIONS FROM THE RESEARCH

An analytical procedure was devised and applied, and the statements of the hypothesis were satisfied.

The majority of the companies investigated appeared to have a system of elements which is reasonably safe. In particular, most of the managements suit the other four elements of the companies, although a few were found which would benefit by improving some elements.

Although the investigation has indicated that most of the firms examined in the Sydney region are assessed as "safe" for one reason or another (low materials or process hazard, or good technology, appropriate human presence or good management) the freedom of many from being involved in a disaster still depends, to a very large extent, on the low probability of such random events.

THE INVESTIGATIONS (IN THE PRESENT)

During the years since finishing the research many accident investigations have been performed, and some of these add to the above conclusions. Citations for these investigations cannot be given, as details of the information may relate to legal proceedings, therefore only a very general outline of each is stated. As the general content of this paper relates to the chemical industry the first examples will be those which have caused injuries directly by chemicals, then examples of fires and explosions

1. Some members of a family were killed, and others were severely injured, when the gas supply to a fire was interrupted during the night.

2. Cleaning contractors were made ill, hence injured, by aerosol insecticide, automatically-sprayed before they entered premises to perform their work.

3. Garbage collectors were made ill, hence injured, by fumes emitted from garden chemicals picked up from domestic bins, after the plastic containers were crushed and the chemicals were mixed by the compacting mechanism.

No reason could be found for the gas fire being extinguished and gas continuing to flow, but that's what happened, and the house became flooded with old-fashioned town gas containing carbon monoxide which caused the fatalities and injuries.

The strange feature of the second case is that the property-owners did not coordinate with the firm which installed the automatic spraying system to ensure there was sufficient time for the aerosol to settle or disperse before the cleaners arrived. Alternatively, the owners should have specified spray timing to suit the cleaners' times. And somewhere in the negotiations the owners should have been informed that the sprayed material could cause illness while it was floating in the air, before it settled on the floor and furniture. So the worst feature seemed to be that the system suppliers didn't tell the owners that several hours should elapse before anyone should enter. Or, if they did, the owners didn't pay attention.

The third case, involving the garbage truck, gets down to the difficulty manufacturers have in telling end-users what to do with the products. In general, materials such as those in the case should not be put into garbage bins but should go to waste collection depots, and of course the manufacturer can "design" the label to provide that information on the label. But can the manufacturer ensure that the end-user *follows* such information? Probably not. More to the point, can anyone be at all sure the manufacturer can ensure the end-user actually *reads* that information? Very probably not. Indeed, that case illustrates the sad conclusion that accidents will continue to happen.

Fire, a reaction between a combustible material and oxygen, is a very useful phenomenon and is, almost certainly, a major factor in humans developing civilised society.

However, sometimes fire is uninvited, and occurs because we forget we're surrounded by one of the necessary reactants.

1. At a tyre retreading factory, rubber dust ignited in the exhaust duct.

2. At a plastics manufacturing factory, polystyrene flakes ignited in an air-conveyor duct.

3. Solvent used to wash machined components was spilled when hoses failed by chemical softening, and was ignited by a nearby gas fire, part of the process system.

4. A spill of vegetable oil in a store was covered by an absorbent material, and left overnight for the spill to be soaked up. During the night the mixture of oil and material spontaneously ignited and damaged the building and contents.

5. A paint store ignited when a door hinge was being repaired by welding.

The first four cases caused property damage, the fifth seriously injured one person and slightly injured two others.

The most probable source of ignition in the first case was a spark caused by the wire brush, used to grind the tyres, striking a nail in a tyre, which happened often, and finally the time came when all the right conditions were present and the duct contents ignited. Tests with rubber particles showed they are hard to ignite as a quantity, but finely divided and suspended in an air stream they apparently did, just a matter of getting the right air-to-fuel ratio. A higher air flow rate might have made the mixture too lean. and ignition might not have occurred.

In the second case the source of ignition was probably static electricity, generated by the plastic flakes being conveyed by an air steam through a duct system. It's well known that hydrocarbons will generate static electricity (even liquid hydrocarbon falling freely through air), and as the duct assembly and connected equipment were not earthed it was just a matter of time before a sufficient electrostatic discharge occurred. Tests showed this material was also hard to ignite as a discrete quantity, and again dispersion in an air stream must have been a telling factor.

The third case involved modification to an existing system, an experiment trying to improve the operating conditions by installing a filtering circulation system. In haste, the job was given to a contractor not qualified for the work (he was an ordinary plumber) and he used rubber hoses which softened, hence became slippery, in contact with the solvent. Incidentally, in this case there was no doubt about ease of ignition, the solvent was a typically volatile hydrocarbon liquid. A hose came loose during the morning tea break when no-one was present, solvent sprayed around, and the nearby gas fire ignited it

The fourth one is hard to explain, all one can say is there are cases of vegetable oil, when mixed with some type of dispersed material, have become hot and have ignited surrounding materials. In fact, that happened in a store building at one firm where the author worked, and one can only assume the same happened in this case. This sort of fire is, strictly, an exotherm case, but not resulting in an explosion like the ones mentioned below, only a fire.

The fifth, the paint store, was ready-made for a fire - - - what happened was a real vapour cloud explosion-fire, in fact, partly confined. The welder said solvent fumes were evident before the work started, but management insisted the repair had to be done, and ignition occurred when an arc was struck for the second time.

The first two of these explosion cases are incidents the author has investigated, and the third was discussed at an in-company meeting which the author attended.

1. A truck driver was killed when an acetylene bottle exploded, when he was loading it manually onto the truck.

2. An employee opened a pit in the footpath to get access to cables, leaking LPG-town gas exploded, and the employee was injured.

3. There was loss of control of an exothermic process, the reaction progressed beyond containment pressure, the vessel burst disc opened, and the contents were sprayed over a neighbouring property.

The damage caused by the first case above was so major (the driver's body and most of the truck were both virtually destroyed) that no-one can know what caused the acetylene to explode. However, it was probably due to the bottle being bumped during loading onto the truck, so that the porous material within was broken or dislodged and the acetylene was no longer finely distributed. A record was found of a similar case, years ago, in the USA, when a bottle on the tray of a truck exploded as the truck went over a bump in the road.

The gas leak, in the second case, which lead to the explosion, was due to lack of maintenance of the town's infrastructure, in this case the part which was the responsibility of the gas supplier. The ownership of the system had changed hands at least once, pipes (using different materials at different time) had been laid underground, and there was plenty of evidence that much of the piping was corroded.

The third case, fortunately, didn't hurt anyone, although it frightened the plant operator who was largely responsible for the exothermic process, and it lead to acrimonious conflict between the two neighbouring firms. This one was bad enough, but nowhere near as bad as one in New Zealand several years ago, one which spewed out thousands of litres of partly-reacted chemicals and fouled a suburb.

One may question whether that was really an "explosion". It's classified it as such, because it was a sudden release of pressure, with considerable energy behind it. However, classifying exotherms is tricky, and not all lead to explosions, for example, example (4) above, which only led to an ordinary, open, fire.

Design assumptions can lead to accidents. I have been informed of a case which involved a long tunnel-like machine which produced and packaged an item which is a domestic consumable. The machine was built with a series of doors for inspection and adjustment, all fitted with micro-switches to isolate the drive if a door was opened. But during one shift a fitter opened a door to make adjustments, gimmicked the micro-switch so the machine would run, and put his fingers into a toothed belt drive. Guards and other protective devices needed, but they can often be defeated. After that accident I'm told, the micro-switches were replaced with a light beam across each doorway.

There is, also, an injury case recently described to me of a bucket elevator which was caused to run forward by an imbalance of buckets when some were being replaced. Why did it run forward? Well, design practice with these machines installs an anti-runback device, because when a bucket elevator stops the rising buckets are often full (and the decending buckets are empty) so there is then a tendency for the whole system to run *backwards*. However, no-one ever thought an out-of-balance situation would be caused by buckets being missing on the *rising* side, which could make an elevator run *forward*. This one did, and it removed much of the fitter's lower arm.

Finally, here is a case to illustrate that we don't need high technology, not even old-fashioned electricity, to injure, or even to kill someone. This case, given to me by a lawyer friend, reflects on that.

A young man was employed as a labourer at an abattoir southwest of Sydney. His job was to clean up scraps from the floor and put them in a rubbish bin, He wasn't involved in the actual cutting work, which was performed by skilled personnel. As he passed by one of those cutting up the carcases sliced through what he was working on, and, rather like the way a golfer "follows through" after impacting the ball, had his knife move on from the cut in what one might term "a follow-through-flourish".

The point of the knife entered the young man's body in the chest, on the left side, and penetrated his heart. He died. Paramedics arrived within minutes of frantic phone calls made. They revived him, bundled him into the ambulance and headed for the hospital. On the way to the hospital - - - he died again. The paramedics revived him. He was whizzed into casualty and a surgeon started repairing the damage, in the middle of which -- - he died again. The surgical team revived him again, and patched him up, then finalised the repair work, and as far as we know he is now still alive.

The two features which come out of this case are ---

First, the low level of technology involved in killing him. How many tools are at a lower level in the technology scale than a knife? Any? Well, maybe a few. A knife doesn't even need to be made from steel, it can be made from flint or some other mineral. The Aztecs made very sharp knives from obsidian, a volcanic rock. So, as I've said, low-tech stuff can be equally as deadly as what we think of as high-tech, and engineers need to remember that. On another side of technology, one may assume the young man is glad surgical technology is at the level it is.

Second, the level of chance (or, in more elegant language, the value of the probability) in what happened. Talk about someone being at the wrong place at the wrong time! A fraction of a second, or a spatial difference of a few centimetres, and it would have been a near miss, followed by some highly-flavoured remarks from both sides. But those sorts of margins are what we are often seeing, in accident cases. If we look at this case as a classic risk, it's high consequence-low probability, with the use of low-level technology, and the probability is so low most would say it's not reasonable to consider it as possible. Minor injuries occur all the time in abattoirs, not fatalities.

THE RECENT AUSTRALIAN CASE

In September, 1988, at Longford, where the Bass Strait oil and gas refinery part-owned and operated by Esso is located down south in Victoria, out from the town of Sale, we had a major fire and explosion which killed two and reduced the supply of gas for the whole state of Victoria to a mere trickle for some weeks.

There has been an equally major enquiry, a Royal Commission, and the findings have been published[5], showing among other problems that there were operating faults and proper maintenance practices were not followed. The report of the Commission was quite strange in one respect, it focused overwhelmingly on the technical factors, but a follow-up volume[6] dealt with the organisational aspects.

What happened? The precise failure occurred in one of the three gas plants GP1),

around the absorber tower, through which light oil is circulated to scrub the denser hydrocarbons out of the gas stream, leaving principally methane. The night before the incident the flow of mixed gas-and-oil crude from the Bass Strait platforms had been unusually high in liquids, which raised the liquid level in the bottom of the tower. This level should have been controlled by increasing the heat input, but the steam control valve was misbehaving so manual control was being used, but ineffectively, so the level continued to rise, finally entering the outlet at the bottom of the absorber tower and chilling the rich oil stream leaving the tower. The pumps supplying the oil stream to the top of the tower automatically shut down.

The reboiler heat exchangers became very cold, showing external frost, and started to leak. Then the circulation pumps were restarted, bringing hot oil into the chilled exchangers, and one failed with a brittle fracture, releasing a mixture of liquid and gas hydrocarbons, which rapidly found a source of ignition, setting off an explosion and subsequent fire. The location of the fire, under some major cross-plant pipelines (something Kletz warned about years ago), forced a complete shutdown of all three of the gas plants. In late winter Victoria was without gas for heating and cooking.

The management blamed the operators, particularly the one in the control room at the time. All that was blown up extensively by the media, and led to this author having the following letter published in the major Sydney newspaper:

This note follows from my letter last year (Herald, 1st October, 1988) which referred to the explosion and fire at Longford and recent reports concerning the enquiry on that event.

The manner in which Esso has laid the cause of the event at the feet of employees relates to a comment I have made several times in the past, sometimes formally at conferences, and occasionally informally in company.

What I have noted, when reviewing man-made disasters in my research, is that management behaviour is like that attributed, rightly or wrongly, to surgeons. It's said of the latter that they can bury their mistakes. If we take that a step further, we may say they bury them in the ground.

Likewise, management can bury their mistakes. Not in the ground, but in the organisation structure. Top management can point down to line management, who can point to supervision, who can point to workers.

I doubt this burial practice fertilises or otherwise improves the organisation structure.

Among the many points which came out in the Commission's report were these: several years earlier Esso had removed engineering staff from Longford (remember one of the factors behind Flixborough?), GP1 which failed was interconnected in many ways with gas plants GP2 and GP3 (does that sound like Piper Alpha?), and the operators lived quite consistently with live alarms (rather like at Three Mile Island?). In addition to those dreadfully familiar items, a HAZOP had not been performed on No. 1 gas plant, and there were training deficiencies. One of the results of the inadequate training was operators allowed departures from safe process conditions to maintain gas output for commercial reasons; so what seems to have been prominent in the minds of those involved in running the gas plant was the need to keep the gas supply going, by expediencies. And, related to training, Exxon, the parent company, had warned all its member-companies, world-wide, of the risk of low-temperature brittle failure.

CONCLUSION FROM INVESTIGATIONS AND LONGFORD
The eleven investigation cases described above have been sorted into categories: six strongly management-related, three related to lack of information (which could be management-related),

one probably due to inadequate training (almost certainly management-related), and one never explained (the gas fire). The injuries in the tunnel-wrapping machine and the bucket elevator were due to design failings (management related), and the abattoir case appears to be the only pure-mischance observed.

The conclusion from all those observations (plus many not recorded here) is that management can very easily be a component in the migration from hazard to incident.

The conclusion from the Longford case is even stronger, supported by the report by the Royal Commission, which pointed at management as a substantial contributor to what happened.

AN OVERALL CONCLUSION

Having reached the point where the author has implicated management as a major factor behind incidents which damage property, and injure and kill people, we should ask ourselves: why is it so? Why does management become a hazard? Is it due to ignorance? Or complacency? Or apathy? Or something else?

The ignorance factor is a strong possibility. The "something else" which has been observed, here, is many of those appointed as industry heads are managing what they do not understand, while those who understand are not allowed to manage as they can. We have, as a recent example of that, the appointment of the retired group managing director of a major bank as chairman of a major chemical firm, for which there may be sound financial reason but one may wonder whether leadership from the top will understand plant-related hazards. Perhaps there was a good reason for that appointment but it's likely the new man will be managing what he understands only imperfectly, maybe does not understand at all.

The complacency factor is also a strong possibility. If nothing has happened for years and years it's rather reasonable to believe nothing will ever happen. At Longford GP1 had been operating for about forty years with no history of imminent disaster, so who would expect what happened on 25th September, 1998?

Apathy, we consider, is unlikely in its usual defined form of not caring, but if we extend it more broadly to include not caring *enough,* of being negligent, then there are certainly examples which agree with that, such as the omission of the HAZOP for GP1, proposed for 1995 but indefinitely deferred.

These become combined, though secondary, when the primary concern of the organisation, hence of the management, is the bottom line, profit. Or, more urgently, survival in the face of competition, which was not the case with Longford, Esso had a near-monopoly, or other external pressure such as customer relations, concerning which Hopkins[6] stated:

> Process upsets which may have had minor commercial consequences were dealt with thoroughly.

The combination of ignorance, complacency and apathy with pressure from the marketplace has been observed in the more "ordinary" cases described above.

A REMEDY? (FOR THE FUTURE)

The only path available to remedying the hazard of management is via information from the past, and a review of the incidents, all of which is analysis of the past. The way from that to the future must be the overall lesson that managers, whether involved in new products, operations, maintenance, or other industrial activities, need to place the correct people in the places which demand those people. But to have that happen we must have high-level managers who accept that those demands exist and are then prepared to face the cost of appointing the right people.

This repeats an old adage: that safety begins at the top. How do we apply it?

MOVING TO THE 2ND GENERATION IN BEHAVIOUR-BASED SAFETY

Thomas R. Krause *, Gordon Sellers [#] and Chris Horn [Φ]
* Behavioral Science Technology, Ojai CA, USA
[#] Behavioural Science Technology International, Bracknell RG12 1JB, UK
Gordon.Sellers@bstsolutions.com
[Φ] GlaxoSmithKline, Worthing, West Sussex BN14 8QH, UK

Behaviour-Based Safety has moved from being a curiosity to becoming an established part of many companies' safety programmes. But what is the right perspective on it – is it a passing fad that will soon die away or, as we saw with HAZOP, is it a foundation methodology for the future? The answer depends on how we see the field of safety and what next steps we take. We discuss typical shortcomings in what some people call behaviour-based safety. We then discuss strategies for maintaining the strengths while addressing the weaknesses, before suggesting two next steps: rethink the old concepts, making the radical proposal that we should take away the emphasis from behaviours and focus instead on the working interface; and use behaviour-based safety methodology as a foundation for organisational change. The paper ends with a case study from a pharmaceutical company that is implementing most features of the '2nd generation' of behaviour-based safety.

Keywords: safety, behaviour, second generation, case study, pharmaceuticals

ESTABLISHING THE NEXT STEP IN BEHAVIOUR-BASED SAFETY

Behaviour-based safety (BBS), pioneered in the early 1980s, has attracted so many imitators that the BBS label no longer means very much. It is time to take stock of the current scene and to draw lessons for the future of behaviour-based safety. We discuss: the origins of BBS; report on current confusions about it; sketch the evolution of an integrated model of BBS; make suggestions for where BBS should move in the future; and close with a case study.

THE ORIGINS OF BBS

BBS came into being as the result of three currents of work done separately with a small degree of overlap. The first was the applied behaviour analysis work of psychologist Judi Komaki, then at the Georgia Institute of Technology in the United States. Komaki was one of a small group of academic applied behavioural analysts working on industrial performance. Her interest was not solely in safety; she was interested in the use of applied behaviour analysis techniques in industry in general. However safety became the focus of her study when one of her students proposed to use behavioural techniques to design a performance improvement at his family's 200-employee food processing plant. As it happened, safety was the area in which the plant most wanted to see performance improvement. Komaki and her associates published an academic paper on their findings in 1978[1].

In 1979, John Hidley and one of us (Tom Krause) were asked by an offshore oil-drilling company in California to help them find innovative ways of improving safety performance. Based on our preliminary analysis of the situation facing this employer, we recommended the use of applied behaviour analysis as an improvement methodology[2]. This was the beginning of BST.

During this same period Gene Earnest and Jim Palmer at Proctor and Gamble were developing a methodology drawn from the behavioural sciences. To our knowledge, Earnest and Palmer were the first to use the phrase "behavior-based safety".

Although similar work in the UK began rather later than in the US, by the late 1980s extensive university research had been applied in industry and a strong body of experience developed through the 1990s, as described by Cooper[3].

CURRENT CONFUSIONS ABOUT BBS

Twenty years later, BBS means many different things to different people. The ambiguity or fuzziness of the term is so far advanced that "BBS" has lost its power to describe anything clearly. For example, some organisations call what they are doing BBS even though they admit they have no involvement of shop-floor personnel in the effort, no operational definitions of critical behaviours, and no continuous improvement mechanism. What they do have is the traditional manager/supervisor audit programme focussed on disciplinary action. The proponents of that approach lose no opportunity to refer to it as "behaviour-based safety".

This is just part of the trend in which all kinds of techniques, including the use of incentives related to accident rates, are labelled "BBS" in an apparent effort to make them more popular. This presents enormous difficulties in communication. One end of the continuum of confusion is the idea that *anything* to do with behaviour, attitude, culture, the worker, etc. is BBS. The next level of confusion is represented by the idea that, to implement BBS, all you have to do is identify some behaviours on a check list, get people to go out and start observing them, apply a lot of reinforcement (including tangible incentives) and then sit back to watch your incident rate fall.

This drastic oversimplification about BBS is troublesome even where the effort is supplemented by standard safety activities. However, this minimalist, "by-the-numbers" version of BBS becomes even more problematic when people offer it as the primary component of a safety effort, instead of as part of an integrated approach that strengthens and supports existing safety systems.

It is hardly surprising that some trade union representatives raise a number of valid concerns about BBS – based on what they have seen labelled as BBS in various organisations – for example:

THE BLAME GAME
Because behaviour-based safety tracks shopfloor behaviour, they predict that it will necessarily turn into fault-finding and blaming.

REDUCED HAZARD MITIGATION
They worry that managers will think that, once they have implemented behaviour-based safety, they can stop pursuing engineering controls for hazard mitigation – so resources will be taken away from facilities, design and maintenance.

DRIVING DATA UNDERGROUND
They believe that, if managers set ambitious targets for the 'numbers' coming out of behaviour-based safety, then they will get the numbers they want – but they may bear little resemblance to reality.

IGNORING SAFETY SPECIALISTS
They also express concern that, because behaviour-based safety encourages the involvement of people who are not safety specialists, this approach bypasses a site's safety specialists and "de-skills" the safety function.

THE EVOLUTION OF BST'S APPROACH TO BEHAVIOUR-BASED SAFETY

Since 1980, BST has helped organisations to implement BBS at more than 1,400 sites around the world. Over that period, like any organisation that is committed to continuous improvement, BST has significantly evolved its Behavioural Accident Prevention Process® or BAPP® technology.

1980 – 1985. In these early years, the method used by BST was management-driven from the top down. BST completed about 15 projects using that supervisor-driven model.

1986 – 1997. From 1986 until about 1995, Krause and his colleagues changed the model to one that was employee-driven. BST integrated Total Quality Management and Organisation Development principles with those of applied behaviour analysis in developing BAPP technology. BST also developed software to store and analyse data generated during behavioural observations, and emphasised feedback as an improvement mechanism and as a type of reinforcement. During this period, BST completed about 200 projects.

1997 – present. Since 1997 the BAPP model has evolved to include more completely the engagement of *all employees*. This occurred in response to the need to address more directly the contradiction that some organisations perceived between an employee-driven process and management accountability. The contradiction does not exist, but failing explicitly to address it allowed misinterpretations to occur.

In spite of warnings to the contrary, some companies implementing BAPP left out the manager and the supervisor. In those companies it was as though people thought that to involve front-line personnel it was necessary to exclude the managers and supervisors. As a result, they put in place change efforts that had strong employee involvement and support, but weak support and commitment from supervisors and managers. It did not take long for organisations to realise that, in order to make a BAPP initiative work over the long run, managers and supervisors had to be involved in appropriate ways.

Some of those ways include: involving some managers and supervisors as equal members of a BAPP steering team, along with front-line employees; training managers and supervisors as observers; developing a datasheet for the management behaviours that support safety ("walking the talk", which is not always easy for managers who are increasingly faced with intense production and financial pressures); using the behavioural safety process to gather "before and after" data to assist other initiatives; using existing departmental continuous improvement teams to develop behavioural action plans to remove intransigent barriers to safe behaviour that have been identified by the observation process; and extending the scope of the behavioural safety process to address other important matters such as product or service quality.

The significance is that the behavioural safety process becomes a method for continuously improving facilities, equipment, design and management system issues. Of BST's current total of implementations, over 1,000 are based on this most current model.

IS BEHAVIOUR-BASED SAFETY STILL THE CORRECT LABEL?

For many years BST's research and development department has analysed hundreds of site data sets containing barriers to safe behaviour. The pie chart in Figure 1 is an analysis of 13,264 behaviours observed at 13 sites.

The pattern of distribution across barriers is similar at these sites to many other sites. Namely, 'facilities & equipment' and 'hazard recognition & response' make up the largest categories, comprising a majority of the barriers to safe behaviours. It is worth noting that this kind of data would not be available if it were not for a behaviour-based methodology that allows it to be gathered. Examining and thinking about these data in consultation with many different organisations has caused BST to take a fresh look at the relationship among causal factors that contribute to injury.

As we now know that barriers to safe behaviour are primarily related to conditions, equipment and management systems, rather than to personal choice, it no longer seems reasonable to state that:

"80 to 95% of injuries are caused by unsafe acts"

However carefully we phrase it, many people still read that as requiring us to make a choice between behaviours and facilities – and implying blame for the worker if he or she acted unsafely.

The focus of our safety improvement efforts has to change from the worker to the systems that enable safe behaviour.

HELPING ORGANISATIONS REDUCE EXPOSURE TO INCIDENTS BY IMPROVING THE WORKING INTERFACE

If we analyse injuries exhaustively, looking at a variety of organisations across industries over a period of several years, what we find is that the actual cause of the great majority of injuries is an interaction between the worker and the facility. We describe this interaction as the Working Interface. Furthermore, we believe that improvement in safety consists of systematically defining and improving this critically important working interface (Figure 2) and we can now change our definition to:

"Incidents are caused by multiple factors which are seen in the working interface. Many exposures are likely to occur before an injury. The specific relationship between exposure and injury varies with type of industry and type of injury."

In spite of much confusion about the essence and the applications of behaviour-based safety, it remains an effective tool for performance improvement, and it is growing stronger and more flexible as more companies adapt it to their unique needs. For companies to succeed with BBS, it is important for them to look beyond the label and understand what constitutes an effective system. And for BBS to continue to thrive, it must continue to evolve, retaining those characteristics that are effective, while addressing perceived weaknesses.

GOING BEYOND SAFETY

Most companies are looking for ways to:

- Engage their employees in problem solving;
- Develop their employees' capacity to respond to challenges; and
- Use data-based tools to make improvements.

We are now demonstrating that behaviour-based safety methodology is a model for organisational change by applying it to such diverse issues as:

- Improving quality in manufacturing processes;
- Improving student life on a college campus;
- Medical error reduction; and
- Improving quality and customer service in a business service company.

CASE STUDY OF BBS AT A UK PHARMACEUTICALS PLANT

Within BST, the change in focus from 'the worker' to 'the systems that enable safe behaviour' has not occurred overnight, but has been an evolution over several years. This can be seen in the experience of the major multinational pharmaceuticals company SmithKline Beecham (now GlaxoSmithKline) that in 1998 launched pilot implementations of BST's BAPP technology at two of its sites – one at Worthing UK and the other at Clifton, NJ, USA. Since then, BAPP implementations have begun at three more of the company's sites – in Ireland, Kenya and Argentina. This brief case study reports on safety gains at the UK site.

Following its August 1998 launch of behaviour-based safety, the Worthing site's twelve-month moving average for lost time accidents (LTAs) has improved steadily (Figure 3). An important factor of this success is the contribution of the site's trained BAPP observers who consistently meet or exceed their targets – in 2000 they completed 3,309 observations against their target of 3,114 (based on one observation per observer per week).

ACTIVE STEERING TEAMS AND OBSERVERS

The site comprises both primary and secondary production. Using reactors, filters, dryers and pumps, primary operations include large-scale fermentation, extraction and fine chemical processing. Secondary operations include bulk powder processing, producing finished tablets and capsules, and product packaging using high speed machinery. Using two steering committees, one for primary production and one for secondary production, the site implemented the process in seven production units out of a total of ten business units.

A BST consultant began training the two steering committees together in July 1998. The committee members in turn trained many of their colleagues as observers. The observers use the data sheets to record the rates at which their colleagues are using the identified safe or at-risk behaviours. After an observation, the observers use two-way feedback to reinforce the safe behaviours they have seen. They then talk about any at-risk behaviour they may have seen. When it is within the control of the observed personnel to avoid an at-risk behaviour, one of the aims of the feedback discussion is for them to agree that in future they will use the identified safe behaviour.

When existing procedures or conditions prevent this change from being within the control of the worker, the observers record that information along with their colleagues' thoughts on how to remove barriers to safe behaviour. Problem-solving teams then use this observation data to make improvements. (This is what BST would now describe as "improving the working interface").

FACING UP TO THE COMMUNICATION CHALLENGES

The first challenge was a need for communication across seven business units using many different work patterns. There was also a need for good communication through all levels of the organisation, including team leaders and managers. In addition, the observers needed ongoing feedback to remind them of the value of their work, to motivate them, and to keep them calibrated with emerging observation targets.

The first site-wide BAPP co-ordinator was especially effective at promoting the process and grabbing people's attention. For a Worthing site open day in May 1998, just before the BBS process was launched, he set up an exhibition stand featuring literature and videos on the BAPP approach to safety. He and the BST consultant were on hand to chat informally about the process and implementation. He then developed a briefing pack for other presenters to use and, to achieve continuity across all seven business units, this pack reproduced the slides and handouts from the exhibition stand. The steering committees used this pack to conduct approximately five presentations per work area covering every shift, totalling 40 to 50 presentations over the entire site.

In addition, the BAPP team produced and published a double-page introductory article in the site's quarterly magazine and have since gone on to launch a very readable behaviour-based safety newsletter.

UNION INVOLVEMENT
The AEEU and TGWU are both represented at the site, and members of the unions were appointed to positions on the steering committees. The site-wide co-ordinator comments that, "A conscious effort was made to involve the unions from the start and because of that we have a very good relationship with them over behaviour-based safety". The co-ordinator of the secondary area steering committee has been a TGWU safety representative for several years and she notes that, "Before we had behaviour-based safety, everyone in my department expected me to solve all their safety problems. Now I have a group of observers and steering team members who help to spread the load and get better involvement."

ADDRESSING OBSERVER CONCERNS
To keep observers in the loop, the steering committees issue reports and conduct regular meetings that are keyed to observer concerns. These communications emphasise the gains the site has made based on observation data.

To remove some of the time pressure on observers, the site is using an alternative feedback method that they call 'hindsight feedback'. When they observe colleagues performing some high priority production jobs, instead of directly engaging in two-way feedback the observers return after the job is completed to conduct a feedback session. This procedure lets the observers conduct observations when they have time to do so and when the observed person is actively engaged; then it lets the observed personnel receive the feedback after the priority job is complete.

CELEBRATING THE GAINS
GlaxoSmithKline Worthing sees its success in various ways. Its lost time accident rate shows continuous improvement. The site's observers are meeting and beating their targets. In March and April of 1999, for the first time in 10 years the site had zero reportable injuries for two consecutive months. According to the current site-wide co-ordinator, beyond those numbers the site's safety culture is improving as more people understand the connection between using the identified critical safe behaviours and reducing their exposure to injury.

REFERENCES
1. Komaki, J., Barwick, K.D. and Scott, L.R., 1978, A Behavioral Approach to Occupational Safety, *Journal of Applied Psychology*, 63(4): 434-445
2. Krause, T.R., Hidley, J.H. and Lareau, W, 1984 (July), Behavioral Science Applied to Industrial Accident Prevention, *Professional Safety*
3. Cooper, D., 1998, Improving Safety Culture: A Practical Guide, John Wiley & Sons

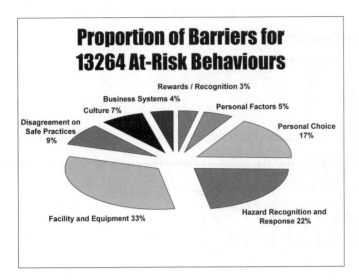

Figure 1. Analysis of at-risk behaviours at 13 sites

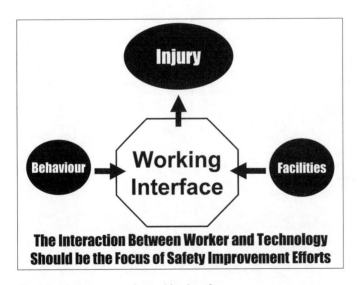

Figure 2. Injuries occur at the working interface

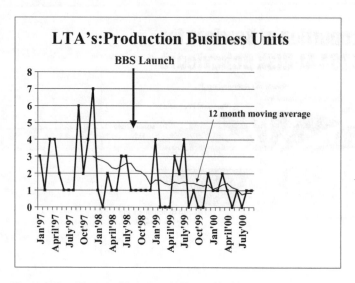

Figure 3. Lost Time Accidents have fallen since the launch of BBS

DEMONSTRATION OF ALARP WITHIN COMAH SAFETY REPORTS

Dr Jerry R. Mullins and Mr Vimal K. Patel

AEA Technology Consulting, Safety Management Group, Risley, Warrington, Cheshire, WA3 6AT, UK.

The implementation of the SEVESO II Directive (COMAH Regulations as it is implemented in the UK) requires operators to demonstrate that major accident risks are as low as is reasonably practicable (ALARP). Meeting this requirement entails carrying out some form of risk assessment and then assessing whether further controls are required. Guidance produced by the UK Chemical Industries Association [1] addresses risk assessment and demonstration of ALARP in relation to on-site occupied buildings but does not address hazards which are difficult to quantify in terms of numerical risk, involve process operators, pose off-site risks or threaten the environment. A more generalised approach to risk assessment/demonstration of ALARP is required to address the variety of hazards associated with chemical sites. This paper will provide examples that demonstrate how such approaches can be successfully applied to COMAH safety reports. An important component of the ALARP demonstration is identifying the range of possible risk reduction measures and then choosing the right one. Ranking of risk reduction options and selection of the optimum solution is discussed for practical situations.

Key words: As Low As Reasonably Practicable (ALARP), Quantified Risk Assessment (QRA), Risk Reduction Measures, Control of Major Accident Hazards (COMAH)

BACKGROUND TO SAFETY REPORT REQUIREMENTS

The COMAH Safety Report Assessment Manual [2] states that operators are required to demonstrate that major accident hazards have been identified and the necessary measures taken to prevent such accidents and limit their consequences to persons and the environment. Decisions about the acceptability of existing risks and the requirement for additional safeguards generally require some form of risk assessment.

The risk assessment approach used to identify and evaluate the risks can be undertaken in a number of ways such as quantitative, semi-quantitative, qualitative or a combination of these. The most suitable approach for a particular hazardous site will be dependent upon the consequences of the event and the magnitude of the risk for example, whether the consequences are confined on-site or extend off-site to significant populations or environmental features will be important factors.

INTRODUCTION

This paper will provide a demonstration of the application of semi-quantitative risk assessment in decision making by means of a case study involving a UK major hazard installation. The purpose of the case study was to undertake a risk assessment for the site in order to identify and evaluate the major accident hazards, assess the acceptability of the risk and make decisions on any required additional risk reduction measures in accordance with the ALARP principle. The basis for the identification of major accident hazards has been structured around brainstorming sessions involving application of a set of guidewords to the various site operations. The assessment of risk has been carried out using a semi-quantitative risk assessment approach in which a relative rank or weight is assigned to each consequence and its likelihood and then an overall risk value assigned on the basis of an agreed risk matrix. Risks have been assigned as high, medium or low and rules applied governing application of risk reduction measures to each risk category.

RISK ASSESSMENT METHODOLOGY

The identification of hazards (including major accident hazards) has been undertaken by means of brainstorming sessions involving application of a set of standard guidewords to a list of the various facilities and a description of the activities undertaken in each facility. The list of assessed facilities included all significant inventories of dangerous substances as defined under COMAH (toxic, flammable, ecotoxic etc.). The list of guidewords adopted for the study was as follows:

- Mechanical failure (corrosion etc)
- Natural external events (extreme weather)
- Man - made external events (fire/explosion etc)
- Impact (vehicles, cranes etc)
- Operator error (incorrect procedure etc)
- Maintenance error (equipment fitted incorrectly etc)
- Equipment failure (stirrers etc)
- Extreme internal conditions (temperature/ pressure/ level/ flow etc)

The brainstorming sessions assigned a relative rank or weight to each accident consequence and its likelihood (Table 1 and Table 2) in order to determine an overall risk ranking in accordance with an agreed risk matrix (Table 3). The definitions in the Tables were based on internal company risk procedures, these definitions will differ from company to company, but the basic concepts remain the same.

Hazard scenarios for this case study were rated using scales of 1 – 4 for consequence and likelihood with level 4 representing the highest loss and frequency.

Consequence categories are assigned on a worst case basis, assuming that only passive safeguards are in operation (i.e. those that require no human intervention). If credit is to be given to passive safeguards then these will need to be fit for purpose and well-maintained e.g. a bund should be in a good state with no leakage.

The approach for assigning likelihood ratings starts with the plant operating experience using the above table. If the event has happened once or more in the past five years on the plant or a similar one then the frequency is assigned a likelihood rating of 4. If an accident has occurred once or more on a longer timescale then the likelihood rating is 3. If no accidents with similar consequences have occurred then the maximum likelihood rating would be once in 100 years or a level 3. The next step is to look at the safeguards in place. If there are effective passive and/or active safeguards in place then the likelihood rating can be reduced to level 2. This is a subjective judgement, which is made by group consensus and is influenced by the generic failure rates of those safeguards. If a high level of protection, including passive engineered safeguards and administrative controls, is in place then a level 1 can be assigned. Level 1 probabilities are intended to be used sparingly and only after considerable thought.

Table 1: Consequence Ratings

Consequence Level	Consequence Definition	Example of Losses On-Site	Examples of Losses Off-Site
4	Off-Site Hazard	• Multiple Severe Injuries • Large Spills and Releases • Property Damage • Business Interruption	• Large Scale Evacuation • Major Property Damage • Major Environmental Impact
3	On-Site Hazard	• 1 Fatality or Severe Injury • Significant Spills and Releases • Property Damage • Business Interruption	• 1 or 2 LTA Injuries • Evacuation; Shelter-in-Place • Significant Property Damage • Environmental Impact
2	In Building Hazard	• Medical Treatment Cases • Multiple First Aid Cases • Medium Spills and Releases • Property Damage	• Nuisance Impact (odours, noise, traffic etc.)
1	Hazard Confined to Local Work Area	• 1 – 2 First Aid Cases • Small Spill or Release that is contained	• No discernible Impact

Table 2: Likelihood Ratings

Likelihood Level	Likelihood Definition	Frequency Range
4	Frequent Occurrence	> Once every 5 years
3	Occasional Occurrence	> Once every 100 years
2	Unlikely Occurrence	Between 100 years to 10,000 years
1	Very Unlikely	< Once every 10,000 years

Each combination of consequence and likelihood is assigned a risk ranking. These risk rankings are allocated as high, medium or low risk in accordance with the following risk matrix (Table 3).

Table 3: Risk Matrix

		Likelihood			
		1	*2*	*3*	*4*
Consequence	*1*	1	2	3	4
	2	2	4	6	8
	3	3	6	9	12
	4	4	8	12	16

Where:

Risk Level	Risk Definition
1 –3	Low Risk
4 – 9	Medium Risk
9 – 16	High Risk

Once risk rankings have been calculated for each identified hazard, the following rules are applied for dealing with each risk category. Those scenarios identified as high risk should have additional safeguards applied to them to reduce the risk rating to a lower level. As general guidance, the implementation of one additional robust safeguard would reduce the likelihood by one level and two additional robust safeguards would reduce the likelihood by two levels. Those scenarios identified as medium risk should have additional safeguards considered and if reasonably practicable, then these should be implemented. Low risk scenarios are considered to be adequately controlled. However, if there are simple additional safeguards which can be applied, then these should be implemented.

CASE STUDY EXAMPLE: TANKER UNLOADING OPERATION AT A UK HAZARDOUS INSTALLATION

The following case study provides an example of the application of the risk assessment methodology as described above. The extracted example is for the road tanker unloading operation for the site. Solvent contained within road tankers is being unloaded into bulk storage tanks for use on-site.

RESULTS OF ASSESSMENT

The results of the risk assessment involving the road tank unloading operation are detailed in Annex 1. The table also includes a listing of the existing safeguards under the headings: prevention, control and mitigation.

ACCEPTABILITY OF RISKS

The risk assessment for the road tanker unloading operation (Annex 1) indicates that for the identified scenarios the risks fall within the high and medium classification of risk. There are no low risk scenarios. In accordance with the above methodology, the site is required to identify and implement a safeguard or safeguards to reduce high risks to a lower risk category and in the case of medium risks to implement a further safeguard or safeguards where reasonably practicable in terms of cost-benefit.

The high-risk scenario (i.e. Operator error leading to incorrect connection) was reviewed by the site management in terms of the adequacy of the existing safeguards. The selected action was to carry out a more detailed risk evaluation study to verify the high-risk status and; if necessary, identify additional safeguard(s) that will reduce the risk to ALARP levels.

In the case of the medium risk scenarios, the actions identified by the site management were as shown in Table 4.

Table 4: Identified Medium Risk Scenarios

Hazardous Scenarios	Location/ effected area	Site Response
Tanker drive away resulting in loss of containment	Tanker Unloading Area/ On-Site effects	• Consider the use of wheel chocks during unloading operations • Consider automatic shut-off on detection of fault condition and audible alarm • Consider de-coupling the Tanker from the truck when the tanker is positioned within the unloading bay area
Vehicle impact onto road tanker resulting in fire and loss of containment	Tanker Unloading Area/ On-Site effects	• Consider placing warning barriers, moveable barriers or closure of unloading area by gates when tankers are in position
Flame impingement onto road tanker resulting in fire	Tanker Unloading Area/ On-Site effects	• Safeguards have been assessed to be appropriate and no further measures are required
Mechanical failure of unloading hoses resulting in loss of containment	Tanker Unloading Area/ On-Site effects	• Consider automatic shut-off on detection of fault condition and audible alarm

USE OF STANDARDS, BEST PRACTICE ETC. IN SELECTION OF SAFGUARDS

The demonstration of ALARP requires arguments to be presented which demonstrate the adequacy of the safeguards in place. For hazards that are essentially confined on-site and where the risk is not considered high, this demonstration can generally be restricted to showing that the safeguards in place plus proposed measures will ensure compliance with legislation, codes of practice, appropriate standards and any other simple improvements. In other cases, for example where hazards extend off-site and/or risks are high, then safeguards in addition to those required above may be required. Appropriate selection of such safeguards is likely to require consideration of how the proposed safeguards would contribute to the prevention, control and mitigation of major accident hazards.

HIERARCHIAL APPROACH TO SELECTION OF SAFEGUARDS

The use of a hierarchical approach to the selection of control measures will help to ensure that priority is given to those safeguards that eliminate or minimise major accident hazards by "inherently safe" design and prevention measures rather than place over reliance on control and mitigation measures. The design stage represents the best opportunity to put such considerations into effect; however they may also be applied to modifications and installation of additional safeguards in existing plant. Another aspect of the hierarchical approach to the selection of control measures is that preference should be given to engineered safeguards rather than managerial controls. This is a reflection of the fact that human error is a major factor in many accidents.

The detailed implementation of such a hierarchical approach to the selection of safeguards will vary from site to site, however, this approach can be used to determine practical options for the management of hazards and risk and in turn provide justification that risks are ALARP.

Annex 1: Extract from the site risk assessment. Road Tank Unloading Operation

Item No.	Major Accident Hazard including description of consequence of hazard	Consequence	Safeguards			Frequency	Risk
			Preventive measures	Control measures	Mitigation measures		
1	Mechanical failure of unloading hoses e.g. corrosion etc resulting in loss of containment	1	• Hoses fit for purpose, designed to appropriate standards • Visual inspection of hoses prior to use • Hoses are pressure tested at lease once a year	• All transfer operations are supervised by competent persons • Isolation valve on tanker outlet	• Spillage procedure • Operator training for Spills • Site drainage system contained	4	4 M
2	Flame impingement onto road ranker resulting in fire/ explosion	3	• Permit to Work system for hot working in the area • Housekeeping procedure • Earthing of tankers, hoses and equipment while unloading	• Hazardous area zoned • Unloading procedure • No smoking policy	• Operator supervision • Fire extinguishers • Fire sprinkler system • Emergency plan	2	6 M
3	Vehicle impact onto road tanker whilst unloading resulting in loss of containment	3	• Designated unloading areas • Site speed limit of 5 mph		• Operator supervision • Forklift driver training • Site drainage system Contained	2	6 M
4	Operator error (incorrect connections) resulting in loss of containment	3			• Manual isolation valves On tanker and tanks • Operator training • Emergency stop buttons For pumps located in the unloading area	4	12 H
5	Tanker drive away resulting in loss of containment	3	• Road tanker air brake System	• Manual isolation valves	• Spillage procedure • Operator supervision • Spillage kits • Site drainage system contained	2	6 M

CONCLUSIONS

This paper provides an example of the application of semi-quantitative risk assessment in decision making by means of a case study involving a UK major hazard installation.

The aim of the study was to identify the major accident hazards for the site and determine whether existing risks were ALARP. For the high-risk scenario identified in the study, further quantitative assessment was identified as necessary in order to verify the classification of the high-risk scenario and if necessary identify further safeguards which will reduce the risk to ALARP levels using a method of cost-benefit analysis. For the identified medium risk scenarios, practical options were identified after consideration of their effectiveness in terms of prevention, control and mitigation and what is required to meet industry best practice. Demonstration of ALARP also requires appropriate evidence that the identified measures will be implemented. To meet this requirement, the identified actions were incorporated into a site action plan.

REFERENCES

[1] Guidance for the Location and Design of Occupied Buildings on Chemical Manufacturing Sites, Chemical Industries Association, February 1998.
[2] COMAH Safety Report Assessment Manual, Predictive Aspects, Part 2 Chapter 3, Health and Safety Executive.

A REGULATORY VIEW OF DETERMINISTIC SAFETY ANALYSIS IN THE NUCLEAR INDUSTRY (SOME LESSONS FOR THE PROCESS INDUSTRY?)

Dr. Andy Trimble, HM Principal Inspector (Nuclear Installations)
HM Nuclear Installations Inspectorate, St. Peter's House, Balliol Road, BOOTLE
L20 3LZ

The aim of this paper is to show the how engineering fault analysis forms a major plank in the safety assessment of Nuclear Plant and how such analysis may be carried out. The paper briefly outlines the regulatory and legal framework for UK nuclear licensed sites in our non prescriptive, goal setting safety regime.

HSE publishes a great deal of guidance. The prime relevant sources are Tolerability of Risk (TOR) and Safety Assessment Principles for Nuclear Plants (SAPs). This led to the development and application of internal guidance on Deterministic Safety Analysis (DSA) which has its roots in Nuclear Chemical Plant assessment and is based on considering design basis faults. Design basis faults are those that, without the appropriate safety systems, are foreseeable within a plant lifetime. DSA forms the major input into the quality required from any such safety systems required to prevent, terminate or mitigate fault sequences. This highlights DSA as the bedrock of safety analysis for nuclear plants which is consistent with international practice.

AIMS

This paper introduces a non probabilistic part of demonstrating safety which has been an underlying principle in the UK's approach to nuclear safety regulation. Here it is called deterministic safety assessment. It is usually complemented by a probabilistic analysis. As part of propagating sound practice and corporate learning, it seemed reasonable to share this way of thinking with the process industries. This is particularly relevant as the guidance stemmed from interactions between ourselves and Nuclear Chemical Plant licensees. The annex summarises the guide which may be bench marked against corporate safety assessment guidance.

In common with the goal setting principles of safety regulation in the UK, the guidance, summarised in the annex, is not a detailed prescription or a single permissible approach that needs to be followed. The guide is intended to assist HSE's Nuclear Inspectors in using consistent approaches to making judgments. In line with the injunction in safety law, all this is subject to the test "so far as is reasonably practicable", better known as As Low As Reasonably Practicable - ALARP (see later).

INTRODUCTION

The legal requirement for a safety case for UK Nuclear Installations stems from the conditions attached to Licenses granted under the Nuclear Installations Act 1965 (as amended). Such cases have been a feature of the licensing regime since its inception. The safety case is a key feature of nuclear safety regulation. The current licence requirement is for an adequate safety case for operations that may affect safety. The Health and Safety Executive's Nuclear Installations Inspectorate (NII) is charged, amongst other things, with administering this licensing function including assessment of such safety cases. Regulating adherence to the conditions attached to licenses (including the safety case assessment) is part of the nuclear safety permissioning regime.

Licensees carry out their duty to protect workers and members of the public by establishing safety standards to ensure radiation doses from both accidents and normal operations are ALARP. NII's has a duty among other things to see that licensees develop, achieve and maintain such standards, to ensure that any necessary safety precautions are taken and to inspect and enforce safety law by means of its powers under the licence and relevant legislation. Thus, NII has to satisfy itself that the licensee is managing safety to an adequate standard, and take the necessary regulatory action to ensure standards are maintained and, where reasonably practical, improved. In all this, the licensee remains solely responsible for safety.

The point is that NII does not prescribe in detail how the licensees should comply with their legal obligations. It is for licensees to present their criteria and safety cases. NII then judges them against the SAPs [1] which are high level goals. NII has also developed a series of assessment guides to complement SAPs and assist in achieving consistency in a regime where there is considerable scope for flexibility and a need for judgment by the regulator. It is also important to realise that the ALARP principle drives an ongoing improvement in safety standards in the light of the current technical understanding, changes to limits and best practice.

THE STANDARD LICENCE

The heart of the nuclear regulatory control system is the licence and its attached conditions. NII can, at any time, attach conditions to a licence which appear necessary or desirable in the interest of safety. The most relevant here include:

a. LC23. OPERATING RULES
(1) The licensee shall, in respect of any operation that may affect safety, produce an adequate safety case to demonstrate the safety of that operation and to identify the conditions and limits necessary in the interests of safety. Such conditions and limits shall hereinafter be referred to as operating rules.

b. LC1. INTERPRETATION
(1) In the conditions set out in this Schedule to this licence, unless the context otherwise requires, the following expressions have the meanings hereby respectively assigned to them, that is to say -
........"operations" includes maintenance, examination, testing and operation of the plant and the treatment, processing, keeping, storing, accumulating or carriage of any radioactive material or radioactive waste and "operating" and "operational" shall be construed accordingly;..............

c. LC14. SAFETY DOCUMENTATION
(1) Without prejudice to any other requirements of the conditions attached to this licence the licensee shall make and implement adequate arrangements for the production and assessment of safety cases consisting of documentation to justify safety during the design, construction, manufacture, commissioning, operation and decommissioning phases of the installation.

d. LC27. SAFETY MECHANISMS, DEVICES AND CIRCUITS
The licensee shall ensure that a plant is not operated, inspected, maintained or tested

*unless suitable and sufficient safety mechanisms, devices and circuits are properly
connected and in good working order.*

In making its regulatory decisions NII must make judgments about compliance
with LCs. This is, in part, achieved using the relevant Safety Assessment Principles.
For example Principle 27 (P27) states the purpose of Design Basis Accident Analysis
(part of Deterministic Safety Analysis) is to provide information relevant to trip
settings, plant operational limits (Operating Rules) and plant operating instructions for
fault conditions and P26 which addresses the minimum requirements for the
sufficiency of safety systems .

TOLERABILITY OF RISK & SAFETY ASSESSMENT PRINCIPLES

Tolerability of Risk (TOR) originates from a recommendation in the 1986
report of the Sizewell Inquiry [3] into the UK's first Pressurised Water Reactor
(PWR). Public comment was invited and TOR was republished [2]. It discusses how
people normally approach risk, shows how industrial risks (and nuclear risks in
particular) are regulated, the nature of risk from radiation and how these are
calculated. In doing this it established three levels of risk:

a. a risk which is so great or the outcome so unacceptable that it must be
refused altogether - which can be described as intolerable risks: these cannot be
justified except in extraordinary circumstances

b. a risk which is or has been made so small that no further precaution is
necessary - the "broadly acceptable" region where no *detailed* working is needed to
show that risks are ALARP.

c. risks that fall between these two states, that have been reduced to the
lowest level reasonably practicable taking into account the detriment of further risk
reduction. The injunction laid down in safety law is that any such risk must be reduced
so far as is reasonably practicable. This is the ALARP or Tolerability region

TOR goes on to quantify these regions for individual risks which, in turn, are
interpreted into some of the quantitative limits found in SAPs. These are set out as
basic safety limits (BSLs) and basic safety objectives (BSOs). There was no intent to
imply that showing how these are achieved by probabilistic safety assessment (PSA)
is the most important element of safety cases. Indeed, HSE has given other statements
that emphasise the more deterministic underlying approach adopted in UK nuclear
safety regulation [6]. This paper shows a way to meet that more deterministic aim.

SAPs are at the "Principle" level and are used to guide inspectors' assessment
for all nuclear installations. They are intended to promote consistent regulatory
decisions. They are not standards imposed on licensees but have been published so
that anyone who is interested can be aware of the safety guidance against which
licensees' safety cases will be judged. They are non prescriptive and are intended for
use with new plant and major plant modifications. However, they are also used in
safety reviews of older plant, required under licence conditions, for comparison with
modern standards and to give a benchmark against which any argument on what is
reasonably practicable can be set.

The bulk of the SAPs set out NII's views on good engineering practice and are
regarded as the basis of safe design. It is only by matching the quality of the
engineering to the harm potential of the operation that fault tolerance in the plant and
its operation can be demonstrably met. This could be interpreted as a definition of

"deterministic" for these purposes. Also, the PSA should help in making decisions to achieve a balanced plant design, i.e. one with no undue reliance on any particular design feature. The PSA should also show that risk targets have been met.

To assist in meeting HSE's policies of consistency and proportionality NII has drafted a series of assessment guides. This paper is primarily concerned with the guide on Deterministic Safety Analysis, which helps define its role and the term deterministic.

TECHNICAL SAPs - DEFINITIONS

The SAPs explicitly state that the technical aspects are fundamentally important to engineering a demonstrably safe, fault tolerant plant. The aspects considered are [7]:

a. Deterministic safety analysis (DSA)

b. Probabilistic safety analysis (PSA sometimes known as QRA)

c. Severe accident analysis (SAA)

d. Good Engineering Practice (GEP)

e. Waste Management

Dealing with each of these broad areas in turn:

DSA: which by definition includes Design Basis Accident Analysis, is a robust demonstration of fault tolerance. It links directly to the engineering principles which call for a preferred series of responses to faults. These vary from designs that are inherently safe to those that may require operator intervention in the fault sequence. The important feature of DSA is that any uncertainty is allowed for by conservatism. Often this conservatism is in the input data and requires expert judgments about the degree of conservatism appropriate to any particular case. DSA is concerned with faults with larger harm potential and not normally with more minor events.

PSA: The main purpose of PSA is to demonstrate a balanced design and it may also show that risks are minimised. The great strength of PSA is this overview. It is not covered by DSA which deals with faults on a fault by fault basis. Undue reliance should not be placed on the numbers produced by PSA. These numbers are usually rather uncertain and so, while they are very useful in comparative terms, they must be used with caution as a definitive quantification of the overall risks from the operation considered. PSA is usually carried out using best estimate data.

SAA: A severe accident is one which is not necessarily expected in a plant lifetime but has the potential for high doses or environmental damage. It is not necessary for this potential to be realised (Three Mile Island was a severe accident but there was no release of radiological significance). The prime difference between DSA and SA is in the way that data is used. SA is based on best estimates and as may well be bounded by the DSA if the level of conservatism is high. However, a sound understanding of the underlying phenomena during such accidents avoids the need for introducing unnecessary conservatism and hence unfruitful expenditure. The main aim of SA is to provide an input to emergency planning and to identify reasonably practical design improvements that can be implemented at reasonable cost.

GEP: In every industry there are both pressures to reduce costs and increase cost effectiveness. However, most companies and most industries set basic standards below which any design should not fall. This ensures that for harm potentials smaller than would be covered by DSA, the learning experience of the company and/or the industry is taken into account. Often GEP is embodied in design manuals or company standards. Quality engineering should not stray outside this standard.

Waste Management: There are major additional external constraints as well as those required for safety. Much regulation is concerned with implementing government policy and GEP. Plainly, this also reflects public opposition to ill considered waste accumulation and storage (disposal is dealt with under Environmental Legislation administered by the Environment Agency).

DSA

This engineering fault analysis or Deterministic Safety Assessment forms the bedrock on which the safety case is built. The rigour in such analysis is directly linked to the harm potential or hazard. This is a key idea in deterministic analysis as harm potential is related primarily to the inherent characteristics of the processed material. It is a qualitative measure of the radioactivity (broadly equivalent to toxicity), mobility and driving force. Thus a mobile, highly active material which can undergo self heating (e.g. high level liquid waste) has a higher harm potential than low level solid waste encapsulated in cement. Although the guide gives broad classes of harm potential the reality is that harm potential is a continuous variable and we judge each case on its merits. The guide addresses the rigour and conservatism appropriate to the classes or categories of nuclear plants.

It is important to understand that DSA deals exclusively with faults - deviations from the operating envelope - and does not consider normal operation except as the state from which faults develop. Therefore, the only consideration or constraint DSA puts on normal operation is the plant state the fault starts from.

In order to carry out DSA on a process it is essential to have a sound technical understanding of that process and plant. Much of the basic information is either identical to that needed for design or closely related to it. There is an ongoing iteration between the designer and safety analyst in the search for a suitable and sufficiently safe design, one which is economic, environmentally acceptable and operable. The outcome is that the options for the underlying processes are assessed and an informed decision made about the preferred option (optioneering). There are similar considerations for existing plant in periodic review but the options for change in order to achieve ALARP will be limited by what already exists.

The DSA technique is conceptually simple and follows the logic in Figure 1. Decisions must be taken and in most cases their order is not vitally important. There is one exception to this. There is a decision node labeled "low consequence". The intention is to remove the analysis burden where the consequences are low. However, this decision must only be carried out after the harm potential or hazard has been judged. The intention is not to place high reliance on mitigation (often filtration on nuclear chemical plant) but rather to soundly engineer the process for defence in depth in the first place. This decision must only be taken in the light of the overall assessment. In case of doubt, we would expect the decision to be prudently based.

The foundation for all this work is fault identification. The main characteristics we seek are that this has been carried out in a structured and comprehensive way. Such techniques might include HAZOP (Hazard and Operability studies) and FMEA (Failure Mode and Effect Analysis). In each case it is important that the individuals involved understand the underlying processes in the plant. The result should be a list of all potential faults for the plant (which may be grouped). As the design evolves the balance of faults changes and so further fault identifications are carried out. In addition, the act of analysing the fault may identify further faults or knock on effects. These should also be analysed. It is very important to ensure that a change on one part of a complex plant does not have an unanalysed knock on effect on another part. The faults so identified become the Fault Schedule. The analysis takes each fault or groups of faults and analyses them in a technique very akin to event tree analysis. The technique simply assumes the fault initiation occurs and examines how the plant responds (usually without any safeguard). Depending on the harm potential of the sequence being considered, the safeguards are then put in place as part of the design and their quality constraints flow from their safety function (see later). One of the key aspects of this type of work is the iteration between the analysts and the designers or operators in the search for improvements to meet ALARP.

The options for dealing with faults during iteration are prioritised on what is known as the P61/P62 hierarchy (relating to Principles P61 and P62, in SAPs). P61 says, in essence, that faults should be avoided by safe passive means if possible. P62 says that the sensitivity to faults should be minimised. These concepts should be at the front of every engineer's mind when designing or analysing plant. It is a drive toward inherent safety (see Annex). It is difficult to overestimate the importance of this hierarchy and this has been the thrust of several initiatives on the part of HSE for some years [4,5]. Intrinsic or inherent safety should be the goal of all designers.

For plants which already exist (especially nuclear plants where access is often either difficult or impossible) the response to this hierarchy can be different to that for plants in design. At this stage the Reasonably Practicable or ALARP principle takes effect. Whilst the ALARP concept from TOR is easy to understand, in DSA the concept is not so easy to apply. The surrogate developed from many years of experience has been to establish the "modern standard". This is compared with what exists and those modifications that improve safety are highlighted. The judgment about what to implement is a combination of the balance of plant life, the hazard potential, the current deficit in performance, costs and benefits. The judgments in nuclear plant are often made on the basis of national and international experience. It is important to note, that it may be acceptable to partly meet the safety shortfall where a safety gain can be made at reasonable cost. However, a case based on cost-benefit analysis alone is unlikely to be sufficient since it would not normally address the deterministic drivers.

In summary the fundamental DSA technique is simple:

     a.   assume the fault occurs with the worst consequences (usually qualitatively).

     b.   assume the worst allowable plant state in terms of feeds, impurities, plant availability and other conditions including start up and shut down .

     c.   develop a technical description of how a fault develops and the engineering calculations which demonstrate how the system or plant behaves under that fault condition. Do not assume any control or safety provision operates correctly. Often this will be a transient analysis.

     d.   define the safety systems available to prevent, terminate or mitigate the fault on the basis of its significance.

e.   determine if these meet the characteristics of quality safety systems e.g. P61/P62 hierarchy, single failure proof, diverse, redundant, segregated, capable of detecting the fault under fault conditions and so on. For more frequent faults, single failures in the safety system is assumed. This is one route for deciding how many redundant trains will be needed in some safety systems. In particular, safety related items which are maintained on line should be assumed to be in the worst maintenance state.

f.   assess the effectiveness of the safety systems on a proportionately conservative basis to demonstrate adequate performance.

g.   judge the adequacy of the safety systems against the Principle 25 criteria of no dose and at least one barrier intact except in the most severe cases and, ideally, having an accident rate less than 10^{-7} per annum for major accidents. For lower consequence faults such a frequency is likely to be both unnecessary and expensive given the potential harm from that fault. It is often the case that surrogate or subordinate rules can be developed to help engineers and analysts demonstrate adequate reliability.

In many cases faults can be considered as transients from steady state and modeling the time variation of some parameters can vary from simple to extremely complex. The more complex calculations are often carried out with computer codes e.g. Computational Fluid Dynamics (CFD). If such codes are used, they should be validated (ensure the code models plant behavior as accurately as possible with due conservatism) and verified (ensure that both the code and the input data are as correct as possible).

Uncertainties which lead to undue constraints on operations can often result in research and development either to look at ways of better preventing or terminating the fault or to reduce conservatism in the analysis by increasing confidence in the underpinning data. Also, the conservatism in the analysis helps develop a design that is robust and can tolerate unforeseen faults e.g. Three Mile Island's containment was not designed for the potential hydrogen ignition insult but, because the design was conservative, it tolerated it. Managing conservatism is covered further in the annex.

The results of such analyses give outputs that put constraints on the operations in question. These are referred to in total as the Safe Operating Envelope for the plant or operation. Licence Condition 23 calls for Limits and Conditions and these are usually derived from the DSA as shown in Figure 1.

CONCLUSION

Deterministic Safety Analysis is a very wide ranging technique intended to demonstrate the robustness of nuclear plant to tolerate relatively frequent faults. The technique is quite different to the more usual fault trees used for PSA (QRA) and serves a different purpose. DSA requires a detailed and comprehensive professional knowledge of how the operations (plants) respond to faults. This can involve anything from simple hand calculation to complex CFD computer models. The rigour and conservatism is a matter of judgment but increasing rigour and increasing conservatism is expected as the harm potential and uncertainty increase.

ANNEX - EXTRACT FROM THE GUIDE

This guide gives inspectors an interpretation of deterministic safety analysis (DSA) together with many of the associated engineering principles used in the assessment of licensees' safety cases. DSA will be used for the integrated concept of a robust demonstration of plant fault tolerance.

SAPs use the term DBAA, design basis accident analysis and so DSA incorporates DBAA and is closely related to it. Deterministic covers qualitative and quantitative, non-PSA aspects of assessments.

There are two functions of DSA that together encapsulate its essence:

a. DSA, together with the engineering justification, as presented in safety cases, provides a robust demonstration of fault tolerance in a proportionate manner;

b. DSA is an input into the engineering design to allow a judgment about the quality that needs to be built into the plant and thus achieve adequate reliability.

General: It is important to note that DSA and the inherent safety of the plant tend to deal with non trivial accidents with the aim of providing defence in depth in a proportionate manner. If the resulting plant is engineered on a sound, robust basis then good engineering practice should ensure less significant events are catered for. PSA should also catch any other identified fault.

It is also important to note that the order of the steps in the logic in Figure 1 is not usually important and that iteration will mean revisiting many aspects as designs evolve. The diagram does not show the multiple iterations that may be necessary.

In DBAA and DSA, uncertainties are dealt with by conservatism in the transient and radiological analyses. Similarly, P82 states that "The design should be conservative . . . ". It is convenient to distinguish between these "conservatisms". The analysis conservatism is preferred as it then permeates through to the engineering to deliver the safety function. Conversely, the margins built into the engineering using such features as robust, prudent design and large factors of safety to generate margins can make an equally valid contribution. It is always possible to balance one against the other or to balance conservatisms within analyses. Therefore, both conservatism and the engineering margins must be judged to yield an outcome that is both safe with an appropriate over design but not so over engineered as to make the outcome disproportionate, illogical or unworkable.

Source ID & Operating modes: The practice of identifying fault types or groups by identifying the characteristics of the activity source (see also Harm Potential later) with a top down approach is one of the key differences between a deterministic case and PSA. It is linked to P19 where faults are analysed as fault groups by taking the characteristics of the most restrictive fault as representative of the group. This allows analysis to be carried out in a comprehensible and suitably robust manner with a clarity that is often difficult with probabilistic techniques.

All initiating faults: This is the bottom up form of initiating fault identification and should generate a comprehensive and near complete overall fault schedule. There are different interpretations of SAPs for DSA purposes:

a. use either the full fault listing as the fault schedule;

b. use the listing derived from the P15 technique;   or

    c. use the reduced set which has been subject to the engineering out and low consequence filters to generate the fault schedule.

    These faults or fault groups are then associated with their protection to generate the overall schedule. For the purposes of DSA either of the second two reduced set fault listings would be adequate. The key aspect is that a formal fault identification system has been used. The aim of the fault schedule is to show how faults have been identified and traced through the analysis. It is acceptable, and often desirable, to group faults rather than repeatedly analyse similar faults. Demonstration of completeness is still required.

    It is important to note that initiating faults may originate in one plant on a multi plant site before propagating to where the consequence could potentially be realised. This should be covered by appropriate interface arrangements if the fault is not traced through the complete fault sequence.

    Engineer out: (or design out) it is important to distinguish between faults which cannot happen, often because of technical choices to achieve inherently safer plant, and those which are very remote such as incredibility of failure cases (IOF). Faults which are engineered out are related to both of these. It then becomes physically impossible, provided the passive engineering and system configurations are maintained, for the fault to develop. Thus, the analysis should show the engineering and system configuration can be preserved and any change to these configurations should be assessed with the safety functions clearly in mind before changes are made. If gross failure would invalidate the case, in the absence of an IOF case, it may be necessary to make an incredibility of gross failure[1] (IOGF) argument. In all such cases maintenance would be expected to cover assurance of continued function by reference to appropriate schedules and, if necessary, repairs would be expected in a short timescale to keep the safety case valid or, if this is not possible, there should be another equivalent way of assuring continued safety function.

    Low consequence: (not part of DSA) these are fault sequences, assessed on a conservative basis, unlikely to give doses in excess of the Ionising Radiations Regulations (IRR) annual whole body limits (or equivalent if other limits are more restrictive). Much depends on the assessment techniques but the aim is to remove the analysis burden where the upper consequence bound is low. Good practice should give an adequate answer in such cases. However, for any fault which passes this test (yes leg), there should be some form of safety measure. The quality and reliability expected from that safety measure should be proportionate to the harm potential. Care must be taken to account for the harm potential under consideration before deciding the fault is low consequence.

    IOF: (not normally part of DSA) these arguments should be extremely rare but, if used, do need to be rigorous (P70). By convention, the failure frequency associated with such cases is taken to be 10^{-7} p.a. Thus an IOF argument is automatically taken down the BDBA leg. It is difficult to see how to avoid a severe accident analysis since the fault is likely to be severe and should be analysed as a severe accident.

---

[1]IOGF is used in this guide as shown (there are other interpretations). An example might be where a case depends on a static pressure generated by the pipe configuration to ensure a positive pressure gradient into the active medium under all reasonably foreseeable conditions. Thus the pipe configuration must be maintained yet the pressure would not be compromised by, say, a minor valve leak or a pin hole in a weld. A guillotine break would invalidate the case and is GROSS FAILURE.

It is also acceptable in some circumstances to use a multi legged argument (similar to an IOF argument). In these circumstances, where no single leg of the argument is sufficient to support the case, it may be possible to show that a combination of nominally lower quality safety provisions can cumulatively give the same degree of safety assurance as a smaller number of more robust systems. The legs of such a case should be as independent as possible to avoid common cause effects.

Severe accident analysis and Beyond Design Basis Analysis (BDBA) are not part of DSA. Both are carried out on a best estimate basis. Often BDBA will be bounded within the conservatisms of the DSA. BDBA is not expected outside PSA.

The basis for safety assessments has been established both in law and in published documents. Thus, the rigour expected can be judged on the basis of radioactive inventory, radio toxicity, "driving force" and mobility - the harm potential.

a.   Highest tier: typically, operating reactor cores, highly active plant and equivalents2, unplanned criticality - full application of DSA with all assumptions rigorously justified. Full conservatism in analysis unless there is a sound justification for the values and / or modeling chosen. Codes and calculations should be fully validated.

b.   Intermediate tier: typically reactor waste stores, medium active plant and equivalents[2] - DSA to be applied as far as is possible, assumptions must be reasonable and capable of justification. A due level of prudence would be expected in the assumptions and analysis. The modeling should be shown to be appropriate.

c.   Lowest tier plant: typically low active waste handling, other low active plant and equivalents - detailed DSA is often not justified on the grounds of harm potential although it would be expected if the unit operations were being used elsewhere and the potential faults had already been modeled there (the cost of transferring the expertise is minimal) or where the analysis is very simple and easy to perform. Use "conservative best estimates" if the analysis is done at all.

For the purposes of P25 dose assessments there should be no doses from design basis fault sequences except in the most severe case where they should not exceed 100 mSv on a conservative basis (P25b). The equivalent dose for a worker should not exceed 200 mSv on a conservative basis (P25c). (These can be considered success criteria and may be compared to the BSO and BSL, although such comparisons are very inexact).

Of particular importance are P61 & 62 - these give the preferred response to faults. Use of dose minimisation by introducing mitigation factors into the release calculations should not be the first option in a DSA case. This is because such analysis does not take account of defence in depth and cannot usually be shown robust unless there is a guarantee that the physical phenomena modeled in the justification will be those prevailing during that fault. Thus, it is prudent to adopt the approach that prevention is better than cure. The following hierarchy has been developed:

---

[2]equivalence can be demonstrated by example where plutonium plants and HA plants have similar rigour in their analyses. The term equivalent is used to ensure every plant either has a "home" or is outside this regime because it has no safety significance in DSA. However, there may well be cases where inactive operations are claimed as safety measures and these should be engineered to a proportionate standard depending on the degree of reliance placed on them and the harm potential of the associated operation(s).

a. the design should be such that hazards are avoided (intrinsic or inherent safety);

b. the design should use passive features without undue reliance on control or safety systems;

c. any failure or fault should produce no significant deviation other than an indication that the fault has happened;

d. the plant should be brought to a safe state by continuously available safety measures or, if not practical, safety measures that need to be brought into operation;

e. administrative safety measures are an option where there is no reasonable alternative;

f. finally, mitigation (filtration / scrubbing) is then taken into account.

The aim is to be as near the top of this list as possible. This is not exactly what SAPs say but represents a strongly preferred interpretation. As a matter of good practice mitigating systems such as filtration and / or personal protective equipment (PPE) would be expected and it may well be that credit can and should be taken but they should not be the first "port of call". There will always be cases where mitigation is the only high reliability safety measure. This does not mean that there should be any lessening of effort to enhance the quality of the engineering higher up the hierarchy (even if it cannot be shown to be fully effective as a high quality system). Hence, only rarely should mitigation be the sole safety measure for faults analysed by DSA. Thus the outcome should be a plant or operation which has proportionate defence in depth (P65). This will be driven by the principles that allow no single failure to compromise the safety function (P78) and the best use of segregation, diversity and redundancy (P68, 79, 80 & 81). This hierarchy is consistent with HSE guidance.

The output from DSA is included in the schedule of safety systems and may be compared with the safety measures derived by other means. The expected outcome would be a list of faults related to the claimed protection often embodied in the Fault Schedule. There is an interface here, between the analysts and the other engineering specialisms who take the DSA output as an input. Iteration between the DSA inspector and other inspectors in the assessment of licensees cases for adequacy and sufficiency is extremely important in seeking a holistic view. The basis for trip settings, limits, Operating Rules (ORs), Operating Instructions (OIs) and Emergency OI's (EOI's) are included in this assessment.

Numeric Reliability: This is part of the ongoing iteration in the search for adequacy and sufficiency. The main use is to ensure that the application of the robust engineering principles has produced a reliable, workable solution being measured by this somewhat diverse technique. Ideally the overall numeric reliability at which the fault is realised to non trivial consequences should be at frequencies below which the figure ceases to have significance 10^{-7}p.a. but pragmatically, provided there are sufficient non-quantified safety measures then a numeric value lying proportionately between the BSO and BSL given in P45 - Plant Damage Frequencies would normally be good enough. There may be cases where very significant deterministic arguments cannot be quantified. In such cases full account should be taken of past precedent and, if there is no alternative, judgment should be used to designate a conservative reliability (P40 & P70). This judgment would be expected to be the exception.

DSA needs to show on a system by system basis (selected from the fault schedule or a group of faults) and for each fault associated with the selected system:

a.   how the fault, if it develops, is terminated or mitigated: one expected technique is to assume the initiating event happens and follow how the plant reacts. This requires a technical analysis of the variables such as flow, mechanical loads, temperature / heat and rates of reaction and can be summarised as "a technical description of how a fault develops with the engineering calculations which demonstrate how the system or plant behaves under that fault condition" . The technique used must be appropriate to the underlying process(es);

b.   the analysis continues with the engineered provisions are provided to detect and, if necessary, terminate the fault (see P61/62 hierarchy), what operator actions are required and, finally, how the effects are mitigated;

c.   how the limits and conditions are set and how these plant items achieve the claimed reliability to meet such demands. Conditions refer to plant or system configurations that describe the safe working envelope of the operation(s) being considered.

These are all done on the basis of worst normally permitted states in terms of plant configuration and plant inputs. This is the main constraint DSA puts on normal operation. This technique is akin to event tree analysis since it represents a sequence in time with multiple potential outcomes depending on success or failure of the engineered provisions and operator actions. The outcome can be seen as somewhat diverse from fault tree treatments in isolation. Fault tree techniques are more useful in supporting the logic where engineered provisions or operator actions might fail.

Inspectors should be able to satisfy themselves that the plant which has been analysed is that which has been designed. This correspondence is vital to ensure the validity of the analysis and this correspondence should continue throughout plant life

The approach for existing plants to demonstrate ALARP is:

a.   establish the existing standard - this includes not only changes in published standards but also the "standard" "what would the plant look like if it were designed today". This drives optioneering studies which may find alternatives which meet the safety intent differently to the existing "standard". To ensure the LC23 demonstration this optioneering should be transparent.

b.   examine the plant and establish what safety improvement is reasonably practical in terms of changes. This should be on a twofold basis - first, if the plant continues to the end of its expected life. Second there will be further modifications that might be made if the plant were to operate longer. In this case, the reasonably practical modifications should be listed taking the overall plant life as twice the design life or a further 20 years, which ever is longer.

c.   if the plant operates beyond the expected life then those extended life modifications should be carried out as well as others that have become reasonably practical in the light of changing standards and knowledge.

It would be unusual for the entire design concept of a plant to be changed and radical change to many plants will be impractical. Thus, the reasonably practicable options will be limited. The yardstick is the P61/62 hierarchy of preferred responses to faults. So arguments for existing plants should be similar to those for plant in design but the comparison with the P61/62 hierarchy and considerations of what is possible, or reasonably practical, may give different safety measures to achieve the safety function.

There may be cases (particularly when assessing older plant):

a. where reliability cannot be proven;

b. where the doses incurred to carry out such modifications to provide the target reliability could prove prohibitive;

c. where the increment in hazard potential during the modification would be unacceptable.

In such cases it will be necessary to make a proportionate argument on the basis of ALARP. Such arguments should include consideration of partial achievement to achieve a safety gain as well as full implementation. This is because partial achievement may be at reasonable cost without other undue detriment.

REFERENCES

1. Safety Assessment Principles for Nuclear Plants   HSE   1992

2. The Tolerability of Risk from Nuclear Power Stations   HSE   1992

3. Sizewell B Public Inquiry Report by Sir Frank Layfield   Dept of Energy

4. INSIDE PROJECT AND THE INSET TOOLKIT: CEC Environment programme 1990-94, Contract No. EV5V-CT94-0416 "Inherently safer approaches to the design of chemical process plant" HSE Contract No 3225/R71.04

5. DRAFT Health & Safety Guide: Successful Design for Health & Safety To be published.

6. Evidence from the Health and Safety Executive To the HOUSE OF LORDS SELECT COMMITTEE ON SCIENCE AND TECHNOLOGY, Inquiry on The Management of Nuclear Waste. Para 25 Submitted by: Jenny Bacon, Director General Health and Safety Executive. January 1998

7. The Use of Deterministic Analysis in Safety Cases for High Hazard Plant, G A Trimble. Proceedings of a conference on Safety Cases: Cross Industry comparisons of best practice. IBC 2001

ACKNOWLEDGMENT AND DISCLAIMER

Thanks go to very many in HSE's Nuclear Installations Inspectorate for help and advice in developing this paper and the guide it describes. The opinions here are those of the author. No part of this paper should be taken as definitive interpretation of HSE or NII policy, the law, or their application.

Figure 1 – DSA Logic Diagram

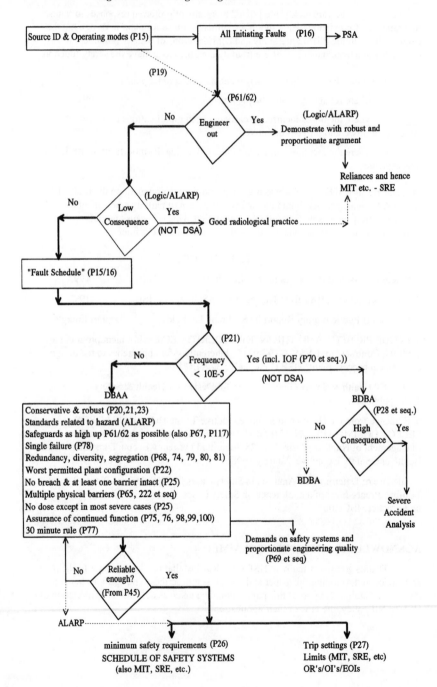

POSITIVE AND NEGATIVE EXPERIENCE WITH THE NEW COMAH REGIME IN THE SPECIALITY CHEMICALS INDUSTRY

Christopher J. Beale, Ciba Specialty Chemicals, PO Box 38, Bradford, West Yorkshire. BD12 0JZ. UK.
MIChemE

Ciba Water and Paper Treatments operate two 'top tier' COMAH sites in the UK. A COMAH Safety Report was issued for both sites in 2000 - one covered about 50 plants and storage areas and was submitted in three phases; the other covered 4 plants and storage areas and was submitted as an integrated report. A team from Ciba have been working on these reports for two years and the Competent Authority has been assessing these reports over the last year. Experience has been gained in a wide range of areas : administration of the COMAH regime, impacts of COMAH on running the business, technical issues, sitewide issues, integrating safety and environmental risk assessments, making the COMAH demonstration and demonstrating ALARP. This paper discusses the positive and negative impacts that COMAH has produced.

COMAH, major hazards, risk assessment

1. INTRODUCTION.

1.1 Overview Of Ciba Water And Paper Treatments UK Operations.

Ciba Specialty Chemicals operate an integrated chemical manufacturing site at Bradford, UK and a smaller manufacturing site at Grimsby, UK within the Water and Paper Treatments business. The Bradford site consists of about twenty tank farms for bulk chemical storage and about twenty production areas, some inside buildings and others in outdoor areas. These production areas are supported by two power stations and a number of warehouse units. The Grimsby site is much smaller and consists of bulk and packaged raw material storage areas, a production building and a warehouse.

The sites handle a wide range of hazardous chemicals with the potential for fire, explosion, toxic and environmental impact damage as a result of an accident. The production plants use a range of batch, semi-batch and continuous processes, mainly based around acrylate chemistry.

Historically, both sites have fallen within the 'Top Tier' requirements of the CIMAH Regulations (CIMAH, 1984) and have had to produce a number of CIMAH Safety Reports covering different areas of the site. Both sites now fall within the 'Top Tier' requirements of the COMAH Regulations (COMAH, 1999) and full COMAH Safety Reports have been submitted for each site.

As the Bradford site is complex, the COMAH Safety Report was submitted as a 'core' report and two 'part ' reports. The Grimsby site is much simpler, so the COMAH Safety Report was submitted as a single integrated report.

1.2 Overview Of COMAH Regime.

The COMAH Regulations are complicated and this paper is not intended to describe the details of the regulations. These details can be found in publications such as (HSE, 1999a), (HSE, 1999b) and (EA, 1999).

It is important to understand that there are some key differences between the COMAH Regulations (COMAH, 1999) and the CIMAH Regulations (CIMAH, 1984) which pre-dated the COMAH Regulations, particularly :

- The scope of COMAH is more wide ranging, covering generic categories of chemicals, chemicals categorised with the R50, R51 and R53 'dangerous to the environment' risk phrases, process as well as storage activities and establishments rather than individual installations. Furthermore, individual smaller quantities of hazardous chemicals which are individually below the COMAH threshold inventory but together exceed the threshold inventory must be aggregated under the COMAH Regulations.
- The Competent Authority has a duty to prohibit activities if he considers that 'serious deficiencies' exist at the installation.
- There is an increased emphasis on safety management systems (SMS) and a requirement to have a Major Accident Prevention Policy (MAPP) in place to ensure that the SMS specifically addresses major accidents to man and the environment.
- Equal emphasis is placed on the environmental and safety aspects of major accident hazard risks.
- The operator must demonstrate that 'all means necessary' (interpreted in the UK using the ALARP (As Low As Reasonably Practicable) principle) have been taken to eliminate, control and mitigate major hazard risks at the site.

1.3 Aims Of Paper.

This paper summarises practical experience that has been gained with the COMAH regime for two very different chemical manufacturing sites. This experience includes preparing and submitting the Safety Reports as well as feedback from the Competent Authority and is summarised under the following three categories :

- Benefits of the COMAH regime (**Section 3**).
- Problems associated with the COMAH regime (**Section 4**).
- Difficulties encountered with COMAH implementation (**Section 5**).

Important factors which have to be addressed when planning a COMAH Safety Report are also summarised (**Section 2**) together with those factors which were considered to be critical for producing the Safety Report (**Section 6**).

2. IMPORTANT FACTORS FOR PLANNING THE COMAH SAFETY REPORT.

The following eight factors have been found to be particularly important when planning a COMAH Safety Report :

- Assessing the extent of information gathering which is required for a complex site.
- Deciding the level of detail which is required for different sections of the report, particularly for process area risk assessment.
- Getting the balance right between allocating staff to prepare the report and to continue running the business.
- Structuring the report as a phased report or an integrated report.
- Identifying areas where a sitewide approach should be taken rather than a plant-by-plant approach.
- Deciding the amount of consequence modelling that is required.
- Using a qualitative, semi-quantitative or fully quantitative approach for risk assessment within the report.
- Involving the Competent Authority in the planning process or presenting a 'fait accompli'.

2.1 Extent Of Information Gathering.

It is very difficult to accurately assess the amount of time and effort which is required for producing the report, particularly if it is the first report that the company has produced. COMAH differs significantly from CIMAH (as described in **Section 1.2**) and some of these differences have a major impact on the workload that is required for producing the Safety Report. Three areas in particular have been found to be particularly resource intensive : assessing the risks associated with process (as opposed to storage) areas, integrating environmental and safety risk assessment and making the COMAH demonstration.

It is important that these problems are identified early in the report production process as additional or specialist resources may be required to complete the work.

2.2 Level Of Detail In Report.

A balance has to be struck between producing a usable document and producing a document that is so massive that it is impossible to understand. This implies that different aspects of the report will contain different levels of detail. A sensible approach would be to present more detail where risks are assessed as being highest or risk controls most critical.

Particular care is required when assessing process areas as batch plants are likely to produce wide ranges and large numbers of different chemicals. It would be impractical to describe the risks associated with each process, so some form of generic approach is required, linking with existing reports and processes that the site uses.

As the Safety Report will be in the public domain, it is essential that the team preparing the report constantly consider some key questions : will the published information give away commercially confidential information? And will the information be a potential security risk? There are mechanisms for excluding some information from the public domain if these criteria are likely to be breached, but it would often be less risky to exclude the information completely.

Under the old CIMAH regime, operators could confidently submit layout drawings, plans, process and instrumentation (P&iD) drawings mass and energy balances, safe in the knowledge that it would not be in the public domain and that it mainly concerned the less commercially sensitive areas of the operations, namely storage. Process information is potentially much more valuable and it is important that this is not accidentally published in the COMAH Safety Report when it is commercially sensitive.

2.3 Resource Allocation Of Key Staff.

The report production process is likely to require intensive efforts from environmental and safety specialists in the company over a six month (straightforward report) to two year (complicated site report) time frame. There is a real risk that key staff will become isolated from their normal business roles and the quality of other activities (new projects, auditing, safety initiatives etc) may suffer. A careful balance has to be struck in this area. Positive benefits can, however, flow from the COMAH Safety Report if it is of high quality, making it easier to make decisions about major hazards in the site's future.

2.4 Phased Or Integrated Report Structure.

Integrated sites which were covered by the 'top tier' requirements of the CIMAH Regulations were given the opportunity to submit one integrated COMAH Safety Report or a first 'core' report supplemented by additional detailed reports over a longer timeframe.

The benefits of producing an integrated report are :

- Completing the report within a shorter timeframe so key staff can move to other projects.
- The Competent Authority can obtain an early view of the whole major hazards risk profile for the site.
- A reduction in duplication of information within the report, depending on how the report is structured.
- Paying lower fees to the Competent Authority under the charging arrangements as they should be able to assess an integrated report more efficiently.

The main disadvantage with the integrated approach is the pressure it can place on key safety and environmental staff during the report production process.

2.5 Areas Where A Sitewide Approach Is Useful.

Where an activity is carried out consistently across the site, time and effort can be saved and clarity can be improved by describing that aspect of the safety report on a sitewide basis. This will typically apply to areas such as safety management systems, emergency response, some parts of maintenance, risk assessment methodology and the engineering design process.

It is useful to identify those areas where a sitewide approach will be beneficial early in the report production process.

2.6 Extent Of Consequence Modelling.

Consequence assessment can be performed in a number of ways, depending on the hazard which is being assessed. Quantitative modelling is very useful for objectively assessing certain types of hazard but can be time consuming. Some hazards are difficult to model accurately and practically in a quantitative manner and are best assessed qualitatively (eg. using expert judgement or reviewing the impacts of previous similar accidents in the industry).

It is important to define the ground rules for consequence modelling early in the project so that the amount of modelling is manageable and does not obscure the key facts in the safety report. Areas which can be difficult to model include the effects of chemical runaway reactions, internal fires in vessels, combustion and by-products and dust explosions.

2.7 Risk Assessment Methodology.

If the safety report is to be useful as a living document, it is important that :

- It can be updated easily and the risk assessment techniques used within the report are clearly understood by site staff.
- It uses a risk assessment methodology which is consistent with other site risk assessment processes, whether these are qualitative, semi-quantitative or fully quantitative.
- It uses a risk assessment methodology which is consistent with other site major hazard risk assessment methodologies, such as those used for assessing the risks to people in occupied buildings.
- Frequency assessments provide a consistent and objective framework for assessing and ranking risks rather than a distraction for discussing the significance of minor differences between the absolute values of very small numbers.

It is therefore important to agree the frequency and risk assessment methodologies early in the report production process, ensuring that information is presented in a consistent and comparable format throughout the report.

2.8 Involvement Of Competent Authority.

The introduction of new legislation is a learning process for the regulator and the regulated alike. When the legislation is complex, such as the COMAH Regulations, it is very useful for both parties to understand the problems, anticipated solutions and plans of the other party. This can often be achieved by holding regular meetings with the Competent Authority to ensure that the following types of issue are covered :

- The rules of engagement are agreed for the charging regime : when is an activity chargeable? How will the Competent Authority provide notification that the activity is chargeable? To whom will invoices be submitted? Will the operator be charged when inexperienced staff are used on the Competent Authority's team?
- The operator understands the availability of existing and planned guidance on the new legislation.

- Areas where problems are anticipated are identified eg. modelling the effects of batch reactions.
- Planned report structures and timescales for submission (operator) and assessment (regulator).

Regular meetings will probably be required because much of this information is dynamic, subject to change over time.

Table 1 summarises these key factors.

3. BENEFITS OF THE COMAH REGIME.

The COMAH legislation covers a broader spectrum of a company's major hazard risks than the previous CIMAH legislation covered and therefore forms a more logical basis for risk management. A major flaw with the old CIMAH legislation was that it often divided manufacturing sites into a complex and illogical number of CIMAH and non-CIMAH areas.

In practice, this meant that most attention was often focused on the wrong areas because of legal scoping defintions. For example, acrylamide bulk storage tanks were included within the scope of CIMAH but extremely flammable methyl chloride and tri-methylamine tanks were excluded. Accidents involving acrylamide only had the potential to affect areas which were local to the tank because of the physical and toxicological properties of the liquid. Methyl chloride and tri-methylamine storage vessels had the potential to BLEVE (Boiling Liquid Expanding Vapour Explosion) which would cause significant damage within hundreds of metres of the vessels. All of these chemicals will be covered within the scope of COMAH.

The benefits gained from COMAH will depend on whether operating companies view COMAH as an administrative burden or as an opportunity to improve corporate risk management. By taking a positive attitude to the new legislation, the following benefits can be gained :

- improved involvement of people throughout the organisation in controlling major accident hazard risks.
- better communication of hazards and risks within and outside the organisation.
- more effective corporate risk management.

Table 1   Key Factors For Compiling the COMAH Safety Report

Ref	Key Factor		Difficult Areas	
2.1	Extent of information gathering.	Assessing process risks	Integrating safety and environmental risk assessments	Making the COMAH demonstration
2.2	Level of detail in report.	Batch plants	Commercial confidentiality issues (P&IDs, mass / energy balances)	Security concerns (plans, layouts)
2.3	Resource allocation for key staff.	Neglecting normal jobs	Pressure on EHS staff	Assuring safety report quality
2.4	Phased or integrated report structure.	Efficiency of assessment by Competent Authority	Compliance cost	Resources required for integrated reports
2.5	Areas where a sitewide approach is useful.	Reducing duplication within the safety report	Identifying areas where consistent approaches are used	Clarity of presentation of information
2.6	Extent of consequence modelling.	Complexity and practicality of modelling technique	Availability of generic data	Clarity of presentation of information
2.7	Risk assessment methodology.	Ease of updating safety report	Consistency with sitewide risk assessment techniques	Consistency with other risk assessment initiatives (eg. occupied buildings)
2.8	Involvement of Competent Authority.	Administrative arrangements	Report structures and timescales	Interpretation of legislative requirements

3.1 Involvement Of People Throughout The Organisation In Controlling Risks.

As operating companies and the Regulatory Authorities gain more experience with the COMAH regime, so companies will have to ensure that staff at all levels within the organisation are involved in risk management. This will help to ensure that senior management adopt realistic and operable systems of work that take account of the real issues that are relevant on the shop floor as well as the strategic issues that the company has to address.

There are often widely different perceptions of risk within an organisation. Operators may have ignored or trivialised certain risks; management may just assume that all risks are well understood; safety specialists may have developed an overly theoretical view of risk levels. The COMAH Safety Report can be a useful tool for developing a common understanding of risk levels within a company if it is clearly written and people throughout the organisation are involved in preparing and understanding the report.

It is also possible to use the data and summaries within the Safety Report as a basis for safety and environmental training programmes. This can improve team-working as different people become more aware of the role that they and their colleagues play in minimising risk levels in the organisation as a whole.

3.2 Improved Risk Communication.

If the COMAH Safety Report is well written, it should summarise a wide range of complex data about major accident hazards in a clear form. This will help staff throughout the organisation to have a better understanding of risk levels and how they adversely or positively affect these risks.

Nowadays, risk levels have to be communicated to a wide range of interested groups : corporate head office departments, insurers, auditors, Regulatory Authorities, neighbouring communities and the media. Risk communication to these groups will be facilitated by having clear and comprehensive summary data available.

3.3 More Effective Risk Management.

Information about major accident hazard risks tends to be spread throughout the organisation and is often presented in different formats in each area. It can be difficult to obtain an accurate sitewide view of the company's risks. Some areas where risk management has been improved include :

- **Highlighting gaps in available information** for some older plants and peripheral activities such as fuel storage.
- **Identification of areas where risk controls are inadequate** such as maintenance activities for safety critical functions which are not being performed properly.
- **Prioritising areas where additional risk reduction measures are required** such as older plants which no longer meet new plant design standards.

- **Assessing the effectiveness, completeness and practicality of the emergency plan.**
- **Defining a basis for planning future site development** taking account of the effect of this development on existing and predicted future risk levels.

4. PROBLEMS ASSOCIATED WITH THE COMAH REGIME.

Some of the potential problems associated with the COMAH regime have been discussed in **Section 2**. Particular problems have been encountered in the following areas :

- Publication of information that may prejudice site security.
- Publication of information that may prejudice commercial confidentiality.
- Cost of compliance with COMAH.
- Consultation distances and hazardous substances consent.
- Different attitudes to implementation of Seveso II directive across Europe.

4.1 Site Security.

COMAH Safety Reports will be made available to the public to satisfy governmental commitments to increase public access to environmental information. This should help to increase the public's confidence about risks associated with neighbouring major hazards installations and lead to public pressure to improve those installations whose performance does not meet acceptable standards.

It is, however, possible that the information could be used maliciously by arsonists or terrorist groups. The COMAH Safety Report is likely to contain a lot of detailed information about the most vulnerable areas within chemical plants. Older sites often have major hazard tank farms, tanker loading / offloading facilities and plants close to the site boundary and most sites will have vulnerable gas lines and warehouses close to the site boundary.

The operating company has to assess escalation risks (where accidents start in one area of the site and spread to affect adjacent areas). This can only meaningfully be completed with reference to the specific location of equipment within the site. This information would be very useful to a potential arsonist or saboteur.

Major accident hazard frequencies are historically low, even on high risk plants. Great care must be taken to ensure that arson and sabotage do not start to contribute significantly to these risk levels because of the publication of major accident hazard data in the public domain.

It is possible to apply for confidentiality for some sections of the report on the grounds that publication poses a threat to national security or on the advice of the local Police Authority. In reality, many sites will not pose a threat to national security and many local Police Authorities will be unfamiliar with COMAH and the chemical industry.

Furthermore, confidence in the Safety Report may be undermined if sections of the report are unavailable and confidential. There may be a perception that the chemical company has something to hide. This means that the operating company has to be very careful about the way that information is presented in the Safety Report, particularly where (i) layouts and plans are presented and (ii) activities are close to the site boundary and vulnerable to attack.

4.2 Commercial Confidentiality.

Under the CIMAH regime, the operating company could provide sensitive information to the Regulatory Authorities with confidence because it would be treated confidentially. A large amount of information has to be presented in the COMAH Safety Report and operating companies may inadvertently disclose sensitive commercial information about their processes and operations.

This is particularly important for layout drawings, plans, process and instrumentation (P&iD) drawings and mass and energy balances.

4.3 Cost Of Compliance.

The UK Competent Authorities will be charging operating companies for assessment work associated with COMAH. No such charges were levied under the previous CIMAH regime. Five particular issues cause concern to operating companies :

- The high hourly fee rate that will be charged for assessment, which is significantly higher than the rate that many top safety consultancies would charge for similar work.
- Fears that operating companies may have to pay these high rates for junior staff from the Competent Authority.
- Difficulties in budgeting for future assessment work by the Competent Authority due to the lack of a pre-agreed scope for the work to be carried out.
- Diverting management time to control the costs which are being charged for assessment by the Competent Authority. This is particularly difficult when the invoices for such work are vague and do not clearly relate to specific activities.
- Fears that these additional costs will erode the international competitiveness of European chemical companies.

4.4 Consultation Distances And Hazardous Substances Consent.

Many operating companies were initially assigned very large Public Information Zones (PIZ) around their sites because of the methodology that the Competent Authority used for calculating these zones. The operating company has to provide defined information to people living within these zones under the COMAH Regulations.

The problem arose because the Competent Authority chose to calculate the PIZ's from the relatively limited information which was submitted by operating companies in their Hazardous Substances Consent applications rather than the detailed information that was submitted to the same Competent Authority in the COMAH Safety Reports. This caused problems to some companies because their PIZ's suddenly grew by factors of 5 to 10 as a result of the change from CIMAH to COMAH.

This caused an additional bureaucratic burden on the companies which were affected but the problem was solvable by making the Hazardous Substances Consent form more detailed.

4.5 European Implementation Of Seveso II Directive.

There are real concerns that the competitiveness of the UK process and manufacturing industries is being eroded because :

-   The legislation has been enacted more quickly in the UK compared to some other European countries.
-   The legislation is being implemented more thoroughly in the UK compared to some other European countries.

5. DIFFICULTIES WITH IMPLEMENTATION OF THE COMAH REGULATIONS.

This section discusses some of the difficult areas that have been identified in producing COMAH Safety Reports.

5.1 Human Factors And People Issues.

Many older onshore plants were designed before human factors issues were given prominence in plant design. These older plants are therefore often not designed to effectively address human factors issues. Similarly, many procedures and operator competence assurance programmes did not use the latest techniques and few management of change procedures directly assessed the people issues associated with planned changes. This makes it very difficult to make the required human factors COMAH demonstrations for this type of plant. Some of the issues can, however, be addressed by improvement plans but will require many years of work.

5.2 Major Accident Prevention Policy (MAPP).

This may appear to duplicate elements of many company's existing Safety Management Systems (SMS) and operating companies may feel that a MAPP can be created simply by changing the word 'hazard' to 'major accident hazard' where it appears in their existing systems.

Many elements of the SMS are aimed at controlling operational safety and environmental risks. The MAPP is intended to extend these systems to ensure that they also address low frequency / high consequence major accident hazards. The practicalities of introducing and operating an effective MAPP within the framework of COMAH are still unclear to many companies.

5.3 Interpretation Of 'All Means Necessary'.

At first sight, this phrase suggests that risk removal or reduction measures should always be implemented regardless of cost contradicting the well established UK concept of ALARP (As Low As Reasonably Practicable). The UK Regulatory Authorities have indicated that they will be interpreting 'all means necessary' using the ALARP principle. Alternative interpretations of the concept could start to threaten the commercial performance of European chemical companies whilst achieving very low real reductions in risk.

5.4 Demonstration That Risks Are 'ALARP'.

There are a number of demonstrations which are required in the COMAH safety report. One of these requires the operator to demonstrate through a risk assessment process that risk levels are As Low As Reasonably Practicable (ALARP). In some industries, such as the offshore oil and gas industry, there are well established methodologies for making this type of demonstration. These methodologies are often less well suited to the onshore process industries where the range of hazards is often more diverse, the potential risk reduction measures less obvious and the cost drivers more wide ranging.

The following techniques are available, but all of them have disadvantages in an onshore context :

- Quantitative risk analysis, option analysis and formal cost benefit analysis. This would be expensive to implement practically and accurately in many onshore situations and does not easily address the range of cost drivers (safety, environmental, commercial, insurance etc) that exist using a consistent framework.
- Risk matrix analysis focusing on the most significant risks that are identified within the matrix. This is often a workable method but suffers from a lack of objectivity and still leaves a large range of hazards to be assessed for a complex site.
- Code compliance. This is how many decisions, particularly for engineering issues, are and have been made. Although this method is easy to apply, it suffers from a lack of a formal assessment of different options, some codes have a higher status than other codes and there are often grey areas within codes and standards.

As more experience is gained within the onshore industries, more efficient and satisfactory methods may evolve for addressing this issue.

5.5 Demonstration For Older Plants.

These plants were often built when design, legislative and documentation standards were lower than they are today. It is often very difficult to make a coherent COMAH demonstration for this type of plant without doing a lot of additional work. In some cases, companies may even choose to close down some plants as this additional work would make the plant's operations uneconomic.

5.6 Inherent Safety.

Inherent safety opportunities have to be considered under the COMAH regime. It will only be practical to maximise the opportunities for inherent safety at a very early stage in a plant's lifecycle when fundamental decisions are to be made. Inherent safety opportunities will be limited for existing older plants.

5.7 Batch Reactions.

Some plants may be used for producing a wide range of different products using batch reactions. Describing and assessing every batch reaction will be impractical and it will be necessary in many cases to group reactions into generic categories eg. Nitrations.

5.8 Environmental Risk Assessment.

Environmental risk assessment is a technique which is still in it's infancy compared to the approaches which are used for safety risk assessments. Many operating companies have limited skills in this area and will struggle to produce assessments to the required standard.

The safety and environmental risk assessments have to be integrated within the COMAH Safety Report. In many accident scenarios, one of safety or environment will dominate the consequences of the accident. It is important to avoid excessive detail when assessing environmental risks when the scenarios are clearly not going to constitute a MATTE (Major Accident To The Environment). On the other hand, sufficient detail has to be provided to demonstrate that environmental risks have been assessed in an integrated approach with safety risks.

5.9 Consequence Modelling.

Accepted techniques exist for modelling the consequences of many of the accidents associated with the bulk storage of hazardous chemicals. This is not the case for many process accidents such as reactor runaways and dust explosions. Simplifying assumptions can often be made but this will affect the accuracy of the modelling.

It is also very difficult to assess the consequences of releases of combustion products from a fire and by-products from an uncontrolled chemical reaction. This is because :

– It is difficult to assess the source term defining exactly which chemical species have been released. Some of the released chemicals are often formed when plastic packaging materials burn and react with burning chemicals.
– The energy associated with the release just prior to loss of containment cannot be calculated accurately.
– Dispersion modelling techniques do not accurately model the interaction between the intense energy of a fire and the energy of the released vapour cloud.

5.10 Occupied Buildings.

A major initiative was started by the UK Health & Safety Executive to ensure that the risks to onsite personnel in occupied buildings on chemical sites were acceptable. For many companies, significant efforts were required to produce these occupied buildings risk assessments. Unfortunately, this initiative clashed with the COMAH implementation timescales making it very difficult for companies to resource the compliance requirements for both initiatives.

6. CRITICAL FACTORS FOR PRODUCING A COMAH SAFETY REPORT.

Based on the experience gained at these two UK sites, the following process appears to be effective for producing a COMAH Safety Report :

1. List the requirements of the COMAH Regulations using a checklist format.

2. Identify information gaps covering plant descriptions, material properties, hazard identification, risk assessment and safety management systems by comparing existing available information with the COMAH checklist.

3. Decide which gaps can be filled using internal resources and competencies and produce a programme for filling all of the gaps using internal and specialist external resources where required.

4. Produce the report and ensure that key personnel in the organisation 'buy in' to the report where it affects their areas.

5. Produce and implement a prioritised action plan for addressing any deficiencies in risk management encompassing technical, management systems and human factors aspects.

6. Assess future plant changes against the information contained within the COMAH Safety Report.

7. CONCLUSIONS.

Depending on the attitude of operating companies and the Regulatory Authorities, the COMAH Safety Report will either be an expensive administrative burden or a useful tool which can improve corporate risk management.

There are still many uncertainties about the details of producing and maintaining the Safety Report but, over time, many of these issues are likely to be clarified as organisations gain more experience.

Two objective measures of the success of the COMAH Regulations could, however, be used but will only be revealed in future years : 'have the normalised UK major accident safety and environmental accident statistics improved?' and 'have companies moved production facilities to other parts of the world where compliance costs are lower'.

8. REFERENCES.

(CIMAH, 1984)   The Control Of Industrial Major Accident Hazards Regulations, 1984.
(COMAH, 1999) The Control Of Major Accident Hazards Regulations, 1999.
(EA, 1999)   'Guidance On The Environmental Risk Assessment Aspects Of COMAH Safety Reports', Environment Agency. 1999.
(HSE, 1999a)   'A Guide To The COMAH Regulations, 1999', 1999.
(HSE, 1999b)   'Preparing Safety Reports, COMAH Regulations, 1999', 1999.

MOVING FORWARD FROM ASSESSMENT TO INSPECTION - HOW GOOD IS COMAH?

Phil Scott, HM Principal Inspector
Hazardous Installations Directorate, Health & Safety Executive, Government Buildings, Ty Glas, Llanishen, Cardiff CF14 5SH
© Crown Copyright 2001.   Reproduced with the permission of the Controller of Her Majesty's Stationery Office.

The COMAH Regulations 1999 set dates by which operators of 'Top-Tier' sites have to produce safety reports, and the key one of February 2001 having passed means that the majority of UK operators have now completed their first reports. Only those that were not designated new major accident hazard sites prior to COMAH need not yet have done so, and these have until February 2002. So what has been the experience so far of the standard of reports and the likely effectiveness of them in preventing major accidents? Certainly the first two years has not been trouble free, as the two parts of the Competent Authority (CA) have begun to work together, operators have struggled with the requirement for demonstration of safe operation, and both operators and regulators alike have met the challenge of the workload involved in COMAH.

The paper will review the outcome of the first round of safety reports, and the CA's priorities for dealing with initial assessments.   Most importantly, the paper will look forward to the next phase, as the CA begins to move from assessment of reports to inspection of COMAH establishments. Using case studies of two actual incidents that occurred at top tier sites before submission of the safety reports, the question of how likely it was that the incidents might have been prevented if the safety reports had been available and assessed will be examined. Finally the paper will outline some of the particular challenges for the future, for both the CA and industry, as COMAH develops and the public become more aware of the changes it introduces to control of major accidents.

Keywords: COMAH; Competent Authority; Inspection

INTRODUCTION

Many view the COMAH bandwagon as having got off to a somewhat shaky start along the route to delivering improved control of major accident hazards, and cite a range of problems that have afflicted industry and both sides of the Competent Authority (CA) over the first couple of years.   When difficulties are highlighted (and before they have had a realistic chance for solutions to filter through) it is easy to lose sight of the progress made so far in developing the systems COMAH calls for both within the CA and industry. It is also equally easy to lose sight of the 'bigger picture' around COMAH – it's not just about safety reports and their assessment, but a longer-term mechanism for combining assessment with inspection.

There have undoubtedly been (and continue to be) some operational problems with COMAH. This is hardly surprising given the enormity of the jump from the previous regime, CIMAH, to COMAH. In its implementation of the Seveso II Directive, the UK has led the field and encountering operational problems associated with this has followed with a certain inevitability.

This paper presents a personal view, from a regulator's perspective, of the state of the game so far and based on experience of dealing with safety reports and inspection arrangements to date. It also considers the relative importance of inspection in the combined assessment / inspection / improvement cycle: the stage has currently been reached where many COMAH top-tier companies have had their safety reports assessed and there is a move now to much greater emphasis on inspection after the prevalence of assessment so far. A central proposition of this paper is that the inspection phase is the most important element in judging the relative success of COMAH in being able to prevent or at least control major accidents.

EARLY EXPERIENCE WITH COMAH AND SAFETY REPORTS

The 'first round' of safety reports, i.e. those submitted and which began assessment around February 2000, included a substantial number where the quality of presentation and level of information anticipated and expected by the regulators fell well short of expectations, and did not meet the minimum requirements set in Schedule 4 Part 2 of the COMAH regulations. Equally, it has to be said, most were at least acceptable and some were very good quality – so it is, and was, clearly possible for the required standard to be produced. A figure of 40% has been quoted for the level of safety reports from that first round being 'rejected' or returned to operators as requiring further work. That figure is somewhat misleading, as it was affected by a few operators submitting many volumes or modules for the same site or sites that all suffered from the same intrinsic deficiencies in approach – but nevertheless, the 'safety reports returned' rate was higher than anticipated.

In addition to individual feedback to operators on their safety reports, in summer 2000 the CA produced a letter on the early lessons from safety reports, that it circulated to all COMAH TT operators. The intention was to be as open as possible and to draw attention to the emerging problems. The letter highlighted the following main issues from safety reports:

a) Descriptions of safety management systems (SMS) which failed to focus specifically upon the **management** of major accident hazards;

b) A failure to demonstrate the link between the major accident hazards and the measures for prevention control and mitigation. This was a key issue.

c) Descriptions in the reports of what the SMS looked like, rather than why and how it demonstrates that all necessary measures have been taken to control major accident hazards.

d) A failure to demonstrate that there is a systematic approach to evaluating major accident risks.

e) A failure to show that human factors, in particular the part that human failure can play in initiating major accidents and the reliability of safeguards which depend on human action were understood and addressed adequately.

f) The risk assessment process had not been robust enough. Operators had not demonstrated that the results from the assessment of the major accident risks had been taken forward and used as the basis of the process to select, prioritise and schedule further risk reduction measures to reduce risks as low as is reasonably practicable (ALARP). This was also a key issue.

Fuller details were given in the letter on the main problems. The hope was that this information would assist in the process of getting better quality safety reports, both for those operators who had had them returned and also for those who were in the process of preparing them for February 2001 submission.

It was disappointing to say the least, therefore, to find that with the February 2001 reports there was still a substantial number where the information was inadequate and they were returned to the operators. In the area covered by one operational Unit for example (Merseyside, Wales, West Midlands and West of England), out of 52 safety reports received in the first quarter 13 have been returned to the operators – 25%. After an initial assessment (the CA carries out an initial read of all safety reports to ensure the presence of the essential information required by the Regs, before committing to a full and detailed assessment process) this was undoubtedly the appropriate action in the circumstances – the reports were clearly deficient in their coverage. It is the intention of the CA to operate in a cost-effective way both in terms of using its resources on viable reports and also to save operators unnecessary charges for work on reports that would patently fail to meet the assessment criteria.

In many cases, whether reports have been rejected or not, there have been serious concerns amongst assessors that the information presented in reports indicates that necessary measures to prevent major accidents (i.e. safety management systems or hardware controls) may not be present on the plant. Where this concern exists, the course of action is to carry out an early inspection to check – and invariably, experience has been that the conditions or provision on plant is substantially better than that presented in the safety report. Many operators are not doing themselves justice, and certainly not doing the company any favours, by failing to properly describe and present in a logical fashion the information about how they control major accident potential. The concept of demonstration is at the heart of this, and clearly the CA has not got over in all cases what it is expecting to see, and some operators have failed to make a reasonable attempt at showing that what they have on site to prevent major accidents will work.

CURRENT DEVELOPMENTS WITH COMAH

The section above focussed on some of the early experiences of dealing with safety reports, and clearly there have been some problems. So what is being done to develop COMAH to address these issues?

The large jump involved in moving from the previous CIMAH regime to implementing the Seveso II Directive by the COMAH Regulations is epitomised by the following fundamental changes that COMAH has brought, and which were at least contributory to the early experiences:

- Formation of the CA by amalgamating HSE and Environment Agency input;
- A Safety Report Assessment Manual, used by the CA and available also to industry and anyone else via the Internet, which sets down the criteria against which safety reports will be assessed;
- The requirement for Demonstration in safety reports of safe operation;
- The concept of 'Domino' or knock-on effects from one major hazard site to another.

The most recent (and forthcoming) developments in each of these aspects will now be summarised.

COMPETENT AUTHORITY

The early challenges in bringing together the Environment Agency (concentrating on the environmental hazard potential) and HSE (taking the lead on safety and health) into an efficient joint regulator have been well documented, and there has been very good progress towards meeting these challenges. This has happened at the strategic level, via a Single Implementation Project that has set a framework for commonality between the two organisations. But it has also happened at local level, by individual HSE and EA teams coming together to produce joint working on COMAH safety reports and to present a more unified approach to operators. The COMAH system provided from the very early stages for common assessment of safety reports – inspectors from EA and HSE being part of the same assessment team, using the same criteria set out in the Safety Report Assessment Manual, and providing a single conclusion to an operator.

The output from a completed assessment is an inspection plan, phased over anything up to 4 years after the assessment in the first year. These are joint inspection plans that combine the identified needs from the assessment team covering HSE (regulatory inspector as well as specialist inspectors) and EA inspectors. The system is transparent to the operator, who has broad details of what the inspection issues are to be. These inspections are now beginning to be carried out.

The process has been less progressive for COMAH lower-tier sites, but EA and HSE teams are now developing and implementing joint inspection plans for these sites too - developed from a hazard-based approach by inspectors from each part of the CA sitting down to review past intelligence about a particular site and determining which aspects of an operation need to be inspected and with what priority. It will take some time for these inspection plans to be produced and implemented for all lower-tier sites, but the process has begun.

DEMONSTRATION

The problems with identifying exactly what is required for a demonstration of safe operation in a safety report has been an issue that has dogged COMAH from the start. These concerns have been expressed extensively within the CA, but quite properly industry representatives have also voiced their concern long and loud. There has been a very reasonable call for better clarification and examples of what a good demonstration comprises. It is in response to this latter stimulus that some action is being taken.

Earlier this year, a Working Group was convened at Huddersfield jointly by the CA and industry representatives via the Chemicals Industry Association, to explore the issues and to identify a way forward. 4 sub-Groups were formed with the task of developing guidance in specific areas on the level of detail required when providing information on the prevention and limitation of major accidents. At the time of writing this guidance is shortly to be published, and the results are awaited with interest both by regulators and industry in the anticipation of some much-needed clarification.

DOMINO

The concept of Domino was introduced for the first time with COMAH. The basic proposition is that if there are 2 or more major hazard sites close to each other with the potential for an incident to happen with effects outside the site boundary, there is a potential for an incident at one site to escalate by causing an incident at an adjacent site also. The COMAH regulations require the CA to identify such sites, by writing to operators and Emergency Planners, so as to stimulate a transfer of information between operators and emergency planners that can be taken into account in off-site emergency plans.

The CA identified Domino sites by means of the Consultation Distances used for assessing the suitability of land-use planning applications in the vicinity of major hazard installations. Each major hazard site has a zone assigned to it the size of which is based on the nature, quantity and usage of hazardous substances; this is used between the local planning authority and HSE to identify and provide advice on land-use planning proposals. The zones provided a rough-and-ready but viable way of identifying Domino sites. Where Consultation Distances from 2 or more sites overlap, and particularly where the overlap encompasses a hazardous installation such as a major storage or process vessel, the sites concerned have been designated Domino sites and required to begin the information exchange and consider what steps need to be taken. At the time of writing the sites have been identified and the activity is currently between operators and emergency planners to consider the implications. Full details are now included as a separate Chapter of the Safety Report Assessment Manual.

SAFETY REPORT ASSESSMENT MANUAL (SRAM)

Changes are afoot with the Safety Report Assessment Manual, which sets out the detailed criteria that the CA uses to assess safety reports against and also provides the process steps the CA operates under. The SRAM has been made fully available via the Internet, and operators who have to prepare safety reports are strongly encouraged to use it to inform the development of their reports.

A review was planned from the outset, to take account of lessons the CA had learned from the first round of safety reports and also feedback from industry. This will be an iterative process of monitoring, reviewing and implementing which will continue indefinitely in response to changing needs and changing information, but the first round of changes are now imminent. The full changes will be publicised through various committees such as Advisory Committee for Dangerous Substances, Chemical Industries Forum, and through industry contacts. Some of the key areas of change however are expected to be:

- Providing a view from assessors dealing with predictive or consequence analysis in safety reports at an early stage, to ensure that the measures considered in a report are proportionate to the level of risk from an operation;
- Greater emphasis on meeting company management where information in safety reports is insufficient and more is needed, to explain exactly what is needed;
- Where 'further information' is requested and provided, this information being part of the safety report and consequently being included on the public register;
- A better targeted Conclusions Letter after assessment, which sets out clearly the main elements of the planned inspection and verification programme.

This latter point is key to providing a link from the assessment process to the inspection phase, the importance of which is considered in the next part of this paper.

FROM ASSESSMENT TO INSPECTION

The Safety report assessment process by a multi-disciplinary assessment team is intended to achieve two basic things: firstly, to conclude on whether the safety report provides an adequate picture of control of major accident hazards at a site, including whether or not there are any serious deficiencies indicated in the measures taken on site to prevent major accidents. And secondly, to identify a programme of issues that members of the team need to inspect on site to verify the information in the report and to check on the physical and safety managerial standards of control. These latter inspection issues will be prioritised so that the most pressing are done soonest and the remainder programmed over anything up to 4 years after assessment. In some cases the issues can be dealt with on site by one inspector, in other cases a team approach (for example, an audit) may be necessary.

An important feature of the inspection plan is that it should be transparent to the operator, both in terms of content and approximate timings so that the operator knows what is in store. Indeed, 'best practice' in this area is for good liaison and exchange of information from the CA to the operator and vice versa so that issues are fully in the open.

The two essential parts of COMAH implemented by the CA, assessment and inspection, have to be seen as working in tandem. COMAH is not just about assessment, and it certainly does not finish with the conclusion of the assessment process – it is only beginning. The effectiveness of COMAH in identifying the potential for major incidents and for preventing them is more likely to derive from the inspection part of the process than from the assessment stage – this is increasingly becoming clear from the assessments completed so far, the inspections carried out after them, and perhaps most importantly incidents that occur. Incidents often provide a very good indicator, albeit after the event, of how well or how badly an operator manages safety to the degree of thoroughness needed for the highest hazard sites.

The next part of this paper will look at two recent incidents as a form of case study to evaluate whether assessment of a safety report alone would be likely to indicate problems that the regulator (or indeed industry) could act on, and hence prevent incidents. While two incidents are not capable of making a case one way or another, they are relevant here for several reasons:

- Both involved COMAH top-tier sites;
- Both involved serious incidents at companies where management thought they had good safety management and control systems;
- Both involved issues that needed to be considered in COMAH safety reports.

Both incidents also resulted in prosecution by HSE under the Health and Safety at Work etc. Act after detailed (and costly!) investigation, and fines imposed after guilty pleas. In as much as they have been dealt with by the courts the facts are therefore a matter of public record, however for the purposes of this paper the circumstances have been anonymised so as not to identify the companies concerned – the principles are what are relevant here to the point being made.

CASE 1 – IGNITION OF TOXIC AND FLAMMABLE GAS

In this incident, two contract welders were burned while working to repair a leak on a pipework system carrying a gas that was both toxic and flammable, when an escaping gas cloud ignited. A system of gas blowers was used to draw gas from one part of the process to another. One of the gas blowers was to be taken off line by the fitting of blanking plates while another put on line by the removal of blanking plates. To achieve this, isolation valves were used to isolate the parts of the plant concerned.

When re-instating a gas blower on line, a leak was detected at a flange. The contractors, under the supervision of a Shift Manager, attempted to seal the leak but a large release occurred which ignited and engulfed the two men. They escaped with burns and problems from inhalation of combustion fumes and the toxic gas, and fortunately made a full recovery.

The investigation revealed a number of factors that led to the accident:

(i)   A special operating procedure was in use for the work, which had been done many times before. The procedure called for a very accurate control of pressure within the gas circuit, to reduce the possibility of leak on the part being worked on. It was clear from the investigation however that the instrumentation provided was neither designed nor capable of balancing pressures with sufficient accuracy and reliability to be able to perform such an operation reliably.

(ii)   In any event, the instruments were not noted on any inspection and maintenance schedules, and no records of any maintenance could be produced.

(iii)   The work also relied upon the closure of isolation valves to prevent the movement of gas. In the investigation it transpired that the isolation valve on the inlet side could not be closed, as it had not been maintained. Indeed, the Permit to Work issued for the job noted that the valve was "passing gas".

A combination of these factors therefore led to the release of the gas, and its subsequent ignition, from which 2 men were fortunate to escape alive. But could these factors have been identified before the event?

The safety report would have been required to contain details of a number of relevant factors. As part of the safety management system description, details of the maintenance and inspection systems and the control and supervision of contractors would have to be documented. There would also need to be details of how risk assessments were organised and undertaken, both for routine and maintenance work. The Permit to Work system would also have to be described. There would need to be a demonstration in the report that the measures taken by the company were proportionate to the hazard, and were effective i.e. were working. For a site such as this, both Process Safety and Mechanical Engineering assessors would have been included in the safety report assessment team and would have looked at many of the circumstances surrounding the work being done during this incident.

In most cases operators describe systems in place on the basis of how they anticipate they will work, rather than thinking about how they might not. At this site, as an example, the operator would have been able to highlight a maintenance and inspection system that was ostensibly detailed, well structured and computer-based. The company used a criticality approach to items to be maintained, and reasonable frequencies for inspection of items on the schedules had been set. Some of this could even have been demonstrated, for example by choosing suitably representative areas and detailing the actions taken. All very reasonable – except that in practice it was not working! The company's own investigation concluded among other things that the planning of the job was inadequate, the operating procedure was inadequate, there were deviations from procedures, the maintenance strategy for isolation valves was inadequate, and there were errors of judgement by personnel involved in the task.

If the company had done a sufficiently rigorous job in looking at it's own systems, it may (but would not with certainty) have discovered its own failings and could then have plugged the gaps. But the CA assessors, faced with an outwardly reasonable description of what was otherwise a comprehensive system, would have had little chance at the assessment stage of uncovering the true picture. This is only likely to have been possible during inspection, when the maintenance system would be given a thorough site inspection by examining systems, checking records, and asking questions of responsible individuals about how things worked in practice and where they sometimes might not.

If the system of balancing the gas pressures across the plant had been described, that is likely to have been sufficiently unusual for it to have raised queries at the assessment stage or more likely for it to be noted as an inspection issue for more detailed consideration under the inspection plan.

In terms of the relative effectiveness of assessment or inspection in preventing this accident, 1 – 0 to inspection.

CASE 2 – RELEASE OF HYDROCHLORIC ACID FROM A STORAGE VESSEL

The second incident relates to a release of concentrated (35%) hydrochloric acid (HCl) from a storage vessel, after bolts securing a flange at the base of the vessel failed and allowed a release of 20 tonnes of acid into the vessel bund.

The vessel was a 40-tonne capacity vertical storage vessel, in a common bund with five other vessels. At the base of the vessel was a nozzle and flange for a level measurement transmitter. The incident happened without warning, when two flange studs failed under acid attack and allowed the flange to open. HCl sprayed due to the head of hydrostatic pressure from the flange and into the bund; an acid mist also began to form and to drift off-site, where it was later smelled a few hundred metres away. Water curtains were set up around the bund, to knock down the acid mist and prevent it leaving the site, and the combined acid and water spray began to fill the bund.

After an hour or so, when the bund level had risen to about half full, part of the bund lining (specifically, the sealant in the expansion joints of the bund) failed under acid attack and the contents of the bund were lost onto adjacent concrete and eventually into the ground.

The investigation revealed the following failings that led directly to the accident and its consequences:

(i)   The flange gasket had been passing acid for some time; this had been playing on the flange stud bolts until they had completely corroded through and failed.

(ii)   There was visual evidence of substantial corrosion around the flange and adjacent pipework, as well as other nearby metalwork including the base of the vessel itself, and evidence of dripping acid on the concrete of the bund floor. This evidence could and should have been noted and acted upon.

(iii)   The bund itself had not been coated to resist acid, and the sealant in the expansion joints of the concrete forming the bund had not been maintained and gave practically no resistance to acid/water mix in the bund.

(iv)   The company had previous experience of corrosion problems with stud bolts used to make flange connections on hydrochloric acid duty.

As with the previous case, would any of these factors have been transparent in a safety report so as to be able to identify action necessary to prevent the incident?

The safety report would ostensibly present a very encouraging picture when describing the safety management system and in particular the maintenance inspection system. A completely new, state of the art system was in the process of being introduced to replace an existing system that was itself apparently well structured.   In addition the company management had shown a positive and progressive interest in maintaining high standards of safety and health across a range of issues.

The vessel concerned, in common with other vessels, had an external as well as an internal inspection frequency established – 2 years external and 5 years internal in this case. The inspection history showed internal inspections had been carried out in 1994 and 1996 (i.e. more than the set frequency) and a further external inspection in 1998.   There was a detailed scope of inspection in a written procedure.

However on closer investigation, the procedure did not include any flanges and fittings as part of the inspections; there was no requirement in the procedure to examine these, let alone dismantle them and examine the condition of bolts, gaskets etc.   There was a general pipework inspection programme, but nothing to cater for the particular hazards of hydrochloric acid duty.   Apart from the failure to include the flanges and fittings as part of the inspection schedule, the weakness of the whole system was epitomised by the fact that there had been a recent painting programme for the vessels that had resulted in painting over the substantial corrosion already present.

Again in this case there was nothing in the safety report descriptions to alert assessors to the developing problems.   The description of the maintenance and inspection systems would be more than adequate to satisfy the assessment criteria, and this could have been backed up by demonstration (even for the vessel concerned) that the measures were effective and were being carried out – inspection records were available for the vessel.   It is highly unlikely that even the most suspicious inspector carrying out an assessment would have guessed that the procedure fell short of the flanges and fittings – though if this had been identified, then a request for further information would in all probability have drawn attention to the intrinsic weakness.   What is far more likely is that an inspection programme to verify the claimed records and dealing with the condition of the storage vessels would have picked up the very obvious corrosion, and led to the right questions being asked and the appropriate action being initiated.

2 – 0 to inspection over assessment?

MOVING INSPECTION ON

A central argument of this paper is that COMAH is not just about assessment, but has to be seen in the wider context of a combined assessment and inspection scheme, the two parts of which need to work together to have the maximum chance of preventing major accidents at COMAH sites.   It is the authors view that there has been a little too much made of the early problems with the assessment process and not enough about the longer term benefits of a structured, transparent system that combines an assessment process leading to the identification of inspection issues that are then examined in detail appropriate to the hazard and risk potential.

The two cases considered above do not, it is fully accepted, make a conclusive case for the value of inspection over assessment any more than they demonstrate what an effective tool COMAH in its widest sense can be.   However, experience of many major incidents that have occurred at high hazard sites has shown time and time again that a structured inspection is one of the most successful ways of challenging beliefs about the effectiveness of safety measures and identifying the potential for things to go wrong.   The efforts of operators to identify these issues, and then to set them out in safety reports, is enhanced by the 'fresh pair of eyes' approach from the regulator working toward the same goal.

The challenge for the CA is how best to use its resources. The assessment process alone is extremely resource-intensive, and in the first assessments of an operator's reports ties up a substantial amount of expertise that is then not available for inspection. In the medium to longer term, the inspection plan produced from assessment has to marshal the correct mix of skills in the assessment team – specialists inspectors dealing with particular disciplines such as process safety or human factors, regulatory inspectors assessing safety management systems, and Environment Agency inspectors dealing with potential environmental impact. Furthermore, the whole process and proposed inspection strategy must be transparent to the operator so that they can see both the rationale for what is proposed as well as the detail of when it will happen and how much it will cost them.

From shaky beginnings, when neither the CA nor industry really knew what COMAH had in store, enormous progress has been made in developing the systems and understanding needed. A great deal is still to be done, but after much effort over safety report assessment the key stage has been reached where the benefits of implementing inspection plans at many COMAH sites can be realised.

COMAH IMPLEMENTATION IN A MULTI-SITE ORGANISATION

Dennis O'Leary HSE Team Leader Bacton Delivery Area SNS Upstream, BP.
Andy Stanley Technical Director, RAS Risk Management Consultants, Chester.

This paper will set out the BP experience in developing a successful multi-site approach to the COMAH Regulations. It will set out the background to COMAH, the key differences between CIMAH and COMAH and the functions of the CA. It will show how a robust and transparent approach is essential in being able to deliver on the COMAH objective in a multisite organisation, that of avoiding catastrophes. Discussion of the ongoing challenge of sustaining the safe management and control of all BP's operations is included. The paper will go on to discuss how the benefits of developing close working relationships with others, including the Competent Authority (CA) can be realised. The paper closes with a brief summary of COMAH and the role of permissioning regimes in the future.

BACKGROUND

In the hydrocarbons and chemical industry, an explosion at the Flixborough chemical plant in 1974 killed 28 workers, this was followed by an incident in 1976 at Seveso in Italy in which a runaway reaction led to widespread contamination of land with dioxin.

These incidents prompted the EC to examine the way in which major hazards were controlled across Europe and led to the passing of an EC Directive – the Seveso Directive (82/501/EEC). In Great Britain this Directive was implemented by the 1984 Control of Major Industrial Accident Hazards (CIMAH) regulations. During the period 1984 through to 1994 further tragic events resulted in a review of the operation of the Seveso Directive.

This revealed that there were a number of weaknesses and omissions causing the EC to issue the Seveso II Directive (96/82/EC). In Great Britain the new directive was implemented primarily by the 1999 Control Of Major Accidents Hazards (COMAH) regulations. The SEVESO Directive or for the UK the CIMAH Regulations applied to all UK facilities that met certain specified criteria. The criteria were focussed on the use or processing of certain specified and named substances.

MOVING FROM CIMAH TO COMAH

In the 1980s when the CIMAH regulations were introduced, BP decided that a common approach to the submission of Safety Reports would be beneficial for many reasons. A network of safety professionals from all BP UK top tier sites was established. The function of this network was to provide guidance on the structure and content of Safety Reports and review the feedback that individual sites received on their submissions.

As in many other organisations, during the last few years the BP organisation has changed enormously. BP in the mid 90s moved to a business unit structure, in 1999 merged with Amoco and acquired Arco in 2000. It is now a substantially larger and more diverse organisation than ever before. There are now some 15 top tier and 19 lower tier sites in the UK alone, each predominantly in different business units and in geographically diverse and sometimes challenging locations.

The COMAH network of safety professionals initially established under CIMAH is now charged with the same and some additional responsibilities under COMAH. One of the first responsibilities the group faced, was how do we take the learning's from our previous CIMAH submissions and include them in our approach to COMAH.

BP had gained some experience in a [1]pilot COMAH project discussed by Ian Hamilton BP at the HAZARDS XIV Conference (Paper 7 1998). This work was undertaken prior to the merger with Amoco in January 1999.

Following the merger, it was decided to use the heritage Amoco Bacton Gas Terminal Complex as the location where much of the development of an approach to meeting and piloting the BP COMAH framework should be undertaken. This decision was made for a number of reasons, in that it would be one of the first locations which had to comply with the COMAH Regulations and was a relatively simple top tier site.

The 'old' BP CIMAH liaison network had developed a significant amount of guidance which was contained within a CIMAH 'toolbox'. BP Sunbury took ownership in 1999 for developing this CIMAH 'toolbox' into a COMAH 'toolbox'.

Thus, the development of the BP COMAH framework and the BP COMAH toolbox is enabling BP to deliver consistent COMAH reports whilst fully including site specific circumstances.

THE REGULATIONS

The COMAH regulations are a development from CIMAH and importantly have included some of the thinking from Lord Cullen's Report following the Piper Alpha tragedy (167 killed) and the subsequent Offshore Safety Case Regulations (1992). The Offshore Safety regulations, the more recently introduced Railways regulations and now the COMAH regulations come under the generic heading of permissioning regimes.

The clear requirement within the permissioning regimes in the UK is one of generating a Safety Report. The HSE have recently issued a recent discussion document on regulating high hazard industries setting out a number of basic principles. The second of these principles defines the basis for major hazard legislation by establishing that there is a legal duty on such industries to manage the risks and requiring them to:

➢ Identify hazards and assess the risks, using appropriate risk assessment methods, develop effective control measures and keep a current documentary record of all this
➢ Include design, hardware, systems, organisation, procedures and human factors in a coherent whole
➢ Implement control measures that are suitable and keep them up to date

➢ Make and test arrangements for managing emergencies and mitigating their consequences.

THE COMPETENT AUTHORITY

Seseo II imposes additional requirements on member states for the creation of a Competent Authority, in the UK this has been realised through various formal organisational arrangements between the HSE and Environment Agency (England and Wales), the HSE and Scottish Environment Agency for Scotland. The Competent Authority is charged with ensuring :

➢ The conclusions of the review of the safety report must now be communicated to the operator
➢ There is a requirement for a five year inspection plan to verify the contents of the safety report
➢ That the report is made available to the general public
➢ The duty to prohibit use where the measures taken by the operator for the prevention and mitigation of major accidents are "seriously deficient"
➢ Setting up a system for land use planning around major hazard sites
➢ The introduction of charging for all COMAH related activities
➢ The submission of safety reports at both the design and operational stages for a new establishment

KEY DIFFERENCIES BETWEEN CIMAH AND COMAH

So what are the key differences between CIMAH and COMAH? The previous discussion has centred on some of the high level differences. However a discussion around some of the detail differences is now important.

The following are the significant differences:

➢ The need to demonstrate rather than describe. This one area has possibly led to more communication than any other aspect of the COMAH regulations. The issue being; when has sufficient demonstration been achieved.
➢ The appropriate use of risk assessment methods, where safety and environmental risk need to be considered equally. This is an interesting difference to previous permissioning legislation in this area, (IE Offshore Safety Case Regulations) as there is no specific requirement to use QRA or any other risk assessment methods, which are available. The emphasis here, is on the appropriate selection and effective use of the risk assessment methods.
➢ The public domain aspects of COMAH. A significant difference in that the COMAH reports are now available on the Public Register. The reports therefore are not written to satisfy just the regulations and the regulator, but also the needs of the community. Clearly this could present some operators with specific concerns, if they have been operating previously in an atmosphere of distrust.

> Domino effects need to be considered. This has and is proving to be a difficult area to fully implement. It requires the sharing of detailed information, sometimes between highly competitive organisations.
> Onsite as well as offsite risk needs to be considered, whereas under CIMAH offsite risk was the primary focus.
> Human Factors, the role of people in managing abnormal or emergency situations and the testing of the adequacy of emergency response plans and their implementation.

BUSINESS OPPORTUNITY OR THREAT

The authors believed we needed to develop a mindset or philosophy to meeting the regulations.

Should we approach the regulations positively so that they work for us and add value to our business. Thereby seeing the new regulations as an opportunity to build trust with the local community through the development of a robust and transparent Safety Report whilst at the same time deliver on the objective of the regulations.

Or, alternatively should we view the regulations as a threat, IE, Approaching the regulations as just more red tape that we must comply with, which will be yet another overhead for the business to manage.

Although it may seem an obvious choice to the reader of this paper, how often do organisations take time to consider what should be the approach to new Regulations?

For BP we chose the former perspective – to treat the COMAH Regulations as a business opportunity.

BP APPROACH TO IMPLEMENTING THE REGULATIONS

The BP approach to implementing the COMAH regulations can best be described by reference to the diagram on the next page. Essentially the guidance that was published at the time, by the various agencies was obtained and evaluated.

Other guidance that became available, such as the Chemical Industry Association (CIA) guidance on Occupied Buildings was included. For clarity only two references to guidance are shown, although a huge amount of other guidance has was reviewed.

It should be noted, although the SEVESO II document was available in 1997, published guidance really only became available during the latter half of 1999 and thereafter. Therefore much of the work that was developed in BP during that period was done in an environment without guidance from the Competent Authority.

BP APPROACH TO IMPLEMENTING THE REGULATIONS

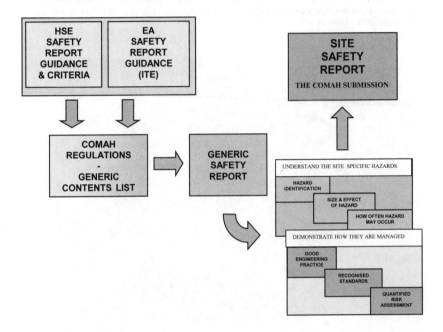

Following this data search, the COMAH regulations and the associated CA COMAH Safety Report Assessment Manual (SRAM) were reviewed in detail. Interestingly, it became clear very quickly that the structure of the Regulations would not necessarily lead to a well-structured and easily understood or readable Safety Report.

These aspects were considered important because of the various stakeholders who needed to be able to access the information contained within the report. The stakeholders considered, being the CA, the management, the workforce, and the general public.

The Generic BP COMAH Safety Report framework was thus developed.

The framework is a key to developing a robust and consistent approach to the COMAH regulations across all UK BP top tier and lower tier sites.

It is important to point out, the CA was also keen to ensure consistency of report submissions, and indeed has set up the CA organisation to be able to deliver on this. The arrangements the CA have in place centre around the LUPI principle (Lead Unit Principle Inspector.

The role of this designated individual is to ensure that issues common at all sites operated by one named organisation, such as HARM criteria, etc are managed centrally. The perceived benefit of this approach is to ensure all sites can use the same fundamental criteria, agreed centrally and not subjected to endless parallel and expensive CA scrutiny.

DEVELOPING A MAJOR ACCIDENT PREVENTION POLICY

Developing the Major Accident Prevention Policy (MAPP) was, intriguingly difficult. Why? Well BP common to many other organisations has for many years, since the 1974 [2]HASWA Act put in place various Health and Safety policies. The picture below shows the 13 elements of the BP Policy.

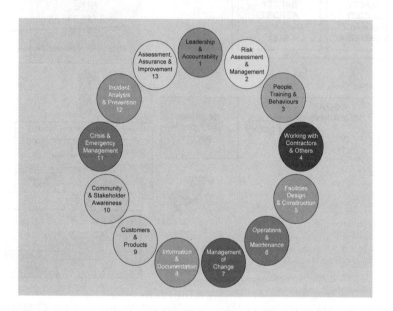

These elements cover the full spectrum of our activities, from the management of major accident hazards through to the reduction of slips trips and falls. However the COMAH regulations specifically ask organisations to address Major Accident Hazards within the MAPP. A further complication arose in that; typically policies were made at the highest level within organisations. This is common to BP also. So how could we link and demonstrate a high level policy document to what happened at the site level.

Our approach was to look in detail at our BP group wide policy, reference all of the elements within our Safety Management System ([3]GHSER) and then identify all the key areas for the management of major accident hazards.

We then decided, we needed a group wide MAPP which is totally transparent to the Group wide Safety, Health and Environment policy, but specifically addresses major accident hazards. We also needed a site MAPP, linking the Group wide MAPP to the site, but now referring to the organisation and arrangements at the site level. This at first seems a complicated arrangement, however it is in fact, very simple, because the documents are transparent to each other

DEVELOPING A COMAH FRAMEWORK FOR ALL UK SITES

The development of the BP COMAH framework or model was an iterative process. Reflecting our continuous learning the development of the model began before the regulations, criteria and guidance were finalised, IE in 1999.

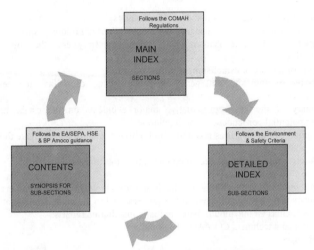

THE STRUCTURE OF THE BP FRAMEWORK OR MODEL.

The framework or model has been developed so that it can be applied at any of the BP sites across the UK. The aim being to avoid any unnecessary repetition of effort and provide a consistency in our approach to the regulations. The model enables the focus to be the management of major accident hazards, rather than being distracted by deciding what the structure of the Safety Report should be.

There are three parts to the framework or model, the company, the establishment and the installation reports. The Company Report is common to all sites across the UK. It describes the structure of the Company and the common elements across the Company. It is common for all BP UK COMAH sites, and is updated by the Company centrally, rather than by the establishment or site. It is submitted with and forms part of every establishment's safety report. It contains information such as:

> The company HSE Policy, Major Accident Prevention Policy (MAPP) and Business Policies
> A Description of Company Structure
> The HSE Management System Framework (Getting HSE Right)
> The Company internal networks
> The technical Practices and references used by the Company
> The Company Incident Reporting Systems
> The Company Emergency and Crisis Management
> The Group or Company Assurance

The biggest and most important part of the model is the Establishment Report.
This is where the demonstrations are made to show how the objectives of the regulations
are delivered at site level. The establishment report describes the common features across
the establishment. It forms the bulk of the submission presented and contains information
such as:

> A description of the site location and its surroundings
> The inventories of dangerous substances on site and their hazardous properties
> The details of the establishment HSE management system, the roles and
  responsibilities
> The details of the site or establishment infrastructure.
> The details of the site emergency response plans, capability and testing
  arrangements.
> A summary of the key representative major accidents on the establishment
  including potential consequences and likelihood
> A description of the measures taken to avoid, prevent, control and mitigate the key
  major accidents
> Justification that the measures are commensurate with the risks

The Installation report, which invariably has much less text, is where either commercially
sensitive or security information is placed, and is not essential to the main demonstrations.
For complex sites such as Grangemouth there are many Installation reports.
BP has also developed a technical COMAH "Toolbox".
This covers such aspects as:

> Identification of representative scenarios
> Possible outcomes (fires, explosions, pressure burst, missiles, toxic clouds)
> Criteria for harm (to people, property and the environment)
> Calculation of consequences
> Assignment of likelihood's
> Domino methodology
> Estimating risk levels
> Modelling the effect of control and mitigation measures
> Demonstration that risks are adequately managed

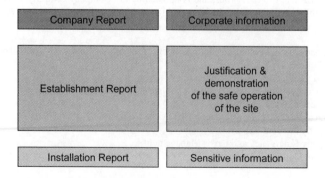

HOW THE ESTABLISMENT REPORT WORKS.

The Major Accident Prevention Policy (MAPP) drives the establishment report. The description provides the source information for the risk assessment. This source information includes all of the substances and quantities on site or foreseeable as coming to site. The description includes the site, surrounding area and any specific issues – such as SSSI. A full site wide safety and environmental risk assessment using appropriate risk assessment methods and associated tools is then undertaken. Therefore a mixture of quantitive and qualitative risk assessments usually varying from site to site, dependent on the complexity of the hazards identified.

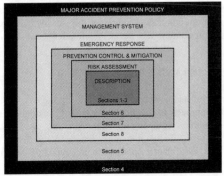

The results of the risk assessment are used to test the prevention, control, mitigation measures and emergency response systems. The prevention, control and mitigation details are developed using the risk hierarchy of avoid, combat and control.

The management system then ensures that all the prevention, control and mitigation measures are in place and managed to meet the expectations as laid out in the Major Accident Prevention Policy.

THE BENEFITS OF THIS APPROACH

What are the benefits of this approach? The model provides support and enables the development of a COMAH Safety Report that is transparent and robust.

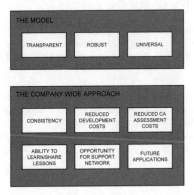

We believed that a robust transparent approach is essential, for as stated before for the first time the Safety Report will be available to the public. In many respects our continued community licence to operate will depend on the success of the Safety Report. Therefore although technical accuracy is paramount, delivering on the much wider objective is equally important.

The universal nature of the model facilitates this consistent application of the COMAH regulations across all our BP UK (and perhaps European) sites. We are able to share our experience and lessons learnt from a very broad base of application. This has and is reducing our Safety Report development costs because the generic challenges can be solved once only. It has and is reducing the costs associated with the CA assessments due to the consistent submissions from our sites. The approach is already being considered as a new way of looking at existing legislation like the Offshore Safety Case Regulations.

THE LEARNING'S FROM 2000 AND 2001

Given that the BP Bacton report has now been [4]'accepted' by the CA what has been the key learning's from the BP approach to meeting the COMAH regulations and are these learning's transferable throughout the company and industry?

The COMAH regulations are significant step forward in regulating MAH's. Some key learning's are:

1. Adopting the right mindset is the first step
2. Understand the objective of the regulations
3. Undertake a gap analysis of what is in place and what needs to be in place
4. Engage the management and workforce and grow their understanding on how they can effectively contribute
5. Deliver on the gap analysis, keep the report live

The CA is now developing their ideas around their safety inspection philosophy to enable them to verify consistently how organisations are delivering on the site COMAH submissions. It is clear already, even at this early stage of COMAH compliance and development that a huge amount of work is still to be done.

LEARNING'S, OPERATOR VIEW OF THE CA

The Competent Authority approach across the country appears to be inconsistent. The authors believe this is due to a number of factors, not least the number of inspectors available and the training provided, but also the number of new sites that now come under the regulations.

Organisational preparedness for the COMAH regulations could have been much improved had a reasonable timescale for the full implementation of the regulations been allowed. The SHARPP pilot and the subsequent work undertaken at Bacton during 1999 was against a backdrop of little or in some areas of the regulations, no guidance from the CA.

The time required to complete a COMAH report, through undertaking the description, hazard identification, risk assessments and putting in place of appropriate management systems to adequately demonstrate how all the Major Accident Hazards can be managed, for some sites, is a huge undertaking.

That is not to say that these sites did not have adequate systems in place, clearly they did. However undertaking a sensible 'gap analysis' between what was in place and what needed to be done to satisfy the regulations can be a lengthy process.

LEARNING'S FOR OTHER OPERATORS

Developing a consistent, robust and transparent approach to the regulations can be done. Sustaining a consistent approach can deliver huge benefits, not least in delivering on the COMAH objective of avoiding catastrophes. It can also deliver in a real business bottom line sense.

Adopting an appropriate mindset is fundamental. However once this has been achieved, continuing to look past the regulations towards the spirit of the regulations can lead to other benefits. An example of this, at one of our sites where the CIA guidance for Occupied Buildings is being discussed, the site safety engineer has been able to demonstrate to the site management how the safety benefits for taking the office, admin buildings and people of site, will also provide real cost savings. Given the current topical discussion around the CONOCO Humber Oil Refinery this is perhaps, timely.

SO THE CHALLENGES WE FACED AND CONTINUE TO FACE ARE

1. Ownership. If the safety report is to deliver real value, it is vital that the safety report is not seen as the property of the HSE department but is owned by line management. The COMAH report will be the main document against which the company will be judged in any inspection carried out by the CA (and also in any incident investigation). It is therefore essential that the systems and procedures documented in the report are an accurate reflection of what actually happens on site and that line management are aware of this.
2. Communication. The safety report identifies the potential major accidents and the key risk control measures in place to prevent such accidents. If these key risk control measures are to remain effective, it is important that workers at all levels understand the consequences of their failure. The safety report is often seen as an excellent reference document. The challenge is to distil and communicate the findings of a long and complex document into a format which is easily digestible to all, so that it can be integrated into every day working practice.
3. A Living Document. Because safety reports are prepared and revised to a specific timetable, they inevitably represent a snapshot of the facility at a particular time. Ideally the safety report would be a living document continuously developing as the facility evolves with time. The need for the document to reside in the public domain along with the CA's comments severely limits the possibility of a single living document.
4. A Seamless Approach. The offshore and onshore approach to safety reports is substantially different, such that very different approaches often apply to equipment

connected together by a single pipeline. In an ideal world the approach would be the same either end of the pipe.

5. Communicating with the public. Safety reports will be made available to the public. Under the regulations, industry has no obligation to advertise the availability of reports or enter into a debate over their contents. However, there is a real opportunity for industry to take a more proactive role, engaging the public in debate and listening to and addressing their concerns.

THE FUTURE – PERMISSIONING REGIMES

So what of the future? The Piper Alpha disaster has been mentioned briefly. The current enquiry into Ladbroke Grove rail tragedy and the various railway failures have focussed governmental, regulatory and public concern around the effectiveness of permissioning regimes. In deed it is perhaps by no co-incidence that Lord Cullen is heading up the Ladbroke Grove enquiry.

What is clear, is that a greater emphasis is now being placed on safety reports due to public scrutiny. The need to understand new regulations, not from the perspective of meeting the requirements of the regulations slavishly, more from a perspective of the community licence to operate is becoming ever more real.

The regulator is now taking a much more robust view of human factors and the role they play in initiating Major Accidents. Major Accident Hazards now include environmental aspects, Major Accidents to the Environment (MATTE). The recently introduced Human Rights Act is likely to focus more thinking and resources into effectively managing this aspect of our business.

ONSHORE AND OFFSHORE ASPECT

So what does this mean for BP ? BP is a Global organisation operating Major Accident Hazards sites in a variety of geographically challenged locations. In the UK this is exemplified typically by our onshore and offshore hydrocarbons facilities. We are now looking to ways of how the management of major accident hazards can be improved and undertaken in a more consistent and robust manner across all our facilities.

The work undertaken in meeting the COMAH regulations is already spilling into our thinking for this, such that we believe we can derive more benefit from meeting the Offshore Safety Case Regulations. This is an important area, which is now coming into focus. We believe that much of the benefits realised to date from the Offshore Safety Case regulations have predominantly been due to necessary hardware improvements, such as blast wall protection, Emergency Shutdown Systems, fire & gas systems etc.

Further benefits should be achieved if we focus or concentrate on people and systems. A basic premise is that the safety case regime and practice has contributed to much good learning and knowledge. However, this knowledge is often ineffective in reducing the risks from Major Accident Hazards (MAH). BP are seeking to "unlock" the potential for this knowledge to become effective in the management of major accident hazards.

Within permissioning regimes, COMAH reports or the Offshore Safety Case must demonstrate that the duty holder has an effective safety management system (SMS). Duty holders generally make this demonstration by describing their SMS in the safety case document.

However, it is evident that the system for Management of Major Accident Hazards as described in the safety case and the actual day-to-day management of MAH can be significantly different. The reasons for these differences are complex, but are associated with the different purposes and perspectives that people have in 1) documenting a management system and 2) operating an installation. The following table characterises these two perspectives of management of MAH:

Perspective 1	Perspective 2
"Objective" idealised, theoretical view of risk	View of risk based on experience and perception
Idealised and generic view of reliability	Realistic and specific view of reliability
Decisions based on simplification and analysis	Decisions based on judgement and experience
Solutions tend to be neat, logical	Solutions tend to be expedient (1001 things to do)
Management of MAH is described in safety case	management of MAH is dealt with by the safety case
Main problem solving tools are QRA and cost-benefit analysis	Problems solved through discussion / getting the job done
'Objective' view of reality	*Perception is reality*

'Specialists' typically use a 'rational' definition of risk as a basis for decision making. Their decision making tools include QRA and cost-benefit analysis. 'Non-specialists' tend to make decisions based on experience and judgement.

These different approaches are also associated with different views of management of MAH. One group seeks to precisely define safety critical elements, associated performance standards and verification activities, while the other group needs to deal with major accident hazards as only one of a large number of (often conflicting) issues.

These polarised perspectives may caricature two approaches but serve to illustrate the extreme differences that exist. In practice, 'specialists' will seek input to their models from those with relevant operational experience, but the obtained information may be difficult to incorporate into the models. On the other hand, the 'non-specialists' will base their decision-making on experience and judgement and sometimes ask for analysis to support decisions, however, the necessary timescale for decision often discourages analysis.

How can these different views of management of MAH be reconciled?

How can the management of MAH be improved in such an environment?

Today, many organisations empower their workforce to be creative in business and exercise and implement their own ideas. This empowerment leads to many positive ideas and actions, and a few negative outcomes which can be tolerated. However, for safety issues, traditional command and control structures still operate. In particular, managers apply control techniques to assist the management of MAH, but near-misses continue to occur. So why do major accident near-misses continue to occur?

Many systems have been introduced on offshore installations to aid management of MAH. The systems are introduced with a clear objective, but over time the focus shifts from delivery of the objective to delivery against the system. People lose sight of the real objective, which is control of hazards.

> **Permit To Work**
> The PTW system is often treated as a paper system that demands compliance, rather than a system for managing hazards - the job can not start until the paperwork is completed. This attitude devalues the system. Evidence of lack of management control tends to be corrected by introducing new systems e.g. task-base risk assessment.

So, the challenge is: To make people think more about the function of the management system and think less about how to satisfy the management system itself.

Clearly much useful work can still be undertaken in this area.

Perhaps BP's progress can be a subject for our submission to the HAZARDS XVII conference next year.

References:

1. SHARPP project (Safety Report Handling Assessment and Review Principles and Processes)
2. 1974 HASWA Act, Health & Safety at Work Etc Act 1974, following the Robens report.
3. GHSER, BP Safety Management System known as Getting Health, Safety and Environment Right.
4. Accepted. The CA does not officially accept COMAH reports. A 'Conclusions' letter is sent to the operator of the site, which states whether Regulation 4 has been achieved and what further measures the CA would like the operator to consider.
5. A Guide to the Control of Major Accident Hazard Regulations 1999, ISBN 0-7176-1604-5
6. HAZARDS XIV Cost Effective Safety, ISBN 0-85295-416-6

COMAH AND THE ENVIRONMENT – LESSONS LEARNED FROM MAJOR ACCIDENTS 1999 - 2000

Aidan Whitfield
Environment Agency, Goldhay Way, Orton Goldhay, Peterborough, PE2 5ZR, UK
© Crown Copyright 2001. Reproduced with the permission of the Controller of
Her Majesty's Stationery Office.

In April 1999, the Control of Major Accident Hazards Regulations 1999 (COMAH),
came into force in Great Britain, implementing the requirements of the Seveso II
Directive 96/82/EC. The Competent Authority (CA) for the COMAH regulations in
England and Wales comprises the Health and Safety Executive (HSE) working
jointly with the Environment Agency (EA) (and in Scotland, the HSE working with
the Scottish Environment Protection Agency (SEPA)). This arrangement reflects
the requirements to ensure the protection of both persons and the environment. The
COMAH regulations superseded the Control of Industrial Major Accidents Hazard
Regulations 1984 (CIMAH), which were implemented by HSE alone.

The first COMAH major accident with environmental consequences was in
July 1999 at a chemicals storage facility operated by Tees Storage, at Seal Sands,
Middlesborough. Sixteen (16) tonnes of sodium cyanide solution leaked from a
storage tank into the ground, polluting the groundwater and the River Tees. This
incident occurred only 4 months after the regulations came into force and provided
an early test for the workings of the CA. It was one of the 11 COMAH major
accidents which were reported to the European Commission in the first year of
operation of the regulations (1999/2000).

Another COMAH major accident with environmental consequences occurred in
October 2000 at a waste management and treatment facility operated by Cleansing
Services Group (CSG), at Sandhurst in Gloucestershire. A major fire started in the
early hours of the morning, during a severe storm, and approximately 60 local
residents were evacuated. The Fire Service were unable to gain access to fight the
fire and the Police set up a "Gold Control" to manage the incident. Three days later
the River Severn burst its banks flooding the site and the local residents were
evacuated for a second time. The CA deployed significant resources to investigate
the incident, make the site safe and handle the public concern about health impacts.

This paper examines the causes of the incidents, their investigation and the
regulatory actions taken by the CA. It also considers some of the longer term
lessons learned.

KEYWORDS COMAH, Environment, Tank Bunds, European Commission
Reportable Accidents (ECRAs), Waste Establishments, Flooding.

INTRODUCTION

The first European Council directive concerned with controlling major accident hazards
involving dangerous substances was adopted in 1982. Known as the "Seveso" directive,
(82/501/EEC), it was incorporated into UK law by means of the Control of Industrial Major
Accidents Hazards Regulations 1984 (CIMAH). The regulations were primarily aimed at
protecting people, and enforcing them was the responsibility of the Health and Safety
Executive (HSE). In 1996, it was superseded by the "Seveso II" directive (96/82/EC). The
principal changes were a broadening of scope to include a wider range of dangerous
substances and enhanced requirements to protect the environment. Most of the requirements

of "Seveso II" have been implemented by the COMAH Regulations 1999 which supersede the 1984 CIMAH regulations. The Competent Authority (CA), for the purposes of the COMAH regulation in England and Wales, is the HSE and the EA acting jointly. Similarly in Scotland, it is the HSE and Scottish Environment Protection Agency (SEPA) acting jointly.

The HSE and the Agencies have often worked closely together, particularly on the investigation of industrial accidents which have had consequences for both human health and the environment. However, the requirements of the COMAH regulations to act jointly as a CA presented a particular set of challenges. The 3 organisations have brought complementary skills into this "arranged marriage"; HSE have 15 years' experience of implementing the previous CIMAH regime and protecting people, whilst the Agencies have experience in environmental regulation and public access to information. As is so often the case, the devil has been in the detail, bringing together 3 sets of procedures, working practices, computer systems, etc.

The general duty of the COMAH regulations is that "Every Operator shall take all measures necessary to prevent major accidents and limit their consequences to persons and the environment". The regulations apply to approximately 1200 establishments in total in Scotland, England and Wales. Approximately 800 are lower tier establishments which must prepare a Major Accident Prevention Policy (MAPP) and an on-site emergency plan. The remaining 430 establishments with larger inventories of dangerous substances are classified as top tier and are subject to additional requirements, including submitting a safety report to the CA and developing off-site emergency plans.

CYANIDE SPILLAGE AT TEES STORAGE, MIDDLESBROUGH, JULY 1999

Tees Storage (now Vopak Ltd) operates a bulk chemicals storage facility at Seal Sands near Middlesbrough in NE England. The facility was built in the 1960's on an area of reclaimed mudflats adjacent to the River Tees and has jetties providing good access by ship. There are over 150 tanks on the site of up to 8,000 tonnes capacity, storing a range of chemicals and oil products. It is a top tier COMAH establishment and was previously top tier under CIMAH.

During the afternoon of 21st July 1999, a worker discovered that a storage tank containing 750 tonnes of 30% sodium cyanide solution was leaking and there was a pool of liquid in the bund. The company informed HSE and the Environment Agency and immediately started transferring the contents of the tank into another tank. There were no injuries and since the primary concern was of environmental pollution, the Agency took the lead under COMAH.

The first concern for the CA was to ensure the safety of their own staff and a training session was arranged for the following morning, at one of the local companies that uses cyanides. Inspectors then visited the site and found that the company had completed the transfer of the tank contents and were preparing to pump the cyanide spillage out of the bund. Only 4 tonnes was recovered from the bund out of the 16 tonnes of cyanide solution that had leaked. The remaining 12 tonnes had leaked into the ground through the permeable base of the bund. The operator had also stopped the discharge of liquid effluent from the site into the River Tees. The Agency took samples from the effluent system, which confirmed that cyanide had entered the river, and Tees Storage commissioned a contractor to sink a series of boreholes around the tank. Agency fisheries staff surveyed the river by boat for several days, taking samples and looking for any evidence of environmental harm. Initial levels of cyanide in the river were measured at 40 µg/l, dropping to 10 µg/l within four days (20 µg/l for 96 hours is a lethal dose to freshwater fish). There was no evidence of harm to fish and samples of plankton were found to be normal. Tees Storage co-operated fully with the investigation and paid £20,000 towards the cost of the environmental monitoring work carried out by the Agency.

The tank was examined by an HSE Specialist Inspector and the cause of the leak was found to be a weld slag inclusion which had been formed during the original fabrication of the tank in 1977. Water had penetrated between the inclusion and the parent weld during tank cleaning operations, causing rust to form, dislodging the inclusion and creating a leak path. The bund consisted of a cast concrete wall and was only designed to provide lateral containment, preventing any spillage from spreading out over the site. This was sufficient to protect people, by confining any toxic or flammable hazard to the vicinity of the tank. However, it was demonstrably inadequate to protect the environment because the base of the bund was permeable and permitted the spillage to leak into the ground and subsequently into the river.

Two days after the incident, the Agency served a COMAH prohibition notice on Tees Storage prohibiting the use of the tank until actions had been taken to allow it to be operated safety. This was the second COMAH prohibition notice served by the CA, only 4 months after the Regulations had come into force. A press release was also issued the same day. The Agency subsequently charged Tees Storage with a breach of its discharge consent under Section 85 of the Water Resources Act 1991. The case was heard at Hartlepool Magistrates Court on 13 June 2000 and the Operator pleaded guilty to discharging up to 100 mg/1 of cyanide into the river compared to the 8 mg/1 allowed in their consent. They were fined £5,000 with £640 costs.

The incident at Tees storage revealed a tank bunding problem of which the Agency had not previously been aware. Further investigations by the Agency have revealed that bunds of similar design to those at Tees Storage are in widespread use in the UK. The Agency is particularly concerned because great efforts have been made in recent years to clean up the River Tees and it is now a salmon river with seals breeding in the estuary for the first time in living memory. The potential environmental damage resulting from a major pollution incident is therefore much greater than it was when the facility was built in the 1970s. The cost of retrofitting a proper "environmental protection" bund to a tank of this size would come to several hundred thousand pounds. The cost of retrofitting such bunds to all the tanks at Tees Storage would exceed the current asset value of the site. The Agency and HSE have nominated a "tank bunding" Lead Inspector to liaise with the chemical storage industry and co-ordinate the approach to be taken. The magnitude of the problem is being evaluated and consultants have been commissioned to carry out a research project involving risk assessment and cost benefit analysis, funded jointly by the CA and the chemical storage industry.

A further lesson concerns the age of the tank. It was built in 1977 to the normal industrial standards of the day and might typically have been expected to have a projected life span of 30 to 40 years. It could therefore be argued that it is reaching the end of its life and should be replaced. This situation applies to a large proportion of the infrastructure used in the chemical and process industries, that was built during the 1960's and 1970's and is still in use today.

MAJOR ACCIDENTS REPORTED TO THE EUROPEAN COMMISSION – 1999/2000

The COMAH regulations require the CA to report to the European Commission (EC) details of any COMAH major accident which exceeds the thresholds laid down in the "Seveso II" directive. The incident at Tees Storage was one of 11 EC Reportable Accidents (ECRA's) which occurred in the first year of operation of the COMAH regulations, from April 1999 to March 2000.

The regulations define "major accident", and all four parts of this definition must be satisfied for an incident to be classed as a COMAH major accident, ie it must be an occurrence at a COMAH establishment, resulting from loss of control, involving a dangerous substance and with the potential to cause harm. It must then satisfy one of 4 criteria to become an ECRA. Three of these criteria relate to the magnitude of the accident; loss of >5% of top tier inventories, specified harm to persons (eg 1 death or evacuation exceeding 500 person hours) or specified harm to the environment (eg significant damage to more than 10 km or river). The fourth criteria is that "a near miss" can be reported if it is a particular technical interest for preventing major accidents.

The CA is carrying out an analysis of the 11 ECRA's which occurred in 1999/2000 and intends to publish a report by late 2001. The important features to note are:

- There were 11 ECRA's in total and there are 1200 COMAH establishments. Hence the accident frequency rate is one per 110 establishments per annum. This demonstrates that the UK has no grounds for complacency on its safety record.

- Seven of the ECRA's were reportable because of the loss of >5% of the top tier threshold inventory.

- Four of the ECRA's were reportable because of harm to people, one involved the death of a worker (when sampling a cyanide solution at BASF, Middlesbrough on 20/12/99) and the other three involved evacuations exceeding 500 person hours.

- None of the ECRA's was reportable because of actual harm to the environment or as a near miss.

FIRE AT CSG, SANDHURST, OCTOBER 2000

Cleansing Service Group Ltd (CSG), operate a hazardous waste treatment facility and transfer station at Sandhurst, near Gloucester. The site was originally a brick works, then from 1860, a tar works. CSG purchased the site in 1972 and developed it into a waste treatment facility. There was a history of complaints from local residents regarding odours and nuisance. The site operated under a waste management licence issued by the Environment Agency and was subject to regular inspections. HSE has also inspected the site under the Health & Safety at Work Act 1974 (HSW74). It has been notified to the CA as a COMAH lower tier establishment though it was not previously regulated under CIMAH.

In the early hours of 30th October 2000, during a severe storm, a major fire started in a waste storage area. The site was unoccupied at the time and the fire service arrived to find the fire blocking the only access road and preventing them from gaining access. Waste aerosol cans were exploding and a series of larger explosions occurred when the contents of drums of toxic and flammable chemicals were released into the air. The overall management of the incident was the responsibility of Gold Control set up by Gloucester Police. Approximately 60 people were evacuated from their homes by the emergency services and 13 persons, mainly emergency service personnel, were taken to hospital as a precautionary measure during the fire, but none was admitted. The fire service gained access to the site from upwind across fields and extinguished the fire by 18.00 hours.

An incident room was set up by the Agency and staffed by Agency and HSE personnel within four hours of the incident starting. On the morning of 31st October, they were allowed access to the site to begin their investigations. Approximately 180 tonnes of mixed chemical wastes including some pesticides and chlorinated hydrocarbon solvents stored within the waste transfer station were consumed in the fire. Not all the materials involved in the fire were dangerous substances as defined in COMAH. In particular, only a maximum of 1.1 tonnes of very toxic substances were involved (compared with the lower tier threshold figure of 5 tonnes.)

Agency flood warnings indicated that the site, which is alongside the River Severn, would flood within days and actions had to be taken to make the site safe by moving fire-damaged and other material on site beyond the reach of floodwaters. When the flooding did occur on 3rd November 2000, the local residents had to be evacuated for a second time. The site was surrounded by floodwater and could only be accessed by boat, which hampered the clean up and investigation. On some days when boats were not used, the site was monitored by staff using helicopters and infrared cameras. Serious flooding continued until 22nd November and high flood water levels continued to threaten the site, which flooded again in December.

In the weeks following the incident, there were a large number of reports of illness from local residents, which were investigated by the local Health Authority. None of the 17,500 tests carried out on over 500 environmental samples, by the Agency and Tewkesbury Borough Council, indicated any significant levels of contaminants off-site. Modelling of the incident by HSE indicated that a "dangerous dose" of toxic materials would not have occurred beyond the site boundary. Gloucestershire Health Authority (GHA) does not believe there is any conclusive evidence of long-term impairment of the health of any member of the public. Monitoring of the health of the local population is continuing.

The Agency also committed significant resources to dealing with the concerns raised by the local residents about the operation of the site, and any possible off-site effects. Communication channels were set up to provide information and to listen to the concerns of residents and their representatives, including Councillors and the Member of Parliament. These channels included a local drop-in centre, daily question and answer briefings and media interviews. Senior Agency staff met with residents the Wednesday after the incident and a public meeting was held the week after the fire, attended by the Agency and HSE (and other members of Gold Control). There was a high level of media and political interest in the incident and the CA has had to submit progress reports to the Deputy Prime Minister[1][2].

Investigation by the CA and the fire service determined that the seat of the fire was in a compound which contained:

- 12 x 1te containers of isopropyl alcohol

- 24 x 200 litre drums of acetone

- 60 x 200 litre drums containing "laboratory smalls" (laboratory waste chemicals of all types in a variety of small containers, packed into 200 litre drums)

- 125 x 200 litre & 4 x 1 te containers and smaller drums of mixed wastes (mostly flammable solvents, adhesives and resins).

The cause of the incident has not been established. The identification of fuel and oxygen are straightforward but is has been more difficult to identify the ignition source that initiated this fire. Arson or a leakage of pyrophoric materials have been considered. Another possibility is that there was a loss of containment of the "laboratory smalls" eg as a result of drums being blown over by storm force winds. The chemicals could then have reacted together, generating heat and eventually igniting a sensitive material.

The Agency issued a notice of suspension to the Waste Management Licence (WML) for the site the day after the incident. This prevented the site from receiving further waste materials until CSG took appropriate actions. A COMAH prohibition notice and two improvement notices under the Health and Safety at Work Act were also served. In March 2001, CSG notified the CA that the inventories of dangerous substances on the site in future would be less than the COMAH thresholds. Investigations into possible breaches of the law are continuing and there may be a public enquiry.

Issues raised by the CSG incident include:

1 Were the waste operations being carried out at Sandhurst unique in any way? (If not, then similar risks might be present on the other 22 COMAH waste establishments (17 in England & Wales and 5 in Scotland)).

2 How many COMAH establishments are at risk of flooding? (Such industrial facilities are often situated near rivers or estuaries to provide cooling water and/or transport links).

3 Was the segregation of the storage for different classes of wastes such as oxidising, flammable and toxic materials adequate?

4 Were the physical storage conditions insecure? (The drums containing "laboratory smalls" were stacked two high and may have been blown over by high winds).

5 Was the site access adequate? (There was a single access road, which was blocked by the fire because of the wind direction).

6   Were the provisions for retaining contaminated fire water on site adequate?

7   The costs of the incident to the Operator have been very high in terms of site clean-up, loss of business and loss of reputation. There is a significant level of local concern and pressure to bring about the permanent closure of the site. Money spent to prevent such accidents may well be a good investment.

8   The Agency and HSE have also incurred considerable costs in terms of the resources allocated to handling the incident (though some of these costs may be recoverable from the Operator either as direct COMAH charging or through the awarding of costs by the courts).

LEARNING THE LESSONS FROM COMAH "ENVIRONMENTAL" INCIDENTS

The Environment Agency has selected 4 issues as its inspection priorities for 2001/02 and the first 3 of these result directly from the experience of the two incidents described in this paper. The inspection priorities are:

1   Bunding of tanks containing dangerous substances.

2   Flooding (both fluvial and tidal)

3   COMAH waste establishments

4   Domino Designations resulting from the effects of dangerous substances in the water abstractions of COMAH establishments.

These two incidents also raise wider issues that may challenge some long-held assumptions regarding risk assessment in the process industries.

The environment has usually been regarded as the victim of industrial accidents. The CSG incident and the widespread flooding last winter demonstrate that operators must take into account environmental factors which might initiate major accidents or worsen their consequences. The Environment Agency believes that global warming is already happening and that the future will involve more severe weather events, ie flooding, storm-force winds, lightning strikes and even tornadoes. These changes need to be considered carefully in the design and operation of processes handling dangerous substances.

The increasing age of equipment is also a growing concern. Much of the equipment used in the process industries was built in the 1960's and may typically have been expected to have a projected life span of 30 to 40 years. Some of that equipment has been scrapped as plants have been modernised but much of it remains in use. Will it continue to operate safely for 40, 50, or even 60 years? This problem has been carefully considered in the nuclear industry as the Magnox power stations have come to the end of their lives. Other sectors of industry may need to look more closely at this issue to ensure that the risks have been properly assessed. Power stations, oil refineries, gas terminals, chemical plants and chemical storage facilities are among the industries faced with these problems.

CONCLUSIONS

The Environment Agency and SEPA have responded to the challenge of the COMAH regulations and are working with HSE to make the CA a success. Environmental concerns are therefore being addressed by the COMAH regulations as was the intention of the "Seveso II" directive.

There were 11 ECRAs during the first year of the COMAH regulations. A wider understanding will only be possible when the trends of several years' data can be seen. It will also be useful to compare the performance of the UK with other European countries.[3]

Through implementation the COMAH regulations, and responding to incidents, the CA is discovering new issues that need to be addressed to ensure the protection of persons and the environment. From tank bunding to planning for climate change, there is still plenty of work to be done.

REFERENCES

1. Joint report by the Health and Safety Executive and the Environment Agency, 2001, Report for the Deputy Prime Minister the Right Honourable John Prescott MP into the major fire on 30 October 2000 at Cleansing Services Group Ltd, Upper Parting Works, Sandhurst Lane, Sandhurst, Gloucester, GL2 9NQ – Version 4.1.
   Available on the Environment Agency website http://www/environment-agency.gov.uk/regions/midlands

2. Joint report by the Health and Safety Executive and the Environment Agency, 2001, Progress report for the Deputy Prime Minister the Right Honourable John Prescott MP on Cleansing Services Group Ltd, Upper Parting Works, Sandhurst Lane, Sandhurst, Gloucester, GL2 9NQ – Final version.
   Available on the Environment Agency website http://www/environment-agency.gov.uk/regions/midlands

3. Kirchsteiger, K. 2001, How Frequent Are Major Industrial Accidents in Europe? Trans I Chem E. Vol 79 Part B.

FIGURES

Figure 1   Tees Estuary including Tees Storage Ltd

Figure 2   Tees Storage Ltd. Sodium Cyanide Leak

Figure 3   CSG Ltd. Fire on 30/10/2000

Figure 4   CSG Ltd. Compound 3 after the fire

Figure 5   CSG Ltd. Compound 1 after the fire

Figure 6   CSG Ltd. Flooding on 4/11/2000

"DEMONSTRATION" UNDER COMAH – PROBLEMS AND PARTNERSHIP.

Dr Ken Patterson, Process Safety Manager, Hickson & Welch, Wheldon Road, CASTLEFORD, West Yorkshire, WF10 2JT, UK
Nick Berentzen, Head of Occupational Safety, Chemical Industries Association, Kings Buildings, Smith Square, LONDON, SW1P 3JJ, UK

The introduction of the COMAH (SEVESO II) regulations into the UK has proved a major undertaking both for the companies required to write new Safety Reports and for the regulators who are required to assess them. The regulations introduce a number of new requirements but one has proved particularly troublesome to both regulated and regulator - the concept of "demonstration".

Although the Competent Authority (HSE, SEPA and EA) were able to offer some assistance with what was to be expected in the "demonstration of safe operation" by an operator, the concept has proved difficult for many. The CA have been refining their ideas in the light of the first submissions and operators have been trying to decide both how to demonstrate safe operation and what level of detail is required in the Safety Report to make it acceptable to the CA.

To answer this problem the UK Chemical Industries Association (CIA) and the CA ran a joint workshop in March 2001 to produce four worked examples of demonstration. The aim of the workshop was to produce a consensus view of what constitutes an acceptable demonstration, both to operators and to the CA. The demonstrations were to be made available to operators to help them in writing Safety Reports and were to be used by the regulators as examples of acceptable practice.

In the event it did not prove possible to write the demonstrations in the time available. Consensus was reached on a number of points which it was agreed were required, but on other matters, operators and the CA were not able to agree the level of detail which it is reasonable to require in a Safety Report. The conclusions of the four working groups at the workshop are being collated and are discussed here. They will be jointly published by HSE and CIA and will be available by the time of the Hazards XVI conference.

This rest of the paper discusses some problems operators have been having with the COMAH Regulations. It also discusses the problems operators have encountered in writing COMAH safety reports, especially the "demonstration" of safe operation, and the ways the regulators have worked with operators to overcome these problems.

COMAH, Demonstration, Safety Reports

BACKGROUND

The UK transposed the European Union's SEVESO II directive into domestic law as the COMAH – Control of Major Accident Hazards – Regulations (1999). HSE was intimately involved throughout the negotiations on the new directive and had a major hand in giving them their final shape. At both UK and EU levels, the new regulations were intended to produce a significant change in the way major hazard sites were regulated. All the major EU players, from the European Parliament to the EU Major Hazards Bureau, have made their mark on the regulations or their implementation. In the UK the introduction of the new regulations has seen the formation of a new Competent Authority (CA) made up jointly of the HSE and EA (HSE and SEPA in Scotland) and the recruitment of additional regulatory staff. The UK regulators have made no secret that they are looking to the new regulations to produce new ways of working – both by the regulators and by operators – with greater openness, especially to the public.

Sadly, the period since the regulations came into force has seen a marked change in the relationship between many UK chemical companies and their regulators, especially HSE. The change has not been for the better. Operators have found the new regulations difficult to implement and very onerous in both cash costs and in internal resource. Most operators have - however unfairly - felt the attitude of HSE (as the lead regulator in the CA) to be unhelpful and confrontational. To their credit, the regulators have recognised this concern and taken action to improve the way they are handling relationships with operators. Most especially, as this paper describes, they have co-operated with a team formed by the CIA (UK Chemical Industries Association) to try to answer one of the areas of difficulty, that of "demonstration" of safe operation (the duty placed on operators under Schedule 4, part 1 of the regulations).

PROBLEMS WITH COMAH INTRODUCTION

Traditionally, operators of major chemical sites in the UK have had open co-operative relationships with HSE, though always with a recognition that HSE was prepared to take enforcement action, including prosecution, when it was justified. In the past there has been a recognition of the expertise available on both sides and a willingness to learn from each other. HSE and EA have both been prepared to listen to industry's concerns and ensure that (where legally and politically possible) their guidance reflected what could be achieved as well as what was desirable. Since the introduction of COMAH, many companies feel that Inspectors' attitudes have undergone a marked change, away from the co-operative attitudes of the past to a more rule bound approach.

This change in relationships can be attributed to a number of things but in our view three stand out: the introduction of charging; the sharp increase in the Consultation Distance (CD) around many sites; and the problems of understanding what the regulators want in a Safety Report, especially how the requirement to "demonstrate ... adequate safety and reliability" (COMAH regulations, schedule 4 paragraph 3) can be met. Both charging and site CDs are being discussed elsewhere and will not be discussed at length. However, in this context, they cannot be ignored.

CHARGING FOR INSPECTION AND SAFETY REPORT ASSESSMENT

Charging (at a very high rate) was an explicitly political decision, taken at a high level in government. The decision will not be changed but there is no doubt that charging is viewed with unhappiness by the chemical industry and has a damaged relationships with the regulators. It is not just the cost, though that does hurt. Part of the problem is the unpredictability of the non-negotiable charges which can be incurred in any given year. There is also a very wide suspicion that the regulators' activities have been distorted to focus on activities which can be charged for. Many "simple" accidents have somehow become COMAH related whilst others seem to be ignored. HSE inspectors looking at their watches and saying "Well the next section of my visit is chargeable" does not encourage frank detailed, open discussions. In one case, HSE inspectors stopped attending regular meetings with a regional Chemical Industry safety group (a Responsible Care Cell) because the work was not chargeable. This has happily been reversed but the distrust has lived on. There is an urgent need for a simple, transparent charging scheme which does not distort priorities and does not unduly penalise what is a very safe industry.

CONSULTATION DISTANCES

If charging was a political decision, the decisions about how site Consultation Distances should be calculated are much more difficult to disentangle. When asked, the DETR (Department of the Environment, Transport and the Regions: the UK Government department responsible for planning law and the sponsoring department for both HSE and EA) suggested that the decisions were technical and taken by HSE. HSE, on the other hand, suggested that options were offered and DETR chose the one they favoured. There is no doubt about the consequences which have been quite serious in some cases - not for chemical companies (yet) but for the communities and Local Authorities around chemical sites.

The operators of chemical sites have worked with both HSE and EA/SEPA year on year to improve their standards and thereby reduce the risks - to the environment, to safety and to health – on and around their sites. However, seemingly at the stroke of an administrative pen, Local Authorities have found that consultation distances have grown enormously, sometimes by a factor of 6. This means that the area covered can be more than 30 times greater than before and the effect on development in the community around a chemical site can be devastating. As an example, the Local Authority for the Hickson & Welch site has now been advised that it should not allow the rebuilding of the local public library, on its existing site, for its existing purpose.

In some areas, operators are now seen as the "problem" and relationships with the community and Local Authorities have deteriorated. Sites are being pressed to give up their rights to hold chemicals, a move which would, in the longer term, undermine the competitive position of the UK chemical industry. Worst of all, the current position threatens to undermine the whole basis of UK planning controls around Major Hazard sites. In a number of areas, Local Authorities are seeking alternative advice to that given by HSE and are writing planning policies which will allow them to discount HSE planning advice when it suits them. This is an outcome neither the regulators nor the industry can be happy with and it is to be hoped that the current review reportedly being undertaken (mid-summer 2001) will have a positive and constructive outcome.

PROBLEMS WITH SAFETY REPORTS
These problems form the backdrop to the difficulties companies are having writing their COMAH Safety Reports (SRs). Companies' difficulties with SRs cover most of the possible topics in a COMAH report, from the breadth of information to be covered, to the depth of detail required in dealing with specific matters. More disturbingly, exploring these difficulties has displayed a wide divergence between the stated expectations of the UK Competent Authority (CA) and the way companies have interpreted the duties placed upon them to provide information in their SRs.

There is no doubt that the CA has tried to give a lead in understanding (most of) the duties. This is perhaps, not surprising though certainly very welcome. After all the UK legislation was prepared by the regulators and a number of people inside HSE had a major hand in framing the EU directive. The HSE, in particular, has published a very large amount of information and guidance designed to assist operators to write their SRs (ref 1,2). Unfortunately the guidance is not always consistent. Indeed the structure of a safety report suggested in the internal HSE guidance on report assessment (the Safety Report Assessment Manual – SRAM – not published in the conventional sense but available from the HSE internet site: ref 3) differs from that suggested in the HSE "official" guidance (HSG190, "Preparing Safety Reports" ref 2). There is also the feeling that HSE (in particular) published a lot of guidance but then abandoned operators to write safety reports.

In fact, HSE did give further guidance to operators based on the common problems they found in the first SRs submitted, for example by sending a letter to top-tier sites involved in writing SRs (ref 4) and by making presentations to a number of conferences. However, the perception of having been set a complicated test by the CA, being given a tight timetable to write the SR and then being marked on the result – with the CA as judge, jury and executioner – is widespread amongst operators.

THE MEANING OF DEMONSTRATION
From discussions with operators and regulators it is clear that the term demonstration has been viewed as fairly all encompassing, by both the CA and those writing safety reports. It is accepted that the term covers not only technical matters around a particular installation but the whole way a site or company operates. Thus there is no dispute that setting out the company's Safety Management System, and showing that it complies with the principles set out in HSG65 (ref 5) (or an equivalent standard), is an essential part of the demonstration of safe operation. Likewise, procedures for handling emergencies; training for staff at all levels; and methods for assessing and understanding the hazards of the chemicals and processes on site, are all a part of the overall demonstration which are required in the Safety Report.

Accepting that they are part of the demonstration of safe operation certainly does not lessen the problem of writing a SR which adequately deals with these matters. However, the outline of what is required to deal with these subjects is fairly clear. They were dealt with in most recent CIMAH safety reports, for example. Though issues of detail and interpretation (to comply with the requirements of COMAH rather than CIMAH) remain, the basic information and systems should already be firmly in place. For example, for Safety Management Systems the standards are set out in HSG65. HSE inspectors have for several years been discussing with operators of Major Hazard sites how they should comply with those standards. Whilst a company's system may require improvement or writing up in a new way for COMAH, both the underlying structure of the Management System and its basic documentation should have been in place by the time the first COMAH safety reports came to be written. And in general, this will have been achieved by co-operation, cajoling and consent between the regulators and the operator.

DEMONSTRATING THE DETAIL

Whilst many parts of the COMAH report may have been in existence before implementation, HSE (especially) have made it quite clear that COMAH is a major change and they were not looking for a simple re- packaging of existing material in a new way. For the regulators, a COMAH SR was never meant to be a simple revision of a CIMAH SR with a few environmental considerations thrown in.

Perhaps one of the key phrases, used by a number of HSE inspectors, has been "we are looking for demonstration not assertion". Occasionally inspectors would add something along the lines of: "What we mean is, it is no good just giving us a description of your operation and saying you are safe like you did in your CIMAH safety report". This is apparently easy to understand; though when HSE inspectors were challenged to explain it in greater depth they found it more difficult. Usually as the questions became more detailed the answers became more fuzzy and reference was increasingly made to the SRAM (referred to above) or "SRAGs" (installation specific assessment guidance) which either had been or were to be published.

A HYPOTHETICAL PLANT

Consider a fictitious case, say a phosgene generation plant. It is clear that the simple statement: "We operate plant Q to make 300 tonnes of phosgene per annum in accordance with our site procedures and in equipment built to the appropriate standards", is not an exhaustive demonstration of safe operation – even if the statement is absolutely true. But then consider mechanical integrity of the plant (bought in as a proprietary unit from abroad). It will have a reaction vessel which will operate at elevated temperature and pressure. The vessel will have a pressure rating and be subject to the Pressure System Regulations. The site has a safety management system which includes a computer-based planned maintenance system (recently audited by the EA) and has a contract with external assessors to inspect vessels and to give reports. The company has the (satisfactory) reports on the vessel from the assessors, on file, on site.

To most operators, the existence of an auditable system, which complies with the Pressure System regulations and is known to the regulators to be working, would seem to be an adequate demonstration of safety of the pressure vessel (which is one small part of the overall safety of the phosgene plant). The problem is that there are an infinite (or at least large) number of questions that could be asked about this vessel. What was the design standard? How does this compare with the latest British Standard? How do you justify any differences between the two standards? If the vessel was built before the last revision of the British Standard has the vessel been reassessed? How was the re-assessment done? Who did the re-assessment? What were the competencies of the person(s) doing the assessment? What steps did the operator take to satisfy themselves that these were the right competencies and that they were actually held?

Then to consider a different aspect: what is the effect of operation at elevated temperature? Has the vessel been de-rated for this operation? Was a standard used to do this de-rating? Why did the operator use this standard? If a standard was not used what is the justification for the method used? Who judged that this was an acceptable method? What is the reliability of the temperature control system? Has the vessel been assessed against the maximum possible temperature which could be reached if the temperature control system fails? How is this temperature arrived at? What about a co-incident pressure excursion?

EFFECT ON SAFETY DEPARTMENTS

Clearly, the number of apparently reasonable questions can be made to grow very rapidly. And I should stress that questions very like these have been asked - in writing - by the CA before they would accept operators' safety reports. Each question on its own has obviously seemed reasonable and justifiable to one member of the CA's assessment team. The net effect however is neither reasonable nor justifiable – not reasonable because there must be a point at which safe operation has been demonstrated without every possible question being answered and not justifiable because asking and answering all these questions will not add to the safety of the plant, its operators or the wider community. Indeed the opposite is now widely felt to be true by many operators. So much effort is being put into writing COMAH Safety Reports, that "normal" safety work is not being done. As an example, on the Hickson & Welch site in 2000 about 50% of all the effort of the SHE department went into writing the COMAH safety report. The net benefits do not justify the time spent.

It is worth noting that this problem is not a function of the way an operator has tried to write the demonstration of safety and is not related to the actual safety of the installation being described. The problem clearly exists for any descriptive, non-quantitative method. It also exists for more formal methods of demonstration, such as the "bowtie/lines of defence" methods used by many companies (including H&W). It certainly also exists for quantitative methods of assessment where many questions can be asked about the source, reliability and applicability of the data being used even before questions are asked about the details of the plant being assessed.

ACCEPTABLE RISK

The current HSE view of acceptable levels of risk is set out in "Reducing Risks, Protecting People" (ref 6) where HSE argues that showing that a plant has a particular risk level associated with it (where ever that lies on the conventional ALARP diagram), is not adequate to comply with the ALARP principle for high hazard plants. There is now a need to show what further measures could be/ could have been used to reduce risks still further. Where they are not used the operator will need to show an assessment to "demonstrate" that their rejection is acceptable. This assessment is, in the same way, open to the same type of detailed questioning. Again, the need in COMAH to take "all measures necessary to prevent major accidents" (how can an operator demonstrate that they have assessed "all measures"? in what detail?) shows the extent of the problem which exists for all safety reports, whatever assessment methods are used.

It must be remembered that this is a problem of description, not of safety. The problem is one of writing a demonstration; not of operating a safe plant. Where any part of the CA has had reservations about the safety or operation of a plant they have used their existing powers under Health and Safety or Environmental Protection legislation to bring about improvement. Even when serving Improvement Notices for inadequacies in Safety Reports, the CA have not generally been asking for changes to plant or management systems. The notices have been for changes or additions to the Safety Report, leaving the fundamental safety of the plant unchanged.

OFFER TO CO-OPERATE

The problems outlined above were one of the subjects discussed at the "Implementing Seveso II" conference held in London in November 2000. The conference also had presentations from the regulators and the regulated in other EU member states. These presentations tended to highlight the much more relaxed attitude to the implementation timetable being taken in the other member states. They also tended to show a much more collaborative approach to the production of Safety Reports in other countries, with inspectors working with companies to produce a report acceptable to everyone. A very notable example of this was Holland where inspectors were members of the project boards in companies producing SRs, guiding companies through the SR writing process. This will ensure that the finished report will be of the form required by the Dutch CA and makes the idea of the Dutch CA rejecting an operator's report nonsensical (though all too familiar in the UK).

The presentation to the conference by one of us (ref 7) focussed on the UK experience and the problems operators were having with the regulations. Other presentations, notably from Colin Pinder of BP (ref 8) and Dave Mercer of Vopak (ref 9), discussed how individual companies had dealt with "demonstration" in their reports and the difficulties they had encountered. All the companies involved, even those who had worked with HSE writing "trial" SRs before the regulations came into force, had great difficulty understanding and complying with the CA's requirements. It was also felt by operators that the CA had adopted a very confrontational approach with a rapid use of Improvement Notices if a company did not produced what the CA considered a satisfactory report at the first attempt. The regulator's view seemed to be that the CA had produced more guidance than ever before, including guidance on the way reports would be assessed, and it was up to companies to provide the CA with what was required. Any failure of understanding or of commission was to be laid at the operator's door and "punished" by serving an Improvement Notice, something reported to the public and noted by many corporate head offices as a serious black mark against a site's SHE performance. Given the non-British ownership of much of the UK Chemical Industry and the fact that SHE performance is used both for deciding the location of future investment and for determining managerial rewards, the service of an Improvement Notice is a serious event in most companies. Not surprisingly, this has given a situation in which operators feel very unhappy about the CA's approach to COMAH and feel that that the problems industry has had in writing safety reports are not being understood or addressed by the CA.

It must be said that this message was understood by the CA at the conference and engendered considerable debate, both on the conference floor and in the breaks between sessions. In discussion, the idea of a workshop to try to answer some of these concerns by developing some model demonstrations was developed.

AIMS AND APPROACH OF THE WORKSHOP

From the outset the workshop was seen as a co-operative venture between the regulators and operators. The principal aim was to develop a number of demonstrations which could be used by both sides – by the operators as models when writing demonstrations for their own processes and by the regulators as a yardstick to judge the adequacy of the demonstration offered in submitted Safety Reports. Provided a common understanding could be reached, both sides felt that some of the heat could be taken out of this part of COMAH report writing – which would be a step to restoring relations to a more normal footing.

Clearly, in any reasonable time the demonstrations could only deal with a small area of a Safety Report – operators spend months writing their reports. There was no intention to deal with areas of the report such as the environment around a site, the safety management system or issues of competency and training. The demonstrations were necessarily limited to the technical matters around particular parts of the installation. To give a reasonable spread, four demonstrations were proposed: a batch reactor; a warehouse and associated storage; bulk liquid storage; and the mechanical integrity of pressurised equipment. These are still very wide areas and so, to enable a focused discussion, a more detailed description of the supposed installation was provided for each case study. There is a danger in this; the more detailed the description the less easily applicable the demonstration to other plants or sites. However without the descriptions little progress could have been made. The descriptions were written by operators with each particular type of plant to ensure reasonable accuracy and coverage of the essential points. They are not reproduced here but are available from the authors on request (and will be available at the conference).

FORM OF THE WORKSHOP

As the workshop was to be a co-operative venture the aim was to have equal numbers of operators and CA members present, 12 from each side. Two days were set aside for the workshop, which was held in Dalton Grange, Huddersfield, courtesy of Syngenta. Following an introduction, the workshop was to split into groups with each group comprising 3 from each side. Each group was intended to discuss one of the demonstrations in detail and then, if time allowed, go on to considering one or more of the other case studies. Finally the groups would come back together and discuss their conclusions ("consensualise" them) and the demonstrations would then be taken away and written up. As an aside, one remark made by a member of the CA team in one of the pre-meetings, is worthy of note. Having seen the timetable he remarked "Yes, but what will they [the groups] do on day two?" To an operator who has struggled firstly to understand demonstration and then has spent some months writing a safety report, this remark points to an apparent serious misunderstanding, in some parts of the CA at least, of the difficulties and the effort required to write a Safety Report.

OUTCOME OF THE DISCUSSIONS

The CA fielded Inspectors from HSE, EA and SEPA, ensuring that all the regulators were represented. The industry representatives likewise covered a good cross section of operators: from dedicated storage sites, to large production facilities and including a range of smaller chemical sites. The CA brought slightly more than their quota of members to the workshop which enabled some (useful) overlap between groups but otherwise the workshop ran to plan, though the timetable proved to be very tight with discussions continuing across all the breaks and over dinner. However, none of the groups was able to fulfil the aim of the workshop in the time available, as none of them was able to write up an agreed demonstration. Neither the tightness of the timetable nor the failure to deliver the demonstrations during the two days, was a surprise to the operators present. Some groups did manage to get closer to the aim of the workshop and produce an outline of a demonstration, though others (notably the batch reactor group) found that there were quite large differences between what the operators felt was reasonable to incorporate in a safety report, and what the representatives of the regulators felt would be required for an acceptable demonstration. The final, plenary session of the workshop allowed the whole group to discuss the outcome of each of the working groups. This session did clearly point up the areas of agreement, which were considerable, as well as highlighting the areas where disagreement remained. Following the workshop, one member of each group undertook write up a summary of the discussions. These have been incorporated into the work described below.

SUBSEQUENT WORK

Following the meeting, HSE, EA and CIA representatives have met to produce a guidance document, based on the workshop's discussions, but also informed by the CA's experience of reading a (rapidly increasing) number of safety reports. The guidance is intended to be published by the CIA and is aimed at helping both those CIA members yet to submit their safety reports and at helping the Competent Authority assessors decide what is a reasonable level of detail to include in a safety report. It should be stressed that the guidance will be about the level of detail that is required to make a demonstration in a safety report. It is not intended to show what is required to control the risks of a major hazard plant adequately. It is expected that inspectors will, in the course of visit over the lifetime of the report, follow up the information given in a demonstration, both to audit the information and to explore the systems described in much greater detail.

At the time of writing the guidance is not (quite) complete but it will consist of a set of general principles to follow when making demonstrations, plus a table showing the details required for demonstrations for a short list of 'top events' associated with each of the four cases. The guidance will be published in the autumn of 2001 and will be available (and described in more detail) at the conference.

1. "A guide to the Control of Major Accident Hazard Regulations 1999", L111, HSE Books, 1999

2. "Preparing Safety Reports: Control of Major Accident Hazard Regulations 1999", HSG190, HSE Books, 1999

3. "COMAH Safety Report Assessment Manual", Available to download from the HSE web site at www.HSE.gov.uk/chid/COMAH2/

4. "Early lessons on COMAH Safety Reports", standard letter sent by the CA to COMAH top tier sites, 2000

5. "Successful health and safety management", HSG65 (revised), HSE Books, 1997

6. "Reducing risks, protecting people", HSE discussion document, 1999, available from the HSE web site at www.HSE.gov.uk/discdocs/closed/dde11.pdf

7. "COMAH – an Industry View", Ken Patterson, Hickson & Welch Ltd, presented at "Implementing SEVESO II Conference", London, 6 – 8 November 2000. Paper and presentation available via the HSE web site at www.HSE.gov.uk/hid/seveso2/main.htm

8. "COMAH – Progress to date: Demonstration and SMS", Colin Pinder, BP Amoco, presented at "Implementing SEVESO II Conference", London, 6 – 8 November 2000. Paper and presentation available via the HSE web site www.HSE.gov.uk/hid/seveso2/main.htm

9. "Seveso I to Seveso II – from Describe to Demonstrate", Dave Mercer, Vopak, presented at "Implementing SEVESO II Conference", London, 6 – 8 November 2000. Paper and presentation available via the HSE web site www.HSE.gov.uk/hid/seveso2/main.htm

HUMAN OPERATOR ASSESSMENT-BASIS FOR A SAFE WORKPLACE IN THE PROCESS INDUSTRY

Ph.D.Ionel Iorga-The Romanian National Research Institute for Occupational Safety(INCDPM),Bucharest

Rear adm.Ph.D.Dan Ionescu-INCDT COMOTI RA,Bucharest,Romania

Ph.D.Stefan Kovacs – The Romanian National Research Institute for Occupational Safety(INCDPM),Bucharest, e-mail:icpm00@softnet.ro

Scientific Researcher Camelia Creanga-INCDT COMOTI RA,Bucharest,Romania

The human operator is the core of good functioning for almost every technical installation, in the civil or military field. About 75% of the occupational accidents are provoked by the human operator. Assessment of the human operator from the safety point of view will be the first step toward a safer workplace. Unfortunately, the assessment process of the human operator is a very subjective job, considering the mostly subjective parameters that are defining him.

This paper shows aspects of the design and application of a better and objective safety assessment system for the human operator, considering all the definitory categories for his/hers safety, like training, physical state, psychical state, stress, attitudes and so on. The system was built on the basis of operational analysis, robotics theory and also the most advanced information instruments available. Searching the space state of the man-machine system in its workplace instance, there could be defined optimum state functions that are balancing the need for efficiency with the safety requirements. The assessment system is using checklists to compute these functions and then is cross-checking these functions against reference values. On the basis of the calculated optimum values, a general score for the human operator is calculated, being compared then with reference scores for various activities inside the process industry. The general score and optimum state functions offer indications about actions that must be taken to improve the safety of the human operator, and actions like a better training, moving to another workplace and so on. The system has a multilevel architecture, starting with base level-basic assessment, done by complex checklists, a middle level for assessing the safety of process specific activities and a final level for assessing the operator's safety at his workplace.

The implementation of this system has started in pilot centers from Romania's process industry, till now being obtained very promising results. Some of these results are also presented in this paper.

Keywords

Human operator assessment, optimum state functions, safety functions, safety assurance

GENERALITIES

Incidents and occupational accidents are taking place into the workspace. Here, because of the human error or because of the malfunctioning of the various installations accidents occur. So, in developing a human operator assessment system, the starting point will be the workplace. There could be defined two categories of state functions, considering the man-machine environment:

-Workplace state functions

-Human operator state functions

Optimum of workplace state functions is given by the parameters of machine and working environment
The human operator(HO) is merely "forgotten" from the safety assessment because of the mainly subjective analysis results that are obtained. But, sadly, the human operator is the main or indirect cause of the most incidents and occupational accidents.
"Static" HO states are defining the readiness of the human operator in performing in safe conditions.
"Dynamic" HO states or functions are defining the dinamic activity developed by the operator to perform his task. Dynamic HO functions could be delimited in:
-Threshold functions: are defining the (succesfull) end of a task and start-up of another task
-Performance functions:are defining the safety performance in doing one specific task .These performance functions could be considered as beeing optimum driven towards optimum workplace state functions
Considering the subjective trend of the most human assessment systems, the main goal of the common research developed by the two Romanian National Institutes, INCDPM and INCDT COMOTI RA [1]was to develop a more objective safety assessment system for the human operator involved in process activities. In doing that, we meet the necessity to define some theoretical basis of human operator analysis inside work space. The existing theories were centered around the human performance at the workplace, the safety aspect being neglected or treated not so well. Our secondary goal was to test our assessment system in real conditions and to develop it so as to became an efficient tool in safety assessment. Some aspects of this research are presented in this paper.

WORKPLACE STATES AND THE ASSESSMENT PROCESS

The assessment process and its consequences are presented in Figure 1.

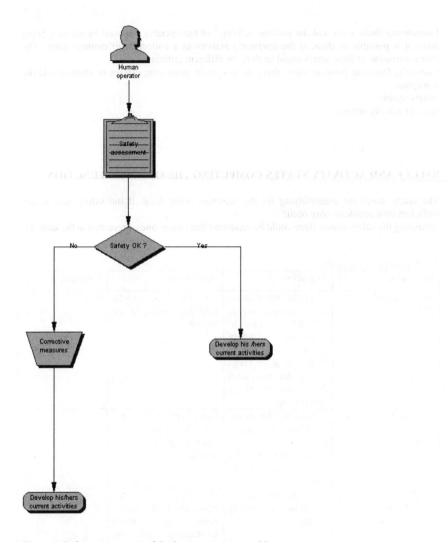

Figure 1-Safety assessment of the human operator and its consequences

The space of workplace's states [2] is a very interesting thing to analyze; practically, these states are leading to a normal functioning of the system or toward occupational accidents. By analogy with robotics it is possible to define at the workplace, two distinct areas:
-the main activity area, in which the human operator is moving so as to perform the process;
-the auxiliary area, in which the human operator is moving for auxiliary tasks, for recreation or for other reasons;

Considering these areas and the canonic activity [3] of the operator imposed by the task being done, it is possible to think at the operator's activity as a collection of distinct states. The characterization of these states could be done on different criteria.

Currently, from our point of view, there are two main interesting classes of states inside the workplace:

-safety states;

-current activity states;

SAFETY AND ACTIVITY STATES-COMPUTING THE OPTIMUM FUNCTION

The safety states are exemplifying for the activities being done. If the safety state is not sufficient then accidents may occur.

Analyzing the safety states, there could be separated three main ones, presented in the table 1:

Table 1-Main Safety States

State name	Transition	Description	Reference values
Ideal Safety State (ISS)	–>all the other states are moving toward this state in case of unlimited safety resources <–all the other states are departing from this state in really functioning	Describes the 100% safe functioning of the system	9...10
Normal Safety State (NSS)	–>towards ISS in the condition of safety supply; <–towards USS in the condition of system decay;	Describes the normal(current) functioning of the system	(5) 6..8
Un-desired Safety State (USS)	–>toward NSS in the condition of safety supply	Describes the critical(from the safety point of view) functioning of the system	0...4(5)

Considering a 0..10 evaluation scale with 0-most negative and 10 most favorable ,we could define reference values for these safety states as shown in the above table.

The reference values are useful in analyzing the results of checklists against these values.

Safety states could be given by statistic data [4] for various activities, analyzing the accidents, incidents and near incidents on a five to ten years period. This analysis could be refined selecting just the events produced by the human operator. For example, considering the reference values presented above, these could be connected to specific events like in the table below.

Table 2-Reference values and number of events at the workplace

Safety State Name	ISS	NSS	USS
Reference values	9..10	6..8	0..5
Number of near incidents in the latest 5 years	0..1	2..15	more than 15
Number of incidents in the latest 5 years	0	1..5	more than 5
Number of accidents in the latest five years	0	1..3	over 3

Analyzing the activity states, is possible to identify three main states, presented below:
-preparation state: in which the process is prepared;
-process state: execution of activity;
-disposal state: in which the by-products are eliminated;

By mapping [5] the safety states on the activity states and taking into account that the main safety problems are in the process sate, we obtain table 3.

Table 3-Mapping of the safety states on the activity states

Activity State/Safety State	Ideal Safety State	Normal Safety State	Un-desired Safety State
Preparation State	9..10	5..8	0..4
Process State	9..10	6..8	0..5
Disposal State	9..10	5..8	0..4

Returning to the human operator, we could identify some main attributes of his safety at the workplace, as these attributes could increase or decrease the safety level; in this paper we are proposing a shorthand list of attributes, presented in table 4:

Table 4-Human operator specific attributes

Attribute name	Describes
Training	Specific safety training of the human operator
Physical state	Physical state of readiness of human operators
Psychical state	Psychical state of readiness of human operators
Stress	Stress level imposed by a specific activity
Attitudes	Attitudes required to perform a specific activity
Conformism-dynamism	Conformism to the activity being done; tendencies to overreact or to do something

Attribute name	Describes
	else in case of a monotone activity

These attributes are caught using complex checklist systems, so as to be as objective as possible. When completed, the checklists are giving specific scores for all these attributes; these scores are converted into a safety state parametric functions, specified as fs(attribute)=value and also in an activity parametric function specified as fa(attribute)=value that combined together give the optimum state function.

The optimum [6]function will be computed as

$$fopt=optimum(fs,fa) \; [1]$$

This optimum function could also be analyzed on a 0 to 10 scale. Our experience in implementation of the system shows that a satisfactory range of values would be between 7..9.

DYNAMIC HUMAN OPERATOR FUNCTIONS

Using a probabilistic approach it is possible to define a general safety function as

$$Gsafe=f \, (X1,X2,...Xn) \; [2]$$

where $X1$= exposure to the risks;
$X2..Xn-1$= exposure variables;
Xn represents the specific safety function slope factor;

Regarding the performance of the worker at his workplace it is possible to define two distinct types of safety functions that could contain the safety aspects of the human operator's activity.

-THE SAFETY PERFORMANCE FUNCTION SPF is directly connected to a specific task or subtask and is describing the safety needs from the human operator, so as to safely perform the mentioned task or subtask;

-THE SAFETY THRESHOLD FUNCTION STF is a connector that describes the safety links between a task and the next one, so that if task n-1 is performed safely task n could start but if task n-1 ended in failure task n will not start.

This alternation between safety performance functions and safety threshold functions is presented below in figure 2.

The chain of safety functions at workplace

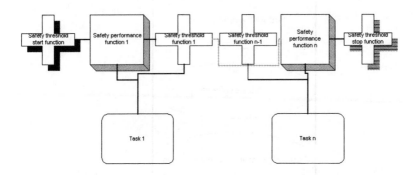

Figure 2 The chain between safety performance functions and safety threshold functions

It is possible to see that, the performance functions are co-responding to a specific task and the threshold functions are gateway functions between the tasks.

SAFETY PERFORMANCE FUNCTIONS (SPF)

The safety performance function is directly mapped to a specific task [7]. For example, at a lathe, the first task is to start the machine. For doing this, the worker:
-1. must be able to carry on and load the material to be processed into the lathe;
-2. must verify the active zone of the lathe so as, at starting up, no materials will be caught and projected into the worker or his/hers colleagues;
-3. must verify the material being processed, so that this material is solidly fixed into the rotating part of the lathe and could not be projected at start-up;
-4. must verify the processing tool, so that is the required tool for the material being processed, this tool is solidly fixed and is not touching the material at starting the machine.
-5. must verify the existence of oil in the oil reservoir and also the functioning of oil pump;
-6. must verify if the lathe is plugged in and if the alimentation cord is safe;
-7. must know on which button to push;
Considering all these auxiliary activities needed to start the lathe, we could define some specific states describing the safety of the human operator.
These states could be evaluated by an auditor   on a 0..10 scale, so as 0 is equivalent to extremely bad and 10 to ideal from the safety point of view .
We can imagine these states as safety filters between risks and the human operator, as shown in the figure 3.
In this example, we are considering the states presented in the table below-their assessment was done so as to assure a minimal safety:

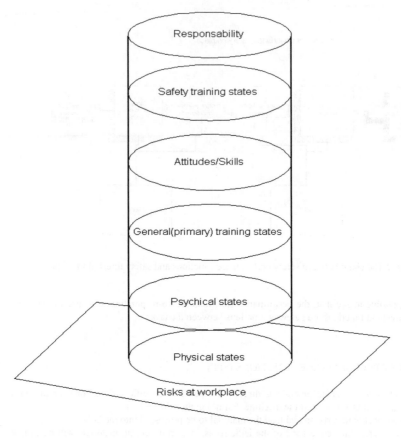

Figure 3 The safety states filter between risk and human operator

A mapping of the safety states on the activities presented in this example is shown in table 5.

Table 5 Safety states vs. activity

No	State	Example activity no.	Safety Estimation
1	General training	2..7	5..6
2	Safety training	2..7	6
3	Physical	1	6
4	Psychical	1..7	5
5	Skills	2..6	6
6	Attitudes	2..6	5
7	Responsibility	1..7	6

A special attention must be given to the Responsibility State. The table 6 is detailing its components

Table 6 Responsibility components

No	Component (Responsibility for...)	Description
1	Supervision	The operator has supervision duties and must fulfill them in order to accomplish his task
2	Policy	Must follow the established policies of the company
3	Methods	Must follow established methods in order to accomplish his tasks and it is /it is not required to establish his own methods.
4	Materials and Supplies	Must efficiently allocate the required materials and supplies to perform the task
5	Confidence and Trust	From the supervisor and from his/hers co-workers
6	Contacts	For ordinary contacts, required by the work process and also from immediate contacts in emergency cases
7	Cooperative service and joint activity	Activity together with his/hers co-workers and also with third parties
8	Records and reports	Must record all the problems and report them to his superiors
9	Machinery and Equipment	Must use, preserve and maintain the machinery and equipment in an adequate state of safety
10	Safety for others	Must perform his/hers activity so as to preserve and improve other's safety
11	Personal safety	Must preserve and improve his/hers safety

We could define Minimal Safety Performance Functions (MSPF) as, those safety performance functions that are just assuring safety against serious accidents ,developing into invalidity or death , without balancing with productivity and efficiency at work.

Analyzing this table, is possible to see that we can describe a Minimal Safety Performance Function, MSPF for this task of starting the lathe , by giving values to the component states, so as to assure the minimal protection against severe accidents. We could consider a MSPF for a Safety Estimation around 5 or 6.

A superior step, the Optimal Safety Performance Functions (OSPF) could be defined as the functions that are assuring safety against the majority of accidents (not including here the minor incidents or the occupational diseases provoked by stress or repetitive work) in co-relation with productivity and efficiency at work. Regarding the previous table, we could consider an OSPF if the Safety Estimation is around 8.

How will this estimation affect the productivity and efficiency ? Firstly, by lowering the time required to perform the task. Secondly , by raising the efficiency of the activity and thirdly by making the activity more secure.

SAFETY THRESHOLD FUNCTIONS (STF)

STF's are the connectors between the tasks that are done at the workplace during the work process. On the simplest thought, STF's can be imagined as a 0..1 functions with the 0 value when the precedent task fails and 1 when the task is performed in safety conditions. This is the simplest way to imagine the threshold. However, in the real life, a task could fail but not obviously, so the next task could start even if the precedent ends in failure. So, it will be better to imagine the threshold functions in the fuzzy domain.

A more lucrative approach is to imagine the threshold functions at the workplace during a work process as coupled functions, the initial function-Safety Threshold Start Function STSTAF(as shown in Figure 2) starting with value 1. Depending on the outcome of various performance functions, this coupled function descends discretely towards the 0 value. When the threshold function is 0 then a serious event (incident, accident or technical error) occurs and the next performance function is not started.

The Safety Threshold Stop Function STSTOF acts a a safety report regarding the whole task. If STSTOF is less than 1 then something wrong happened and the process must be audited to see what went wrong.

The scope of threshold functions is to give a dynamic approach to the human operator problem and also to act as a guiding wire between the various activities being performed to execute a task.

The Immediate Threshold Safety Function ITSF describes the decision of the human operator to perform a potential dangerous task. ITSF could be described by the following values:

- 0 –when the human operator considers the task too dangerous and is not performing;
- 0< and >1 when the human operator performs conditioned the task; for example, being asked to polish a piece of iron at the polishing machine he asks for safety glasses and also for safety gloves.
- 1 –when the human operator is performing the task

This ITSF could describe the start-up point of accident building, considering just the human factor. Contrary to the other threshold functions ITSF is an aprioric function.

All the other functions could be considered as after event (aposterioric) functions.

THE HUMAN ASSESSMENT SYSTEM

The developed safety system will be multi-level structured. This multi-level approach [8]assures an efficient assessment in accordance with the safety needs.

There could be defined three levels for the assessment.

Immediate-before entering the workplace, so as to be safe at the workplace-able to perform

Mid-term-to assure safety for him-able to work safely

Long term-to assure safety for him and his/hers co-workers; to be aware of the safety problems and to actively pursue safety-able to manage safety at workplace

In the following paragraph we are presenting some aspects of this system

The main idea is that we could scientifically design objective checklists, using the definitory attributes presented previously.

For example, we consider the training attribute.

What are the goals desired from such an attribute ?

-First, we want that the worker, at his/hers workplace to have sufficient general training so as to perform correctly his/hers work tasks. So, we must check the general training.

-The safety training is an essential point. We must check the general safety training (knowledge of risks), the safety training specific to the main task, to the auxiliary activities and also to the transport duties.

-For a safe workplace is not sufficient that a single worker is safety prepared. All his/hers team fellows must share the same safety training. So , we must check out the safety training image of the fellow workers-in the idea that such workers exist.

The checklist sample for the training attribute is presented below.

Table 7- Checklist sample for the training component

Question
1. On a 0..10 scale, evaluate your general training, regarding the activities performed on the workplace
2. On a 0..10 scale, evaluate your training, taking into account the main activity performed by you at the workplace
3. On a 0..10 scale, evaluate your training, taking into account the auxiliary activities performed by you at the workplace
4. On a 0..10 scale, evaluate your training, taking into account the general safety training -Do you know the safety measures, rules and norms that are in usage in your activity ?
5. On a 0..10 scale, evaluate your training, taking into account the general safety training- i.e. the knowledge of risks, general prevention measures, etc.
6. On a 0..10 scale, evaluate your safety training, taking into account the main activity performed by you at the workplace -Do you master the main activity ? -Are you informed fully about the risks involved ? -Do you know the usage of the personnel protective equipment and other safety equipment ? -Are you ready to perform specific rescue activities and to give first aid if necessary ?
7. On a 0..10 scale, evaluate your safety training, taking into account the auxiliary activities performed by you at the workplace -Do you master the activities that are to be done , auxiliary to the main activity ? -Do you know the risks involved in these activities ?
8. On a 0..10 scale, evaluate your safety training, considering the transport activities performed by you
9. On a 0..10 scale, evaluate the safety knowledge of your team colleagues regarding your main activity
10. On a 0..10 scale, evaluate the safety knowledge of your team colleagues regarding the auxiliary activities developed at your workplace
11. On a 0..10 scale, evaluate the safety knowledge of your team colleagues regarding the transportation activities
12.On a 0..10 scale evaluate the possibility to be a work accident casualty , considering your actual training –lower marks for a greater possibility, higher marks for a low possibility
13. On a 0..10 scale, evaluate the possibility to be a work accident casualty, considering the training of your colleagues –lower marks for a greater possibility, higher marks for a low possibility

Question
14. On a 0..10 scale, evaluate the possibility to be a work accident casualty, considering your safety training –lower marks for a greater possibility, higher marks for a low possibility
15. On a 0..10 scale, evaluate the possibility to be a work accident casualty, considering the safety training of your colleagues –lower marks for a greater possibility, higher marks for a low possibility

The algorithm is relatively simple.

$$Nt = Kw* Nw + Kcw * Ncw + Ks* Ns [3]$$

The media of worker's assessment [9] (Nw) is pondered with a coefficient (Kw) dependent on the worker's experience and previous work and safety results. The media of co-workers assessment-regarding a specific worker (Ncw) is pondered by a coefficient (Kcw) dependent on the team experience and results in safety assurance. The media of the supervisor's assessment (Ns) regarding the worker is pondered by a coefficient (Ks)dependent on his/hers experience and safety results.   Some example values for this coefficients are presented in the table below

Table 8-Example of coefficients

Case	Kw	Kcw	Ks
Apprentice with a normal team and a good supervisor (no accidents)	0.44	0.2	0.35
Apprentice with a normal team and supervisor (few accidents)	0.55	0.15	0.3
Worker with a normal team and a good supervisor (no accidents or few accidents)	0.6..0.65	0.1..0.2	0.25..0.3
Low qualified worker with a similar team and a good supervisor(no accidents or a few accidents)	0.3..0.4	0.05..0.1	0.5..0.65
High qualified worker with a similar team and a good supervisor (no accidents or a few accidents)	0.7	0.1	0.2

$$Kw+Kcw+Ks=1[4]$$

The proposed system is developed as a pilot now and will be fully functional in the second part of 2002.

REFERENCES

1.Creanga C.,Darabont D.,Ionescu D.,Kovacs St.,Methods for safety assessment at the workplace,OID-ICM, 2000

2.Creanga C.,Ionescu D.,Nepotescu M., Human operator assessment-basis for a safe workplace in the process industry, in Safety Now! (www.safetynow.ro), November 2000,December 2000,January 2001

3.Shneiderman, B. (1998). Designing the user interface: Strategies for effective human-computer interaction (3rd ed.). Reading, MA: Addison-Wesley.

4.Sikora, C. A. and Swan, R. (1998). Perceived usability and system complexity. Asia Pacific Computer Human Interaction 1998, 76-81.

5.Sincell, J., Perez, R. J., Noone, P., and Oberhettinger, D. (1998). Redundancy verification analysis - an alternative to FMEA for low cost missions. 1998 Proceedings Annual Reliability and Maintainability Symposium, 54-60.

6.Song, I. and Froehlich, K. (1994). Entity-relationship modeling. IEEE Potentials, 13(5), 29-34.

7.Spool, J. M., Scanlon, T., and Snyder, C. (1998). Product usability: Survival techniques. Proceedings of CHI '98 Human Factors in Computing Systems, 113-114.

8.Weinschenk, S., Jamar, P., and Yeo, S. C. (1997). GUI design essentials. New York: John Wiley & Sons.

9.Yang, K. and Kapur, K. C. (1997). Customer driven reliability: Integration of QFD and robust design. 1997 Proceedings Annual Reliability and Maintainability Symposium, 339-345.

A METHODOLOGY FOR THE ASSESSMENT OF DUST EXPLOSION RISKS: INTEGRATION INTO A GENERIC ASSESSMENT SYSTEM.

*Haesch G., *Kanuga K., [+]Lambert P. G.,*Milburn T., [+]Owen O. J. R., [+]Ward R. J.
*Degussa Raylo Chemicals 1021 Hayter Road Edmonton, T6S 1A1 Alberta, Canada
[+]Degussa Fine Chemicals Seal Sands, Middlesbrough, UK, TS2 1UB.

Risk management covers the whole business process and has been the subject of numerous publications. This paper covers one critical part of the risk management process, namely the control of hazards specific to the manufacture and handling of chemicals. In particular it discusses the *integration of a* method for assessing the risks from dust explosions with an existing system that examines chemical reaction hazards. This revision to the original system also allows the assessment of vapour phase explosions, powder handling hazards & occupational hygiene hazards to be performed.

COMPASS (Computerised Process Assessment Safety System)[1] was originally conceived to assess only the thermal hazards and risks from chemical reactions. However, the use of a common system based on the properties of materials *in combination* with defined operations & plant, allows assessment of a wider range of hazards. Methods were available in house for the assessment of risk with the exception of those from dust explosions. A new method was developed for the safe, rapid and cost effective assessment of potential dust explosions for integration into COMPASS. The approach which has been adopted is similar to that used in the Laporte "Vapour Phase Explosion" guide[2].

The integration of this methodology into the company systems has resulted in common high standards, guides and codes of practice at all manufacturing sites. The approach enhances awareness of the hazards and the tolerable residual risk results in cost-effective controls.

The methodology outlined in this paper was developed for Laporte, and specifically for the fine chemicals group. During the first half of 2001, Laporte was purchased by Degussa.

Keywords: Dust explosions, risk assessment, generic systems

INTRODUCTION

The Speciality Chemical industry is under increasing pressure to provide a manufacturing service that is not only safe but also cost effective & rapid.

Laporte Fine Chemicals is well established in the toll-manufacturing sector. Here, the ability to respond rapidly is of paramount importance. Many modern chemical processes use new reagents and introduce complex reaction hazards. It is therefore important to have assessment systems that are based on modern concepts, employ best practice, and which allow rapid, uniform but effective assessment of these hazards.

Laporte manufactures chemicals at twenty-two sites worldwide. The Catalyst & Initiator Group, the Fine Chemicals Group & the Performance Chemicals Group have businesses & manufacturing operations in Australia, Austria, Brazil, Canada, Germany, Korea, Spain, South Africa, Thailand, The Netherlands, France, U.K. and U.S.A.

These businesses operate with different national cultures and regulatory bodies. They use muti purpose plant, face differing hazards and levels of operational complexity, as well as rapid change. It is essential that the company has an approach to managing the hazards and risks associated with chemical processes that recognises these differences but also provides a rigorous, rapid yet flexible approach. Methodologies that require an analysis on a case by case basis have short term advantages but could not be sustained nor supported in the medium to long term. Generic systems are required, preferably that use simple and similar strategies.

COMPASS

COMPASS[1] was originally conceived in order to assess only the thermal hazards and risks from chemical reactions. However, we soon realised that since the risk and consequence were dependent on the properties of the substance(s) and how they were to be processed on a particular scale, COMPASS could have a wider use. It became very clear that the full power of developing an integrated chemical properties database could best be exploited by developing a series of models to cover the range of assessments required to handle chemicals safely. We therefore developed a range of standards based on the principle that the basis of safety and its control system need to address the properties of materials *in combination* with defined operations and plant. These standards included generic approaches for the assessment of organic peroxide manufacture, vapour phase explosions and occupational hygiene, in addition to chemical reaction hazards. One area where no consistent approach was used was for dust explosions. A new methodology has been written and is being integrated into COMPASS. It should be noted that generic systems, of necessity, need to be conservative but practicable.

COMPASS is a system that guides the user through a series of assessments. It can be used at a number of levels. At its most basic, it will guide the user through the assessments required for control of vapour phase explosions, dust explosions, reaction hazards and toxic hazards, prompting for relevant information. There is an expert system built in that will guide the user through the assessment, interpret the answers and flag up warnings where appropriate.

At a higher level, there are calculation routines that will allow knowledgeable staff to determine properties such as boiling rates and cooling efficiency.

Help screens are also aimed at providing enough background to enable the user to understand what the programme is doing at each stage of the assessment.

Data is stored in a central database that contains detailed information on the physical and toxicological hazards of a wide variety of chemicals.

DUST EXPLOSION MODULE

There have been numerous excellent publications[3,4,5] providing information or methods for the prevention or minimisation of dust explosion risks. However we were unable to locate a strategy that suited the needs of the businesses in the company. The main reasons were:

- Many small sites with little or no local in-house specialist knowledge on dust explosions
- Fast turn round in projects with many process / plant changes
- Businesses with pilot plants operating at small to medium scale with limited campaigns
- Extremely high cost pharmaceutical products & intermediates
- Limited availability of materials for test purposes
- Businesses operating at high levels of GMP / FDA quality compliance standards
- Businesses operating with high potency materials
- A need to support growth by decentralising the hazards assessments

A standard was required which allowed minimum or no testing in some circumstances yet provided a basis of safety that was sufficiently robust and within our tolerable limit criteria (internal equivalent of as low as reasonably practicable, ALARP). It should be noted that the module was designed for Laporte and was based on an intimate knowledge of the businesses, their technical ability, plant, operations, chemistry etc. The suitability for other businesses has not been assessed. Therefore the list of operations may not be exhaustive or even appropriate for all other businesses.

BASIC PRINCIPLES
Many processes involving powders and dusts, suspended or accumulated, have the potential to lead to fire, explosion or decomposition in the presence of oxygen. The risk of dust explosions increases as more and more products take the form of powders or require the use of powders during manufacture. Indeed, modern complex molecules have shown a tendency to be easier to ignite and to produce stronger explosions than the simpler molecules produced a quarter of a century ago. Currently, there are approximately 50 dust explosions per year in the U.K. In Europe, it is close to one a day on average. Many are secondary explosions initiated by ignition of a flammable vapour cloud in the vicinity. The initial explosion may ignite further dusts and powders that have accumulated on level surfaces. The damage caused by dust explosions is generally worse than that caused from vapour phase explosions. This emphasises the need for proper housekeeping to ensure that these incidents are not escalated.
A dust explosion can only occur if there is a flammable atmosphere (an explosive dust mixed with air/oxidant) and an ignition source. The conditions required to ignite dust clouds are dependent on several factors;

- The dust must be explosible. Solids are grouped in three classifications.

  Explosible   (UK Group A)
  Non-explosible   (UK Group B)
  Complex   (Hybrids of vapour & dust)

- The dust must have a particle size distribution that will allow the propagation of flame
- The dispersed cloud or suspension must have sufficient oxidant to support combustion.
- The dust cloud must be within the explosible range
- Sufficient ignition energy must be in contact with the dust cloud in order to ignite it

DEFINING THE BASIS OF SAFETY FOR THE PREVENTION & PROTECTION AGAINST DUST EXPLOSIONS.
The requirement to ensure safe handling and processing of powders and dusts relies on the operational effectiveness of employees and equipment to ensure that at least two of the above conditions are removed during operation. The basis of safety must be maintained through the lifetime of the process.

The probability of a dust explosion during processing is related to the properties of materials, such as the minimum ignition energy, K_{st} value etc. together with the nature of the operation being performed and the equipment used. One can therefore specify the level of safety required for any powder – operation combination.

A set of simple flowcharts and matrices has been developed which allow the combination of intrinsic and extrinsic factors to be easily assessed. The output for a given combination dictates controls and conditions for operations to be performed at tolerable levels of risk.

The specification of the level of safety required is a six-stage process and is described below.

STAGE 1: DETERMINE THE CORRECT GUIDANCE TO FOLLOW.
The purpose of Flow Chart 1 (see figure 1 at end of paper) is to ensure that the correct guidance is being followed. If the powder has no explosive properties then dust explosivity is not a problem. If the powder is wet then there is little or no dust explosivity hazard if the solvent is not flammable and is present at levels above ca 25%[4]. If the powder is wet to between 10% and 25% then dust explosions are possible but depend to a great extent on the ability to raise a dust cloud. If the solvent is flammable and present at levels greater than 1% then a vapour phase explosion (VPE) model[2] should be used as the vapour phase explosion presents a greater risk.

If the particle size is above 400μ[8], then a dust explosion is unlikely to propagate and so there is little dust explosion problem.(Other sources, for example the I Chem E guides [4], give a value of 500μ, however for internal use, and given the recent data[8] we are confident with the lower value). It should be emphasised that if fines can be formed, by attrition or otherwise, then the material should be treated as having the properties of a fine powder .Flow Chart 1 accepts the concept that testing (either for dust explosivity properties or particle size) is not always possible, practical or desirable. In such circumstances, the user of this guide has two options. A DEFAULT level of safety (LEVEL 3d) may be used, or the powder can be assigned a classification of High risk (see stage 2). In order to avoid misuse, these options can only be applied with approval of a knowledgeable person .

If Flow Chart 1 takes the exit "NO DUST EXPLOSIVITY PROBLEM" or "USE VPE", then the required action is self-explanatory.

If Flow Chart 1 takes the exit "USE DUST GUIDE DEFAULT LEVEL 3d", then the user can go straight to table 2 showing the requirements for ensuring this basis of safety.

If Flow Chart 1 takes the exit " ASSUME HIGH RISK POWDER", or "USE DUST GUIDE", then stage 2 is required.

STAGE 2 : CLASSIFYING DUSTS AND POWDERS
The matrix below (table 1) classifies powders according to three criteria.
  The K_{st} value,
  The minimum ignition energy (MIE) and
  The bulk resistivity (R_b).
 The numbers in the classification tables are listed in this order.

Table 1 Dust classification

CLASSIFICATION	1	2	3
K_{st} value	K_{st} 1	K_{st} 2	K_{st} 3
M.I.E.	> 50 mJ	10 – 50 mJ	< 10 mJ
Bulk Resistivity	$< 10^6 \ \Omega m$	$10^6 – 10^9 \ \Omega m$	$> 10^9 \ \Omega m$
HIGH RISK	3,3,3	3,2,3	2,3,2
	3,3,2	2,2,3	2,3,3
	3,3,1	3,2,2	3,1,3
MEDIUM RISK	2,2,1	1,2,2	1,3,3
	2,2,2	3,2,1	3,1,2
	2,3,1	1,2,3	1,3,2
LOW RISK	1,1,3	1,2,1	2,1,3
	1,1,2	2,1,1	3,1,1
	1,1,1	2,1,2	1,3,1

All powders can be assigned a K_{st}, MIE and R_b classification. The combination of these classifications (in that order) categorises powders into three bands of low, medium and high risk.

For example a powder that is K_{st} 2, with an MIE of 8mJ and bulk resistivity of 10^{10} Ωm would be classified as a 2,3,3 material & a powder that is K_{st} 1, with an MIE of 30mJ and bulk resistivity of 10^6 Ωm would be classified as a 1,2,2 material.

Once the classification is known, it is possible to move to stage 3.

STAGE 3 : OPERATIONAL RISKS (TABLE 2)

All common operations have been classified as low, medium, high or very high risk.

Note: many plant operations require a combination of powder movement, charging, discharge etc. As different hazards and risks can be present at each step, each must be reviewed separately.

The criteria below were based on the propensity of a given operation to generate:

Combustible dust cloud

Heat source or ignition source

Charge on a solid

If all three were likely then the operation was classed as very high, if two were likely the operation was classed as high, etc. This table contains approximately 15% of the available operational risk charts, which could not be published in full in this paper.

Table 2 Operational Risks

OPERATION	0 LOW	1 MEDIUM	2 HIGH	3 VERY HIGH
Solids Movement				
Vibrating table			H*	
Conveyor belt (continuous)		M*		
Bucket elevator Open				VH
Pneumatic (only an issue if >1m)				VH
Vacuum			H*	
Disc			H*	
Screw feeder (closed flights)			H*	
Chutes >2m				
Non conductive/not inerted				VH
Conductive/not inerted			H	
Non conductive/inerted			H	
Conductive/inerted		M		
Chutes <2m				
Non conductive/not inerted			H	
Conductive/not inerted		M		
Non conductive/inerted	L			
Conductive/inerted	L			

* Discharges move up 1 level $^+$Seek advice on these operations.

† This may be a significant flammable hazard that could initiate a secondary dust cloud explosion. This classification, whilst strictly correct for dust clouds alone, is misleading where there is a flammable vapour present. Under these circumstances, it is recommended that this be treated using a Vapour Phase Explosion model in addition to a Dust Explosion model. (Footnotes are for the full table.)

Table 3 Operation/Material Matrix

MATERIAL CLASSIFICATION	OPERATIONAL CLASSIFICATION			
	Low Risk	Medium Risk	High Risk	Very High Risk
Low Risk	Level 1	Level 1	Level 1	Level 1
Medium Risk	Level 1	Level 2	Level 2/3	Level 2/3
High Risk	Level 2	Level 2/3	Level 3	Level 3

Note: For high resistivity solids (*,*,3), earthing cannot be used as the sole basis of safety (LEVEL 2 minimum).

STAGE 4 : USE OF OPERATIONS/MATERIALS MATRIX
During stage 2 and stage 3 the operation and powder will have been classified. The operations/material matrix (table 3) above specifies a level of safety for any combination of operation and material. The majority of combinations are specific, however some combinations need a further review.

If a specific level of safety of 1 or 2 is defined, then it is possible to move directly to stage 6. If the level is 2/3 or 3, then stage 5 must be used.

STAGE 5 : SELECTING THE APPROPRIATE BASIS OF SAFETY.
Where stage 4 requires a level 2/3, Flow Chart 2 (see figure 2 at end of paper) differentiates between the use of level 2 and level 3 depending on risk and consequence. This is achieved by reviewing the quantities used in total and/or at any one time.

Where stage 4 requires a level 3, Flow Chart 2 differentiates between the different protective systems that may be used (LEVEL 3c containment, LEVEL 3v venting or LEVEL 3s suppression).

The flow chart also covers all operations/powders combinations and is therefore a double check of stage 4.

STAGE 6 : DEFINING REQUIREMENTS OF THE BASIS OF SAFETY
By following the preceding stages, a level of safety will have been specified for the material/operation combination. These levels obviously increase the rigour, reliability and security of the control systems moving from BASIC to Level 4. The requirements are listed in table 4 below.

It cannot be stressed enough that good housekeeping, including the avoidance of dust layers and major ignition sources, is a BASIC level of safety. Almost all significant damage and/or injuries from dust explosions result from the SECONDARY event rather than the primary. Typically the primary event will shake a structure, room or equipment and dislodge powders sufficient to result in a secondary explosion. This event is usually involving larger quantities in a larger volume with no protective systems.

Note: Where other modules of COMPASS, such as those to control hazards from flammable gases and vapours, are used in combination with the dust module, the basis of safety must reflect the whole process, not only the control measures from one module.

Level 1 and Level 2 are preventative levels of safety.

Level 3 incorporates the preventative measures of LEVEL 2 <u>PLUS</u> one of the following:

    (c) Containment of the overpressure by the equipment/structure

    (v) Venting the overpressure through a properly designed bursting panel and discharge system

    (s) Suppression of the explosion by extremely rapid addition of an inert diluent/phlegmatiser to stop the explosive reaction

    (d) The default system requires a high reliability of preventative measures

Approval should be sought for the use of level 3(c) or level 3(d) and expert advice must be taken and implemented before 3(v) or 3(s) can be operated.

Level 4 has no common solution. Expert advice must be sought.

For the purposes of the guide, specified Laporte persons were designated as either "Knowledgeable Persons", "experts" or both.

Table 4 Requirements for the Basis of Safety for dust explosions.

LEVEL	REQUIREMENT
BASIC LEVEL:	Good housekeeping, avoidance of dust layers, no electrical ignition sources. Proper use of electrical zones
LEVEL 1: **Preventative**	BASIC LEVEL <u>PLUS</u> Earthing and bonding of equipment, minimising electrostatic ignition sources, earthing people (not a requirement if MIE > 50 mJ). Use earthed scoops / solids movement systems (not a requirement if MIE > 50 mJ). An electrostatics guide should be consulted.
LEVEL 2: **Preventative**	LEVEL 1 <u>PLUS</u> <u>Either:</u> Inerting with N_2, CO_2, steam to <6% oxygen (or ½ MOC (Minimum or limiting oxygen concentration) if known, whichever is lower) <u>OR:</u> Dilution with air or other suitable material to reduce the dust concentration below 5 $g.m^{-3}$

LEVEL 3:
 Preventative +
 Protective
	LEVEL 2 <u>PLUS</u>
	 Protective system (c) Containment
	                        (v) Venting
	                        (s) Suppression

DEFAULT LEVEL: **LEVEL 3d,** agreed with a knowledgeable person	LEVEL 2 <u>PLUS</u> all of the following: Reliability of inerting, or dilution (see Vapour Phase Explosion and Inerting Guides) Avoidance of ignition sources Closed system Isolated area (typically this would be a full enclosure often with blow-out panels, but it could be interpreted in other ways. In all cases, the agreement of a knowledgeable person must be obtained.) High integrity earth continuity testing
LEVEL 4:	Seek expert advice

THE ASSESSMENT REPORT

Once the chemical properties database has been updated with the relevant test results, COMPASS will automatically display these when the Dust Explosion Assessment module is opened (see figure 3), as well as the calculated Dust Hazard Rating. The user is then guided through a set of questions driven by the expert system and based on the decision trees shown above. The system then displays the appropriate basis of safety and the systems required to support it. The full assessment, including the questions asked and the responses given, can be printed out together with the system requirements. Part of the assessment from which the report is generated is shown in figure 4.

EXAMPLES.

1. A new pharmaceutical intermediate needed to be produced for ongoing trials. The quantity required was ca 200 kg, but this could only be manufactured in lots of 65kg or so. The intermediate was the final stage in a multi-step synthesis and was itself the final step before the bulk active ingredient. As such, the product was very valuable both financially and in the ability to produce more material. As an intermediate, there was only limited toxicity data available but the end pharmaceutical product was known to have potent pharmacological properties. There were no data on dust explosivity and little physical property data.

The manufacturing plant operates to current good manufacturing practice (cGMP) and has obligations to comply with standards required by the Food and Drug Administration (FDA). In addition, the safety management system (SMS) and hazards management system (HMS) are regularly audited by independent people using recognised methodologies. The isolation, drying and packing was planned to be via centrifuge, small double cone dryer operating at 6-7 rpm and direct discharge via a closed system into lined 50kg fibreboard kegs. Using the dust assessment module of COMPASS the business decided that they did not wish to generate dust explosivity data because:

> No material was available
>
> Hazards involved to persons performing the tests
>
> The small quantity being produced
>
> High cost of material for testing
>
> The business would not operate the process any differently because of FDA, GMP, SMS requirements, even if the material had been shown to be low hazard or even non explosible.

Using flow chart 1 (see figure 1) the exit "use default level 3d" was chosen. This was approved by competent persons internally. The plant was reviewed as part of the hazard study and the requirements of level 3d verified to be in place, maintained and calibrated.

2. A product expansion involved the inclusion of a new formulating facility. Powder from an existing plant was taken in flexible intermediate bulk containers (FIBCs) to the feed hopper of the formulating unit. The design specification for the throughput was greater than 1500 tonne per annum. Measurements on the powder had previously shown the following properties

> K_{st} 331 bar m/s
>
> MIE   10mJ
>
> Bulk resistivity 2.5×10^{15} Ωm

The new formulating unit consisted of a number of unit operations such as screw feeds, hoppers & dust collection. These units were treated separately using the dust module of COMPASS. For this paper, only the feed and intermediate discharge hoppers will be considered. Using flow chart 1, the exit was "use dust guide, flow chart 2". It should be noted that the default level 3d could not be used as data was available on the material and this takes precedence. In addition approval would not have been obtained from the in house specialists given the properties of the material and the scale of operation.

From table 1 it is obvious that the material is classified as a high risk. The unit operations were each classified as medium risk. From table 3 this combination requires a level 2/3 basis of safety and therefore requires clarification using flow chart 2. This brought the assessor to "protective system must be used". There was no information to show that the hoppers had been designed to withstand any specific overpressure so level 3c was not evaluated further. Level 3v was considered as both hoppers had an area available that could be fitted with a venting panel. Using the VDI 3673 method[4], with;

K_{st} of 350 bar m/s,

Volume of the two units as $0.96m^3$ and $0.24 m^3$,

Reduced explosion pressure (P_{red}) as 0.4 bar

Vent bursting pressure (P_{stat}) as 0.1 bar and

Vent duct of less than 3m,

the vent areas were calculated as $0.37m^2$ and $0.13m^2$ respectively. Note that level 3v requires a vent *in addition* to the preventative measures from levels 1 & 2.

CONCLUSION

Similar principles to those described above are used for the vapour phase explosion assessment. The Reaction Hazards module has been described elsewhere[1]. The Occupational Hygiene module works on a similar principle using our banding system (which is broadly similar to the CIA banding system[6]) and COSHH Essentials[7]. This link will form the subject of another paper. This method of assessing risk using a combination of material banding with an operational risk rating has been shown to have wide application.

This approach provides the ability for rapid assessment for safe scale up and manufacture. It also provides a mechanism for consistent standards, smoother process and technology transfer. The methodology enhances line management involvement, allows integration of hazards and risk assessments and incorporates safety, health & environment in the early stages of process development.

REFERENCES

1 Lambert P G, Phillips J and Ward R J., 19-21 June 2001, A computerised process assessment safety system (COMPASS), 10th International Symposium on Loss Prevention & Safety Promotion in the Process Industries. Paper number 105/1049 Stockholm .

2 Scilly N F, Owen O J R, Wilberforce J K., 26-29 Sept. 1995, The control of confined vapour phase explosions. International Conference & Workshop on Modelling & Mitigating the Consequences of Accidental Releases of Hazardous Materials, New Orleans,

3 Abbott, J Prevention of Fire and Explosions in Dryer, 2nd Ed, IChemE, ISBN 0 85295 2570

4 I. Chem E. Monograph Guide to dust explosion protection:

Part 1: Venting. ISBN 0 85295 293 7

Part 2: Ignition prevention, containment, inerting, suppression and isolation. ISBN 0 85295 222 8

Part 3: The venting of weak explosions and the effect of vent ducts. ISBN 0 85295 230 9

5 Equipment & Protective Systems Intended for Use in Potentially Explosive Atmospheres (ATEX 137, Directive 99/92/EC). See EUR-LEX www.europa.eu.int/eur-lex/

6 COSHH - guidance on allocating occupational exposure bands (Reg 7), 1997, CIA ISBN 1 85897 048 2

7 COSHH Essentials. Easy steps to control chemicals. HS(G)193. H.S.E. Books. ISBN 0 7176 2421 8

8　Beck H., Glienke N., Moehlmann C.,BIA report HVBG, Combustion and explosion characteristics of dusts, Berofsgenossenschaftliches Institut fur Arbeitssicherheit (BIA), November 1997. ISBN 3 88383 469 6

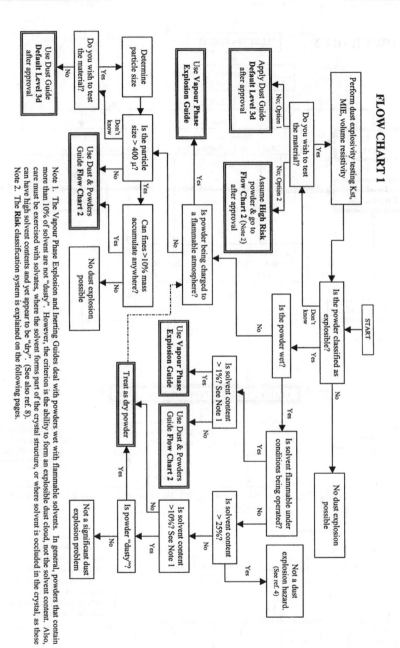

FLOW CHART 1

Note 1. The Vapour Phase Explosion and Inerting Guides deal with powders wet with flammable solvents. In general, powders that contain more than 10% of solvent are not "dusty". However, the criterion is the ability to form an explosible dust cloud, not the solvent content. Also, care must be exercised with solvates, where the solvent forms part of the crystal structure, or where solvent is occluded in the crystal, as these can have high solvent contents and yet appear to be "dry". (See also ref. 8).

Note 2. The **Risk** classification system is explained on the following pages.

Figure 1. Flow Chart 1.

FLOW CHART 2

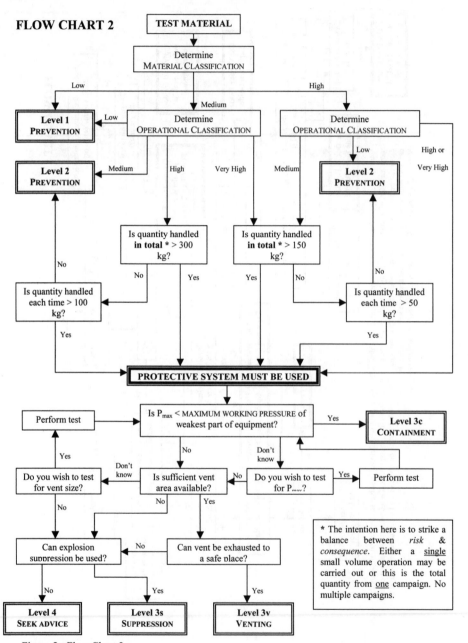

Figure 2. Flow Chart 2.

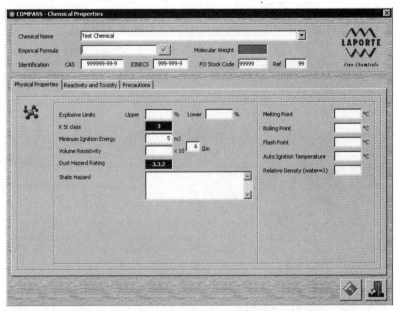

Figure 3. The physical properties screen showing the dust hazard rating.

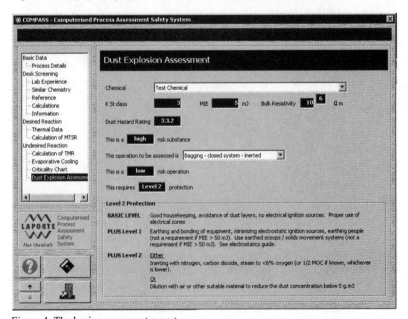

Figure 4. The basic assessment report.

SORPTION OF CADMIUM USING A NATURAL BIOSORBENT AND ACTIVATED CARBON

P. J. Lloyd-Jones, J. R. Rangel-Mendez and M. Streat
Department of Chemical Engineering, Loughborough University, Leicestershire. LE11 3TU, UK

This paper investigates the use of commercially available and modified activated carbon and a natural biosorbent for the removal of cadmium from water. A wood based activated carbon, AUG WHK, was acid oxidised to enhance its metal binding capacity. The leaves of a water fern, Azolla filiculoides were separated from the roots and ground into particles and acid washed to create a uniform hydrogen form adsorbent. These materials were subsequently studied for the removal of cadmium ions from aqueous solution. The sorption performance of these materials for cadmium is compared. The physical structure of the adsorbents has been investigated using scanning electron microscopy, nitrogen and amino acid content and BET surface area. Carbon adsorbents were characterised by N2 adsorption at 77K before and after oxidation, and a quantitative determination of weak-acid surface groups was carried out by direct titration. The BET surface area decreased considerably after oxidation, however, the total amount of oxygen-containing surface groups was 3.3 times higher compared to the untreated adsorbent. Cadmium adsorption isotherms were performed at pH values of 4, and 6 showing an increase in capacity as pH increases. The maximum capacity for the sorbents was 0.08, 0.33, 1.40 mmol/g for the three adsorbents: unoxidised WHK, Azolla filiculoides and acid oxidised WHK, respectively. Kinetic experiments showed that the materials were all rapid adsorbents of cadmium, with 80% of capacity reached in 0.2 hours for all three materials.

Keywords: cadmium, biosorbent, activated carbon, granular carbon, adsorbents, kinetics, oxidation.

INTRODUCTION

The presence of heavy metals in effluents is a world-wide environmental problem. There are a wide range of industries that produce heavy metal waste, therefore efficient and cost effective methods of water treatment are essential. Cadmium is prominent on the EU Black List of priority pollutants that are highly toxic and a serious threat to life. It is a carcinogen and causes damage to the kidneys. Cadmium is used extensively in electroplating due to its corrosion resistance and is a component in the expanding market for rechargeable batteries. Concentrations of the metal can reach 100ppm in surrounding areas adjacent to mines, smelters and Ni-Cd battery plants. Therefore, cost-effective methods of removing this trace metal are in great demand. At present a number of technologies, such as chemical precipitation, electroplating, evaporation, adsorption and ion exchange, are used to treat heavy metal containing wastewaters. Conventional chelating ion exchange resins can be effective but their production costs are a limiting factor. The above methods, other than adsorption and ion exchange, are not efficient or cost effective when the concentrations of metal ions are as low as 100ppm and the required concentration in the treated water is almost at the limit of detection [1].

Adsorption has been widely applied for the removal of trace contaminants from potable water, domestic water and industrial effluents. Sorption of heavy metals on activated carbon is not a simple process because it depends on several factors such as water chemistry and the surface reactivity of the adsorbent material. Granular activated carbons are extensively used in wastewater treatment for the removal of a wide range of contaminants. They possess high mechanical rigidity, well defined pore size distribution and offer extensive surface area for sorption of metal ions from aqueous solutions.

The use of naturally occurring plants as biosorbents for the removal of trace toxic metals is extensively studied on the laboratory scale but has not yet found widespread industrial application. Biosorption defines processes that remove contaminants from wastewater by either metabolic or physico-chemical pathways [2]. Many biological materials have been investigated for their ability to remove cadmium ions from solution. These include bacteria [3], fungi [4] and most commonly algae [5,6,7]. When considering biomass as a commercial process, the abundance and availability of the material are important considerations. In the case of algae, seaweeds can be harvested directly or received as recycled waste from the algin production industry. *Azolla filiculoides* is a fast free-growing "weed" that re-produces prodigiously, covering and blocking many waterways around the world. Biosorbents generally have a lower capacity than commercial ion exchange resins and modified activated carbons, however, they are regenerable and low-priced. *A. filiculoides* has already been shown to be very effective in repeatedly removing many pollutants from waste waters [8,9,10], including cadmium [11].

It is the aim of this work to compare the cadmium sorption capacity abilities of a commercial and modified granular activated carbon and a natural biosorbent. Sorption isotherms and kinetic experiments were performed to describe their performance. Samples were characterised, chemically and physically, by acid/base titration, pH titration, nitrogen and amino acid content, BET surface area and Scanning Electron Microscopy.

EXPERIMENTAL

MATERIALS

A. filiculoides was received from The University of Liverpool, Department of Biological Sciences. This was frozen in liquid nitrogen and the leaves separated from the roots. The leaves were then selected as they had shown a significantly greater cadmium sorption capacity than the roots. These were then ground into particles using a mortar and pestle. The particles were dried and sieved to 170-210μm. A wood based granular activated carbon WHK, supplied by AUG Germany, was sieved to a particle size fraction of 170-210μm, washed carefully with distilled water and then dried in an oven at 378K until no change in weight was observed. Cadmium solution was prepared using $CdCl_2 \cdot H_2O$ laboratory grade purchased from May & Baker Ltd., Dagenham, England. Sodium hydroxide, nitric acid, hydrochloric acid and potassium chloride were prepared from analytical reagents supplied by Fisher, UK. Aldrich Chemicals, USA, supplied volumetric standard solutions of sodium hydroxide, sodium carbonate, and HPLC grade ethanol. Sodium hydrogen carbonate and sodium ethoxide solutions were prepared from analytical reagents purchased from Aldrich Chemicals, USA.

CHARACTERISATION

Surface Area
The Surface area of granular activated carbons was obtained by nitrogen adsorption and desorption at 77 K using a Micromeritics ASAP2010 automatic surface area analyser. The samples were outgassed for 24 hours at 378 K under a vacuum of <10 μmHg.

Scanning Electron Microscopy (SEM)
Scanning Electron Microscopy pictures of granular carbons and *A. filiculoides* were taken using a Cambridge Stereoscan 360 operated at an accelerating voltage of 10 kV.

Nitrogen Analysis
Nitrogen analyses for biosorbent were conducted using the Kjelhdahl Method [12]. Duplicate 1g samples of *A. filiculoides* and native and dealginated seaweeds: *Ascophyllum nodosum* and *Lessonia flavicans* (both supplied gratis by Kelco, UK) were weighed on filter paper and placed into digestion vessels on a Buchi B435 digestion unit. The nitrogen control sample was a known weight of ammonium sulphate (to calculate process efficiency). The samples were then heated for 45 minutes at 623 K with sulphuric acid and catalyst pellets, to complete the hydrolysis stage. The hydrolysed product was steam distilled for 3 minutes using a Buchi 323 Kjeldahl distillation unit. The resulting distillate was titrated against a 0.1M hydrochloric acid solution, using screened methyl red indicator in a 2% boric acid solution.

Amino Acid Analysis
Samples of *A. filiculoides* were hydrolysed in order to liberate the amino acids. This was achieved by adding 0.5ml of 0.1M phenol (to reduce oxidation) and 4.5ml of 6.6M HCl to 100mg of the sample. The samples were heated at 383 K for 24 hours and then allowed to desiccate until dryness. Distilled water was twice added and evaporated to ensure removal of all HCl. The amino acids were then obtained as hydrochlorides. The samples were analysed by ion exchange High Performance Liquid Chromatography (HPLC) using a Kontron Analytical Chromakon 500. The results were compared against standards and quantities of each amino acid were ascertained.

pH Titration
15 ml of a 0.1M NaCl solution was added to 25ml Erlenmeyer flasks. The solution pH was varied by adding, a total volume of 5 ml, 0.1M NaOH, HCl and/or distilled de-ionised water. Then, 10mg of neutrally buoyant adsorbent particles, <90 μm, were added to the flasks. The samples were stirred for 48 hours at room temperature to allow them to reach equilibrium. The initial (before the addition of adsorbent) and final pH were measured. Blank samples, under the same conditions, were titrated at the same time for comparison. The electrophoretic mobility of the equilibrated samples was measured using a Malvern Instruments Zetasizer 3000HSA.

Acid/Base Titration
The distribution of oxygen-containing groups was analysed by direct titration using the Boehm method [13]. The samples were contacted with bases of different strength, NaOH, $NaCO_3$, $NaHCO_3$ and $NaOC_2H_5$ (dissolved in HPLC grade ethanol). A pre-determined amount of adsorbent was placed in a 50 ml conical flask and then contacted with 20 ml of each alkali solution. The flask was sealed and stirred using an orbital shaker at 300 min⁻¹ for seven days. The solution was filtered using a 0.2 μm PTFE syringe top filter to remove adsorbent particles. Finally a 5 ml aliquot was titrated with volumetric standard solution of

HCl, using a glass burette (tolerance ± 0.02ml), with methyl red as indicator. A simple mass balance was used to determine the ion exchange capacity of each oxygen-containing group.

Batch Sorption
A pre-determined amount of adsorbent was added to a 100ml conical flask containing 50ml of cadmium solution, of known initial concentration and pH. Samples were agitated by an orbital shaker at 300 min^{-1} at room temperature. The cadmium solution pH was checked and adjusted daily by addition of 0.1M NaOH or HCl until a constant pH was attained. The samples were deemed to have achieved equilibrium when no significant change in pH was observed (± 0.1 units) in a 24-hour period. The equilibrated samples were filtered using a 0.2μm PTFE syringe top filter to remove the adsorbent particles and then analysed for cadmium concentration, using a Varian SpectraAA-200 atomic adsorption spectrophotometer in flame mode at 228.8nm wavelength. Blank samples using the same solutions under the same conditions without adsorbent were prepared for comparison.

Kinetic Experiments
990ml of distilled water was added to a round-bottomed flask. Then, 1 g of adsorbent was placed into a rotating basket made of perspex and plastic mesh (opening 50 μm) [14]. The basket containing adsorbent was placed in the reactor and connected to a stirrer. The adsorbent was contacted with distilled water for 1 hour prior to the start of the experiment to allow trapped air to diffuse out and in the case of the biomass for particle swelling. 10ml of cadmium solution, of known initial concentration, was added to the reactor and the timer and the stirrer motor (set at 250 min^{-1}) started immediately. This was noted as the zero-time of the experiment. Samples were collected at certain time intervals and analysed for cadmium concentration. The experiments were run for up to 3 hours and the temperature was kept at 298 K by a temperature control unit.

RESULTS AND DISCUSSION

NITROGEN CONTENT AND AMINO ACID ANALYSIS
Previous metal sorption experiments on seaweed algae have attributed metal removal to functional groups present as part of the polysaccharide algin [15]. However, a significant residual metal sorption capacity remains after the alginates have been chemically removed [16]. It was suggested that this residual capacity can be attributed to functional groups associated with protein in the material. Protein is composed of a polymer of amino acids joined by primary amine and carboxyl groups. It is the functionality of the side chain that is of importance in metal binding. Amino acids contain a wide variety of side chains but only two are ionised in the pH range of interest i.e. the carboxylic groups on aspartic and glutamic acid (see Figure 1).

Table 1 Nitrogen content of several biomaterials

Material	Percent Nitrogen	Estimated Percent Protein*
Azolla filiculoides	3.80	23.76
De-alginate *Lessonia flavicans*	3.20	20.02
Lessonia flavicans	1.90	11.86
De-alginate *Ascophyllum. nodosum*	1.66	10.38
Ascophyllum nodosum	0.79	4.94

* Using AOAC international protein factor of 6.25

The biomaterials were analysed for nitrogen and this value was converted to a protein concentration using the general Association of Official Analytical Chemists (AOAC) factor of 6.25, which assumes the nitrogen content of the protein is 16%. Table 1 shows a high nitrogen content per unit mass for the dealginated seaweeds. *A. filiculoides* contains more than twice the nitrogen content of native *L. flavicans* and *A. nodosum*.

Figure 2 shows that *A. filiculoides* has a high concentration of the useful amino acids that may be involved in metal binding. 14.2% of the amino acids were aspartic acid and 10.2% glutamic acid.

OXYGEN-CONTAINING GROUPS
Figure 3 shows the concentration and type of functional groups on activated carbons. It can be seen that the concentration of oxygen-containing groups increases considerably after acid oxidation, but not in equal proportion. As-received granular activated carbon (WHK) contains carbonyl surface groups in the highest concentration. Acid oxidation results in an increase of 2, 3, 5 and 9 times higher for carbonyl, lactonic, phenolic and carboxyl groups, respectively. It is clear that carboxyl groups are introduced in the highest concentration, which will render acid oxidised carbon (WHK) more efficient in the treatment of drinking water since carboxyl groups are completely dissociated at near-neutral pH [17].

PH TITRATION
The surface chemistry of the adsorbents is extremely important in the sorption of metal ions and has to be studied in detail. The point of zero charge (PZC) is a useful parameter and can be determined by pH titration. PZC is the pH at which the net surface charge (internal and external) is zero [18]. This point can be deduced in Figure 4. The PZC for commercial granular carbon is at pH 4.5 whereas after acid oxidation it is shifted to pH 3.5. This behaviour is attributed to an increase in acidic surface groups, e.g. carboxyl, phenolic and carbonyl. The increase of these functional groups is also reflected in high concentration of ions released, H^+, with increasing pH (see Figure 4). The surface is positively charged in conventional and modified granular carbon WHK at pH values below the PZC where the oxygen-containing groups are undissociated and the adsorbent is able to remove anionic species. On the other hand, at pH values greater than the PZC, the sorbent surface becomes increasingly negative due to the dissociation of weakly acidic oxygen-containing groups. Hence, the adsorbent surface is able to attract and exchange cations in solution.

Alternatively, *A. filiculoides* has a proton binding curve that does not show a PZC within the experimental range (above pH 2). This means that the charge on the surface is always negative which is characteristic of a weak acid cation exchanger.

ELECTROPHORETIC MEASUREMENTS

The zeta potential (ZP) obtained by electrophoretic measurements at different pHs is reported in Figure 5. ZP is an index of the magnitude of interaction between colloidal particles. Colloidal suspensions/dispersions of fine particles in a liquid phase possess an electric charge that depends on the nature of the solid surface and the surrounding medium [19]. The point of zero net external surface charge is defined as the isoelectric point (IEP), which is located at the crossover point shown in Figure 5. The IEP for commercial and modified granular carbon is at pH 2.19 and 0.90 respectively, whereas for *A. filiculoides* it is at a pH of 1.42. The surface charge below and above the IEP can be explained in terms of the protonation and dissociation of oxygen-containing groups. It has already been mentioned that the PZC relates to the internal and external surface, whereas the IEP refers only to the external surface of the adsorbent. Hence, it can be deduced that the distribution of acidic surface groups is not homogeneous since the IEP is located at lower pH values. This indicates that the concentration of acidic groups is higher at the external surface as compared to the interior of the adsorbent.

SCANNING ELECTRON MICROGRAPHY

The SEMs presented in Figure 6 show the surface morphology of commercial and modified carbons, respectively. Un-oxidised carbon shows a well-defined and regular distribution of pores, whereas the oxidised sample shows irregular openings and roughness produced by chemical erosion. This is reflected in the loss of surface area. In comparison, the SEM of *A. filiculoides* leaves shows no sign of porosity.

BATCH EXPERIMENTS

Natural biosorbent, *A. filiculoides*, commercial and oxidised granular activated carbons, WHK, were tested for the removal of cadmium from aqueous solution. The sorption of cadmium at an equilibrium concentration of 0.8mM and pH 6 was 3.7 times higher for *A. filiculoides* than for commercial WHK (see Figure 7). Under the same conditions acid oxidised WHK showed 4 times higher cadmium capacity than *A. filiculoides*. This was expected since the concentration of oxygen-containing groups, found by acid/base titration, increased after chemical modification. However, BET surface area of the oxidised carbon decreased from 1912 to 714m^2/g due to the chemical reaction. An adsorbent with this surface area is entirely suitable for water treatment. The tendency for cadmium uptake is also reflected in the proton binding curves and electrophoretic mobility measurements. The concentration of ions released and zeta potential *versus* pH increases in the following order: commercial WHK, *A. filiculoides* and acid oxidised WHK. These results are in total agreement with the amount of cadmium removed by the adsorbents investigated in this research.

The effect of pH on adsorption was investigated and is reported in Figure 8. An increase of 53.12 and 58.33 % in cadmium uptake at 0.8mM was found when the solution pH was increased from 4 to 6 for *A. filiculoides* and oxidised granular carbon WHK, respectively. This is attributed to increased dissociation of acidic surface groups as the pH increases. For example the pK values of carboxylic groups lies between 2 and 5 [20,17].

Table 2 Freundlich isotherm parameters for the adsorption of cadmium

Material	pH	$k, \left[\frac{l^{1/n}}{mg^{1-1/n}g^{-1}} \right]$	n	R
A. filiculoides	4	0.161	2.915	0.995
A. filiculoides	6	0.350	5.495	0.989
Acid-ox. WHK	4	0.726	3.401	0.995
Acid-ox. WHK	6	1.267	7.937	0.988
Un-ox. WHK	6	0.081	5.208	0.919

The isotherms (Figures 7 and 8) were fitted using the Freundlich adsorption model, which had the best correlation of the experimental data compared with the Langmuir model. The parameters are shown in Table 2.

It has been mentioned that the surface chemistry and the metal speciation in solution are essential parameters to an understanding of the sorption mechanism. The speciation diagram for 0.1M $CdCl_2$ in aqueous solution (see Figure 9) was calculated using the equilibrium constants reported by Stumm and Morgan [21]. Cadmium appears as Cd^{2+}, $CdCl^+$ and $CdCl_2(aq)$ below pH 7.6 in the approximate proportions of 58, 39 and 3 %, respectively. Cadmium precipitates above pH 7.6 as $Cd(OH)_2$. Therefore cation exchange and/or complexation with surface functional groups is the most likely sorption mechanism.

The results presented in this section show that natural biosorbent, *A. filiculoides*, has 3.7 times higher cadmium capacity than commercial granular carbon WHK. Biosorbents are potentially useful for water treatment since they possess satisfactory capacities for metal ions and have a distinct economic advantage. However, it is shown that by oxidising the granular carbon WHK it is possible to obtain a cadmium sorption capacity greater than *A. filiculoides*. The drawbacks are that this process incurs extra cost and reduces the mechanical strength of the material. Oxidised carbons may also leach humic substances during subsequent use in water treatment.

KINETICS
Kinetic data are plotted in Figure 10 and this shows that the adsorption rate for cadmium is extremely fast for all the adsorbents. A significant difference is observed after 0.2 hours, when 94% capacity is reached with activated carbons compared to 82% for the biosorbent. Rapid sorption kinetics in these experiments can be attributed to the relatively small and close size distribution of particles and well-defined pore size distribution for the carbons. It has been shown that there is little or no porosity in the biosorbent, hence there are no internal diffusion constraints in the sorption mechanism.

CONCLUSIONS
The capacity of biomass for cadmium is 4 times greater than as-received commercial granular carbon WHK. The oxidation of commercial activated carbon increases sorption capacity for cadmium by a factor of 15 compared with the as-received material. There is, however, a subsequent loss in surface area due to the chemical reaction. Biosorbents are potentially useful for water treatment since they possess satisfactory capacities for metal ions and have a distinct economic advantage. All the materials displayed fast sorption kinetics, more than

80% capacity was reached in 0.2 hours, making them suitable for conventional column techniques.

ACKNOWLEDGEMENTS

The authors would like to thank for financial assistance during the period of this research, Severn Trent Water PLC and EPSRC. J. R. Rangel-Mendez appreciates the scholarship (ref. 70767/125253) from Consejo Nacional de Ciencia y Technologia (CONACyT), Mexico.

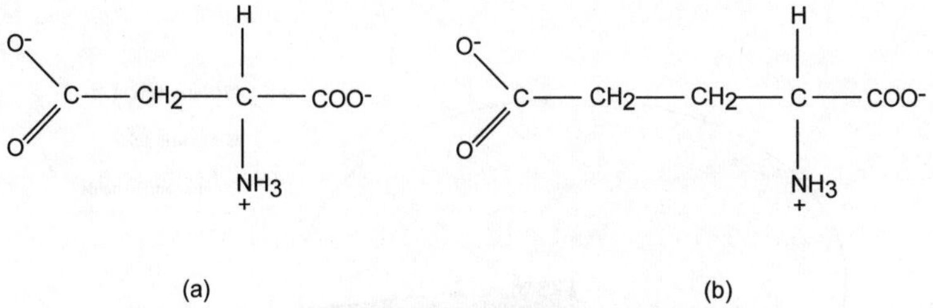

Fig. 1 Amino acids, (a) aspartic acid and (b) glutamic acid

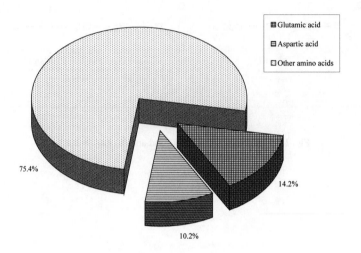

Fig. 2 Amino acid profile of *A. filiculoides*

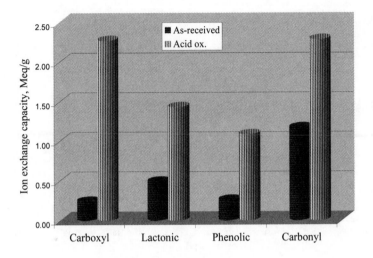

Fig. 3 Oxygen containing groups on conventional and modified granular carbon WHK

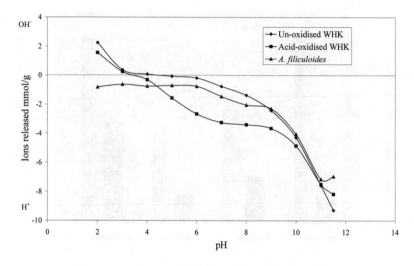

Fig. 4 Proton binding curves for granular carbon WHK and *A. filiculoides*

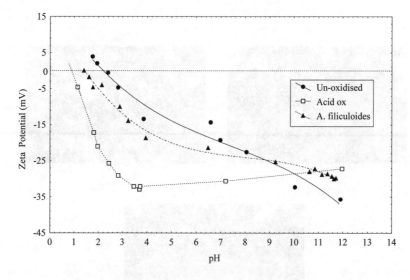

Fig. 5 Electrophoretic mobility measurements using granular carbon WHK and *A. filiculoides*

(a) (b)

(c)

Fig. 6 Scanning Electron Micrographs of: (a) conventional WHK, (b) Acid oxidised WHK, (c) *A. filiculoides*

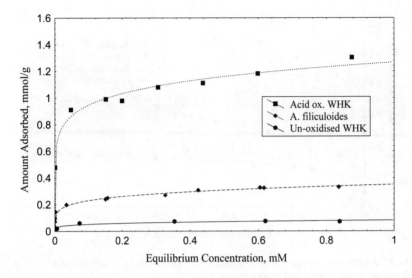

Fig. 7 Equilibrium cadmium sorption isotherms for granular carbon and *A. filiculoides* at pH 6 and room temperature.

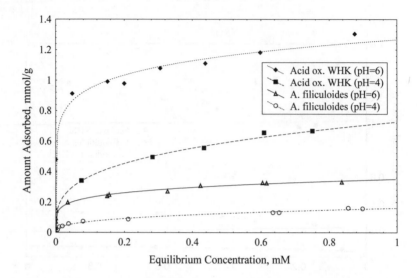

Fig. 8 Equilibrium cadmium sorption isotherms for oxidised granular carbon and *A. filiculoides* at pH 4 and 6, and room temperature.

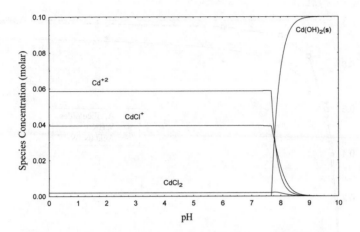

Fig. 9 Speciation diagram of 0.1 M CdCl₂ in aqueous solution at 298.15 K

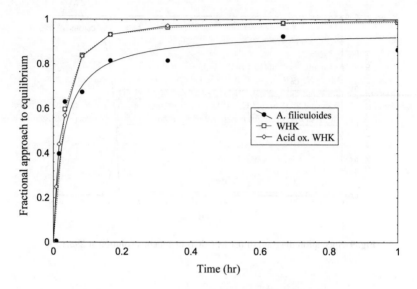

Fig. 10 Comparison of kinetics for granular carbons and the biosorbent

REFERENCES

1. Nriagu, J.O., 1988, A silent epidemic of environmental metal poisoning? Environmental Pollution 50: 139-161

2. Fourest, E., Roux, J., 1992, Heavy metal biosorption by fungal mycelial by-product:mechanisms and influence of pH. Applied Microbial Biotechnology, 37: 399-403

3. Chang, J.S., Law, R., Chang, C.C., 1997, Biosorption of lead, copper and cadmium by biomass of Pseudomonas aeruginosa PU21. Water Research 31: 1651-1658

4. Fourest, E., Canal, C., Roux, J.C., 1994, Improvement of heavy metal biosorption by mycelial dead biomass (*Rhizopus arrhizus, Mucor miehei and Penicillium chrysogenum*): pH control and cationic activation. FEMS Microbiology Reviews 14: 325-332

5. Leusch, A., Holan, Z.R., Volesky, B., 1995, Biosorption of heavy metals (Cd, Cu, Ni, Pb, Zn) by chemically reinforced biomass of marine algae. Journal of Chemical Technology and Biotechnology 62: 279-288

6. Yu, Q., Matheickal, J.T., Yin, P., Kaewswarn, P., 1999, Heavy metal uptake capacities of common marine macro algal biomass. Water Research 33 (6): 1534-1537

7. Matheickal, J.T., Yu, Q., Woodburn, G.M., 1999, Biosorption of cadmium(II) from aqueous solutions of pre-treated biomass of marine alga Durvillaea potatorum. Water Research 33: 335-343

8. Sanyahumbi, D., Duncan, J.R., Zhao, M., Van Hille, R., 1998, Removal of lead from solution by the non-viable biomass of the water fern Azolla filiculoides. Biotechnology Letters 20 No. 8: 745-747

9. De Wet, L.P.D., Schoonbee, H.J., Pretorius, J., Bezuidenhout, L.M., 1990, Bioaccumulation of selected heavy metals by the water fern, Azolla filiculoides Lam. In a wetland ecosystem affected by sewage, mine and industrial pollution. Water SA 16 No. 4: 281-286

10. Zhao, M., Duncan, J.R., 1997, Batch removal of sexivalent chromium by Azolla filiculoides. Biotechnology and applied biochemistry 26: 179-182

11. Sela, M., Fritz, E., Hutterman, A., Tel-Or, E., 1990, Studies on cadmium localization in the water fern Azolla. Physiol. Plan. 79: 547-553

12. Kjeldahl, J.T., 1883, Neue Methode zur Bestimmung des Stickstoffs in organischen Körper, Z. Anal Chem., 22: 366

13. Boehm H.P, 1966, Chemical identification of surface groups, in Eley, D.D., Pines, H. and Weisz, P.B. (eds). Advanees in catalysis 16: 179-274. Academic Press, New York

14. Rangel-Mendez, J.R., Tai M.H., Streat, M., 2000, Removal of cadmium using electrochemically oxidized activated carbon. Trans IChemE 78, part B: 143-147

15. Volesky, B., 1990, Biosorption of heavy metals, CRC Press, Inc., Boca Raton, Florida

16. Malik, D.J., Streat, M., Grieg, J., 1999, Characterisation and evaluation of seaweed-based sorbents for treating toxic metal bearing solutions, Trans IchemE 77 part B: 227

17. Mironov, A.N., Taushkanou, V.P., 1974, *Adsorption and Adsorbents (adsorbtsiya i adsorbenti)*, 2: 32

18. Menendez, J.A., Illan-Gomez, M.J., Leon y Leon, C.A., Radovic, L.R., 1995, "On the difference between the isoelectric point and the point of zero charge of carbons", *Carbon*, 33 (11): 1655-1659

19. Malvern Instruments, 1998, *The measurements of zeta potential using electrophoresis.* Training manual

20. Zubay, G.L., Parson, W.W., Vance, D.E., 1995, Principles of Biochemistry, Wm. C. Brown Publishers

21. Stumm, W., Morgan, J.J., 1981, Aquatic chemistry, John Wiley and Sons

SAFETY AS A NEED/ENVIRONMENT PROTECTION AS A DEED

Ph. D. Stefan Kovacs - The Romanian National Research Institute for Occupational Safety,(INCDPM)Bucharest,e-mail:icpm00@softnet.ro
Scientific Researcher Darabont Doru- The Romanian National Research Institute for Occupational Safety(INCDPM),Bucharest
Marioara Apostol -INCDT COMOTI RA
Scientific Researcher Camelia Creanga - INCDT COMOTI RA

The paper presents the experience of a national (process industry) research institute in checking and balancing the safety needs and also the environmental needs into the design activity. This experience is interesting especially considering the transition towards a market economy and also the various research profiles (including military ones).

The problem was that, taking into account the four main components of the Man-Machine system, the human operator, the task that is done, the machine and the work environment, to fine-tune them so as to obtain maximum safety and a reasonable degree of environmental protection.

In this spirit, a crosscheck assessment system was designed. This system assesses in a first step, the safety at the workplace, and in a second step the environment protection. Using this system, can be defined some specific crises, crises that can further be used at the development of various scenarios and mainly at the development of counter-strike measures. Such crises can be: human- environment crisis, task-environment crisis, machine-environment crisis and work environment-environment crisis. Training can diffuse the human-environment crisis, the task-environment by redesigning the task, the work environment-environment and machine, –environment crisis can be diffused by technical means.

Using statistic casualty and environment data, the paper shows that the work environment-environment crisis and the machine- environment crisis are the most serious and are determinant, if preventive actions are not quickly taken, to major accidents, with human losses and environment irreversible damage.

The developed assessment system is a quick, efficient and objective way to follow safety and environment together.

Keywords:
Safety assessment, environmental assessment, interactions, expert systems

GENERAL ASPECTS

In the design process the designer takes a great responsibility, especially for the future. The designed product will be manufactured, used and when its life cycle is over will be disposed .
All these life stages involves safety risks for the manufacturer, user and disposer and also environmental risks for the work environment and also for the surrounding environment.
The majority of research institutes in Romania are product developers, with design activities. Regarding this aspect, the paper presents the essential aspects of a multi-assessment system,

for safety and the environmental protection, which was developed jointly by the Romanian National Institute for Turboengines Research(INCDT COMOTI RA) and the Romanian National Institute for Safety Research (INCDPM)

THE SAFETY AND ENVIRONMENT ASSESSMENT PROCESS

The simplest way to make a safety assessment for a design is to use checklists so as to verify all the significant safety aspects of the design. A more complex method, named "Safety Integrator"[1] was developed and was presented at SafeCon, in Athens, in June 2000.

When assessing the safety in the design stage, the four components of the Man-Machine system(man, machine, task and environment) must be taken into account. Also, the three main stages of the future product or technology, manufacturing, usage and disposal must be analyzed.

The next figure presents the general schemata of the safety and environment assessment system

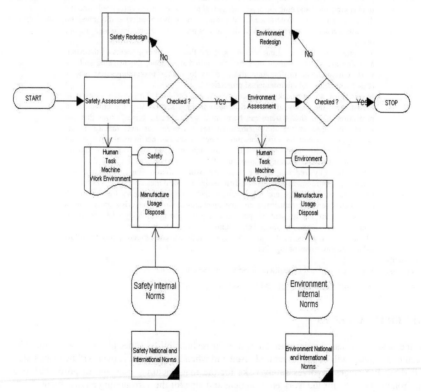

Figure 1.General schemata of the COMOTI assessment system

Undesired events are produced by interactions. The main goal in the safety assessment must be the human operator, so the interactions between various components must be analyzed from this point of view.

The general schemata of the safety assessment is presented in the figure 2

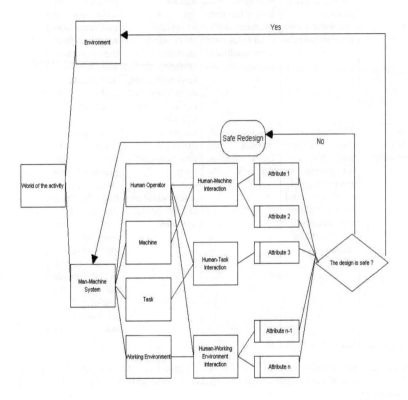

Figure 2. General schemata of the safety assessment process

In this research, the Human-Human and Human-Task interactions could be partially eliminated, because it is difficult for the designer to assess specific workers at the manufacturing point or specific users, without having the necessary data. So, regarding these interactions , the designer must develop the manufacturance specifications and also the user manual in accordance with the safety principles .The important safety problems for the designer are given by the Human-Machine and the Human-Working Environment interactions . These interactions are detailed in the following table.

Table 1.a) Problem identification regarding Human-Machine and Human-Environment
Interactions in the three main life stages of a product

Component	Manufacturing	Usage	Disposal	Observations
Human-Machine	Manufacturing risks, design problems, manufacturer's training, experience and responsibilities	Specific risks in usage, design problems, User's training, attitudes, skills, experience and responsibilities,	Specific risks at disposal regarding human operators, Materials, Disposal training, attitudes, skills, responsibilities, experience and environmental attitudes	Main goal: to optimize the design of the product or technology so that the risks resulting from the Man-Machine interactions will be acceptable
Human-Working Environment	Manufacturing risks, design problems, manufacturer's environmental training and responsibilities, organization's environmental attitudes	Environmental training and Environmental attitudes	Disposable materials, Environmental training, environmental responsibilities, environmental attitudes	Main goal: to optimize the design of the product or technology so that the risks resulting from the man-working environment intractions will be acceptable and the working environment will be relatively safe

Going further , we can eliminate the manufacturing phase from the table, considering that
manufacturing engineers are responsible for this phase. A more detailed analysis will led us to
the following tables:

Table 1.b) Problem identification regarding the Human-Machine(Product)Interaction in the
usage and disposal phases

Component	Usage	Disposal	Observations
Human-Machine	-Specific risks in usage independent from the design; -Risks caused by design problems; -Other risks; -Ergonomic aspects;	-Specific risks at disposal independent from the design; -Risks caused by the design, involving product	Main goal: to optimize the design of the product or technology so that the risks resulting from the Man-Machine (product)interactions will be acceptable. Risks can be identified using the risks list contained in EN

Component	Usage	Disposal	Observations
	-User's training, attitudes, skills, experience and responsibilities,	materials and disposal technologies; -Disposal worker training, attitudes, skills, responsibilities, experience and environmental attitudes	1050

From this table, we could identify two main problems, regarding the human-product interaction at usage and disposal:
-assurance of safety at usage and disposal (including various types of risks and their prevention measures and also the human operator capacities regarding the product);
-assurance of comfort in usage and disposal;

Table 1 c) Problem identification regarding the Human-Working Environment Interaction in the usage and disposal phases;

Component	Usage	Disposal	Observations
Human-Working Environment	-Specific risks independent from the design; -Design problems concerning the work environment; - Environmental training and Environmental attitudes	-Disposable materials; -Environmental training, environmental responsibilities, environmental attitudes	Main goal: to optimize the design of the product or technology so that the risks resulting from the man-working environment interactions will be acceptable and the working environment will be relatively safe

From this table we could identify the two main problems that could be summarized as:
-assurance of the safety regarding the work environment;
-assurance of the comfort regarding the work environment;
It is possible to see that in developing the safety assessment are taken into account some attributes that are described more detailed in the following table.

Table 2. Significant attributes that are influencing the safety assessment

Principal attribute	Description
Specific risks independent from the design	Existing or very probable risks at manufacturing, usage and disposal, risks that are influencing the human operator,

Principal attribute	Description
	excepting the design influence. For example: at the manufacturing process, the processed material is very breakable, splashing with debris
Risks caused by design problems and design problems	Problems connected with ergonomic design or with bad design
Training	Specific activity training so as to perform efficiently
Responsibilities	Responsibilities that must be assumed by the worker and his team to perform optimally the activity
Manufacturing risks	Risks implied by the manufacturing process
Usage risks	Risks implied by the usage of the product
Disposal risks	Risks implied by the disposal of the product
Materials	Component materials of the product;

The final result of the assessment will be the conclusion that the designed product or technology is safety compliant or the necessity to redesign it.

If the safety assessment is acceptable, the next step will be the environment assessment.

The environmental assessment will indicate if the product (or technology) is environmentally friendly or will lead to the definition of specific crisis scenarios, like those presented in the following table.

Table 3. Man-Machine components-environment crisis scenarios

No	Name	Definition	Provoked by	Observations
1	Human-environment or Environment-human crisis	Historically, the first crisis from the apparition of the mankind. The socio-technological crisis caused by the human operator actions with direct or indirect results on the environment; the crisis caused by environment manifestation against the human operator	-the intentional actions of the human operator upon the environment -the accidental actions of the human operator on the environment -the environment adverse influence on the human operator	Could be diffused by : -training, for the part regarding the active actions of the human operator; -using the Personnel Protective Equipments or other specific protection against the surrounding environment;
2	Task-environment or environment [2] task crisis	The technological crisis developed because the execution of specific tasks with impact on the	-the execution of specific tasks with results on the environment	Could be diffused by redesigning the tasks or by specific protection against

No	Name	Definition	Provoked by	Observations
		with impact on the environment ; the crisis developed because the impossibility to execute a task or the deficient task execution because the environment	-the impossibility to execute a task or the deficient task execution because the environment	protection against the surrounding environment; also, could be diffused by changing the task schedule
3	Machine-environment or environment-machine crisis	The technological crisis developed because the improper functioning of the machine (s) involved in a process with adverse effects on the working environment; the crisis developed because the environment effects on the machine	-the improper functioning of the machine -the environment effects on the machine	Could be diffused by a proper maintenance of the machine and adequate protection against environment
4	Working environment-environment crisis	The techno-environmental crisis developed because the mixing between working environment and environment	-improper containing of the working environment	Could be diffused by an adequate separation between the two environments

THE EXPERT APPROACH

We used an expert approach [3], firstly to model the safety and environment assessment process, secondly to capture the heuristic knowledge from the safety and environmental experts and finally to develop expert system modules for assistance in the assessment process and also in the improvement of the situation. Also, the expert approach allows the usage of fuzzy data.

We have chosen an object oriented expert approach. This allows the definition of the following hierarchical structure:

WORLD OF INTEREST-- > CLASSES--> OBJECTS--->ATTRIBUTES

The class components of our model are detailed in the table 4

Table 4. Class components

Man-Machine system	Human operator	Human operator-Environment Interaction	Human operator-Environment crisis	Man-Machine system and environment are general
	Task	Task-Environment Interaction	Task-Environment crisis	static classes. All the interaction and
	Machine	Machine-Environment Interaction	Machine-Environment crisis	crisis classes are dynamic ones
	Working environment	Working environment-Environment Interaction	Working environment-Environment crisis	
Environment		Environment Interaction	Environment crisis	

It is possible to see that from this composition a complex hierarchical structure is born, structure that can satisfy all the major needs of a model.

For the safety assessment, there could be defined specific objects that are describing a part of the world that is assessed. For example, the following table presents some of the objects for the human operator.

Table 5. Objects specific to the Human Operator Class

HUMAN OPERATOR CLASS	Object name	Object possible ranges	Object description
	General training	0..10 or yes/no	Specifies the operator's training regarding the performed activity
	Safety training	0..10 or yes/no	Specifies the specific safety training of the operator regarding the activity being performed
	Physical state	0..10 or yes/no	The state in which the operator is at the beginning of the work, relatively to his physical attitudes
	Mental state	0..10 or yes/no	The state in which the operator is at the beginning of the work, relatively to his psychical attitudes
	Safety responsibility on him/herself	0..10 or yes/no	Responsibility to assure personal safety
	Safety responsibility to co-workers/others	0..10 or yes/no	Responsibility to assure other's safety

The interaction classes have objects that are defining specific parts of environmental aspects. Some of these are presented in the following table:

Table 6. Example of objects specific to the Man-Machine-Environment interactions

Interaction	Specific objects	Description
Human operator-Environment Interaction	Specific environmental training	Describes the necessary training for the human operator so as to conform to the ecologic rules
	Environmental sense	The necessary sense to assure ecological protection
	Preventive attitudes	The possibility to take rapidly preventive attitudes in case of an incoming event
Task-Environment Interaction	Environmental design	The task design that is taking care of ecological aspects
	Task execution	If at the task execution the environment is polluted
	Environmental control	If there is any control after the task fulfillment
Machine-Environment Interaction	Machine design	The environmental correct design of the machine
	Machine maintenance	The maintenance of the machine that is avoiding ecological problems like spills, etc.
	Machine environmental control	The environmental control of the machine output
Working environment-Environment Interaction	Work environment maintenance	The environmental maintenance of the work environment

The following figure shows the graphical representation of the classes that were built inside the model.

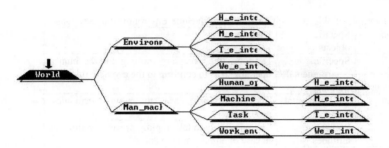

Figure 3   Component classes of the model

The Human-Environment, Machine-Environment, Task-Environment and Work Environment-Environment Interactions were defined with both Environment and Human Operator, Machine, Task and Work Environment as their parent classes. This definition allows the inheritance of all the general properties dependent on the Environment and also on the Man+Machine components.

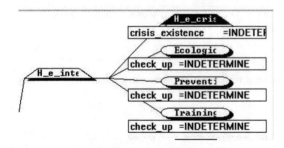

Figure 4. The components of Human Operator-Environment Class

In the previous figure the resultant class, Human Operator-Environment Crisis appears. The attribute for this class, crisis_ existence is activated when a specific rule is triggered, as in the next figure.

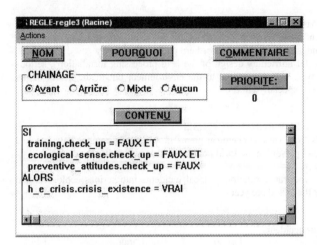

Figure 5. The rule that triggers the activation of the Human Operator-Environment Crisis Class

It is possible to see that there were introduced some example attributes for exemplifying the rule, attributes that are defined as belonging to the Human Operator-Environment Interaction; these attributes, by taking the No (FAUX) values are activating the class Human Operator-Environment Crisis with its attribute crisis _existence.

The next figure shows parts of the tracing process of the trial run

Figure 6. Part of the tracing process of the trial run

STATISTICAL ASPECTS

Putting together occupational accidents and environmental accidents data it is possible to see that machine –environment and work environment-environment crisis are the most serious from the environmental point of view.

We would present just some case examples to confirm our theory, in the following paragraphs.

A)MACHINE-ENVIRONMENT CRISIS
In the metal processing industries, significant ecological incidents are resulting especially from the lead processing industry located in the northern part of the country.
Because of the environmental unfriendly design of the lead processing installations, serious and irreversible damages were caused not just to the environment but to the health of the population living in the area ,especially children.

B)WORK ENVIRONMENT-ENVIRONMENT CRISIS
Uncontained cyanide spills from various chemical plants in the eastern regions have reached the rivers, killing the fish and poisoning the local population that was eating the dead fish.

The next table is showing the transformation of local incidents into serious ecological and occupational accidents, for the last three years

Table 7.Incidents vs. serious accidents [4]

Year	1998	1999	2000
Reported incidents	20	25	30
Serious accidents	5	11	19

The next table makes the connection between the reported incidents and design causes

Table 8.Incidents caused by design problems [4]

Year	1998	1999	2000
Reported incidents	20	25	30
Design caused incidents	15	21	26

CONCLUSIONS

Some aspects of the development and functioning of an assessment system for multi-stage assessment were presented in this paper.
In the first stage, the system is assessing the safety design of a product ,technology or service, respectively the safety at the manufacturing, usage and disposal of a product or service.
In the second stage, the system is assessing the environmental outcome of the usage of the product , technology or service and is developing (or not, if it is not the case) crisis scenarios for the interactions between the components of the Man-Machine system and the environment.
If the product is safe and environmental friendly it could be developed further, being manufactured, distributed and used accordingly with the indications.
If the product is not in conformance with the safety and environmental established rules, it is redesigned till it becomes conformant.

REFERENCES

1.Creanga Camelia- New tendencies in safety implementation towards the design phase.Safety Integrators and design safety audit. (PDF document) In SafetyNet page www.safetynet.de
2.Creanga Camelia-Environmental protection as a design need, in Researches in Safety, no.23,May 2000, pg.447-449
3.Creanga Camelia and Kovacs Stefan-Expert systems for safety assessment, MEDINF 1998
4.Internal Labour Minstry Statistics,1998-2000
5.Germain Arnold,Rowan Roane-Safety,Health and Environmental Management,A Practitioner Guide,a publication of Risk Management Institute,Inc.1998
6.Petersen Dan-Techniques of Safety Management(A Systems Approach),Goshen NY,1989

KNOWLEDGE-BASED APPROACH FOR THE IDENTIFICATION AND ASSESSMENT OF HAZARDS DUE TO STATIC ELECTRICITY

A. Kraus, H.-G. Schecker
AG PCV, University of Dortmund, Dortmund, Germany

ABSTRACT
To improve the identification of hazards due to static electricity in process plants the use of a knowledge-based system is suggested. The identification and the assessment of electrostatic hazards is carried out by using a systematic safety assessment methodology. Thus a thorough analysis of plants is comprehensively assisted. This facilitates process engineers with special knowledge about the examined process or experts in the field of static electricity to apply the system.

A systematic approach is necessary due to the large amount of knowledge in this field. The CENELEC-Report R044-001 (February 1999) „Guidance and recommendations for the avoidance of hazards due to static electricity" serves as a basis for the knowledge-based decision system. To validate the decisions of the system the results of the generated safety report are compared with expert opinions. Case histories about explosion accidents caused by static electricity are used to carry out the validation of the system.

The assessment of hazards due to static electricity will be done by linking information about the apparatus and the materials. Special processing situations are also recognised. Starting from that suitable safety measures can be selected. In demanding cases the need for further expert advice is indicated to avoid misjudgements. But the strong point of the system is that every part of the equipment will be checked in view of electrostatic hazards and the results are listed thus generating a safety report.

INTRODUCTION
In order to be able to assess the hazards caused by electrostatic discharges, extensive knowledge is required from the fields of electrostatic, chemistry and process engineering. The comprehensive knowledge on electrostatic charging currently available is therefore concentrated on only a few experts mainly in the big companies of the chemical industry.

The application of knowledge as given by guidelines e.g. the CENELEC Report R044-001 "Guidance and recommendations for the avoidance of hazards due to static electricity" and other publications on a concrete processing situation is often not possible for a non-expert in the field of hazards caused by electrostatic discharges due to a lack of practical experience. To enable an active access to the experiences about detecting and preventing potential hazards, it is a necessity for the knowledge-based system to offer a systematic procedure to identify and assess hazards that is close to industrial practice.

To improve the acceptance of the knowledge-based system the validation of the implemented knowledge is done with case histories descriptions.

EXPERT SYSTEMS

Algorithmic programming languages like FORTRAN and PASCAL are not sufficient for an efficient knowledge representation in the field of safety science. Especially to appropriately describe expert knowledge in the field of electrostatic discharges and explosion protection, it is necessary to have tools that provide object- and rule-structures and offer suitable inference strategies.

In the past most of the available expert systems were not able to fulfil the high expectations they were faced to. These expectations were forced not at least because of terms like "artificial intelligence" which are used with the development of expert systems. A less demanding - but simplifying- definition for knowledge-based systems could be:

Knowledge-based systems are computer-based decision tools that store and save the knowledge of experts by means of special knowledge representation forms, like "If-Then-Rules" and "Class/Object-Structures", to put this competence at the user's disposal.

After the conceptional phase the knowledge acquisition and modelling forms an important step in expert system development. During this step the knowledge model is formulated in co-operation of the domain experts and the knowledge engineers. The implementation of the knowledge model has to be independent from the used tools and should be carried out with adequate software-tools.

HAZARDS CAUSED BY ELECTROSTATIC DISCHARGES

Electrostatic discharges are a potential ignition source for explosive atmospheres. They can become effective as an ignition source for gas/air-, vapour/air- (above flammable liquids) and dust/air-mixtures. Plant components as well as products might cause electrostatic charging and give rise to the possibility of a discharge which may ignite an explosive atmosphere.

Charging of products or plant components occurs when surfaces are separated from each other. Surface in this connection stands for the phase boundary of solids or liquids. Charging arises only when one of the materials involved in the separation process is not conductive (insulator). Therefore charge relaxation is not possible because of too high separating velocities [1].

There are several kinds of electrostatic discharges: spark discharges, brush discharges, propagative brush discharges, cone or bulking discharges, corona discharges, lightening like discharges, super brush discharges. The occurrence of these gas discharges can be determined by the properties of the involved materials. Furthermore one also has to pay attention to the processing variables.

When reaching a sufficiently high charging, ignition effective discharges may occur [2]:

- between an isolated or grounded conductive object and a charged isolated conductive object as well as
- between an isolated or grounded conductive and a charged non-conductive material.

DANGEROUS PROCESSING SITUATIONS CAUSED BY ELECTROSTATIC DISCHARGES

The following examples for dangerous processing situations caused by ESD show the great variety of ways of looking at a problem and the various variables that have to be taken into account. These parameters are a result of the various process sequences that

lead to electrostatic charging. During practical safety assessments in the field of electrostatic discharges the following processing situations may occur:
- A dust is poured out of a non-conductive bag.
  Because of the separation of dust and bag, both, the product and the container are charged.
- A powder is filled into an agitated vessel.
  The product as well as the non-conductive container can be charged because of the separation process. Therefore gas discharges could occur. These may ignite a vapour-air-mixture which is present over a flammable liquid in the vessel.
- A surface of a flammable, non-conductive, charged liquid gets close to grounded conductive installations.
  Because the non-conductive surface of the liquid gets very close to grounded installations of the apparatus, brush discharges may occur. They could ignite a vapour-air-mixture over the flammable liquid.
- A non-conductive liquid flows through a fine filter.
  Due to the large surface area between the solid and the non-conductive liquid inside the fine filter, the liquid could be charged up very high.

SYSTEMATIC PROCEDURE WHILE SAFETY ASSESSMENT

The aim of the systematic safety assessment with the help of the knowledge-based system is to detect and assess hazards caused by electrostatic discharges. As a consequence adequate safety measures can be chosen to achieve a reliable and safe plant operation. These safety measures are based on guidelines or regulations e.g. [2].

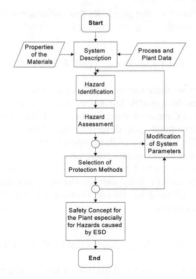

Fig. 1: Proceeding of the knowledge-based system during the systematic safety assessment of hazards caused by electrostatic discharges

To attain a systematic proceeding of the system the following concepts have been developed and implemented into the knowledge-based system. The first concept in Fig. 1 shows the basic structure of the procedure while safety assessment of hazards caused by electrostatic discharges. The procedure should ensure the inclusion of all aspects that have to be taken into account.

The data about the plant and processed material which is necessary for the safety assessment is provided by the user. An examined process is described by its safety characteristics, electrical properties, process parameters and also plant data.

The goal of the hazard identification is to determine the occurrence of explosive atmosphere inside the plant and in the surroundings of the plant. Therefore qualitative and quantitative safety characteristics are valued first of all independently from potential ignition sources [3]. In this way it is possible to identify dangers caused by the properties of the products. The assessment of the occurrence of explosive atmospheres is described with safety characteristics which are dependent from the state of matter. Also, process parameters like e.g. an increased temperature have an influence on the hazard identification process.

If the formation of an explosive atmosphere is possible a systematic hazard assessment is carried out with respect to the occurrence of ignition sources and the incenditivity of them for an existing fuel/air-mixture. The plant and its surroundings are divided into zones, which distinguish the probability of the occurrence of explosive atmospheres.

At the end of the examination the system chooses suitable safety measures. The result of the hazard evaluation is the basis for the development of a safety concept for one apparatus but also for the whole plant. The plant periphery as well as moveable objects should be taken into account. Safety measures have to be determined according to the zone assignment.

By modifying different system properties their influence on the result of the safety assessment can be examined.

MODELLING OF THE PROCESS STRUCTURE FOR COMPUTER-BASED ASSESSMENT

Another important step for the computer-based hazard assessment is the representation of the examined process by a model. The assessment of hazards caused by electrostatic discharges requires the information about the links between several parts of a process plant (e.g. pipes or apparatus). The different parts of the process plant can be represented by objects. The links between these objects represent the electric connections.

Based on this model of the process plant the safety assessment is carried out. The procedure during the assessment of hazards caused by electrostatic discharges invokes the graphical user interface to ask the user for unknown properties. The model of the process forms the basis for the graphical user dialogue which is described in connection with the examples given below.

ASSESSMENT OF IGNITION SOURCES CAUSED BY ELECTROSTATIC DISCHARGES

During the safety assessment, a detailed analysis of the hazards caused by electrostatic discharges is carried out. The structure of the evaluation is shown in Fig. 2.

At first materials are analysed which are involved in the process. Products, plant equipment as well as persons in the surroundings of the analysed part of the plant have to be examined. At this point of the assessment one can decide which kinds of discharges may principally occur. After this, the operating and plant parameters have to be taken into account to be able to analyse the occurrence of possible discharges in detail. This includes parameters which are connected with the process mode e.g. the flow velocity or the surface area between the filter and the fluid during microfiltration. Furthermore the surroundings of the analysed process have to be taken into account. For the evaluation of the different kinds of discharges the occurrence of these discharges is not proved. If the prerequisites for the occurrence of a discharge are given, then the ignition source is regarded as potentially existing. Afterwards the effectiveness of the possible ignition source for the existing explosive atmosphere is assessed. The list of ignition sources and their incendivities given in Fig. 2 is not complete but they represent the valid valuation of the incendivities.

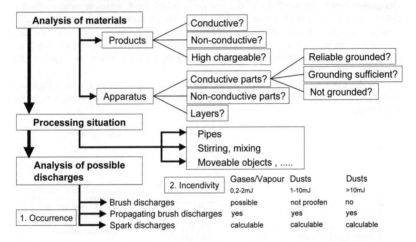

Fig. 2: Procedure during hazard evaluation of ignition sources caused by electrostatic charging.

This procedure constitutes the second, more detailed concept to achieve a systematic assessment of the examined processing situation. The following chapter describes exemplary the necessary steps to be taken when analysing spark discharges.

APPLICATION OF THE GENERAL PROCEDURE
The analysis of different process modes is explained by an example which shows the difficulties of applying the general structure as given in Fig. 2. But, nevertheless, this structure is necessary to ensure that all details for a complete assessment are included.

The first example discussed is a filter which is cleaned in situ by using pulses of pressurised air. This example is given as a case history by Lüttgens and Wilson [4]. The filter bag is supported by a metal basket. Electrostatic charging seems to be not a problem because of the lack of moving parts inside the system. But an ungrounded metal basket could get highly charged because of the separation between filter bag and the basket during a pulse with pressurised air.

During the assessment the user dialogue of the knowledge-based system has to point out to the user that the conductive metal basket could get charged if it is not reliably grounded. Therefore it is necessary to implement knowledge about the structure of this part of the plant. These rules have to transform the input of the user into a form that can be evaluated according to the structure given in Fig. 2.

The application of the procedure described in Fig. 2 for practical cases shows the difficulties for a user with basic knowledge in explosion protection. This user can not take an evaluation of the dangerous situation with common terms like „conductive material" or „sufficient grounding".

The following example discusses the problems which occur while applying the practical experiences in the assessment procedure within a computer-based system.

The filling process is shown in Fig. 3 as part of a flowchart. The non-conductive, chargeable dust is conveyed out of the silo into a metal drum, which is weighed during filling. During this operation near the drum and inside the hose an explosive atmosphere occurs. The dust is charged during the conveyance out of the silo.

Spark discharges may occur, if conductive parts of the plant are not grounded. In the example spark discharges can occur by charging the metal drum, the scale or the supporting rings of the hose.

In the evaluated process only the metal drum can be charged up so highly that incendiary discharges may occur. The grounding of the conductive drum has to be examined.

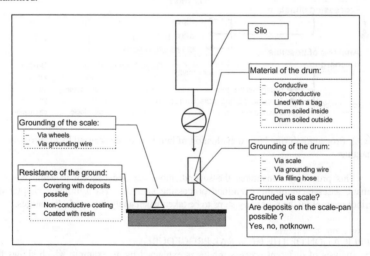

Fig. 3: Drums are filled with dust out of a silo. The drums stand on a moveable scale. Example for the graphical user dialogue with pull-down-menus which allow the specification of the examined process by the user.

The grounding of the drum is a necessary safety measure. A reliable grounding can be achieved by different measures. The drum can be grounded via the scale or via a grounding wire which is connected to the drum before the filling. If the grounding is done via the scale, which is required for an automatic filling process, it must be guaranteed that the scale is grounded and that the scale-pan is not soiled or covered with non-conductive material. The scale itself must be reliably grounded too.

In the given example propagating brush discharges can be excluded due to the fact, that there is no strong charging mechanism like pneumatic conveying. Conveying the powder by gravity does not lead to the necessary high charging for propagating brush discharges. There are also no non-conductive areas in the examined plant which could get charged.

Brush discharges as well as corona discharges cannot be avoided when handling large amounts of medium or non-conductive powders [2]. In the presented case the dust/air-mixture has a minimum ignition energy (MIE) of higher then 5 mJ. The brush discharges cannot ignite this dust/air-mixture. Problems with brush discharges from charged dusts may occur if occasionally a flammable mixture with a lower MIE (e.g. explosive solvent/air-mixture) is present where the brush discharges take place. This indicates that every change in the order of events of the process has to be examined very carefully not to overlook important details.

The examples shows that it is necessary to take into account many details of the concrete process. Therefore it is not possible to describe for example the spark discharges only in general terms. For a computer-based hazard assessment it is necessary to register all details. The user's attention should be drawn to hazardous situations which are relevant in practice. That is why many cases must be analysed during the development of the expert system. From these examples one can derive the parameters to describe specific hazard situations.

The general, systematic procedure derived from the examination of the case histories can be validated with a set of case histories which can be found e.g. in [4].

The user dialogue is supported by a graphical dialogue in which the details of the process are shown. The user has to specify the process to be analysed via pull-down menus. The inputs are evaluated by the expert system and hence included in the assessment of hazards which might be detected.

APPLICATION OF THE EXPERT SYSTEM IN INDUSTRIAL PRACTICE

Different applications of the expert system are possible. While planning a plant, the expert system can give safety advice to avoid hazards caused by electrostatic discharges. The expert system could be used by plant managers to recognize hazards which have been overlooked during the safety assessment in a working plant. Furthermore a repetition of the assessment is necessary, if a process is going to be modified. Safety engineers with practical experience in explosion protection can use this tool to assess potential hazards caused by electrostatic discharges.

The practical application of the expert system facilitates the identification of possible hazards. The results given by the system indicate the necessity for further examinations by experts.

SUMMARY

With the presented knowledge-based system possible hazards caused by electrostatic discharges can be detected and assessed. The system provides a detailed assessment of different processing situations with proposals for safety measures. Potential hazards in explosive atmospheres of dusts, gases and liquids are examined.

The first part during the development of the knowledge-based system is the systematic structuring of the knowledge. The result is a comprehensive and structured summary of the knowledge in this field, that allows hazard assessments independently from the development of the knowledge-based system. This method is the prerequisite to easily extend, validate and maintain the knowledge-based system.

The second part of the development consists of the implementation of the knowledge in the knowledge-based system. To emphasize potentially dangerous operations a graphical user interface has been introduced.

In the result of the safety assessment the knowledge-based system gives references to guidelines and regulations, and the necessity for further examinations by experts is indicated.

LITERATURE

[1]   Lüttgens, G., Glor, M.: Understanding and controlling static electricity, Ehningen, Expert-Verlag (1989).

[2]   European Committee for Electrotechnical Standardization: CENELEC-Report R044-001, Safety of machinery - Guidance and recommendations for the avoidance of hazards due to static electricity (1999).

[3]   Hauptverband der gewerblichen Berufsgenossenschaften: Richtlinien für die Vermeidung der Gefahren durch explosionsfähige Atmosphäre mit Beispielsammlung - Explosionsschutzrichtlinien (EX-RL), Carl Heymanns Verlag, ZH 1/10, (1996).

[4]   Lüttgens, G., Wilson, N.: Electrostatic hazards, Butterworth-Heinemann (1997).

INDEX